# Contents in Brief

**Focal Points and Connections**
See page T17 for key.

**About the Cover**

Fractions and decimals and the relationship between fractions and decimals are featured topics in Fourth grade. On the cover, the pitcher is wearing a fraction. It is equivalent to 0.5. Have students find the other fraction on the cover that is equivalent to 0.5.

**Three Horizontally Aligned Programs**

- Common vocabulary
- Common manipulatives
- Common authors
- Common technology
- Common Professional Development

**Grade 4**

NSF-funded, integrated performance assessment aligned with investigative instruction

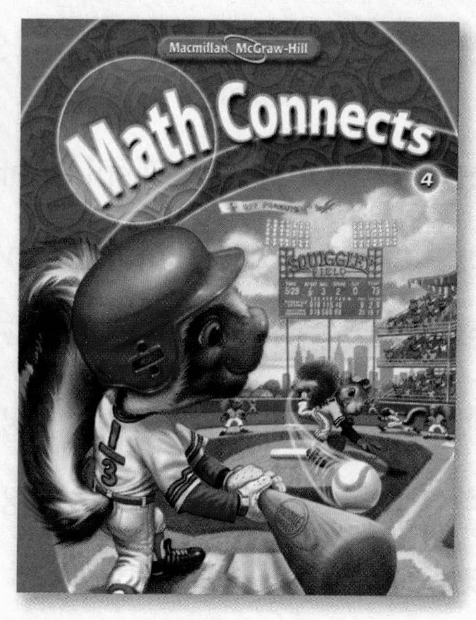

**Grade 4**

Intensive Intervention for students two or more years below grade level (Tier 3 RTI)

The McGraw·Hill Companies

 **Macmillan/McGraw-Hill**



Send all inquiries to:
Macmillan/McGraw-Hill
8787 Orion Place
Columbus, OH 43240-4027

ISBN: 978-0-02-105745-0 *(Teacher Edition)*
MHID: 0-02-105745-1 *(Teacher Edition)*
ISBN: 978-0-02-105733-7 *(Student Edition)*
MHID: 0-02-105733-8 *(Student Edition)*

*Math Connects,* Grade 4

Printed in the United States of America.

5 6 7 8 9 10 11 12 13 14 WEB/LEH 19 18 17 16 15 14 13 12 11 10

# Benefits of Student Edition Organization

***Math Connects***, grade 4 Student Edition, has a 4-part organization.

1. **Start Smart** gets students ready for grade 4 with a review of key math standards from grade 4 that are prerequisites for grade 4.
2. **Chapters 1-15** Each chapter has coherent groups of lessons focused on related grade 4 math standards and the NCTM Focal Points.
3. **Preparing for Standardized Tests** provides test success tips, step-by-step solutions for standards-based multiple-choice questions, and an extensive practice section to review before your state test.
4. **Looking Ahead** prepares students for success with lessons on several key math standards.

The organization and pacing of ***Math Connects*** helps ensure in-depth coverage of all grade 4 standards, success on your state test, and a good start for grade 5.

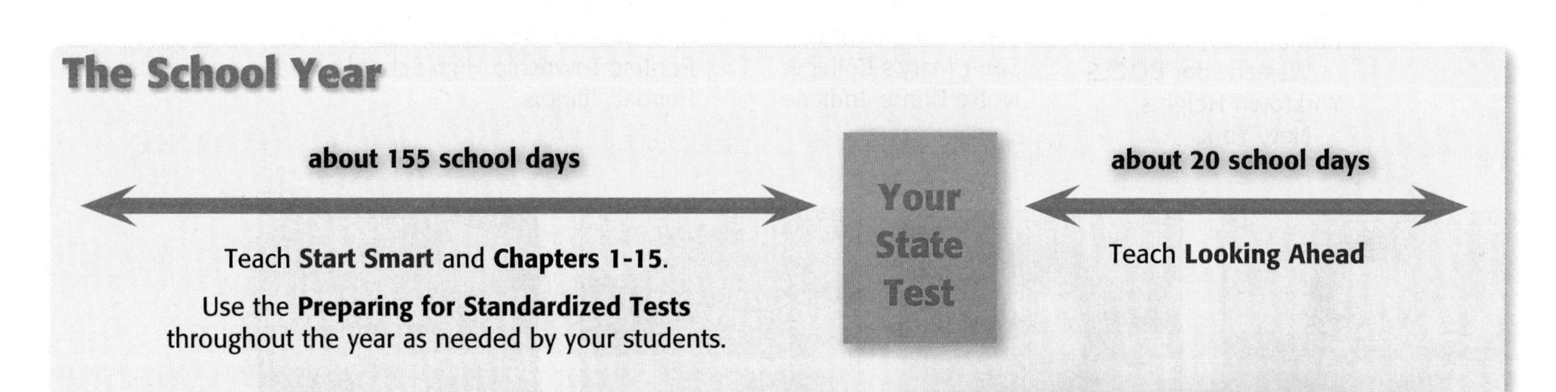


**Pacing Guide**
Each chapter includes days for review and assessment.

| Start Smart | Optional |
|---|---|
| Chapter 1 | 9 days |
| Chapter 2 | 10 days |
| Chapter 3 | 13 days |
| Chapter 4 | 11 days |
| Chapter 5 | 10 days |
| Chapter 6 | 8 days |
| Chapter 7 | 9 days |
| Chapter 8 | 12 days |
| Chapter 9 | 8 days |
| Chapter 10 | 12 days |
| Chapter 11 | 12 days |
| Chapter 12 | 13 days |
| Chapter 13 | 9 days |
| Chapter 14 | 10 days |
| Chapter 15 | 9 days |
| **Total** | 155 days |
| **State Test** | |
| **Looking Ahead** | 20 days |

# Authors

**Mary Behr Altieri**
Putnam/Northern Westchester BOCES
Yorktown Heights, New York

**Don S. Balka**
Professor Emeritus
Saint Mary's College
Notre Dame, Indiana

**Roger Day, Ph.D.**
Mathematics Department Chair
Pontiac Township High School
Pontiac, Illinois

**Philip D. Gonsalves**
Mathematics Coordinator
Alameda County Office of Education and California State University East Bay
Hayward, California

**Ellen C. Grace**
Mathematics Consultant
Albuquerque, New Mexico

**Stephen Krulik**
Professor Emeritus Mathematics Education
Temple University
Cherry Hill, New Jersey

**Carol E. Malloy, Ph.D**
Associate Professor of Mathematics Education
University of North Carolina at Chapel Hill
Chapel Hill, North Carolina

**Rhonda J. Molix-Bailey**
Mathematics Consultant
Mathematics by Design
Desoto, Texas

**Lois Gordon Moseley**
Staff Developer
NUMBERS: Mathematics Professional Development
Houston, Texas

**Brian Mowry**
Independent Math Educational Consultant/Part-Time Pre-K Instructional Specialist
Austin Independent School District
Austin, Texas

**Christina L. Myren**
Consultant Teacher
Conejo Valley Unified School District
Thousand Oaks, California

**Jack Price**
Professor Emeritus
California State Polytechnic University
Pomona, California

**Mary Esther Reynosa**
Instructional Specialist for Elementary Mathematics
Northside Independent School District
San Antonio, Texas

**Rafaela M. Santa Cruz**
SDSU/CGU Doctoral Program in Education
San Diego State University
San Diego, California

**Robyn Silbey**
Math Content Coach
Montgomery County Public Schools
Gaithersburg, Maryland

**Kathleen Vielhaber**
Mathematics Consultant
St. Louis, Missouri

## Contributing Authors

**Donna J. Long**
Mathematics Consultant
Indianapolis, Indiana

FOLDABLES® **Dinah Zike**
Educational Consultant
Dinah-Might Activities, Inc.
San Antonio, Texas

# Consultants

Macmillan/McGraw-Hill wishes to thank the following professionals for their feedback. They were instrumental in providing valuable input toward the development of this program in these specific areas.

## Mathematical Content

**Viken Hovsepian**
Professor of Mathematics
Rio Hondo College
Whittier, California

**Grant A. Fraser, Ph.D.**
Professor of Mathematics
California State University, Los Angeles
Los Angeles, California

**Arthur K. Wayman, Ph.D.**
Professor of Mathematics Emeritus
California State University, Long Beach
Long Beach, California

## Assessment

**Jane D. Gawronski, Ph.D.**
Director of Assessment and Outreach
San Diego State University
San Diego, California

## Cognitive Guided Instruction

**Susan B. Empson, Ph.D.**
Associate Professor of Mathematics and Science Education
University of Texas at Austin
Austin, Texas

## English Learners

**Cheryl Avalos**
Mathematics Consultant
Los Angeles County Office of Education, Retired
Hacienda Heights, California

**Kathryn Heinze**
Graduate School of Education
Hamline University
St. Paul, Minnesota

## Family Involvement

**Paul Giganti, Jr.**
Mathematics Education Consultant
Albany, California

## Literature

**David M. Schwartz**
Children's Author, Speaker, Storyteller
Oakland, California

## Vertical Alignment

**Berchie Holliday**
National Educational Consultant
Silver Spring, Maryland

**Deborah A. Hutchens, Ed.D.**
Principal
Norfolk Highlands Elementary
Chesapeake, Virginia

# Reviewers

Each Reviewer reviewed at least two chapters of the Student Edition, giving feedback and suggestions for improving the effectiveness of the mathematics instruction.

**Ernestine D. Austin**
Facilitating Teacher/Basic Skills Teacher
LORE School
Ewing, NJ

**Susie Bellah**
Kindergarten Teacher
Lakeland Elementary
Humble, Texas

**Megan Bennett**
Elementary Math Coordinator
Hartford Public Schools
Hartford, CT

**Susan T. Blankenship**
5th Grade Teacher – Math
Stanford Elementary School
Stanford, KY

**Wendy Buchanan**
3rd Grade Teacher
The Classical Center at Vial
Garland, TX

**Sandra Signorelli Coelho**
Associate Director for Mathematics
PIMMS at Wesleyan University
Middletown, CT

**Joanne DeMizio**
Asst. Supt., Math and Science Curriculum
Archdiocese of New York
New York, NY

**Anthony Dentino**
Supervisor of Mathematics
Brick Township Schools
Brick, NJ

**Lorrie L. Drennon**
Math Teacher
Collins Middle School
Corsicana, TX

**Ethel A. Edwards**
Director of Curriculum and Instruction
Topeka Public Schools
Topeka, Kansas

**Carolyn Elender**
District Elementary Math Instructional Specialist
Pasadena ISD
Pasadena, Texas

**Monica Engel**
Educator Second Grade
Pioneer Elementary School
Bolingbrook, IL

**Anna Dahinden Flynn**
Math Teacher
Coulson Tough K–6 Elementary
The Woodlands, TX

**Brenda M. Foxx**
Principal
University Park Elementary
University Park, MD

**Katherine A. Frontier**
Elementary Teacher
Laidlaw
Western Springs, IL

**Susan J. Furphy**
5th Grade Teacher
Nisley Elementary
Grand Jct., CO

**Peter Gatz**
Student Services Coordinator
Brooks Elementary
Aurora, IL

**Amber Gregersen**
Teacher – 2nd Grade
Nisley Elementary
Grand Junction, CO

**Roberta Grindle**
Math and Language Arts Academic Intervention Service Provider
Cumberland Head Elementary School
Plattsburgh, NY

**Sr. Helen Lucille Habig, RSM**
Assistant Superintendent/ Mathematics
Archdiocese of Cincinnati
Cincinnati, OH

**Holly L. Hepp**
Math Facilitator
Barringer Academic Center
Charlotte, NC

**Martha J. Hickman**
2nd Grade Teacher
Dr. James Craik Elementary School
Pomfret, MD

**Margie Hill**
District Coordinating Teacher for Mathematics, K–12
Blue Valley USD 229
Overland Park, KS

**Carol H. Joyce**
5th Grade Teacher
Nathanael Greene Elementary
Liberty, NC

**Stella K. Kostante**
Curriculum Coach
Roosevelt Elementary
Pittsburgh, PA

**Pamela Fleming Lowe**
Fourth Grade eMINTS Teacher
O'Neal Elementary
Poplar Bluff, MO

**Lauren May, NBCT**
4th Grade Teacher
May Watts Elementary School
Naperville, IL

**Lorraine Moore**
Grade 3 Math Teacher
Cowpens Elementary School
Cowpens, SC

**Shannon L. Moorhead**
4th Grade Teacher
Centerville Elementary
Anderson, SC

**Gina M. Musselman, M.Ed**
Kindergarten Teacher
Padeo Verde Elementary
Peoria, AZ

**Jen Neufeld**
3rd Grade Teacher
Kendall
Naperville, IL

**Cathie Osiecki**
K–5 Mathematics Coordinator
Middletown Public Schools
Middletown, CT

**Phyllis L. Pacilli**
Elementary Education Teacher
Fullerton Elementary
Addison, IL

**Cindy Pearson**
4th/5th Grade Teacher
John D. Spicer Elementary
Haltom City, TX

**Herminio M. Planas**
Mathematics Curriculum Specialist
Administrative Offices-Bridgeport Public Schools
Bridgeport, Connecticut

**Jo J. Puree**
Educator
Lackamas Elementary
Yelm, WA

**Teresa M. Reynolds**
Third Grade Teacher
Forrest View Elementary
Everett, WA

**Dr. John A. Rhodes**
Director of Mathematics
Indian Prairie SD #204
Aurora, IL

**Amy Romm**
First Grade Teacher
Starline Elementary
Lake Havasu, AZ

**Delores M. Rushing**
Numeracy Coach
Dept. of Academic Services-Mathematics Department
Washington, DC

**Daniel L. Scudder**
Mathematics/Technology Specialist
Boone Elementary
Houston, TX

**Laura Seymour**
Resource Teacher Leader – Elementary Math & Science, Retired
Dearborn Public Schools
Dearborn, MI

**Petra Siprian**
Teacher
Army Trail Elementary School
Addison, IL

**Sandra Stein**
K–5 Mathematics Consultant
St. Clair County Regional Educational Service Agency
Marysville, MI

**Barb Stoflet**
Curriculum Specialist
Roseville Area Schools
Roseville, MN

**Kim Summers**
Principal
Dynard Elementary
Chaptico, MD

**Ann C. Teater**
4th Grade Teacher
Lancaster Elementary
Lancaster, KY

**Anne E. Tunney**
Teacher
City of Erie School District
Erie, PA

**Joylien Weathers**
1st Grade Teacher
Mesa View Elementary
Grand Junction, CO

**Christine F. Weiss**
Third Grade Teacher
Robert C. Hill Elementary School
Romeoville, IL

# Mathematics Teacher Handbook

# Table of Contents

## PreK–12 Mathematics: Focus on Grade 4

# Welcome to Math Connects

## Concepts • Skills • Problem Solving

The only true vertically aligned PreK–12 Mathematics Curriculum

***Math Connects*** offers three dimensions of vertical alignment.

### ❶ Content Design

Vertical content alignment is a process that ensures you and your students experience an articulated, coherent sequence of content from grade level to grade level. This provides you with the assurance that content is introduced, reinforced, and assessed at appropriate times in the series, eliminating gaps and unnecessary duplication. You are able to target your instruction to student needs because you are not teaching content intended to be covered later or that students have previously mastered.

### ❷ Instructional Design

Our strong vertical alignment in instructional approach from PreKindergarten through Algebra 2 provides a smooth transition for students from elementary to middle school to high school. Our common vocabulary, technology, manipulatives, lesson planning, and Data-Driven Decision Making reduces the confusion students often encounter when transitioning between grade levels without this built-in articulation.

### ❸ Visual Design

The student pages of ***Math Connects*** have a consistent visual design from grade to grade. This aids students' transition from elementary school to middle school and from middle school to Algebra 1. Students are more likely to succeed when they are already familiar with how to navigate student pages.

PreK-2

3–5

# 5 Keys to Success

## ❶ Backmapping

According to College Board research, about 80% of students who successfully complete Algebra 1 and Geometry by 10th grade attend and succeed in college. (Changing the Odds: Factors Increasing Access to College, 1990) ***Math Connects*** was conceived and developed by backmapping with the final result in mind–student success in Algebra 1 and beyond.

## ❷ Balanced, In-Depth Content

***Math Connects*** was developed to specifically target the skills and topics that give students the most difficulty, such as Problem Solving, in each grade span.

| Grades K–2 | Grades 3–5 |
|---|---|
| 1. Problem Solving<br>2. Money<br>3. Time<br>4. Measurement<br>5. Fractions<br>6. Computation | 1. Problem Solving<br>2. Fractions<br>3. Measurement<br>4. Decimals<br>5. Time<br>6. Algebra |
| **Grades 6–8** | **Grades 9–12** |
| 1. Fractions<br>2. Problem Solving<br>3. Measurement<br>4. Algebra<br>5. Computation | 1. Problem Solving<br>2. Fractions<br>3. Algebra<br>4. Geometry<br>5. Computation<br>6. Probability |

– *K–12 Math Market Analysis Survey,* Open Book Publishing, 2006

## ❸ Ongoing Assessment

***Math Connects*** includes diagnostic, formative, and summative assessment; data-driven instruction; intervention options; and performance tracking, as well as remediation, acceleration, and enrichment tools throughout the program.

## ❹ Intervention and Differentiated Instruction

A three-tiered Response To Intervention (RTI) is provided.

TIER 1 **Daily Intervention** Reteach masters and Alternative Strategy suggestions address concepts from a different modality or learning style.

TIER 2 **Strategic Intervention** Teachers can use the myriad of intervention tips and ancillary materials, such as the Strategic Intervention Guide (1–5) and Study Guide and Intervention (6–8).

TIER 3 **Intensive Intervention** For students who are two or more years below grade level, ***Math Triumphs*** provides step-by-step instruction, vocabulary support, and data-driven decision making to help students succeed.

## ❺ Professional Development

***Math Connects*** includes many opportunities for teacher professional development. Additional learning opportunities in various formats–video, online, and on-site instruction–are fully aligned and articulated from Kindergarten through Algebra 2.

6–8 | Pre-Algebra and Algebra 1 | Geometry and Algebra 2

# The Research Base

Continuous research with teachers, students, academician, and leading experts helps to build a solid foundation for ***Math Connects.***

## 1 Program Development Research

- Evaluating state and local standards
- Qualitative market research
- Academic content research

For more detailed information about our classroom research results, please consult the ***Math Connects*** *Program Efficacy Research Report.*

# for *Math Connects*

## 2 Formative Research

- Pedagogical research base
- Classroom field tests
- Teacher advisory boards
- Academic consultants and reviewers

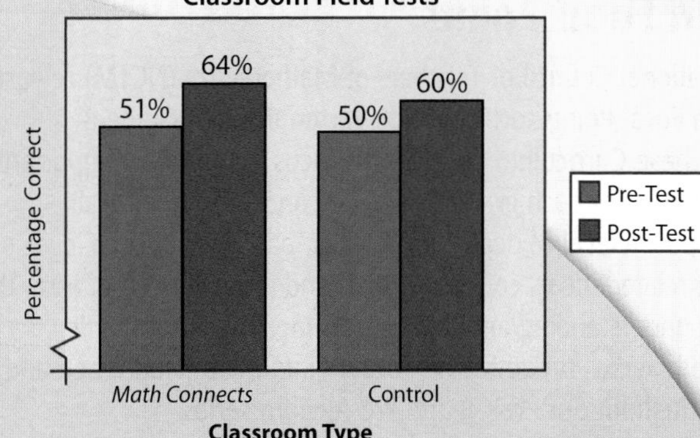


Students using a field test of the ***Math Connects*** program **(experimental group)** had ***higher*** pre-test to post-test gains than students using other textbook programs **(control group)**.

## 3 Summative Research

- Evidence of increased test scores
- Quasi-experimental program efficacy research
- Longitudinal studies
- Qualitative program evaluations

Access all ***Math Connects*** research at macmillanmh.com.

# NCTM Focal Points

## The NCTM Focal Points

In 2006, the National Council of Teachers of Mathematics (NCTM) released the Curriculum Focal Points for Pre-Kindergarten through Grade 8 Mathematics. These Curriculum Focal Points focus on the most important mathematical topics for each grade level. The concepts are vertically-aligned and expect a level of depth, complexity, and rigor at each level. They comprise related ideas, concepts, skills, and procedures that form the foundation for understanding and lasting learning. The Focal Points emphasize depth versus breadth. The Focal Points will be addressed and highlighted throughout our PreK-8 and Pre-Algebra series.

## What is the benefit to you in your classroom?

These Focal Points identify content for each grade level that should be mastered in order for your students to have true mathematical understanding–being able to not only calculate the answer, but to explain the answer and how to apply the calculation. The NCTM Focal Points were used as the basis in the development of ***Math Connects.*** The authors have incorporated the Focal Points into the content to assist you in building depth of understanding.

| NCTM Focal Points for Grade 4 | Supporting Chapters in ***Math Connects*** |
|---|---|
| *Number and Operations and Algebra* | Chapters 4, 5, 6, 7 |
| *Number and Operations* | Chapters 13, 14, 15 |
| *Measurement* | Chapters 11, 12 |
| **Connections to the Focal Points** | |
| Algebra | Chapters 2, 5 |
| Geometry | Chapters 9, 10, 11, 12 |
| Measurement | Chapter 9 |
| Data Analysis | Chapter 3 |
| Number and Operations | Chapters 1, 2, 8, 13, 14, 15 |

**The Curriculum Focal Points identify key mathematical ideas for this grade. They are not discrete topics or a checklist to be mastered; rather, they provide a framework for the majority of instruction at a particular grade level and the foundation for future mathematics study. The complete document may be viewed at www.nctm.org/focalpoints.**

**KEY**

**G4-FP1** Grade 4 Focal Point 1
**G4-FP2** Grade 4 Focal Point 2
**G4-FP3** Grade 4 Focal Point 3
**G4-FP4C** Grade 4 Focal Point 4 Connection
**G4-FP5C** Grade 4 Focal Point 5 Connection
**G4-FP6C** Grade 4 Focal Point 6 Connection
**G4-FP7C** Grade 4 Focal Point 7 Connection
**G4-FP8C** Grade 4 Focal Point 8 Connection

**G4-FP1** *Number and Operations* **and** *Algebra:* **Developing quick recall of multiplication facts and related division facts and fluency with whole number multiplication**

Students use understandings of multiplication to develop quick recall of the basic multiplication facts and related division facts. They apply their understanding of models for multiplication (i.e., equal sized groups, arrays, area models, equal intervals on the number line), place value, and properties of operations (in particular, the distributive property) as they develop, discuss, and use efficient, accurate, and generalizable methods to multiply multidigit whole numbers. They select appropriate methods and apply them accurately to estimate products or calculate them mentally, depending on the context and numbers involved. They develop fluency with efficient procedures, including the standard algorithm, for multiplying whole numbers, understand why the procedures work (on the basis of place value and properties of operations), and use them to solve problems.

**G4-FP2** *Number and Operations:* **Developing an understanding of decimals, including the connections between fractions and decimals**

Students understand decimal notation as an extension of the base-ten system of writing whole numbers that is useful for representing more numbers, including numbers between 0 and 1, between 1 and 2, and so on. Students relate their understanding of fractions to reading and writing decimals that are greater than or less than 1, identifying equivalent decimals, comparing and ordering decimals, and estimating decimal or fractional amounts in problem solving. They connect equivalent fractions and decimals by comparing models to symbols and locating equivalent symbols on the number line.

**G4-FP3** *Measurement:* **Developing an understanding of area and determining the areas of two-dimensional shapes**

Students recognize area as an attribute of two-dimensional regions. They learn that they can quantify area by finding the total number of same-sized units of area that cover the shape without gaps or overlaps. They understand that a square that is 1 unit on a side is the standard unit for measuring area. They select appropriate units, strategies (e.g., decomposing shapes), and tools for solving problems that involve estimating or measuring area. Students connect area measure to the area model that they have used to represent multiplication, and they use this connection to justify the formula for the area of a rectangle.

## Connections to the Focal Points

**G4-FP4C** *Algebra:* Students continue identifying, describing, and extending numeric patterns involving all operations and nonnumeric growing or repeating patterns. Through these experiences, they develop an understanding of the use of a rule to describe a sequence of numbers or objects.

**G4-FP5C** *Geometry:* Students extend their understanding of properties of two-dimensional shapes as they find the areas of polygons. They build on their earlier work with symmetry and congruence in grade 3 to encompass transformations, including those that produce line and rotational symmetry. By using transformations to design and analyze simple tilings and tessellations, students deepen their understanding of two-dimensional space.

**G4-FP6C** *Measurement:* As part of understanding two-dimensional shapes, students measure and classify angles.

**G4-FP7C** *Data Analysis:* Students continue to use tools from grade 3, solving problems by making frequency tables, bar graphs, picture graphs, and line plots. They apply their understanding of place value to develop and use stem-and-leaf plots.

**G4-FP8C** *Number and Operations:* Building on their work in grade 3, students extend their understanding of place value and ways of representing numbers to 100,000 in various contexts. They use estimation in determining the relative sizes of amounts or distances. Students develop understandings of strategies for multidigit division by using models that represent division as the inverse of multiplication, as partitioning, or as successive subtraction. By working with decimals, students extend their ability to recognize equivalent fractions. Students' earlier work in grade 3 with models of fractions and multiplication and division facts supports their understanding of techniques for generating equivalent fractions and simplifying fractions.

# Program Philosophy

## Balanced Instruction, Vertically-Aligned from Grades PreK through Algebra 1

The vertical alignment of ***Math Connects*** PreK-8 and ***Algebra 1*** incorporates a balance of instruction throughout. These programs provide students a balanced approach to mathematics by:

- investigating concepts and building conceptual understanding.
- developing, reinforcing, and mastering computational and procedural skills.
- applying mathematics to problem-solving situations.

This sequence of Student Edition pages illustrates the vertically-aligned development of the conceptual understanding and corresponding computational and procedural skills for an important algebra topic.

**Primary** Students use two-color counters to model addition sentences. This activity forms a basis for future understanding of and success in solving algebraic equations.

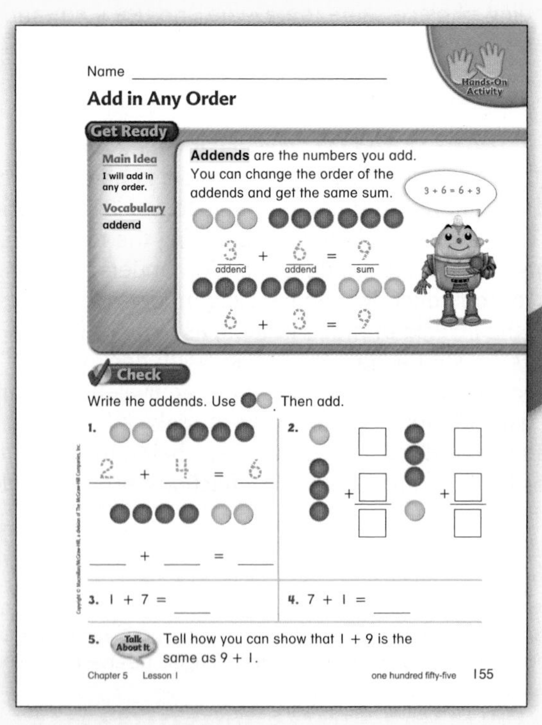

Name ______________________

Hands-On Activity

**Add in Any Order**

**Get Ready**

**Main Idea**
I will add in any order.

**Vocabulary**
addend

**Addends** are the numbers you add. You can change the order of the addends and get the same sum.

$3 + 6 = 6 + 3$

$3 + 6 = 9$ (addend, addend, sum)

$6 + 3 = 9$

**Check**

Write the addends. Use counters. Then add.

1. $2 + 4 = 6$ ; ___ + ___ = ___
2. ☐ + ☐ = ☐ ; ☐ + ☐ = ☐
3. $1 + 7 =$ ____
4. $7 + 1 =$ ____
5. Talk About It: Tell how you can show that $1 + 9$ is the same as $9 + 1$.

Chapter 5 Lesson 1 — one hundred fifty-five 155

*Math Connects*, Grade 1, Student Edition, page 155

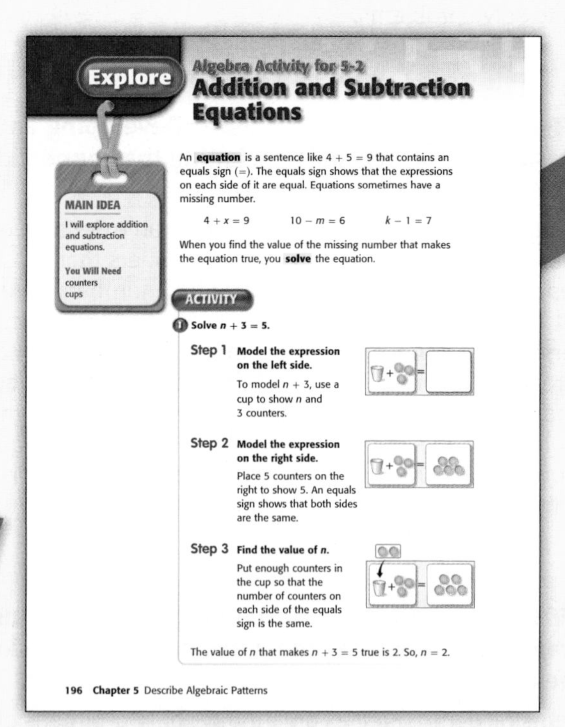

**Explore**

Algebra Activity for 5-2

**Addition and Subtraction Equations**

**MAIN IDEA**
I will explore addition and subtraction equations.

**You Will Need**
counters
cups

An **equation** is a sentence like $4 + 5 = 9$ that contains an equals sign (=). The equals sign shows that the expressions on each side of it are equal. Equations sometimes have a missing number.

$4 + x = 9$ $\quad$ $10 - m = 6$ $\quad$ $k - 1 = 7$

When you find the value of the missing number that makes the equation true, you **solve** the equation.

**ACTIVITY**

1 Solve $n + 3 = 5$.

**Step 1** **Model the expression on the left side.** To model $n + 3$, use a cup to show $n$ and 3 counters.

**Step 2** **Model the expression on the right side.** Place 5 counters on the right to show 5. An equals sign shows that both sides are the same.

**Step 3** **Find the value of $n$.** Put enough counters in the cup so that the number of counters on each side of the equals sign is the same.

The value of $n$ that makes $n + 3 = 5$ true is 2. So, $n = 2$.

196 Chapter 5 Describe Algebraic Patterns

*Math Connects*, Grade 4, Student Edition, page 196

**Intermediate** Students build on their experience with counters to using cups and counters to model and solve addition and subtraction equations. The exercises are designed to help students bridge the gap from using cups and counters to solving equations symbolically.

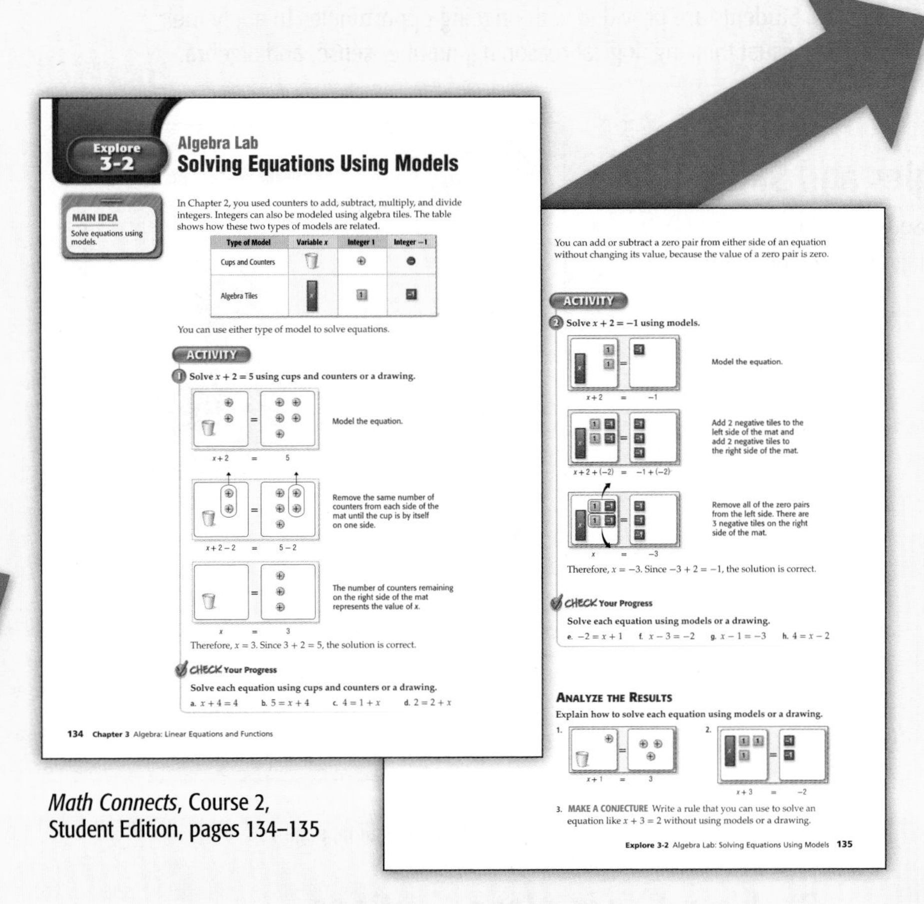

## Explore 3-2 Algebra Lab
## Solving Equations Using Models

**MAIN IDEA**
Solve equations using models.

In Chapter 2, you used counters to add, subtract, multiply, and divide integers. Integers can also be modeled using algebra tiles. The table shows how these two types of models are related.

| Type of Model | Variable $x$ | Integer 1 | Integer −1 |
|---|---|---|---|
| Cups and Counters | | | |
| Algebra Tiles | $x$ | 1 | −1 |

You can use either type of model to solve equations.

**ACTIVITY**

**1 Solve $x + 2 = 5$ using cups and counters or a drawing.**

$x + 2 = 5$ — Model the equation.

$x + 2 - 2 = 5 - 2$ — Remove the same number of counters from each side of the mat until the cup is by itself on one side.

$x = 3$ — The number of counters remaining on the right side of the mat represents the value of $x$.

Therefore, $x = 3$. Since $3 + 2 = 5$, the solution is correct.

**CHECK Your Progress**

**Solve each equation using cups and counters or a drawing.**

a. $x + 4 = 4$ b. $5 = x + 4$ c. $4 = 1 + x$ d. $2 = 2 + x$

134 Chapter 3 Algebra: Linear Equations and Functions

You can add or subtract a zero pair from either side of an equation without changing its value, because the value of a zero pair is zero.

**ACTIVITY**

**2 Solve $x + 2 = -1$ using models.**

$x + 2 = -1$ — Model the equation.

$x + 2 + (-2) = -1 + (-2)$ — Add 2 negative tiles to the left side of the mat and add 2 negative tiles to the right side of the mat.

$x = -3$ — Remove all of the zero pairs from the left side. There are 3 negative tiles on the right side of the mat.

Therefore, $x = -3$. Since $-3 + 2 = -1$, the solution is correct.

**CHECK Your Progress**

**Solve each equation using models or a drawing.**

e. $-2 = x + 1$ f. $x - 3 = -2$ g. $x - 1 = -3$ h. $4 = x - 2$

**ANALYZE THE RESULTS**

**Explain how to solve each equation using models or a drawing.**

1. $x + 1 = 3$
2. $x + 3 = -2$
3. **MAKE A CONJECTURE** Write a rule that you can use to solve an equation like $x + 3 = 2$ without using models or a drawing.

Explore 3-2 Algebra Lab: Solving Equations Using Models 135

*Math Connects*, Course 2,
Student Edition, pages 134–135

**Middle School** Students represent the variable *x* as a cup, as a counter, or as a written *x*. In this Algebra Lab, students make the transition from cups and counters to the more abstract algebra tiles. In the next lesson, students solve simple equations symbolically.

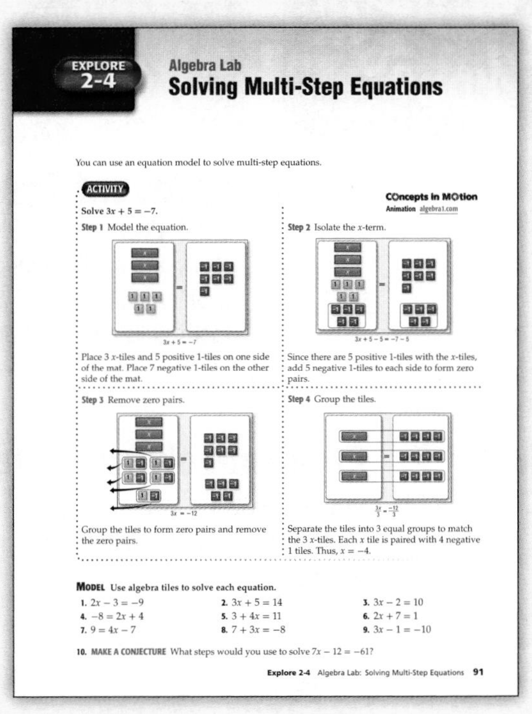

## EXPLORE 2-4 Algebra Lab
## Solving Multi-Step Equations

You can use an equation model to solve multi-step equations.

**ACTIVITY**

Concepts in MOtion
Animation algebra1.com

**Solve $3x + 5 = -7$.**

**Step 1** Model the equation.

$3x + 5 = -7$

Place 3 $x$-tiles and 5 positive 1-tiles on one side of the mat. Place 7 negative 1-tiles on the other side of the mat.

**Step 2** Isolate the $x$-term.

$3x + 5 - 5 = -7 - 5$

Since there are 5 positive 1-tiles with the $x$-tiles, add 5 negative 1-tiles to each side to form zero pairs.

**Step 3** Remove zero pairs.

$3x = -12$

Group the tiles to form zero pairs and remove the zero pairs.

**Step 4** Group the tiles.

$\frac{3x}{3} = \frac{-12}{3}$

Separate the tiles into 3 equal groups to match the 3 $x$-tiles. Each $x$ tile is paired with 4 negative 1 tiles. Thus, $x = -4$.

**MODEL** **Use algebra tiles to solve each equation.**

1. $2x - 3 = -9$
2. $3x + 5 = 14$
3. $3x - 2 = 10$
4. $-8 = 2x + 4$
5. $3 + 4x = 11$
6. $2x + 7 = 1$
7. $9 = 4x - 7$
8. $7 + 3x = -8$
9. $3x - 1 = -10$
10. **MAKE A CONJECTURE** What steps would you use to solve $7x - 12 = -61$?

Explore 2-4 Algebra Lab: Solving Multi-Step Equations 91

*Glencoe Algebra 1*,
Student Edition, page 91

**Algebra 1** Students continue the use of algebra tiles to investigate solving multi-step equations. In the next lesson, students apply the procedure developed in the Algebra Lab to a symbolic approach.

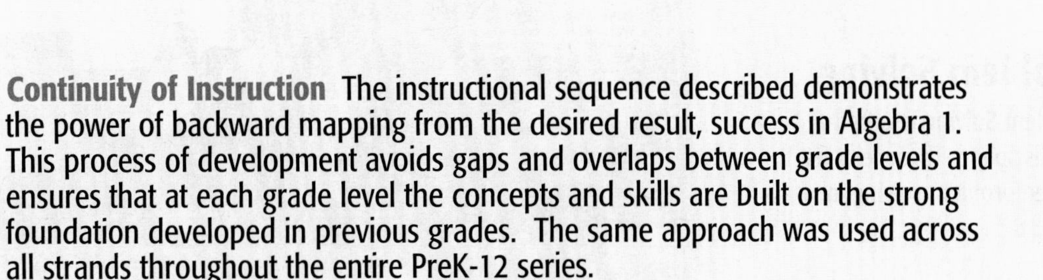

**Continuity of Instruction** The instructional sequence described demonstrates the power of backward mapping from the desired result, success in Algebra 1. This process of development avoids gaps and overlaps between grade levels and ensures that at each grade level the concepts and skills are built on the strong foundation developed in previous grades. The same approach was used across all strands throughout the entire PreK-12 series.

# Program Philosophy Balance of Instruction

## Relevant Problem Solving

***Math Connects*** provides students with the appropriate development of problem-solving strategies, skills, and applications from PreK through grade 5. In grades 6–8, students continue to learn and apply problem-solving skills and strategies. Students are provided with ongoing opportunities to apply their math skills and solve problems using visual thinking, logical reasoning, number sense, and algebra.

### Problem-Solving Strategies and Skills

**Problem-Solving Strategy** or **Skill** lessons introduce students to multiples methods for solving problems all using the *four-step* plan.

- Understand
- Plan
- Solve
- Check

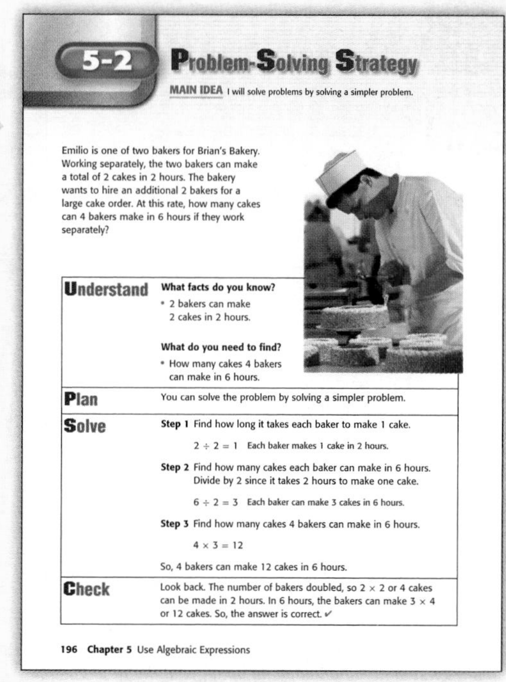

5-2 Problem-Solving Strategy

MAIN IDEA I will solve problems by solving a simpler problem.

Emilio is one of two bakers for Brian's Bakery. Working separately, the two bakers can make a total of 2 cakes in 2 hours. The bakery wants to hire an additional 2 bakers for a large cake order. At this rate, how many cakes can 4 bakers make in 6 hours if they work separately?

| | |
|---|---|
| Understand | What facts do you know?<br>• 2 bakers can make 2 cakes in 2 hours.<br>What do you need to find?<br>• How many cakes 4 bakers can make in 6 hours. |
| Plan | You can solve the problem by solving a simpler problem. |
| Solve | Step 1 Find how long it takes each baker to make 1 cake.<br>$2 \div 2 = 1$ Each baker makes 1 cake in 2 hours.<br>Step 2 Find how many cakes each baker can make in 6 hours. Divide by 2 since it takes 2 hours to make one cake.<br>$6 \div 2 = 3$ Each baker can make 3 cakes in 6 hours.<br>Step 3 Find how many cakes 4 bakers can make in 6 hours.<br>$4 \times 3 = 12$<br>So, 4 bakers can make 12 cakes in 6 hours. |
| Check | Look back. The number of bakers doubled, so $2 \times 2$ or 4 cakes can be made in 2 hours. In 6 hours, the bakers can make $3 \times 4$ or 12 cakes. So, the answer is correct. ✓ |

196 Chapter 5 Use Algebraic Expressions

*Math Connects,* Grade 5
Student Edition, page 196

### Problem-Solving Investigations

Problem-Solving Investigation lessons help students learn to choose appropriate strategies and apply them in problem-solving situations.

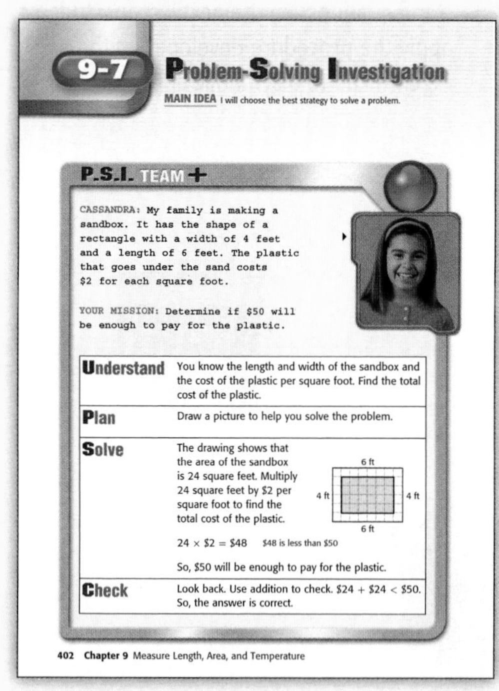

9-7 Problem-Solving Investigation

MAIN IDEA I will choose the best strategy to solve a problem.

P.S.I. TEAM +

CASSANDRA: My family is making a sandbox. It has the shape of a rectangle with a width of 4 feet and a length of 6 feet. The plastic that goes under the sand costs $2 for each square foot.

YOUR MISSION: Determine if $50 will be enough to pay for the plastic.

| | |
|---|---|
| Understand | You know the length and width of the sandbox and the cost of the plastic per square foot. Find the total cost of the plastic. |
| Plan | Draw a picture to help you solve the problem. |
| Solve | The drawing shows that the area of the sandbox is 24 square feet. Multiply 24 square feet by $2 per square foot to find the total cost of the plastic.<br>$24 \times \$2 = \$48$ $48 is less than $50<br>So, $50 will be enough to pay for the plastic. |
| Check | Look back. Use addition to check. $\$24 + \$24 < \$50$. So, the answer is correct. |

402 Chapter 9 Measure Length, Area, and Temperature

*Math Connects,* Grade 3
Student Edition, page 402

### Real-World Problem Solving

Each chapter has a Problem Solving lesson that makes a tie to another discipline. These lessons encourage students to see problem solving in real-world applications.

Problem Solving in Science

EMPERORS OF THE ICE

There are 17 different types of penguins. Emperor penguins are the tallest and heaviest penguins. An Emperor penguin is over 3 feet tall and can weigh from 42 to 101 pounds. The average Emperor penguin weighs 66 pounds and can swim 15 miles per hour.

About 200,000 pairs of Emperor penguins live in 40 different groups in Antarctica. Penguins huddle together to share their body heat during the cold winter temperatures and bitter winds.

Did You Know? Emperor penguins usually dive 60 to 70 feet. An average dive lasts 3 to 6 minutes.

Real-World Math

Use the information on pages 256 and 257 to solve each problem.

1. Suppose that eight average-sized Emperor penguins are standing together. What is their total weight?
2. Six penguins of varying weights are standing together. What is the least they can weigh? the most?
3. Suppose a penguin's dive lasts 4 minutes. How many times did its heart beat during the dive?
4. How many miles can a penguin swim in 3 hours?
5. Suppose it takes a penguin 3 minutes to walk from its resting place to the place where it dives. What is a reasonable number of times its heart beats in these three minutes before it dives?
6. Based on the following table, estimate how many times a penguin's heart beats after completing all of the activities listed for two minutes each.

Penguin Heartbeat

| Activity | Heartbeat (beats per minute) |
|---|---|
| Resting | 65 |
| Before a dive | 180–200 |
| Hitting the water | 100 |
| Diving | 20 |
| Returning to surface | 200 |

256 Chapter 6 Multiply by One-Digit Numbers

Problem Solving in Science 257

*Math Connects,* Grade 4
Student Edition, pages 256–257

## Real-World Problem Solving Readers

Fiction and nonfiction leveled readers extend problem-solving skills and strategies and make real-world applications. The books are provided for On Level, Sheltered English, and Spanish readers.

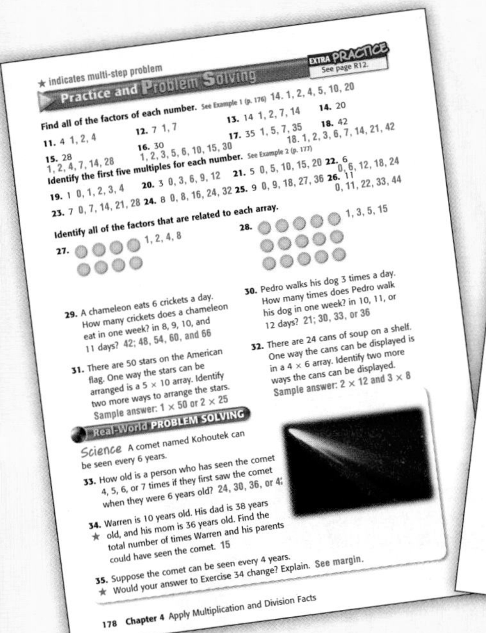

★ indicates multi-step problem

Practice and Problem Solving — EXTRA PRACTICE See page R12.

Find all of the factors of each number. See Example 1 (p. 176)

11. 4 1, 2, 4 12. 7 1, 7 13. 14 1, 2, 7, 14 14. 20 1, 2, 4, 5, 10, 20
15. 28 1, 2, 4, 7, 14, 28 16. 30 1, 2, 3, 5, 6, 10, 15, 30 17. 35 1, 5, 7, 35 18. 42 1, 2, 3, 6, 7, 14, 21, 42

Identify the first five multiples for each number. See Example 2 (p. 177)

19. 1 0, 1, 2, 3, 4 20. 3 0, 3, 6, 9, 12 21. 5 0, 5, 10, 15, 20 22. 6 0, 6, 12, 18, 24
23. 7 0, 7, 14, 21, 28 24. 8 0, 8, 16, 24, 32 25. 9 0, 9, 18, 27, 36 26. 11 0, 11, 22, 33, 44

Identify all of the factors that are related to each array.

27. 1, 2, 4, 8 28. 1, 3, 5, 15

29. A chameleon eats 6 crickets a day. How many crickets does a chameleon eat in one week? in 8, 9, 10, and 11 days? 42; 48, 54, 60, and 66

30. Pedro walks his dog 3 times a day. How many times does Pedro walk his dog in one week? in 10, 11, or 12 days? 21; 30, 33, or 36

31. There are 50 stars on the American flag. One way the stars can be arranged is a 5 × 10 array. Identify two more ways to arrange the stars. Sample answer: 1 × 50 or 2 × 25

32. There are 24 cans of soup on a shelf. One way the cans can be displayed is in a 4 × 6 array. Identify two more ways the cans can be displayed. Sample answer: 2 × 12 and 3 × 8

Real-World PROBLEM SOLVING

Science A comet named Kohoutek can be seen every 6 years.

33. How old is a person who has seen the comet 4, 5, 6, or 7 times if they first saw the comet when they were 6 years old? 24, 30, 36, or 42

34. ★ Warren is 10 years old. His dad is 38 years old, and his mom is 36 years old. Find the total number of times Warren and his parents could have seen the comet. 15

35. ★ Suppose the comet can be seen every 4 years. Would your answer to Exercise 34 change? Explain. See margin.

178 Chapter 4 Apply Multiplication and Division Facts

*Math Connects*, Grade 4
Student Edition, page 162

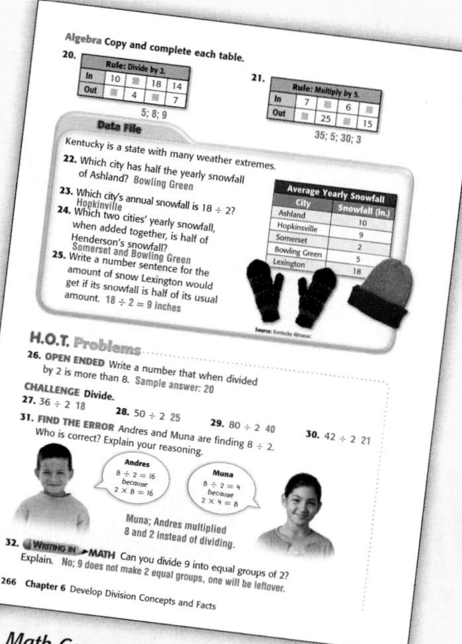

Algebra Copy and complete each table.

20. Rule: Divide by 2.

| In | 10 | ■ | 18 | 14 |
|---|---|---|---|---|
| Out | ■ | 4 | ■ | 7 |

5; 8; 9

21. Rule: Multiply by 5.

| In | 7 | ■ | 6 | ■ |
|---|---|---|---|---|
| Out | ■ | 25 | ■ | 15 |

35; 5; 30; 3

Data File

Kentucky is a state with many weather extremes.

22. Which city has half the yearly snowfall of Ashland? Bowling Green

23. Which city's annual snowfall is 18 ÷ 2? Hopkinsville

24. Which two cities' yearly snowfall, when added together, is half of Henderson's snowfall? Somerset and Bowling Green

25. Write a number sentence for the amount of snow Lexington would get if its snowfall is half of its usual amount. 18 ÷ 2 = 9 inches

Average Yearly Snowfall

| City | Snowfall (in.) |
|---|---|
| Ashland | 10 |
| Hopkinsville | 9 |
| Somerset | 2 |
| Bowling Green | 5 |
| Lexington | 18 |

Source: Kentucky Almanac

H.O.T. Problems

26. OPEN ENDED Write a number that when divided by 2 is more than 8. Sample answer: 20

CHALLENGE Divide.

27. 36 ÷ 2 18 28. 50 ÷ 2 25 29. 80 ÷ 2 40 30. 42 ÷ 2 21

31. FIND THE ERROR Andres and Muna are finding 8 ÷ 2. Who is correct? Explain your reasoning.

Andres: 8 ÷ 2 = 16 because 2 × 8 = 16
Muna: 8 ÷ 2 = 4 because 2 × 4 = 8

Muna; Andres multiplied 8 and 2 instead of dividing.

32. WRITING IN MATH Can you divide 9 into equal groups of 2? Explain. No; 9 does not make 2 equal groups, one will be leftover.

266 Chapter 6 Develop Division Concepts and Facts

*Math Connects*, Grade 3
Student Edition, page 266

## Multi-Step Word Problems

Multi-step word problems are not simple computation problems using the numbers given. Students must analyze exactly what the problem is asking and how to use the information given. These problems are starred in the Teacher Edition.

## H.O.T. Problems

H.O.T. Problems require students to use **Higher Order Thinking** skills to solve problems.

## Looking Ahead

Looking Ahead lessons introduce important concepts and skills that students can use.

*Math Connects,* Grade 5
Student Edition, page LA0–LA1

# Comprehensive Assessment System

## Data-Driven Decision Making

***Math Connects*** offers frequent and meaningful assessment of student progress within the curriculum structure and printed teacher support materials. See pages T22 and T23 for digital assessment solutions.

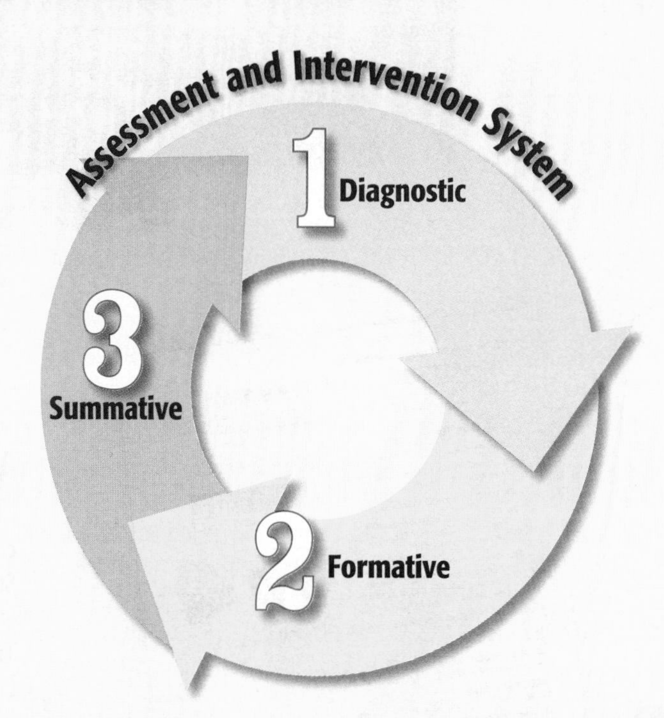


## 1 Diagnostic

**Initial Assessment** Assess students' knowledge **at the beginning of the year** with the *Diagnostic and Placement Tests*. This booklet will help you determine whether your students need additional materials and resources to meet grade-level standards.

**Entry–Level Assessment** Assess students' prior knowledge **at the beginning of a chapter or lesson** with one of the following options.

### Student Edition

- Are You Ready?

### Teacher Edition

- Intervention Options
- 5-Minute Check

### Additional Resources

- Chapter Resource Masters, Chapter Diagnostic Test

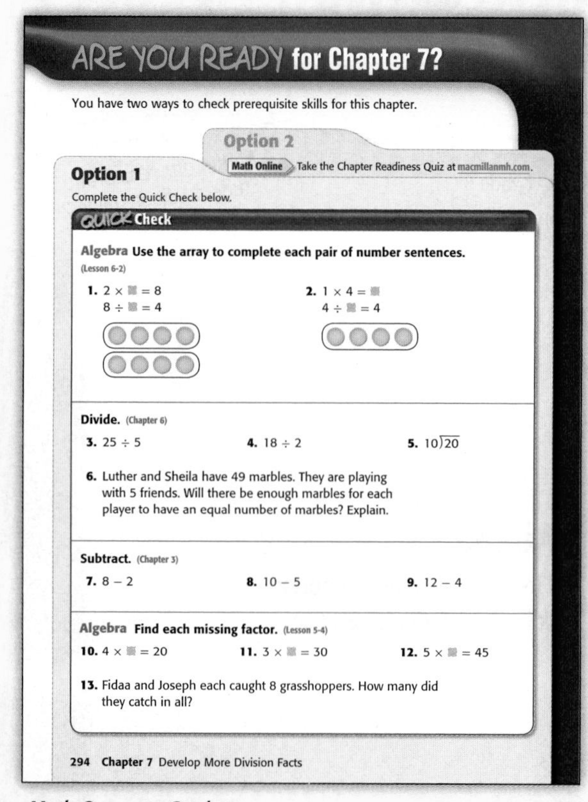

ARE YOU READY for Chapter 7?

You have two ways to check prerequisite skills for this chapter.

**Option 2**

Math Online Take the Chapter Readiness Quiz at macmillanmh.com.

**Option 1**

Complete the Quick Check below.

QUICK Check

**Algebra Use the array to complete each pair of number sentences.** (Lesson 6-2)

**1.** 2 × ■ = 8
8 ÷ ■ = 4

**2.** 1 × 4 = ■
4 ÷ ■ = 4

**Divide.** (Chapter 6)

**3.** 25 ÷ 5 **4.** 18 ÷ 2 **5.** $10\overline{)20}$

**6.** Luther and Sheila have 49 marbles. They are playing with 5 friends. Will there be enough marbles for each player to have an equal number of marbles? Explain.

**Subtract.** (Chapter 3)

**7.** 8 − 2 **8.** 10 − 5 **9.** 12 − 4

**Algebra Find each missing factor.** (Lesson 5-4)

**10.** 4 × ■ = 20 **11.** 3 × ■ = 30 **12.** 5 × ■ = 45

**13.** Fidaa and Joseph each caught 8 grasshoppers. How many did they catch in all?

294 Chapter 7 Develop More Division Facts

*Math Connects*, Grade 3
Student Edition, page 294

# Formative

**Progress Monitoring** Determine if students are progressing adequately as you teach each lesson. Use the assessments to differentiate lesson instruction and practice.

### Student Edition

- Mid-Chapter Check
- Find the Error
- Check What You Know
- Talk About It
- Writing in Math
- Study Guide and Review
- Foldables™

### Teacher Edition

- Alternate Teaching Strategy
- Step 4 (Assess) of the Teaching Plan
- Quick Check
- Data-Driven Decision Making

### Additional Resources

Chapter Resource Masters

- Mid-Chapter Test
- 3 Quizzes

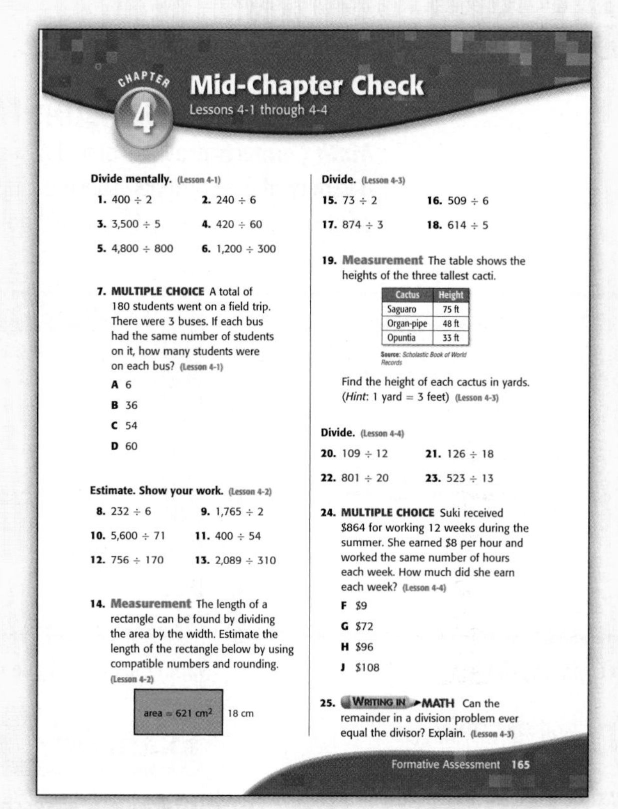

CHAPTER 4 **Mid-Chapter Check**
Lessons 4-1 through 4-4

**Divide mentally.** (Lesson 4-1)

1. 400 ÷ 2
2. 240 ÷ 6
3. 3,500 ÷ 5
4. 420 ÷ 60
5. 4,800 ÷ 800
6. 1,200 ÷ 300

7. **MULTIPLE CHOICE** A total of 180 students went on a field trip. There were 3 buses. If each bus had the same number of students on it, how many students were on each bus? (Lesson 4-1)
   **A** 6
   **B** 36
   **C** 54
   **D** 60

**Estimate. Show your work.** (Lesson 4-2)

8. 232 ÷ 6
9. 1,765 ÷ 2
10. 5,600 ÷ 71
11. 400 ÷ 54
12. 756 ÷ 170
13. 2,089 ÷ 310

14. **Measurement** The length of a rectangle can be found by dividing the area by the width. Estimate the length of the rectangle below by using compatible numbers and rounding. (Lesson 4-2)
   area = 621 $cm^2$ 18 cm

**Divide.** (Lesson 4-3)

15. 73 ÷ 2
16. 509 ÷ 6
17. 874 ÷ 3
18. 614 ÷ 5

19. **Measurement** The table shows the heights of the three tallest cacti.

| Cactus | Height |
|---|---|
| Saguaro | 75 ft |
| Organ-pipe | 48 ft |
| Opuntia | 33 ft |

Source: Scholastic Book of World Records

Find the height of each cactus in yards. (*Hint:* 1 yard = 3 feet) (Lesson 4-3)

**Divide.** (Lesson 4-4)

20. 109 ÷ 12
21. 126 ÷ 18
22. 801 ÷ 20
23. 523 ÷ 13

24. **MULTIPLE CHOICE** Suki received $864 for working 12 weeks during the summer. She earned $8 per hour and worked the same number of hours each week. How much did she earn each week? (Lesson 4-4)
   **F** $9
   **G** $72
   **H** $96
   **J** $108

25. WRITING IN MATH Can the remainder in a division problem ever equal the divisor? Explain. (Lesson 4-3)

Formative Assessment 165

*Math Connects,* Grade 5
Student Edition, page 165

# Summative

**Summative Evaluation** Assess student success in learning the concepts in each chapter.

### Student Edition

- Chapter Test
- Test Practice
- Foldables™

### Teacher Edition

- Data-Driven Decision Making

### Additional Resources

Chapter Resource Masters

- Oral Assessment
- Listening Assessment
- 4 Leveled Chapter Tests
- Cumulative Test

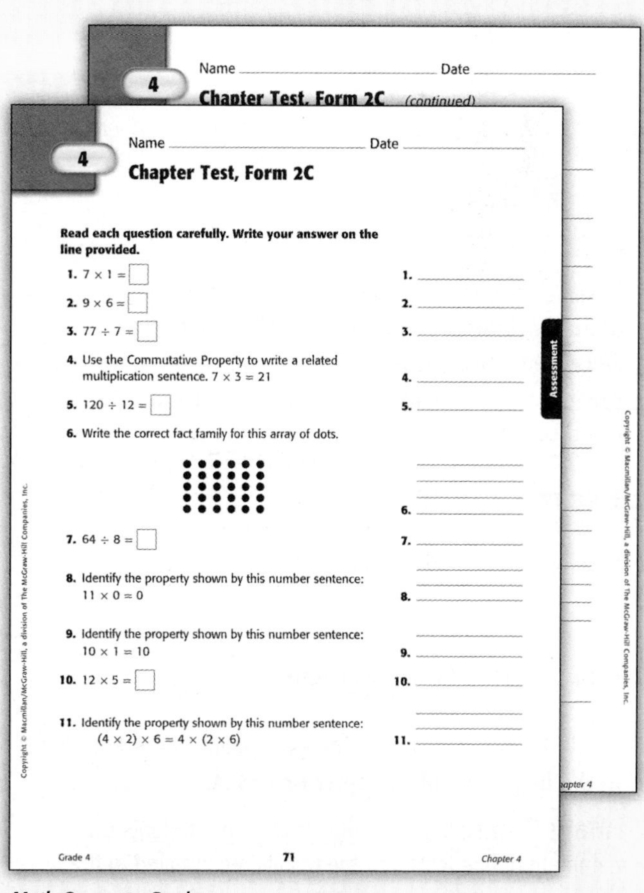

4 Name ______ Date ______
**Chapter Test, Form 2C** *(continued)*

4 Name ______ Date ______
**Chapter Test, Form 2C**

**Read each question carefully. Write your answer on the line provided.**

1. 7 × 1 = ☐
2. 9 × 6 = ☐
3. 77 ÷ 7 = ☐
4. Use the Commutative Property to write a related multiplication sentence. 7 × 3 = 21
5. 120 ÷ 12 = ☐
6. Write the correct fact family for this array of dots.
7. 64 ÷ 8 = ☐
8. Identify the property shown by this number sentence: 11 × 0 = 0
9. Identify the property shown by this number sentence: 10 × 1 = 10
10. 12 × 5 = ☐
11. Identify the property shown by this number sentence: (4 × 2) × 6 = 4 × (2 × 6)

Assessment

Copyright © Macmillan/McGraw-Hill, a division of The McGraw-Hill Companies, Inc.

Grade 4 71 Chapter 4

*Math Connects,* Grade 4
Chapter 8 Resource Masters, pages 71–72

# Comprehensive Assessment System

## Data-Driven Decision Making

***Math Connects*** provides digital assessment options to create, customize, administer, and instantly score a variety of assessments. These digital solutions offer the same quality assessments and reporting as the print resources in easy-to-use technology tools.

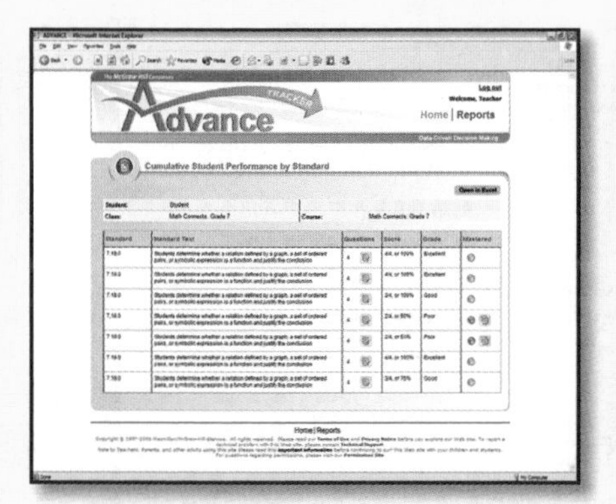

*Math Connects*, Grade 4

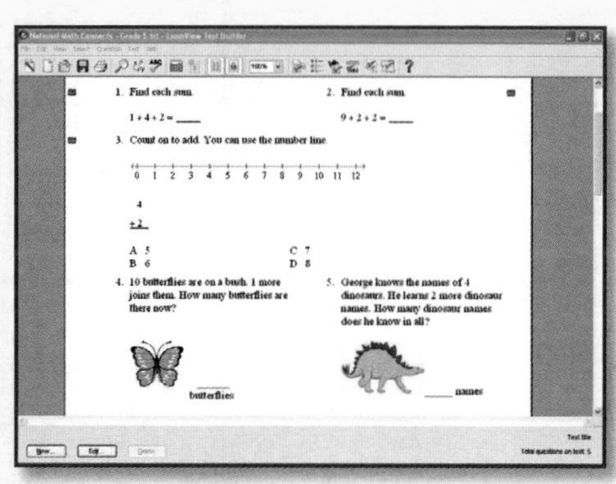

*Math Connects*, Grade 4

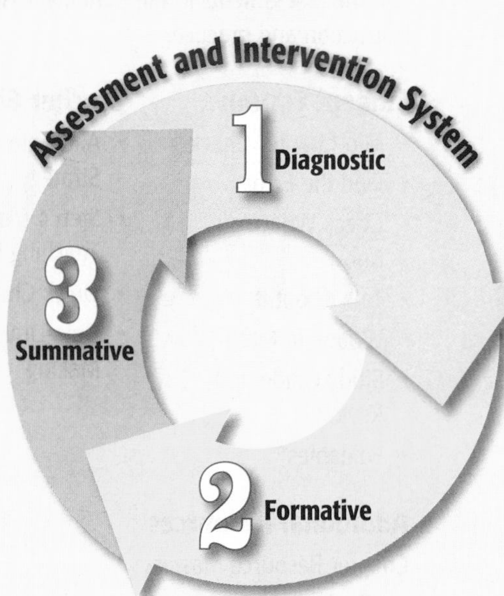

**Advance Tracker** helps teachers administer online tests, diagnose student achievement, and create prescriptive reports for a student or class.

**ExamView Assessment Suite** allows teachers to create and customize their own assessment and assignments. Print in one or two columns to match state test.

## 1 Diagnostic

**Initial Assessment** Assess students' knowledge **at the beginning of the year** with the *Diagnostic and Placement Tests.* These assessments will help you determine whether your students need additional materials and resources to meet grade-level standards.

- Diagnostic and Placement Tests

- Diagnostic and Placement Tests

**Entry-Level Assessment** Assess students' prior knowledge **at the beginning of a chapter or lesson.**

**Math Online** macmillanmh.com Students can complete online tests and the results are emailed to the teacher.

- Chapter Readiness

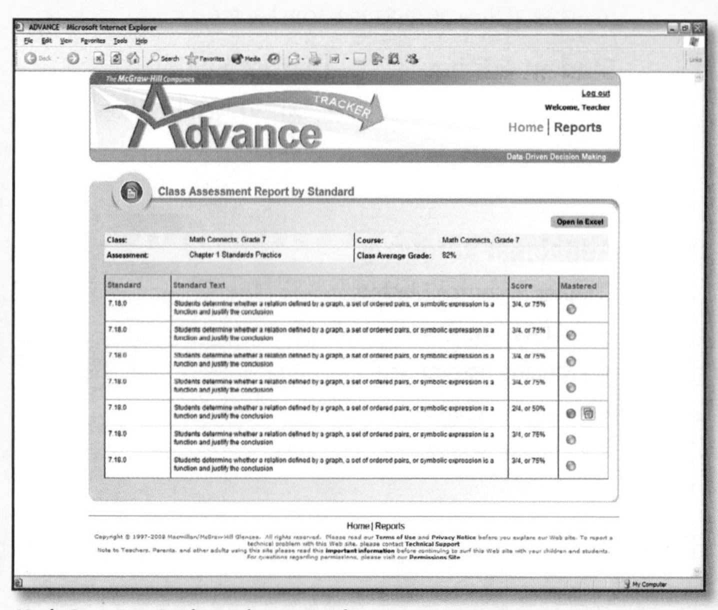


*Math Connects,* Grade 5 Advance Tracker

## Formative

**Progress Monitoring** Determine if students are progressing adequately as you teach each lesson. Use the assessments to differentiate lesson instruction and practice.

- Mid-Chapter Test
- Study Guide and Review

**Math Online** macmillanmh.com

- Self-Check Quizzes

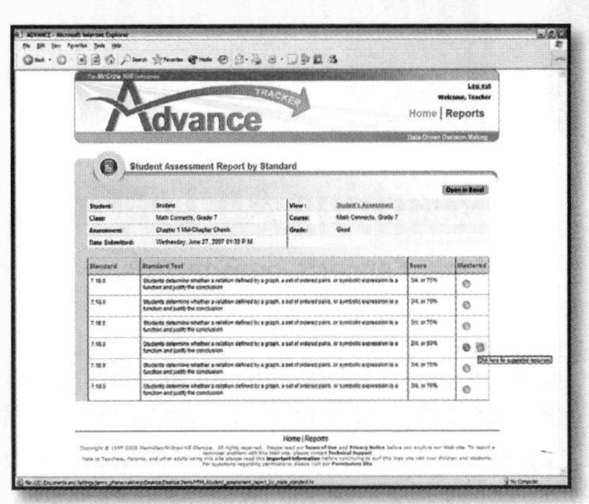


*Math Connects*, Grade 3, Advance Tracker

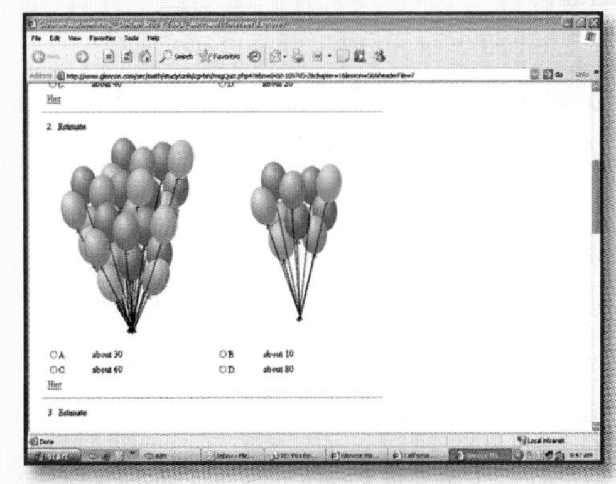


*Math Connects*, Grade 4, Self-Check Quiz

## Summative

**Summative Evaluation** Assess students' success in learning the concepts in each chapter.

- Chapter Tests
- Cumulative Standardized Test Practice

- Chapter Tests
- Cumulative Standardized Test Practice

**Math Online** macmillanmh.com

- Chapter Tests

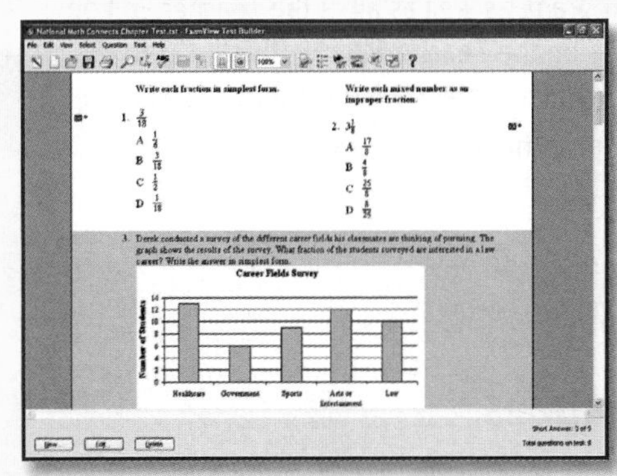


*Math Connects*, Grade 5, ExamView Assessment Suite

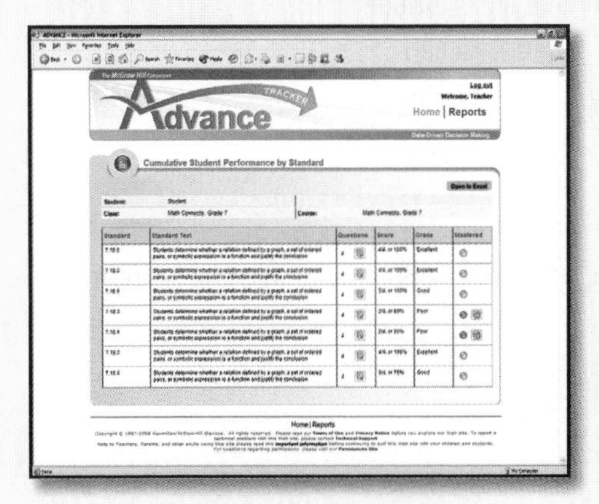


*Math Connects*, Grade 4, Advance Tracker

# Differentiated Instruction

## Reaching All Learners

***Math Connects,*** provides extensive support for reaching all learners.

Every chapter and lesson includes suggestions for identifying and meeting your students' needs. Strategies include differentiation in pacing and student grouping, alternate approaches, ways to enhance instruction with manipulatives, questions to promote higher-order thinking, and language hints.

Personalize instruction for:

- BL Students who are below or approaching grade level
- ELL English language learners
- AL Students who are above or beyond grade level

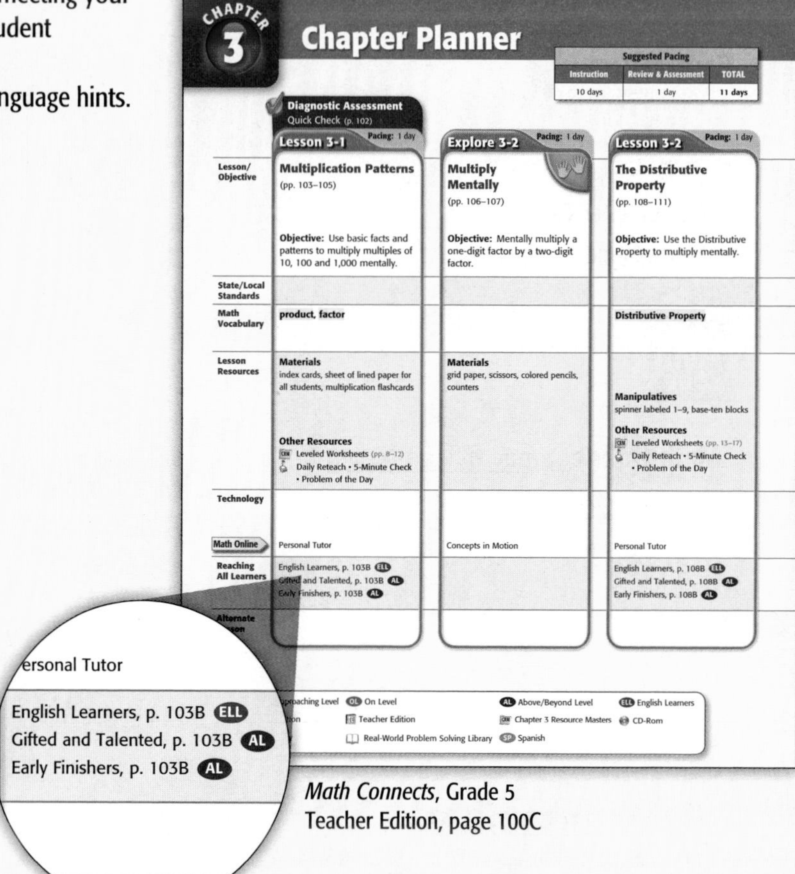

Chapter 3 Chapter Planner

| Suggested Pacing | | |
|---|---|---|
| Instruction | Review & Assessment | TOTAL |
| 10 days | 1 day | 11 days |

Diagnostic Assessment
Quick Check (p. 102)

| | Lesson 3-1 Pacing: 1 day | Explore 3-2 Pacing: 1 day | Lesson 3-2 Pacing: 1 day |
|---|---|---|---|
| Lesson/Objective | **Multiplication Patterns** (pp. 103–105) **Objective:** Use basic facts and patterns to multiply multiples of 10, 100 and 1,000 mentally. | **Multiply Mentally** (pp. 106–107) **Objective:** Mentally multiply a one-digit factor by a two-digit factor. | **The Distributive Property** (pp. 108–111) **Objective:** Use the Distributive Property to multiply mentally. |
| State/Local Standards | | | |
| Math Vocabulary | **product, factor** | | **Distributive Property** |
| Lesson Resources | **Materials** index cards, sheet of lined paper for all students, multiplication flashcards **Other Resources** Leveled Worksheets (pp. 8–12) Daily Reteach • 5-Minute Check • Problem of the Day | **Materials** grid paper, scissors, colored pencils, counters | **Manipulatives** spinner labeled 1–9, base-ten blocks **Other Resources** Leveled Worksheets (pp. 13–17) Daily Reteach • 5-Minute Check • Problem of the Day |
| Technology | | | |
| Math Online | Personal Tutor | Concepts in Motion | Personal Tutor |
| Reaching All Learners | English Learners, p. 103B ELL Gifted and Talented, p. 103B AL Early Finishers, p. 103B AL | | English Learners, p. 108B ELL Gifted and Talented, p. 108B AL Early Finishers, p. 108B AL |
| Alternate Lesson | | | |

OL On Level · AL Above/Beyond Level · ELL English Learners · Teacher Edition · Chapter 3 Resource Masters · CD-Rom · Real-World Problem Solving Library · SP Spanish

Personal Tutor
English Learners, p. 103B ELL
Gifted and Talented, p. 103B AL
Early Finishers, p. 103B AL

*Math Connects*, Grade 5
Teacher Edition, page 100C

## Leveled Exercise Sets

The assignments for each lesson are leveled for students.

- BL Below or Approaching Grade Level
- OL on Grade Level
- AL Above or Beyond Grade Level

## Leveled Resources

All of the blackline masters and transparencies that accompany the program, as well as all of the Teacher Edition pages, are available on the **TeacherWorks Plus™ CD-ROM.** Resources and assignments are leveled for students who are:

- BL Below or Approaching Grade Level
- OL On Grade Level
- AL Above or Beyond Grade Level
- ELL English Language Learners

## Learning Stations

Cross-curricular learning centers offer students guided opportunities to explore chapter concepts as individuals or in small groups. Content areas include:

- Science
- Social Studies
- Reading
- Art
- Health
- Writing
- Music

Learning Station cards are English on one side and Spanish on the other.

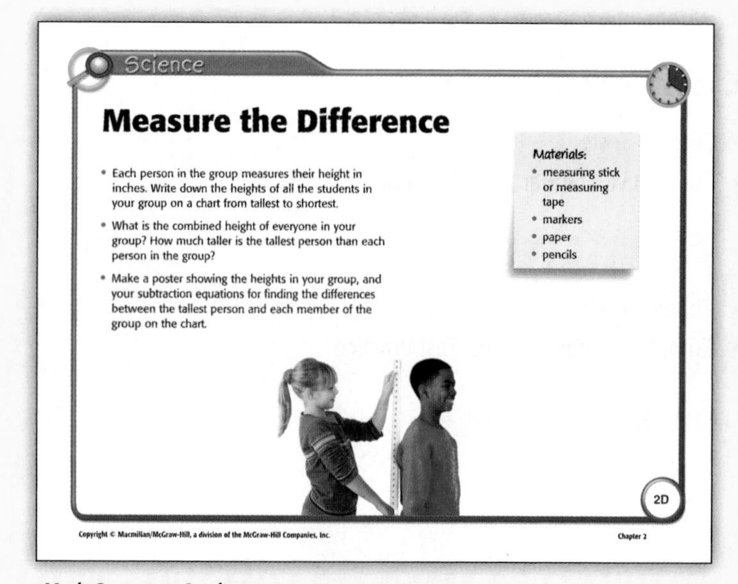

Science

**Measure the Difference**

- Each person in the group measures their height in inches. Write down the heights of all the students in your group on a chart from tallest to shortest.
- What is the combined height of everyone in your group? How much taller is the tallest person than each person in the group?
- Make a poster showing the heights in your group, and your subtraction equations for finding the differences between the tallest person and each member of the group on the chart.

Materials:
- measuring stick or measuring tape
- markers
- paper
- pencils

2D

Copyright © Macmillan/McGraw-Hill, a division of the McGraw-Hill Companies, Inc.

Chapter 2

*Math Connects*, Grade 4
Learning Station Card 2D

## Advanced Learners

Acceleration and Enrichment Resources and assignments for students who are above level may be used with advanced learners. In particular, the **Enrich Masters** provide students with valuable opportunities for extending your lessons.

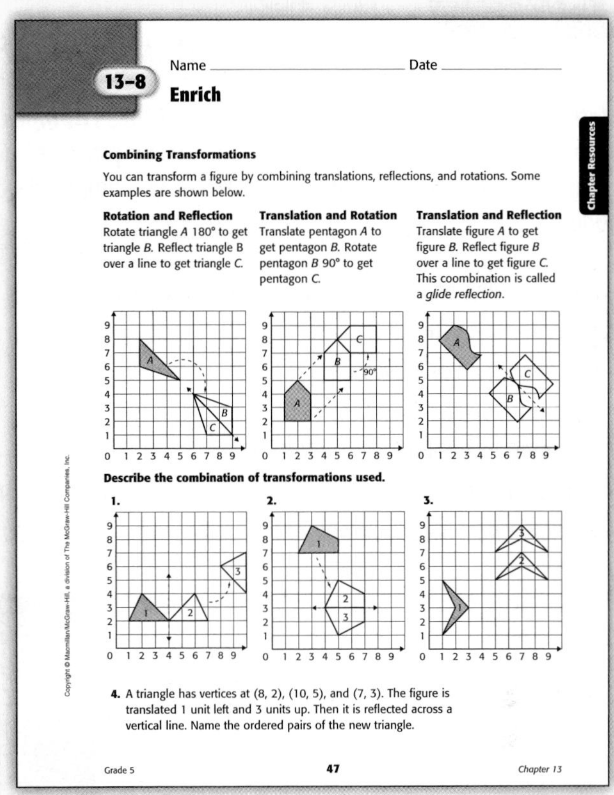

Name ____________ Date ____________

13-8 **Enrich**

Chapter Resources

**Combining Transformations**

You can transform a figure by combining translations, reflections, and rotations. Some examples are shown below.

**Rotation and Reflection** Rotate triangle *A* 180° to get triangle *B*. Reflect triangle B over a line to get triangle *C*.

**Translation and Rotation** Translate pentagon *A* to get pentagon *B*. Rotate pentagon *B* 90° to get pentagon *C*.

**Translation and Reflection** Translate figure *A* to get figure *B*. Reflect figure *B* over a line to get figure *C*. This coombination is called a *glide reflection*.

**Describe the combination of transformations used.**

1.

2.

3.

**4.** A triangle has vertices at (8, 2), (10, 5), and (7, 3). The figure is translated 1 unit left and 3 units up. Then it is reflected across a vertical line. Name the ordered pairs of the new triangle.

Copyright © Macmillan/McGraw-Hill, a division of The McGraw-Hill Companies, Inc.

Grade 5 47 Chapter 13

*Math Connects*, Grade 5,
Chapter 13 Resource Masters, page 47

## ELL English Language Learners

Our authors have identified seven keys for effective instruction with English language learner students and used them throughout the program.

1. Simplify language, not concepts.
2. Activate background knowledge.
3. Teach in multiple modalities.
4. Use core vocabulary and common use verbs.
5. Express mathematical understanding in different ways.
6. Incorporate higher-level problem-solving skills.
7. Provide a mathematics-rich classroom environment.

**The English Language Learners Guide** provides additional support for English language learner students that can be used alone or with core instruction in the Student Edition and Teacher Edition.

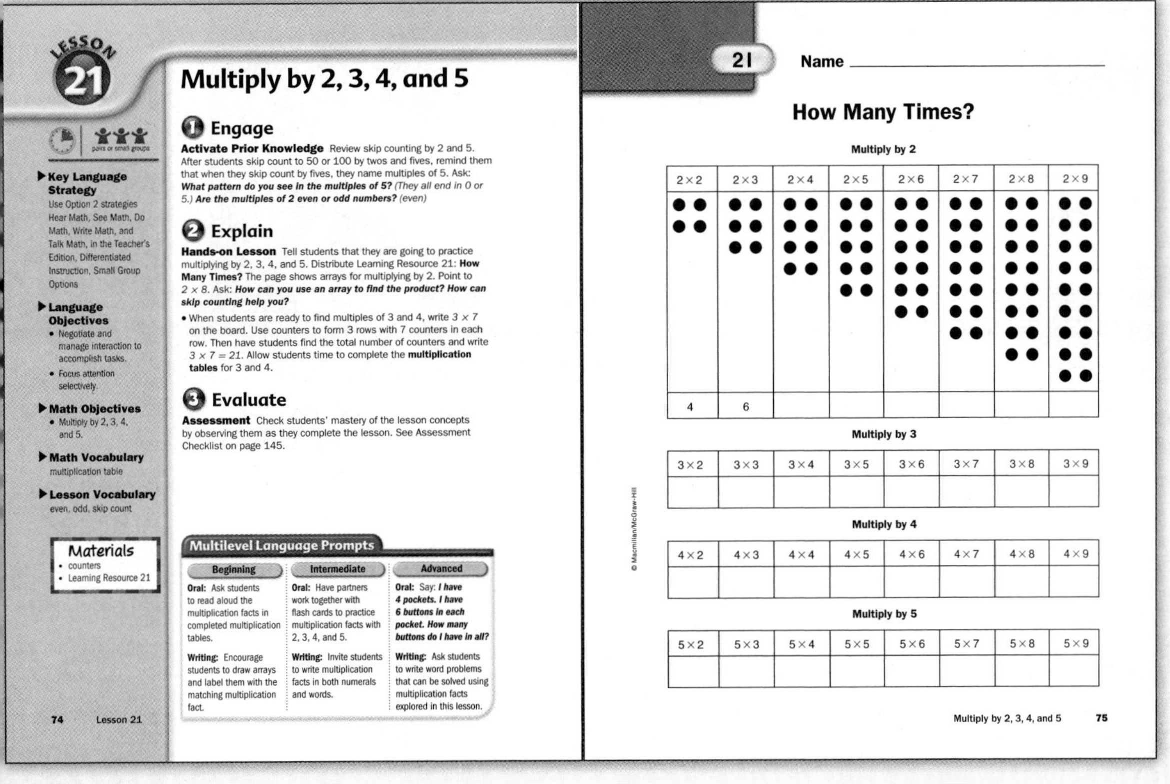

LESSON 21

# Multiply by 2, 3, 4, and 5

pairs or small groups

▶ **Key Language Strategy**
Use Option 2 strategies Hear Math, See Math, Do Math, Write Math, and Talk Math, in the Teacher's Edition, Differentiated Instruction, Small Group Options

▶ **Language Objectives**
- Negotiate and manage interaction to accomplish tasks.
- Focus attention selectively.

▶ **Math Objectives**
- Multiply by 2, 3, 4, and 5.

▶ **Math Vocabulary**
multiplication table

▶ **Lesson Vocabulary**
even, odd, skip count

**Materials**
- counters
- Learning Resource 21

**1 Engage**

**Activate Prior Knowledge** Review skip counting by 2 and 5. After students skip count to 50 or 100 by twos and fives, remind them that when they skip count by fives, they name multiples of 5. Ask: ***What pattern do you see in the multiples of 5?*** *(They all end in 0 or 5.)* ***Are the multiples of 2 even or odd numbers?*** *(even)*

**2 Explain**

**Hands-on Lesson** Tell students that they are going to practice multiplying by 2, 3, 4, and 5. Distribute Learning Resource 21: **How Many Times?** The page shows arrays for multiplying by 2. Point to $2 \times 8$. Ask: ***How can you use an array to find the product? How can skip counting help you?***

- When students are ready to find multiples of 3 and 4, write $3 \times 7$ on the board. Use counters to form 3 rows with 7 counters in each row. Then have students find the total number of counters and write $3 \times 7 = 21$. Allow students time to complete the **multiplication tables** for 3 and 4.

**3 Evaluate**

**Assessment** Check students' mastery of the lesson concepts by observing them as they complete the lesson. See Assessment Checklist on page 145.

**Multilevel Language Prompts**

| Beginning | Intermediate | Advanced |
|---|---|---|
| **Oral:** Ask students to read aloud the multiplication facts in completed multiplication tables. | **Oral:** Have partners work together with flash cards to practice multiplication facts with 2, 3, 4, and 5. | **Oral:** Say: ***I have 4 pockets. I have 6 buttons in each pocket. How many buttons do I have in all?*** |
| **Writing:** Encourage students to draw arrays and label them with the matching multiplication fact. | **Writing:** Invite students to write multiplication facts in both numerals and words. | **Writing:** Ask students to write word problems that can be solved using multiplication facts explored in this lesson. |

74 Lesson 21

21 Name ____________

**How Many Times?**

**Multiply by 2**

| 2×2 | 2×3 | 2×4 | 2×5 | 2×6 | 2×7 | 2×8 | 2×9 |
|---|---|---|---|---|---|---|---|
| 4 | 6 | | | | | | |

**Multiply by 3**

| 3×2 | 3×3 | 3×4 | 3×5 | 3×6 | 3×7 | 3×8 | 3×9 |
|---|---|---|---|---|---|---|---|
| | | | | | | | |

**Multiply by 4**

| 4×2 | 4×3 | 4×4 | 4×5 | 4×6 | 4×7 | 4×8 | 4×9 |
|---|---|---|---|---|---|---|---|
| | | | | | | | |

**Multiply by 5**

| 5×2 | 5×3 | 5×4 | 5×5 | 5×6 | 5×7 | 5×8 | 5×9 |
|---|---|---|---|---|---|---|---|
| | | | | | | | |

© Macmillan/McGraw-Hill

Multiply by 2, 3, 4, and 5 75

*Math Connects*, Grade 3
ELL Guide, pages 74–75

# Blending Your Instruction

## *Basal – NSF-Funded – Tier 3 Intervention*

***Math Connects, IMPACT Mathematics***, and ***Math Triumphs*** provide a three-pronged approach to mathematics instruction. This unique combination provides built-in strategies to easily tip the balance of instruction to a more conceptual approach or to a more skills-based approach, depending on the needs of your students.

These programs are horizontally aligned in the following ways.

- Common vocabulary
- Common manipulatives
- Common teacher planning guides
- Common technology
- Common authors
- Common professional development

## RTI (Response to Intervention)

In the ***Math Connects*** Teacher Editions, the Data-Driven Decision Making chart provides a comprehensive RTI (Response to Intervention) beginning with diagnostic review and continuing with prescriptions at all three RTI tiers.

- **Tier 1** – Leveled exercise sets and leveled resources
- **Tier 2** – Strategic Intervention Guide (1–5), Study Guide and Intervention (6–8)
- **Tier 3** – Intensive Intervention, ***Math Triumphs***

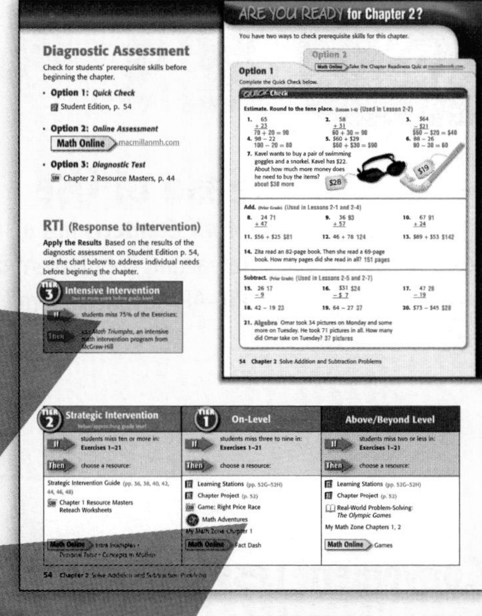


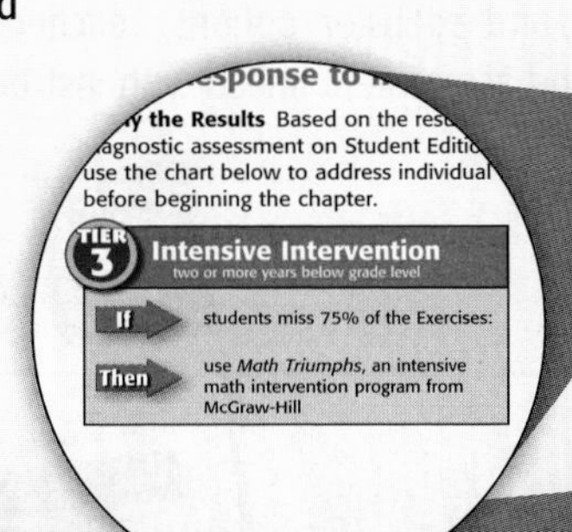

**Apply the Results** Based on the results of the diagnostic assessment on Student Edition p. 54, use the chart below to address individual needs before beginning the chapter.

| TIER 3 Intensive Intervention (two or more years below grade level) |
|---|
| **If** students miss 75% of the Exercises: |
| **Then** use *Math Triumphs*, an intensive math intervention program from McGraw-Hill |

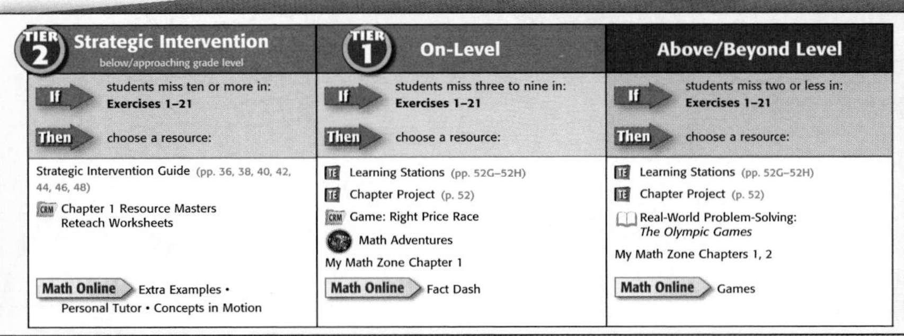

| TIER 2 Strategic Intervention (below/approaching grade level) | TIER 1 On-Level | Above/Beyond Level |
|---|---|---|
| **If** students miss ten or more in: **Exercises 1–21** | **If** students miss three to nine in: **Exercises 1–21** | **If** students miss two or less in: **Exercises 1–21** |
| **Then** choose a resource: | **Then** choose a resource: | **Then** choose a resource: |
| Strategic Intervention Guide (pp. 36, 38, 40, 42, 44, 46, 48)<br>CRM Chapter 1 Resource Masters Reteach Worksheets<br>Math Online Extra Examples • Personal Tutor • Concepts in Motion | TE Learning Stations (pp. 52G–52H)<br>TE Chapter Project (p. 52)<br>CRM Game: Right Price Race<br>Math Adventures<br>My Math Zone Chapter 1<br>Math Online Fact Dash | TE Learning Stations (pp. 52G–52H)<br>TE Chapter Project (p. 52)<br>Real-World Problem-Solving: *The Olympic Games*<br>My Math Zone Chapters 1, 2<br>Math Online Games |

*Math Connects,* Grade 4
Teacher Edition, page 54

The Chapter Planner, also in the Teacher Edition of ***Math Connects,*** references alternative lessons found in ***IMPACT Mathematics.*** These lessons provide opportunities for investigative instruction with hands-on explorations.

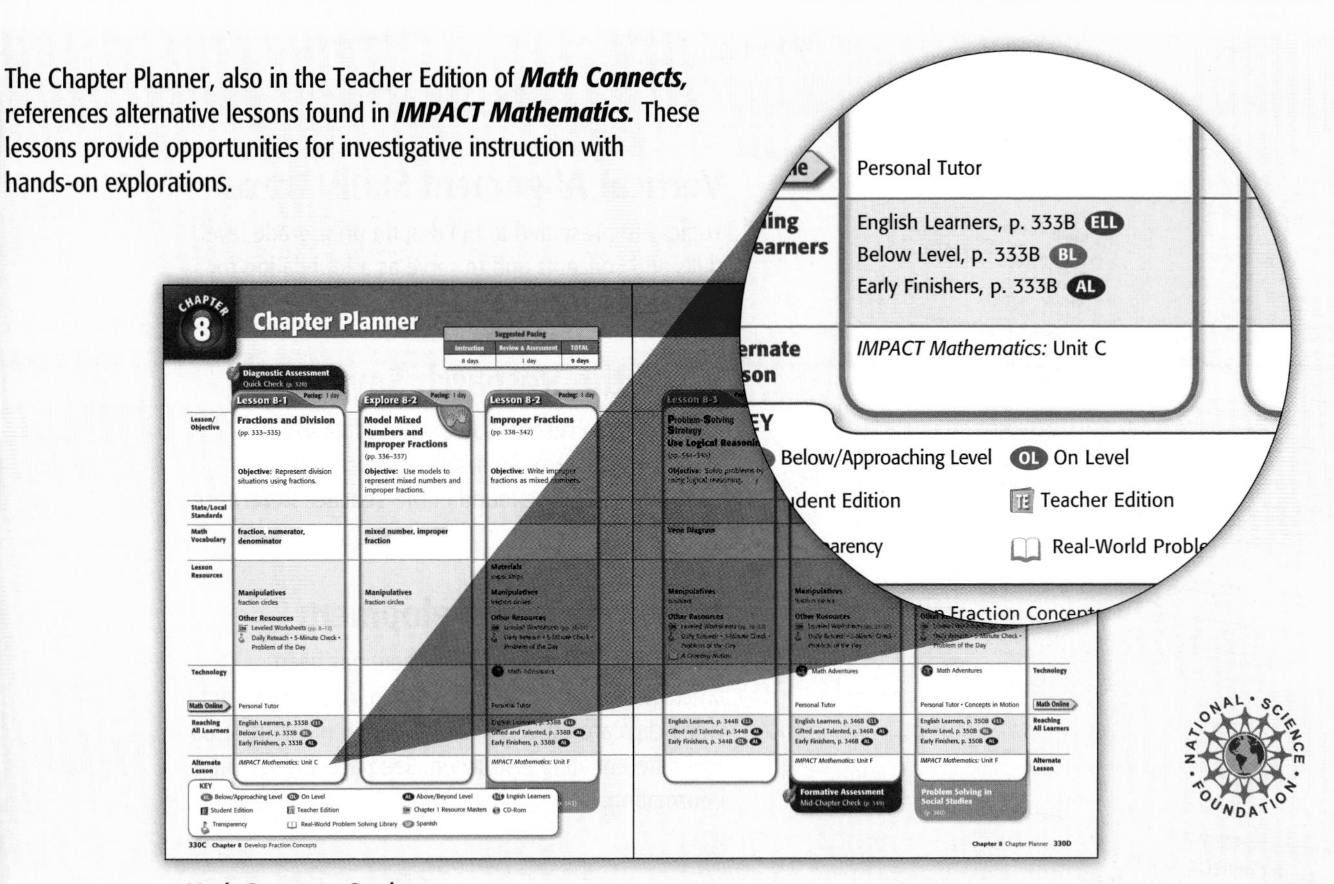


*Math Connects,* Grade 5
Teacher Edition, pages 330C–330D

# Planning for Success

## Ease of Use

***Math Connects*** has a strong instructional model that includes differentiated instructional options, reteaching, reinforcement, and extension options, Teacher Tips to help address various learners, Pre-AP/Advanced items, and assessment linked with instruction.

## Convenient Lesson Planning at Your Fingertips

The **Chapter Overview** helps you plan your instruction by showing the objectives to be covered, suggested pacing, and coverage of Focal Points.

## TeacherWorks™ Plus

This electronic lesson planner contains multi-purpose management software including the Teacher Edition pages, program blackline masters, and daily calendars that make planning a snap.

CHAPTER 4 **Chapter Overview**

**Chapter-at-a-Glance**

In Chapter 4, the emphasis is on the meaning of multiplication and multiplication facts with 2, 4, 5, and 10.

| Lesson | Math Objective | State/Local Standards |
|---|---|---|
| EXPLORE 4-1 Meaning of Multiplication (pp. 157–158) | Use models to explore multiplication. | |
| 4-1 Arrays and Multiplication (pp. 159–161) | Use arrays to multiply. | |
| 4-2 Multiply by 2 (pp. 162–164) | Multiply by 2. | |
| EXTEND 4-2 Model Multiplication (pp. 165–166) | Use technology to multiply. | |
| 4-3 Multiply by 4 (pp. 168–170) | Multiply by 4. | |
| 4-4 Problem-Solving Skill: Extra or Missing Information (pp. 172–173) | Solve a problem by identifying extra or missing information. | |
| 4-5 Multiply by 5 (pp. 174–176) | Multiply by 5. | |
| 4-6 Multiply by 10 (pp. 178–181) | Multiply by 10. | |
| 4-7 Problem-Solving Investigation: Choose a Strategy (pp. 184–185) | Choose the best strategy to solve a problem. | |
| 4-8 Multiply by 0 and 1 (pp. 186–188) | Multiply by 0 and 1. | |

**Develop Multiplication Concepts and Facts**

BIG Idea There are 144 multiplication combinations from $1 \times 1$ to $12 \times 12$, most of which are learned without difficulty. Students can use several different strategies to make sense of multiplication facts.

- Multiplication is repeated addition. For example, $4 \times 3$ is the same as adding the number 4 three times. $(4 \times 3 = 4 + 4 + 4 = 12)$
- Multiplication can be represented visually using arrays. The fact $4 \times 3$ can be demonstrated by an array of pictures or objects with 4 columns and 3 rows.
- Skip counting by a number is the same as multiplying by 1, 2, 3, and so on. To count by 4s, say 4, 8, 12, 16. . .

Use these and other strategies to emphasize the meaning of multiplication. Continued practice in a variety of contexts will lead students to commit facts to memory.

**Algebra** Students learn about the properties of multiplication. This concept will help prepare them for algebra concepts, such as solving equations and inequalities. (Lessons 4-1 and 4-8)

**G3-FP1** *Number and Operations and Algebra:* **Developing understandings of multiplication an[d] ... and strategies for basic multiplication facts ... division facts**

Students understand the meanings of m... of whole numbers through the use of ... equal-sized groups, arrays, area mod... number lines for multiplication, an... partitioning, and sharing for divisi... addition and multiplication (e.g., ... the distributive property) to mult... increasingly sophisticated strateg... solve multiplication and division ... By comparing a variety of solutio... multiplication and division as inv...

**G3-FP4C** *Algebra:* Understand... and the relationship between mult... of algebra readiness that develops a... analysis of patterns and relationships ... division should occur at this grade level... foundation for later understanding of func... describing relationships in context with such ... number of legs is 4 times the number of chairs.

154A Chapter 4 Develop Multiplication Concepts and Facts



*Math Connects*, Grade 3
Teacher Edition, page 154A

**Develop Multiplication Concepts and Facts**

**Skills Trace**
Vertical Alignment

**Second Grade**
**In second grade, students learned to:**
- Multiply by using repeated addition, arrays, and counting by multiples.

**Third Grade**
**During this chapter, students learn to:**
- Multiply by 2, 4, 5, 10, 0 and 1, and use arrays.

**After this chapter, students learn to:**
- Multiply by 3, 6, 7, 8, 9, 11, and 12.
- Multiply by a two-digit number.

**Fourth Grade**
**In fourth grade, students learn to:**
- Multiply by one- and two-digit numbers.
- Find multiples of whole numbers.

**Backmapping and Vertical Alignment** McGraw-Hill's ***Math Connects*** program was concieved and developed with the final results in mind: student success in Algebra 1 and beyond. The authors, using the **NCTM Focal Points and Focal Connections** as their guide, developed this brand-new series by backmapping from Algebra 1 concepts, and vertically aligning the topic so that build upon prior skills and concepts and serve as a foundation for future topics.

**Math Vocabulary**

The following math vocabulary words for Chapter 4 are listed in the glossary of the ***Student Edition.*** You can find interactive definitions in 13 languages in the ***eGlossary*** at macmillanmh.com.

**array** Objects or symbols displayed in rows and columns. (p. 159A)

**Commutative Property of Multiplication** The property that states that the order in which numbers are multiplied does not change the product. (p. 159A)
**Example:** $7 \times 2 = 2 \times 7$

**factor** A number that is multiplied by another number (p. 159A)

**Identity Property of Multiplication** If you multiply a number by 1, the product is that number. (p. 186A)
**Example:** $8 \times 1 = 8 = 1 \times 8$

**multiplication** An operation on two numbers to find their product. It can be thought of as repeated addition. (p. 157A)
**Example:** $3 \times 8 = 24$ can also be written as $8 + 8 + 8 = 24$

**multiply** Find the product of two or more numbers. (p. 157A)

**product** The answer to a multiplication problem. (p. 159A)

**Zero Property of Multiplication** The property that states any number multiplied by zero is zero. (p. 186A)
**Example:** $0 \times 5 = 0$

**Visual Vocabulary Cards**
Use Visual Vocabulary Cards 3, 9, 29, and 37 to reinforce the vocabulary in this lesson. (The Define/Example/Ask routine is printed on the back of each card.)

array

Chapter 4 Chapter Overview 154B

*Math Connects*, Grade 3
Teacher Edition, page 154B

## Vertical Alignment Skills Trace

Topics are presented to build upon prior grade level skills and concepts and to serve as a foundation for future topics.

## What the Research Says

Citations from **research** help to validate ***Math Connects*** program. An additional Research Bibliography can be found in the **Teacher Reference Handbook.**

## Professional Development

Targeted professional development has been articulated throughout the program. Actual classroom video clips are especially helpful when planning lessons and differentiating instruction. See page T32 for more information.

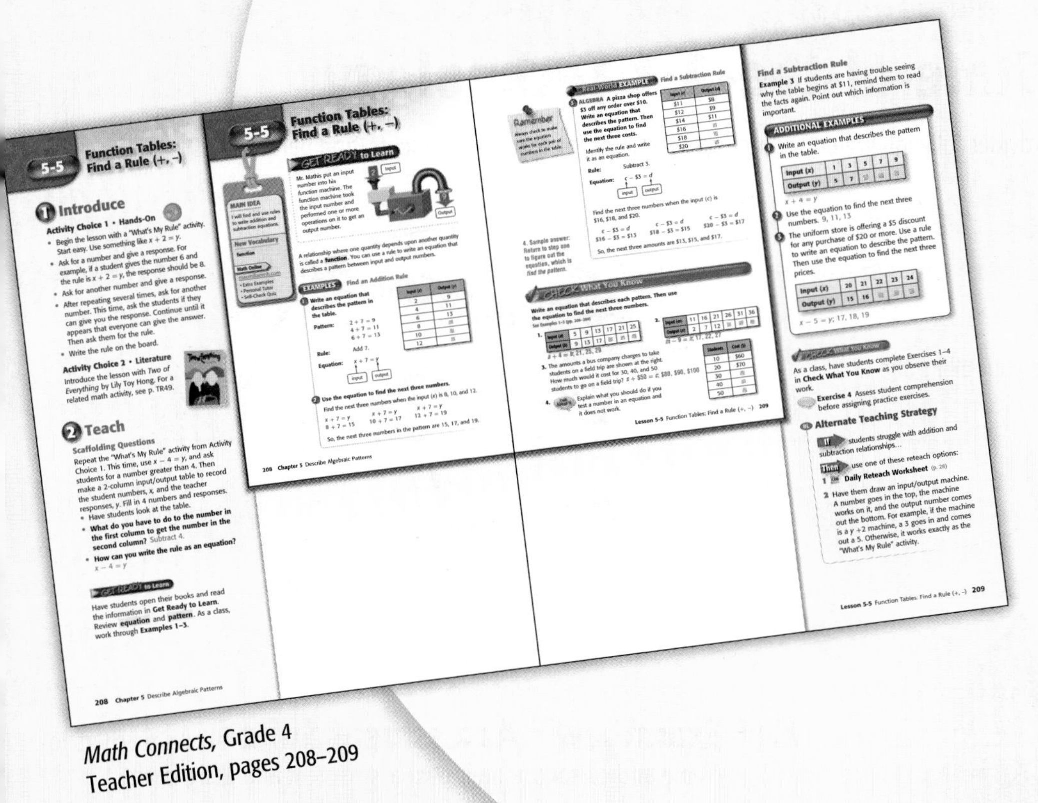

*Math Connects*, Grade 4
Teacher Edition, pages 208–209

## Four-Step Teaching Plan

Organizes your instruction as you **Focus** and **Teach** and help your students **Practice** and **Assess** what they've learned.

## Scaffolding Questions

Each lesson contains **Scaffolding Questions** for you to use to help students investigate and understand the main ideas of the lesson.

## Additional Examples

Each **Additional Example** mirrors the example in the Student Edition. The Additional Examples are also available as a PowerPoint® presentation on the **Interactive Classroom** CD-ROM.

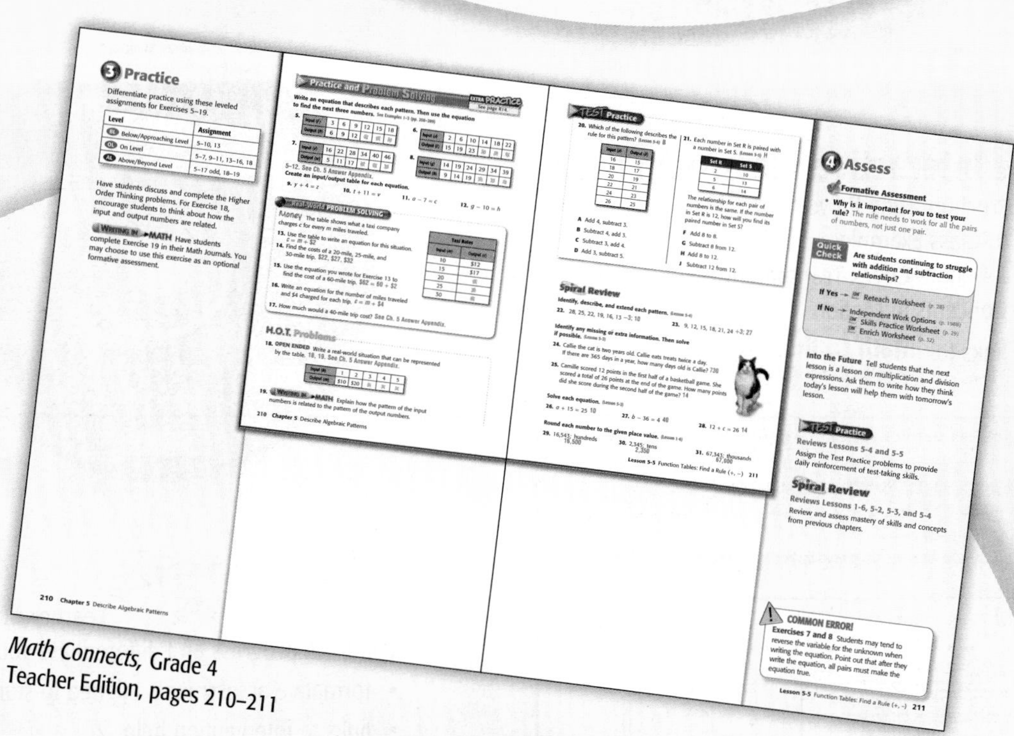

*Math Connects*, Grade 4
Teacher Edition, pages 210–211

## Differentiated Practice

Because most classrooms include students at a wide range of ability levels, **Differentiated Practice** allows you to customize your assignments.

## Vertical Alignment

**Vertical Alignment** at the beginning of each chapter shows the objectives that lead into and follow the current lesson's content for a coherent PreK–12 scope and sequence.

# Planning for Success
## State-of-the-Art Technology

***Math Connects*** provides fully integrated technology resources for teachers, students, and parents.

## For Teachers

**TeacherWorks™ Plus** is your all-in-one planner and resource center.

- entire Teacher Edition
- all print ancillaries
- electronic lesson planner

**ExamView® Assessment Suite** allows teachers to create and customize their own assessment and assignments.

**New features:**

- correlated to state standards
- online content update
- one- or two-column formatting

Use **Interactive Classroom** to guide instruction using PowerPoint ™

- In-Class Examples
- 5-Minute Check Transparencies
- Concepts in Motion
- links to **Math Online**

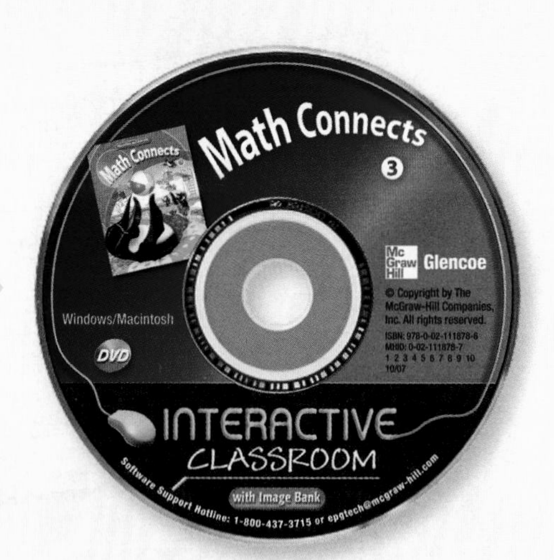


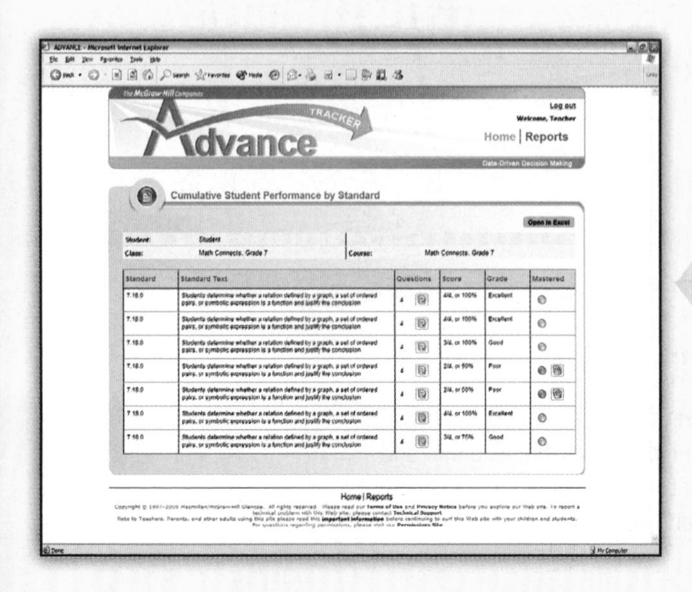


**Advance** TRACKER Learner Management System helps you track progress and differentiate your instruction.

- formative assessments aligned to standards
- links to intervention help

**Other Technology:** My Math Zone (CD-ROM)
Math Songs (English and Spanish, CD-ROM)

## For Students

**StudentWorks™ Plus** is your students' backpack solution.

- entire Student Edition
- all student worksheets
- links to **Math Online**

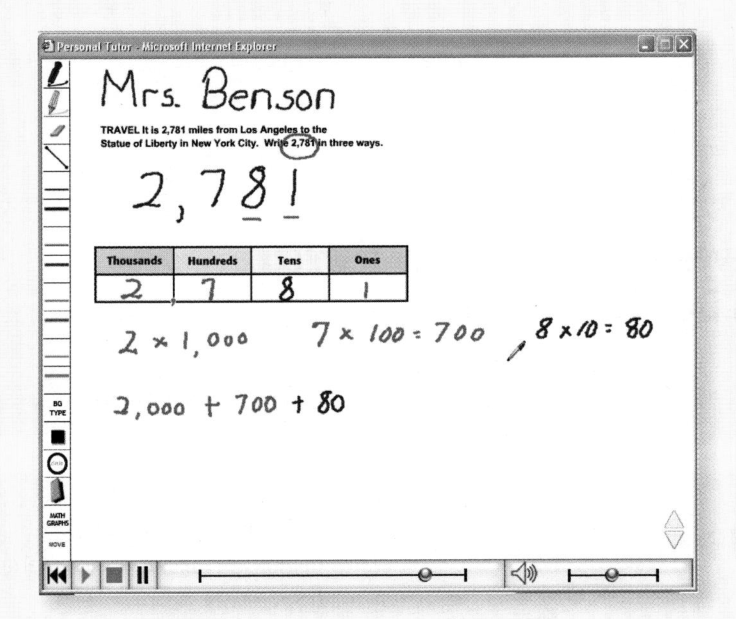


**Math Online** provides a wealth of resources – convenient for students and parents!

- Self-Check Quizzes
- Personal Tutor
- Concepts in Motion
- eGlossary (14 languages)
- And much, much more!

**Math Online** *Math Connect's* **eBook** is easy to use, easy to read, and packed with features.

- links to online study tools and resources right from the page
- includes audio

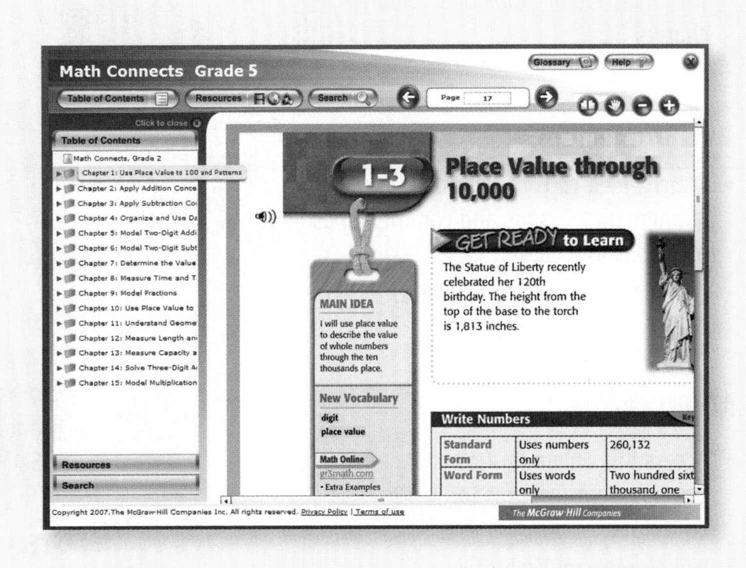


**Other Technology:** Math Adventures with Dot and Ray (online and CD-ROM)
Math Tool Chest (online and CD-ROM)

# PreK-12 Data-Driven Professional Development

McGraw-Hill Professional Development (MHPD) provides a comprehensive plan for mathematics that is fully aligned and articulated with ***Math Connects K–8*** and the ***Glencoe Mathematics*** high school series.

| Professional Development Needs | Online Courses | DVD Workshops | Video Library | Teach-Use-Succeed | Ready-Access Math |
|---|---|---|---|---|---|
| Has immediate classroom application | ✓ | ✓ | ✓ | ✓ | ✓ |
| Builds content knowledge | ✓ | ✓ | | | ✓ |
| Promotes best teaching practices | | ✓ | ✓ | | |
| Supports new and experienced teachers | ✓ | ✓ | ✓ | ✓ | ✓ |
| Allows customization of courses | ✓ | ✓ | | | ✓ |
| Can be self-paced | ✓ | ✓ | | ✓ | ✓ |
| Adaptable for various timeframes | ✓ | ✓ | ✓ | ✓ | ✓ |
| Is grade-level specific | | | ✓ | ✓ | ✓ |
| Promotes a learning community | ✓ | ✓ | | | ✓ |
| Provides vertically-aligned content | ✓ | ✓ | ✓ | | ✓ |
| Helps with RTI (Response to Intervention), Tiers 1–3 | ✓ | ✓ | ✓ | | ✓ |

## Use students' mathematics achievement data to help develop a targeted Professional Development Plan.

### Accredited Online Courses

(available for purchase)

- Watch video clips of math classrooms Complete interactive exercises Develop electronic portfolios.
- Complete each 3- to 5-hour online module one segment at a time.
- University credit (additional tuition charge)

### DVD Workshops

- Watch video clips of classroom mathematics lessons and commentaries by leading educators.
- Complete lessons and activities.

### MHPD Online

- Access this online Professional Development resource for K–12 educators.
- Link to relevant Web sites.
- Download grade-level student resources.

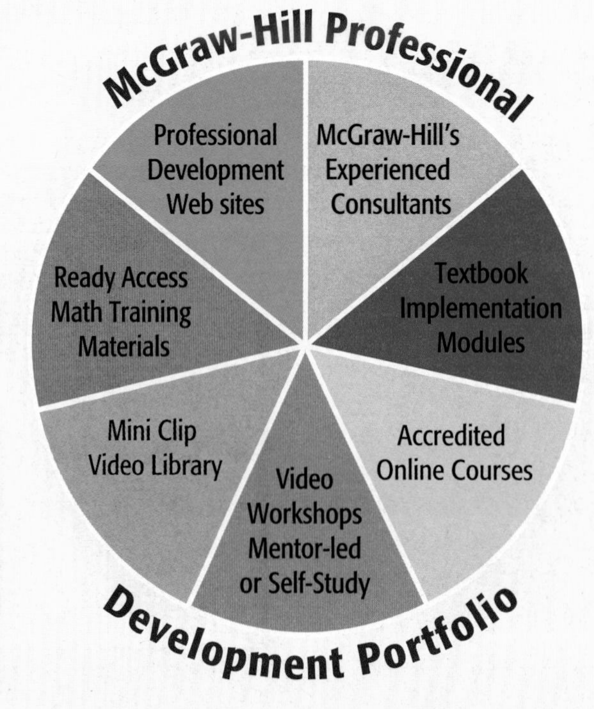


### Video Library **Math Online**

- Access hundreds of K–12 video clips.
- See clips that illustrate mathematics content and instructional strategies.
- Watch demonstrations or commentaries by math specialists

### Teach-Use-Succeed Textbook Implementation Modules

- Watch an experienced teacher demonstrate the *Math Connects* K–8 Student Editions, Teacher Editions, and program ancillaries
- Online or DVD

### Ready-Access Math, Personalized Professional Development

- Access training materials for nearly 300 mathematics professional development lessons.
- Create a customized sequence of professional development sessions.
- Deliver 45–60 minute after-school professional development sessions.

Teacher Edition

Macmillan McGraw-Hill

# Math Connects

4

Volume 2

Authors

Altieri • Balka • Day • Gonsalves • Grace • Krulik
Malloy • Molix-Bailey • Moseley • Mowry • Myren
Price • Reynosa • Santa Cruz • Silbey • Vielhaber

Mc Graw Hill Macmillan/McGraw-Hill

Table of Contents

# Contents

## Start Smart

### H.O.T. Problems

# CHAPTER 1 Use Place Value to Represent Whole Numbers

**Focal Points and Connections**

**G4-FP8C** Number and Operations

# Solve Addition and Subtraction Problems



**Focal Points and Connections**

**G4-FP4C** Algebra
**G4-FP8C** Number and Operations

**Test Practice** 61, 67, 69, 83, 89, 90, 91

**H.O.T. Problems**
**Higher Order Thinking** 57, 61, 67, 74, 82

**WRITING IN MATH** 57, 61, 63, 67, 68, 69, 71, 74, 77, 82, 89

# Chapter 3 Organize, Display, and Interpret Data

**Focal Points and Connections**

**G4-FP7C** Data Analysis

**Test Practice** 101, 107, 111, 127, 139, 140, 141

**H.O.T. Problems**
**Higher Order Thinking** 97, 101, 107, 110, 114, 126, 130

**WRITING IN MATH** 97, 101, 103, 107, 110, 111, 114, 117, 119, 123, 126, 130, 139

# Apply Multiplication and Division Facts



**Focal Points and Connections**

**G4-FP1** Number and Operations and Algebra

# CHAPTER 5 Describe Algebraic Patterns



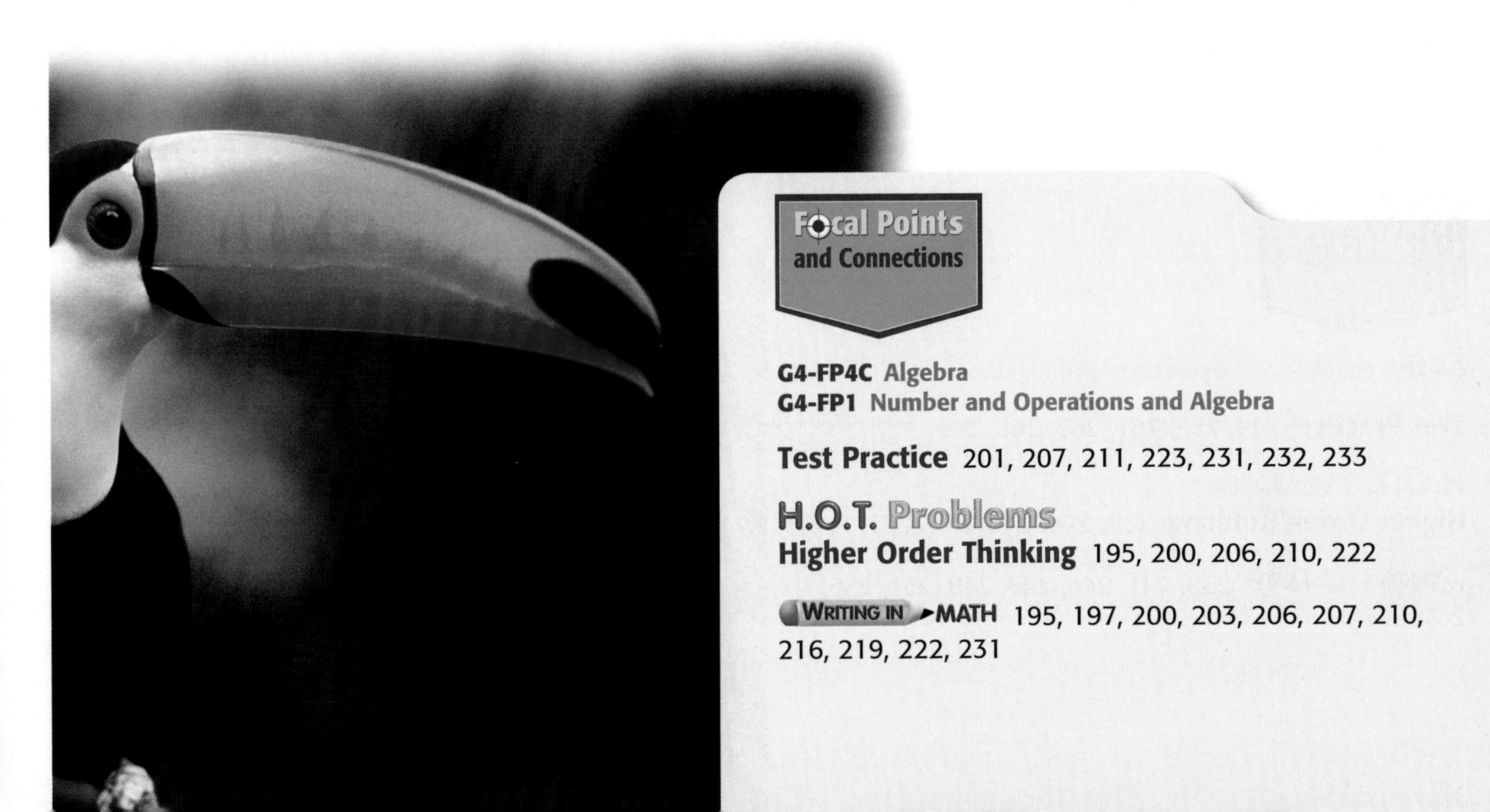

**Focal Points and Connections**

**G4-FP4C** Algebra
**G4-FP1** Number and Operations and Algebra

# CHAPTER 6 Multiply by One-Digit Numbers



**Focal Points and Connections**

# CHAPTER 7 Multiply by Two-Digit Numbers

**G4-FP1** Number and Operations and Algebra

**Test Practice** 279, 287, 291, 305, 306, 307

**H.O.T. Problems**
**Higher Order Thinking** 275, 279, 286, 290, 298

WRITING IN MATH 275, 279, 281, 283, 286, 287, 290, 295, 298, 305

# CHAPTER 8 Divide by One-Digit Numbers

**G4-FP8C** Number and Operations

**Test Practice** 319, 325, 329, 345, 353, 354, 355

**H.O.T. Problems**
**Higher Order Thinking** 315, 319, 324, 329, 334, 338, 345

**WRITING IN MATH** 312, 315, 319, 321, 324, 325, 329, 331, 334, 338, 345, 353

# CHAPTER 9 Identify and Describe Geometric Figures

**Focal Points and Connections**

**G4-FP6C** Measurement
**G4-FP5C** Geometry

# Chapter 10 Understand and Develop Spatial Reasoning

**G4-FP5C** Geometry

**Test Practice** 403, 409, 415, 433, 434, 435

**H.O.T. Problems**

**Higher Order Thinking** 397, 403, 408, 415, 420, 424

WRITING IN ▸MATH 397, 399, 403, 405, 408, 409, 411, 415, 417, 420, 424, 433

# Measure Length, Area, and Temperature

**G4-FP3** Measurement
**G4-FP5C** Geometry

# CHAPTER 12 Measure Capacity, Weight, and Volume

**G4-FP3** Measurement
**G4-FP5C** Geometry

**Test Practice** 489, 495, 501, 507, 515, 523, 531, 532

**H.O.T. Problems**
**Higher Order Thinking** 489, 491, 494, 500, 506, 510, 515, 523

WRITING IN MATH 485, 491, 497, 503, 506, 519, 531

# CHAPTER 13 Describe and Compare Fractions

**Focal Points and Connections**

**G4-FP2** Number and Operations
**G4-FP8C** Number and Operations

# Chapter 14 Use Place Value to Represent Decimals

**Focal Points and Connections**

**G4-FP2** Number and Operations
**G4-FP8C** Number and Operations

# Chapter 15 Add and Subtract Decimals

**Focal Points and Connections**

**G4-FP2** Number and Operations
**G4-FP8C** Number and Operations

# Looking Ahead



# Problem-Solving Projects



## H.O.T. Problems

# Student Handbook

## Built-In Workbook



## Reference

# To the Student

As you gear up to study mathematics, you are probably wondering, "What will I learn this year?"

- **Number and Operations:** Estimate and find products of whole numbers, including multidigit whole numbers.
- **Number and Operations:** Understand decimals and relate fractions and decimals.
- **Measurement:** Understand and find areas of two-dimensional figures.

Along the way, you'll learn more about problem solving, how to use the tools and language of mathematics, and how to THINK mathematically.

# How to Use Your Math Book

Have you ever been in class and not understood all of what was being presented? Or, you understood everything in class, but got stuck on how to solve some of the homework problems? Don't worry. You can find answers in your math book!

- **Read** the MAIN IDEA at the beginning of the lesson.
- **Find** the New Vocabulary words, **highlighted in yellow**, and read their definitions.
- **Review** the EXAMPLE problems, solved step-by-step, to remind you of the day's material.
- **Refer** to the EXTRA PRACTICE boxes that show you where you can find extra exercises to practice a concept.
- **Go** to Math Online where you can find extra examples to coach you through difficult problems.
- **Review** the notes you've taken on your FOLDABLES.
- **Refer** to the Remember boxes for information that may help you with your examples and homework practice.

# Chapter Overview

## Chapter-at-a-Glance

In Chapter 9, the emphasis is on identifying and describing two-dimensional figures, three-dimensional figures, and angles.

| Lesson | | Math Objective | State/Local Standards |
|---|---|---|---|
| **9-1** | **Three-Dimensional Figures** (pp. 359–361) | Identify and describe three-dimensional figures and identify and draw nets. | |
| **9-2** | **Two-Dimensional Figures** (pp. 362–365) | Identify, describe, and classify two-dimensional figures. | |
| **9-3** | **Problem-Solving Strategy: Look for a Pattern** (pp. 366–367) | Solve problems by looking for a pattern. | |
| **9-4** | **Angles** (pp. 368–370) | Identify, describe, and classify angles. | |
| **9-5** | **Triangles** (pp. 372–375) | Identify, describe, and classify triangles. | |
| **9-6** | **Quadrilaterals** (pp. 376–378) | Identify, describe, and classify quadrilaterals. | |
| **9-7** | **Problem-Solving Investigation: Choose a Strategy** (pp. 380–381) | Choose the best strategy to solve a problem. | |

## Identify and Describe Geometric Figures

**BIG Idea** Students have learned to use the attributes of geometric figures to form classes of figures. Students now extend their knowledge by using attributes of additional polygons and solid figures. They identify and describe angles. Students should use manipulatives or visuals as they examine the geometric figures. It continues to be important for students to use geometric language to describe and classify two- and three-dimensional figures.

**Algebra** Students work with the look for a pattern strategy. This strategy prepares them for algebra concepts, such as writing equations and identifying functions. (Lesson 9-3)

**Measurement** Students identify and describe two- and three-dimensional and solid figures. This prepares them for measurement concepts, such as finding area, perimeter, and volume. (Lessons 9-1 and 9-2)

**G4-FP6C** ***Measurement:*** As part of understanding two-dimensional shapes, students measure and classify angles.

**G4-FP5C** ***Geometry:*** Students extend their understanding of properties of two-dimensional shapes as they find the areas of polygons. They build on their earlier work with symmetry and congruence in grade 3 to encompass transformations, including those that produce line and rotational symmetry. By using transformations to design and analyze simple tilings and tessellations, students deepen their understanding of two-dimensional space.

## Skills Trace

### Vertical Alignment

**Third Grade**

**In third grade, students learned to:**

- Identify, classify, and describe attributes of polygons, including triangles, quadrilaterals, and other common three-dimensional objects.
- Identify congruent two-dimensional figures.
- Use concrete models to create two-dimensional figures with lines of symmetry.

**Fourth Grade**

**During this chapter, students learn to:**

- Identify, describe, and classify two-dimensional figures, geometric objects, and angles.
- Identify and describe three-dimensional figures and identify and draw nets.

**After this chapter, students learn to:**

- Find the perimeter and area of geometric figures.

**Fifth Grade**

**In fifth grade, students learn to:**

- Identify characteristics of triangles and quadrilaterals.
- Sketch translations, reflections, and rotations.
- Identify transformations.

**Backmapping and Vertical Alignment** **McGraw-Hill's *Math Connects*** program was conceived and developed with the final results in mind: student success in Algebra 1 and beyond. The authors, using the **NCTM Focal Points and Focal Connections** as their guide, developed this brand-new series by backmapping from Algebra 1 concepts, and vertically aligning the topics so that they build upon prior skills and concepts and serve as a foundation for future topics.

## Math Vocabulary

The following math vocabulary words for Chapter 9 are listed in the glossary of the ***Student Edition***. You can find interactive definitions in 13 languages in the ***eGlossary*** at macmillanmh.com.

**acute angle** An angle with a measure greater than 0° and less than 90°. (p. 368A)

**angle** A figure that is formed by two rays with the same endpoint. (p. 368A)

**obtuse angle** An angle that measures greater than 90° but less than 180°. (p. 368A)

**polygon** A closed plane figure formed using line segments that meet only at their endpoints. (p. 362A)

**right angle** An angle with a measure of 90°. (p. 368A)

**three-dimensional figure** A solid figure. It has length, width, and height. (p. 359A)

**two-dimensional figure** A plane figure. It has length and width. (p. 362A)

**Visual Vocabulary Cards**

Use Visual Vocabulary Cards 2 and 38 to reinforce the vocabulary in this lesson. (The Define/Example/Ask routine is printed on the back of each card.)

CHAPTER 9

# Chapter Planner

| Suggested Pacing | | |
|---|---|---|
| Instruction | Review & Assessment | TOTAL |
| 7 days | 1 day | **8 days** |

**Diagnostic Assessment**
Quick Check (p. 358)

| | Lesson 9-1 (Pacing: 1 day) | Lesson 9-2 (Pacing: 1 day) | Lesson 9-3 (Pacing: 1 day) |
|---|---|---|---|
| **Lesson/ Objective** | **Three-Dimensional Figures** (pp. 359–361)<br>**Objective:** Identify and describe three-dimensional figures and identify and draw nets. | **Two-Dimensional Figures** (pp. 362–365)<br>**Objective:** Identify, describe, and classify two-dimensional figures. | **Problem-Solving Strategy Look for a Pattern** (pp. 366–367)<br>**Objective:** Solve problems by looking for a pattern. |
| **State/Local Standards** | | | |
| **Math Vocabulary** | **three-dimensional figure**, **face**, **edge**, **vertex**, **net** | **two-dimensional figure**, **polygon**, **triangle**, **quadrilateral**, **pentagon**, **hexagon**, **sides** | |
| **Lesson Resources** | **Materials**<br>grid paper, tape or glue, scissors<br>**Manipulatives**<br>geometric solids<br>**Other Resources**<br>CRM Leveled Worksheets (pp. 8–12)<br>Daily Reteach • 5-Minute Check • Problem of the Day | **Materials**<br>construction paper, scissors, glue, colored pencils<br>**Manipulatives**<br>pattern blocks, geometric solids<br>**Other Resources**<br>CRM Leveled Worksheets (pp. 13–17)<br>Daily Reteach • 5-Minute Check • Problem of the Day | **Manipulatives**<br>pattern blocks<br>**Other Resources**<br>CRM Leveled Worksheets (pp. 18–22)<br>Daily Reteach • 5-Minute Check • Problem of the Day<br>*Solving the Pyramid Puzzle* |
| **Technology** | | Math Tool Chest<br>Math Adventures | |
| **Math Online** | Personal Tutor | Personal Tutor | |
| **Reaching All Learners** | English Learners, p. 359B ELL<br>Gifted and Talented, p. 359B AL<br>Early Finishers, p. 359B OL AL | English Learners, p. 362B ELL<br>Gifted and Talented, p. 362B AL<br>Early Finishers, p. 362B OL AL | English Learners, p. 366B ELL<br>Below Level, p. 366B BL<br>Early Finishers, p. 366B OL AL |
| **Alternate Lesson** | | | |

**KEY**
- BL Below/Approaching Level
- OL On Level
- AL Above/Beyond Level
- ELL English Learners
- SE Student Edition
- TE Teacher Edition
- CRM Chapter 9 Resource Masters
- CD-Rom
- Transparency
- Real-World Problem Solving Library

# Identify and Describe Geometric Figures

| | Lesson 9-4 (Pacing: 1 day) | Lesson 9-5 (Pacing: 1 day) | Lesson 9-6 (Pacing: 1 day) |
|---|---|---|---|
| **Lesson/ Objective** | **Angles** (pp. 368–370)<br>**Objective:** Identify, describe, and classify angles. | **Triangles** (pp. 372–375)<br>**Objective:** Identify, describe, and classify triangles. | **Quadrilaterals** (pp. 376–378)<br>**Objective:** Identify, describe, and classify quadrilaterals |
| **State/Local Standards** | | | |
| **Math Vocabulary** | **angle**, **right angle**, **acute angle**, **obtuse angle** | **isosceles triangle**, **equilateral triangle**, **scalene triangle**, **obtuse triangle**, **acute triangle**, **right triangle** | **rectangle**, **square**, **rhombus**, **parallelogram**, **trapezoid** |
| **Lesson Resources** | **Materials**<br>circle with two perpendicular lines drawn on it, compass, paper clips<br>**Other Resources**<br>CRM Leveled Worksheets (pp. 23–27)<br>Daily Reteach • 5-Minute Check • Problem of the Day | **Materials**<br>craft sticks, triangles made from construction paper, ruler, clay<br>**Other Resources**<br>CRM Leveled Worksheets (pp. 28–32)<br>Daily Reteach • 5-Minute Check • Problem of the Day | **Manipulatives**<br>pattern blocks<br>**Other Resources**<br>CRM Leveled Worksheets (pp. 33–37)<br>Daily Reteach • 5-Minute Check • Problem of the Day |
| **Technology** / **Math Online** | Math Adventures<br>Personal Tutor | Math Adventures<br>Personal Tutor | Math Adventures<br>Personal Tutor |
| **Reaching All Learners** | English Learners, p. 368B ELL<br>Below Level, p. 368B BL<br>Early Finishers, p. 368B OL AL | English Learners, p. 372B ELL<br>Gifted and Talented, p. 372B AL<br>Early Finishers, p. 372B OL AL | English Learners, p. 376B ELL<br>Gifted and Talented, p. 376B AL<br>Early Finishers, p. 376B OL AL |
| **Alternate Lesson** | | | |
| | **Formative Assessment**<br>Mid-Chapter Check (p. 371) | | **Game Time**<br>Shape Up (p. 379) |

# Chapter Planner

## Lesson 9-7

**Pacing:** 1 day

| | Lesson 9-7 |
|---|---|
| **Lesson/ Objective** | **Problem-Solving Investigation** <br> **Choose a Strategy** <br> (pp. 380–381) <br> **Objective:** Choose the best strategy to solve a problem. |
| **State/Local Standards** | |
| **Math Vocabulary** | |
| **Lesson Resources** | **Materials** <br> scissors, grid paper <br> **Manipulatives** <br> paper money <br> **Other Resources** <br> CRM Leveled Worksheets (pp. 38–42) <br> Daily Reteach • 5-Minute Check • Problem of the Day <br> *Solving the Pyramid Puzzle* |
| **Technology** | |
| **Math Online** | Personal Tutor |
| **Reaching All Learners** | English Learners, p. 380B ELL <br> Gifted and Talented, p. 380B AL <br> Early Finishers, p. 380B OL AL |
| **Alternate Lesson** | |

**Problem Solving: Art** (p. 382)

**Summative Assessment**
- Study Guide/Review (p. 384)
- Chapter Test (p. 389)
- Test Practice (p. 390)

## Assessment Options

### Diagnostic Assessment

- SE *Option 1:* Quick Check (p. 358)
- *Option 2:* Online Quiz macmillanmh.com
- CRM *Option 3:* Diagnostic Test (p. 44)
- CRM *Option 4:* Chapter Pretest (p. 45)

### Formative Assessment

- TE Alternate Teaching Strategies (in every lesson)
- SE Talk About It (in every lesson)
- SE Writing in Math (in every lesson)
- SE Check What You Know (in every lesson)
- TE Ticket Out the Door (p. 361)
- TE Yesterday's News (pp. 365, 375)
- TE Name the Math (p. 378)
- SE Mid-Chapter Check (p. 371)
- CRM Lesson Quizzes (pp. 46–48)
- CRM Mid-Chapter Test (p. 49)

### Summative Assessment

- SE Chapter Test (p. 389)
- SE Test Practice (p. 390)
- CRM Vocabulary Test (p. 50)
- CRM Leveled Chapter Tests (pp. 55–66)
- CRM Cumulative Test Practice (pp. 69–71)
- CRM Oral Assessment (pp. 51–52)
- ExamView® Assessment Suite
- Advance Tracker

## Mc Graw Hill Professional Development

Targeted professional development has been articulated throughout **McGraw-Hill's *Math Connects*** program. The **McGraw-Hill Professional Development Video Library** provides short videos that support the **NCTM Focal Points and Focal Connections.** For more information visit macmillanmh.com.

Model Lessons

Instructional Strategies

## Assessment Tips

Vocabulary is an essential part of geometry and it requires students to be able to "say it," "read it," "write it," "define it," and "draw it."

- Have students create vocabulary cards for each word in the chapter.
- Conduct a vocabulary interview each day with a couple of different students.
- Ask them to tell you all about one of their vocabulary cards, providing the word, definition, and drawing.
- Probe for their understanding of the vocabulary words and record your observations on index cards that can be put in their file folders.

## Teacher Notes

# Learning Stations

## Cross-Curricular Links

### Writing

individual | VISUAL

**How Did the Student Cross the Road?**

- Write a detailed description of your journey to school, using what you know about figures.
- What kinds of angles do you observe along the way? How are they formed? What shapes do you remember seeing? How would you classify them? What about three-dimensional figures?
- Share your description with the class.

My Figure Journey to School

When I first leave my apartment building, which is a rectangular prism, I turned the corner toward the bus stop. The corner is a right angle.

**Materials:**

- paper
- pencil

### Art

individual | LOGICAL

**Solid Architecture**

Before an architect submits his or her plans to build a real building, several smaller models are made. Design your ideal school building: make a model using three-dimensional figures made out of paper.

- Choose patterns to make three-dimensional figures out of white paper, and cut them out. Follow fold lines on the original patterns, and tape the faces of each three-dimensional figure together. Use the ends of a paper towel tube to make end circles.
- Make your building by taping together your solids, using a piece of cardboard as a base. Then write a description detailing which three-dimensional figure you used.

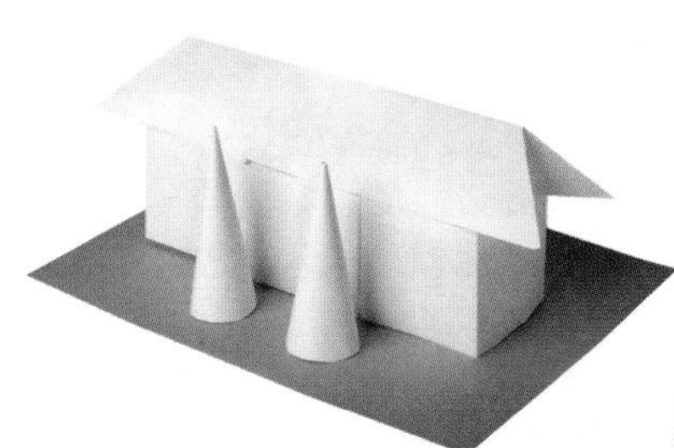

**Materials:**

- patterns for cones, cubes, triangular and rectangular prisms
- white paper
- scissors
- paper towel tubes
- tape

### Reading

pair | LOGICAL

**Pair Up**

- Read *A Pair of Socks* by Stuart J. Murphy by yourself or with your partner. Then, make a pairing game using triangles.
- Each partner cuts out two pairs of matching obtuse triangles, two pairs of matching acute triangles, and two pairs of matching right triangles from cardboard (that is 12 triangles in all). Each partner puts his or her triangles in a basket.
- Now, switch baskets. On the count of 3, dump out the triangles in your baskets and match them up. The first one to match his or her triangles wins. Classify the triangles together when your race is finished.

**Materials:**

- *A Pair of Socks* by Stuart J. Murphy
- cardboard
- scissors
- 2 baskets

# Identify and Describe Geometric Figures

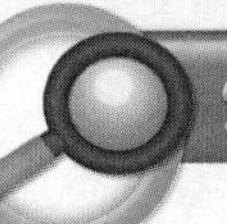

## Science

### Crystal Shapes

Crystals grow in several different shapes and sizes. Familiar-shaped crystals are as close as your salt shaker.

- Using your magnifying glass, look at the crystals of the three materials on the table: iodized salt, kosher salt, and sugar.
- What shape are the crystals of each material? Name the solid that most resembles the shape of these crystals.
- How are the crystals of each material similar? How are they different? Explain.

**Materials:**
- magnifying glass
- iodized salt
- kosher salt
- sugar
- paper
- pencil

## Music

### Figure Challenge

Musical instruments are all made using different two- and three-dimensional figures. Can you recognize them all?

- You and your partner will look at a series of pictures of musical instruments. For each instrument, name as many two- and three-dimensional figures as you can spot. Do not show your partner your list until you have finished.
- Compare your lists. If you both wrote down the same figures for a given instrument, cross off the ones that match. The person with the most figure names remaining wins the Figure Challenge, and if neither one of you has any figure names left after you compare, you both win!

**Materials:**
- pictures of musical instruments
- paper
- pencils

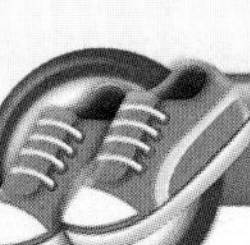

## Health

### The Food Pyramid

Did you know that even the way you eat can be described as a three-dimensional figure? How does your eating plan shape up?

- Take a look at the Food Pyramid. On the poster, it appears as a two-dimensional figure, but it is named after a three-dimensional figure. Why do you think it is called the Food Pyramid and not the Food Triangle?
- Make your own customized Food Pyramid. Trace a pyramid pattern onto paper, cut it out, fold it, and tape it together. Then divide your pyramid into levels, as seen on the Food Pyramid poster. For each level, write on your pyramid the kinds of foods you like that fall into that category.

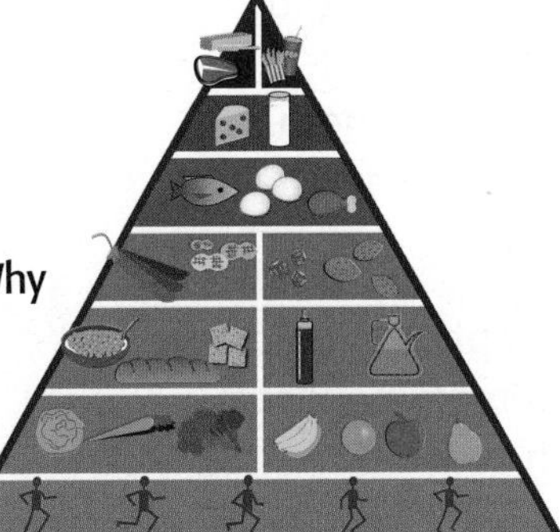

**Materials:**
- poster of the Food Pyramid
- pyramid pattern for tracing and cutting
- colored markers
- tape
- paper

CHAPTER 9

# Introduce the Chapter

## Real World: Is It two- or three-dimensional?

**Materials:** magazines, scissors, glue, paper

Share with students that they are going to learn about two- and three-dimensional figures in this chapter. Explain that there are many two- and three-dimensional figures in their world.

If necessary, have students share examples of two- and three-dimensional figures before they begin the activity.

Provide students with magazines, scissors, glue, and paper. Have them search through the magazines for two- and three-dimensional figures found in the real world.

Ask them to cut the figures out of the magazine and glue them on their paper to make a collage.

Direct students to Student Edition p. 356. Have students read the paragraph at the top of the page.

- **What are some examples of rectangles that you found?** Answers will vary.
- **What other figures did you find?** Answers will vary.

## WRITING IN ▶MATH

**Starting the Chapter**
Have students write about two- and three-dimensional figures. Suggest that they give examples of two or three and draw pictures when possible.

**Key Vocabulary** Introduce the key vocabulary in the chapter using the routine below.

Define: An angle is a figure that is formed by two *rays* with the same *endpoint*.
Example: Point out angles in the classroom.
Ask: What are some other angles you see in the classroom?

**Read-Aloud Anthology** For an optional reading activity to introduce this chapter's math concepts, see the Read-Aloud Anthology on p. TR33.

CHAPTER 9

# Identify and Describe Geometric Figures

**BIG Idea** **What are two-dimensional and three-dimensional figures?**

A **two-dimensional figure** has length and width.
A **three-dimensional figure** has length, width, and height.

**Example** Two-dimensional and three-dimensional figures are often found in traffic signs.

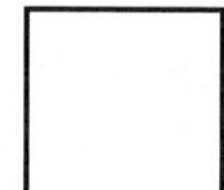

### What will I learn in this chapter?

- Identify, describe, and classify two- and three-dimensional figures.
- Identify angles.
- Identify and make nets.
- Solve problems by looking for a pattern.

### Key Vocabulary

**three-dimensional figure**
**two-dimensional figure**
**polygon**
**angle**

Math Online ▶ **Student Study Tools at macmillanmh.com**

356 **Chapter 9** Identify and Described Geometric Figures

## Chapter 9 Project

### A Banner of Shapes

Students make a banner of cloth shapes.

- Students use fabric paints or cloth and glue to create shapes on 10-by-10 inch white sheeting blocks. If using cloth, they will need scissors to cut out shapes. Any cloth can be used. Fabric paint is good for representing lines, rays, and angles.
- Students write the names of the shapes under each one, using fabric paint or glitter glue. Cloth blocks can be sewn together in a long banner or fused together using fusible webbing.
- Before attaching the blocks together, challenge students to categorize the blocks into polygon groups, angles, and lines and arrange the banner in that order.

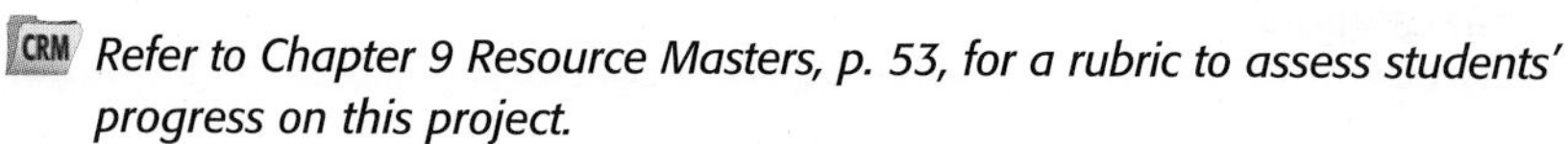

CRM *Refer to Chapter 9 Resource Masters, p. 53, for a rubric to assess students' progress on this project.*

FOLDABLES Study Organizer

Make this Foldable to help you organize information about geometric figures. Begin with 8 sheets of notebook paper.

1. **Staple** the sheets of notebook paper together to form a booklet.

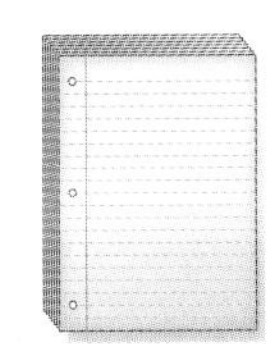

2. **Cut** a tab as shown. On the third page, make the tab longer, and so on.

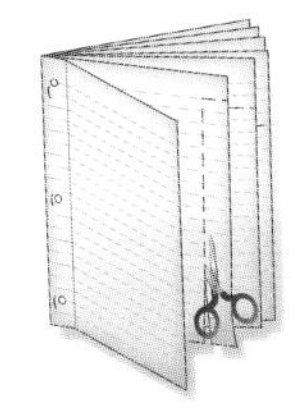

3. **Write** the chapter title on the cover. Label each tab with a lesson number.

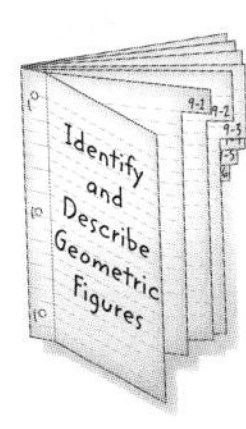




## ELL National ESL Standards Alignment for Chapter 9

| Lesson, Page | ESL Standard | Modality | Level |
|---|---|---|---|
| 9-1, p. 359B | Goal 3, Standard 1, g | Auditory, Linguistic | Intermediate |
| 9-2, p. 362B | Goal 1, Standard 3, k | Kinesthetic, Linguistic | Beginning |
| 9-3, p. 366B | Goal 2, Standard 2, i | Kinesthetic | Beginning |
| 9-4, p. 368B | Goal 2, Standard 1, h | Logical, Visual | Beginning |
| 9-5, p. 372B | Goal 2, Standard 2, c | Linguistic, Kinesthetic | Intermediate |
| 9-6, p. 376B | Goal 1, Standard 1, b | Interpersonal, Auditory/Visual | Advanced |
| 9-7, p. 380B | Goal 2, Standard 1, a | Intrapersonal | Intermediate |

The National ESL Standards can be found in the Teacher Reference Handbook.

## FOLDABLES Dinah Zike's Foldables

Guide students through the directions on p. 357 to create their own Foldables graphic organizers for geometric figures. Students may also use their Foldables to study and review for chapter assessments.

**When to Use It** Lessons 9-1, 9-2, 9-4, and 9-6. (Additional instructions for using the Foldables with these lessons are found on pp. 371 and 384.)

## Chapter 9 Literature List

| Lesson | Book Title |
|---|---|
| 9-1 | **Sir Cumference and the Sword in the Cone**<br>Cindy Neuschwander |
| 9-2 | **Shape Up! Fun With Triangles and Other Polygons**<br>David A. Adler |
| 9-3 | **A Cloak for the Dreamer**<br>Aileen Friedman |
| 9-4 | **Angles are Easy as Pie**<br>Robert Froman |
| 9-5 | **Bridges**<br>Ken Robbins |
| 9-6 | **Kathy Ross Crafts Triangles, Rectangles, Circles and Squares!**<br>Kathy Ross |
| Any | **A Pair of Socks**<br>Stuart J. Murphy |

- Read the Math at Home letter found in the Chapter 9 Resource Masters, p. 4, with the class and have each student sign it. (A Spanish version is found on p. 5.)
- Send home copies of the Math at Home letter with each student.

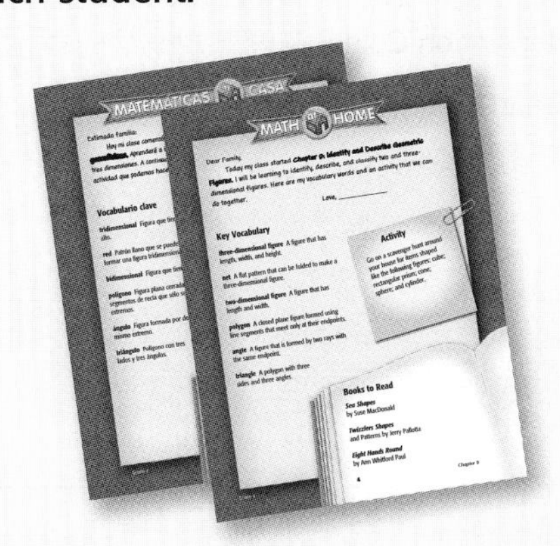

# Diagnostic Assessment

Check for students' prerequisite skills before beginning the chapter.

- **Option 1:** ***Quick Check***

  SE Student Edition, p. 358

- **Option 2:** ***Online Assessment***

  **Math Online** macmillanmh.com

- **Option 3:** ***Diagnostic Tests***

  CRM Chapter 9 Resource Masters, p. 44–45

# RTI (Response to Intervention)

**Apply the Results** Based on the results of the diagnostic assessment on Student Edition p. 358, use the chart below to address individual needs before beginning the chapter.

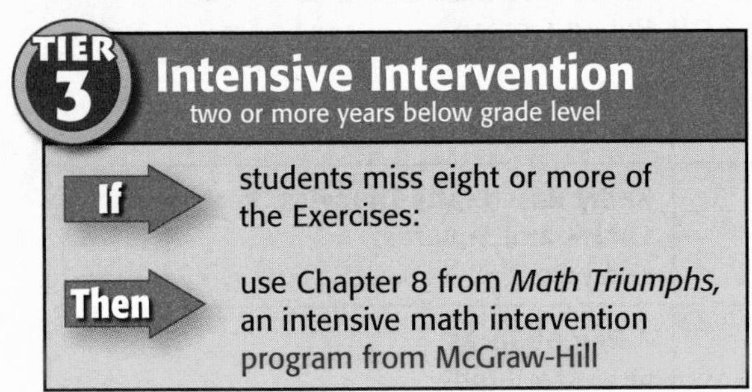

| TIER 3 Intensive Intervention<br>two or more years below grade level | |
|---|---|
| **If** | students miss eight or more of the Exercises: |
| **Then** | use Chapter 8 from *Math Triumphs,* an intensive math intervention program from McGraw-Hill |

## ARE YOU READY for Chapter 9?

You have two ways to check prerequisite skills for this chapter.

**Option 2**

**Math Online** Take the Chapter Readiness Quiz at macmillanmh.com.

**Option 1**

Complete the Quick Check below.

**QUICK Check**

**Identify each figure.** (Prior Grade) (Used in Lesson 9-1)

1. sphere

2. 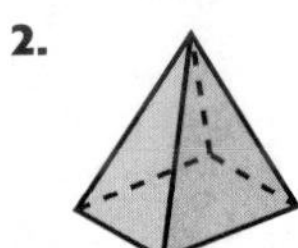 pyramid

3. 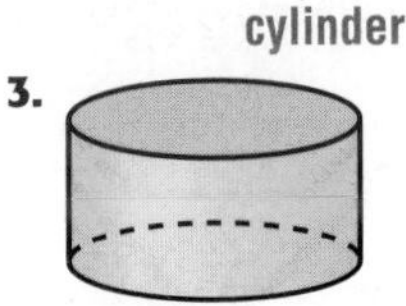 cylinder

4. Identify the three-dimensional figure that represents the objects at the right. cube

**How many sides does each figure have?** (Prior Grade) (Used in Lesson 9-2)

5. 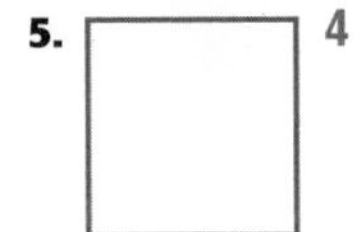 4

6. 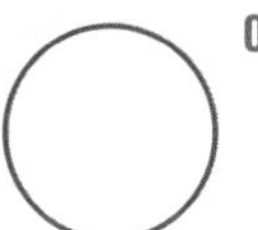 0

7. 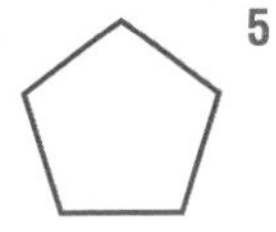 5

8. The musical instrument at the right resembles a triangle. How many sides does the instrument have? 3 sides

**Identify each figure.** (Prior Grade) (Used in Lesson 9-2)

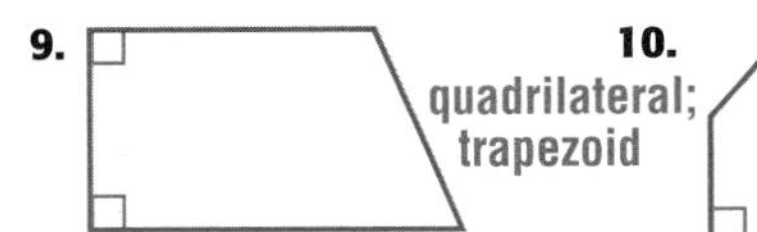

9. quadrilateral; trapezoid

10. pentagon

11. quadrilateral; rectangle

**358 Chapter 9** Identify and Describe Geometric Figures

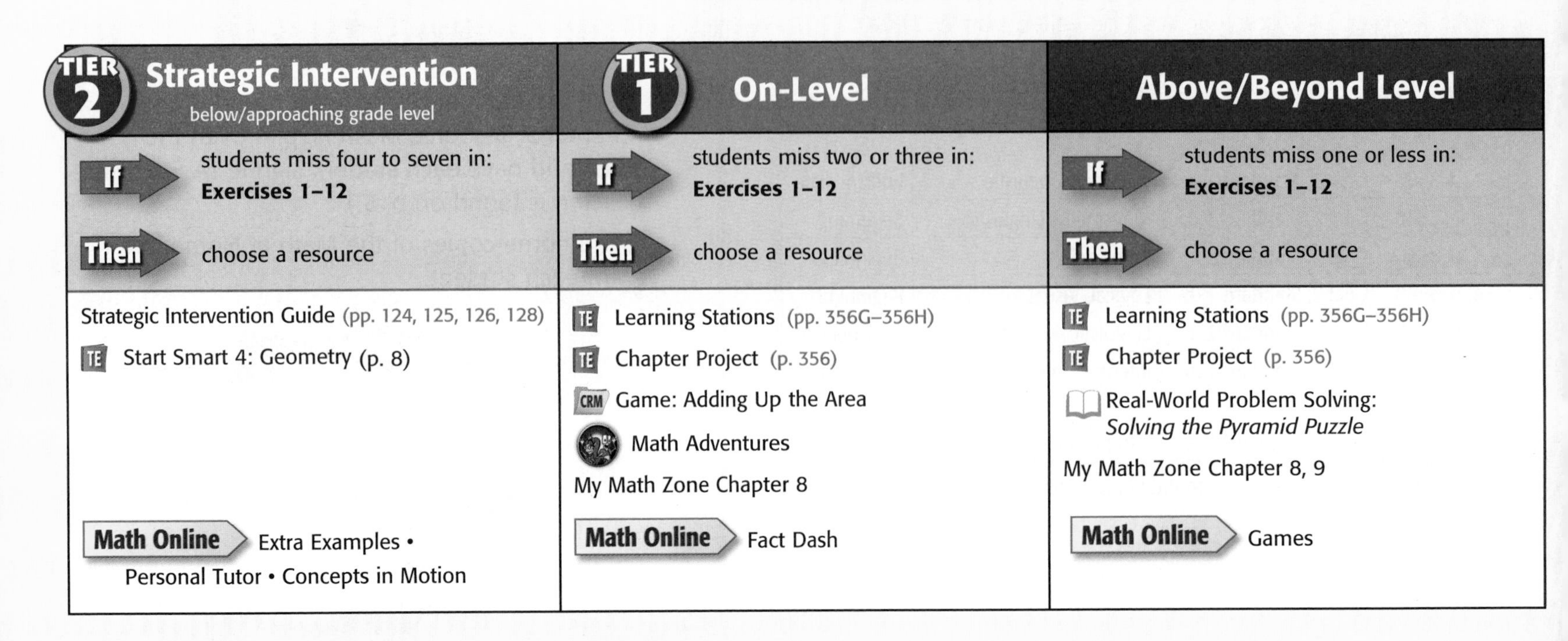

| TIER 2 Strategic Intervention<br>below/approaching grade level | TIER 1 On-Level | Above/Beyond Level |
|---|---|---|
| **If** students miss four to seven in: **Exercises 1–12** | **If** students miss two or three in: **Exercises 1–12** | **If** students miss one or less in: **Exercises 1–12** |
| **Then** choose a resource | **Then** choose a resource | **Then** choose a resource |
| Strategic Intervention Guide (pp. 124, 125, 126, 128)<br>TE Start Smart 4: Geometry (p. 8)<br>**Math Online** Extra Examples • Personal Tutor • Concepts in Motion | TE Learning Stations (pp. 356G–356H)<br>TE Chapter Project (p. 356)<br>CRM Game: Adding Up the Area<br>Math Adventures<br>My Math Zone Chapter 8<br>**Math Online** Fact Dash | TE Learning Stations (pp. 356G–356H)<br>TE Chapter Project (p. 356)<br>Real-World Problem Solving: *Solving the Pyramid Puzzle*<br>My Math Zone Chapter 8, 9<br>**Math Online** Games |

LESSON 9-1

# Three-Dimensional Figures

## Lesson Planner

### Objective

Identify and describe three-dimensional figures and identify and draw nets.

### Vocabulary

**three-dimensional figure**, **face**, **edge**, **vertex**, **net**

### Resources

**Materials:** grid paper, tape or glue, scissors

**Manipulatives:** geometric solids

**Literature Connection:** *Sir Cumference and the Sword in the Cone* by Cindy Neuschwander

**Teacher Technology**

TeacherWorks • Interactive Classroom

## Daily Routine

Use these suggestions before beginning the lesson on p. 359.

### 5-Minute Check

(Reviews Lesson 8-9)

**Divide. Use estimation to check.**

1. $2\overline{)5{,}378}$ 2,689
2. $3\overline{)2{,}349}$ 783
3. $7\overline{)8{,}577}$ 1,225 R2
4. $5\overline{)4{,}120}$ 824
5. $5,144 ÷ 6 $857 R2
6. $2,831 ÷ 3 $943 R2

### Problem of the Day

The normal boiling point of gold is 2,660°C. The normal boiling point of silver is 2,193°C. What is the least temperature at which both silver and gold will boil? 2,660°C

### Focus on Math Background

Three-dimensional figures can also be called names such as 3-D (three-dimensional) shapes, solids, solid figures, and solid shapes. Reminding students that all of these titles have the same meaning may eliminate some confusion later on. In previous grades, students learned to identify cubes, rectangular prisms, cones, pyramids, cylinders, and spheres. In this lesson, students will extend their understanding by naming the number of faces, edges, and vertices figures have. Students will also use nets to make three-dimensional figures and be able to identify the figure the net will make.

### Building Math Vocabulary

Write the lesson vocabulary words and their definitions on the board.

Group the students into pairs. Give each pair a rectangular prism such as a shoebox. Have them identify for each other a face, an edge, and a vertex. Have them sketch a net of the prism.

#### Visual Vocabulary Cards

Use Visual Vocabulary Card 48 to reinforce the vocabulary introduced in this lesson. (The Define/Example/Ask routine is printed on the back of each card.)

# Differentiated Instruction

## Small Group Options

Option 1 — VISUAL, SPATIAL

### Gifted and Talented AL

**Materials:** 1-inch grid paper, crayons/markers, scissors

- Hand students these instructions and provide the necessary tools.
- The packaging industry uses what you have learned about nets to design containers for their new products. They want containers that are neither too big or too small.
- Use 1-inch grid paper and cut 4 separate nets like Exercises 18 or 20 in this lesson.
- Put each of them together to form cubes. Pretend that the cubes are toy cars.
- Use more grid paper and design a box to fit these 4 pieces.
- Finally, color your box, give your toy company a name, or perhaps even color your toy cars. Explain your work to the class and put it on display.

Option 2 — AUDITORY, LINGUISTIC

### English Language Learners ELL

**Materials:** drawings of shapes
**Core Vocabulary:** shapes, label, name
**Common Use Verb:** say
**Hear Math** This strategy uses the students' native languages to activate background knowledge.

- Draw shapes on the chalkboard.
- Ask students to draw them on paper and label them in their native languages.
- Write labels for shapes and pronounce them. Have students repeat.
- Have students label their shapes in English as well.
- Call out a name of a shape and ask a student to tell you the name in his or her native language.

## Independent Work Options

Option 1 — VISUAL, SPATIAL

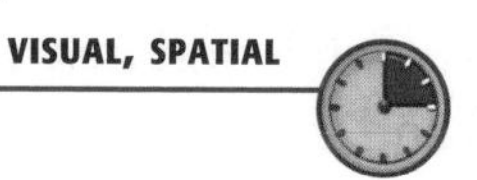

### Early Finishers OL AL

**Materials:** paper, pencil, straight edge, tape or glue, scissors

- Have students make nets of what they think will make rectangular prisms. When they finish, ask them to cut out their nets and glue or tape them together to see if they actually do form rectangular prisms.
- Repeat the process until they have nets that actually form rectangular prisms.

Option 2

### Student Technology

**Math Online** macmillanmh.com

Personal Tutor • Extra Examples

Option 3

### Learning Station: Art (p. 356G)

Direct students to the Art Learning Station for opportunities to explore and extend the lesson concept.

Option 4

### Problem-Solving Practice

Reinforce problem-solving skills and strategies with the Problem-Solving Practice worksheet.

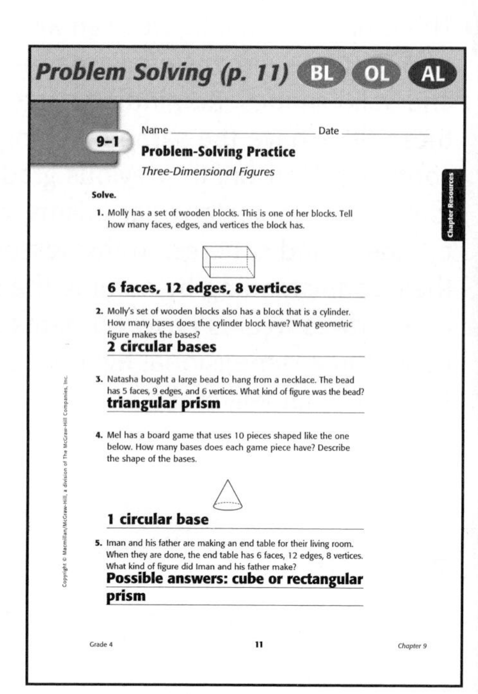

**Problem Solving (p. 11)** BL OL AL

Name ________ Date ________

9–1 **Problem-Solving Practice**
*Three-Dimensional Figures*

**Solve.**

1. Molly has a set of wooden blocks. This is one of her blocks. Tell how many faces, edges, and vertices the block has.
**6 faces, 12 edges, 8 vertices**
2. Molly's set of wooden blocks also has a block that is a cylinder. How many bases does the cylinder block have? What geometric figure makes the bases?
**2 circular bases**
3. Natasha bought a large bead to hang from a necklace. The bead has 5 faces, 9 edges, and 6 vertices. What kind of figure was the bead?
**triangular prism**
4. Mel has a board game that uses 10 pieces shaped like the one below. How many bases does each game piece have? Describe the shape of the bases.
**1 circular base**
5. Iman and his father are making an end table for their living room. When they are done, the end table has 6 faces, 12 edges, 8 vertices. What kind of figure did Iman and his father make?
**Possible answers: cube or rectangular prism**

Grade 4 11 Chapter 9

# 9-1 Three-Dimensional Figures

## GET READY to Learn

The dog crate shown resembles a three-dimensional figure. A **three-dimensional figure** is a solid figure. It has length, width, and height.

**MAIN IDEA**

I will identify and describe three-dimensional figures, and identify and draw nets.

**New Vocabulary**

- three-dimensional figure
- face
- edge
- vertex
- net

**Math Online**

macmillanmh.com
- Extra Examples
- Personal Tutor
- Self-Check Quiz

- A **face** is a flat side.
- Two faces meet at an **edge**.
- A **vertex** is where three or more faces meet.

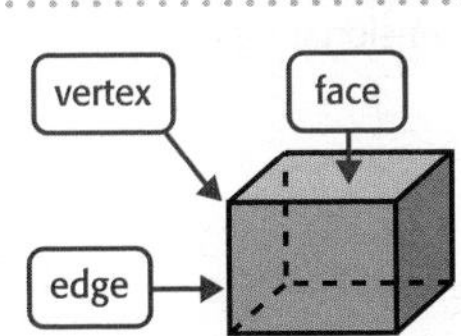


### Three-Dimensional Figures (Key Concepts)

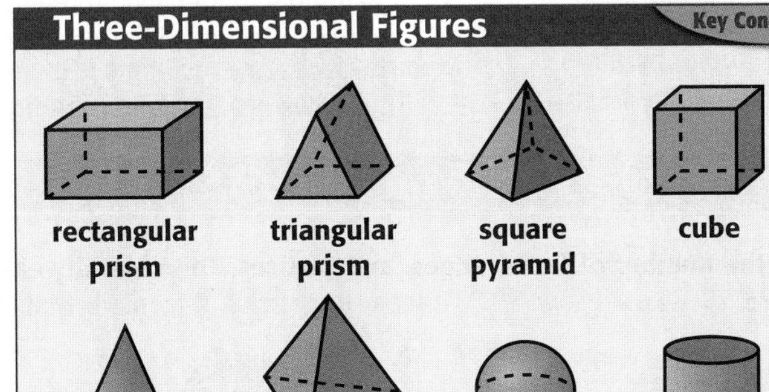


### Real-World EXAMPLE: Identify Three-Dimensional Objects

**1 GIFTS Tell the number of faces, edges, and vertices. Then identify the shape of the gift box.**

It has 6 faces, 12 edges, and 8 vertices. The gift box is a rectangular prism.



# 9-1 Three-Dimensional Figures

## 1 Introduce

### Activity Choice 1 • Hands-On

- Divide the class into groups of three. Provide groups with models of three-dimensional figures such as prisms, pyramids, cones, spheres, and cylinders.
- Have each group answer the following questions about their three-dimensional figures: Answers will vary depending on the three-dimensional figure.
- **Are the sides curved or flat?**
- **How many sides are there?**
- **Are there edges on your figure?**
- Make a table that includes the name of each figure, type of sides, number of flat sides, number of points, and number of edges on the board. Have students fill in the information that they find. Explain that you will be talking more about the parts of different three-dimensional figures in this lesson.

### Activity Choice 2 • Literature

Introduce the lesson with *Sir Cumference and the Sword in the Cone* by Cindy Neuschwander. For a related math activity, see p. TR55.

## 2 Teach

### Scaffolding Questions

Show students an example of a rectangular prism, such as a box. Identify one of the faces of the prism by pointing to it.

- **How many faces does the prism have?** 6

  Point to one of the edges.
- **How many edges does the prism have?** 12

  Point to one of the vertices.
- **How many vertices does the prism have?** 8
- **Where is there an edge in the classroom?** Sample answer: where the walls meet

### GET READY to Learn

Have students open their books and read the information in **Get Ready to Learn**. Introduce **three-dimensional figure**, **face**, **edge**, **vertex**, and **net**. As a class, work through **Example 1**.

## Hands-On Mini Activity

Distribute grid paper, tape, and scissors for the hands-on activity. Have students use their grid paper to draw a net like the one shown.

### Identify Three-dimensional Objects

**Example 1** If students have problems identifying the number of faces, edges, and vertices, provide them with a model.

**ADDITIONAL EXAMPLE**

1. Tell the number of faces, edges and vertices. Then identify the figure.
   It has 2 faces, 2 edges, 0 vertices. The paper towel roll is a cylinder.

**CHECK What You Know**

As a class, have students complete Exercises 1–8 in **Check What You Know** as you observe their work.

**Exercise 8** Assess student comprehension before assigning practice exercises.

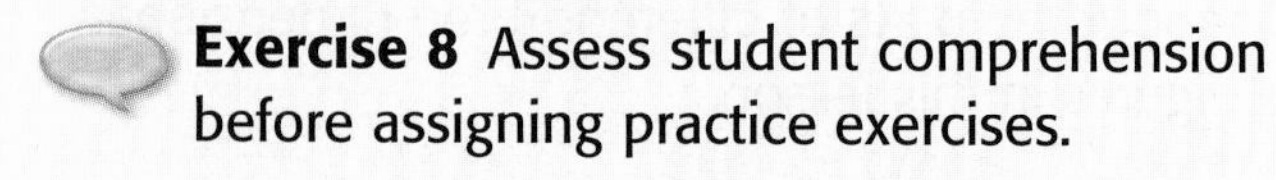

## BL Alternate Teaching Strategy

**If** students have trouble recognizing solid figures...

**Then** use one of these reteach options:

1 CRM **Daily Reteach Worksheet** (p. 8)

2 Take a geometry walk through the school. Have students locate examples of each type of three-dimensional figure studied in this lesson. Ask students to list the examples they observe.

After returning to the classroom, discuss the types of items observed. Make a list on the board of the names of the three-dimensional figures and examples of each.

### Exercise Alert!

**Exercise 12** A cone is a circular solid. It does not fit the exact definitions for plane solids. For example, a cone has 1 vertex, even though 3 or more faces never meet.

A **net** is a two-dimensional figure that can be folded to make a three-dimensional figure.

**Vocabulary Link**

net

**Everyday Use** threads or wires woven together to form a bag-like figure used for trapping something

**Math Use** a two-dimensional figure that can be folded to make a three-dimensional figure

8. Sample answer: A triangular prism has rectangular sides and a triangular pyramid has triangular sides.

### Hands-On Mini Activity

**Step 1** Using grid paper, draw and cut out the net shown.

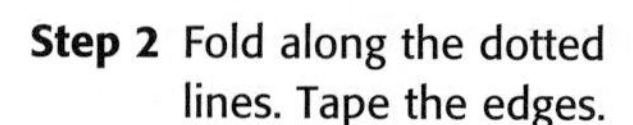

**Step 2** Fold along the dotted lines. Tape the edges.

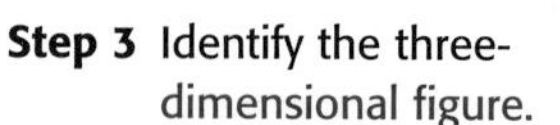

**Step 3** Identify the three-dimensional figure.

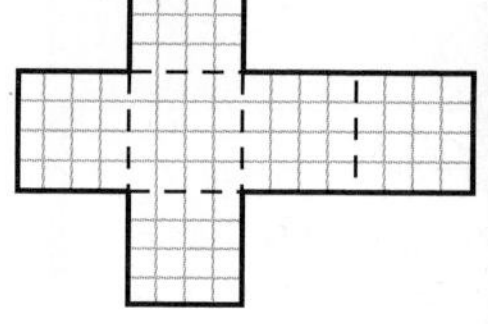

1. Draw another net that could be used to form a cube. See students' work.
2. Identify the three-dimensional figure the net shown at the right makes. triangular pyramid

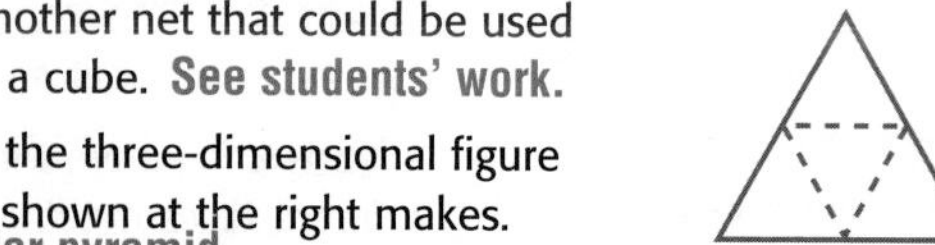

3. Explain how to identify a three-dimensional figure from its net without folding the paper. if the faces are rectangles, the figure is a prism; if the faces are triangles, the figure is a pyramid

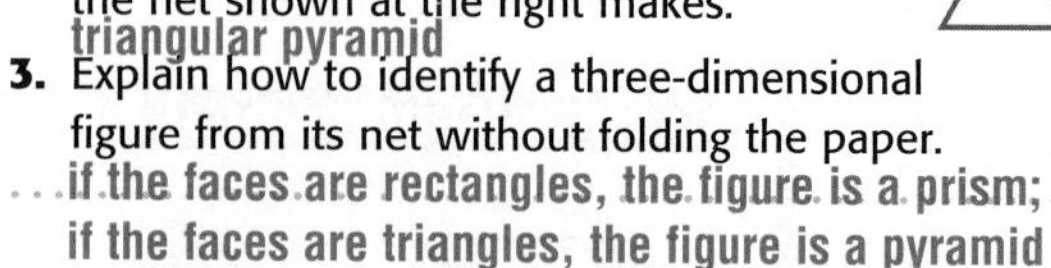

## CHECK What You Know

**Tell the number of faces, edges, and vertices. Then identify each figure.** See Example 1 (p. 359) 3. 0 edges, 0 vertices, 2 faces; cylinder

1. 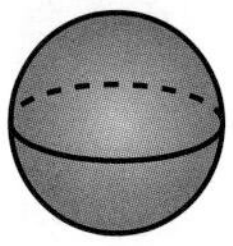 none; sphere

2. 5 faces, 6 vertices, 9 edges; triangular prism

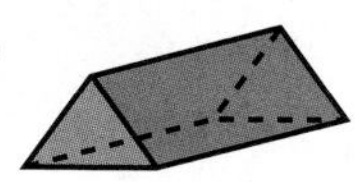

3.

**Identify the three-dimensional figure each net makes.**

4. rectangular prism

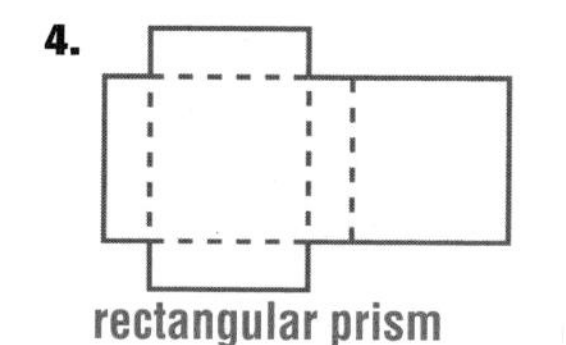

5. cube

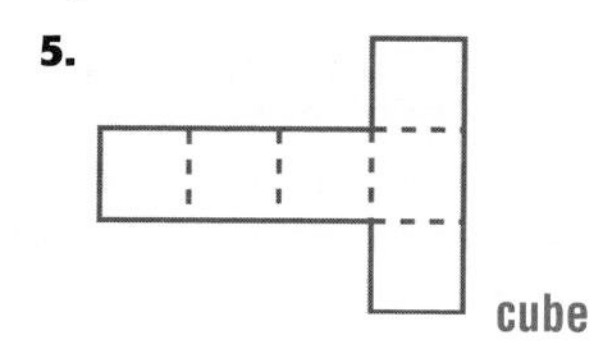

6. triangular prism

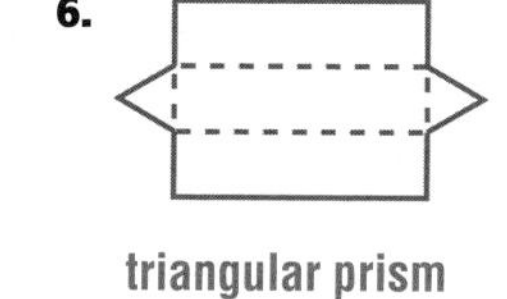

7. Name two three-dimensional figures that have 6 faces. Sample answer: cube and rectangular prism

8. Talk About It Compare a triangular prism and a triangular pyramid.

360 **Chapter 9** Identify and Describe Geometric Figures

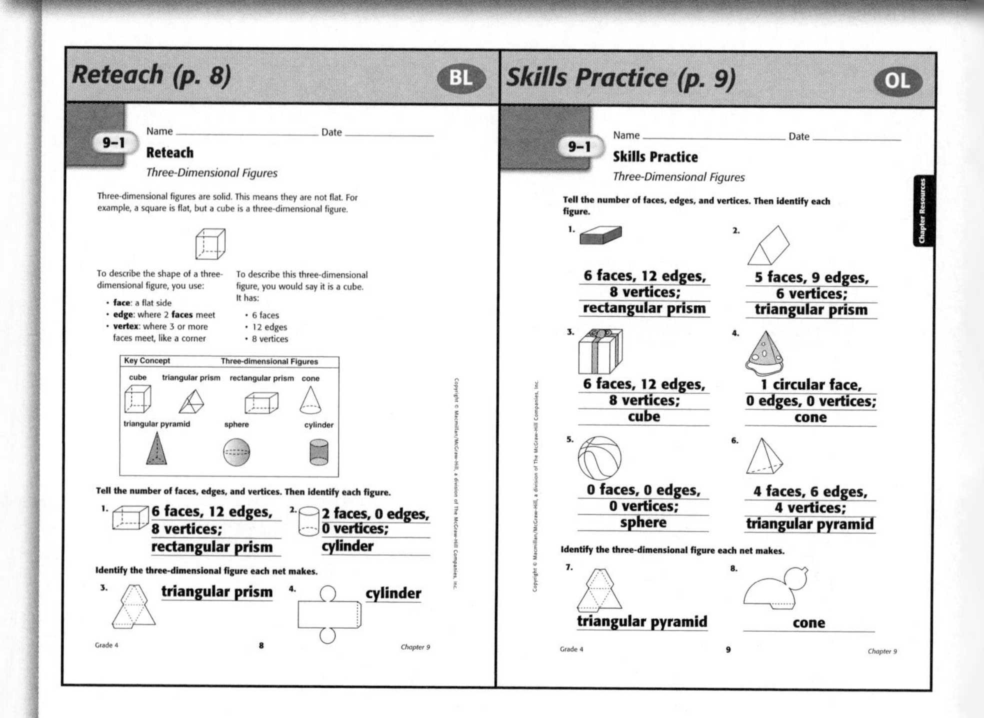

**Reteach (p. 8)** BL

9–1 Name ______ Date ______

**Reteach**

*Three-Dimensional Figures*

Three-dimensional figures are solid. This means they are not flat. For example, a square is flat, but a cube is a three-dimensional figure.

To describe the shape of a three-dimensional figure, you use:

- **face**: a flat side
- **edge**: where 2 **faces** meet
- **vertex**: where 3 or more faces meet, like a corner

To describe this three-dimensional figure, you would say it is a cube. It has:

- 6 faces
- 12 edges
- 8 vertices

Key Concept — Three-dimensional Figures: cube, triangular prism, rectangular prism, cone, triangular pyramid, sphere, cylinder

**Tell the number of faces, edges, and vertices. Then identify each figure.**

1. 6 faces, 12 edges, 8 vertices; rectangular prism
2. 2 faces, 0 edges, 0 vertices; cylinder

**Identify the three-dimensional figure each net makes.**

3. triangular prism
4. cylinder

Grade 4 8 Chapter 9



**Skills Practice (p. 9)** OL

9–1 Name ______ Date ______

**Skills Practice**

*Three-Dimensional Figures*

**Tell the number of faces, edges, and vertices. Then identify each figure.**

1. 6 faces, 12 edges, 8 vertices; rectangular prism
2. 5 faces, 9 edges, 6 vertices; triangular prism
3. 6 faces, 12 edges, 8 vertices; cube
4. 1 circular face, 0 edges, 0 vertices; cone
5. 0 faces, 0 edges, 0 vertices; sphere
6. 4 faces, 6 edges, 4 vertices; triangular pyramid

**Identify the three-dimensional figure each net makes.**

7. triangular pyramid
8. cone

Grade 4 9 Chapter 9

Chapter Resources

## Practice and Problem Solving

See page R23.

**Tell the number of faces, edges, and vertices. Then identify each figure.**
See Example 1 (p. 359) 9. 8 vertices, 12 edges, 6 faces; rectangular prism

9\.

10\. 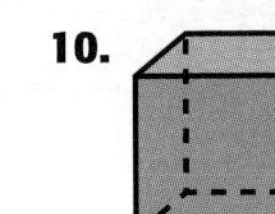 8 vertices, 12 edges, 6 faces; cube

11\. 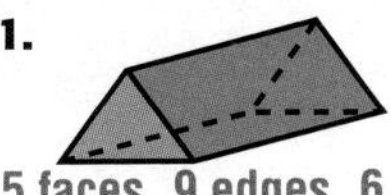 5 faces, 9 edges, 6 vertices; triangular prism

12\. 1 vertex, 0 edges, 1 face; cone

13\.  2 faces, 0 edges, 0 vertices; cylinder

14\.  none; sphere

**Identify the three-dimensional figure each net makes.** 17. triangular pyramid

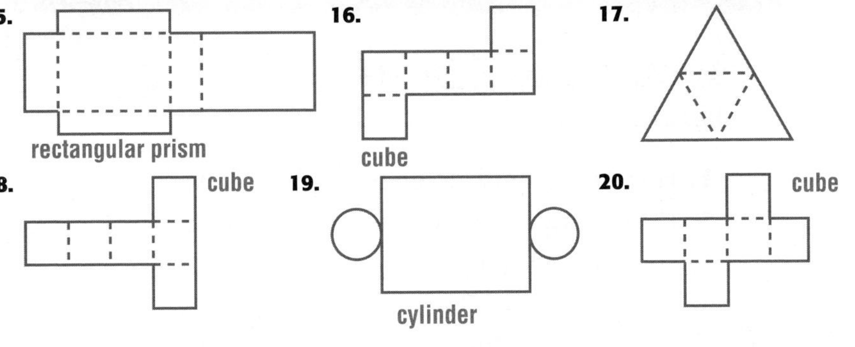

15\. rectangular prism

16\. cube

17\.

18\. cube

19\. cylinder

20\. cube

21\. This three-dimensional figure has 4 faces, 6 edges, and 4 vertices. What figure is it? triangular pyramid

22\. This three-dimensional figure can be made using 2 circles and 1 large rectangle. What figure is it? cylinder

### H.O.T. Problems

23\. **OPEN ENDED** Draw a three-dimensional figure. Then describe its faces, edges, and vertices. 23–25. See Ch. 9 Answer Appendix.

24\. **WHICH ONE DOESN'T BELONG?** Identify the figure that does not belong with the other three. Explain.

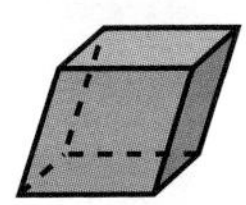 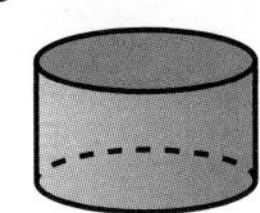 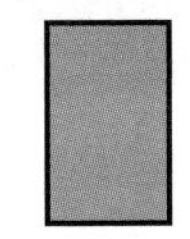 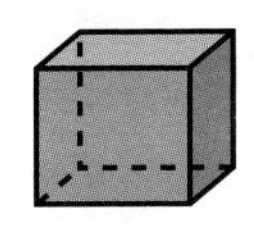

25\. **WRITING IN MATH** Compare a cone and cylinder.



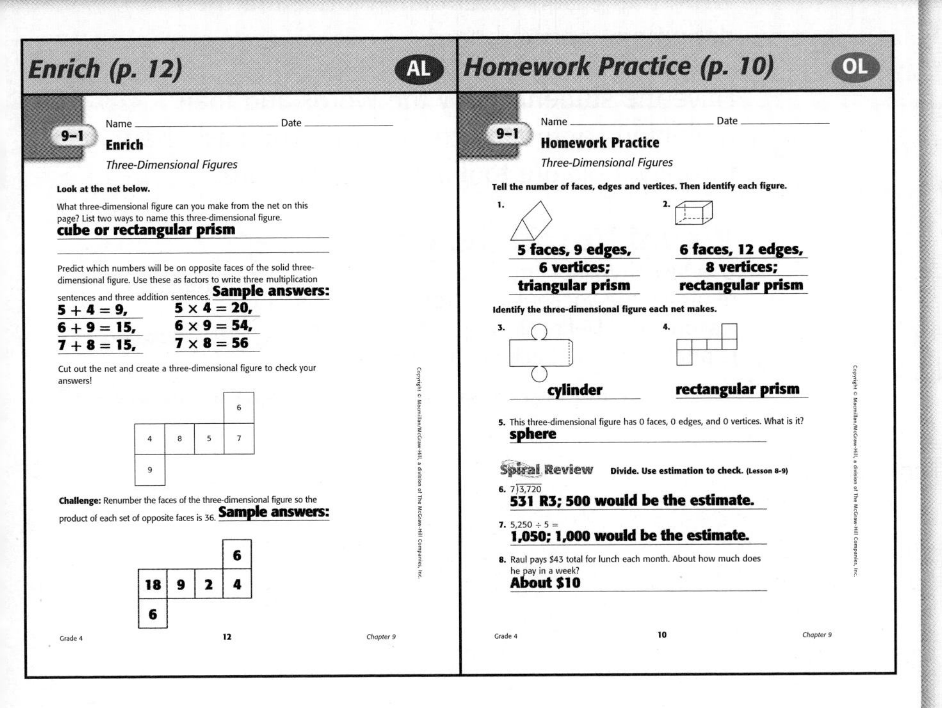

**Enrich (p. 12)** AL

9-1 Name ______ Date ______
**Enrich**
*Three-Dimensional Figures*

**Look at the net below.**

What three-dimensional figure can you make from the net on this page? List two ways to name this three-dimensional figure.
**cube or rectangular prism**

Predict which numbers will be on opposite faces of the solid three-dimensional figure. Use these as factors to write three multiplication sentences and three addition sentences. **Sample answers:**
**5 + 4 = 9, 5 × 4 = 20,**
**6 + 9 = 15, 6 × 9 = 54,**
**7 + 8 = 15, 7 × 8 = 56**

Cut out the net and create a three-dimensional figure to check your answers!

**Challenge:** Renumber the faces of the three-dimensional figure so the product of each set of opposite faces is 36. **Sample answers:**

Grade 4 12 Chapter 9

**Homework Practice (p. 10)** OL

9-1 Name ______ Date ______
**Homework Practice**
*Three-Dimensional Figures*

**Tell the number of faces, edges and vertices. Then identify each figure.**

1\. **5 faces, 9 edges, 6 vertices; triangular prism**

2\. **6 faces, 12 edges, 8 vertices; rectangular prism**

**Identify the three-dimensional figure each net makes.**

3\. **cylinder**

4\. **rectangular prism**

5\. This three-dimensional figure has 0 faces, 0 edges, and 0 vertices. What is it? **sphere**

**Spiral Review** Divide. Use estimation to check. (Lesson 8-9)

6\. 7)3,720 **531 R3; 500 would be the estimate.**

7\. 5,250 ÷ 5 = **1,050; 1,000 would be the estimate.**

8\. Raul pays $43 total for lunch each month. About how much does he pay in a week? **About $10**

Grade 4 10 Chapter 9

## 3 Practice

Differentiate practice using these leveled assignments for Exercises 9–25.

| Level | Assignment |
|---|---|
| BL Below/Approaching Level | 9–11, 15–18, 21 |
| OL On Level | 9–13, 15–19, 21, 24 |
| AL Above/Beyond Level | 9–21 odd, 23–25 |

Have students discuss and complete the Higher Order Thinking problems. Have them compare their answers with a partner and work out any incorrect answers.

**WRITING IN MATH** Have students complete Exercise 25 in their Math Journals. You may choose to use this exercise as an optional formative assessment.

## Assess

### Formative Assessment

- **How are a sphere and a cylinder alike? How are they different?** Sample answer: Both have a surface that is curved, not flat. A cylinder has two round faces and two edges, but a sphere does not.
- **Give an example of a rectangular prism.** Answers will vary. Sample answer: shoebox

**Quick Check** **Are students continuing to struggle with three-dimensional figures and their nets?**

**If Yes** → Strategic Intervention Guide (p. 124)

**If No** → Independent Work Options (p. 359B)
CRM Skills Practice Worksheet (p. 9)
CRM Enrich Worksheet (p. 12)

**Ticket Out the Door** Ask students to quickly sketch a net of any of the three-dimensional figures they learned about in this lesson. Ask them to identify the three-dimensional figure that the net would make.

LESSON 9-2

# Two-Dimensional Figures

## Lesson Planner

### Objective

Identify, describe, and classify two-dimensional figures.

### Vocabulary

**two-dimensional figure**, **polygon**, **sides**, **triangle**, **quadrilateral**, **pentagon**, **hexagon**, **octagon**

### Resources

**Materials:** construction paper, scissors, glue, colored pencils

**Manipulatives:** pattern blocks, geometric solids

**Literature Connection:** *Shape Up! Fun With Triangles and Other Polygons* by David A. Adler

**Teacher Technology**

TeacherWorks • Interactive Classroom • Math Tool Chest

## Daily Routine

Use these suggestions before beginning the lesson on p. 362.

### 5-Minute Check

(Reviews Lesson 9-1)

1. How many vertices does a sphere have? 0
2. How many faces does a cylinder have? 2
3. Describe a triangular pyramid. Sample answer: It has a triangular base, 4 faces, 6 edges, 4 vertices
4. Name a solid figure that has 5 faces, 8 edges, and 5 vertices. square pyramid

### Problem of the Day

There are 10 pencils in each box and 12 boxes in each carton. James orders 1 carton and 3 boxes. How many pencils did he order? 150 pencils

### Focus on Math Background

In the previous lesson, students explored figures that do not lie entirely in one plane. In this lesson, they will consider figures that do lie in one plane. Remind students that *two-dimensional figures* can also be called *plane shapes* or figures because they lie in one plane. Students, at the very least, have experience with common polygons such as triangles, rectangles, and squares. At this grade level, students are not given a formal definition of a polygon. Instead they are told informally that polygons are two-dimensional figures with three or more sides, and they do not have curved sides. When appropriate, students will be given a formal definition of a polygon.

A *polygon* is a closed figure in a plane that is formed from line segments that meet only at their endpoints.

### Building Math Vocabulary

Write the lesson vocabulary words and their definitions on the board.

Have the students copy the words and their definitions onto a piece of paper. Then ask them to draw a picture to illustrate each word.

**Visual Vocabulary Cards**

Use Visual Vocabulary Cards 38 and 41 to reinforce the vocabulary introduced in this lesson. (The Define/Example/Ask routine is printed on the back of each card.)

# Differentiated Instruction

## Small Group Options

**Option 1** LOGICAL, SPATIAL

### Gifted and Talented AL

**Materials:** index cards

- Challenge students to write logical statements using the terminology presented in the lesson. Students' statements should explain relationships among the various two-dimensional figures.
- Provide students with starter sentences to fill in, such as: All ____ have ____. Some ____ are ____. No ____ have ____.
- Students should then make a second set without naming the two-dimensional figure (leave it blank).
- Students should use their pairs in small groups. They should lay them out facedown in a grid and play concentration to rematch the pairs.

**Option 2** KINESTHETIC, LINGUISTIC

### English Language Learners ELL

**Materials:** pipe cleaners

**Core Vocabulary:** number of sides, name, copy

**Common Use Verb:** can tell

All equilateral triangles have acute angles.

Some quadrilaterals are trapezoids.

No parallelograms have intersecting lines.

**Talk Math** This strategy uses native language and manipulatives to help students name and internalize two-dimensional figures.

- Draw a triangle.
- Have students copy with their pipe cleaners and count the sides.
- Prompt students to name the shape in English or in their native languages.
- Say: "The **number of sides** can tell you its name."
- Discuss similarities of native and English figure names. Repeat for other figures.

**English Language Learners (p. 169) ELL**

45 Name ____

**3-Dimensional Shapes**

| Cube | Triangular Pyramid | Rectangular Prism |
|---|---|---|
| ____ faces<br>____ edges<br>____ vertices | ____ faces<br>____ edges<br>____ vertices | ____ faces<br>____ edges<br>____ vertices |
| **Cylinder** | **Square Pyramid** | **Cone** |
| ____ bases<br>____ edges | ____ faces<br>____ edges<br>____ vertices | ____ bases<br>____ edges<br>____ vertices |

2- and 3-Dimensional Figures 169

*Use this worksheet to provide additional support for English Language Learners.*

## Independent Work Options

**Option 1** LOGICAL

### Early Finishers OL AL

**Materials:** paper, pencils

- Students draw a line on the paper. Then they keep drawing lines or curves until they have created a closed figure. Then have them tell whether the figure is a polygon or not.
- Ask the students to draw figures that contain curves, as well as polygons.

**Option 2** Tech Link

### Student Technology

**Math Online** macmillanmh.com

Math Tool Chest Attributes

Personal Tutor • Extra Examples

Math Adventures

**Option 3**

### Learning Station: Science (p. 356H)

Direct students to the Science Learning Station for opportunities to explore and extend the lesson concept.

**Option 4**

### Problem-Solving Practice

Reinforce problem-solving skills and strategies with the Problem-Solving Practice worksheet.

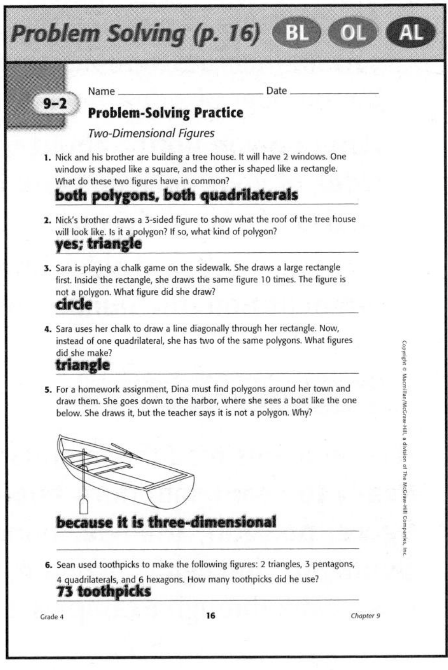
**Problem Solving (p. 16) BL OL AL**

9–2 Name ____ Date ____

**Problem-Solving Practice**

*Two-Dimensional Figures*

1. Nick and his brother are building a tree house. It will have 2 windows. One window is shaped like a square, and the other is shaped like a rectangle. What do these two figures have in common?
**both polygons, both quadrilaterals**
2. Nick's brother draws a 3-sided figure to show what the roof of the tree house will look like. Is it a polygon? If so, what kind of polygon?
**yes; triangle**
3. Sara is playing a chalk game on the sidewalk. She draws a large rectangle first. Inside the rectangle, she draws the same figure 10 times. The figure is not a polygon. What figure did she draw?
**circle**
4. Sara uses her chalk to draw a line diagonally through her rectangle. Now, instead of one quadrilateral, she has two of the same polygons. What figures did she make?
**triangle**
5. For a homework assignment, Dina must find polygons around her town and draw them. She goes down to the harbor, where she sees a boat like the one below. She draws it, but the teacher says it is not a polygon. Why?
**because it is three-dimensional**
6. Sean used toothpicks to make the following figures: 2 triangles, 3 pentagons, 4 quadrilaterals, and 6 hexagons. How many toothpicks did he use?
**73 toothpicks**



Grade 4 16 Chapter 9

# Two-Dimensional Figures

## 1 Introduce

### Activity Choice 1 • Hands-On

Show students several models of figures that do not have curved surfaces. Hold them up one at a time. For example, hold up a square pyramid.

- **How many faces does this three-dimensional figure have?** 5
- **Are the faces all the same shape?** no
- Point to a triangular face. **What is the shape of this face called?** triangle
- Point to the square face. **What is the shape of this face called?** square
- Repeat for the other three-dimensional figures.

### Activity Choice 2 • Literature

Introduce the lesson with *Shape Up! Fun With Triangles and Other Polygons* by David A. Adler. For a related math activity, see p. TR56.

## 2 Teach

### Scaffolding Questions

Divide the class into groups. Give each group a different set of shapes: triangles, quadrilaterals, pentagons, hexagons, or octagons. Make sure the figures are not all regular.

- **What do you call a two-dimensional figure with 3 sides? with 4 sides? with 5 sides? with 6 sides? with 8 sides?** triangle; quadrilateral; pentagon; hexagon; octagon
- Ask students to describe the polygons in their sets. In their descriptions, they should include the number of sides and angles.
- **What do you notice about the number of sides of your polygons and the number of angles of your polygons?** They are the same.
- **Can the number of sides of a polygon be different from the number of angles?** no

### GET READY to Learn

Have students read the information in **Get Ready to Learn**. Introduce **two-dimensional figure**, **polygon**, **triangle**, **quadrilateral**, **pentagon**, **hexagon**, **octagon**, and **sides**. As a class, work through **Examples 1–3**.



# 9-2 Two-Dimensional Figures

**MAIN IDEA**

I will identify, describe, and classify two-dimensional figures.

**New Vocabulary**

two-dimensional figure
polygon
sides
triangle
quadrilateral
pentagon
hexagon
octagon

**Math Online**

macmillanmh.com
- Extra Examples
- Personal Tutor
- Self-Check Quiz

### GET READY to Learn

These are traffic signs that you may see every day. What shapes are the signs?

The shapes of the signs are two-dimensional figures. A **two-dimensional figure** is a plane figure. It has length and width. **Polygons** are closed plane figures that have three or more line segments called **sides**.

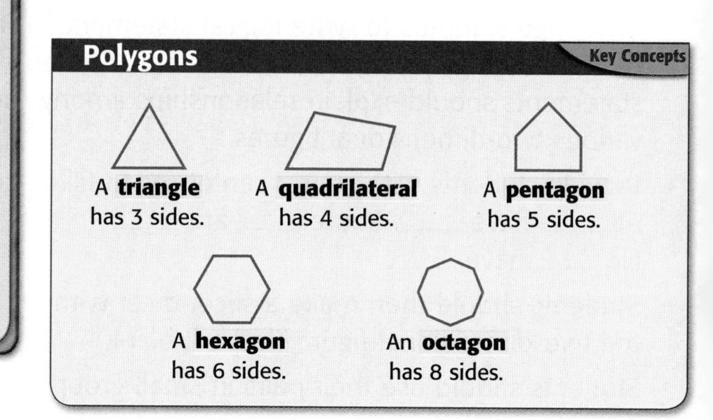

**Identify a Polygon**

**1 SPORTS Identify the shape of home plate.**

Look at the shape of the home plate. It has 5 sides.

So, this figure is a pentagon.

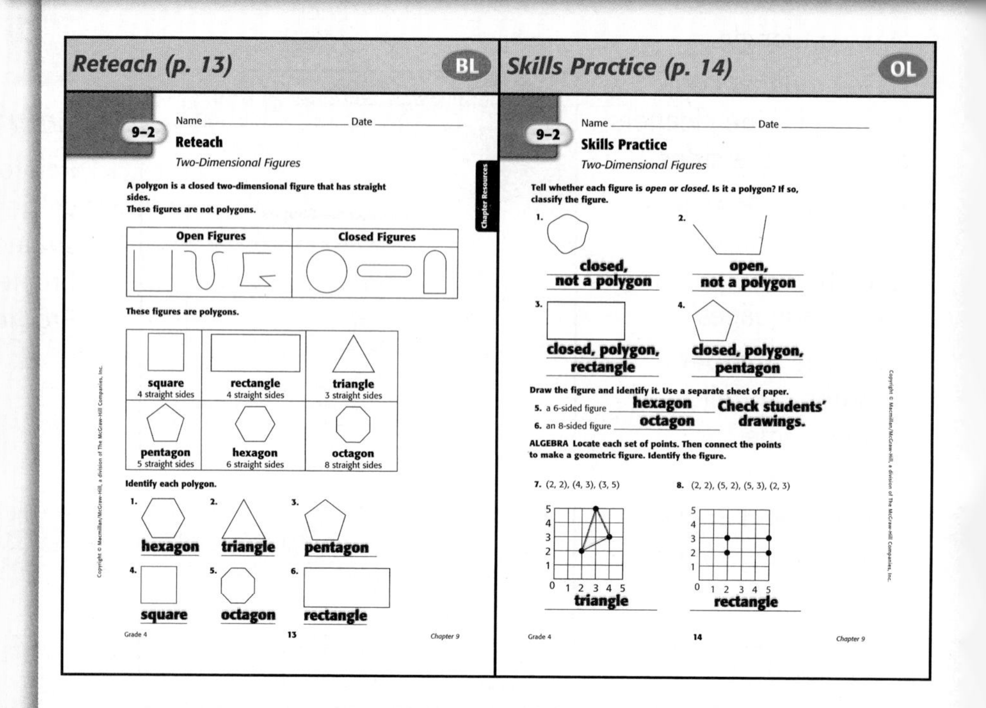

**Reteach (p. 13)** BL

9-2 Reteach
*Two-Dimensional Figures*

Name ________ Date ________

A polygon is a closed two-dimensional figure that has straight sides.
These figures are not polygons.

| Open Figures | Closed Figures |
|---|---|

These figures are polygons.

| square<br>4 straight sides | rectangle<br>4 straight sides | triangle<br>3 straight sides |
|---|---|---|
| pentagon<br>5 straight sides | hexagon<br>6 straight sides | octagon<br>8 straight sides |

Identify each polygon.

1. hexagon 2. triangle 3. pentagon
4. square 5. octagon 6. rectangle

Grade 4 13 Chapter 9

**Skills Practice (p. 14)** OL

9-2 Skills Practice
*Two-Dimensional Figures*

Name ________ Date ________

Tell whether each figure is *open* or *closed*. Is it a polygon? If so, classify the figure.

1. closed, not a polygon
2. open, not a polygon
3. closed, polygon, rectangle
4. closed, polygon, pentagon

Draw the figure and identify it. Use a separate sheet of paper.

5. a 6-sided figure hexagon Check students' drawings.
6. an 8-sided figure octagon

ALGEBRA Locate each set of points. Then connect the points to make a geometric figure. Identify the figure.

7. (2, 2), (4, 3), (3, 5) triangle
8. (2, 2), (5, 2), (5, 3), (2, 3) rectangle

Grade 4 14 Chapter 9

A circle is not a polygon because it does not have straight sides. Other shapes are not polygons as well.

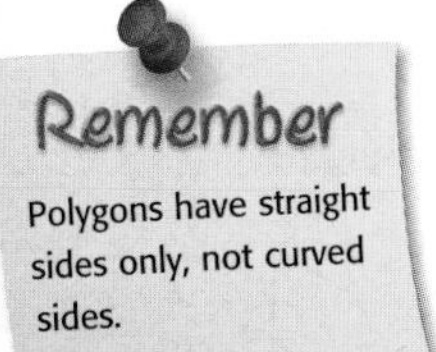


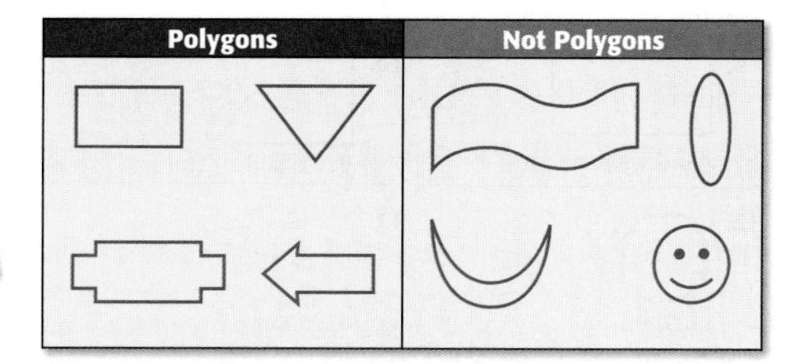


**EXAMPLES** Identify a Polygon

**Tell whether each shape is a polygon.**

The figure has curved sides. It is not a polygon.

The figure has 6 straight sides. It is a polygon.

## CHECK What You Know

**Identify each polygon.** See Example 1 (p. 362)

**1.** quadrilateral

**2.** 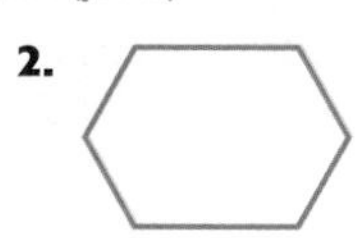 hexagon

**3.**  octagon

**Tell whether each shape is a polygon.** See Examples 2 and 3 (p. 363)

**4.**  no

**5.**  yes

**6.**  yes

**7.** Identify the shape of the nut. hexagon

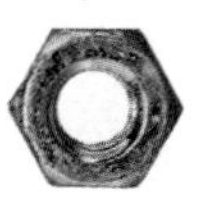

**8.** Talk About It If we take a quadrilateral and cut it into two pieces, what shapes could the pieces be? Sample answer: triangles



**Enrich (p. 17)** AL

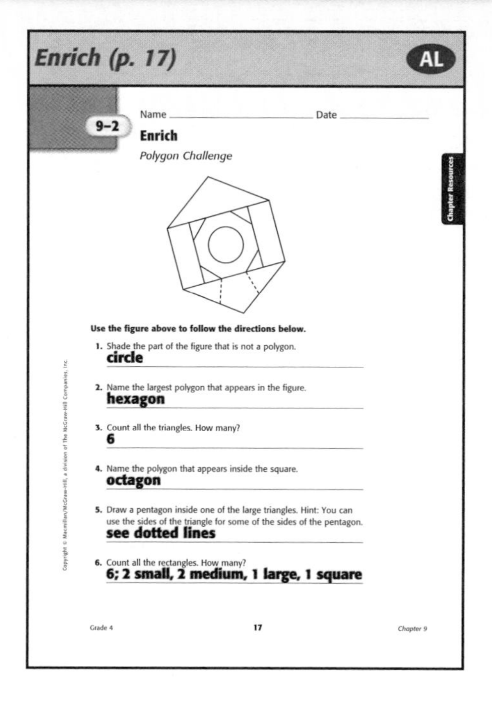

9–2 Name ______ Date ______

**Enrich**

*Polygon Challenge*

**Use the figure above to follow the directions below.**

1. Shade the part of the figure that is not a polygon. **circle**
2. Name the largest polygon that appears in the figure. **hexagon**
3. Count all the triangles. How many? **6**
4. Name the polygon that appears inside the square. **octagon**
5. Draw a pentagon inside one of the large triangles. Hint: You can use the sides of the triangle for some of the sides of the pentagon. **see dotted lines**
6. Count all the rectangles. How many? **6; 2 small, 2 medium, 1 large, 1 square**

Grade 4 17 Chapter 9

### Identify a Polygon

**Example 1** Students may have trouble identifying polygons that are not regular. Encourage them to always count the number of sides a polygon has before identifying the polygon.

## ADDITIONAL EXAMPLES

**1** Identify the shape of a face on a milk carton. rectangle

**2** Tell whether the shape is a polygon. no

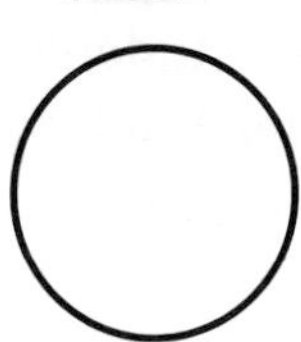

**3** Tell whether the shape is a polygon. yes

### CHECK What You Know

As a class, have students complete Exercises 1–8 in **Check What You Know** as you observe their work.

**Exercise 8** Assess student comprehension before assigning practice exercises.

## BL Alternate Teaching Strategy

**If** students have trouble distinguishing among pentagons, hexagons, and octagons…

**Then** use one of these reteach options:

1. CRM **Daily Reteach Worksheet** (p. 13)
2. Have them trace the figures in their books, cut them out, and glue them on a piece of construction paper. Then ask them to count the sides and label each polygon. Display these papers around the classroom.
3. Tech Link Have students use Math Tool Chest to help complete the problem-solving exercises.

# 3 Practice

Differentiate practice using these leveled assignments for Exercises 9–29.

| Level | Assignment |
|---|---|
| BL Below/Approaching Level | 9–14, 15–17, 21–22 |
| OL On Level | 9–22, 25–26, 28 |
| AL Above/Beyond Level | 10–26 even, 27–29 |

Have students discuss and complete the Higher Order Thinking problems. Have them discuss their answers with a partner and make any corrections necessary.

**WRITING IN ▶MATH** Have students complete Exercise 29 in their Math Journals. You may choose to use this exercise as an optional formative assessment.

### COMMON ERROR!

**Exercises 21–22** Students may have trouble finding the polygons in these pictures. Copy the pictures. Have the students use colored pencils to trace the polygons they see in the picture before they identify them.



## Practice and Problem Solving

EXTRA PRACTICE See page R23.

**Identify each polygon.** See Example 1 (p. 362)

**9.** 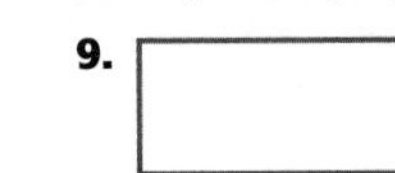 quadrilateral

**10.** 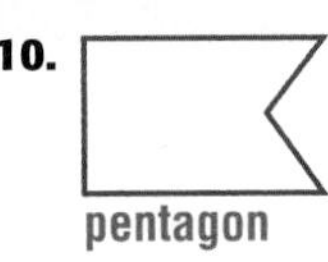 pentagon

**11.** 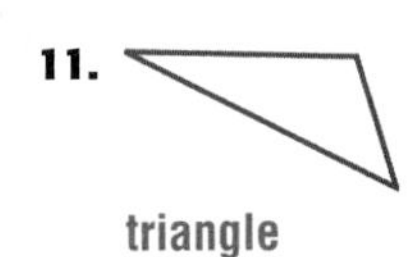 triangle

**12.** 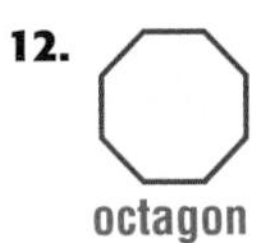 octagon

**13.** 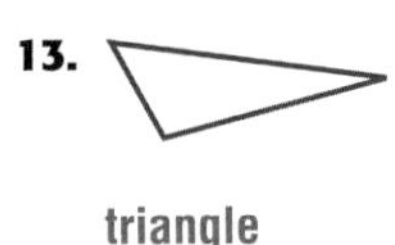 triangle

**14.**  hexagon

**Tell whether each shape is a polygon.** See Examples 2 and 3 (p. 363)

**15.** 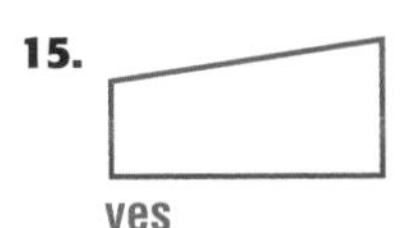 yes

**16.** 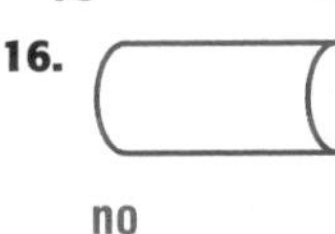 no

**17.**  yes

**18.**  no

**19.**  yes

**20.**  no

**Identify two polygons on each real-world object.**

**21.**  Sample answer: triangles and quadrilaterals

**22.**  Sample answer: triangles and quadrilaterals

23. Sample answer: triangles and quadrilaterals

### Real-World PROBLEM SOLVING

**Art** Polygons and other shapes are used in the painting *Castle and Sun*.

**23.** Name two polygons in the painting.

**24.** Is the sun a polygon? Explain. No; It is a circle and does not have any straight lines.

**25.** What polygon is in the painting most often? quadrilateral

**26.** What polygon in the painting has the most sides? quadrilateral

## H.O.T. Problems

27. **OPEN ENDED** Draw and identify a polygon. See students' work.

28. **FIND THE ERROR** Carlota and Gabe are drawing a polygon. Who is correct? Explain.

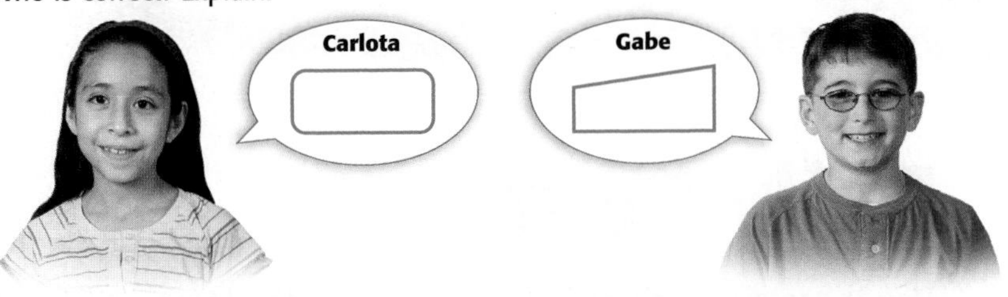


Sample answer: Gabe; The shape Carlota drew has curved lines.

29. **WRITING IN MATH** Write about a real-world object that is made of polygons. Sample answer: A ladder; it has quadrilaterals, and it can form a triangle when it is open.

## TEST Practice

30. Which figure can form a cube when folded on the dotted lines without overlapping? (Lesson 9-1) B

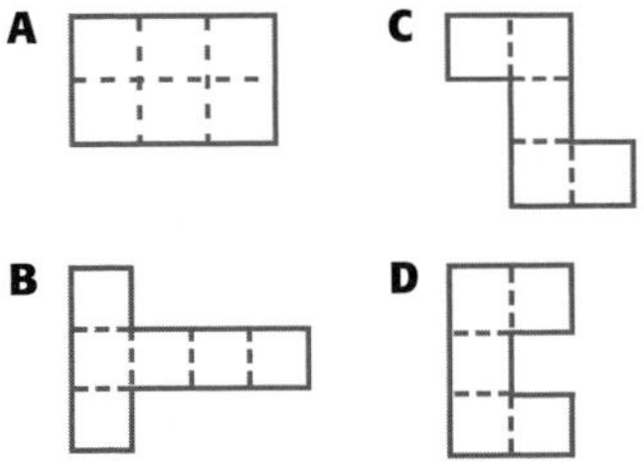

A

C 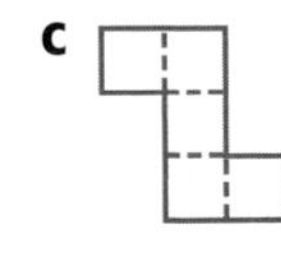

B 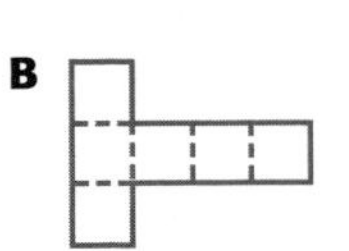

D 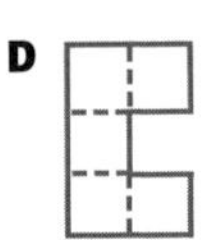

31. Which statement about these figures is true? (Lesson 9-2) H

F There is one polygon.

G These are all polygons.

H There are two polygons.

J None of these are polygons.

## Spiral Review

**Identify each figure. Then tell the number of faces, edges, and vertices.** (Lesson 9-1)

32.

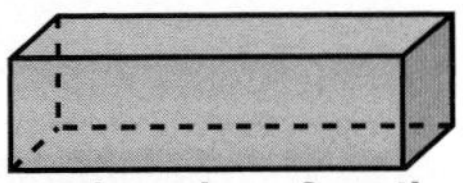

rectangular prism; 8 vertices, 12 edges, 6 faces

33. 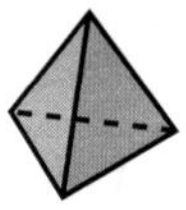  triangular pyramid; 4 faces, 6 edges, 4 vertices

**Divide. Use estimation to check.** (Lesson 8-9)

34. 6,204 ÷ 3

35. $7,816 ÷ 8

36. 5)9,675

37. 7)$7,371

34–37. See Ch. 9 Answer Appendix.



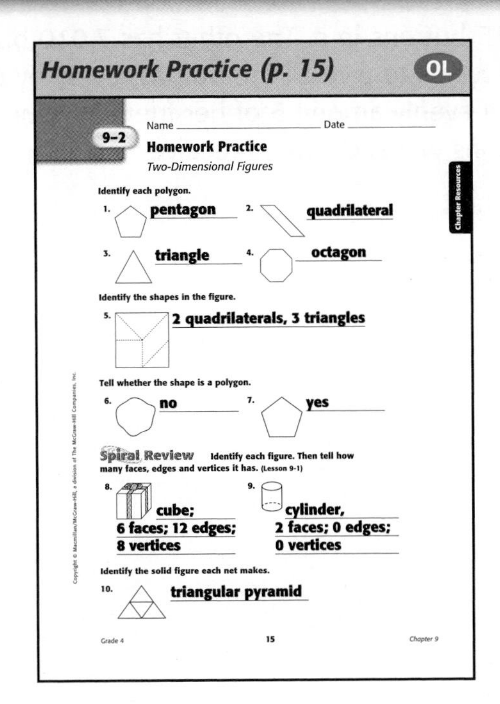

**Homework Practice (p. 15)** OL

Name ________ Date ________

9-2 **Homework Practice**

*Two-Dimensional Figures*

**Identify each polygon.**

1. pentagon
2. quadrilateral
3. triangle
4. octagon

**Identify the shapes in the figure.**

5. 2 quadrilaterals, 3 triangles

**Tell whether the shape is a polygon.**

6. no
7. yes

**Spiral Review** Identify each figure. Then tell how many faces, edges and vertices it has. (Lesson 9-1)

8. cube; 6 faces; 12 edges; 8 vertices
9. cylinder, 2 faces; 0 edges; 0 vertices

**Identify the solid figure each net makes.**

10. triangular pyramid

Grade 4 15 Chapter 9

# Assess

## Formative Assessment

Ask the students the following questions:

- **What are the names of 5 different types of polygons?** triangle, quadrilateral, pentagon, hexagon, octagon
- Have students choose their favorite polygon, draw it, tell why it is a polygon, and, if possible, name it. Answers will vary. Sample answer: A drawing of a triangle. It is a polygon because it is a two-dimensional figure with three sides; triangle.

**Quick Check** **Are students continuing to struggle with identifying, describing, and classifying two-dimensional figures?**

**If Yes** → Strategic Intervention Guide (p. 125)

**If No** → Independent Work Options (p. 318B)
CRM Skills Practice Worksheet (p. 14)
CRM Enrich Worksheet (p. 17)

**Yesterday's News** How did the information you learned about three-dimensional figures in Lesson 9-1 help you with what you learned today about two-dimensional figures?

## TEST Practice

### Reviews Lessons 9-1 and 9-2

Assign the Test Practice problems to provide daily reinforcement of test-taking skills.

## Spiral Review

### Reviews Lessons 8-9 and 9-1

Review and assess mastery of skills and concepts from previous chapters.

# 9-3 Problem-Solving Strategy
# Look for a Pattern

## Lesson Planner

### Objective

Solve problems by looking for a pattern.

### Resources

**Manipulatives:** pattern blocks

**Literature Connection:** *A Cloak for the Dreamer* by Aileen Friedman

**Teacher Technology**
TeacherWorks • Interactive Classroom

**Real-World Problem Solving Library**
**Math and Science: *Solving the Pyramid Puzzle***
Use these leveled books to reinforce and extend problem-solving skills and strategies.

Leveled for:
- OL On Level
- ELL Sheltered English
- SP Spanish

For additional support, see the Real-World Problem Solving Teacher Guide.

## Daily Routine

Use these suggestions before beginning the lesson on p. 366.

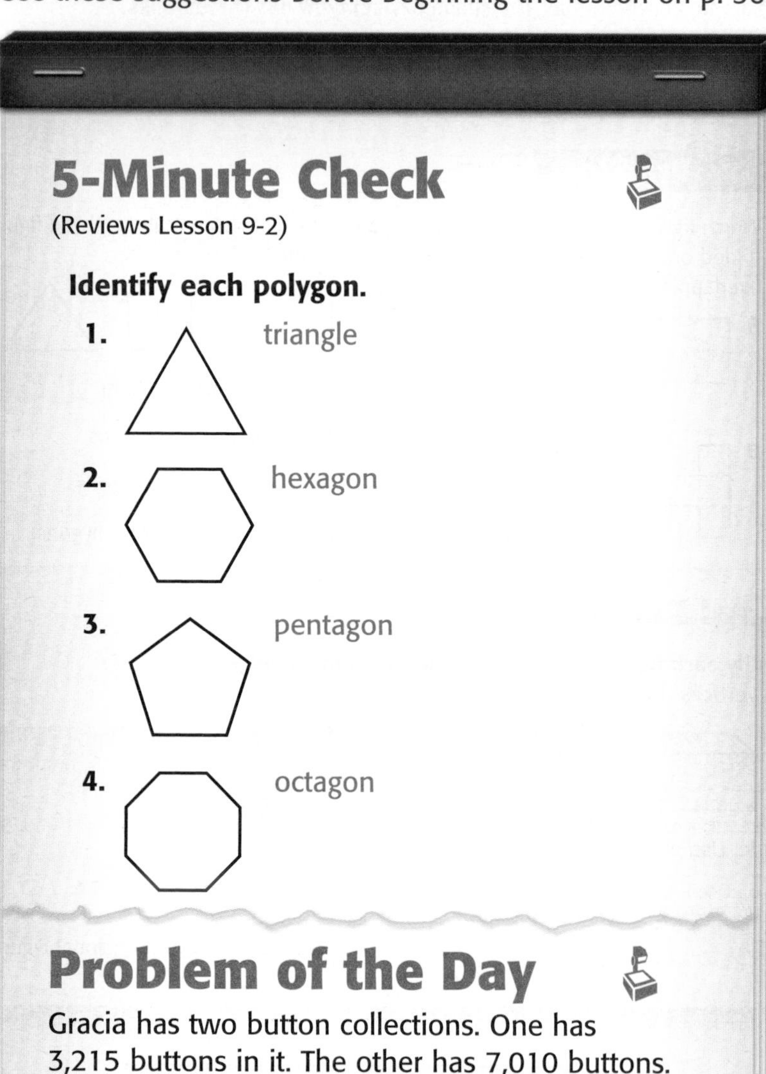

### 5-Minute Check
(Reviews Lesson 9-2)

**Identify each polygon.**

1. triangle
2. hexagon
3. pentagon
4. octagon

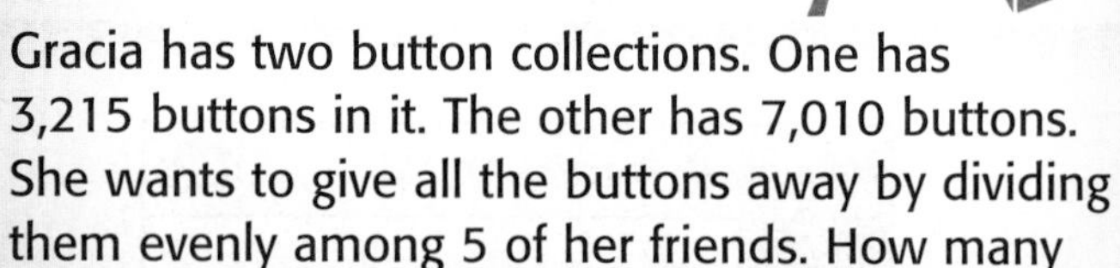

### Problem of the Day

Gracia has two button collections. One has 3,215 buttons in it. The other has 7,010 buttons. She wants to give all the buttons away by dividing them evenly among 5 of her friends. How many buttons will each friend receive? 2,045

# Differentiated Instruction

## Small Group Options

LOGICAL

### Option 1 Below Level BL

**Materials:** pattern blocks

- Ask students to pretend they are designing the tile floor pattern for a room in a new house. Have them use pattern blocks to create a unique tile floor pattern.
- You may want to document the students' work by taking pictures of the tile patterns.

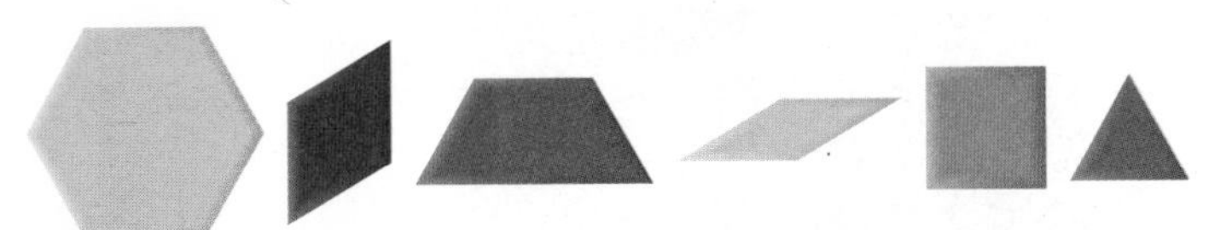

KINESTHETIC

### Option 2 English Language Learners ELL

**Materials:** attribute blocks
**Core Vocabulary:** continue, pattern base, read
**Common Use Verb:** place

**Do Math** This strategy activates patterning background knowledge and practices extending it to help internalize shapes.

- Give each student various colored blocks.
- Ask students to lay the blocks on the table in a pattern.
- After students have begun the pattern, ask them to write on the pattern how the pattern will continue for the next 5 steps.
- Allow students to switch pattern bases and repeat with a new pattern.
- Encourage students to "read" the pattern by naming the shapes, for example, triangle, square, hexagon, triangle, hexagon, and so forth.

## Independent Work Options

VISUAL, SPATIAL

### Option 1 Early Finishers OL AL

**Materials:** paper and pencil

- Pose the following problem to students:

The school supply store sells blank CDs for $1 each or $8 for a box of 12. First estimate which is the best buy. Then find the exact amount. Which problem solving strategy did you use?
Best buy is $8 for 12. Strategies for estimation will vary.

### Option 2 Student Technology

**Math Online** macmillanmh.com

Personal Tutor • Extra Examples

### Option 3 Learning Station: Reading (p. 356G)

Direct students to the Reading Learning Station for opportunities to explore and extend the lesson concept.

# 1 Introduce

### Activity Choice 1 • Review

- Write the following problem on the board:

  *Amara gave her sister 4 hats last week. She gave her best friend 2 hats yesterday. Amara's mom gave her 5 new hats this morning. Amara now has 12 hats. How many hats did Amara have originally?*
- **What strategy would you use to solve this problem? Why?** work backward; When it asks you how many she had originally, it gives you a hint to work backward.
- **How many hats did Amara have originally?** 13 hats

### Activity Choice 2 • Literature

Introduce the lesson with *A Cloak for the Dreamer* by Aileen Friedman. For a related math activity see p. TR56.

# 2 Teach

Have students read the problem on tile patterns. Guide them through the problem-solving steps.

**Understand** Using the questions, review what students know and need to find.

**Plan** Have them discuss their strategy.

**Solve** Guide students to use the look for a pattern strategy to solve the problem.

- **Look at the colors of the tiles. Is there a pattern? Explain.** yes; red, green, blue, yellow
- **Continue applying the pattern to all the tiles. Which tiles are missing?** 2 blue, 1 green, 1 yellow, and 1 red

**Check** Have students look back at the problem to make sure that the answers fits the facts given.

- **Will 2 blue, a yellow, a green, and a red tile complete the pattern on the floor?** yes

### COMMON ERROR!

**Exercise 7** Problems of this type can be confusing to students. Encourage them to make a table or list to help organize their work.



# 9-3 Problem-Solving Strategy

**MAIN IDEA** I will solve problems by looking for a pattern.

Amado is helping his dad put tile on a table top. They are laying the tiles in a pattern. They have run out of tiles and need to buy more. What color of tiles need to be purchased to complete the table?

| | |
|---|---|
| **Understand** | **What facts do you know?**<br>• You know the tiles form a pattern.<br>• You know they need to buy more tiles.<br>**What do you need to find?**<br>• Find the tile colors that need to be purchased. |
| **Plan** | Look for a pattern. Then continue the pattern to find the missing tiles. |
| **Solve** | There are two rows of tile, and the tiles repeat red, green, blue, and yellow.<br>In the first row, the missing tiles are blue and green. In the second row, the missing tiles are red, blue, and yellow.<br>So, Amado and his father need 2 blue, 1 green, 1 red, and 1 yellow tile. |
| **Check** | Look back. The answer makes sense for the facts given. So, the answer is correct. ✓ |



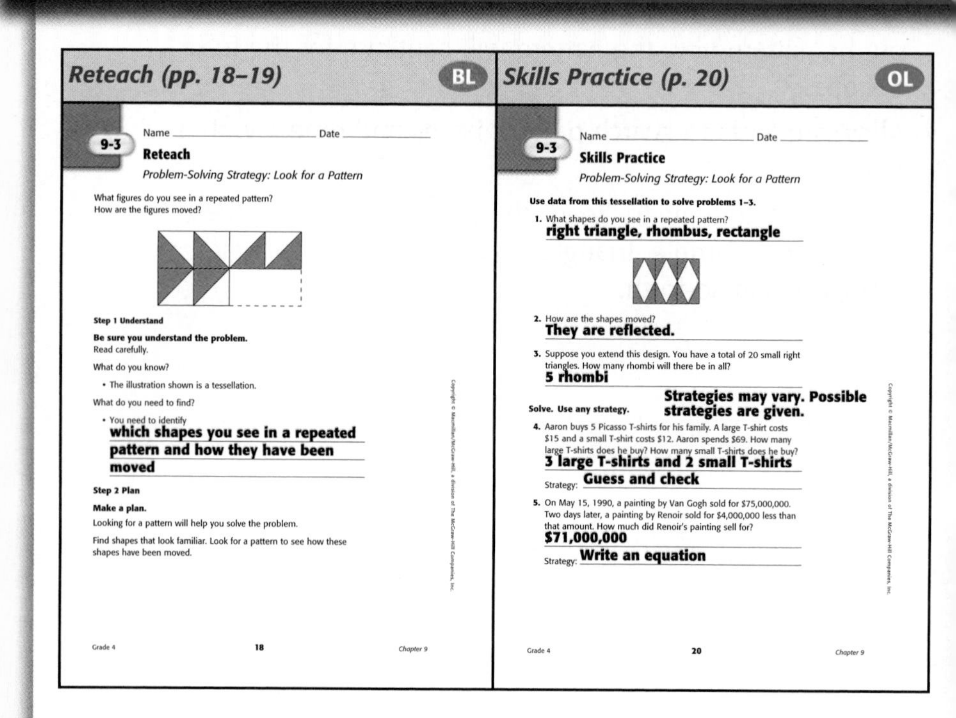

**Reteach (pp. 18–19)** BL

9-3 Name ______ Date ______

**Reteach**

*Problem-Solving Strategy: Look for a Pattern*

What figures do you see in a repeated pattern?
How are the figures moved?

**Step 1 Understand**

**Be sure you understand the problem.**
Read carefully.

What do you know?

- The illustration shown is a tessellation.

What do you need to find?

- You need to identify **which shapes you see in a repeated pattern and how they have been moved**

**Step 2 Plan**

**Make a plan.**

Looking for a pattern will help you solve the problem.

Find shapes that look familiar. Look for a pattern to see how these shapes have been moved.



Grade 4 18 Chapter 9

**Skills Practice (p. 20)** OL

9-3 Name ______ Date ______

**Skills Practice**

*Problem-Solving Strategy: Look for a Pattern*

**Use data from this tessellation to solve problems 1–3.**

1. What shapes do you see in a repeated pattern? **right triangle, rhombus, rectangle**
2. How are the shapes moved? **They are reflected.**
3. Suppose you extend this design. You have a total of 20 small right triangles. How many rhombi will there be in all? **5 rhombi**

**Solve. Use any strategy.** **Strategies may vary. Possible strategies are given.**

4. Aaron buys 5 Picasso T-shirts for his family. A large T-shirt costs $15 and a small T-shirt costs $12. Aaron spends $69. How many large T-shirts does he buy? How many small T-shirts does he buy? **3 large T-shirts and 2 small T-shirts**

   Strategy: **Guess and check**
5. On May 15, 1990, a painting by Van Gogh sold for $75,000,000. Two days later, a painting by Renoir sold for $4,000,000 less than that amount. How much did Renoir's painting sell for? **$71,000,000**

   Strategy: **Write an equation**



Grade 4 20 Chapter 9

## ANALYZE the Strategy

**efer to the problem on the previous page.** 1, 4. See Ch. 9 Answer Appendix.

**1.** How do you identify a pattern in a problem-solving situation?

**2.** If Amado and his dad used 36 tiles, how many tiles would they use of each color? 9 red, 9 green, 9 blue, 9 yellow

**3.** Suppose Amado and his dad laid 3 more rows of tiles. How many green tiles would they need in all? 10

**4.** Look back at Exercise 3. Check your answer. Explain how you know the answer is correct.

## PRACTICE the Strategy

**EXTRA PRACTICE**
See page R23.

**olve. Use the look for a pattern strategy.**

**5.** Draw the next three figures in the pattern below. Explain.

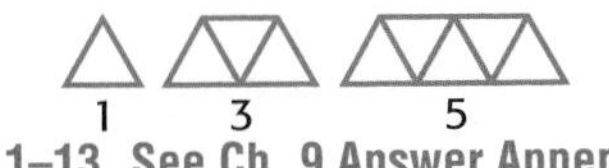

See Ch. 9 Answer Appendix.

**6. Algebra** Copy and complete the table. What is the pattern? Multiply by 4.

| Input ($g$) | Output ($h$) |
|---|---|
| 6 | 24 |
| 8 | 32 |
| 5 | 20 |
| 3 | ■ 12 |
| ■ 9 | 36 |

**7.** Claudia will arrive at the airport on the first plane after 9 A.M. Planes arrive every 45 minutes after 6 A.M. When will Claudia's plane arrive? 9:45 A.M.

**8.** Ming found 8 seashells on the first day, 20 on the second day, and 32 on the third day. If the pattern continues, how many shells will she find on the fifth day? 56 shells

**9.** Describe the pattern below. Then find the missing number. Multiply by 2; 16

2, 4, 8, ■, 32

**10.** Two hikers take turns carrying a backpack. The first hiker carries the pack. They change every 3 miles. They have hiked 14 miles so far. How many times have they changed? Who has the pack now? 4 times; the first hiker

**11. Algebra** A pattern of figures is shown below. Draw the next two figures. Explain your pattern.

1 3 5

11–13. See Ch. 9 Answer Appendix.

**12. Geometry** A border on a scrapbook page has a repeating design that shows a triangle, a pentagon, and a hexagon. Draw the first eight figures in the pattern.

**13. WRITING IN MATH** Create a pattern with geometric figures. Give it to a classmate and see if he or she can continue it.



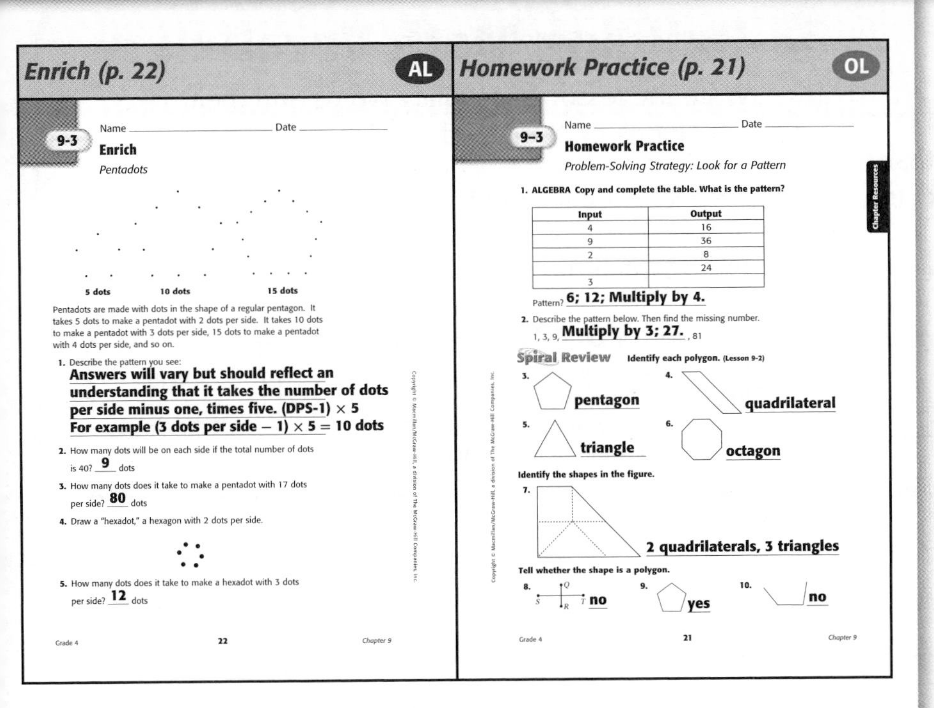

**Enrich (p. 22)** AL

9-3 Name ________ Date ________

**Enrich**

*Pentadots*

5 dots 10 dots 15 dots

Pentadots are made with dots in the shape of a regular pentagon. It takes 5 dots to make a pentadot with 2 dots per side. It takes 10 dots to make a pentadot with 3 dots per side, 15 dots to make a pentadot with 4 dots per side, and so on.

1. Describe the pattern you see: **Answers will vary but should reflect an understanding that it takes the number of dots per side minus one, times five. (DPS-1) × 5 For example (3 dots per side − 1) × 5 = 10 dots**
2. How many dots will be on each side if the total number of dots is 40? **9** dots
3. How many dots does it take to make a pentadot with 17 dots per side? **80** dots
4. Draw a "hexadot," a hexagon with 2 dots per side.
5. How many dots does it take to make a hexadot with 3 dots per side? **12** dots

Grade 4 22 Chapter 9

Copyright © Macmillan/McGraw-Hill, a division of The McGraw-Hill Companies, Inc.

**Homework Practice (p. 21)** OL

9–3 Name ________ Date ________

**Homework Practice**

*Problem-Solving Strategy: Look for a Pattern*

**1. ALGEBRA Copy and complete the table. What is the pattern?**

| Input | Output |
|---|---|
| 4 | 16 |
| 9 | 36 |
| 2 | 8 |
| | 24 |
| 3 | |

Pattern? **6; 12; Multiply by 4.**

2. Describe the pattern below. Then find the missing number.
1, 3, 9, **Multiply by 3; 27.**, 81

**Spiral Review** **Identify each polygon.** (Lesson 9-2)

3. **pentagon**
4. **quadrilateral**
5. **triangle**
6. **octagon**

**Identify the shapes in the figure.**

7. **2 quadrilaterals, 3 triangles**

**Tell whether the shape is a polygon.**

8. Q S R T **no**
9. **yes**
10. **no**

Grade 4 21 Chapter 9

Chapter Resources

Copyright © Macmillan/McGraw-Hill, a division of The McGraw-Hill Companies, Inc.

**Analyze the Strategy** Use Exercises 1–4 to analyze and discuss the problem-solving strategy.

### BL Alternate Teaching Strategy

**If** students have trouble using the look for a pattern strategy...

**Then** use one of these reteach options:

1. CRM **Daily Reteach Worksheet** (pp. 18–19)
2. Provide students with additional practice using this strategy. Have students create 5 of their own patterns on a piece of paper. Tell them to exchange their patterns with other students. Have them take turns solving each other's pattern problems.

## 3 Practice

### Using the Exercises

**Exercise 11** You may want to provide students with pattern blocks.

## 4 Assess

### Formative Assessment

Pose the following problem to students:

*Your mom has decided to give you some money. On the first day she gives you 1 penny. On the second day she gives you 2 more pennies. On the third day she gives you 3 more pennies. This continues for 15 days.*

- **How many pennies will your mom give you on the tenth day?** 10
- **How many pennies will your mom give you on the fifteenth day?** 15
- **How much money will you have at the end of the 15 days?** 120 pennies or $1.20

**Quick Check** **Are students continuing to struggle with using the look for a pattern strategy?**

**If Yes** → Strategic Intervention Guide (p. 128)

**If No** → Independent Work Options (p. 366B)
CRM Skills Practice Worksheet (p. 20)
CRM Enrich Worksheet (p. 22)

LESSON 9-4

# Angles

## Lesson Planner

### Objective

Identify, describe, and classify angles.

### Vocabulary

**angle**, **right angle**, **acute angle**, **obtuse angle**

### Resources

**Materials:** circle with two perpendicular lines drawn on it, compass, paper clips

**Literature Connection:** *Angles are Easy as Pie* by Robert Froman

**Teacher Technology**
TeacherWorks • Interactive Classroom

## Daily Routine

Use these suggestions before beginning the lesson on p. 368.

### 5-Minute Check

(Reviews Lesson 9-3)

**Solve. Use the look for a pattern strategy.**

While on vacation, Paul collected pine cones. On Sunday, he collected 2. On Monday, he collected 9. On Tuesday, he collected 16. If this pattern continues, how many pine cones will he collect on Friday? 37

### Problem of the Day

A $10 bill is almost 16 cm long. Suppose $10 bills are put in a 1-meter long row from end to end. The value of the money in the row would be about how much? Explain. (100 cm = 1 m) about $60; 6 bills would measure 6 × 16 cm = 96 cm or about 1 meter.

### Focus on Math Background

In previous grades, students have used a "corner" as a representation of a right angle and used this representation to identify whether an angle is smaller than a right angle, a right angle, or greater than a right angle. In this lesson, students give angles names such as acute, right, or obtuse. They also learn the measures associated with these angles. An angle is:

- *acute* if its measure is greater than 0° and less than 90°
- *right* if its measure is 90°
- *obtuse* if its measure is greater than 90° and less than 180°
- *straight* if its measure is 180° (Note: straight angles are not defined at this level.)

### Building Math Vocabulary

Write the lesson vocabulary words and their definitions on the board.

Have the students use the vocabulary words to make a crossword puzzle. When they finish, have them switch puzzles with a classmate and solve.

**Visual Vocabulary Cards**
Use Visual Vocabulary Card 2 to reinforce the vocabulary introduced in this lesson. (The Define/Example/Ask routine is printed on the back of each card.)

# Differentiated Instruction

## Small Group Options

### Option 1 Below Level BL

SPATIAL, LINGUISTIC

**Materials:** paper, scissors

- Help students draw and cut out a circle. Fold the circle in half.
- Ask, "What part of the circle is left? What is the measure of the angle?" half, 180°
- Repeat with 90°, 270°, and 360°.

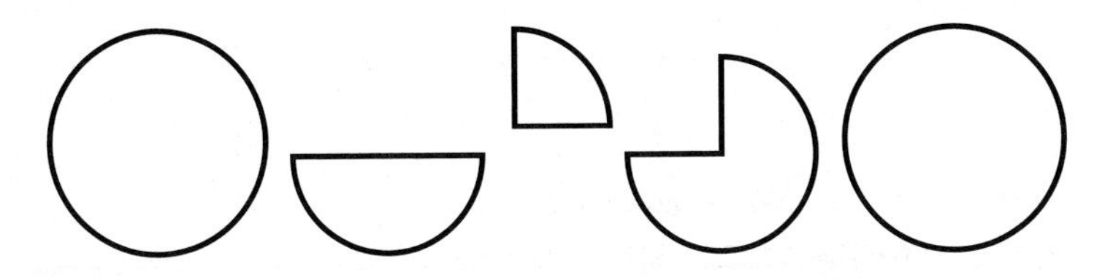

### Option 2 English Language Learners ELL

LOGICAL, VISUAL

**Materials:** note cards, clock
**Core Vocabulary:** straight, lesser, greater
**Common Use Verb:** raise

**Do Math** This strategy helps students to use a familiar object to understand the concept of angles.

- Use a clock to demonstrate different angles.
- Have students label three note cards with *straight*, *lesser*, and *greater* on one side and *acute*, *right*, and *obtuse* on the other side.
- Guide students to draw the angles on the appropriate card.
- After several drawings have been completed, call out an angle or show a clock and ask students to raise the card that names the angle.
- Repeat as time permits.

*English Language Learners (p. 171)* ELL

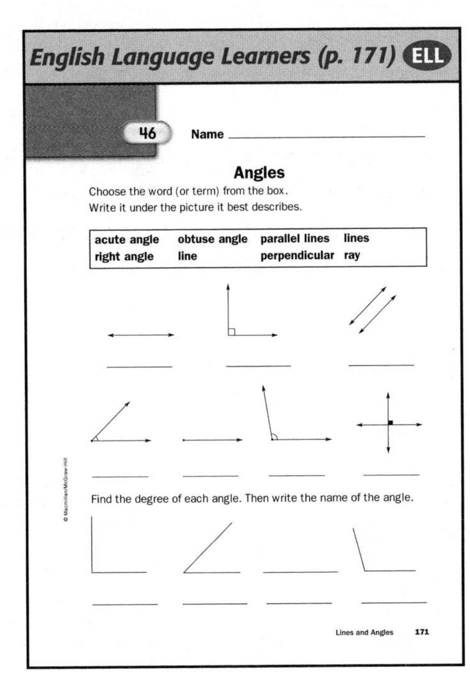

46 Name ____________

Angles

Choose the word (or term) from the box.
Write it under the picture it best describes.

| acute angle | obtuse angle | parallel lines | lines |
| --- | --- | --- | --- |
| right angle | line | perpendicular | ray |

Find the degree of each angle. Then write the name of the angle.

Lines and Angles 171

*Use this worksheet to provide additional support for English Language Learners.*

## Independent Work Options

### Option 1 Early Finishers AL OL

VISUAL, SPATIAL

**Materials:** paper, pencil, straightedge, crayons or markers

- Draw a design or picture with at least two acute angles, at least 2 obtuse angles, and at least 1 right angle. Label the angles.
- If time allows, color the design or picture with crayons or markers.

### Option 2 Student Technology

Tech Link

**Math Online** macmillanmh.com

Personal Tutor • Extra Examples

Math Adventures

### Option 3 Learning Station: Writing (p. 356G)

Direct students to the Writing Learning Station for opportunities to explore and extend the lesson concept.

### Option 4 Problem-Solving Practice

Reinforce problem-solving skills and strategies with the Problem-Solving Practice worksheet.

*Problem Solving (p. 26)* BL OL AL

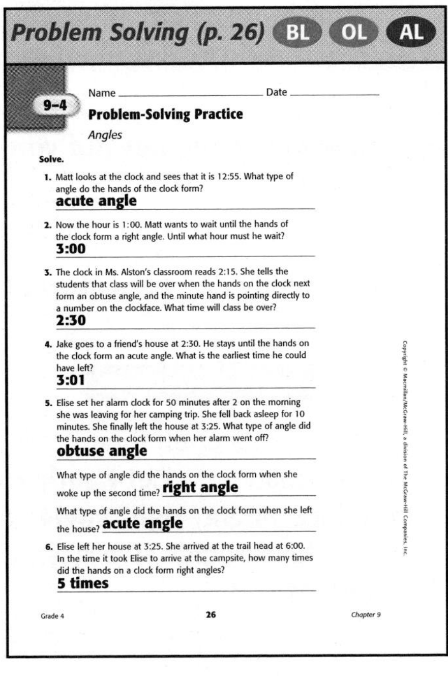

9-4 Name ____________ Date ____________

**Problem-Solving Practice**

*Angles*

**Solve.**

1. Matt looks at the clock and sees that it is 12:55. What type of angle do the hands of the clock form?
**acute angle**
2. Now the hour is 1:00. Matt wants to wait until the hands of the clock form a right angle. Until what hour must he wait?
**3:00**
3. The clock in Ms. Alston's classroom reads 2:15. She tells the students that class will be over when the hands on the clock next form an obtuse angle, and the minute hand is pointing directly to a number on the clockface. What time will class be over?
**2:30**
4. Jake goes to a friend's house at 2:30. He stays until the hands on the clock form an acute angle. What is the earliest time he could have left?
**3:01**
5. Elise set her alarm clock for 50 minutes after 2 on the morning she was leaving for her camping trip. She fell back asleep for 10 minutes. She finally left the house at 3:25. What type of angle did the hands on the clock form when her alarm went off?
**obtuse angle**
What type of angle did the hands on the clock form when she woke up the second time? **right angle**
What type of angle did the hands on the clock form when she left the house? **acute angle**
6. Elise left her house at 3:25. She arrived at the trail head at 6:00. In the time it took Elise to arrive at the campsite, how many times did the hands on a clock form right angles?
**5 times**

Grade 4 26 Chapter 9

# 9-4 Angles

## 1 Introduce

### Activity Choice 1 • Hands-On

- Start by reading the following to the students:
  The Babylonians in about 2400 B.C. lived in Mesopotamia, now southern Iraq. They used a number system based on 60. Some believe they divided the circle into 360 degrees because $6 \times 60 = 360$ degrees. Others believe that they watched the planets and the sun. They knew it took 360 days for the sun's path to complete a total circuit. Either way, that is how we got a 360° circle.
- Divide the class into groups of 2 or 3. Give each group a circle with two perpendicular lines on it as shown in the figure above. Have them use a paper clip as a pointer. They will use their pointer to help them visualize benchmark angles of 90, 180, 270, and 360 degrees.

### Activity Choice 2 • Literature

Introduce the lesson with *Angles are Easy as Pie* by Robert Froman. For a related math activity, see p. TR56.

## 2 Teach

### Scaffolding Questions

Have students use the pointer from Activity Choice 1. Have students position the pointer at 0° (straight up). Remind students that there are 360° in the circle. Ask them to move the pointer $\frac{1}{4}$ turn.

- **How many degrees did you move? Explain.** 90°; $360° \div 4 = 90°$
- Have them move the pointer $\frac{1}{2}$ turn.
- **How many degrees did you move?** 180°

### GET READY to Learn

Have students open their books and read the information in **Get Ready to Learn**. Introduce **angle**, **right angle**, **acute angle** and **obtuse angle**. As a class, work through **Examples 1–3**.



# 9-4 Angles

**MAIN IDEA**

I will identify, describe, and classify angles.

**New Vocabulary**

angle
right angle
acute angle
obtuse angle

**Math Online**

macmillanmh.com

- Extra Examples
- Personal Tutor
- Self-Check Quiz

### GET READY to Learn

Brent's teacher assigned ten problems for homework. Brent started his homework at 4:00 P.M. He completed it at the time shown. How far has the minute hand turned?

An **angle** is a figure made from two rays that have the same endpoint. Angles are measured in degrees (°).

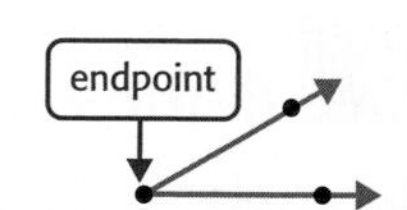


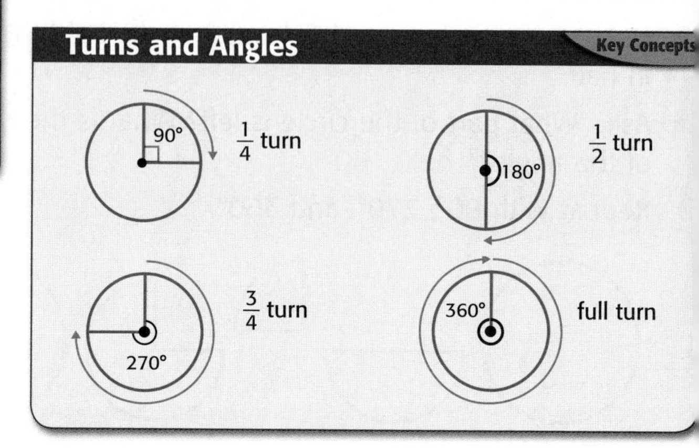


### Real-World EXAMPLE — Turns and Angles

**1 MEASUREMENT Refer to the clock above. Write how far the minute hand has turned in degrees and as a fraction.**

Compare the angle shown on the clock to the angles shown in the Key Concepts box.

So, the angle shown on the clock is 90° or a $\frac{1}{4}$ turn.

368 **Chapter 9** Identify and Describe Geometric Figures

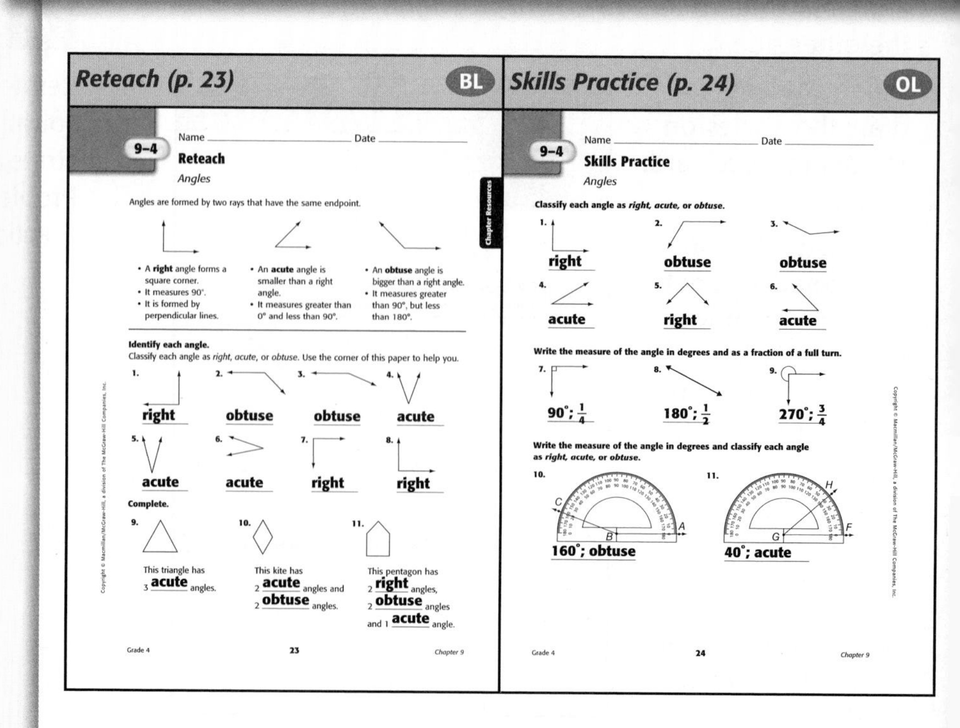

**Reteach (p. 23)** BL

9–4 Name ________ Date ________

**Reteach**

*Angles*

Angles are formed by two rays that have the same endpoint.

- A **right** angle forms a square corner.
- It measures 90°.
- It is formed by perpendicular lines.

- An **acute** angle is smaller than a right angle.
- It measures greater than 0° and less than 90°.

- An **obtuse** angle is bigger than a right angle.
- It measures greater than 90°, but less than 180°.

**Identify each angle.**
Classify each angle as *right*, *acute*, or *obtuse*. Use the corner of this paper to help you.

1. right
2. obtuse
3. obtuse
4. acute
5. acute
6. acute
7. right
8. right

**Complete.**

9. This triangle has 3 **acute** angles.
10. This kite has 2 **acute** angles and 2 **obtuse** angles.
11. This pentagon has 2 **right** angles, 2 **obtuse** angles and 1 **acute** angle.

Grade 4 — 23 — Chapter 9

Chapter Resources



**Skills Practice (p. 24)** OL

9–4 Name ________ Date ________

**Skills Practice**

*Angles*

**Classify each angle as *right, acute,* or *obtuse*.**

1. right
2. obtuse
3. obtuse
4. acute
5. right
6. acute

**Write the measure of the angle in degrees and as a fraction of a full turn.**

7. 90°; $\frac{1}{4}$
8. 180°; $\frac{1}{2}$
9. 270°; $\frac{3}{4}$

**Write the measure of the angle in degrees and classify each angle as *right, acute,* or *obtuse*.**

10. 160°; obtuse
11. 40°; acute

Grade 4 — 24 — Chapter 9

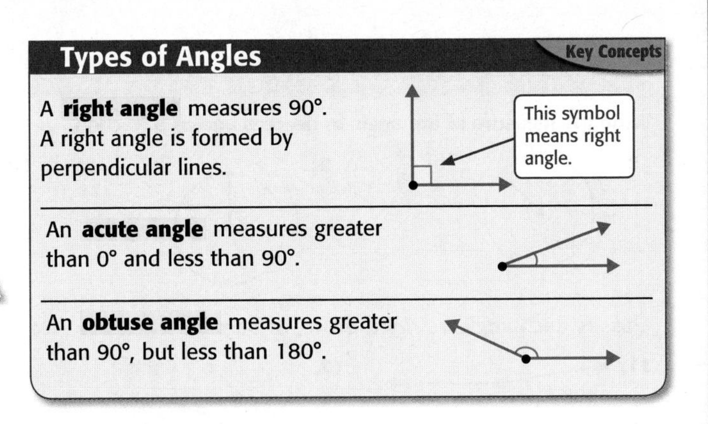

## Types of Angles

Key Concepts

A **right angle** measures 90°. A right angle is formed by perpendicular lines.

This symbol means right angle.

An **acute angle** measures greater than 0° and less than 90°.

An **obtuse angle** measures greater than 90°, but less than 180°.

## EXAMPLES Classify an Angle

**Classify each angle as *right*, *acute*, or *obtuse*.**

**2** The angle is 90°. So, it is a right angle.

**3** The angle is greater than 90° and less than 180°. It is an obtuse angle.

. Sample answer: An acute angle is less than 90°. An obtuse angle is greater than 90 and less than 180°. A right angle is 90°.

## CHECK What You Know

**Write the measure of each angle in degrees and as a fraction.** See Example 1 (p. 368)

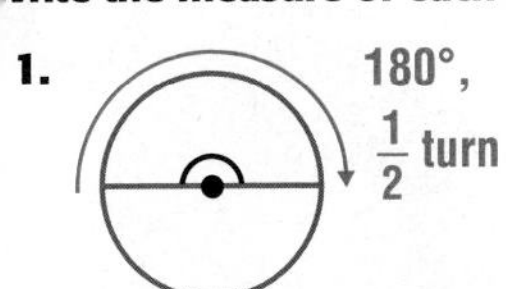

**1.** 180°, $\frac{1}{2}$ turn

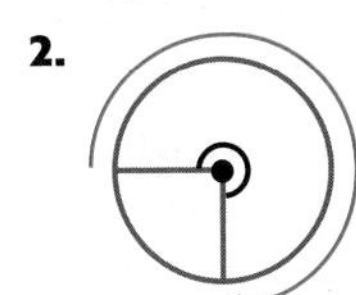

**2.** 270°, $\frac{3}{4}$ turn

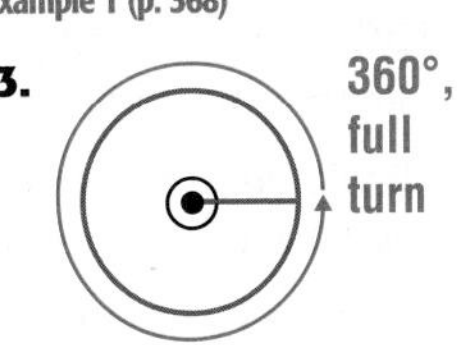

**3.** 360°, full turn

**Classify each angle as *right*, *acute*, or *obtuse*.** See Examples 2 and 3 (p. 369)

**4.** acute

**5.** right

**6.** obtuse

**7.** Talk About It: Describe what makes each type of angle an *acute*, *obtuse*, or *right* angle.



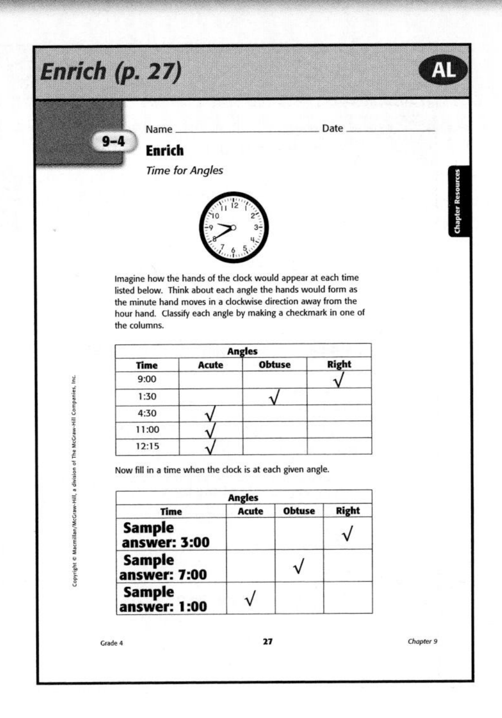

Enrich (p. 27) AL

Name ____________ Date ____________

9-4 **Enrich**

*Time for Angles*

Imagine how the hands of the clock would appear at each time listed below. Think about each angle the hands would form as the minute hand moves in a clockwise direction away from the hour hand. Classify each angle by making a checkmark in one of the columns.

| | Angles | | |
|---|---|---|---|
| Time | Acute | Obtuse | Right |
| 9:00 | | | √ |
| 1:30 | | √ | |
| 4:30 | √ | | |
| 11:00 | √ | | |
| 12:15 | √ | | |

Now fill in a time when the clock is at each given angle.

| | Angles | | |
|---|---|---|---|
| Time | Acute | Obtuse | Right |
| **Sample answer: 3:00** | | | √ |
| **Sample answer: 7:00** | | √ | |
| **Sample answer: 1:00** | √ | | |

Grade 4 27 Chapter 9

Chapter Resources



## Classify an Angle

**Example 2** Remind students that if an angle has a right angle symbol in it, then it must be a right angle. If there is no symbol, then you have to prove that it is a right angle.

## ADDITIONAL EXAMPLES

**1** Write how far the minute hand has turned in degrees and as a fraction of a full turn.
180° or $\frac{1}{2}$ turn

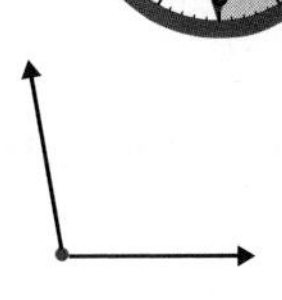

**2** Classify the angle as *acute*, *obtuse*, or *right*. obtuse

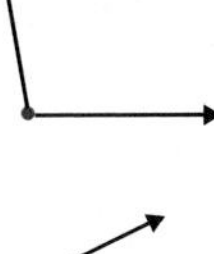

**3** Classify the angle as *acute*, *obtuse*, or *right*. acute

## CHECK What You Know

As a class, have students complete Exercises 1–7 in **Check What You Know** as you observe their work.

**Exercise 7** Assess student comprehension before assigning practice exercises.

## BL Alternate Teaching Strategy

**If** students have trouble classifying acute, right, and obtuse angles…

**Then** use one of these reteach options:

1. CRM **Daily Reteach Worksheet** (p. 23)
2. Have several students come to the board and draw right angles. Discuss the right angles.

   Have several other students come to the board and draw acute angles. Discuss the variety of acute angles. Repeat with obtuse angles.

# 3 Practice

Differentiate practice using these leveled assignments for Exercises 8–22.

| Level | Assignment |
|---|---|
| BL Below/Approaching Level | 8–10, 14–16, 18 |
| OL On Level | 8–14, 17–21 |
| AL Above/Beyond Level | 9–19 odd, 21–22 |

Have students discuss and complete the Higher Order Thinking problems. Point out to students that they can use the corner of a piece of notebook paper to approximate a right angle.

**WRITING IN MATH** Have students complete Exercise 22 in their Math Journals. You may choose to use this exercise as an optional formative assessment.

# 4 Assess

### Formative Assessment

Have the students answer the following questions.

- **How would you compare a right angle with an acute angle?** The measure of a right angle is greater than that of an acute angle.
- **How would you compare a right angle with an obtuse angle?** The measure of a right angle is less than that of an obtuse angle.

**Quick Check** **Are students continuing to struggle with identifying, describing, and classifying angles?**

**If Yes** → Small Group Options (p. 368B)

**If No** → Independent Work Options (p. 368B)
CRM Skills Practice Worksheet (p. 24)
CRM Enrich Worksheet (p. 27)

**Into the Future** Tell students that tomorrow's lesson will be about classifying triangles by their angles. Ask them to write about how today's lesson will help them with the next lesson.

## COMMON ERROR!

**Exercises 19 and 20** You may want to bring a compass to class to show how it can be used to find directions.



## Practice and Problem Solving

EXTRA PRACTICE See page R24.

**Write the measure of the angle in degrees and as a fraction.** See Example 1 (p. 368)

**8.** 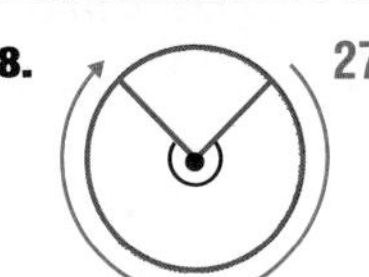 $270°, \frac{3}{4}$ turn

**9.** 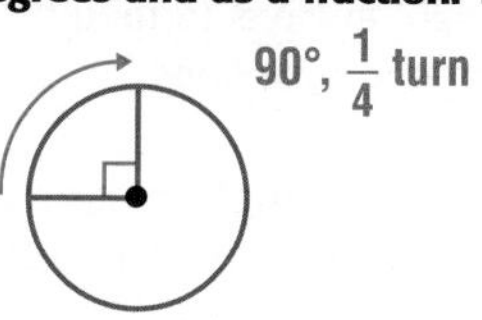 $90°, \frac{1}{4}$ turn

**10.** 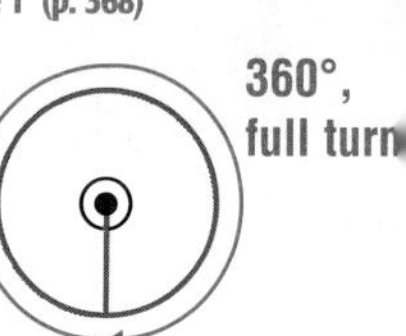 360°, full turn

**Classify each angle as *right, acute,* or *obtuse*.** See Examples 2 and 3 (p. 369)

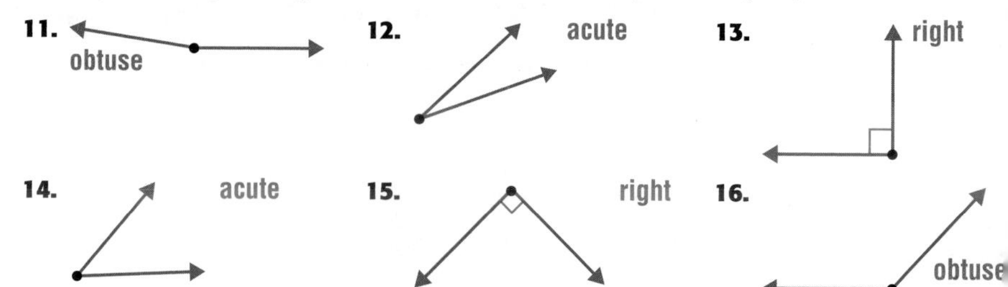

**11.** obtuse

**12.** acute

**13.** right

**14.** acute

**15.** right

**16.** obtuse

**17.** The timer is set to 30 minutes. How many degrees will the dial have turned when the timer goes off? $\frac{1}{2}$ turn, 180°

**18.** Classify the angle shown on the gas gauge below. obtuse

### Real-World PROBLEM SOLVING

*Geography* A compass can be used to find direction. The arrow on a compass always faces north.

**19.** If you are facing north and turn west, what angle could be drawn to represent your movement? $\frac{1}{4}$ turn, 90°

**20.** You are facing east and are told to turn 180°. What direction will you be facing? Write the angle your body has turned as a fraction. west; $\frac{1}{2}$ turn

### H.O.T. Problems

**21. OPEN ENDED** Draw three different acute angles. 21, 22. See Ch. 9 Answer Appendix.

**22. WRITING IN MATH** Choose three objects in your classroom that have angles. Describe how to classify each angle as *acute, obtuse,* or *right.*



*Homework Practice (p. 25)* OL

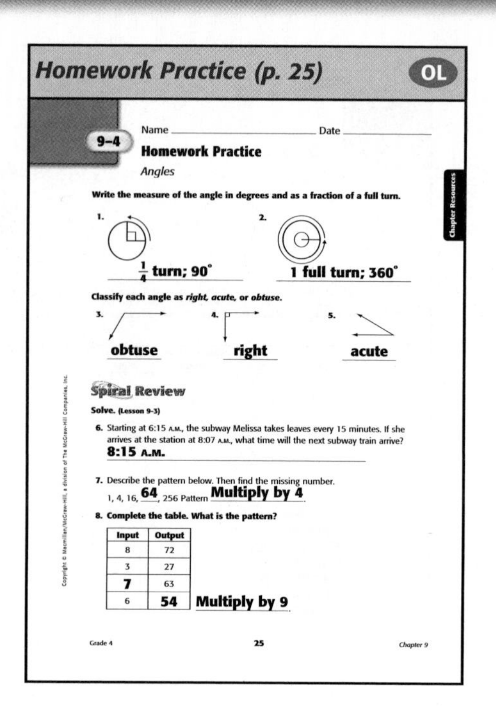
Name ______ Date ______

9–4 **Homework Practice**
*Angles*

Chapter Resources

**Write the measure of the angle in degrees and as a fraction of a full turn.**

1. $\frac{1}{4}$ turn; 90°
2. 1 full turn; 360°

**Classify each angle as *right, acute,* or *obtuse*.**

3. obtuse
4. right
5. acute

**Spiral Review**

**Solve.** (Lesson 9-3)

6. Starting at 6:15 A.M., the subway Melissa takes leaves every 15 minutes. If she arrives at the station at 8:07 A.M., what time will the next subway train arrive? **8:15 A.M.**

7. Describe the pattern below. Then find the missing number.
1, 4, 16, **64**, 256 Pattern **Multiply by 4**

8. Complete the table. What is the pattern?

| Input | Output |
|---|---|
| 8 | 72 |
| 3 | 27 |
| **7** | 63 |
| 6 | **54** |

**Multiply by 9**

# Mid-Chapter Check

Lessons 9-1 through 9-4

15. Sample answer: No, A polygon has only two dimensions while a solid has three dimensions

**ell the number of faces, edges, and ertices. Identify each figure.** (Lesson 9-1)

1. 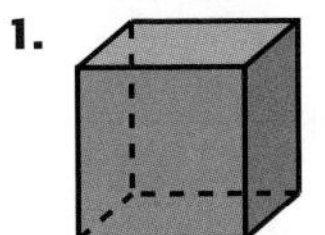

2. 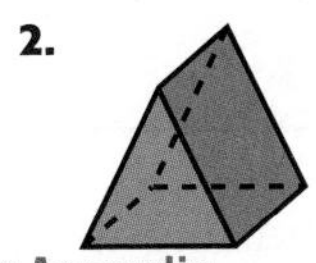

, 2. See Ch. 9 Answer Appendix.

3. Identify the three-dimensional figure the net would make. (Lesson 9-1)

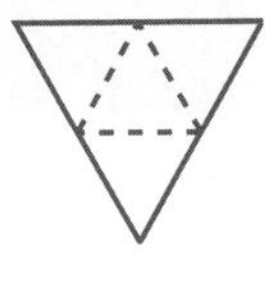

triangular pyramid

**dentify each polygon.** (Lesson 9-2)

4. quadrilateral

5. 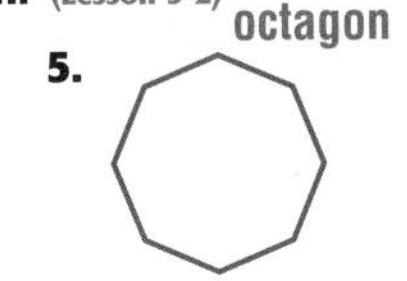

octagon

6. **MULTIPLE CHOICE** Look at the figures below. Which statement is true? (Lesson 9-2) B

**A** There is one polygon.

**B** These are all polygons.

**C** There are two polygons.

**D** None of these are polygons.

7. Identify two polygons on the bird house. (Lesson 9-2)

Sample answer: rectangle and pentagon

8. **MULTIPLE CHOICE** What is this figure called? (Lesson 9-2) F

**F** hexagon

**G** triangle

**H** octagon

**J** pentagon

**For Exercises 9 and 10, solve. Use the look for a pattern strategy.** (Lesson 9-3)

9. Describe the pattern in 3, 9, 27, ■, 243. Then find the missing number.
Multiply by 3; 81

10. A ferry leaves a harbor every 35 minutes starting at 6:30 A.M. Davion plans to take the first ferry after 8 A.M. When will his ferry leave? 8:15 A.M.

**Write the measure of each angle in degrees and as a fraction.** (Lesson 9-4)

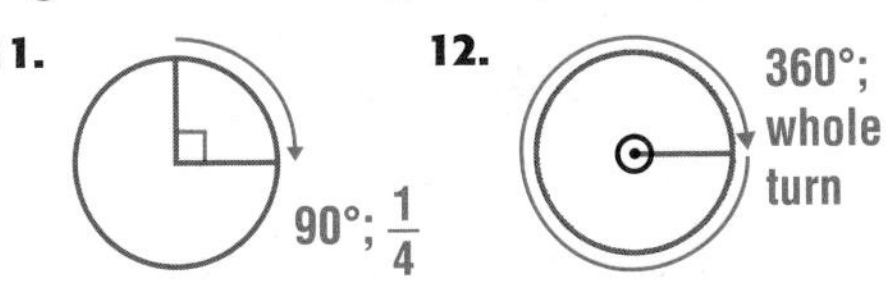

11. 90°; $\frac{1}{4}$

12. 360°; whole turn

**Classify each angle as *right*, *acute*, or *obtuse*.** (Lesson 9-4)

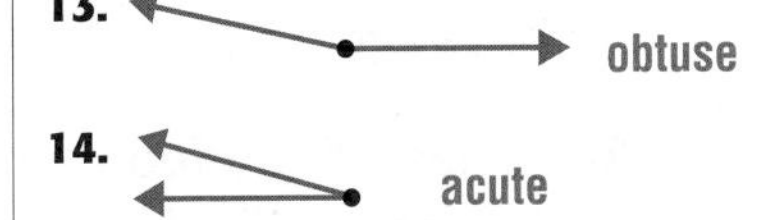

13. obtuse

14. acute

15. **WRITING IN MATH** Can a figure be a polygon and three-dimensional? Explain. (Lesson 9-2)

Formative Assessment 371

# Mid-Chapter Check

## Lessons 9-1 through 9-4

### Formative Assessment

Use the Mid-Chapter Check to assess students' progress in the first half of the chapter.

Customize and create multiple versions of your Mid-Chapter Check and the test answer keys.

### FOLDABLES Dinah Zike's Foldables

Use these suggestions to incorporate the Foldable during the chapter.

**Lessons 9-1, 9-2** Students identify, describe, and classify two- and three-dimensional figures beneath the top left tab. Store vocabulary, physical examples, and student work in pocket.

**Lesson 9-4** Students identify, describe, and classify angles beneath the tab. Store vocabulary, physical examples, and student work in pocket.

# Data-Driven Decision Making

Based on the results of the Mid-Chapter Check, use the following resources to review concepts that continue to give students problems.

| Exercises | State/Local Standards | What's the Math? | Error Analysis | Resources for Review |
|---|---|---|---|---|
| **1–3** Lesson 9-1 | | Identify, describe, and classify three-dimensional objects. | Confuses "faces," "edges," and "vertices." Does not know "cube," "triangular prism." | Strategic Intervention Guide (pp. 124, 125, 126, 128) CRM Chapter 9 Resource Masters (Reteach) Math Adventures My Math Zone Chapter 9 Math Online Extra Examples • Concepts in Motion |
| **4–8, 15** Lesson 9-2 | | Identify, describe, and classify two-dimensional figures. | Does not know names of shapes. Does not understand "polygon." | |
| **11–14** Lesson 9-4 | | Measure and classify angles. | Does not know "right," "acute," "obtuse." Does not know to put degrees over 360 to get fraction for circle angle. | |

LESSON 9-5

# Triangles

## Lesson Planner

### Objective

Identify, describe, and classify triangles.

### Vocabulary

**isosceles triangle**, **equilateral triangle**, **scalene triangle**, **right triangle**, **acute triangle**, **obtuse triangle**

### Resources

**Materials:** craft sticks, triangles made from construction paper, ruler, clay

**Literature Connection:** *Bridges* by Ken Robbins

**Teacher Technology**

TeacherWorks • Interactive Classroom

## Daily Routine

Use these suggestions before beginning the lesson on p. 372.

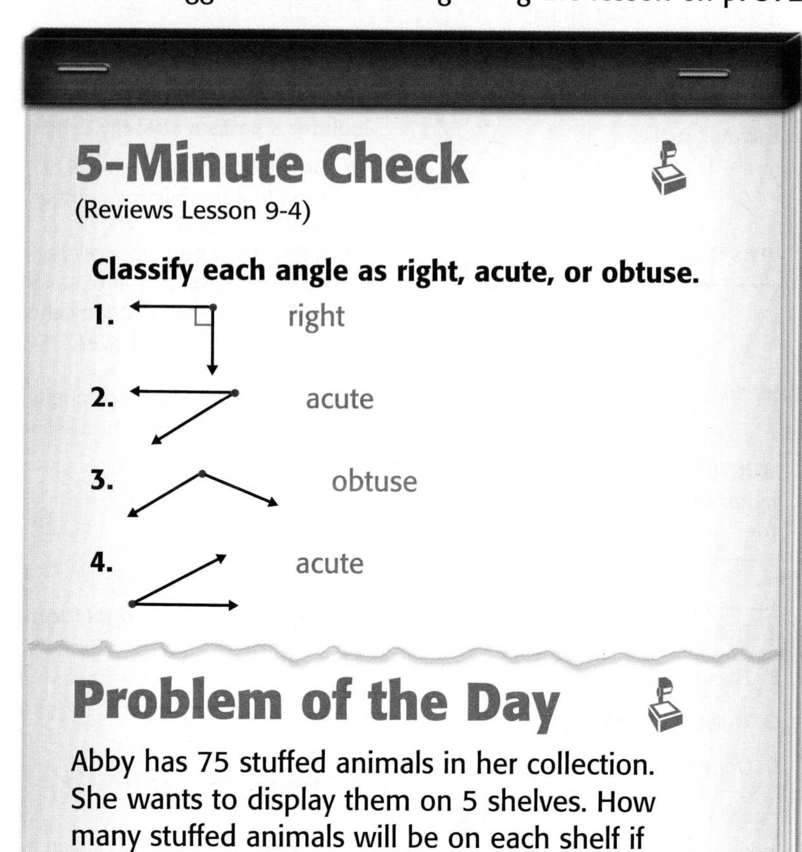

### 5-Minute Check

(Reviews Lesson 9-4)

**Classify each angle as right, acute, or obtuse.**

**1.** right

**2.** acute

**3.** obtuse

**4.** acute

### Problem of the Day

Abby has 75 stuffed animals in her collection. She wants to display them on 5 shelves. How many stuffed animals will be on each shelf if the same number of stuffed animals are on each shelf? 15 stuffed animals

### Focus on Math Background

Triangles can be classified by their sides (equilateral, isosceles, and scalene) and by their angles (acute, right, and obtuse). In the previous grade, students learned to classify triangles by their sides. At this level they use and extend their knowledge to include classifying triangles by their angles.

### Building Math Vocabulary

Write the lesson vocabulary words and their definitions on the board.

Have each student draw an example of each of the vocabulary words, label the examples, and tell why they chose the label they did.

# Differentiated Instruction

## Small Group Options

KINESTHETIC

### Option 1 Gifted and Talented AL

**Materials:** plain paper, scissors, ruler, pencil

- Say to students: "I want you to use what you learned in this lesson to decide how much information you need to draw a triangle. For instance, you know one angle is 90° and one angle is 45°, and the length of the side between those two angles is 5 cm. Can you finish drawing a triangle?" yes
- Describe this triangle. It is a right triangle or an isosceles triangle.
- What if you know the length of two sides, 4 cm and 7 cm, and one angle of 30 degrees? Can you complete the drawing of a triangle? no
- Have students continue to work with angles and sides until they can tell you that they need to know angles and one side to draw a complete triangle.

LINGUISTIC, KINESTHETIC

### Option 2 English Language Learners ELL

**Materials:** chart paper, construction paper, tape/glue
**Core Vocabulary:** tape, matches, description
**Common Use Verb:** cut out
**Do Math** This strategy increases comprehensibility of math vocabulary through cooperative groups.

- Post 6 pieces of chart paper around the room with an example of a triangle and its description on each piece.
- Review vocabulary such as side, angle, obtuse, scalene, acute, etc.
- Divide the class into six groups to cut out triangles in various shapes.
- Give each group one piece of chart paper.
- Students should tape the triangle that matches each description to the chart paper.
- After a minute, tell students to travel to the next piece of paper.
- Continue until done. Discuss as time permits.

## Independent Work Options

LOGICAL, VISUAL, SPATIAL

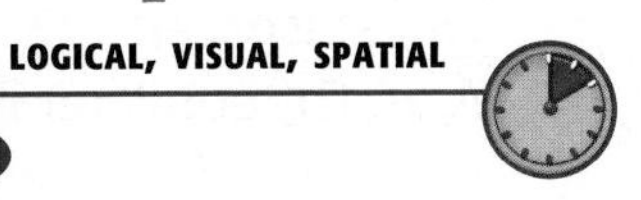

### Option 1 Early Finishers OL AL

**Materials:** scissors, construction paper

- Ask students to cut out 8 triangles of different shapes and sizes. Have them label the back of each triangle with its two classifications, such as equilateral and acute.

**Obtuse Isosceles**

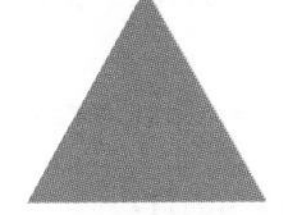

**Acute Equilateral**

**Right Scalene**

### Option 2 Student Technology

**Math Online** macmillanmh.com

Personal Tutor • Extra Examples

 Math Adventures

### Option 3 Learning Station: Reading (p. 356G)

Direct students to the Reading Learning Station for opportunities to explore and extend the lesson concept.

### Option 4 Problem-Solving Practice

Reinforce problem-solving skills and strategies with the Problem-Solving Practice worksheet.

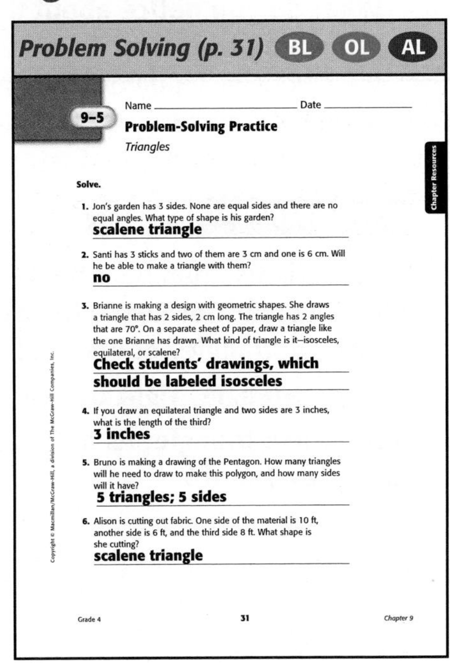

*Problem Solving (p. 31)* BL OL AL

9–5

Name ____________ Date ____________

**Problem-Solving Practice**

*Triangles*

**Solve.**

1. Jon's garden has 3 sides. None are equal sides and there are no equal angles. What type of shape is his garden?
   **scalene triangle**
2. Santi has 3 sticks and two of them are 3 cm and one is 6 cm. Will he be able to make a triangle with them?
   **no**
3. Brianne is making a design with geometric shapes. She draws a triangle that has 2 sides, 2 cm long. The triangle has 2 angles that are 70°. On a separate sheet of paper, draw a triangle like the one Brianne has drawn. What kind of triangle is it—isosceles, equilateral, or scalene?
   **Check students' drawings, which should be labeled isosceles**
4. If you draw an equilateral triangle and two sides are 3 inches, what is the length of the third?
   **3 inches**
5. Bruno is making a drawing of the Pentagon. How many triangles will he need to draw to make this polygon, and how many sides will it have?
   **5 triangles; 5 sides**
6. Alison is cutting out fabric. One side of the material is 10 ft, another side is 6 ft, and the third side 8 ft. What shape is she cutting?
   **scalene triangle**

Chapter Resources



Grade 4 31 Chapter 9

# 9-5 Triangles

## 1 Introduce

### Activity Choice 1 • Hands-On

- Provide student groups with one set of construction paper triangles of the following types: isosceles (3 of different shapes, labeled A, B, C); equilateral (3 of different sizes, labeled D, E, F), and scalene (3 of different shapes, labeled G, H, I).
- Ask the students to label each angle in each triangle as right, obtuse, or acute.
- Have students use a ruler to measure and label the length of each side.

### Activity Choice 2 • Literature

Introduce the lesson with *Bridges* by Ken Robbins. For a related math activity, see p. TR56.

## 2 Teach

### Scaffolding Questions

Use the triangles from Activity 1 above to discuss the following questions as a class.

- **Are there any triangles whose sides are all the same length?** yes Label these triangles equilateral.
- **Are there any triangles where exactly 2 sides are the same length?** yes Label these triangles isosceles.
- **What do you notice about the sides of the 3 remaining triangles?** Sample answer: Each of their sides has a different length. Label these triangles scalene.

### GET READY to Learn

Have students open their books and read the information in **Get Ready to Learn**. Introduce **isosceles triangle**, **equilateral triangle**, **scalene triangle**, **right triangle**, **acute triangle**, and **obtuse triangle**. As a class, work through **Examples 1 and 2**.

# 9-5 Triangles

**MAIN IDEA**

I will identify, describe, and classify triangles.

**New Vocabulary**

- right triangle
- acute triangle
- obtuse triangle
- isosceles triangle
- equilateral triangle
- scalene triangle

**Math Online**

macmillanmh.com

- Extra Examples
- Personal Tutor
- Self-Check Quiz

### GET READY to Learn

This sandwich is cut in half. What figure does each half resemble?

There are many different types of triangles. You can classify triangles by the measure of their angles

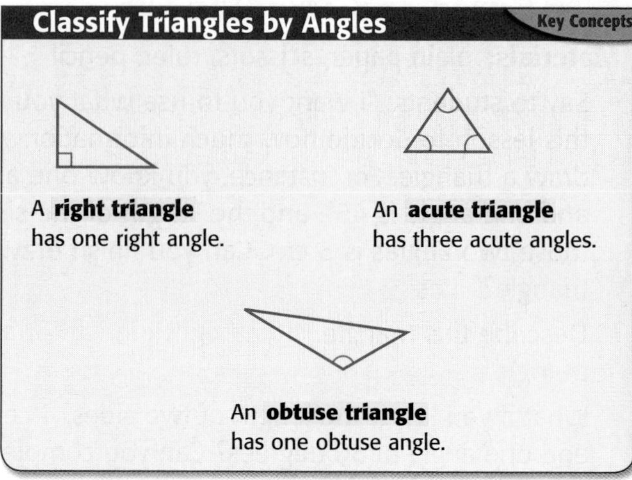

**Classify Triangles by Angles** — Key Concepts

A **right triangle** has one right angle.

An **acute triangle** has three acute angles.

An **obtuse triangle** has one obtuse angle.

**EXAMPLE** Classify by Angles

**1** **Classify the triangle. Use *right, acute,* or *obtuse*.**

Since there is one obtuse angle, the triangle is obtuse.



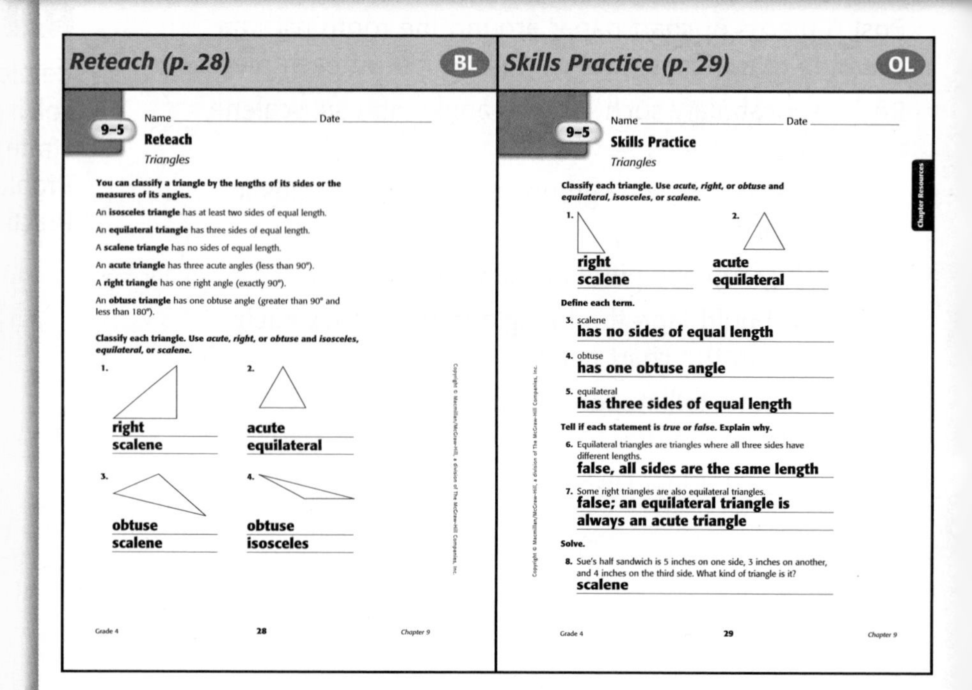

*Reteach (p. 28)* BL

9–5 Name ______ Date ______

**Reteach**

*Triangles*

**You can classify a triangle by the lengths of its sides or the measures of its angles.**

An **isosceles triangle** has at least two sides of equal length.

An **equilateral triangle** has three sides of equal length.

A **scalene triangle** has no sides of equal length.

An **acute triangle** has three acute angles (less than 90°).

A **right triangle** has one right angle (exactly 90°).

An **obtuse triangle** has one obtuse angle (greater than 90° and less than 180°).

**Classify each triangle. Use *acute, right,* or *obtuse* and *isosceles, equilateral,* or *scalene*.**

1. right, scalene
2. acute, equilateral
3. obtuse, scalene
4. obtuse, isosceles



Grade 4 28 Chapter 9

*Skills Practice (p. 29)* OL

9–5 Name ______ Date ______

**Skills Practice**

*Triangles*

**Classify each triangle. Use *acute, right,* or *obtuse* and *equilateral, isosceles,* or *scalene*.**

1. right, scalene
2. acute, equilateral

**Define each term.**

3. scalene — **has no sides of equal length**
4. obtuse — **has one obtuse angle**
5. equilateral — **has three sides of equal length**

**Tell if each statement is *true* or *false*. Explain why.**

6. Equilateral triangles are triangles where all three sides have different lengths. **false, all sides are the same length**
7. Some right triangles are also equilateral triangles. **false; an equilateral triangle is always an acute triangle**

**Solve.**

8. Sue's half sandwich is 5 inches on one side, 3 inches on another, and 4 inches on the third side. What kind of triangle is it? **scalene**

Chapter Resources



Grade 4 29 Chapter 9

Triangles can also be classified by the measure of their angles.

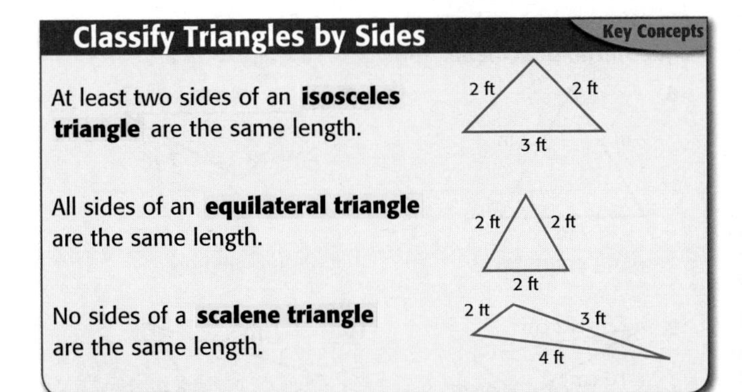

**Classify Triangles by Sides** — Key Concepts

At least two sides of an **isosceles triangle** are the same length.

All sides of an **equilateral triangle** are the same length.

No sides of a **scalene triangle** are the same length.



**EXAMPLE** Classify by Angles and Sides

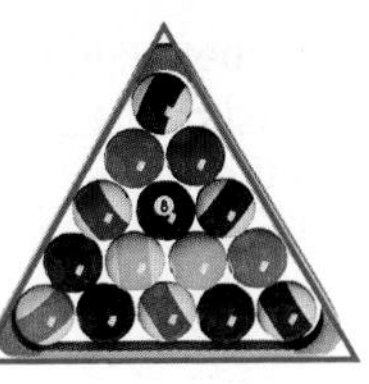

**2** **Classify the triangle. Use *acute, right,* or *obtuse* and *isosceles, equilateral,* or *scalene*.** The triangle has three angles that are less than 90°. The triangle is acute. All of the sides are the same length, so it is also equilateral.

## CHECK What You Know

**Classify each triangle. Use *acute, right,* or *obtuse* and *isosceles, equilateral,* or *scalene*.** See Examples 1 and 2 (pp. 372–373)

**1.** 3 cm, 3 cm, 5 cm — obtuse isosceles

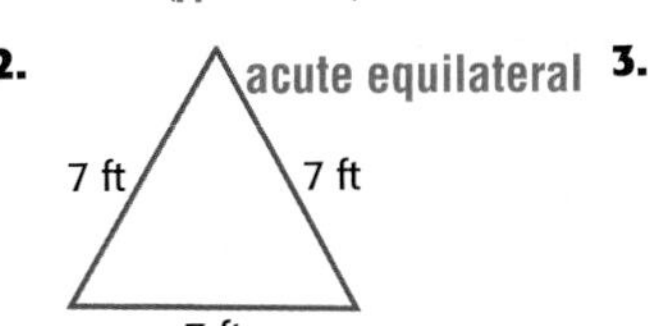

**2.** 7 ft, 7 ft, 7 ft — acute equilateral

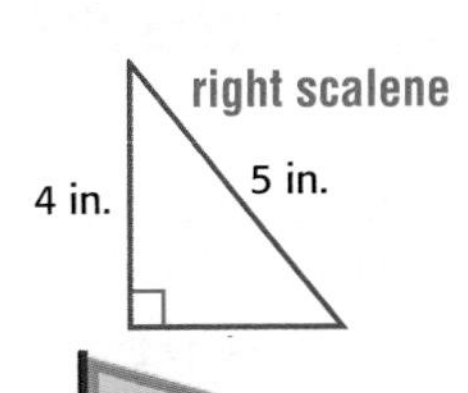

**3.** 4 in., 5 in. — right scalene

**4.** What type of triangle is the pennant? acute scalene

GO TIGERS!

**5.** Talk About It — Two sides of an equilateral triangle measure 3 feet. What is the measure of the third side? Explain.
3 ft; All sides have the same length.



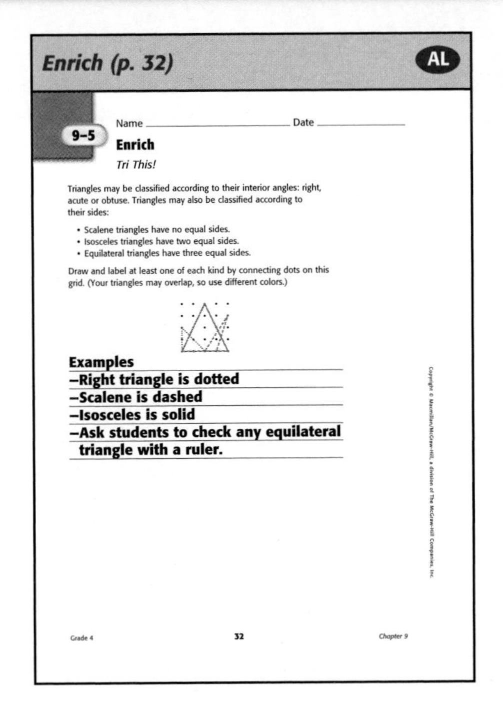

**Enrich (p. 32)** AL

9-5 Name ____ Date ____

**Enrich**

*Tri This!*

Triangles may be classified according to their interior angles: right, acute or obtuse. Triangles may also be classified according to their sides:

- Scalene triangles have no equal sides.
- Isosceles triangles have two equal sides.
- Equilateral triangles have three equal sides.

Draw and label at least one of each kind by connecting dots on this grid. (Your triangles may overlap, so use different colors.)

**Examples**
**–Right triangle is dotted**
**–Scalene is dashed**
**–Isosceles is solid**
**–Ask students to check any equilateral triangle with a ruler.**

Grade 4 32 Chapter 9

### Classify by Sides

**Example 1** Sometimes it is hard for students to determine if an angle is obtuse or right. Show them how to use the corner of a piece of paper to tell if an angle is a right angle or greater than a right angle.

## ADDITIONAL EXAMPLES

**1** Classify the triangle. Use *isosceles, equilateral,* or *scalene*. isosceles

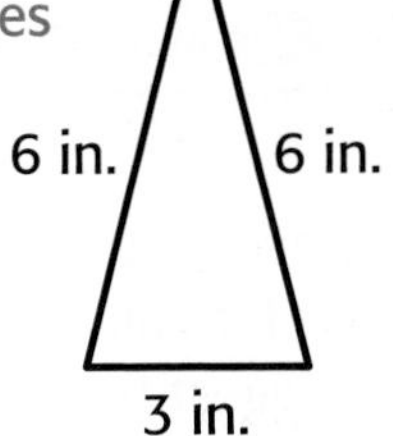



**2** Classify the triangle. Use *acute, right,* or *obtuse*. obtuse

**3** Classify the triangles above. Use *acute, right* or *obtuse* and *isosceles, equilateral,* or *scalene*. acute isosceles; obtuse scalene

### CHECK What You Know

As a class, have students complete Exercises 1–5 in **Check What You Know** as you observe their work.

**Exercise 5** Assess student comprehension before assigning practice exercises.

## BL Alternate Teaching Strategy

**If** students have trouble identifying triangles...

**Then** use one of these reteach options:

1 CRM **Daily Reteach Worksheet** (p. 28)

2 Provide them with craft sticks and clay. (Craft sticks can be broken to make different lengths.) Have groups of students construct examples of each of the following triangles: acute, obtuse, right, scalene, equilateral, and isosceles.

Have students label each type of triangle. Ask students to check to see that each example matches its definition.

# 3 Practice

Differentiate practice using these leveled assignments for Exercises 6–21.

| Level | Assignment |
|---|---|
| BL Below/Approaching Level | 6–8, 12–13, 15–16 |
| OL On Level | 6–13, 16–20 |
| AL Above/Beyond Level | 7–17 odd, 19–21 |

Have students discuss and complete the Higher Order Thinking problems. For Exercise 21, suggest that students draw several equilateral triangles and observe the angles of each.

**WRITING IN ▸MATH** Have students complete Exercise 21 in their Math Journals. You may choose to use this exercise as an optional formative assessment.

### Additional Answer

**17.** Sample answer: The triangle has one obtuse angle, so it is obtuse. The triangle also has three sides of different lengths. So, the triangle is scalene.

### COMMON ERROR!

**Exercises 6–13** Students may classify the triangle only one way. Point out that they should classify the triangle by the lengths of its sides and the measures of its angles.



## Practice and Problem Solving

**Classify each triangle. Use *acute, right,* or *obtuse* and *isosceles, equilateral,* or *scalene.*** See Examples 1 and 2 (pp. 372–373)

**6.**
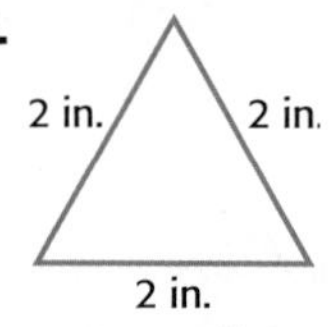

acute equilateral

**7.**
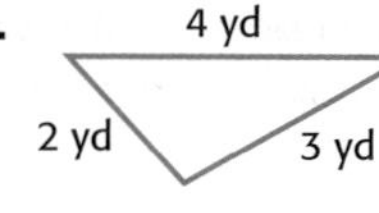

obtuse scalene

**8.**
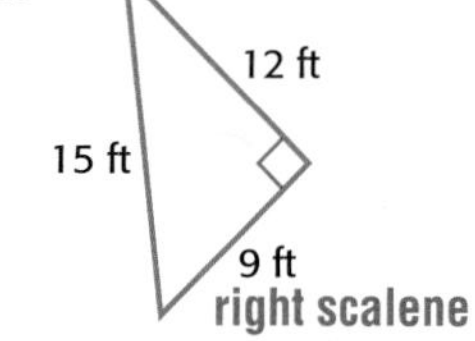

right scalene

**9.** 12 cm, 10 cm, 4 cm
obtuse scalene

**10.**
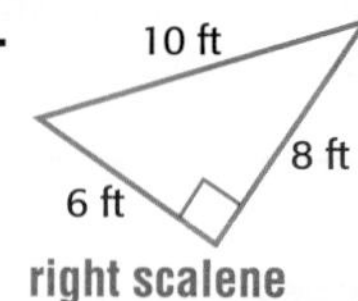

right scalene

**11.**
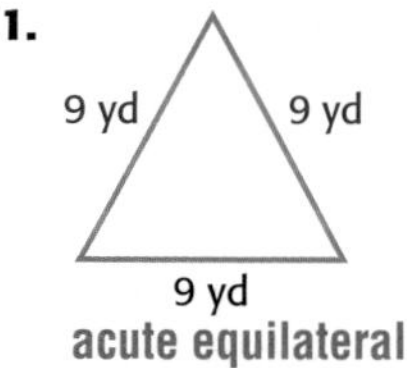

acute equilateral

**12.** Describe the triangle formed by the ladder and the wall. right scalene

**13.** Classify the triangle on the wedge of cheese. obtuse isosceles

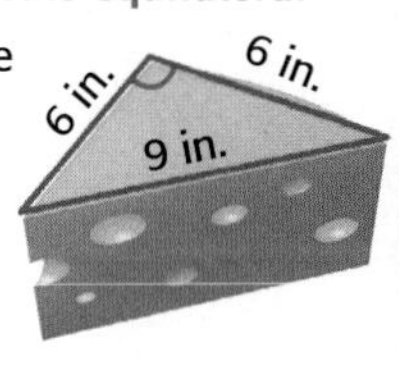


**14. Measurement** Shonda draws an equilateral triangle with 2 sides whose sum equals 12 inches. What is the length of the third side? 6 in.

**15. Measurement** Ross draws an isosceles triangle with sides 5 centimeters and 3 centimeters. What could the measure of the third side be? 3 cm or 5 cm

### Data File

Phoenix is the capital of Arizona. It has the greatest population of any capital city in the United States.

**16.** Classify the triangle formed by Phoenix, Yuma, and Grand Canyon. obtuse scalene

**17.** Explain how you classified the triangle in Exercise 16. See margin.

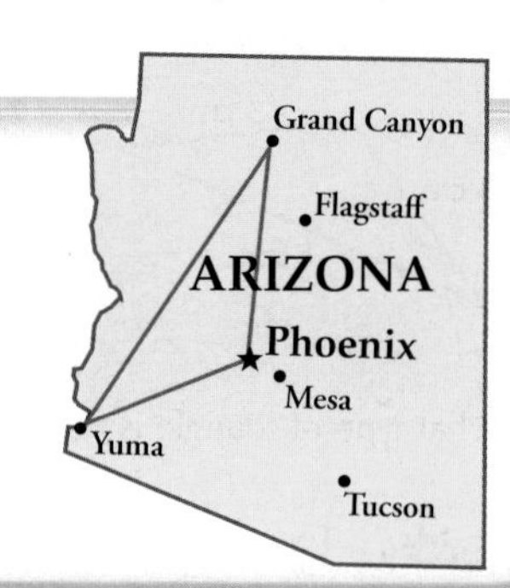

## H.O.T. Problems

**OPEN ENDED** Draw an example of each triangle.

**18.** right scalene triangle 18, 19. See margin. **19.** obtuse isosceles triangle

**20.** **WHICH ONE DOESN'T BELONG?** Identify the term that does not belong with the other three. Explain. Sample answer: scalene; It describes the sides not the angles.

right | obtuse | scalene | acute

**21.** **WRITING IN ▸MATH** Can an equilateral triangle be obtuse? Explain your answer. Sample answer: no; In order to have an obtuse angle, one of the sides has to be longer than the others.

## TEST Practice

**22.** In the figure, which two angles appear to be obtuse? (Lesson 9-4) B

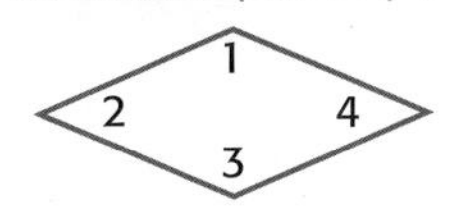


**A** Angles 1 and 2

**B** Angles 1 and 3

**C** Angles 1 and 4

**D** Angles 2 and 4

**23.** What kind of triangle always has 3 acute angles and 3 sides the same length? (Lesson 9-5) H

**F** isosceles

**G** right

**H** equilateral

**J** scalene

## Spiral Review

**Classify each angle as *right, acute,* or *obtuse.*** (Lesson 9-4)

**24.** right

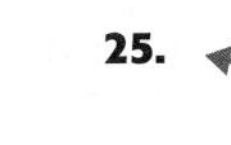

**25.** obtuse

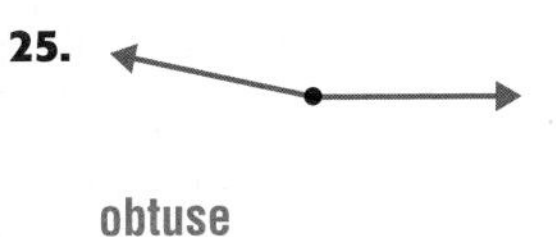

**26.** acute

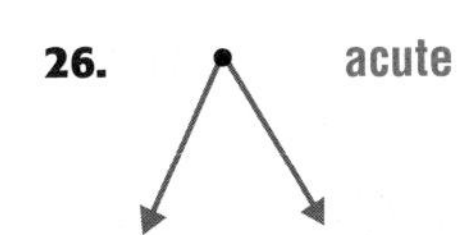

**27.** Suppose the pattern at the right was extended to 30 figures in all. How many pentagons and octagons would there be? (Lesson 9-3)
20 pentagons and 10 octagons

**Identify the first five multiples for each number.** (Lesson 4-9) 31. 0, 11, 22, 33, and 44

**28.** 3
0, 3, 6, 9, and 12

**29.** 5
0, 5, 10, 15, and 20

**30.** 8
0, 8, 16, 24, and 32

**31.** 11

**Lesson 9-5** Triangles **375**

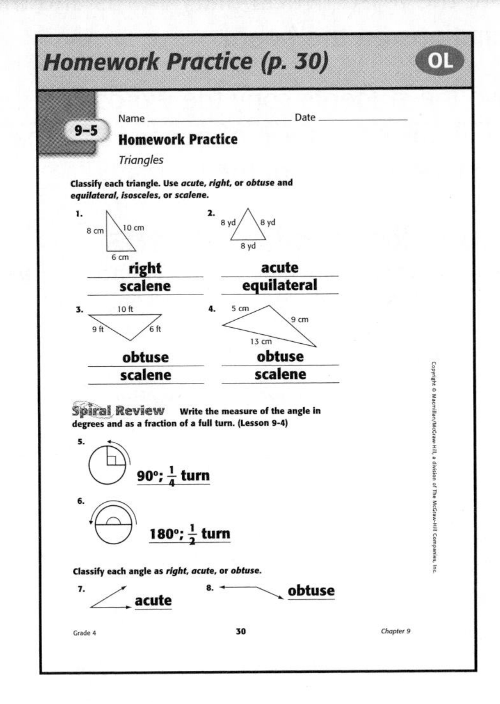

*Homework Practice (p. 30)* OL

9-5 Name ____ Date ____

**Homework Practice**

*Triangles*

Classify each triangle. Use *acute, right,* or *obtuse* and *equilateral, isosceles,* or *scalene.*

1. right scalene
2. acute equilateral
3. obtuse scalene
4. obtuse scalene

**Spiral Review** Write the measure of the angle in degrees and as a fraction of a full turn. (Lesson 9-4)

5. 90°; $\frac{1}{4}$ turn
6. 180°; $\frac{1}{2}$ turn

Classify each angle as *right, acute,* or *obtuse.*

7. acute
8. obtuse

Grade 4 30 Chapter 9

# 4 Assess

### Formative Assessment

Have the students answer the following questions.

- **What are two ways to classify triangles?**
  by sides and by angles
- **What is the difference between an acute triangle and an obtuse triangle?**
  Sample answer: All of the angles of an acute triangle are acute. For a triangle to be obtuse, one angle must be obtuse.

**Quick Check** **Are students continuing to struggle with identifying, describing, and classifying triangles?**

**If Yes** → Strategic Intervention Guide (p. 126)

**If No** → Independent Work Options (p. 392B)
CRM Skills Practice Worksheet (p. 29)
CRM Enrich Worksheet (p. 32)

**Yesterday's News** How did the concepts you learned about angles in Lesson 9-4 help you with today's lesson?

### TEST Practice

**Reviews Lessons 9-4 and 9-5**

Assign the Test Practice problems to provide daily reinforcement of test-taking skills.

### Spiral Review

**Reviews Lessons 4-9, 9-3, and 9-4**

Review and assess mastery of skills and concepts from previous chapters.

### Additional Answers

**18.** Sample answer:

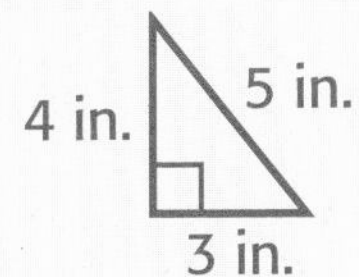


**19.** Sample answer: 5 in. 5 in. 8 in.

LESSON 9-6

# Quadrilaterals

## Lesson Planner

### Objective

Identify, describe, and classify quadrilaterals.

### Vocabulary

**rectangle**, **square**, **rhombus**, **parallelogram**, **trapezoid**

### Resources

**Manipulatives:** pattern blocks

**Literature Connection:** *Kathy Ross Crafts Triangles, Rectangles, Circles & Squares!* by Kathy Ross

**Teacher Technology**

TeacherWorks • Interactive Classroom

## Daily Routine

Use these suggestions before beginning the lesson on p. 376.

### 5-Minute Check

(Reviews Lesson 9-5)

**Draw an example of each triangle.**

1. obtuse isosceles Check drawings.
2. acute scalene Check drawings.
3. acute equilateral Check drawings.

### Problem of the Day

Armando writes these letters on the board in a pattern. What are the next two letters in the pattern? A, B, D, G, K, ___, ___. Describe the pattern.

P, V; Between the first two letters, skip no letters. Between the next two letters, skip 1 letter. Between the next two letters, skip 2 letters, and so on.

### Focus on Math Background

In the previous grade, students learned to identify and describe parallelograms, rectangles, and squares. In this lesson, students extend their knowledge of quadrilaterals to include trapezoids and rhombi. Students also learn to classify quadrilaterals by as many ways as possible. For example, a rectangle is also a parallelogram, and a quadrilateral.

### Building Math Vocabulary

Write the lesson vocabulary words and their definitions on the board.

Have the students copy the words and their definitions on a piece of paper. Have them draw examples for each of the words.

**Visual Vocabulary Cards**

Use Visual Vocabulary Card 35 to reinforce the vocabulary introduced in this lesson. (The Define/Example/Ask routine is printed on the back of each card.)

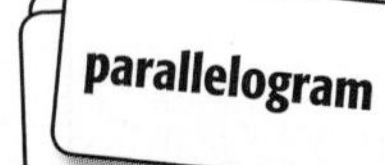

# Differentiated Instruction

## Small Group Options

### Option 1 Gifted and Talented AL

VISUAL, SPATIAL

**Materials:** 11″ × 17″ plain paper, old magazines, glue stick, pen

- Tell students that they are going to create a collage.
- Have students cut pictures from magazines that show the quadrilateral shapes they have studied.
- Have them glue the pictures onto their paper in an interesting way. Ask them to label all the shapes.
- Talk as a class about what they found.
- Find a way to display the students' work to the public.

### Option 2 English Language Learners ELL

INTERPERSONAL, AUDITORY/VISUAL

**Materials:** paper, rulers, scissors
**Core Vocabulary:** definition, walk, around the room
**Common Use Verb:** find

**Talk Math** This strategy promotes conversation using target vocabulary.

- Divide the group in half. One group will write on the strips of paper the definition of each type of quadrilateral. The other group will draw the different quadrilaterals on separate pieces of paper.
- Have each student hold one definition or piece of paper.
- Have students walk around the room to find matches.
- Once they have found their match, have students form a line, taking turns reading their definitions and holding up the matching pictures.
- Write the definitions or key vocabulary on the board if students need a language scaffold.

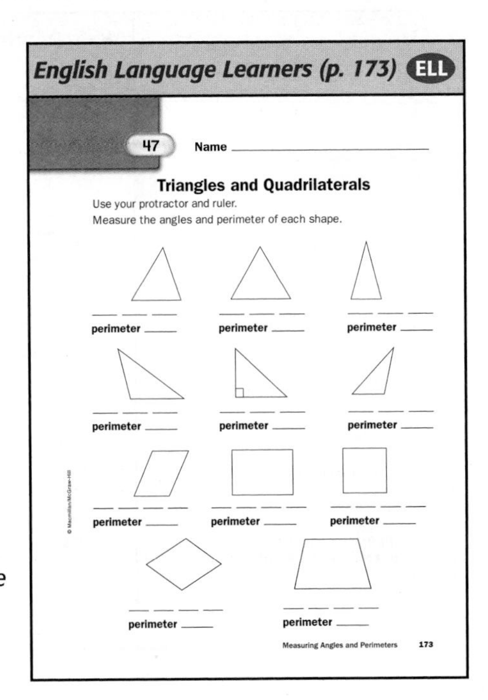
*English Language Learners (p. 173)* ELL

47 Name ______

**Triangles and Quadrilaterals**

Use your protractor and ruler.
Measure the angles and perimeter of each shape.

perimeter ______ perimeter ______ perimeter ______
perimeter ______ perimeter ______ perimeter ______
perimeter ______ perimeter ______ perimeter ______
perimeter ______ perimeter ______

© Macmillan/McGraw-Hill

Measuring Angles and Perimeters 173

*Use this worksheet to provide additional support for English Language Learners.*

## Independent Work Options

### Option 1 Early Finishers OL AL

VISUAL, SPATIAL

**Materials:** grid paper, pencil

- Have students use only the quadrilaterals from this lesson to design the floor plan of a simple house.
- Ask them to draw the design on grid paper. Have them label each of the shapes.

### Option 2 Student Technology

macmillanmh.com

Personal Tutor • Extra Examples

 Math Adventures

### Option 3 Learning Station: Music (p. 356H)

Direct students to the Music Learning Station for opportunities to explore and extend the lesson concept.

### Option 4 Problem-Solving Practice

Reinforce problem-solving skills and strategies with the Problem-Solving Practice worksheet.

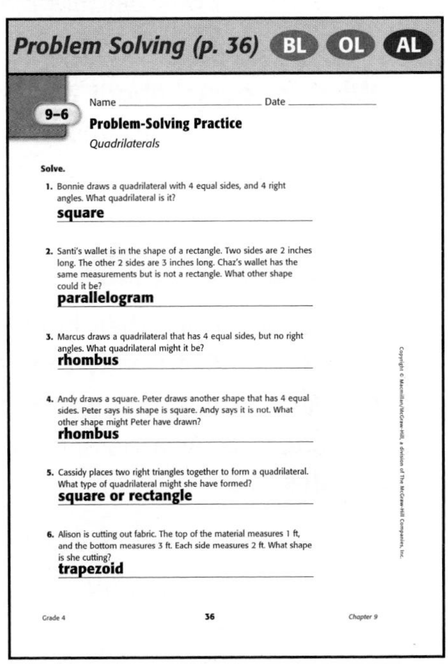
*Problem Solving (p. 36)* BL OL AL

9–6 Name ______ Date ______

**Problem-Solving Practice**

*Quadrilaterals*

**Solve.**

1. Bonnie draws a quadrilateral with 4 equal sides, and 4 right angles. What quadrilateral is it?
   **square**
2. Santi's wallet is in the shape of a rectangle. Two sides are 2 inches long. The other 2 sides are 3 inches long. Chaz's wallet has the same measurements but is not a rectangle. What other shape could it be?
   **parallelogram**
3. Marcus draws a quadrilateral that has 4 equal sides, but no right angles. What quadrilateral might it be?
   **rhombus**
4. Andy draws a square. Peter draws another shape that has 4 equal sides. Peter says his shape is square. Andy says it is not. What other shape might Peter have drawn?
   **rhombus**
5. Cassidy places two right triangles together to form a quadrilateral. What type of quadrilateral might she have formed?
   **square or rectangle**
6. Alison is cutting out fabric. The top of the material measures 1 ft, and the bottom measures 3 ft. Each side measures 2 ft. What shape is she cutting?
   **trapezoid**



Grade 4 36 Chapter 9

# 9-6 Quadrilaterals

## 1 Introduce

### Activity Choice 1 • Hands-On

- Divide the class into groups of 2 or 3. Give each group manipulatives (pattern blocks or other figures) that include different shapes of trapezoids and rhombi.
- Hold up a trapezoid or draw figures similar to the ones the students have. Have students describe the figure using its attributes. If necessary, remind students that an attribute is a physical feature used to describe an object or shape. If students do not describe the pair of parallel sides, ask them to do so.
- Repeat the process with a rhombus.

### Activity Choice 2 • Literature

Introduce the lesson with *Kathy Ross Crafts Triangles, Rectangles, Circles & Squares!* by Kathy Ross. For a related math activity, see p. TR57.

## 2 Teach

### Scaffolding Questions

Use the information gathered in Activity 1 to answer these questions.

- **What attribute does each of your models possess?** They all have four sides.
- Show students a trapezoid.
- **What is special about a trapezoid?** It has exactly one pair of parallel sides.
- Show students a rhombus.
- **What is special about a rhombus?** It has 4 equal sides, and it has two pairs of parallel sides.

### GET READY to Learn

Have students open their books and read the information in **Get Ready to Learn**. Introduce **rectangle**, **square**, **rhombus**, **parallelogram**, and **trapezoid**. As a class, work through **Examples 1–3**.

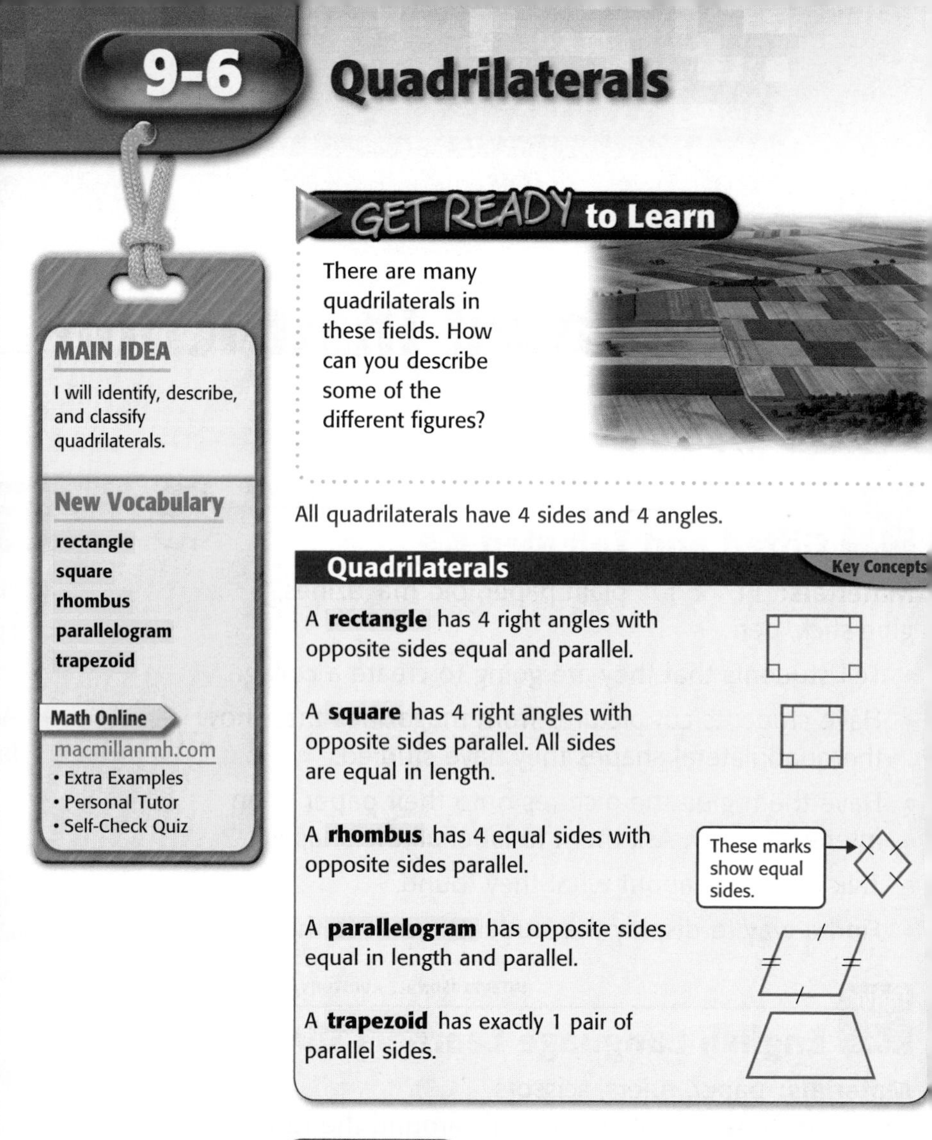

# 9-6 Quadrilaterals

**MAIN IDEA**

I will identify, describe, and classify quadrilaterals.

**New Vocabulary**

rectangle
square
rhombus
parallelogram
trapezoid

**Math Online**

macmillanmh.com
- Extra Examples
- Personal Tutor
- Self-Check Quiz

**GET READY to Learn**

There are many quadrilaterals in these fields. How can you describe some of the different figures?

All quadrilaterals have 4 sides and 4 angles.

**Quadrilaterals** — Key Concepts

A **rectangle** has 4 right angles with opposite sides equal and parallel.

A **square** has 4 right angles with opposite sides parallel. All sides are equal in length.

A **rhombus** has 4 equal sides with opposite sides parallel.

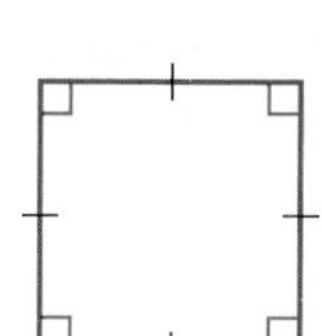

These marks show equal sides.

A **parallelogram** has opposite sides equal in length and parallel.

A **trapezoid** has exactly 1 pair of parallel sides.

**EXAMPLE** Classify a Quadrilateral

1. **Classify the quadrilateral in as many ways as possible.**

   It can be classified as a parallelogram, rectangle, square, and rhombus.

376 **Chapter 9** Identify and Describe Geometric Figures

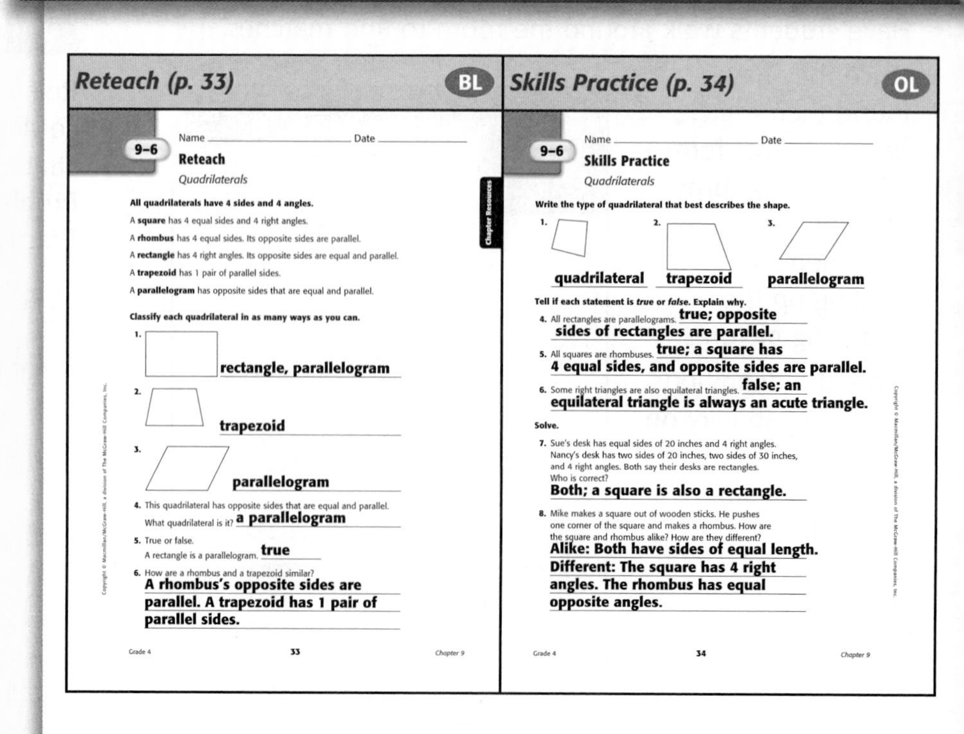

**Reteach (p. 33)** BL

9-6 Name ______ Date ______

**Reteach**

*Quadrilaterals*

**All quadrilaterals have 4 sides and 4 angles.**

A **square** has 4 equal sides and 4 right angles.

A **rhombus** has 4 equal sides. Its opposite sides are parallel.

A **rectangle** has 4 right angles. Its opposite sides are equal and parallel.

A **trapezoid** has 1 pair of parallel sides.

A **parallelogram** has opposite sides that are equal and parallel.

**Classify each quadrilateral in as many ways as you can.**

1. **rectangle, parallelogram**
2. **trapezoid**
3. **parallelogram**
4. This quadrilateral has opposite sides that are equal and parallel. What quadrilateral is it? **a parallelogram**
5. True or false. A rectangle is a parallelogram. **true**
6. How are a rhombus and a trapezoid similar? **A rhombus's opposite sides are parallel. A trapezoid has 1 pair of parallel sides.**

Grade 4 33 Chapter 9

Chapter Resources

Copyright © Macmillan/McGraw-Hill, a division of The McGraw-Hill Companies, Inc.

**Skills Practice (p. 34)** OL

9-6 Name ______ Date ______

**Skills Practice**

*Quadrilaterals*

**Write the type of quadrilateral that best describes the shape.**

1. **quadrilateral**
2. **trapezoid**
3. **parallelogram**

**Tell if each statement is *true* or *false*. Explain why.**

4. All rectangles are parallelograms. **true; opposite sides of rectangles are parallel.**
5. All squares are rhombuses. **true; a square has 4 equal sides, and opposite sides are parallel.**
6. Some right triangles are also equilateral triangles. **false; an equilateral triangle is always an acute triangle.**

**Solve.**

7. Sue's desk has equal sides of 20 inches and 4 right angles. Nancy's desk has two sides of 20 inches, two sides of 30 inches, and 4 right angles. Both say their desks are rectangles. Who is correct? **Both; a square is also a rectangle.**
8. Mike makes a square out of wooden sticks. He pushes one corner of the square and makes a rhombus. How are the square and rhombus alike? How are they different? **Alike: Both have sides of equal length. Different: The square has 4 right angles. The rhombus has equal opposite angles.**

Grade 4 34 Chapter 9

Copyright © Macmillan/McGraw-Hill, a division of The McGraw-Hill Companies, Inc.

Many real-world objects have the shapes of quadrilaterals.

**Real-World EXAMPLES** Real-World Shapes

**2** **VIDEO GAMES** **Write the type of quadrilateral that best describes the shape around the game controller.**

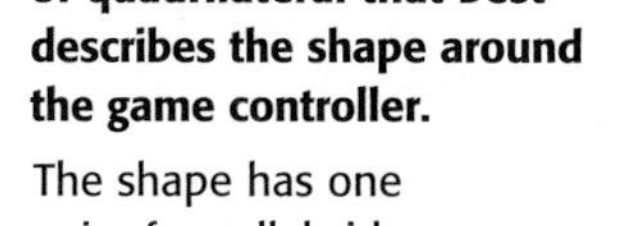

The shape has one pair of parallel sides. So, it is a trapezoid.

**3** **Identify the red shape in as many ways as possible.**

The shape has 4 right angles, with opposite sides equal and parallel. So, it is a rectangle and a parallelogram.

## CHECK What You Know

**Classify each quadrilateral in as many ways as possible.**

See Example 1 (p. 376)

**1.** rhombus and parallelogram

**2.** 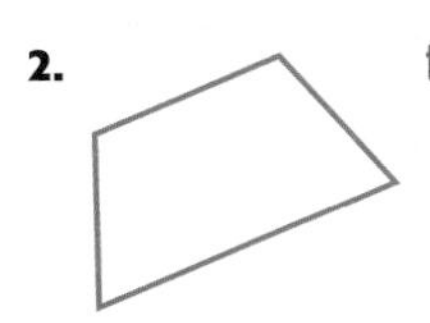 trapezoid

**3.** 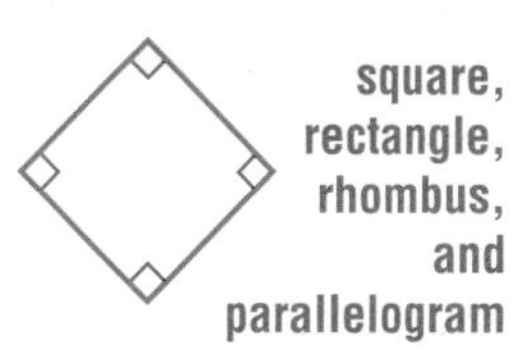 square, rectangle, rhombus, and parallelogram

**Write the type of quadrilateral that best describes the shape.**

See Examples 2–3 (p. 377)

**4.** trapezoid

**5.**  rectangle

**6.**  square

**7.** Talk About It How are a square and a rhombus alike? How are they different? Sample answer: They both have 4 equal sides. A square always has right angles.



**Enrich (p. 37)** AL

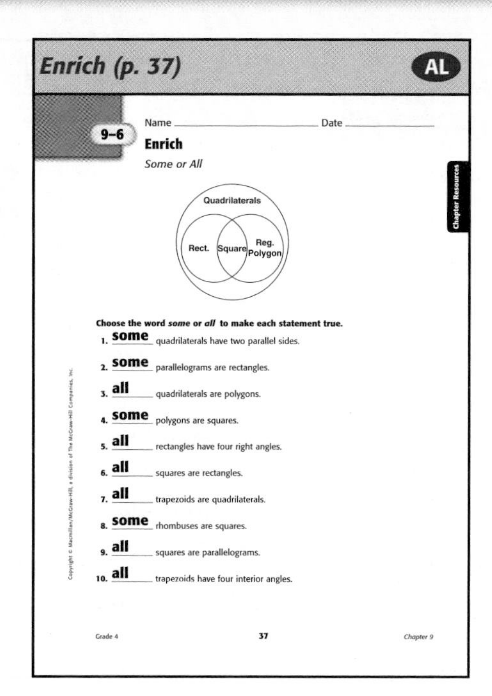

9-6 Name ____ Date ____

**Enrich**

*Some or All*

Quadrilaterals — Rect. | Square | Reg. Polygon

**Choose the word *some* or *all* to make each statement true.**

1. some quadrilaterals have two parallel sides.
2. some parallelograms are rectangles.
3. all quadrilaterals are polygons.
4. some polygons are squares.
5. all rectangles have four right angles.
6. all squares are rectangles.
7. all trapezoids are quadrilaterals.
8. some rhombuses are squares.
9. all squares are parallelograms.
10. all trapezoids have four interior angles.

Grade 4 37 Chapter 9

## Classify a Quadrilateral

**Example 1** Students get confused when one quadrilateral can be classified in so many ways. You may want to help them organize what they know in a graphic organizer.

### ADDITIONAL EXAMPLES

**1** Classify the quadrilateral in as many ways as possible. trapezoid

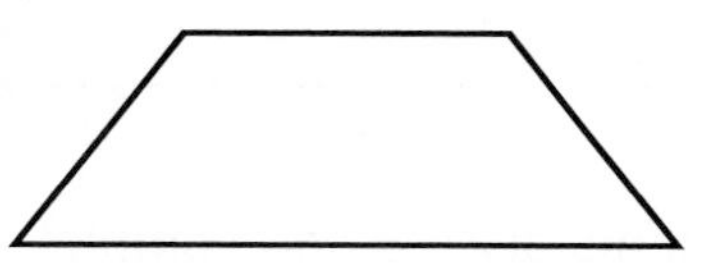

**2** Write the type of quadrilateral that best describes the shape around a calculator. rectangle

**3** Identify the shape outlined. parallelogram

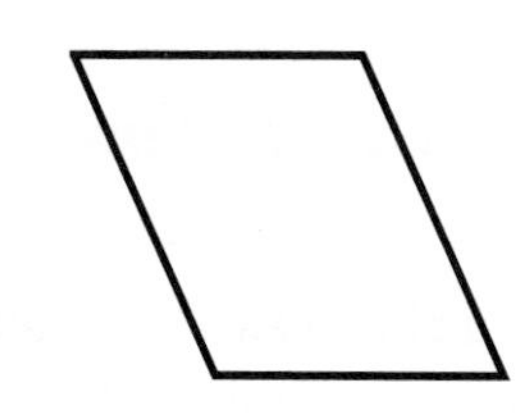

### CHECK What You Know

As a class, have students complete Exercises 1–7 in **Check What You Know** as you observe their work.

**Exercise 7** Assess student comprehension before assigning practice exercises.

## BL Alternate Teaching Strategy

**If** students have trouble classifying quadrilaterals…

**Then** use one of these reteach options:

1 CRM **Daily Reteach Worksheet** (p. 33)

2 Have them take a quiet walk around the school to look for quadrilaterals. Have them keep track of what they find on a piece of paper. Ask them to make a quick sketch, identify the object (such as a window), and write the type of quadrilateral that best describes the shape.

# 3 Practice

Differentiate practice using these leveled assignments for Exercises 8–25.

| Level | Assignment |
|---|---|
| BL Below/Approaching Level | 8–10, 14–17, 20–21 |
| OL On Level | 8–15, 16–23 |
| AL Above/Beyond Level | 8–20 even, 22–25 |

Have students discuss and complete the Higher Order Thinking problems. Have them compare their answers with another student and make any changes necessary.

**WRITING IN ▸MATH** Have students complete Exercise 25 in their Math Journals. You may choose to use this exercise as an optional formative assessment.

# 4 Assess

## Formative Assessment

Have the students answer the following questions:

- **Is a square a rhombus? Explain.** yes; It is a rhombus that has right angles.
- **Is a square a rectangle? Explain.** yes; It is a rectangle with all four sides equal in length.

**Quick Check** **Are students continuing to struggle with identifying, describing, and classifying quadrilaterals?**

**If Yes** → CRM Reteach Worksheet (p. 33)

**If No** → Independent Work Options (p. 332B)
CRM Skills Practice Worksheet (p. 34)
CRM Enrich Worksheet (p. 37)

**Name the Math** Draw and identify a rectangle, square, rhombus, parallelogram, and trapezoid.

**COMMON ERROR!**

**Exercises 20 and 21** Some students may have trouble classifying the quadrilateral from the description. Encourage them to draw a picture.



## Practice and Problem Solving

EXTRA PRACTICE See page R24.

**Classify each quadrilateral in as many ways as possible.**
See Example 1 (p. 376)

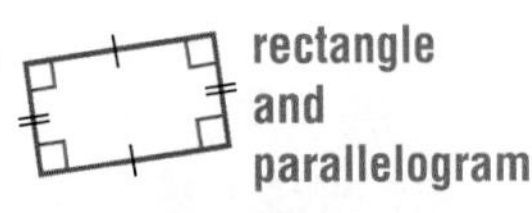

8. rectangle and parallelogram
9. trapezoid
10. parallelogram

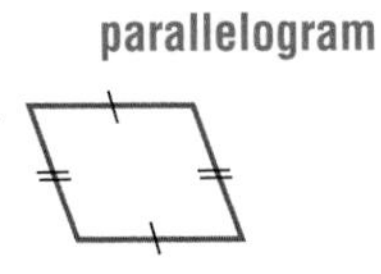

11. trapezoid
12. square, rectangle, rhombus, and parallelogram
13. rectangle and parallelogram

**Write the type of quadrilateral that best describes the shape.**
See Examples 2 and 3 (p. 377)

14. 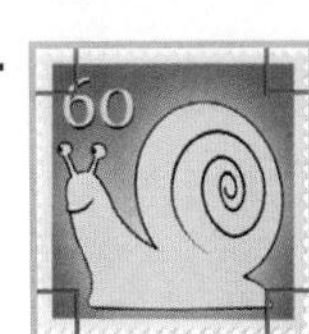

square
15. 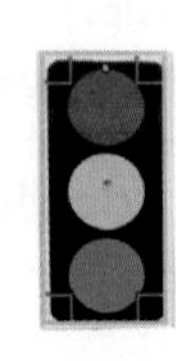 rectangle
16.  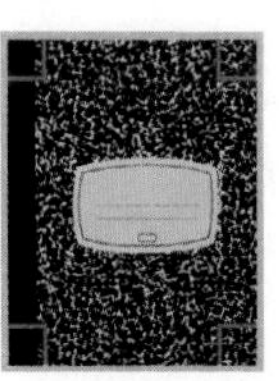 rectangle
17. trapezoid
18.   rectangle
19. 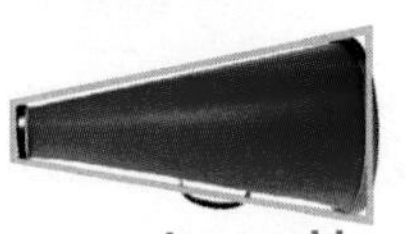 trapezoid

20. A quadrilateral has 4 sides with opposite sides parallel and 4 right angles. Two sides are longer than the others. What is the quadrilateral? rectangle

21. Phillip draws a quadrilateral. All 4 sides are the same length. Its opposite sides are parallel. What figure did he draw? rhombus

### H.O.T. Problems

22. **OPEN ENDED** Draw two quadrilaterals that can be classified as parallelograms. See Ch. 9 Answer Appendix.

**REASONING Tell whether each statement is *true* or *false*. If the statement is false, draw a counterexample.**

23. A rhombus is a square. false; 

24. A rectangle is a parallelogram. true

25. **WRITING IN ▸MATH** True or false: All squares are rectangles, but not all rectangles are squares. Explain. See Ch. 9 Answer Appendix.



**Homework Practice (p. 35)** OL

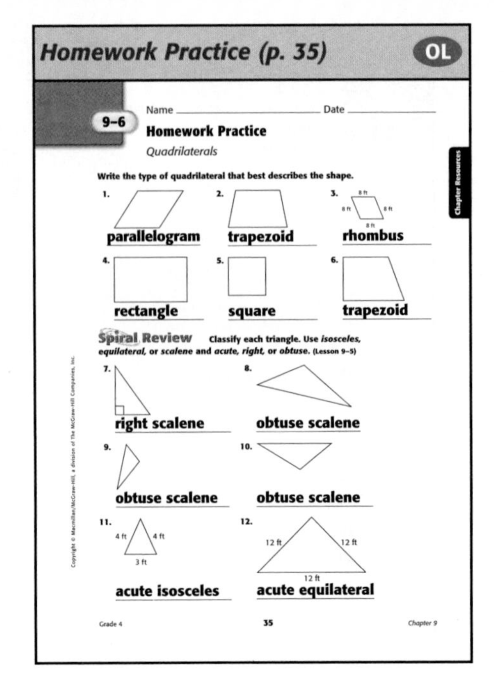

9–6 Name ______ Date ______

**Homework Practice**
*Quadrilaterals*

Write the type of quadrilateral that best describes the shape.

1. parallelogram
2. trapezoid
3. rhombus
4. rectangle
5. square
6. trapezoid

**Spiral Review** Classify each triangle. Use *isosceles, equilateral,* or *scalene* and *acute, right,* or *obtuse.* (Lesson 9–5)

7. right scalene
8. obtuse scalene
9. obtuse scalene
10. obtuse scalene
11. acute isosceles
12. acute equilateral

Grade 4 35 Chapter 9

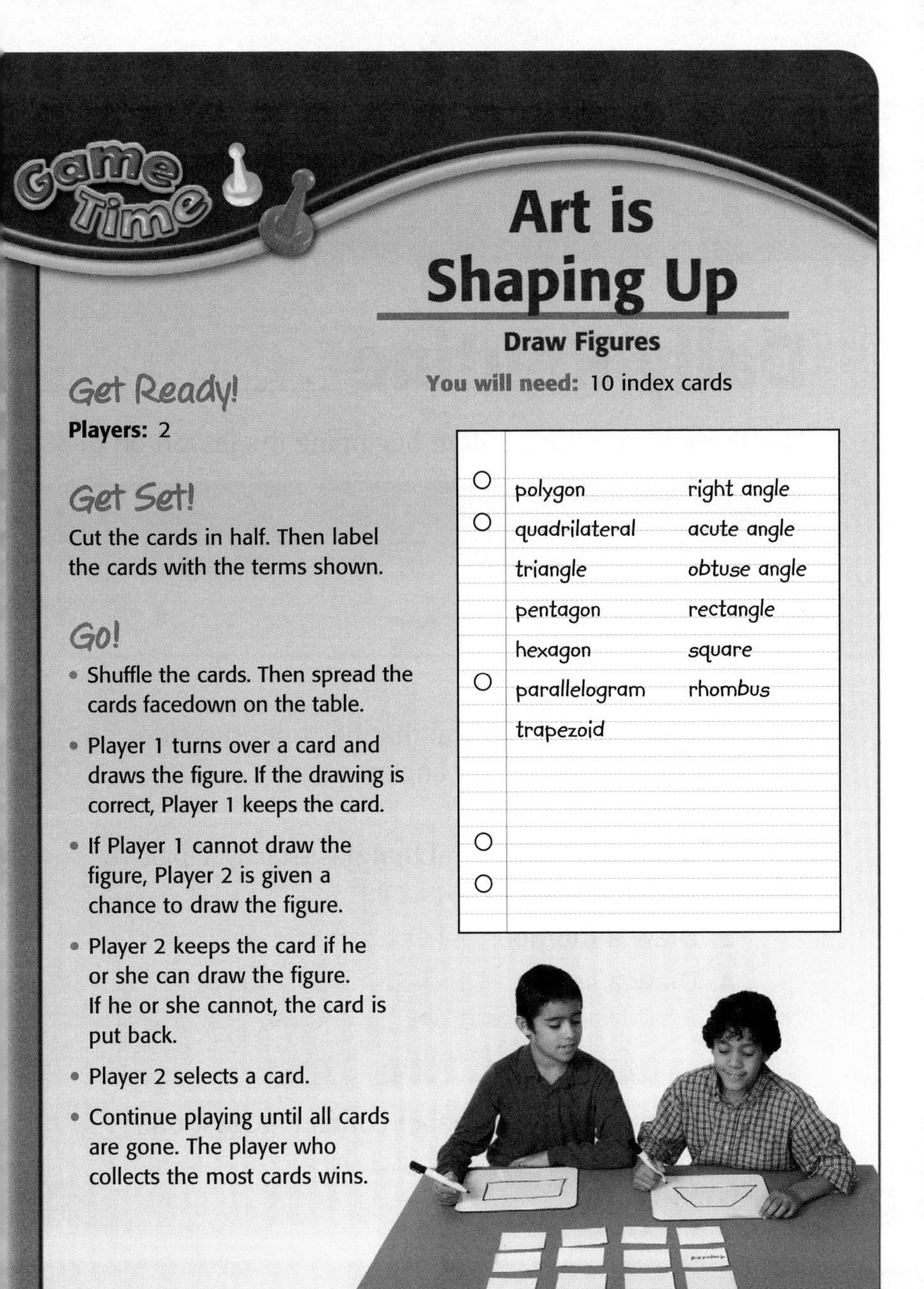

Game Time

# Art is Shaping Up

**Draw Figures**

**You will need:** 10 index cards

**Get Ready!**

**Players:** 2

**Get Set!**

Cut the cards in half. Then label the cards with the terms shown.

| | |
|---|---|
| polygon | right angle |
| quadrilateral | acute angle |
| triangle | obtuse angle |
| pentagon | rectangle |
| hexagon | square |
| parallelogram | rhombus |
| trapezoid | |

**Go!**

- Shuffle the cards. Then spread the cards facedown on the table.
- Player 1 turns over a card and draws the figure. If the drawing is correct, Player 1 keeps the card.
- If Player 1 cannot draw the figure, Player 2 is given a chance to draw the figure.
- Player 2 keeps the card if he or she can draw the figure. If he or she cannot, the card is put back.
- Player 2 selects a card.
- Continue playing until all cards are gone. The player who collects the most cards wins.

**Game Time** Art is Shaping Up **379**

## Differentiated Practice

Use these leveled suggestions to differentiate the game for all learners.

| Level | Assignment |
|---|---|
| BL Below/Approaching Level | Students use illustrations from the chapter to help them identify the figures. |
| OL On Level | Have students play the game with the rules as written. |
| AL Above/Beyond Level | Students write definitions of the figures in addition to drawing them. |

# Art is Shaping Up

**Math Concept:**
**Draw Figures**

**Materials:** 10 index cards, paper, pencils

Introduce the game on p. 379 to your students to play as a class, in small groups, or at a learning station to review concepts introduced in this chapter.

## Instructions

- Students cut cards in half and label one side of each card with one term from the list shown on p. 379.
- Students play in pairs. They shuffle the cards and spread them out facedown on the table.
- Player 1 turns over a card and tries to draw on a white board the item listed on the card. If Player 1 can draw it, he or she gets to keep the card. If Player 1 cannot draw the right figure, Player 2 is given a chance to draw it and keep the card if the figure is drawn correctly. If no one can draw the figure correctly, the card is put back.
- Player 2 selects a card and the same procedure is followed. Play continues until all the cards are gone. The player with the most cards wins.

## Extend the Game

Have students make a memory game using cards that show drawings of the figures in addition to the cards that have names.

# 9-7 Problem-Solving Investigation
# Choose a Strategy

## Lesson Planner

### Objective

Choose the best strategy to solve a problem.

### Resources

**Materials:** scissors, grid paper

**Manipulatives:** paper money

**Teacher Technology**
TeacherWorks • Interactive Classroom

**Real-World Problem Solving Library**
**Math and Science: *Solving the Pyramid Puzzle***
Use these leveled books to reinforce and extend problem-solving skills and strategies.

Leveled for:
- OL On Level
- ELL Sheltered English
- SP Spanish

For additional support, see the Real-World Problem Solving Teacher Guide.

## Daily Routine

Use these suggestions before beginning the lesson on p. 380.

### 5-Minute Check

(Reviews Lesson 9-6)

1. Name a quadrilateral that has opposite sides parallel and 4 right angles. Sample answer: rectangle
2. Name a quadrilateral that has exactly 1 pair of parallel sides. trapezoid
3. Draw a rhombus. Check students' drawings.
4. Draw a square. Check students' drawings.

### Problem of the Day

What letters of the alphabet contain at least one pair of parallel lines? E, F, H, I, N, Z and sometimes M and W

# Differentiated Instruction

## Small Group Options

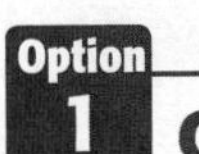

LOGICAL

### Option 1 Gifted and Talented AL

**Materials:** paper and pencil

- Hand students the following problem and T-chart with the missing numbers:

  *Cintia has a number chart with some missing items. She needs help filling in the chart correctly and writing a number sentence that will let her solve other problems for this chart.*

- The missing numbers in the chart are:
  (▲ × 3) + 1 or ▲ + ▲ + ▲ + 1

| 2 | 7 |
|---|---|
| 3 | 10 |
| 4 | 13 |
| 5 | 16 |
| 6 | 19 |
| 7 | 22 |
| 8 | 25 |

INTRAPERSONAL

### Option 2 English Language Learners ELL

**Materials:** index cards, play money
**Core Vocabulary:** draw, various, combine
**Common Use Verb:** make
**See Math** This strategy uses background knowledge to extend students' understanding of shapes.

- Post "$1" and pass out coins.
- Model using 4 quarters to make a square.
- Ask students to come up with various coin combinations that form a named shape and the dollar amount.

- Have students draw the money combinations on an index card and tape it to a poster for that shape.
- Repeat for non-standard shapes, (see art) and have students figure out the dollar amount.

## Independent Work Options

VISUAL, SPATIAL

### Option 1 Early Finishers OL AL

**Materials:** cut out 5 shapes like those on p. 380

- Have students arrange the five pieces from the problem to create other shapes such as a large triangle or bird.
- Have students trace around the pieces of their new arrangement. Then provide a name for the arrangement.

### Option 2 Student Technology

**Math Online** macmillanmh.com

Personal Tutor • Extra Examples

### Option 3 Learning Station: Health (p. 356H)

Direct students to the Health Learning Station for opportunities to explore and extend the lesson concept.

# 9-7 Problem-Solving Investigation

## 1 Introduce

**Activity • Review**

- Present the following problem to students:

  *Jin needs to catch the first bus leaving town after 11 A.M. The busses are scheduled to leave every 20 minutes starting at 8:30 A.M. What time will Jin leave on the bus?*

- **What strategy could you use to solve this problem?** look for a pattern
- **What time will Jin leave on the bus?** 11:10 A.M.

## 2 Teach

Have students read the problem on puzzle pieces. Guide them through the problem-solving steps.

**Understand** Using the questions, review what students know and need to find.

**Plan** Have them discuss their strategy.

**Solve** Guide students to use the act it out strategy to solve the problem.

- **How can you start to arrange the pieces to make a square? Explain.** Cut out the pieces and try different arrangements.
- **Is there only one way to use all of the pieces to form a square?** yes

**Check** Have students look back at the problem to make sure that the answer fits the facts given.

- **Are all the sides the same length?** yes
- **Are all 4 angles right angles?** yes

### ! COMMON ERROR!

**Exercise 3** Students may have trouble drawing this pattern because of the number of squares that it requires. If they have trouble, have them work on grid paper.



# 9-7 Problem-Solving Investigation

**MAIN IDEA** I will choose the best strategy to solve a problem.

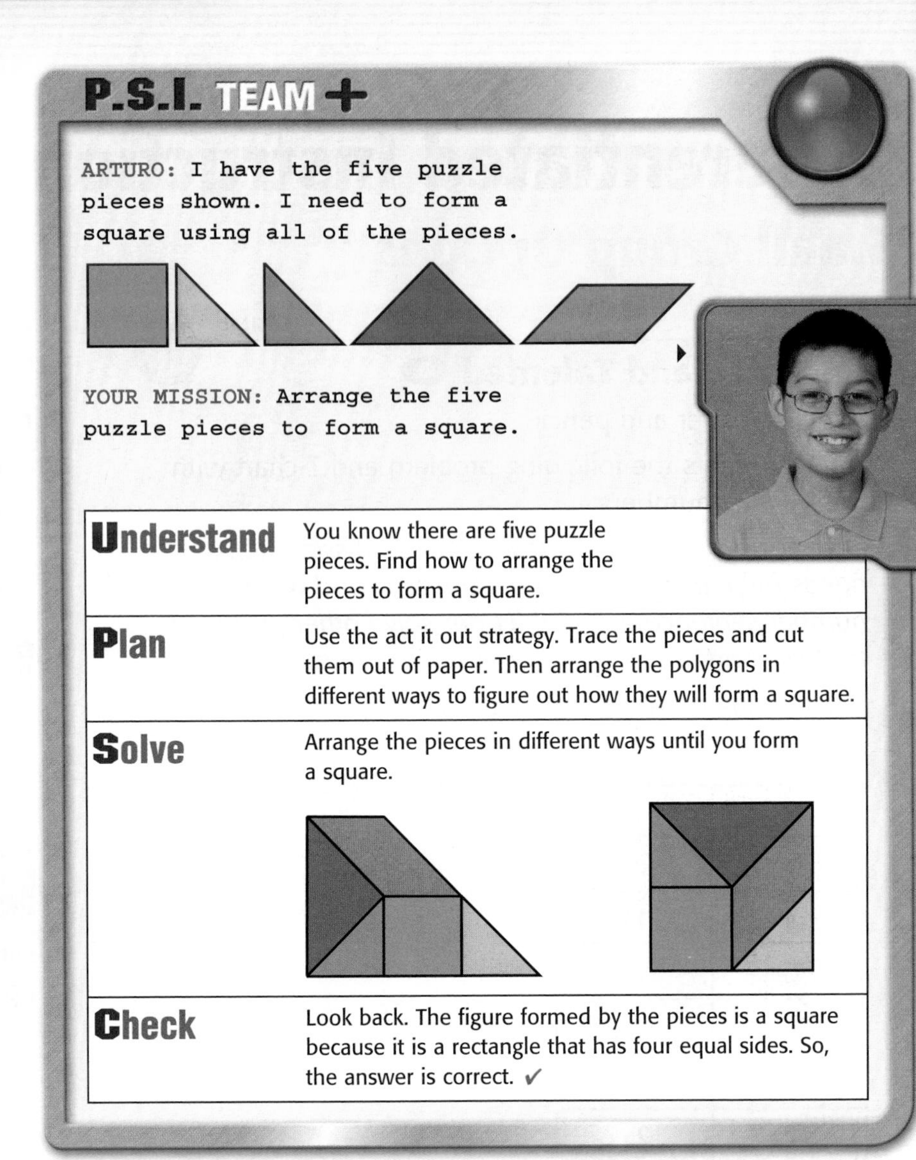

**P.S.I. TEAM +**

ARTURO: I have the five puzzle pieces shown. I need to form a square using all of the pieces.

YOUR MISSION: Arrange the five puzzle pieces to form a square.

| | |
|---|---|
| **Understand** | You know there are five puzzle pieces. Find how to arrange the pieces to form a square. |
| **Plan** | Use the act it out strategy. Trace the pieces and cut them out of paper. Then arrange the polygons in different ways to figure out how they will form a square. |
| **Solve** | Arrange the pieces in different ways until you form a square. |
| **Check** | Look back. The figure formed by the pieces is a square because it is a rectangle that has four equal sides. So, the answer is correct. ✓ |



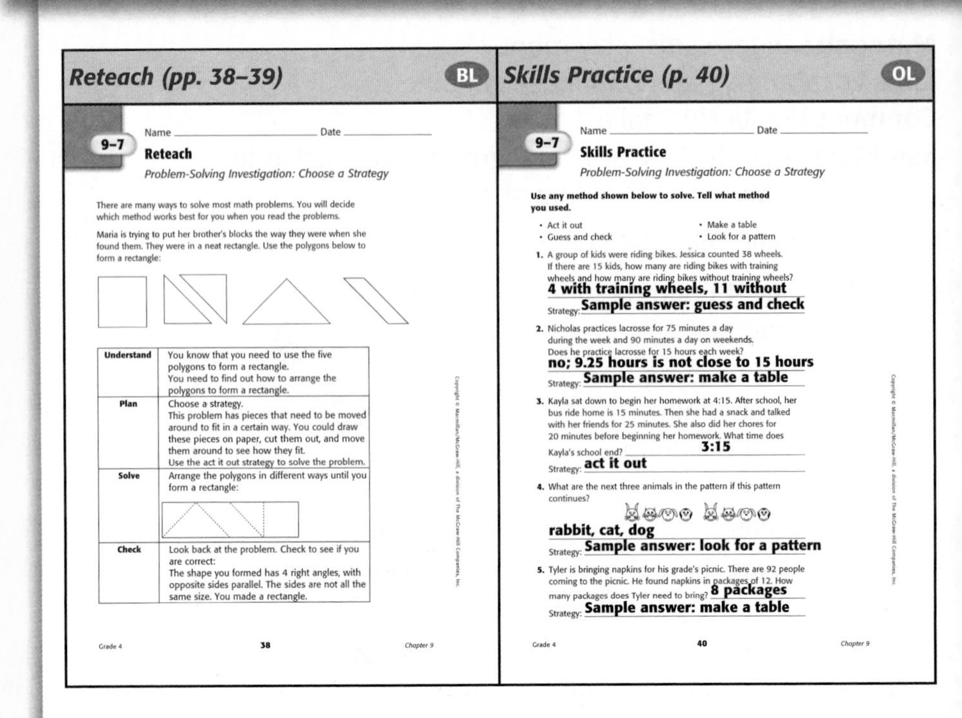

**Reteach (pp. 38–39)** BL

9–7 Name ______ Date ______

**Reteach**

*Problem-Solving Investigation: Choose a Strategy*

There are many ways to solve most math problems. You will decide which method works best for you when you read the problems.

Maria is trying to put her brother's blocks the way they were when she found them. They were in a neat rectangle. Use the polygons below to form a rectangle:

| | |
|---|---|
| **Understand** | You know that you need to use the five polygons to form a rectangle. You need to find out how to arrange the polygons to form a rectangle. |
| **Plan** | Choose a strategy. This problem has pieces that need to be moved around to fit in a certain way. You could draw these pieces on paper, cut them out, and move them around to see how they fit. Use the act it out strategy to solve the problem. |
| **Solve** | Arrange the polygons in different ways until you form a rectangle: |
| **Check** | Look back at the problem. Check to see if you are correct: The shape you formed has 4 right angles, with opposite sides parallel. The sides are not all the same size. You made a rectangle. |

Grade 4 38 Chapter 9



**Skills Practice (p. 40)** OL

9–7 Name ______ Date ______

**Skills Practice**

*Problem-Solving Investigation: Choose a Strategy*

**Use any method shown below to solve. Tell what method you used.**

- Act it out
- Guess and check
- Make a table
- Look for a pattern

1. A group of kids were riding bikes. Jessica counted 38 wheels. If there are 15 kids, how many are riding bikes with training wheels and how many are riding bikes without training wheels? **4 with training wheels, 11 without**
   Strategy: **Sample answer: guess and check**
2. Nicholas practices lacrosse for 75 minutes a day during the week and 90 minutes a day on weekends. Does he practice lacrosse for 15 hours each week? **no; 9.25 hours is not close to 15 hours**
   Strategy: **Sample answer: make a table**
3. Kayla sat down to begin her homework at 4:15. After school, her bus ride home is 15 minutes. Then she had a snack and talked with her friends for 25 minutes. She also did her chores for 20 minutes before beginning her homework. What time does Kayla's school end? **3:15**
   Strategy: **act it out**
4. What are the next three animals in the pattern if this pattern continues?
   **rabbit, cat, dog**
   Strategy: **Sample answer: look for a pattern**
5. Tyler is bringing napkins for his grade's picnic. There are 92 people coming to the picnic. He found napkins in packages of 12. How many packages does Tyler need to bring? **8 packages**
   Strategy: **Sample answer: make a table**

Grade 4 40 Chapter 9

★ indicates multi-step problem

## Mixed Problem Solving

EXTRA PRACTICE
See page R25.

Use any strategy shown below to solve. Tell what strategy you used.

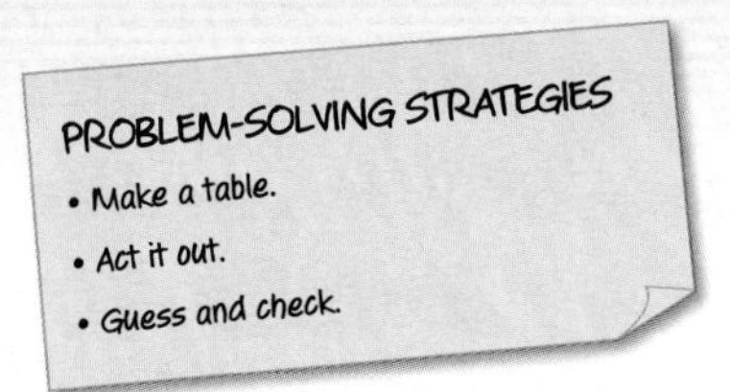


★1. **Measurement** Keli can run 3 miles in 36 minutes. She plans to run each mile one minute faster every 2 weeks. Is it reasonable to say that Keli will be able to run 3 miles in 25 minutes in 3 weeks? Explain.
See Ch. 9 Answer Appendix.

2. Identify a combination of four bills which are worth a total of $50.
two $20, two $5

3. **Algebra** Draw the next three figures in the pattern below.

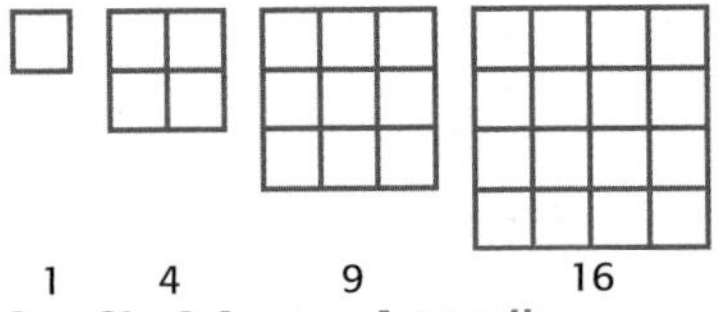


See Ch. 9 Answer Appendix.

★4. Audrey had 8 trading cards. She then bought some packs with 6 cards in each pack. Audrey now has 44 cards. How many packs did she buy?
6 packs

5. Kareem has $20. He wants to buy the items shown. Will he have enough money? Explain.
no; He needs $1.

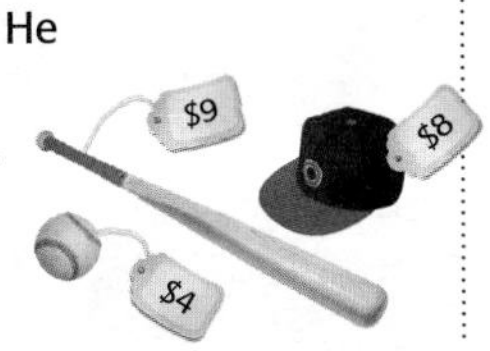

$9 $8 $4

6. **Measurement** Kala wants to download 12 songs on her digital music player. She only has 5 minutes to download the songs. If it takes 30 seconds for Kala to download one song, will she have enough time to download all of the songs? Explain.
no; 12 songs = 6 min

7. **Algebra** The polygons below form a pattern. How many sides will the ninth polygon have? Explain.

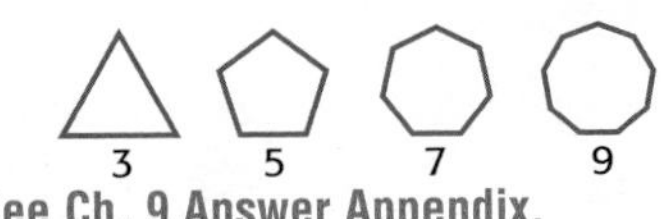


See Ch. 9 Answer Appendix.

★8. Mason has $12. He earns $5 every week for doing chores. Is it reasonable to say that Mason will be able to buy a skateboard that costs $60 in 10 weeks? Explain. Sample answer: yes; He already has $12 and will make $50 in 10 weeks.

★9. A number is multiplied by 2. Then 4 is subtracted from the product. The result is 8. What was the original number? 6

10. **Measurement** During football practice, Tyrell is running drills. He runs 20 yards forward and then 10 yards backward starting at the goal line. How many sets will it take him to reach the other goal line 100 yards away? 9

11. **WRITING IN MATH** Look at Exercise 7. Which problem-solving strategy did you use to find the answer? Explain how you used this strategy to solve the problem.
See Ch. 9 Answer Appendix.



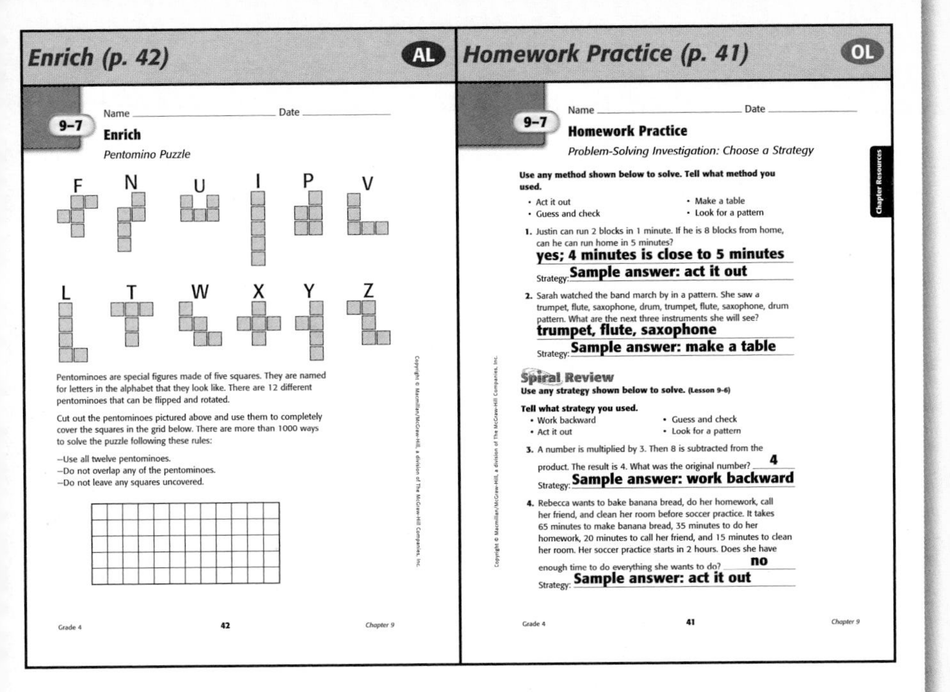

**Enrich (p. 42)** AL

9–7 Name ________ Date ________

**Enrich**

*Pentomino Puzzle*

F N U I P V
L T W X Y Z

Pentominoes are special figures made of five squares. They are named for letters in the alphabet that they look like. There are 12 different pentominoes that can be flipped and rotated.

Cut out the pentominoes pictured above and use them to completely cover the squares in the grid below. There are more than 1000 ways to solve the puzzle following these rules:

–Use all twelve pentominoes.
–Do not overlap any of the pentominoes.
–Do not leave any squares uncovered.

Grade 4 42 Chapter 9

Copyright © Macmillan/McGraw-Hill, a division of The McGraw-Hill Companies, Inc.

**Homework Practice (p. 41)** OL

9–7 Name ________ Date ________

**Homework Practice**

*Problem-Solving Investigation: Choose a Strategy*

**Use any method shown below to solve. Tell what method you used.**

- Act it out
- Guess and check
- Make a table
- Look for a pattern

1. Justin can run 2 blocks in 1 minute. If he is 8 blocks from home, can he can run home in 5 minutes?
**yes; 4 minutes is close to 5 minutes**
Strategy: **Sample answer: act it out**

2. Sarah watched the band march by in a pattern. She saw a trumpet, flute, saxophone, drum, trumpet, flute, saxophone, drum pattern. What are the next three instruments she will see?
**trumpet, flute, saxophone**
Strategy: **Sample answer: make a table**

**Spiral Review**

**Use any strategy shown below to solve.** (Lesson 9-6)

**Tell what strategy you used.**

- Work backward
- Act it out
- Guess and check
- Look for a pattern

3. A number is multiplied by 3. Then 8 is subtracted from the product. The result is 4. What was the original number? **4**
Strategy: **Sample answer: work backward**

4. Rebecca wants to bake banana bread, do her homework, call her friend, and clean her room before soccer practice. It takes 65 minutes to make banana bread, 35 minutes to do her homework, 20 minutes to call her friend, and 15 minutes to clean her room. Her soccer practice starts in 2 hours. Does she have enough time to do everything she wants to do? **no**
Strategy: **Sample answer: act it out**

Grade 4 41 Chapter 9

Chapter Resources

Copyright © Macmillan/McGraw-Hill, a division of The McGraw-Hill Companies, Inc.

## BL Alternate Teaching Strategy

**If** students have trouble deciding which strategy to use to solve a problem…

**Then** use one of these reteach options:

1. CRM **Daily Reteach Worksheets** (pp. 38–39)
2. Read through each problem in the exercises as a class, and decide which strategy would work best to solve each problem.

## 3 Practice

### Using the Exercises

**Exercises 1–10** provide practice using the strategies listed.

**Exercise 2** You may want to give the students play money to help them use the act it out strategy for this exercise.

**Exercises 3 and 7** are models of number patterns. You may want to demonstrate how the numbers relate to the models.

## 4 Assess

### Formative Assessment

Have the students use the exercises from the Mixed Problem Solving to answer the following questions.

- **What strategy could be used to solve Exercise 4?** the act it out strategy
- **What strategy could be used to solve Exercise 7?** the look for a pattern strategy

**Quick Check** **Are students continuing to struggle with choosing the best strategy to solve a problem?**

**If Yes** → Small Group Options (p. 380B)

**If No** → Independent Work Options (p. 336B)
CRM Skills Practice Worksheet (p. 40)
CRM Enrich Worksheet (p. 42)

Problem-Solving

# Lesson Planner

## Objective

Interpret information and data from art to solve problems.

### National Standard 

Students will identify connections between the visual arts and other disciplines in the curriculum.

## Activate Prior Knowledge

Before you turn students' attention to the pages, ask them to discuss garden art.

- **What kinds of materials do artists use to make garden art?** stone, metal
- **What is another name for garden art?** sculpture

## Using the Student Page

Ask students to use the information on pp. 382 and 383 and answer these questions:

- **What is the shape of one face on a cube from *Cluster of Four Cubes*?** square
- **What do *Four-Sided Pyramid* and *Cluster of Four Cubes* have in common?** square base

Problem Solving in Art

# Garden Art

Four-Sided Pyramid

The Sculpture Garden in Washington, D.C., is filled with many figures. It has 17 large sculptures. Many of these sculptures are made of different three-dimensional figures. For example, the *Four-Sided Pyramid* is made of concrete cubes. It is about 32 feet tall and 33 feet wide.

Another sculpture in this garden, *Cluster of Four Cubes,* is made of four metal cubes that spin in the breeze. These cubes are about 9 feet high in the air. *Moondog* is a metal sculpture that has triangles, hexagons, and pentagons in its shape. It is so large you can walk under it!

**Did You Know?**

There are 624 cubes in *Four-Sided Pyramid.*

## Real-World Math

**Use the sculptures *Moondog, Four-Sided Pyramid,* and *Cluster of Four Cubes* to solve each problem.**

1. What geometric figure does *Four-Sided Pyramid* resemble? **square pyramid**
2. How many faces, edges, and vertices does *Four-Sided Pyramid* have? **5 faces, 8 edges, 5 vertices**
3. How many edges does one cube in *Cluster of Four Cubes* have? **12 edges**
4. Can you see a rectangle in the picture of *Moondog*? Explain. **yes; One is formed by the see-through parts of the sculpture.**
5. How many equilateral triangles do you see in the picture of the *Moondog*? **Sample answer: 3**
6. All the edges of the *Four-Sided Pyramid* are equal. What kind of triangles make up the faces? How many triangles are there? **equilateral; 4**
7. Suppose one face of a cube on *Cluster of Four Cubes* is cut diagonally. What kind of triangle will it make? **right isosceles**

Problem Solving in Art 383

## Real-World Math

Assign the exercises on p. 383. Encourage students to choose a problem-solving strategy before beginning each exercise. If necessary, review the strategies suggested in Lesson 8-7, p. 369.

**Exercise 2** Tell students to use the basic shape of the sculpture to answer this question, not the individual figures of the cubes that form the sculpture.

**Exercise 6** Remind students of the types of triangles from which they have to choose.

**Exercise 7** Remind students that they need to identify the shape of one face of a cube in the sculpture first before they can answer this question.

**WRITING IN MATH** Have students create a word problem that uses the information found in the text and in the exercises on pp. 382 and 383.

## Extend the Activity

Have students look at these three pieces of artwork then identify all the two- and three-dimensional figures that they can find.

# Chapter 9 Study Guide and Review

## FOLDABLES Dinah Zike's Foldables

Use these lesson suggestions to incorporate the Foldables during the chapter. Students can then use their Foldables to review for the test.

**Lesson 9-5** Students identify, describe, and classify triangles beneath the top right tab. Vocabulary, physical examples, and student work can be stored in the center pocket.

**Lesson 9-6** Students identify, describe, and classify quadrilaterals beneath the top right tab. Vocabulary, physical examples, and student work can be stored in the center pocket.

## Key Vocabulary

The page references after each word denote where that term was first introduced. If students have difficulty answering Exercises 1–5, remind them that they can use the page references to review the vocabulary terms.

## Vocabulary Review

Review chapter vocabulary using one of the following options.

- **Visual Vocabulary Cards** (2, 35, 38, 41, and 48)
- **eGlossary** at macmillanmh.com



Chapter 9 Study Guide and Review

Math Online macmillanmh.com
- STUDY TO GO
- Vocabulary Review

### FOLDABLES Study Organizer GET READY to Study

**Be sure the following Key Vocabulary words and Key Concepts are written in your Foldable.**

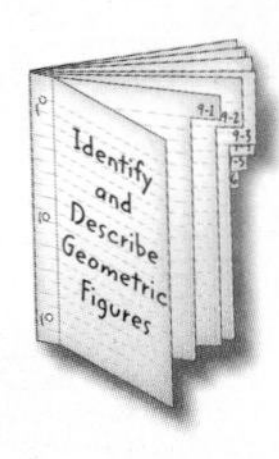


### Key Concepts

- A **three-dimensional figure** is a solid figure with length, width, and height. (p. 359)

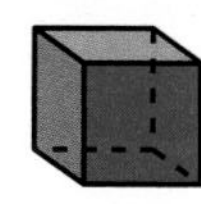

- A **two-dimensional figure** is a plane figure with length and width. (p. 362)

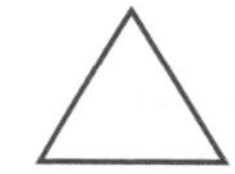

- An **angle** is a figure made from two rays that have the same endpoint. (p. 368)

### Key Vocabulary

**angle** (p. 368)
**polygon** (p. 362)
**three-dimensional figure** (p. 359)
**two-dimensional figure** (p. 362)

### Vocabulary Check

**Decide which vocabulary word best completes each sentence.**

1. A(n) __?__ is a solid figure. three-dimensional figure
2. A(n) __?__ is a figure made from two rays that have the same endpoint. angle
3. A(n) __?__ is a closed plane figure that has three or more line segments. polygon
4. A(n) __?__ has length, width, and height. three-dimensional figure
5. A(n) __?__ is a plane figure that has length and width. two-dimensional figur
6. A(n) __?__ is measured in degrees (°). angle



## Chapter 9 Project

### A Banner of Shapes

Alone, in pairs, or in small groups, have students discuss the results of their completed chapter project with the class. Assess their work using the Chapter Project rubric found in Chapter 9 Resource Masters, p. 53.

## Lesson-by-Lesson Review

### 9-1 Three-Dimensional Figures (pp. 359–361)

**Example 1**
**Identify the shape of the cooking pot. Then tell the number of faces, edges, and vertices.**

The cooking pot is a cylinder.

It has 2 faces, 0 edges, and 0 vertices.

**Identify each figure. Then tell how many faces, edges, and vertices it has.**

**7.** 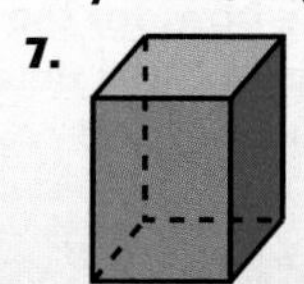

**8.** 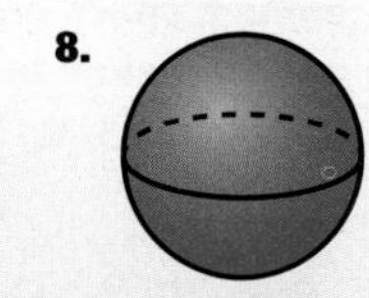

7, 8. See margin.

**9.** Identify the two-dimensional figure the net would make.

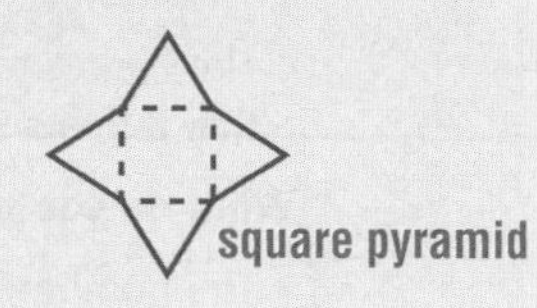

square pyramid

### 9-2 Two-Dimensional Figures (pp. 362–365)

**Tell whether each shape is a polygon.**

**Example 2**

The moon has curved sides. So, it is not a polygon.

**Example 3**

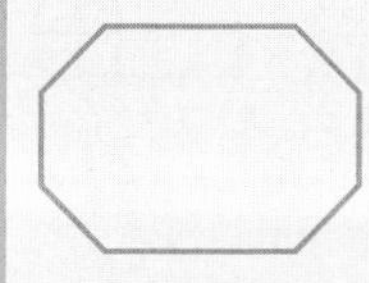

This figure has 8 sides. The sides are straight. So, it is a polygon.

**Identify each polygon.** 10–13. See margin.

**10.** 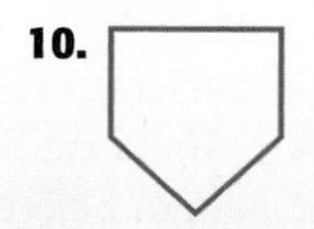

**11.** 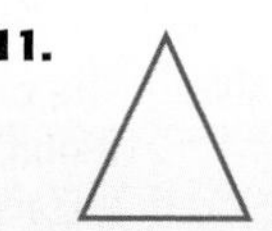

**12.** 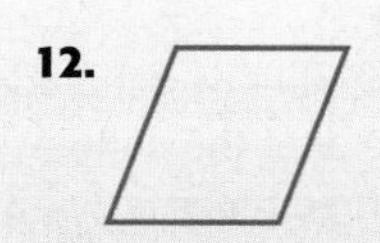

**13.** 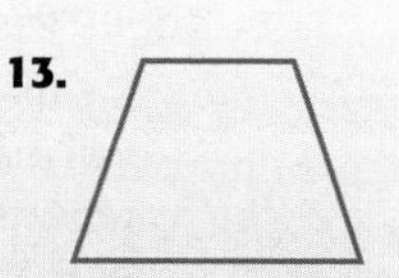

**Tell whether the shape is a polygon.**

**14.**  yes

**15.**  no



# Lesson-by-Lesson Review

Have students complete the Lesson-by-Lesson Review on pp. 384–388. Then you can use ExamView® Assessment Suite to customize another review worksheet that practices all the objectives of this chapter or only the objectives on which your students need more help.

**Intervention** If the given examples are not sufficient to review the topics covered by the questions, use the page references next to the exercises to review that topic in the Student Edition.

### Additional Answers

**7.** rectangular prism; 6 faces; 8 vertices; 12 edges

**8.** sphere; 0 faces; 0 vertices; 0 edges

**10.** pentagon

**11.** triangle

**12.** quadrilateral

**13.** quadrilateral

# Study Guide and Review

## Additional Answers

**16.** Sample answer: The numbers in the pattern are decreasing by 9; 18

**17.** Check students' work.

**20.** Check students' work.

## 9-3 Problem-Solving Strategy: Look for a Pattern (pp. 366–367)

**Example 4**
**Bruce is creating the pattern below on a bowl in art class. There is enough space on the bowl for the pattern below to repeat three times. How many stars will he make?**

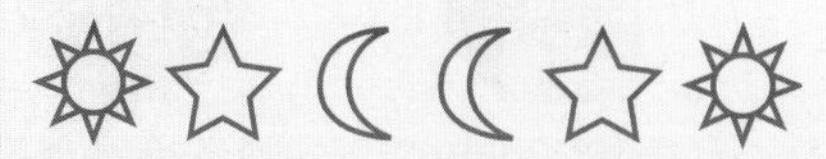

**Understand**

**What facts do you know?**

- The figures form a pattern that repeats three times.

**What do you need to find?**

- The number of stars Bruce will make.

**Plan** Look for a pattern to solve.

**Solve** The pattern is sun, star, moon, moon, star, sun. There are 2 stars in the pattern before it repeats.

So, the number of stars Bruce will make after the pattern repeats three times is 2 × 3 or 6.

**Check** The answer makes sense for the facts given. The answer is correct.

**16.** Describe the pattern below. Then find the missing number.
16, 17. See margin.
45, 36, 27, ■, 9

**17.** Copy and complete the pattern. What are the next two figures in this pattern?

**18.** **Algebra** Copy and complete the table. What is the pattern?

Sample answer: Multiply $x$ by 5.

| Input ($x$) | Output ($y$) |
|---|---|
| 8 | 40 |
| 4 | 20 |
| 9 | 45 |
| 7 | ■35 |
| ■3 | 15 |

**19.** Nell jogged for 8 minutes on Monday, 13 minutes on Tuesday, and 18 minutes on Wednesday. If this pattern continues, how many minutes will Nell jog on Sunday?
38 min

**20.** The pattern below can also be shown as 1, 4, 7, 10. Draw the next two figures. What are the next two numbers?

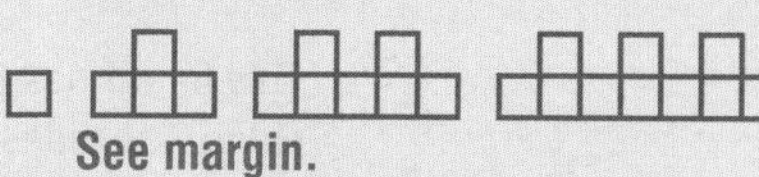

See margin.

**21.** Describe the pattern below. Then find the missing number.
1, 3, 7, 15, ■
times 2 plus 1; 31

## -4 Angles (pp. 368–370)

**Example 5**
**Write the measure of the angle shown below in degrees and as a fraction of a full turn.**

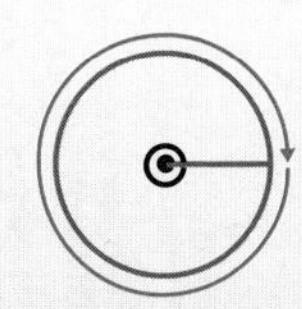

The angle shown is 360° or a full turn.

**Write the measure of each angle in degrees and as a fraction of a full turn.**

**22.** **23.**

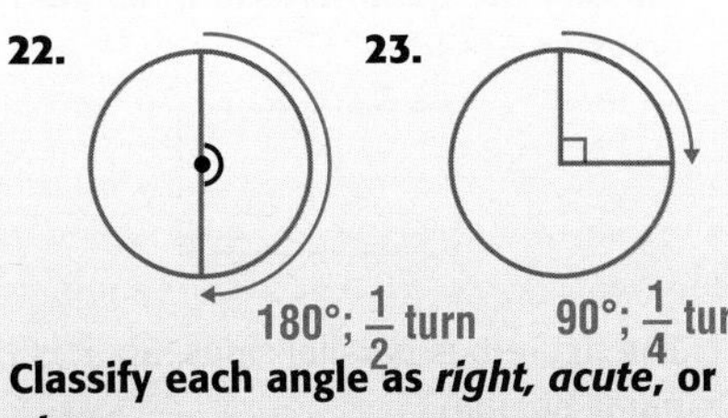

22. 180°; $\frac{1}{2}$ turn
23. 90°; $\frac{1}{4}$ turn

**Classify each angle as *right, acute,* or *obtuse*.**

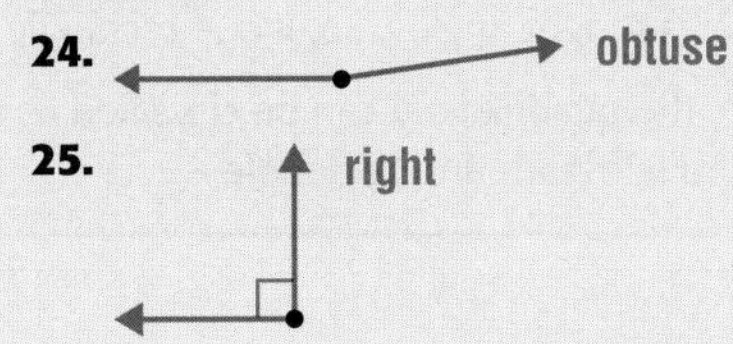

**24.** obtuse

**25.** right

## -5 Triangles (pp. 372–375)

**Example 6**
**Classify the triangle. Use *acute, right,* or *obtuse* and *isosceles, equilateral* or *scalene*.**

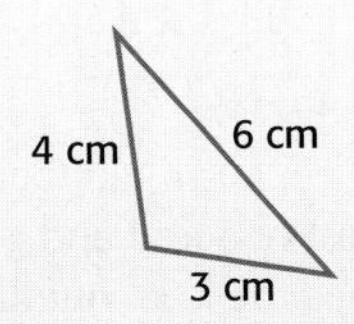


The triangle has one obtuse angle, so it is obtuse.

Since no sides are the same length, the triangle is scalene.

**Classify each triangle. Use *acute, right,* or *obtuse* and *isosceles, equilateral,* and *scalene*.**

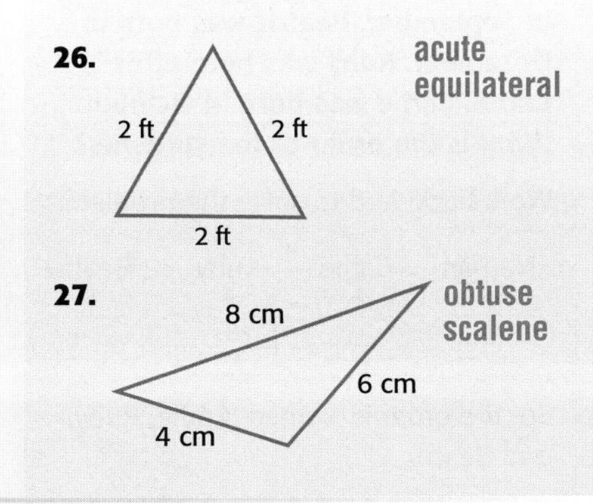


**26.** acute equilateral

**27.** obtuse scalene



**Chapter 9** Study Guide and Review **387**

# CHAPTER 9 Study Guide and Review

## Additional Answers

**29.** rectangle, parrallelogram

**32.** rectangle, parallelogram

**33.** rhombus, parallelogram

**34.**

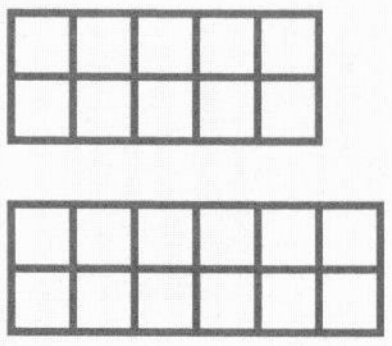

### 9-6 Quadrilaterals (pp. 376–378)

**Example 7**
**Classify the quadrilateral in as many ways as possible.**

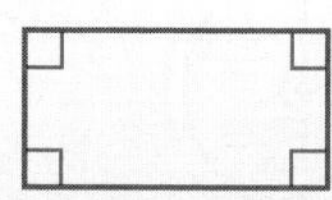

The figure has parallel sides. So, it is a parallelogram.

It has 4 right angles. So, it is a rectangle.

So, the quadrilateral can be classified as a parallelogram and rectangle.

**Classify each quadrilateral in as many ways as possible.** 29. See margin.

**28.** **29.**

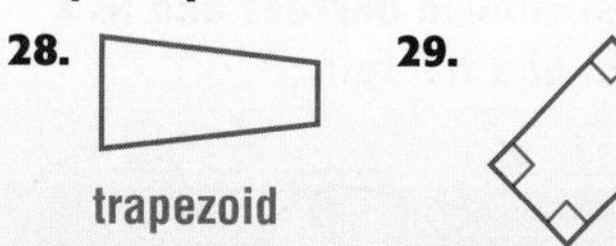

trapezoid

**30.**

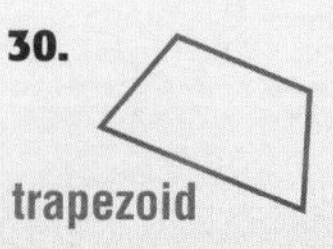

trapezoid

**31.**

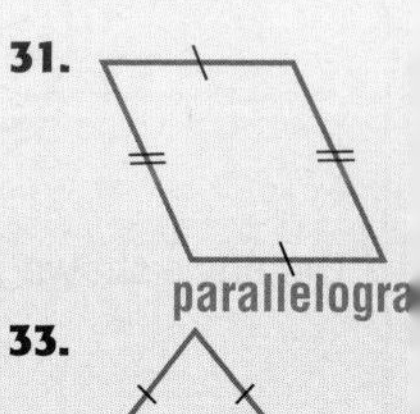

parallelogra

**32.**

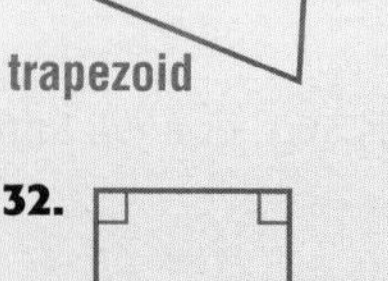

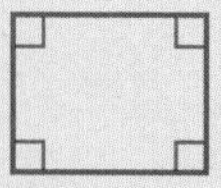

See margin.

**33.**

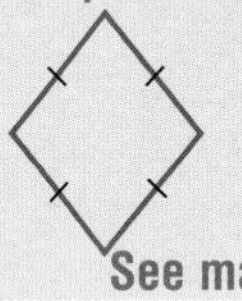

See margi

### 9-7 Problem-Solving Investigation: Choose a Strategy (pp. 380–381)

**Example 8**
**Students are lining up by birthdays. Nathan is first in line. His birthday is in September. Beatriz was born in December. Ruby was born after Carlie. Carlie was born in October. What is the order of the students?**

Work backward to solve the problem.

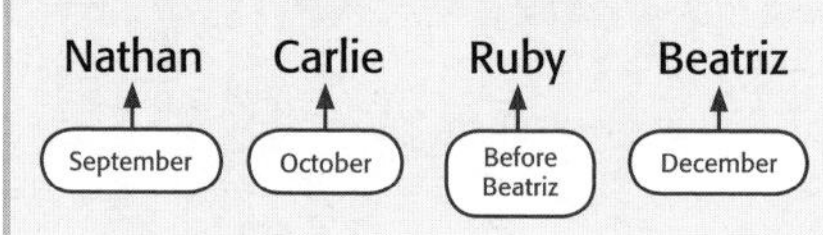


So, the order is Nathan, Carlie, Ruby, and Beatriz.

**Use any strategy to solve.**

**34.** Draw the next two figures in the pattern.

See margin.

**35.** Liana rounds a number to the nearest hundred and gets 200. What is the least number it could be? the greatest number? 150; 249

**36.** **Algebra** Logan has 7 jars of coins. Each jar has 35 coins. How many coins does he have? 245

388 Chapter 9 Identify and Describe Geometric Figures

# Chapter Test

or Exercises 1–3, decide whether each tatement is *true* or *false*.

1. A square is a two-dimensional figure in which all the sides are the same length. true
2. A trapezoid has two pairs of parallel sides. false
3. An obtuse triangle has two obtuse angles. false

4. Identify the three-dimensional figure the net would make. cube

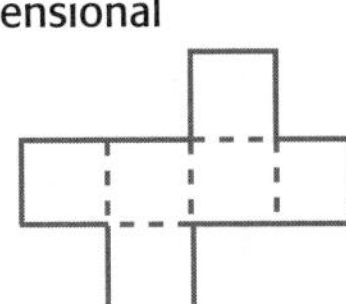

lassify each quadrilateral in as many vays as possible.

5. 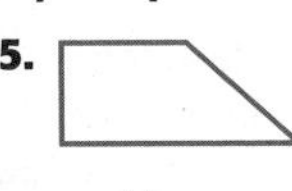 rapezoid

6. 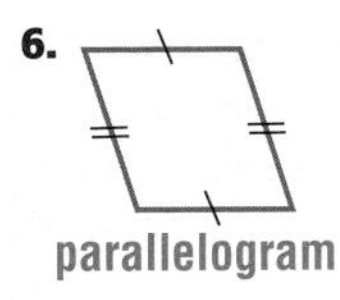 parallelogram

7. **MULTIPLE CHOICE** How many faces does this figure have? C

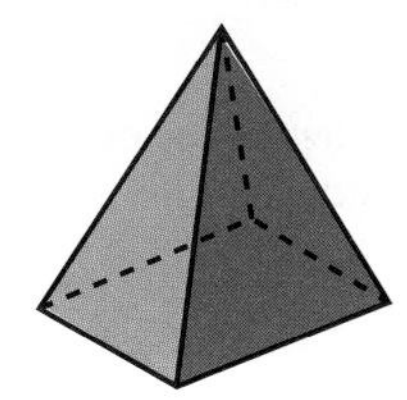

**A** 3 **C** 5
**B** 4 **D** 6

**Classify each triangle. Use *acute, right,* or *obtuse* and *isosceles, equilateral,* or *scalene*.**

8. 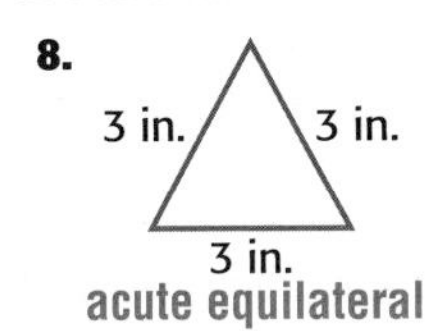

acute equilateral

9. 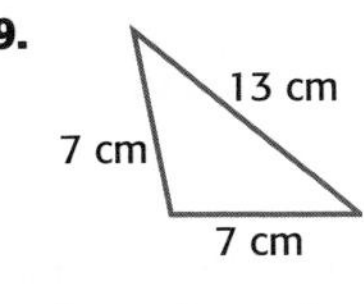

obtuse isosceles

**Classify each angle as *right, acute,* or *obtuse*.**

10. 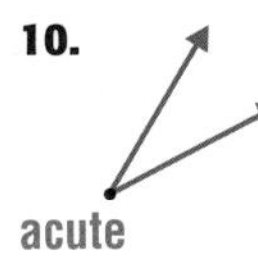 acute

11. 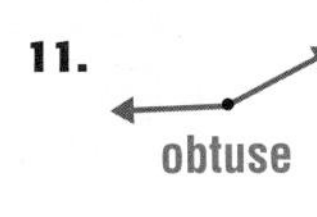 obtuse

12. Draw the next two figures in the pattern below. See Ch. 9 Answer Appendix.

13. **MULTIPLE CHOICE** In the figure below, which angles appear to be acute? J

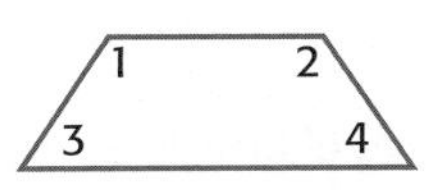


**F** Angles 1 and 2 **H** Angles 2 and 4
**G** Angles 1 and 3 **J** Angles 3 and 4

14. WRITING IN MATH Is it possible to draw an isosceles triangle that is acute? Explain. Draw a picture to support your answer. See Ch. 9 Answer Appendix.



# Chapter 9 Chapter Test

## Summative Assessment

Use these alternate leveled chapter tests to differentiate assessment for the specific needs of your students.

| Leveled Chapter 9 Tests | | | |
|---|---|---|---|
| **Form** | **Type** | **Level** | **CRM Pages** |
| 1 | Multiple Choice | BL | 55–56 |
| 2A | Multiple Choice | OL | 57–58 |
| 2B | Multiple Choice | OL | 59–60 |
| 2C | Free Response | OL | 61–62 |
| 2D | Free Response | OL | 63–64 |
| 3 | Free Response | AL | 65–66 |

BL = below/approaching grade level
OL = on grade level
AL = above/beyond grade level

## Vocabulary Test

CRM **Chapter 9 Resource Masters** (p. 50)

ExamView Assessment Suite Customize and create multiple versions of your Chapter Test and the test answer keys.

# Data-Driven Decision Making

Based on the results of the Chapter Test, use the following to review concepts that continue to present students with problems.

| Exercises | State/Local Standards | What's the Math? | Error Analysis | Resources for Review |
|---|---|---|---|---|
| 10–11, 13 | | Classify angles. | Does not know angle terms "acute," "obtuse," "right," or "straight." | Strategic Intervention Guide (pp. 124, 125, 126, 128)<br>CRM Chapter 9 Resource Masters (Reteach)<br>Math Adventures<br>My Math Zone Chapter 9<br>Math Online Extra Examples • Concepts in Motion |
| 8–9, 14 | | Know definitions of different triangles. | Does not know "isosceles," "equilateral," or "scalene." Draws a triangle with wrong number of equal sides or no equal sides. | |
| 1–4 | | Know definitions of different quadrilaterals. | Does not know "trapezoid," "rectangle," "rhombus," or "parallelogram." | |

# Chapter 9 Test Practice

## Formative Assessment

- Use Student Edition pp. 390–391 as practice and cumulative review. The questions are written in the same style as many state tests.
- You can also use these two pages to benchmark student progress, or as an alternate homework assignment.

Additional practice pages can be found in the Chapter 9 Resource Masters.

CRM **Chapter 9 Resource Masters**
Cumulative Test Practice
- Multiple Choice format (pp. 55–60)
- Free Response format (pp. 61–66)

Create practice worksheets or tests that align to your state standards.

**Math Online** Have students visit macmillanmh.com for additional practice to reinforce your state standards.

# Chapter 9 Test Practice

Cumulative, Chapters 1–9

**Math Online** macmillanmh.com
- Test Practice

**PART 1 Multiple Choice**

**Read each question. Then fill in the correct answer on the answer sheet provided by your teacher or on a sheet of paper.**

**1.** Nara is wrapping a gift in a box shaped like a rectangular prism. How many faces does a rectangular prism have? B

**A** 4 **C** 8
**B** 6 **D** 12

**2.** Which number makes this equation true? J

$126 \div ■ = 9$

**F** 10 **H** 12
**G** 11 **J** 14

**3.** What kind of triangle is shown below? D

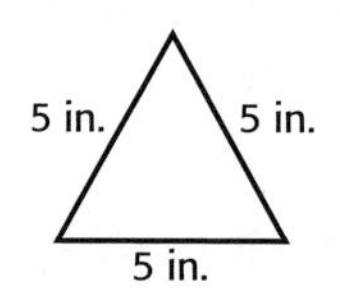


**A** scalene **C** isosceles
**B** right **D** equilateral

**4.** What number comes next in the pattern below? F

20, 17, 14, 11, 8, __

**F** 5 **H** 3
**G** 4 **J** 2

**5.** Which of the following angles appears to be right? A

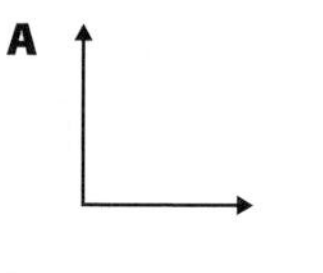
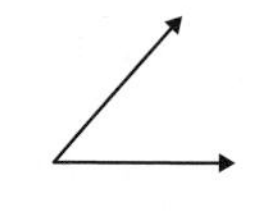


**6.** Tyrell has 162 pennies. He wants to put about the same number of pennies into each of 8 jars. About how many pennies will be in each jar? G

**F** 18 **H** 22
**G** 20 **J** 24

**7.** What solid figure has one circular face and one vertex? A

**A** cone
**B** cylinder
**C** prism
**D** sphere

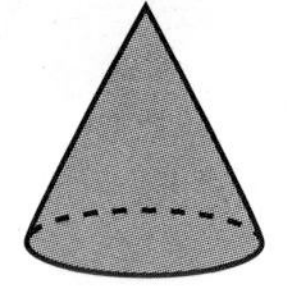



## Test-Taking Tip

Tell students that to estimate the measure of an angle, they should compare it to an angle whose measure they know, such as a 90° angle.

**Preparing for Standardized Tests**
For test-taking strategies and practice, see pages R42–R55.

**8.** Which figure can form a square pyramid when folded on the dotted lines without overlapping? F

**F** 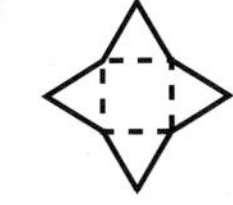

**H** 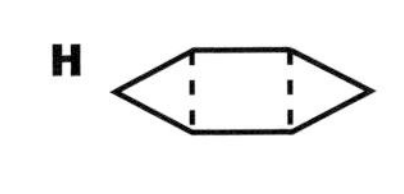

**G** 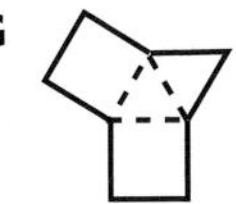

**J** 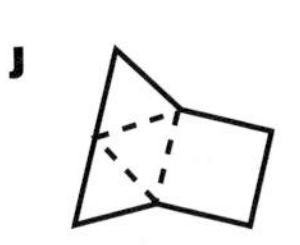

**9.** Gigi has 4 boxes filled with books. Each box can hold 24 books. How many books does she have? C

**A** 68 **C** 96
**B** 88 **D** 120

**10.** Which is the best estimate for $423 \div 7$? G

**F** 50 **H** 70
**G** 60 **J** 80

**11.** A zoo had 1,295 visitors on Tuesday and 1,523 visitors on Wednesday. How many visitors in all on the two days? C

**A** 228 **C** 2,818
**B** 2,808 **D** 2,908

## PART 2 Short Response

**Record your answers on the answer sheet provided by your teacher or on a sheet of paper.**

**12.** How many vertices does a cube have? 8

**13.** Which quadrilateral has exactly one pair of parallel sides? trapezoid

**14.** Tell whether the angle shown below is *acute, obtuse,* or *right.* acute

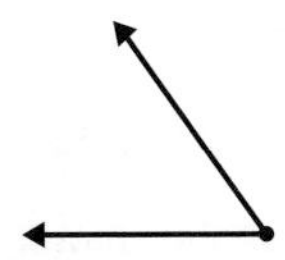

## PART 3 Extended Response

**Record your answers on the answer sheet provided by your teacher or on a sheet of paper.**

**15a.** What is the name of the figure for the net shown below? Explain.

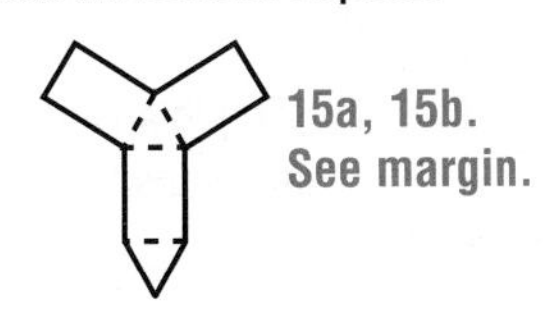

15a, 15b. See margin.

**15b.** How many vertices will the figure have after it is formed? Explain.

| NEED EXTRA HELP? | | | | | | | | | | | | | | | | |
|---|---|---|---|---|---|---|---|---|---|---|---|---|---|---|---|---|
| If You Missed Question... | 1 | 2 | 3 | 4 | 5 | 6 | 7 | 8 | 9 | 10 | 11 | 12 | 13 | 14 | 15a | 15b |
| Go to Lesson... | 9-1 | 5-8 | 9-5 | 9-3 | 9-4 | 8-4 | 9-1 | 9-1 | 6-4 | 8-4 | 2-4 | 9-1 | 9-6 | 9-4 | 9-1 | 9-1 |



# Answer Sheet Practice

Have students simulate taking a state test by recording their answers on a practice recording sheet.

**CRM Chapter 9 Resource Masters**
Student Recording Sheet (p. 71)

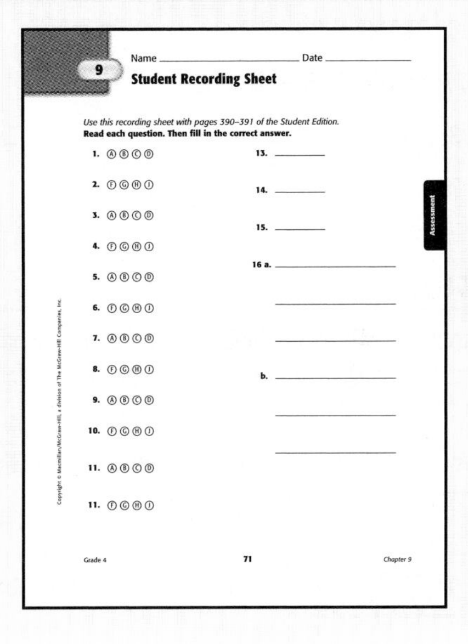
Name ____ Date ____
9 **Student Recording Sheet**
*Use this recording sheet with pages 390–391 of the Student Edition.*
**Read each question. Then fill in the correct answer.**

## Additional Answers

**15a.** Sample answer: triangular prism; The base of the three-dimensional figure is a triangle and the sides' faces are rectangles. So, the three-dimensional figure is a triangular prism.

**15b.** Sample answer: 6; Each triangular base will have 3 vertices. So, the two bases will have $3 + 3$ or 6 vertices.

## Page 361, Lesson 9-1

**23.** Sample answer:

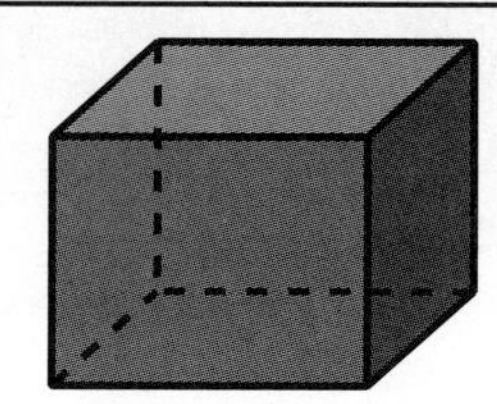

A rectangular prism has 12 edges, 6 faces, and 8 vertices.

**24.** Sample answer: rectangle; A rectangle is a 2-dimensional figure, whereas the other three shapes are solid figures.

**25.** Sample answer: A cone and a cylinder both have a base that is a circle. They are different because a cone has a point at one end, and a cylinder has two bases that are circles.

## Page 365, Lesson 9-2

**34.** 2,068; 6,000 ÷ 3 = 2,000

**35.** $977; $8,000 ÷ 8 = $1,000

**36.** 1,935; 10,000 ÷ 5 = 2,000

**37.** $1,053; $7,000 ÷ 7 = $1,000

## Page 367, Lesson 9-3

**1.** Sample answer: The objects or numbers in a pattern have a special relationship. Determine what the special relationship is by finding how you get from one object/number to the next.

**4.** Sample answer: There are 2 green in each row and 5 rows → 5 × 2 = 10.

**5.** 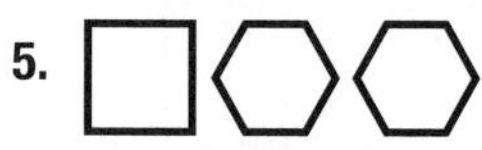 ; The pattern is square, hexagon, hexagon.

**11.** ; The pattern is the number of triangles increases by 2.

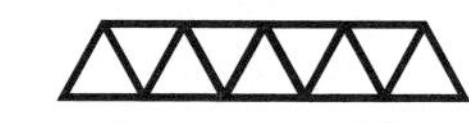

**12.** 

**13.** Sample answer:

## Page 370, Lesson 9-4

**21.** Sample answer:

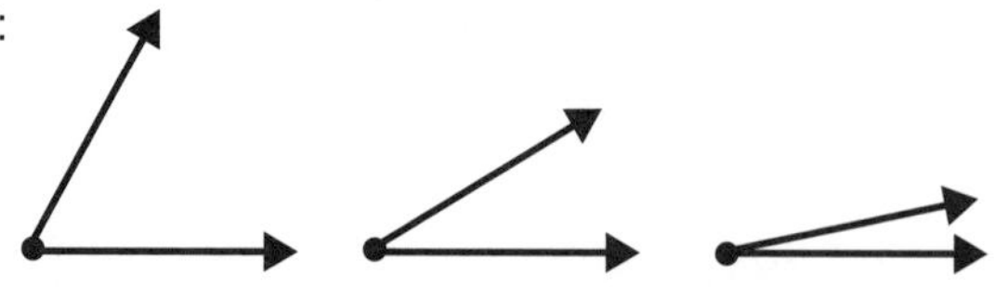

**22.** Sample answer: corner of desk = right; corner of chalkboard = right; spine of open book = obtuse

## Page 371, Mid-Chapter Check

**1.** 6 faces, 12 edges, 8 vertices

**2.** 5 faces, 9 edges, 6 vertices

## Page 378, Lesson 9-6

**22.** 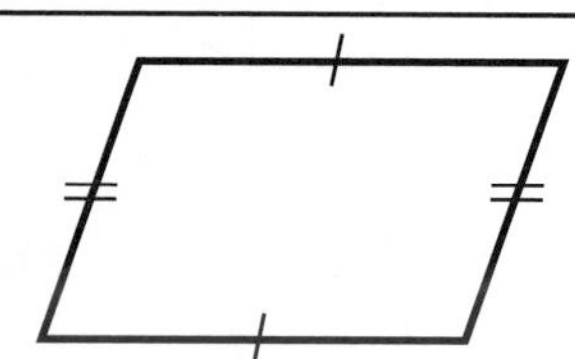

**25.** Sample answer: All squares are rectangles because squares have four right angles as rectangles by definition. All rectangles are not squares, since rectangles may not have all four sides equal in length.

## Page 381, Lesson 9-7

**1.** Sample answer: She will only improve her time by one minute every two weeks. So, in 3 weeks, her total time will only improve by 9 minutes.

**3.** 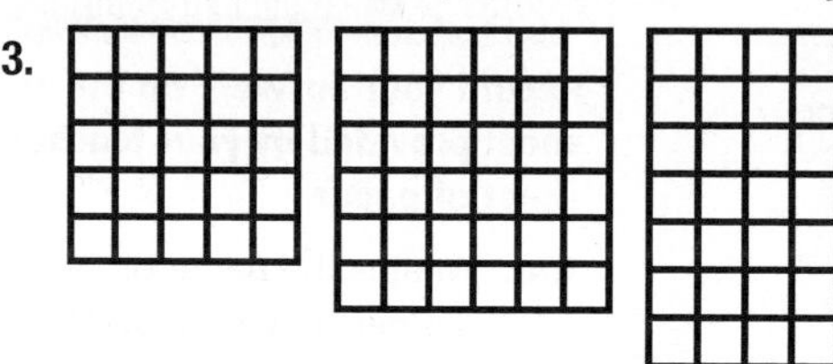

**7.** Sample answer: 19 sides; The pattern is the number of sides on each shape increases by 2.

**11.** Sample answer: The number of sides on the figures shown is 3, 5, 7, and 9. If this pattern continues the ninth polygon will have 19 sides.

## Page 389, Chapter Test

**12.**

**14.** Sample answer: yes;

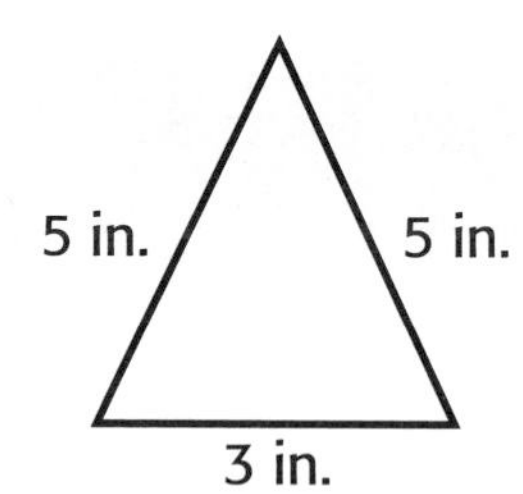

# NOTES

# Chapter Overview

## Chapter-at-a-Glance

In Chapter 10, the emphasis is on identifying parallel and intersecting lines, line segments, and rays; and demonstrating rotations, reflections, and translations using models.

| Lesson | Math Objective | State/Local Standards |
|---|---|---|
| **10-1 Locate Points on a Numbers Line** (pp. 395–397) | Locate points on a number line. | |
| EXPLORE **10-2 Parallel and Intersecting Lines** (pp. 398–399) | Identify and describe parallel and intersecting lines. | |
| **10-2 Lines, Line Segments, and Rays** (pp. 400–403) | Identify and describe lines, line segments, and rays. | |
| **10-3 Problem-Solving Strategy: Make an Organized List** (pp. 404–405) | Make an organized list to solve problems. | |
| **10-4 Find Points on a Grid** (pp. 406–408) | Use ordered pairs to find and name points on a grid. | |
| EXPLORE **10-5 Rotations, Reflections, and Translations** (pp. 410–411) | Explore rotations, reflections, and translations. | |
| **10-5 Rotations, Reflections, and Translations** (pp. 412–415) | Identify rotations, reflections, and translations. | |
| **10-6 Problem-Solving Investigation: Choose a Strategy** (pp. 416–417) | Choose the best strategy to solve a problem. | |
| **10-7 Congruent Figures** (pp. 418–420) | Identify congruent figures. | |
| EXTEND **10-7 Congruent Figures** (p. 421) | Use technology to explore congruent figures. | |
| **10-8 Symmetry** (pp. 422–425) | Identify figures with symmetry. | |

## Understand and Develop Spatial Reasoning

**BIG Idea** In Grade 3, students identify, describe, and compare two- and three-dimensional figures by their attributes. In Chapter 10, students will use this knowledge to recognize the transformations of shapes and to find symmetry. Students will also locate points on a grid. The content learned in this chapter will provide a foundation for topics such as developing geometric definitions, finding ordered pairs, and graphing functions.

**Algebra** Students use ordered pairs to locate and name points on a grid. This work will prepare them for algebra concepts, such as graphing linear equations and functions. (Lesson 10-4)

**G4-FP5C** *Geometry:* Students extend their understanding of properties of two-dimensional shapes as they find the areas of polygons. They build on their earlier work with symmetry and congruence in grade 3 to encompass transformations, including those that produce line and rotational symmetry. By using transformations to design and analyze simple tilings and tessellations, students deepen their understanding of two-dimensional space.

## Skills Trace

### Vertical Alignment

**Third Grade**

**In third grade, students learned to:**

- Identify congruent two-dimensional figures.
- Use concrete models to create two-dimensional figures with lines of symmetry.
- Locate and name points on a number line and grid.

**Fourth Grade**

**During this chapter, students learn to:**

- Identify, describe, and classify lines, line segments, and rays.
- Demostrate rotations, reflections, and translations using concrete models.
- Identify congruent figures.
- Identify figures with symmetry and use reflections to check.
- Find points on a number line.

**After this chapter, students learn to:**

- Find perimeters of polygons and the area of squares and rectangles.

**Fifth Grade**

**In fifth grade, students learn to:**

- Sketch translations, reflections, and rotations on a grid.
- Identify transformations.

**Backmapping and Vertical Alignment McGraw-Hill's *Math Connects*** program was conceived and developed with the final results in mind: student success in Algebra 1 and beyond. The authors, using the **NCTM Focal Points and Focal Connections** as their guide, developed this brand-new series by backmapping from Algebra 1 concepts, and vertically aligning the topics so that they build upon prior skills and concepts and serve as a foundation for future topics.

## Math Vocabulary

The following math vocabulary words for Chapter 10 are listed in the glossary of the ***Student Edition***. You can find interactive definitions in 13 languages in the ***eGlossary*** at macmillanmh.com.

**bilateral symmetry** The property of a figure that allows it to be folded so the two halves match exactly. (p. 422A)

**congruent** Two shapes having the same size and the same shape. (p. 418A)

**coordinate plane** A plane in which a horizontal number line and a vertical number line intersect at a right angle at the point where each line is zero. (p. 406A)

**line of symmetry** A line on which a figure can be folded so that its two halves match exactly. (p. 422A)

**line segment** A part of a line between two endpoints. The length of the line segment can be measured. (p. 400A)

**line symmetry** A line that can be drawn through the figure which splits the figures into 2 halves that match. (p. 422A)

**number line** A line that represents numbers as points. (p. 395A)

**origin** The point (0, 0) on a coordinate graph where the vertical axis meets the horizontal axis, (0, 0). (p. 406A)

**point** An exact location in space. Also refers to a decimal place. (p. 395A)

**reflection** A transformation that flips a figure across a line to make a mirror image of that figure. (p. 410A)

**Visual Vocabulary Cards**
Use Visual Vocabulary Card 7 to reinforce the vocabulary in this lesson. (The Define/Example/Ask routine is printed on the back of each card.)

congruent

CHAPTER 10

# Chapter Planner

| Suggested Pacing | | |
|---|---|---|
| Instruction | Review & Assessment | TOTAL |
| 11 days | 1 day | **12 days** |

**Diagnostic Assessment**
Quick Check (p. 394)

| | Lesson 10-1 (Pacing: 1 day) | Explore 10-2 (Pacing: 1 day) | Lesson 10-2 (Pacing: 1 day) |
|---|---|---|---|
| **Lesson/ Objective** | **Locate Points on a Number Line** (pp. 395–397)<br>**Objective:** Locate points on a number line. | **Parallel and Intersecting Lines** (pp. 398–399)<br>**Objective:** Identify and describe parallel and intersecting lines. | **Lines, Line Segments, and Rays** (pp. 400–403)<br>**Objective:** Identify, describe, and classify lines, line segments, and rays. |
| **State/Local Standards** | | | |
| **Math Vocabulary** | **number line**, **point** | | **lines**, **ray**, **endpoint**, **line segment**, **parallel**, **intersecting**, **perpendicular** |
| **Lesson Resources** | **Materials**<br>number lines<br>**Other Resources**<br>CRM Leveled Worksheets (pp. 8–12)<br>Daily Reteach • 5-Minute Check • Problem of the Day | **Materials**<br>index cards, tape, scissors<br>**Manipulatives**<br>pattern blocks, rulers | **Other Resources**<br>CRM Leveled Worksheets (pp. 13–17)<br>Daily Reteach • 5-Minute Check • Problem of the Day |
| **Technology** | Math Adventures | | Math Adventures<br>Math Songs Track #7 |
| **Math Online** | Personal Tutor | | Personal Tutor |
| **Reaching All Learners** | English Learners, p. 395B ELL<br>Gifted and Talented, p. 395B AL<br>Early Finishers, p. 395B OL AL | | English Learners, p. 400B ELL<br>Below Level, p. 400B BL<br>Early Finishers, p. 400B OL AL |
| **Alternate Lesson** | | | |

**KEY**

BL Below/Approaching Level
OL On Level
AL Above/Beyond Level
ELL English Learners
SE Student Edition
TE Teacher Edition
CRM Chapter 10 Resource Masters
CD-Rom
Transparency
Real-World Problem Solving Library

# Understand and Develop Spatial Reasoning

| | Lesson 10-3 (Pacing: 1 day) | Lesson 10-4 (Pacing: 1 day) | Explore 10-5 (Pacing: 1 day) |
|---|---|---|---|
| **Lesson/Objective** | **Problem-Solving Strategy Make an Organized List** (pp. 404–405) **Objective:** Make an organized list to solve problems. | **Find Points on a Grid** (pp. 406–408) **Objective:** Use ordered pairs to find and name points on a grid. | **Rotations, Reflections, and Translations** (pp. 410–411) **Objective:** Explore rotations, reflections, and translations. |
| **State/Local Standards** | | | |
| **Math Vocabulary** | | **coordinate plane**, **origin**, ***x*-axis**, ***y*-axis**, **ordered pair**, **coordinates** | **transform**, **rotation**, **reflection**, **translation** |
| **Lesson Resources** | **Other Resources**<br>CRM Leveled Worksheets (pp. 18–22)<br>Daily Reteach • 5-Minute Check • Problem of the Day<br>*Trapped in Tar* | **Materials**<br>grid paper, colored pencils or marker<br>**Other Resources**<br>CRM Leveled Worksheets (pp. 23–27)<br>Daily Reteach • 5-Minute Check • Problem of the Day | **Materials**<br>square pattern blocks |
| **Technology** | | Math Songs Track #7 | |
| **Math Online** | Personal Tutor | Personal Tutor | Personal Tutor |
| **Reaching All Learners** | English Learners, p. 404B ELL<br>Below Level, p. 404B BL<br>Early Finishers, p. 404B OL AL | English Learners, p. 406B ELL<br>Below Level, p. 406B BL<br>Early Finishers, p. 406B OL AL | |
| **Alternate Lesson** | | | |

**Formative Assessment**
Mid-Chapter Check (p. 409)

# Chapter Planner

| | Lesson 10-5 Pacing: 1 day | Lesson 10-6 Pacing: 1 day | Lesson 10-7 Pacing: 1 day |
|---|---|---|---|
| **Lesson/ Objective** | **Rotations, Reflections, and Translations** (pp. 412–415)<br><br>**Objective:** Identify rotations, reflections, and translations. | **Problem-Solving Investigation** **Choose a Strategy** (pp. 416–417)<br><br>**Objective:** Choose the best strategy to solve a problem. | **Congruent Figures** (pp. 418–420)<br><br>**Objective:** Identify congruent figures. |
| **State/Local Standards** | | | |
| **Math Vocabulary** | **rotation**, **reflection**, **translation**, **transformation** | | **congruent** |
| **Lesson Resources** | **Materials**<br>dot paper, overhead projector<br><br>**Manipulatives**<br>rhombus pattern block<br><br>**Other Resources**<br>CRM Leveled Worksheets (pp. 28–32)<br>Daily Reteach • 5-Minute Check • Problem of the Day | **Materials**<br>five name tags<br><br>**Other Resources**<br>CRM Leveled Worksheets (pp. 33–37)<br>Daily Reteach • 5-Minute Check • Problem of the Day<br>*Trapped in Tar* | **Manipulatives**<br>pattern blocks, scissors, Geomirrors<br><br>**Other Resources**<br>CRM Leveled Worksheets (pp. 38–42)<br>Daily Reteach • 5-Minute Check • Problem of the Day |
| **Technology** | | | |
| **Math Online** | Personal Tutor | Personal Tutor | Personal Tutor • Concepts in Motion |
| **Reaching All Learners** | English Learners, p. 412B ELL<br>Below Level, p. 412B BL<br>Early Finishers, p. 412B AL | English Learners, p. 416B ELL<br>Gifted and Talented, p. 416B AL<br>Early Finishers, p. 416B OL AL | English Learners, p. 418B ELL<br>Below Level, p. 418B BL<br>Early Finishers, p. 418B OL AL |
| **Alternate Lesson** | *IMPACT Mathematics:* Unit J | | *IMPACT Mathematics:* Unit J |

## Extend 10-7
**Pacing:** 1 day

Tech Link

### Congruent Figures
(p. 421)

**Objective:** Use technology to explore congruent figures.

Math Tool Chest

## Lesson 10-8
**Pacing:** 1 day

### Symmetry
(pp. 422–425)

**Objective:** Identify figures with symmetry and use reflections to check.

**line symmetry**, **line of symmetry**, **bilateral symmetry**, **rotational symmetry**

**Materials**
large regular hexagon figure on paper, crayons or colored pencils, block letters, scissors, dot paper

**Manipulatives**
ruler, pattern blocks, Geomirrors

**Other Resources**
CRM Leveled Worksheets (pp. 43–47)
Daily Reteach • 5-Minute Check • Problem of the Day

Personal Tutor

English Learners, p. 380B ELL
Gifted and Talented, p. 380B AL
Early Finishers, p. 380B OL AL

*IMPACT Mathematics:* Unit J

**Game Time** (p. 425)
**Problem Solving: Science** (p. 426)

**Summative Assessment**
- Study Guide/Review (p. 428)
- Chapter Test (p. 433)
- Test Practice (p. 434)

## Assessment Options

### Diagnostic Assessment
- SE *Option 1:* Quick Check (p. 394)
- *Option 2:* Online Quiz macmillanmh.com
- CRM *Option 3:* Diagnostic Test (p. 49)
- CRM *Option 4:* Chapter Pretest (p. 50)

### Formative Assessment
- TE Alternate Teaching Strategy (in every lesson)
- SE Talk About It (in every lesson)
- SE Writing in Math (in every lesson)
- SE Check What You Know (in every lesson)
- TE Ticket Out the Door (p. 403)
- TE Into the Future (p. 415)
- TE Name the Math (pp. 397, 408)
- SE Mid-Chapter Check (p. 409)
- CRM Lesson Quizzes (pp. 51–53)
- CRM Mid-Chapter Test (p. 54)

### Summative Assessment
- SE Chapter Test (p. 433)
- SE Test Practice (p. 434)
- CRM Vocabulary Test (p. 55)
- CRM Leveled Chapter Tests (pp. 60–71)
- CRM Cumulative Test Practice (pp. 74–76)
- CRM Oral Assessment (pp. 56–57)
- ExamView® Assessment Suite
- Advance Tracker

## McGraw-Hill Professional Development

Targeted professional development has been articulated throughout **McGraw-Hill's *Math Connects*** program. The **McGraw-Hill Professional Development Video Library** provides short videos that support the **NCTM Focal Points and Focal Connections.** For more information visit macmillanmh.com.

Model Lessons

Instructional Strategies

CHAPTER 10

# Learning Stations

## Cross-Curricular Links

### Writing

individual | VISUAL

**Shapely Poetry**

- Think of the shapes that you see around you. How would you describe them?
- Write a poem to describe one of the shapes you see in your classoom. Use mathematics vocabulary in your poem.
- Take turns reading your poem to your partner. Did your partner figure out what you were describing? Did you figure out what your partner was describing?

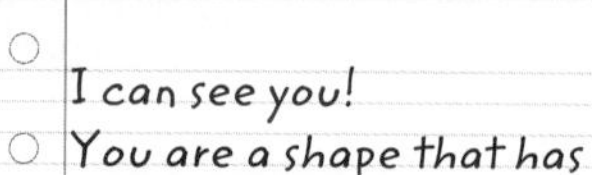


**Materials:**
- paper
- pencil

### Art

pair | SPATIAL

**Butterfly Symmetry**

Can you make a perfectly symmetrical butterfly? Try it and see.

- Each partner folds a piece of paper lengthwise and then unfolds it. On the left side of the fold line, each partner draws one half of a butterfly. Make the wings as fancy as you want.
- Now switch half-butterflies with your partner. Try to draw the right side of the butterfly as an exact mirror image of the left side. Place the mirror on the fold line to reflect the left side. This will help you visualize what you need to draw on the right side. Whose butterfly is more symmetrical?

**Materials:**
- white paper
- markers
- scissors
- mirror

### Reading

pair | LINGUISTIC

**A Line Here And There**

- Read *Lines* by Philip Yenawine by yourself or with a partner.
- What is the difference between parallel lines and perpendicular lines? How might each type of line be important in a polygon?
- Choose one of the artworks in the book and identify as many of the parallel and perpendicular lines that you can.
- Name some polygons in real life that have one type of line or the other. Explain how you know which type of lines the polygon contains.

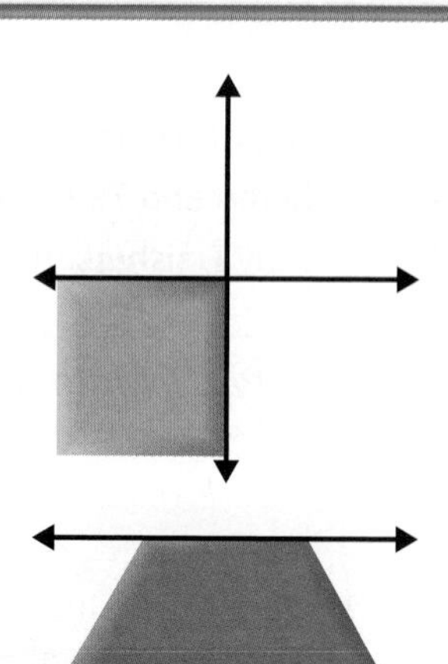

**Materials:**
- *Lines* by Philip Yenawine
- paper
- pencils

## Science

pair | VISUAL

### Scuba Diving Quadrant

Go scuba diving in a graph quadrant, but find your fish fast before you run out of air.

- Each person copies the example coordinate grid on grid paper.
- Each person cuts out 10 fish shapes from construction paper, then selects 10 points on the grid and writes the coordinates of each point on one fish per point.
- Exchange your fish with your partner, set the timer for one minute's worth of air, and find the fish! The first person to plot points for all their fish and beat the timer wins.

**Materials:**
- example coordinate grid
- grid paper
- construction paper
- scissors
- markers
- pencils

## Health

pair | LOGICAL

### Toss the Bean Bags

Toss bean bags and see how many times you can get them into the box.

- Each person tosses 20 bean bags into a box. Partners tally the number of times the bean bags go into the box.
- Determine the total for each partner then place the totals on a number line labeled from 0–20.
- Challenge each other to compare the number of times each person got the bean bag in the box. Try subtracting using the number lines. What was the difference between the greatest number of successful tosses and the least number of successful tosses?

**Materials:**
- 20 small bean bags
- sturdy box to toss the bean bags into
- paper
- pencils

## Social Studies

pair | LOGICAL

### Submarine Search

Build your own submarines and try to find your partner's submarines on a coordinate grid.

- Each person copies the example coordinate grid onto his or her own grid paper.
- Place four line-segments, vertical or horizontal, anywhere on the grid, between three and five units long. Keep the grids hidden from each other.
- Take turns guessing coordinate points on your partner's grid. A hit on a submarine gets you another turn. The first person to find all the other person's submarines wins.

**Materials:**
- example coordinate grid
- grid paper
- pencils

CHAPTER 10

# Introduce the Chapter

## Real World: Designs

**Materials:** pattern blocks, paper

Share with students that they will be developing their spatial reasoning skills by learning about lines, coordinate planes, and transformations.

Give students a half sheet of paper and a set of pattern blocks. Have them choose one of the shapes and use that shape to cover the paper without any gaps or overlaps.

**Did you slide, turn, or flip your shape in order to cover the paper?** Answers will vary. **Which shapes will cover the paper by sliding the figure?** both rhombuses, hexagon, square **Which shapes require turns or flips?** triangle, trapezoid

Direct students to Student Edition p. 392. Have students read the paragraph at the top of the page.

- **What does spatial reasoning allow you to do?** Spatial reasoning allows you to see changes in the world around you.
- **What do you notice about the streets on the map?** Sample answer: It is like a grid the game board pieces move on.

## WRITING IN MATH

**Starting the Chapter**
Ask students to write a short paragraph about different geometric shapes in the classroom. Have them give details about how they are the same and how they are different.

**Key Vocabulary** Introduce the key vocabulary in the chapter using the routine below.

Define: Congruent means having the same size and the same shape.
Example: The tiles on this floor have the same size and shape. They are congruent.
Ask: What are some other congruent items in the classroom?

**Read-Aloud Anthology** For an optional reading activity to introduce this chapter's math concepts, see the Read-Aloud Anthology p. TR35.



CHAPTER 10

# Understand and Develop Spatial Reasoning

**BIG Idea** **What is a transformation?**

A **transformation** is a movement of a figure. The three types of transformations are **translation** (slide), **reflection** (flip), and **rotation** (turn).

**Example** Beth and Daniel are playing chess. Beth is moving the chess piece as shown. This movement is an example of a slide or translation.

### What will I learn in this chapter?

- Find points on number lines and coordinate planes.
- Identify and describe lines, line segments, and rays.
- Explore and identify rotations, reflections, and translations.
- Use rotations, reflections, and translations to identify congruent figures and symmetry in figures.
- Solve problems by making an organized list.

### Key Vocabulary

**number line** **transformation**
**point** **congruent**
**coordinate plane**

**Student Study Tools** at macmillanmh.com

## Chapter 10 Project

**Room Redesign**

Students use coordinate points on a grid to redesign the classroom.

- Students create a coordinate grid mapping their classroom. On the grid, they locate furnishings and other items in the classroom and assign them points.
- Students work in pairs to change the positioning of the furniture in the classroom, and show their new design on a new coordinate grid. They create a key to the grid, listing each item in the room and its corresponding point on the grid.
- Student pairs present their room redesign to the class. Students vote on which design is the best, and if possible, rearrange the room according to the winning design.
- Challenge students to create coordinate grid maps of other areas of the school and redesign those areas using points on the grids.

CRM *Refer to Chapter 10 Resource Masters, p. 58 for a rubric to assess students' progress on this project.*

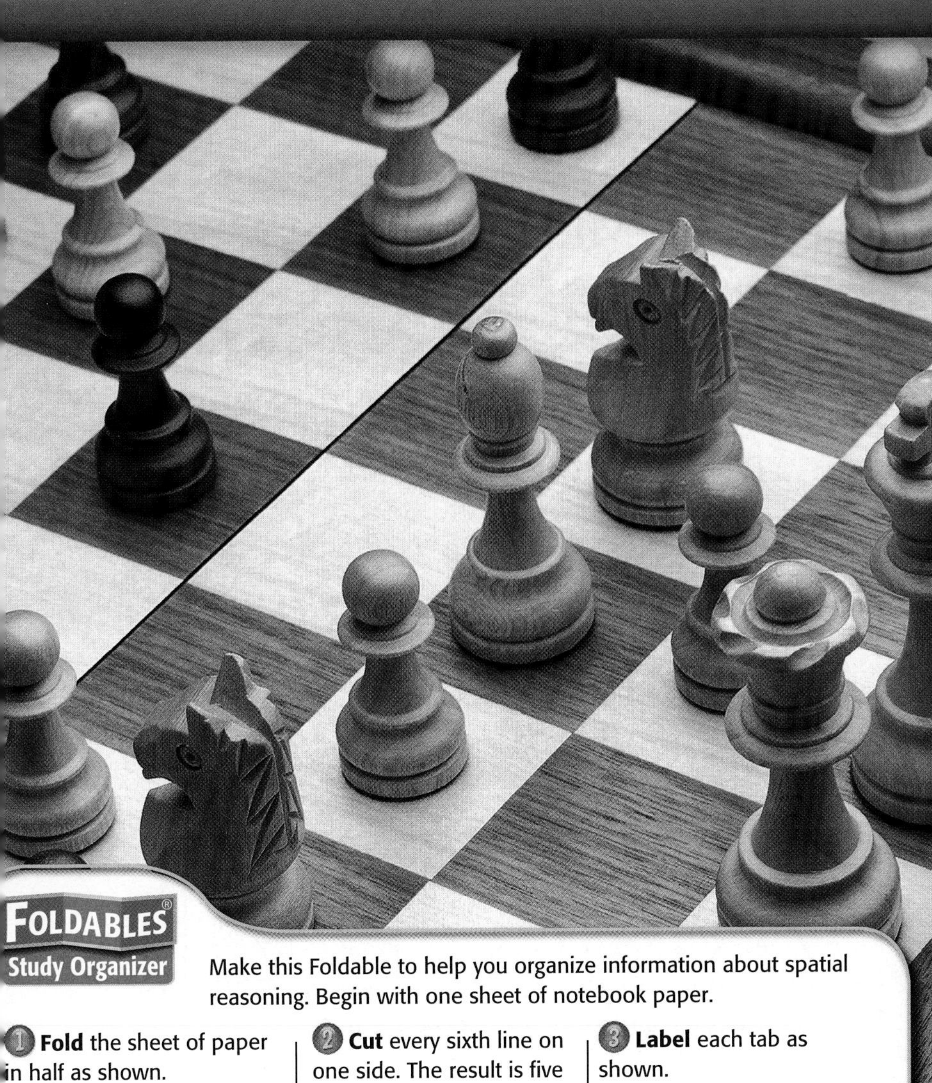

**FOLDABLES® Study Organizer**

Make this Foldable to help you organize information about spatial reasoning. Begin with one sheet of notebook paper.

1. **Fold** the sheet of paper in half as shown.

2. **Cut** every sixth line on one side. The result is five tabs.

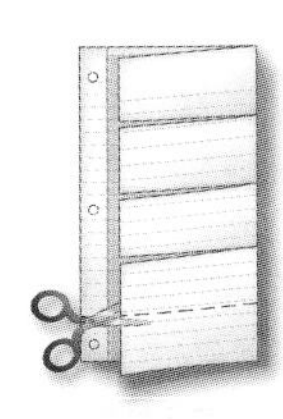

3. **Label** each tab as shown.

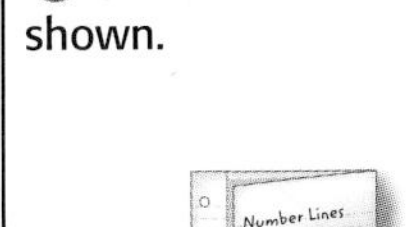

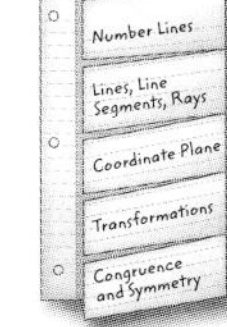




## ELL National ESL Standards Alignment for Chapter 10

| Lesson, Page | ESL Standard | Modality | Level |
|---|---|---|---|
| 10-1, p. 395B | Goal 2, Standard 1, a | Auditory, Kinesthetic | Intermediate |
| 10-2, p. 400B | Goal 1, Standard 3, k | Kinesthetic, Auditory | Beginning |
| 10-3, p. 404B | Goal 2, Standard 3, g | Intrapersonal | Advanced |
| 10-4, p. 406B | Goal 1, Standard 3, j | Visual, Logical | Intermediate |
| 10-5, p. 412B | Goal 2, Standard 2, e | Kinesthetic | Beginning |
| 10-6, p. 416B | Goal 2, Standard 2, b | Linguistic, Intrapersonal | Advanced |
| 10-7, p. 418B | Goal 2, Standard 1, c | Auditory, Spatial/Visual | Advanced |
| 10-8, p. 422B | Goal 2, Standard 1, f | Visual, Social | Intermediate |

The National ESL Standards can be found in the Teacher Reference Handbook.

## FOLDABLES® Dinah Zike's Foldables

Guide students through the directions on p. 393 to create their own Foldables graphic organizers for spatial reasoning. Students may also use their Foldables to study and review chapter assessments.

**When to Use It** Lessons 10-2, 10-4, 10-7, and 10-8. (Additional instructions for using the Foldables with these lessons are found on pp. 409 and 428.)

| Lesson | Book Title |
|---|---|
| 10-1 | **King's Commissioners** Aileen Friedman |
| 10-2 | **Lines, Segments, Polygons** Mindel and Harry Sitomer |
| 10-3 | **Domino Addition** Lynette Long, Ph.D. |
| 10-4 | **G is for Googol: A Math Alphabet Book** David M. Schwartz |
| 10-5 | **Tilling Shapes** Kari Jenson Gold |
| 10-7 | **The Greedy Triangle** Marilyn Burns |
| 10-8 | **Round Trip** Ann Jonas |
| Any | **How Tall, How Short, How Far Away?** David A. Adler |
| Any | **Pezzettino** Leo Lionni |

- Read the Math at Home letter found in the Chapter 10 Resource Masters, p. 4, with the class and have each student sign it. (A Spanish version is found on p. 5.)
- Send home copies of the Math at Home letter with each student.

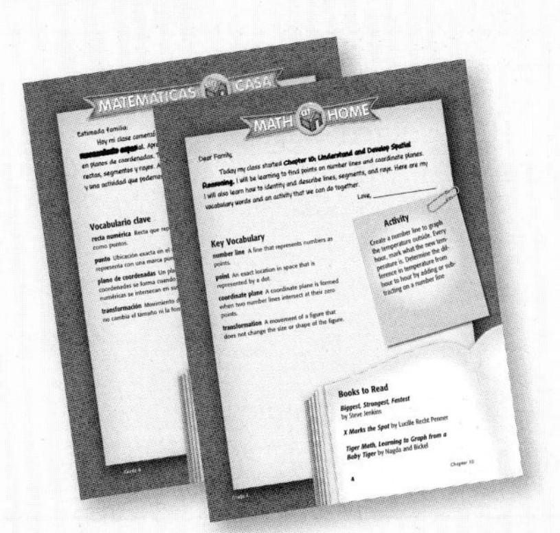

# Diagnose

Check for students' prerequisite skills before beginning the chapter.

- **Option 1:** ***Quick Check***

  SE Student Edition, p. 394

- **Option 2:** ***Online Assessment***

  Math Online macmillanmh.com

- **Option 3:** ***Diagnostic Tests***

  CRM Chapter 10 Resource Masters, pp. 49–50

# RTI (Response to Intervention)

**Apply the Results** Based on the results of the diagnostic test on Student Edition p. 494, use the chart below to address individual needs before beginning the chapter.

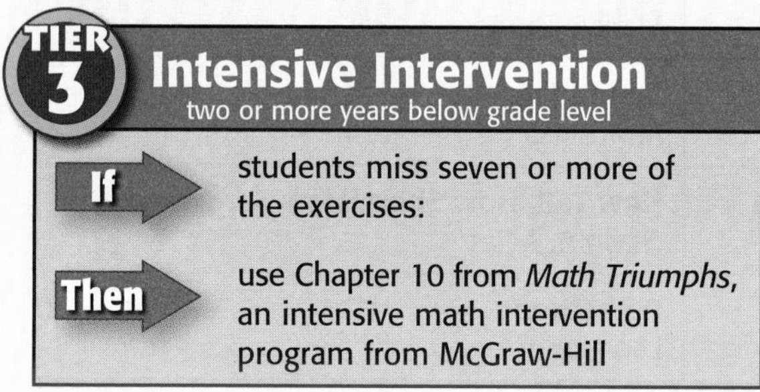

**TIER 3 Intensive Intervention**
two or more years below grade level

**If** students miss seven or more of the exercises:

**Then** use Chapter 10 from *Math Triumphs*, an intensive math intervention program from McGraw-Hill

## ARE YOU READY for Chapter 10?

You have two ways to check prerequisite skills for this chapter.

**Option 2**

Math Online Take the Chapter Readiness Quiz at macmillanmh.com

**Option 1**

Complete the Quick Check below.

### QUICK Check

**Tell whether the dashed line divides the figure in half. Write *yes* or *no*.** (Prior Grade) (Used in Lesson 10-8)

1. 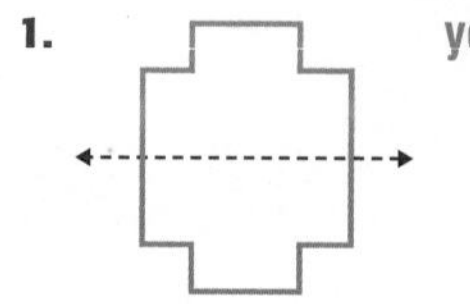 yes

2. 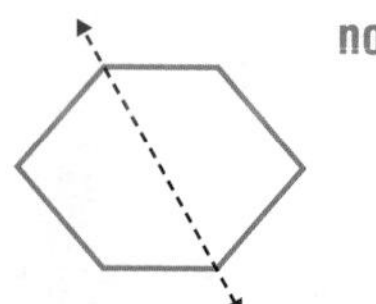 no

3. no

4. Jon is sharing his sandwich with his brother. Is the sandwich divided in half? yes

**Identify the figure that is different.** (Prior Grade) (Used in Lesson 10-7)

5. 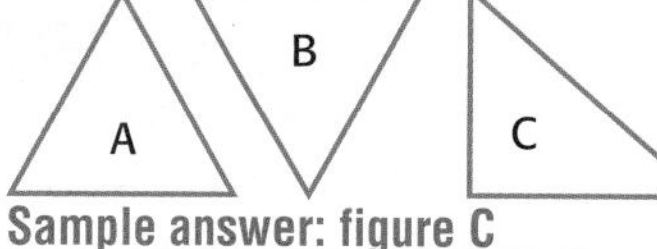

Sample answer: figure C

6. D E F
Sample answer: figure E

**Identify each polygon.** (Lesson 9-2) (Used in Lesson 10-5)

7. octagon

8. pentagon

9. hexagon

10. Peyton is looking in a kaleidoscope. Identify two of the polygons that can be seen. Sample answer: triangles and squares

394 Chapter 10 Understand and Develop Spatial Reasoning

| TIER 2 Strategic Intervention below/approaching grade level | TIER 1 On-Level | Above/Beyond Level |
|---|---|---|
| **If** students miss four to six in: **Exercises 1–10** | **If** students miss two or three in: **Exercises 1–10** | **If** students miss one or less in: **Exercises 1–10** |
| **Then** choose a resource: | **Then** choose a resource: | **Then** choose a resource: |
| Strategic Intervention Guide (pp. 124, 126)<br>CRM Chapter 10 Resource Masters Reteach Worksheets<br>Math Online Extra Examples • Personal Tutor • Concepts in Motion | TE Learning Stations (pp. 492G–492H)<br>TE Chapter Project (p. 492)<br>CRM Game: Count the Stars<br>Math Adventures<br>My Math Zone Chapter 9<br>Math Online Fact Dash | TE Learning Stations (pp. 492G–492H)<br>TE Chapter Project (p. 492)<br>Real-World Problem Solving: *Trapped in Tar*<br>My Math Zone Chapters 9 and 10<br>Math Online Games |

LESSON 10-1

# Locate Points on a Number Line

## Lesson Planner

### Objective

Find points on a number line.

### Vocabulary

**number line**, **point**

### Resources

**Materials:** number lines

**Literature Connection:** *King's Commissioners* by Aileen Friedman

**Teacher Technology**
TeacherWorks • Interactive Classroom

## Daily Routine

Use these suggestions before beginning the lesson on p. 395.

### 5-Minute Check

(Reviews Lesson 9-7)

**Use any strategy to solve. Tell what strategy you used.**

Sophia can score up to 50 points in a computer game. She has scored an average of 38 points per game for 5 games. She wants to beat the high score of 242 points for 6 games. Is it reasonable for Sophia to think she can beat the high score? Sample answer: no; So far, Sophia has 190 points. She would have to score 53 points to beat the high score and she can only score 50 points in a game; make a table strategy.

### Problem of the Day

Mark bought 3 books and Geraldo bought 12 books. If each book cost $5, how much did the two boys spend in all? $75

### Focus on Math Background

A point on a number line is the graph of a single number, and the number is the name of the point. This lesson focuses primarily on numbers between one thousand and one million. The key concept involves the identification of scale on the number line.

### Building Math Vocabulary

Write the lesson vocabulary words and their definitions on the board.

Discuss the terms with the students. Draw a number line and demonstrate how to locate and label points on it.

# Differentiated Instruction

## Small Group Options

LOGICAL

### Option 1 Gifted and Talented AL

**Materials:** chart paper, markers, paper, pencils

- Draw a line with and arrow on each end on the chart paper.
- Place the following numbers in a rectangle below the line, telling the students that these numbers are in the bank: 135, 89, 163, 41, 198.
- Ask the students to draw a number line of their own on the paper and place the numbers on it, as correctly as possible.
- If the students have difficulty beginning, suggest that they set up range numbers such as 0, 50, 100, 150, and 200.
- As the students finish, ask them to compare with each other.

AUDITORY, KINESTHETIC

### Option 2 English Language Learners ELL

**Materials:** masking tape, numbers cards 1 to 10, number cube

**Core Vocabulary:** Where are you?, step, I'm on ___.

**Common Use Verb:** walk forward

**Do Math** This strategy helps students increase understanding of addition by acting out number sentences.

- Make a number line with tape on the floor. Label with number cards.
- Model standing on 0, facing 10.
- Say: **"I'm on zero."** Roll cube and walk forward to that number.
- Have students repeat, adding: ***"Walk*** ___ **steps *forward"*** and asking: **"Where are you?"**
- Prompt students to answer, **"I'm on ___."**
- Repeat as time permits.
- Variation: Pairs of students "race" using two number lines and taking turns walking forward.

## Independent Work Options

LOGICAL

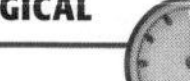

### Option 1 Early Finishers AL

**Materials:** paper and pencil

- Students draw their own number lines using various intervals such as 50, 200, or 2,000. They place letters above the number line to represent missing numbers.
- Have them exchange number lines with other students and name the missing numbers represented by the letters.

### Option 2 Student Technology

**Math Online** macmillanmh.com

Personal Tutor • Extra Examples

Math Adventures

### Option 3 Learning Station: Health (p. 392H)

Direct students to the Health Learning Station for opportunities to explore and extend the lesson concept.

### Option 4 Problem-Solving Practice

Reinforce problem-solving skills and strategies with the Problem-Solving Practice worksheet.

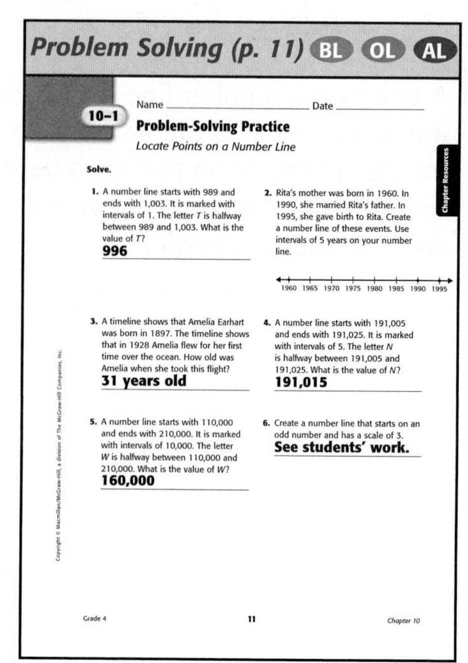

**Problem Solving (p. 11)** BL OL AL

10–1 Name ________ Date ________

**Problem-Solving Practice**

*Locate Points on a Number Line*

**Solve.**

1. A number line starts with 989 and ends with 1,003. It is marked with intervals of 1. The letter *T* is halfway between 989 and 1,003. What is the value of *T*?
   **996**
2. Rita's mother was born in 1960. In 1990, she married Rita's father. In 1995, she gave birth to Rita. Create a number line of these events. Use intervals of 5 years on your number line.
   1960 1965 1970 1975 1980 1985 1990 1995
3. A timeline shows that Amelia Earhart was born in 1897. The timeline shows that in 1928 Amelia flew for her first time over the ocean. How old was Amelia when she took this flight?
   **31 years old**
4. A number line starts with 191,005 and ends with 191,025. It is marked with intervals of 5. The letter *N* is halfway between 191,005 and 191,025. What is the value of *N*?
   **191,015**
5. A number line starts with 110,000 and ends with 210,000. It is marked with intervals of 10,000. The letter *W* is halfway between 110,000 and 210,000. What is the value of *W*?
   **160,000**
6. Create a number line that starts on an odd number and has a scale of 3.
   **See students' work.**

Chapter Resources



Grade 4 11 Chapter 10

# Locate Points on a Number Line

## GET READY to Learn

Andrés is trying to find what whole number is represented by point *T* on the number line.

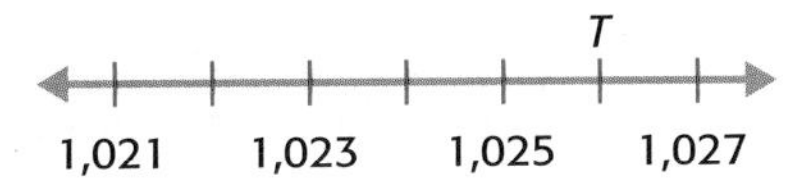


**MAIN IDEA**

will locate points on number line.

**New Vocabulary**

**number line**
**point**

**Math Online**

macmillanmh.com

- Extra Examples
- Personal Tutor
- Self-Check Quiz

A **number line** is a line with numbers on it in order at regular intervals. A **point** is an exact location in space. You can locate points on a number line.

**EXAMPLES** Locate Points on a Number Line

**1 What number is represented by point *T*?**

To find what number point *T* represents, use the number line.

The scale for the number line is in one-unit intervals. Count to find what number point *T* represents.

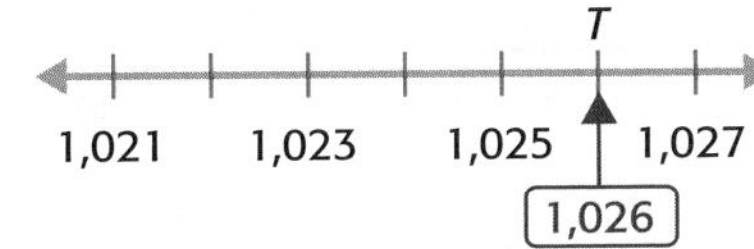


So, point *T* represents 1,026.

**2 What number does point *Z* represent on the number line?**

Locate *Z* on the number line. The scale is in intervals of 5. Count by fives to find what number point *Z* represents.

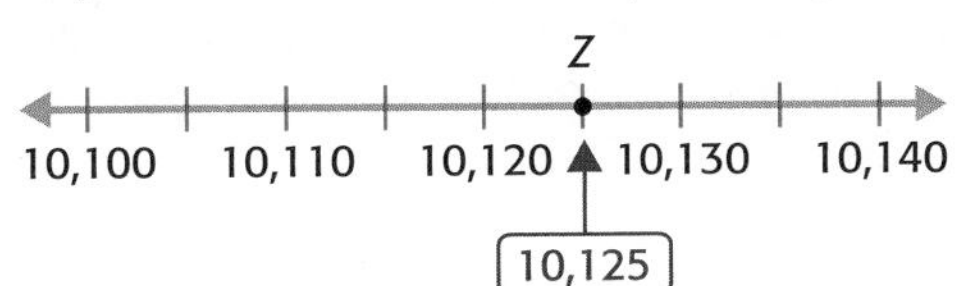


So, point *Z* represents 10,125.

# Locate Points on a Number Line

## 1 Introduce

### Activity Choice 1 • Hands-On

- Write the number 345 on the board. Have volunteers come up and write the next 5 numbers that would follow at intervals of 5. 350, 355, 360, 365, 370
- Write the number 3,400 on the board. **What are the next five numbers that follow in intervals of 200?** Call on different students to give answers. Write answers on board. 3,600; 3,800; 4,000; 4,200; 4,400

### Activity Choice 2 • Literature

Introduce the lesson with *King's Commissioners* by Aileen Friedman. For a related math activity, see p. TR57.

## 2 Teach

### Scaffolding Questions

Draw a number line. Label it with the following: 1,300; 1,350; 1,400; 1,500; 1,550. Note: The spacing between 1,400 and 1,500 will be double the spacing that is between the other numbers.

- Point to the location midway between 1,400 and 1,500. **What number is missing?** 1,450
- **If you continued labeling the number line to the right, what number would come after 1,550?** 1,600
- **How did you determine the missing numbers?** Sample answer: skip counting by fifties

### GET READY to Learn

Have students open their books and read the information in **Get Ready to Learn.** Introduce **number line** and **point**. As a class, work through **Examples 1–3.**

## Name Points on a Number Line

**Example 2** Be sure students understand that the scale is in intervals of fives even though the scale is labeled every other interval, making it appear that the scale is in intervals of 10.

## ADDITIONAL EXAMPLES

**1** Tell what number each letter on the number line represents.

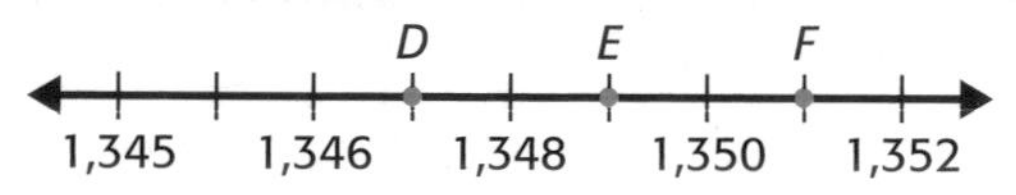


$D = 1{,}347$; $E = 1{,}349$; $F = 1{,}351$

**2** Tell what number point $Z$ represents on the number line. $Z = 12{,}130$

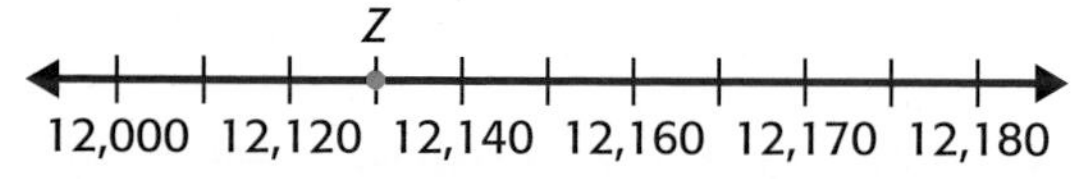


**3** Tell what number point $Z$ represents on the number line. $Z = 181{,}300$

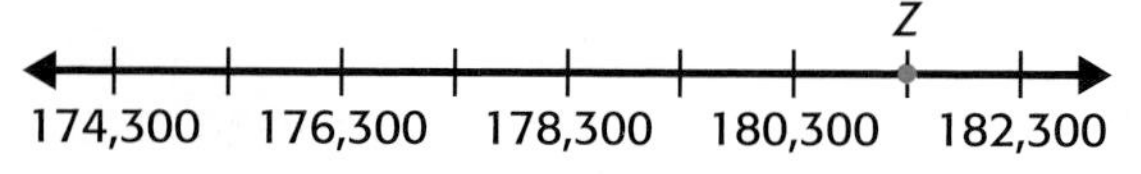


### CHECK What You Know

As a class, have students complete Exercises 1–6 in **Check What You Know** as you observe their work.

**Exercise 6** Assess student comprehension before assigning practice exercises.

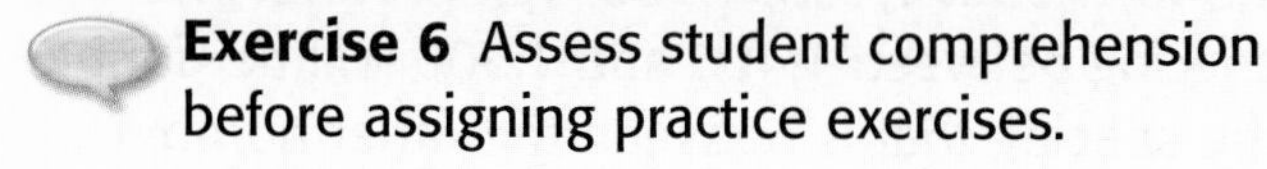

## BL Alternate Teaching Strategy

**If** students have trouble finding points on a number line…

**Then** use one of these reteach options:

1 CRM **Daily Reteach Worksheet** (p. 8)

2 Have students label two number lines starting at 800 in five-unit intervals with one labeled every other interval and the other labeled every two intervals. Lead them to see that they can determine the scale even when the number lines are labeled differently and that once they determine the scale on a number line, they can use it to find points.

### COMMON ERROR!

Students may only use the first two numbers given to determine the interval between the numbers. Remind them to consider all of the numbers shown on the number line.



**EXAMPLE** Locate Points on a Number Line

**3** **What number does point $Z$ represent on the number line?** Locate $Z$ on the number line. The scale is in intervals of 1,000. Count by thousands to find what point $Z$ represents.

Z
151,500 152,500 153,500 155,500 156,500
154,500

So, point $Z$ represents 154,500.

### CHECK What You Know

**Tell what number each letter on the number line represents.**
See Examples 1–3 (pp. 395–396)

**1.**

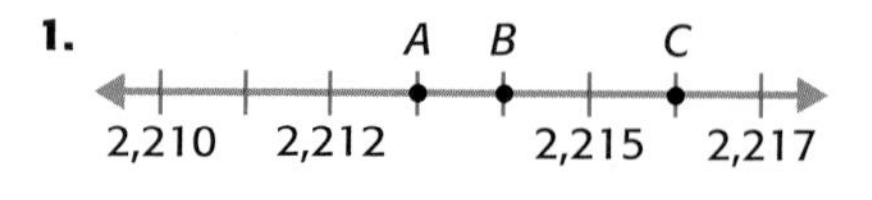


*A*: 2,213; *B*: 2,214; *C*: 2,216

**2.**

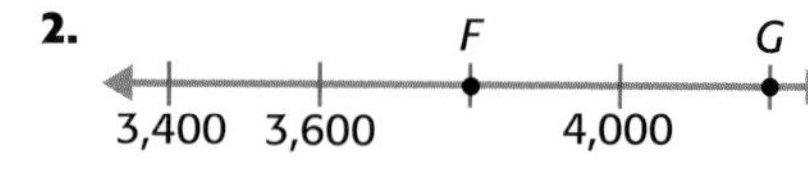


*F*: 3,800; *G*: 4,200

**Tell what number point $Z$ represents on each number line.** See Examples 1–3 (pp. 395–396)

**3.**

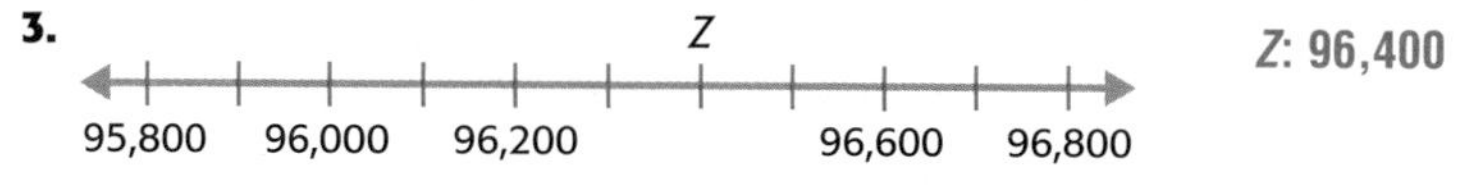


*Z*: 96,400

**4.**

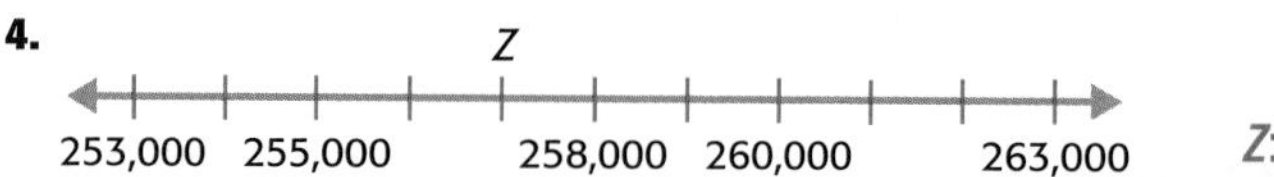


*Z*: 257,000

**5.** In 1787, Delaware became the first state in the United States. In 1803, Ohio became a state. Indiana became a state 13 years after Ohio. Create a number line that has intervals of 10. Locate these points on your number line. See students' work.

**6.** Talk About It Why do most number lines have intervals greater than one? Sample answer: By using intervals greater than one, number lines can show more information.

396 **Chapter 10** Understand and Develop Spatial Reasoning

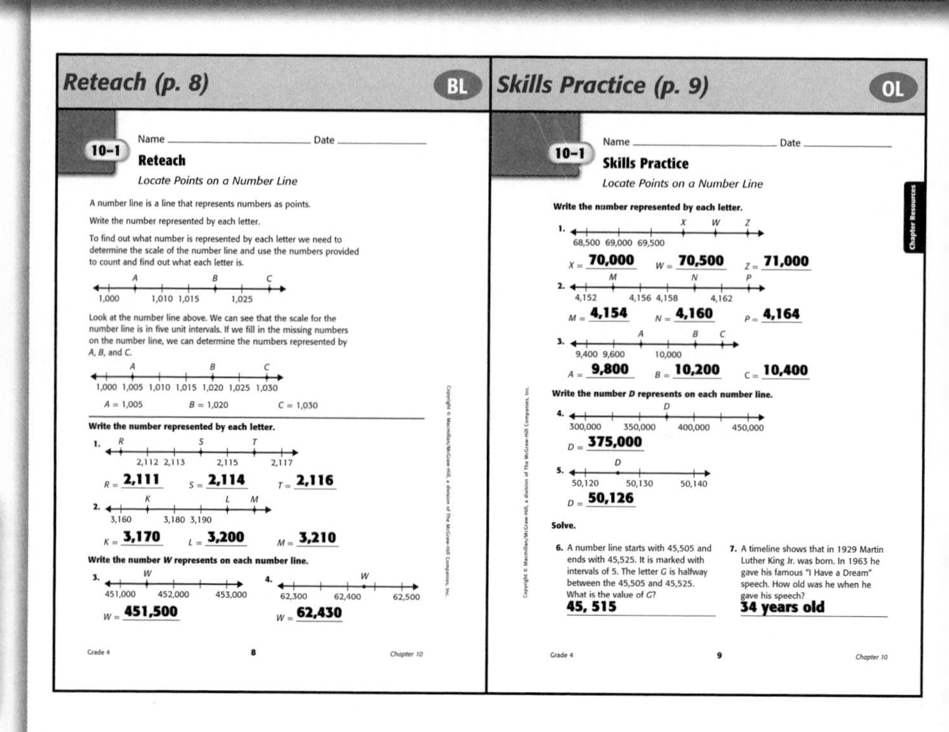

**Reteach (p. 8)** BL

Name ______ Date ______

10-1 **Reteach**

*Locate Points on a Number Line*

A number line is a line that represents numbers as points.

Write the number represented by each letter.

To find out what number is represented by each letter we need to determine the scale of the number line and use the numbers provided to count and find out what each letter is.

A B C
1,000 1,010 1,015 1,025

Look at the number line above. We can see that the scale for the number line is in five unit intervals. If we fill in the missing numbers on the number line, we can determine the numbers represented by A, B, and C.

A B C
1,000 1,005 1,010 1,015 1,020 1,025 1,030
A = 1,005 B = 1,020 C = 1,030

**Write the number represented by each letter.**

1. R S T
2,112 2,113 2,115 2,117
R = **2,111** S = **2,114** T = **2,116**

2. K L M
3,160 3,180 3,190
K = **3,170** L = **3,200** M = **3,210**

**Write the number W represents on each number line.**

3. W
451,000 452,000 453,000
W = **451,500**

4. W
62,300 62,400 62,500
W = **62,430**

Grade 4 8 Chapter 10

**Skills Practice (p. 9)** OL

Name ______ Date ______

10-1 **Skills Practice**

*Locate Points on a Number Line*

**Write the number represented by each letter.**

1. X W Z
68,500 69,000 69,500
X = **70,000** W = **70,500** Z = **71,000**

2. M N P
4,152 4,156 4,158 4,162
M = **4,154** N = **4,160** P = **4,164**

3. A B C
9,400 9,600 10,000
A = **9,800** B = **10,200** C = **10,400**

**Write the number D represents on each number line.**

4. D
300,000 350,000 400,000 450,000
D = **375,000**

5. D
50,120 50,130 50,140
D = **50,126**

**Solve.**

6. A number line starts with 45,505 and ends with 45,525. It is marked with intervals of 5. The letter G is halfway between the 45,505 and 45,525. What is the value of G? **45, 515**

7. A timeline shows that in 1929 Martin Luther King Jr. was born. In 1963 he gave his famous "I Have a Dream" speech. How old was he when he gave his speech? **34 years old**

Grade 4 9 Chapter 10

## Practice and Problem Solving

See page R25.

**ell what number each letter on the number line represents.** See Examples 1–3 (pp. 395–396)

**7.**
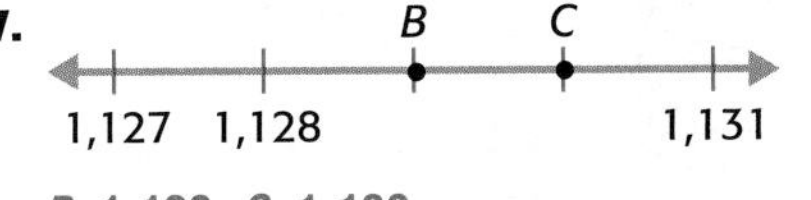

*B*: 1,129; *C*: 1,130

**8.**
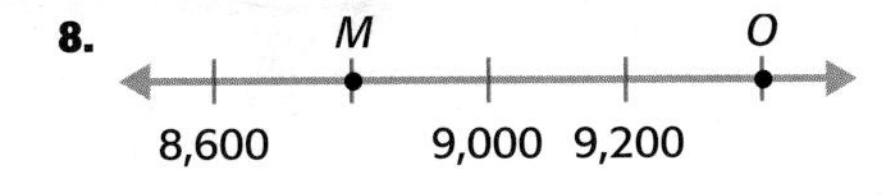

*M*: 8,800; *O*: 9,400

**9.** *S* *T*
7,000 7,500 9,000
*S*: 8,000; *T*: 8,500

**10.** *X* *Y*
6,100 6,200 6,300
*X*: 6,150; *Y*: 6,350

**ell what number point *Z* represents on each number line.** See Examples 1–3 (pp. 395–396)

**1.**
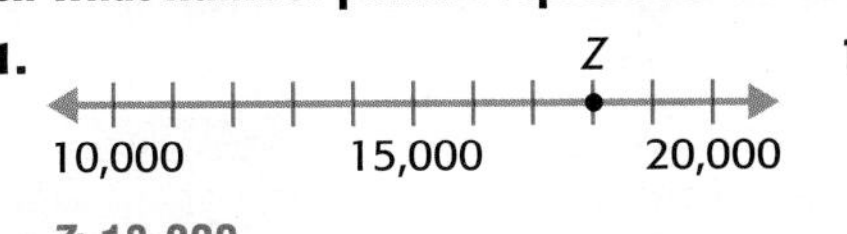

*Z*: 18,000

**12.**
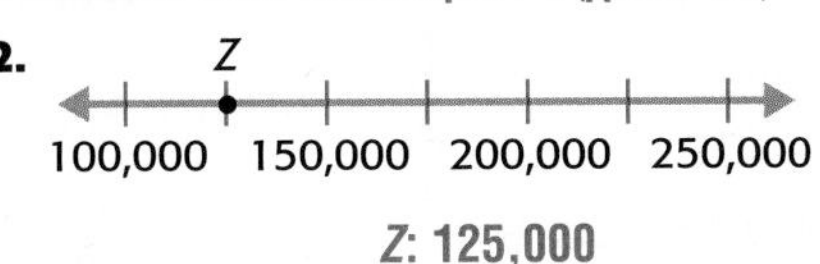

*Z*: 125,000

**3.** *Z*
35,120 35,140 35,160 35,200 35,220
*Z*: 35,180

**4.** *Z*
513,000 514,000 515,000 516,000 517,000 518,000
*Z*: 514,500

**5.** A number line starts with 4,250 and ends on 4,500. It is marked with intervals of 50. The letter *X* is on the third tick mark from the beginning. What is the value for *X*? **4,350**

**6.** A number line starts with 30,405 and ends on 30,415. It is marked with intervals of 1. The letter *N* is halfway between 30,405 and 30,415. What is the value for *N*? **30,410**

### H.O.T. Problems

**7. CHALLENGE** Estimate the number that each letter on the number line represents.

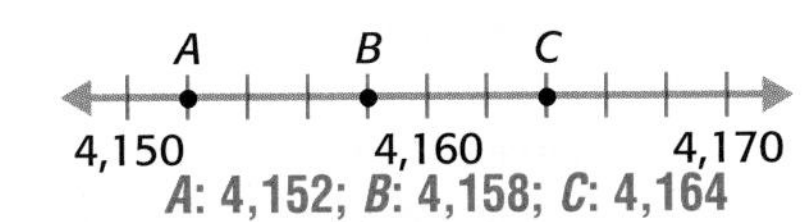

*A*: 4,152; *B*: 4,158; *C*: 4,164

**8.** **WRITING IN MATH** Explain how to locate points on a number line.
See Ch. 10 Answer Appendix.



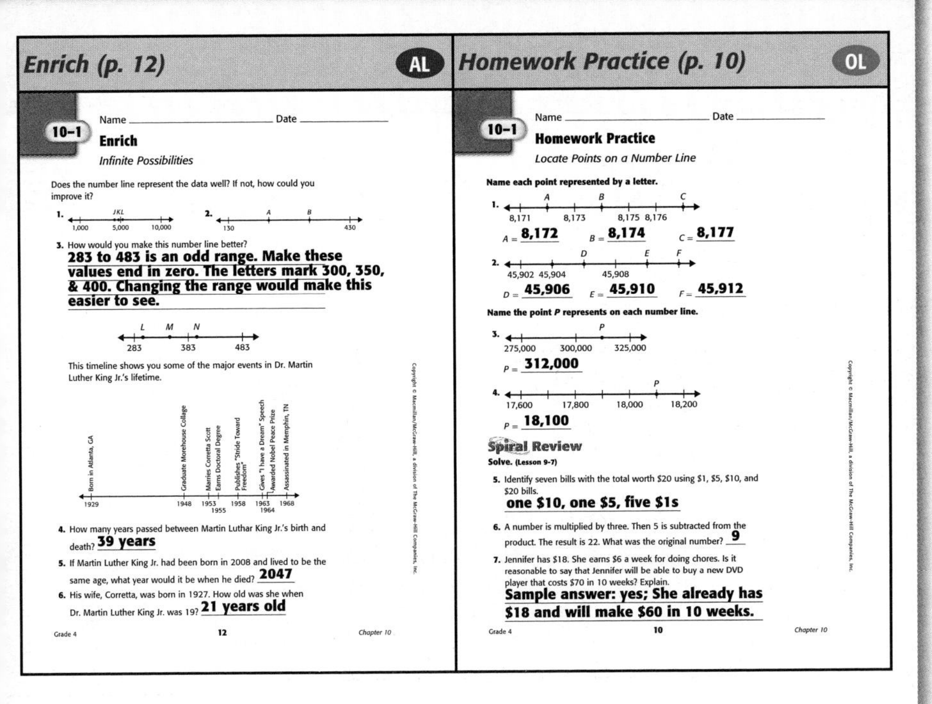

**Enrich (p. 12)** AL

Name ________ Date ________

10-1 **Enrich**
*Infinite Possibilities*

Does the number line represent the data well? If not, how could you improve it?

1. JKL — 1,000 5,000 10,000
2. A B — 150 450

3. How would you make this number line better?
**283 to 483 is an odd range. Make these values end in zero. The letters mark 300, 350, & 400. Changing the range would make this easier to see.**

L M N — 283 383 483

This timeline shows you some of the major events in Dr. Martin Luther King Jr.'s lifetime.

Born in Atlanta, GA; Graduate Morehouse College; Marries Coretta Scott; Earns Doctoral Degree; Publishes "Stride Toward Freedom"; Gives "I have a Dream" Speech; Awarded Nobel Peace Prize; Assassinated in Memphis, TN

1929 1948 1953 1955 1958 1963 1964 1968

4. How many years passed between Martin Luther King Jr.'s birth and death? **39 years**
5. If Martin Luther King Jr. had been born in 2008 and lived to be the same age, what year would it be when he died? **2047**
6. His wife, Coretta, was born in 1927. How old was she when Dr. Martin Luther King Jr. was 19? **21 years old**

Grade 4 12 Chapter 10

**Homework Practice (p. 10)** OL

Name ________ Date ________

10-1 **Homework Practice**
*Locate Points on a Number Line*

**Name each point represented by a letter.**

1. A B C — 8,171 8,173 8,175 8,176
A = **8,172** B = **8,174** C = **8,177**

2. D E F — 45,902 45,904 45,908
D = **45,906** E = **45,910** F = **45,912**

**Name the point *P* represents on each number line.**

3. P — 275,000 300,000 325,000
P = **312,000**

4. P — 17,600 17,800 18,000 18,200
P = **18,100**

**Spiral Review**
**Solve.** (Lesson 9-7)

5. Identify seven bills with the total worth $20 using $1, $5, $10, and $20 bills.
**one $10, one $5, five $1s**

6. A number is multiplied by three. Then 5 is subtracted from the product. The result is 22. What was the original number? **9**

7. Jennifer has $18. She earns $6 a week for doing chores. Is it reasonable to say that Jennifer will be able to buy a new DVD player that costs $70 in 10 weeks? Explain.
**Sample answer: yes; She already has $18 and will make $60 in 10 weeks.**

Grade 4 10 Chapter 10

## 3 Practice

Differentiate practice using these leveled assignments for Exercises 7–18.

| Level | Assignment |
|---|---|
| BL Below/Approaching Level | 7, 9, 11, 13, 16 |
| OL On Level | 7–11, 13, 15, 18 |
| AL Above/Beyond Level | 7–15 odd, 17 and 18 |

Have students discuss and complete the Higher Order Thinking problems. Remind students to draw number lines and label the numbers on the number line at evenly spaced intervals.

Have students complete Exercise 18 in their Math Journals. You may choose to use this exercise as an optional formative assessment.

## 4 Assess

### Formative Assessment

- **Explain how a number line can be used to locate points.** Sample answer: Use the numbers given on the number line to count and locate the points.

**Quick Check** **Are students continuing to struggle with finding points on a number line?**

**If Yes** → Small Group Options (p. 395B)
Strategic Intervention Guide (p. 124)

**If No** → Independent Work Options (p. 395B)
CRM Skills Practice Worksheet (p. 9)
CRM Enrich Worksheet (p. 12)

**Name the Math** Have students write a description that tells what interval they would use to create a number line that shows the numbers from 15,000 to 15,030 with a point at 15,025.

# Lesson Planner

## Objective

Identify and describe parallel and intersecting lines.

## Vocabulary

**parallel**, **intersecting**, **perpendicular**

## Resources

**Materials:** index cards, tape, scissors

**Manipulatives:** pattern blocks, rulers

## 1 Introduce

- Recall for students that people mention cross streets or intersections when giving directions. **What do you think the words *intersection* or *cross street* mean?** Sample answer: The place where streets meet, intersect, or cross each other.
- Have volunteers draw examples of cross streets and intersections on the board. Suggest they use their neighborhood streets. Then draw examples of streets parallel and perpendicular to each other.
- Tell students that the streets are examples of intersecting, parallel, and perpendicular lines.

## 2 Teach

**Activity 1** Distribute pattern blocks and rulers. Check that students align their rulers with the corners of the trapezoid when extending the lines.



Explore

Math Activity for 10-2

# Parallel and Intersecting Lines

**MAIN IDEA**
I will identify and describe parallel and intersecting lines.

**You Will Need**
pattern blocks
paper and pencil
ruler

In this activity, you will use pattern blocks to explore parallel and intersecting lines. You will also decide if the intersecting lines are perpendicular.

**ACTIVITY** Parallel and Intersecting Lines

**1 Use a pattern block to explore parallel and intersecting lines.**

**Step 1 Observe.**
Look at the pattern block shown. There are four corners. At each corner there is a point of intersection, where two lines meet.

**Step 2 Trace the shape.**
Place the pattern block on a piece of paper. Trace the shape.

**Step 3 Extend the lines.**
Extend the lines with a ruler. Notice how the sides intersect above the pattern block.

The top and bottom lines appear to be parallel. That is, they do not intersect and the distance between them is always the same.

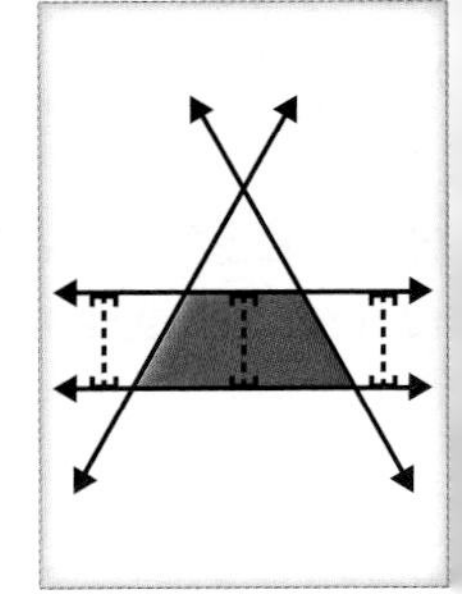

Hands-On Activity

**ACTIVITY** Perpendicular Lines

**2** **Model intersecting lines.**

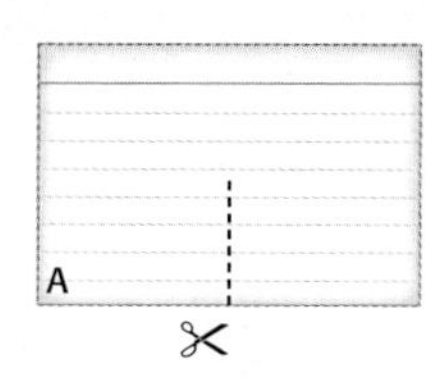


**Step 1** **Label the cards.**
Label the index cards A and B.

**Step 2** **Cut the cards.**
Hold the cards together. Cut a slit halfway through both cards as shown.

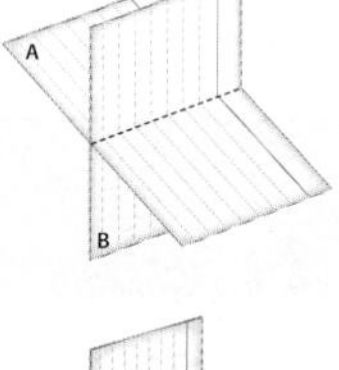


**Step 3** **Form perpendicular lines.**
Insert one card into the slit of the other. Use tape to hold the cards together at right angles. These cards are now perpendicular.

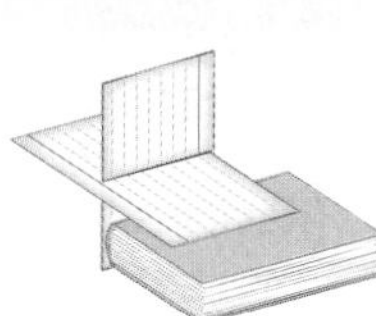

**Step 4** **Identify perpendicular lines.**
Use the cards to identify objects in your classroom that illustrate perpendicular lines.

## Think About It

1. Are any of the intersecting lines perpendicular on the trapezoid? no
2. Name two other shapes that have parallel lines. square, rhombus
3. Name two shapes that have perpendicular lines of intersection. rectangle, right triangle

## CHECK What You Know

**Identify and describe lines as *parallel, intersecting,* or *perpendicular*.**

4. 5. 6.

parallel

7. **WRITING IN MATH** How would you determine if two lines are parallel? Sample answer: Use a ruler to measure the distance between the lines. If distance does not change it is parallel.



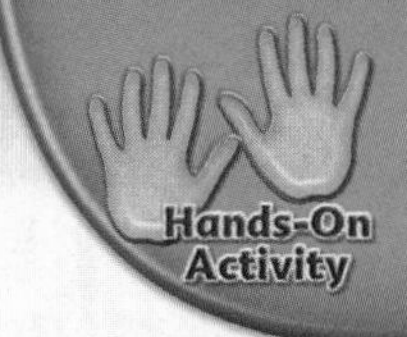


**Activity 2** Make sure students understand that some intersecting lines are perpendicular, not all. You might want to mention that perpendicular lines form a 90° angle when they meet.

## Think About It

Assign Exercises 1–3 in the **Think About It** section to assess student comprehension of the concept presented in the Activity.

# 3 Assess

### Formative Assessment

Use **Check What You Know** Exercises 4–6 to assess whether students comprehend the differences among intersecting, parallel, and perpendicular lines.

**From Concrete to Abstract** Use Exercises 5 and 6 to bridge the gap between identifying lines and justifying that the identification is correct.

LESSON 10-2

# Lines, Line Segments, and Rays

## Lesson Planner

### Objective

Identify and describe lines, line segments, and rays.

### Vocabulary

**line**, **ray**, **endpoint**, **line segment**, **parallel**, **intersecting**, **perpendicular**

### Resources

**Literature Connection:** *Lines, Segments, Polygons* by Mindel and Harry Sitomer

**Teacher Technology**
TeacherWorks • Interactive Classroom • Math Songs Track #7 Lesson Plan

## Daily Routine

Use these suggestions before beginning the lesson on p. 400.

### 5-Minute Check

(Reviews Lesson 10-1)

**Tell what number each letter on the number line represents.**

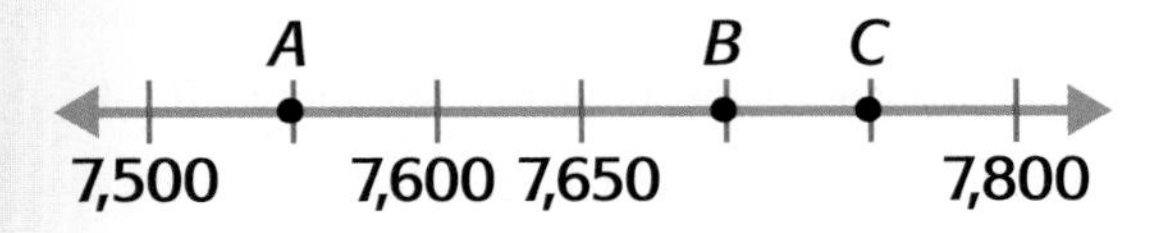


1. *A* 7,550 2. *B* 7,700 3. *C* 7,750

4. Tell what number point *Z* represents on the number line. 25,000

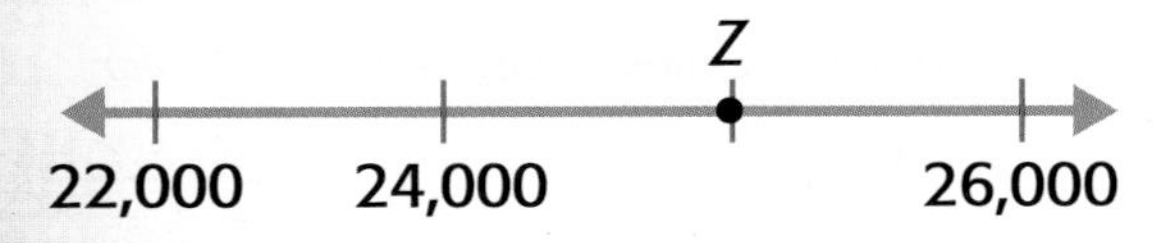


### Problem of the Day

The school drama club sold $640 worth of tickets. If they sold 80 adult tickets at $6 each, how many $4 student tickets were sold? 40 student tickets

### Focus on Math Background

In previous grades, students have studied lines, points, and planes informally. Symbols, definitions, and abstractions have been introduced gradually. Most students at this level have a basic understanding that a right angle makes the corner of a square. Most likely they have used the corner of an index card to check to see if an angle is a right angle or not. This background is essential to this lesson because it helps students understand what it means for two lines to be perpendicular, that is, they meet to form right angles.

### Building Math Vocabulary

Write the lesson vocabulary words and their definitions on the board.

Have the students copy the words and their definitions onto a piece of paper. Then ask them to draw a picture to illustrate each word. Have them label each of their drawings.

# Differentiated Instruction

## Small Group Options

Option 1 — KINESTHETIC

### Below Level BL

Note: While this activity is designed to assess understanding of students having difficulty, it can serve as an energizer for the whole class.

- Have students stand and form a circle around the classroom.
- Say, "Use your arms to show me parallel lines, intersecting lines, perpendicular lines. Use your hands and arms to show me a line segment, a ray, a line."
- Quickly assess anyone having difficulty with any of the concepts and review.
- Do this activity on more than one day.

Option 2 — KINESTHETIC, AUDITORY

### English Language Learners ELL

**Materials:** paper, black and yellow crayons/markers
**Core Vocabulary:** road, line, end
**Common Use Verb:** look

**See Math** This strategy provides the language to describe lines and line relationships cooperatively.

- Say: "**Roads** are what cars drive on. On paper a **road** ***looks*** like a **line**."
- Guide students through drawing and coloring a road map that demonstrates the different types of lines.
- Allow some roads to intersect, be parallel, and be perpendicular.
- Provide the language of each line and relationship as you design the map with the class using the words *start* and ***end.***

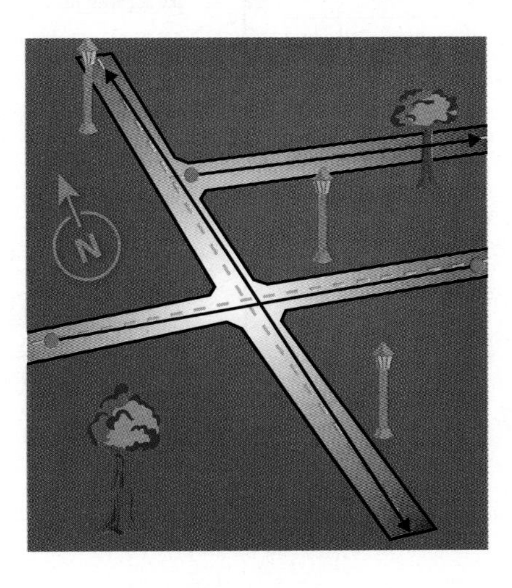

## Independent Work Options

Option 1 — VISUAL, SPATIAL

### Early Finishers OL AL

**Materials:** paper, pencil, crayons or markers, straightedge

- Have students draw a picture that includes parallel, intersecting, and perpendicular line segments.
- Remind them to label their parallel, intersecting, and perpendicular line segments.
- If time allows, have them color the picture.

Option 2

### Student Technology

Math Online macmillanmh.com

Personal Tutor • Extra Examples

Math Adventures

Math Songs, "I Draw the LIne" Track #7

Option 3

### Learning Station: Writing (p. 392G)

Direct students to the Writing Learning Station for opportunities to explore and extend the lesson concept.

Option 4

### Problem-Solving Practice

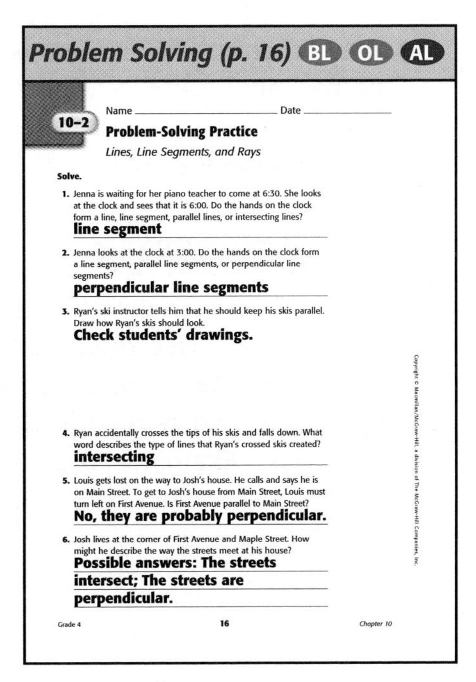

**Problem Solving (p. 16)** BL OL AL

10–2 Name ______ Date ______

**Problem-Solving Practice**

*Lines, Line Segments, and Rays*

**Solve.**

1. Jenna is waiting for her piano teacher to come at 6:30. She looks at the clock and sees that it is 6:00. Do the hands on the clock form a line, line segment, parallel lines, or intersecting lines?
   **line segment**
2. Jenna looks at the clock at 3:00. Do the hands on the clock form a line segment, parallel line segments, or perpendicular line segments?
   **perpendicular line segments**
3. Ryan's ski instructor tells him that he should keep his skis parallel. Draw how Ryan's skis should look.
   **Check students' drawings.**
4. Ryan accidentally crosses the tips of his skis and falls down. What word describes the type of lines that Ryan's crossed skis created?
   **intersecting**
5. Louis gets lost on the way to Josh's house. He calls and says he is on Main Street. To get to Josh's house from Main Street, Louis must turn left on First Avenue. Is First Avenue parallel to Main Street?
   **No, they are probably perpendicular.**
6. Josh lives at the corner of First Avenue and Maple Street. How might he describe the way the streets meet at his house?
   **Possible answers: The streets intersect; The streets are perpendicular.**



Grade 4 16 Chapter 10

# 10-2 Lines, Line Segments, and Rays

## 1 Introduce

### Activity Choice 1 • Hands-On

- Have students volunteer to tell what they know about lines. Discuss their responses.
- Have volunteers come to the board and draw and label examples of lines.
- Tell students that they will be learning about parts of a line.

### Activity Choice 2 • Literature

Introduce the lesson with *Lines, Segments, Polygons* by Mindel and Harry Sitomer. For a related math activity, see p. TR57.

## 2 Teach

### Scaffolding Questions

Draw a line on the board and label it *AB*. Explain that lines are often named by naming two points on the line.

- **What do you think the name of this line is?** line *AB*
- Draw two intersecting lines–one horizontal and one vertical. Label the point of intersection *A*. On the vertical line, label another point on the line *B* and on the horizontal line, label a second point *C*.
- Point to the vertical line. **What is the name of this line?** $\overleftrightarrow{AB}$ or $\overleftrightarrow{BA}$
- **What is the name of the other line?** $\overleftrightarrow{AC}$ or $\overleftrightarrow{CA}$
- **Why do you think we use two points to name lines?** Sample answer: So that in the case of intersecting lines, you know which line you are talking about.

### GET READY to Learn

Have students open their books and read the paragraph under **Get Ready to Learn**. Introduce **line**, **ray**, **endpoint**, **line segment**, **parallel**, **intersecting**, and **perpendicular**. As a class, work through **Examples 1–3**.



# 10-2 Lines, Line Segments, and Rays

**MAIN IDEA**

I will identify and describe lines, line segments, and rays.

**New Vocabulary**

line
ray
endpoint
line segment
parallel
intersecting
perpendicular

**Math Online**

macmillanmh.com
- Extra Examples
- Personal Tutor
- Self-Check Quiz

### GET READY to Learn

Farmers often plant crops like corn in rows. The rows resemble line segments.

### Lines, Rays, Line Segments — Key Concepts

**Words** A **line** is a straight set of points that extend in opposite directions without ending.

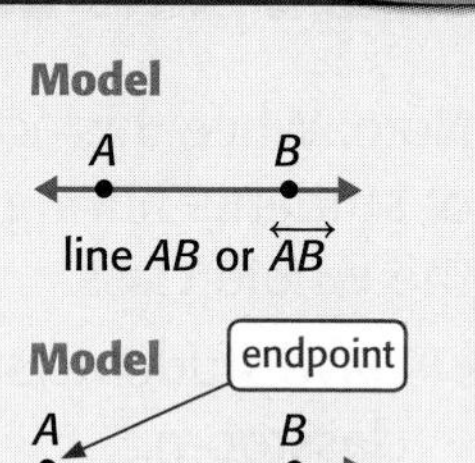

**Model** line *AB* or $\overleftrightarrow{AB}$

**Words** A **ray** is a part of a line that has one **endpoint** and extends in one direction without ending.

**Model** ray *AB* or $\overrightarrow{AB}$

**Words** A **line segment** is a part of a line between two endpoints.

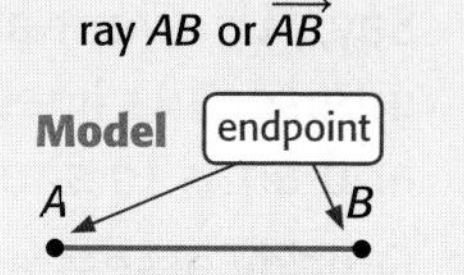

**Model** segment *AB* or $\overline{AB}$

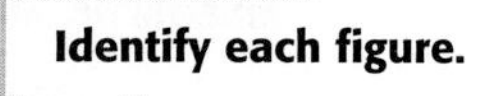

**EXAMPLES** Identify Lines, Rays, or Line Segments

**Identify each figure.**

1.

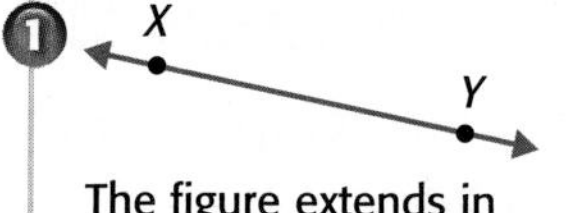

The figure extends in opposite directions without ending. Line *XY* or $\overleftrightarrow{XY}$.

2. The figure has one endpoint and extends in one direction without ending. Ray *AB* or $\overrightarrow{AB}$.



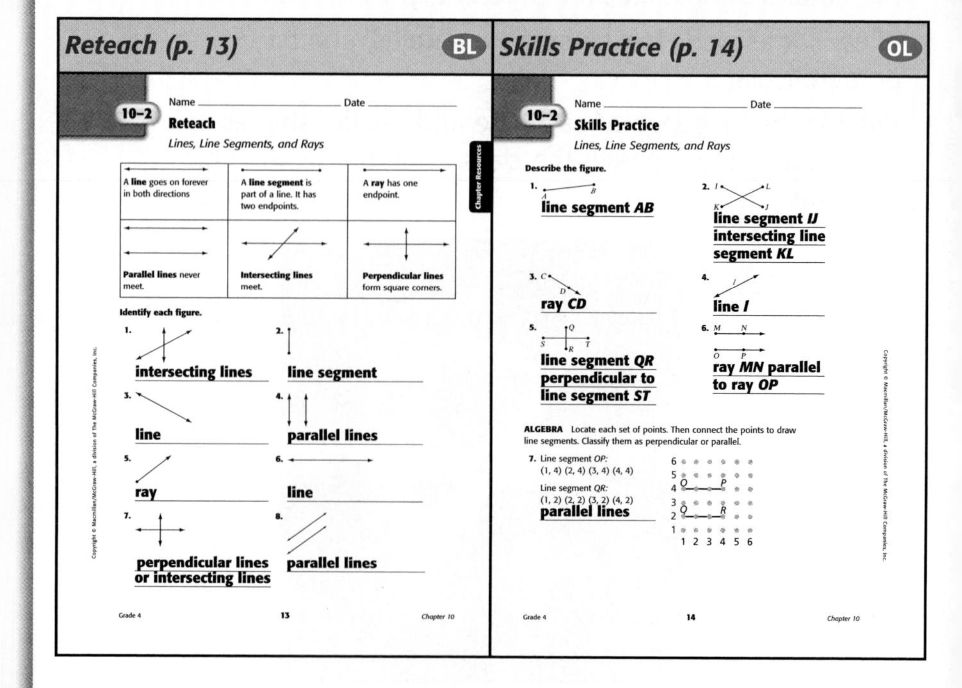

**Reteach (p. 13)** BL

10-2 Reteach
*Lines, Line Segments, and Rays*

| A **line** goes on forever in both directions | A **line segment** is part of a line. It has two endpoints. | A **ray** has one endpoint. |
| --- | --- | --- |
| **Parallel lines** never meet. | **Intersecting lines** meet. | **Perpendicular lines** form square corners. |

**Identify each figure.**

1. intersecting lines
2. line segment
3. line
4. parallel lines
5. ray
6. line
7. perpendicular lines or intersecting lines
8. parallel lines

Grade 4 13 Chapter 10

**Skills Practice (p. 14)** OL

10-2 Skills Practice
*Lines, Line Segments, and Rays*

**Describe the figure.**

1. line segment *AB*
2. line segment *IJ* intersecting line segment *KL*
3. ray *CD*
4. line *I*
5. line segment *QR* perpendicular to line segment *ST*
6. ray *MN* parallel to ray *OP*

**ALGEBRA** Locate each set of points. Then connect the points to draw line segments. Classify them as perpendicular or parallel.

7. Line segment *OP*: (1, 4) (2, 4) (3, 4) (4, 4)
Line segment *QR*: (1, 2) (2, 2) (3, 2) (4, 2)
parallel lines

Grade 4 14 Chapter 10

You can describe lines, rays, and line segments by the way they meet or cross each other. In the previous Explore Activity, you learned how to identify parallel and intersecting lines.

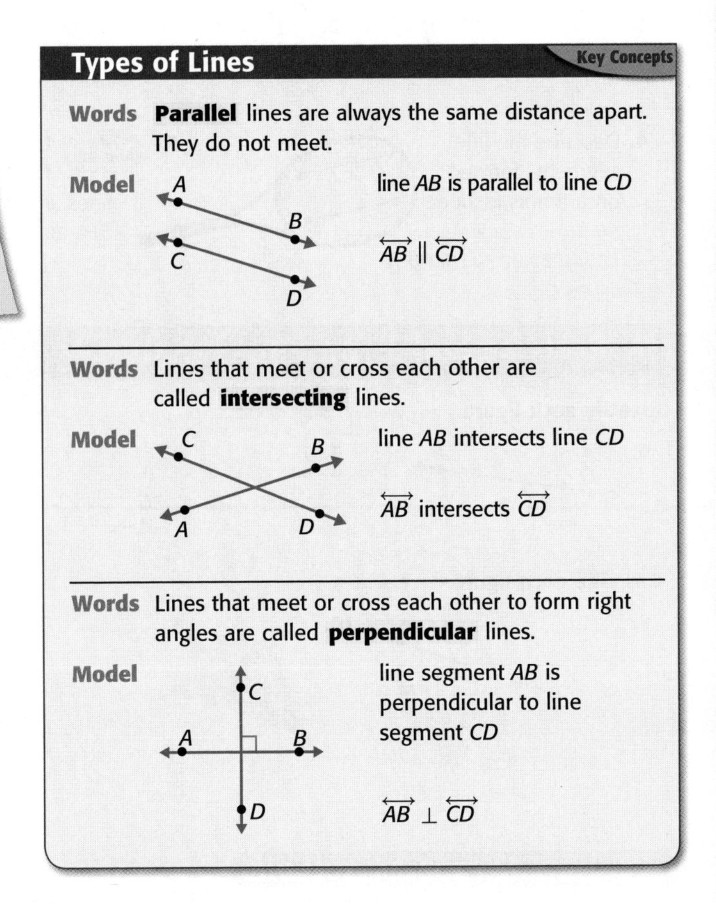

## Types of Lines

Key Concepts

**Words** **Parallel** lines are always the same distance apart. They do not meet.

**Model** line $AB$ is parallel to line $CD$

$\overleftrightarrow{AB} \parallel \overleftrightarrow{CD}$

**Words** Lines that meet or cross each other are called **intersecting** lines.

**Model** line $AB$ intersects line $CD$

$\overleftrightarrow{AB}$ intersects $\overleftrightarrow{CD}$

**Words** Lines that meet or cross each other to form right angles are called **perpendicular** lines.

**Model** line segment $AB$ is perpendicular to line segment $CD$

$\overleftrightarrow{AB} \perp \overleftrightarrow{CD}$

**Remember**

The symbol $\parallel$ means parallel. The symbol $\perp$ means perpendicular. The symbol ⌝ means right angle.

## EXAMPLE Describe Lines, Rays, or Line Segments

**3 Describe the figure.**

The figure shows ray $AB$ and line segment $CD$. Notice that ray $AB$ intersects line segment $CD$.

$\overrightarrow{AB}$ intersects $\overline{CD}$.

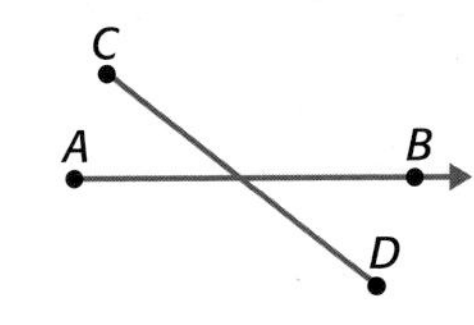




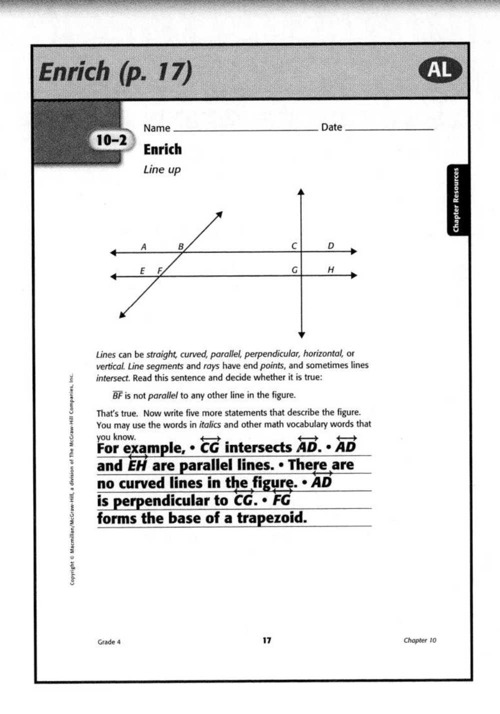

**Enrich (p. 17)** AL

Name ______ Date ______

10-2 **Enrich**

*Line up*

*Lines* can be *straight, curved, parallel, perpendicular, horizontal,* or *vertical. Line segments* and *rays* have end *points*, and sometimes lines *intersect*. Read this sentence and decide whether it is true:

$\overline{BF}$ is not *parallel* to any other line in the figure.

That's true. Now write five more statements that describe the figure. You may use the words in *italics* and other math vocabulary words that you know.

**For example, • $\overleftrightarrow{CG}$ intersects $\overleftrightarrow{AD}$. • $\overleftrightarrow{AD}$ and $\overleftrightarrow{EH}$ are parallel lines. • There are no curved lines in the figure. • $\overleftrightarrow{AD}$ is perpendicular to $\overleftrightarrow{CG}$. • $\overleftrightarrow{FG}$ forms the base of a trapezoid.**



Grade 4 17 Chapter 10

## Describe Lines

**Example 3** Emphasize the importance of labeling lines, line segments, and rays correctly. Remind students that rays are named beginning with the end point.

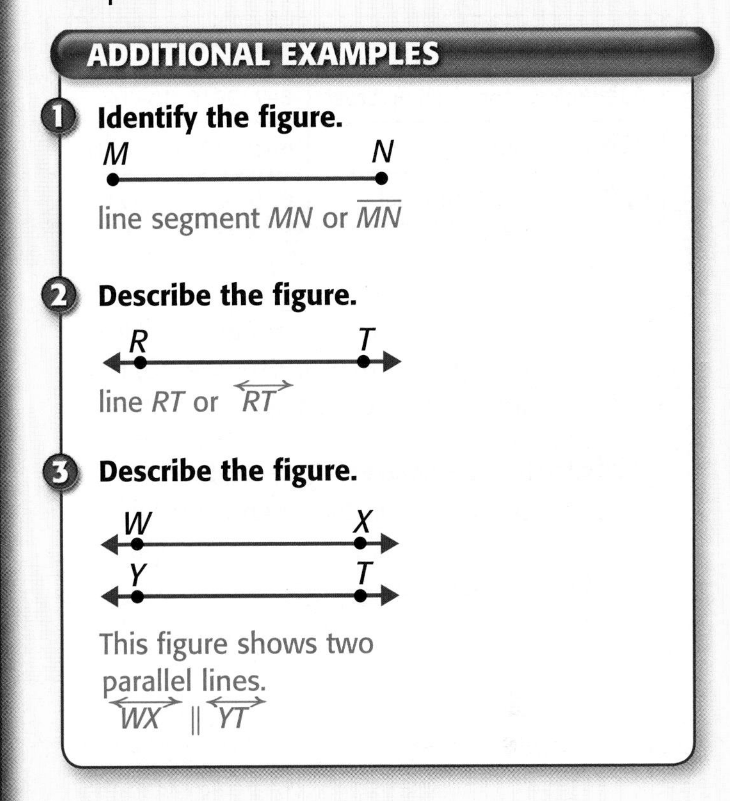

## ADDITIONAL EXAMPLES

**1 Identify the figure.**

line segment $MN$ or $\overline{MN}$

**2 Describe the figure.**

line $RT$ or $\overleftrightarrow{RT}$

**3 Describe the figure.**

This figure shows two parallel lines. $\overleftrightarrow{WX} \parallel \overleftrightarrow{YT}$

## CHECK What You Know

As a class, have students complete Exercises 1–5 in **Check What You Know** as you observe their work.

**Exercise 5** Assess student comprehension before assigning practice exercises.

## BL Alternate Teaching Strategy

**If** students have trouble with the vocabulary terms and labeling...

**Then** use one of these reteach options:

1. CRM **Daily Reteach Worksheet** (p. 13)
2. Have students find examples of parallel, intersecting, and perpendicular lines in the classroom. Ask them to compare the examples and explain the differences. Then have them draw and label their own examples.

# 3 Practice

Differentiate practice using these leveled assignments for Exercises 6–21.

| Level | Assignment |
|---|---|
| BL Below/Approaching Level | 6–7, 9–10, 13–14 |
| OL On Level | 6–10, 12–15, 16–18 |
| AL Above/Beyond Level | 6–14 even, 16–21 |

Have students discuss and complete the Higher Order Thinking problems. For Exercise 20, have students explain their reasoning.

**WRITING IN MATH** Have students complete Exercise 21 in their Math Journals. You may choose to use this exercise as an optional formative assessment.

## COMMON ERROR!

**Exercises 9 and 10** Some students may think that all intersecting lines are perpendicular. Remind them that intersecting lines are perpendicular only if they form a right angle. Have students look at Exercise 10. Point out that the "box" symbol indicates a right angle.

**Identify each figure.** See Examples 1 and 2 (p. 400)

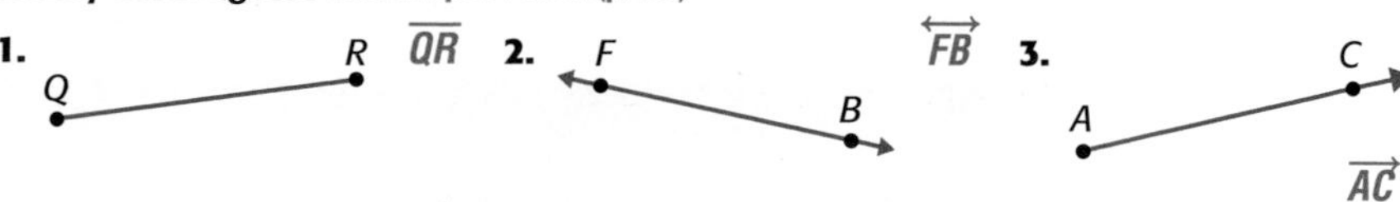


1. $\overline{QR}$
2. $\overleftrightarrow{FB}$
3. $\overrightarrow{AC}$

4. Describe the line segments formed on a tennis racquet. See Example 3 (p. 401)
The lines are parallel.

5. Talk About It List a real-world example for a line segment, parallel lines, and intersecting lines.
See margin.

## Practice and Problem Solving

**Identify each figure.** See Examples 1 and 2 (p. 400)

6. $\overleftrightarrow{DF}$
7. $\overrightarrow{FG}$
8. $\overline{HK}$

**Describe each figure.** See Example 3 (p. 401)

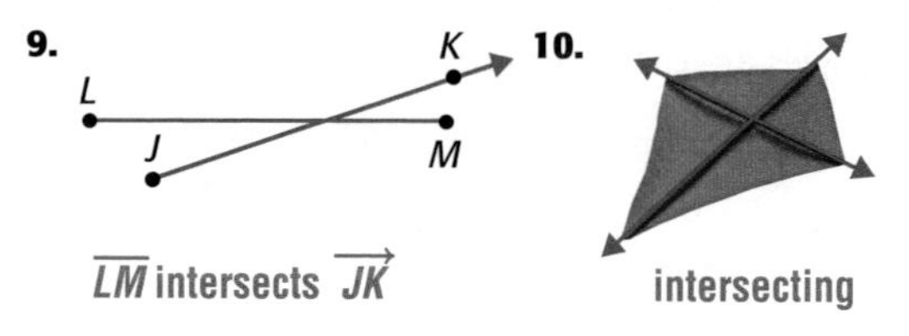


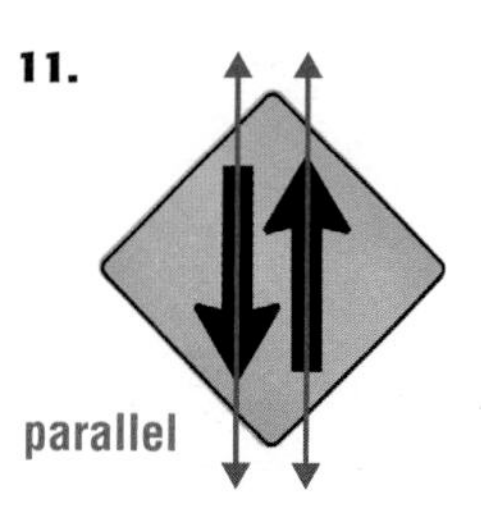

9. $\overline{LM}$ intersects $\overrightarrow{JK}$
10. intersecting
11. parallel

### Real-World PROBLEM SOLVING

**Geography** On a map, streets resemble line segments. Use the map to answer Exercises 12–15.

12. Identify two streets that are parallel to Oak Street.
Sample answer: Center and Pine Streets
13. Tell whether Center Street and Johnston Street are parallel, intersecting, or perpendicular lines. Explain.
See margin.
14. Identify two streets that are parallel.
Sample answer: Queen and School Streets
15. Are there any streets that are intersecting? Explain.
See margin.

Pine St, Oak St, Center St, Main St, Johnston St, Church St, Stephenson St, School St, Queen St



### Additional Answers

5. Sample answer: line segment = edge of a book; parallel lines = edges of a box; intersecting lines = tree branches
13. Sample answer: perpendicular; These two streets cross each other to form right angles.
15. Sample answer: yes; For example, Johnston and Main Streets intersect because any non-parallel streets intersect.

## H.O.T. Problems

16–18. See Ch. 10 Answer Appendix.

**OPEN ENDED** Draw an example of each figure described.

**16.** ray *CD*  **17.** $\overleftrightarrow{DE} \parallel \overleftrightarrow{FG}$  **18.** $\overline{RS}$ intersecting $\overline{TU}$

**REASONING** Tell whether each statement is *true* or *false*.

**19.** If two lines are parallel, they are the same distance apart. true

**20.** If two lines are parallel, they are also perpendicular. false

**21.** WRITING IN ▶MATH Can you draw two lines on a sheet of paper that are both parallel and perpendicular? Explain. See Ch. 10 Answer Appendix.

## TEST Practice

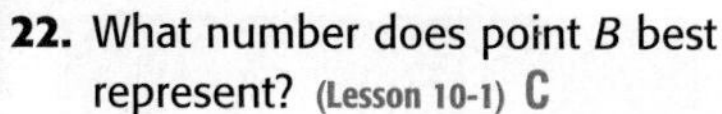

**22.** What number does point *B* best represent? (Lesson 10-1) C

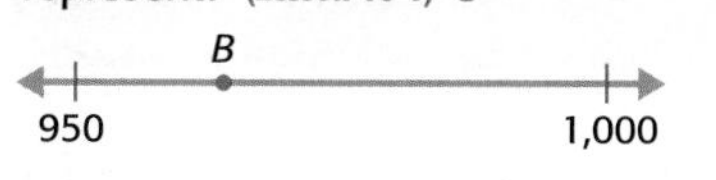


**A** 900

**B** 950

**C** 970

**D** 1,000

**23.** Which figure shows parallel lines? (Lesson 10-2) F

**F**
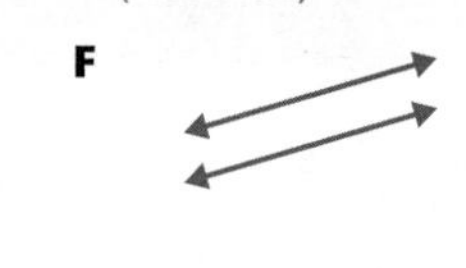

**H**
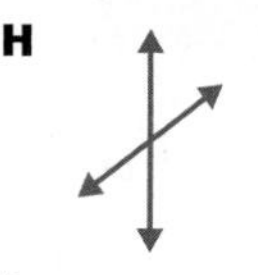

**G**
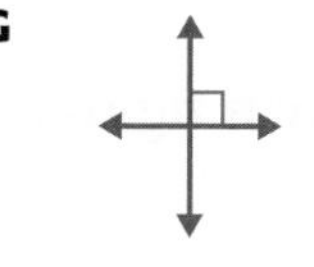

**J**
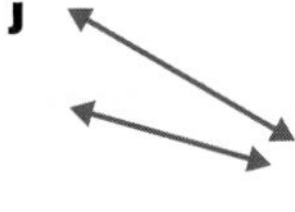

## Spiral Review

**Tell what number each letter on the number line represents.** (Lesson 10-1)

**24.** A, B; 2,000  2,600  3,200  3,800

*A*: 2,300; *B*: 3,500

**25.**

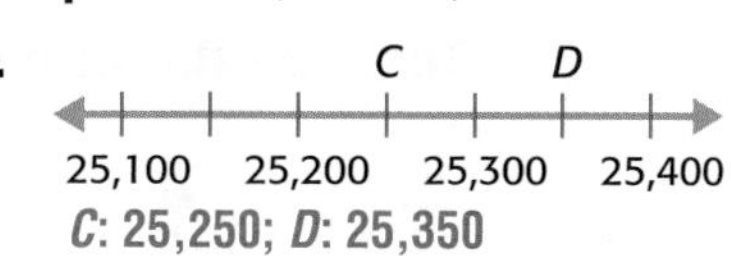


*C*: 25,250; *D*: 25,350

**Algebra** For Exercises 26 and 27, use the table. (Lesson 9-7)

| Game Pieces Needed | |
|---|---|
| Students | Number of Pieces |
| 4 | 36 |
| 7 | 63 |
| ■ | 72 |
| 9 | ■ |
| 10 | 90 |

**26.** Mr. Larson's class is playing a game. The table shows how many playing pieces are needed. Copy and complete the table. students = 8; pieces = 81

**27.** Explain how to find the number of pieces needed if you know the number of students playing. See margin.



### Homework Practice (p. 15) OL

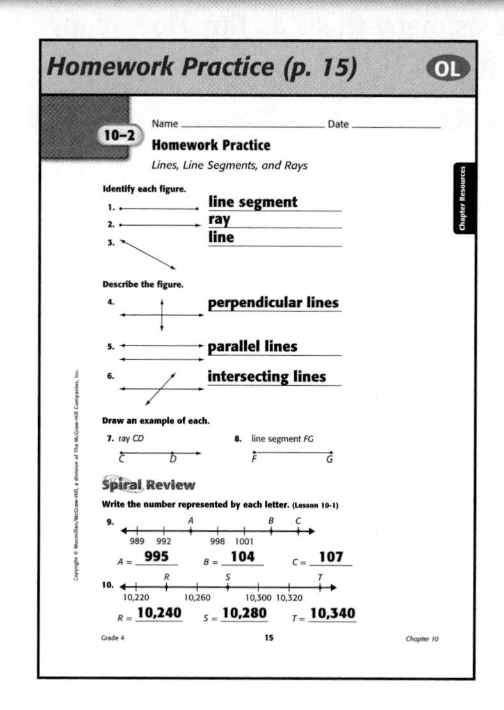


# 4 Assess

## Formative Assessment

- **Explain the difference between a line and a line segment.** A line goes on forever in two directions; a line segment has two endpoints.
- **What are some examples of perpendicular lines?** Sample answers: lines on graph paper that cross, the lines that cross on window panes

**Quick Check** Are students continuing to struggle with identifying, describing, and classifying lines, line segments, and rays?

**If Yes** → Small Group Options (p. 356B)
Strategic Intervention (p. 126)

**If No** → Independent Work Options (p. 356B)
CRM Skills Practice Worksheet (p. 14)
CRM Enrich Worksheet (p. 17)

**Ticket Out the Door** Draw two perpendicular line segments, *XY* and *WZ*, on the board. Tell students to write a description of the figure and give it to you.

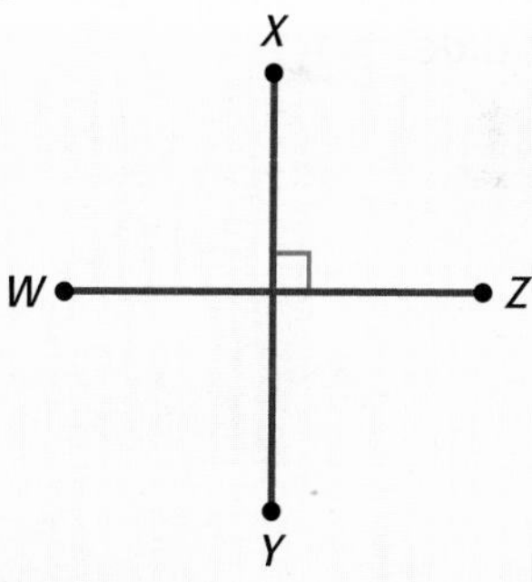


## TEST Practice

### Reviews Lessons 10-1 and 10-2

Assign the Test Practice problems to provide daily reinforcement of test-taking skills.

## Spiral Review

### Reviews Lessons 10-1 and 9-7

Review and assess mastery of skills and concepts from previous chapters.

### Additional Answer

**27.** Sample answer: Multiply the number of students by 9.

# 10-3 Problem-Solving Strategy: Make an Organized List

## Lesson Planner

### Objective

Make an organized list to solve problems.

### Resources

**Literature Connection:** *Domino Addition* by Lynette Long, Ph.D.

**Teacher Technology**

TeacherWorks • Interactive Classroom •

**Real-World Problem Solving Library**
**Math and Science: *Trapped in Tar***
Use these leveled books to reinforce and extend problem-solving skills and strategies.

Leveled for:

- OL On Level
- ELL Sheltered English
- SP Spanish

For additional support, see the Real-World Problem Solving Teacher Guide.

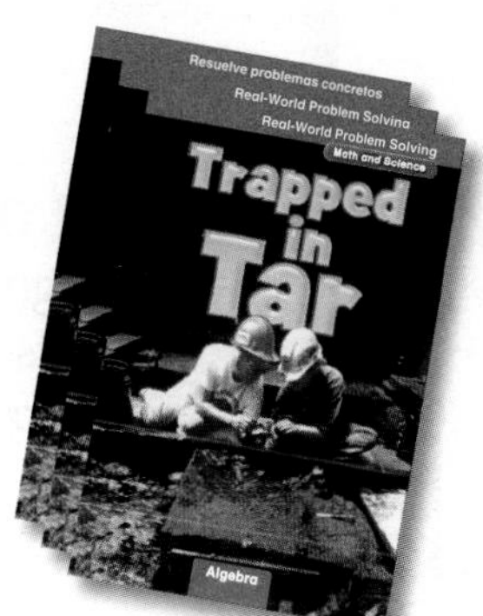


## Daily Routine

Use these suggestions before beginning the lesson on p. 404.

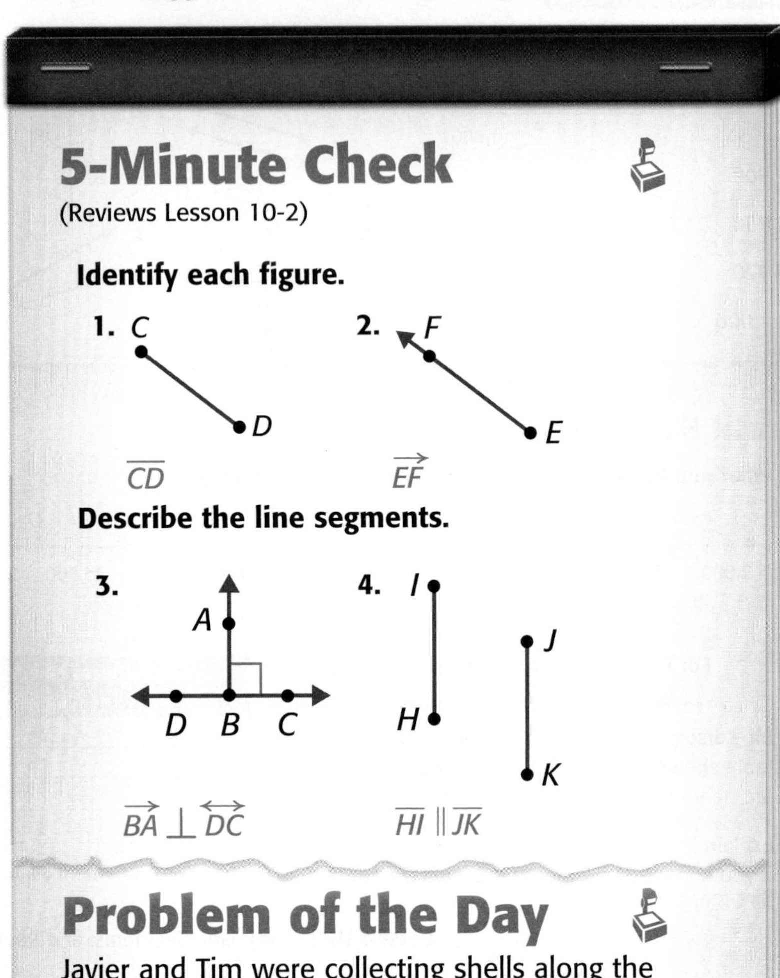

### 5-Minute Check

(Reviews Lesson 10-2)

**Identify each figure.**

**1.** $\overline{CD}$

**2.** $\overrightarrow{EF}$

**Describe the line segments.**

**3.** $\overrightarrow{BA} \perp \overleftrightarrow{DC}$

**4.** $\overline{HI} \parallel \overline{JK}$

### Problem of the Day

Javier and Tim were collecting shells along the beach. Tim found 8 shells. Javier found 3 more than twice as many shells as Tim. How many shells did they find in all? 27

# Differentiated Instruction

## Small Group Options

Option 1 LOGICAL, VISUAL, SPATIAL

### Below Level BL

**Materials:** chart paper, markers, pennies, nickels, dimes, quarters, paper, pencils

Copy the following problem on the chart paper:

*How many different combinations of coins are there to make 31¢?*

- Encourage students to make an organized list of their answers in order to be sure to get them all.
  See students' work.
- Ask students if they see any patterns in the list.
  See students' work.

Option 2 INTRAPERSONAL

### English Language Learners ELL

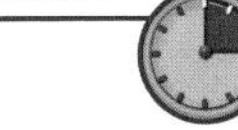

**Materials:** pencil, paper
**Core Vocabulary:** important, remind, brought from home
**Common Use Verb:** take/took
**Write Math** This strategy connects background knowledge of lists to target vocabulary.

- Say, "Lists **remind** us to do something or help us to remember something **important**."
- Have students write a list in their native language of the five most important things they brought from their home country or the five most important things in their homes.
- Say: "Lists can also help people solve math problems."
- After making their lists, have students write a math problem that uses the things they brought from home (in English).
- Discuss problems and how the list helped or did not help them.

## Independent Work Options

Option 1 LOGICAL, VISUAL

### Early Finishers OL AL

**Materials:** four types/colors of wrapping paper, three types/colors of ribbon or bows, paper, pencil.

- Have students find all possible combinations of gift wrap from the given supplies.
- Tell students that exactly one type of paper and one type of ribbon can be used to wrap a package.
- Ask them to display the possible combinations on their poster in an organized list.

| | Yellow ribbon | Blue ribbon | Green ribbon |
|---|---|---|---|
| Purple paper | PP/YR | PP/BR | PP/GR |
| Yellow paper | YP/YR | YP/BR | YP/GR |
| Green paper | GP/YR | GP/BR | GP/GR |
| Blue paper | BP/YR | BP/BR | BP/GR |

Option 2

### Student Technology

Math Online macmillanmh.com

Personal Tutor • Extra Examples

Tech Link

Option 3

### Learning Station: Art (p. 392G)

Direct students to the Art Learning Station for opportunities to explore and extend the lesson concept.

# 10-3 Problem-Solving Strategy

## 1 Introduce

### Activity Choice 1 • Review

- Provide students with the following problem:

  *There are 17 plants in a garden. There are twice as many pepper plants as tomato plants and 3 fewer cucumber plants as pepper plants. How many of each kind of plant is in the garden?*

- **What strategy did you use to solve this problem?** Sample answer: guess and check
- **Solve the problem.** 4 tomato plants; 8 pepper plants; 5 cucumber plants

### Activity Choice 2 • Literature

Introduce the lesson with *Domino Addition* by Lynette Long, Ph.D For a related math activity, see p. TR57.

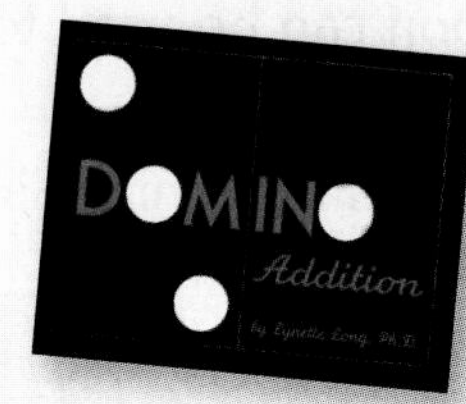

## 2 Teach

Have students read the problem on going camping. Guide them through the problem-solving steps.

**Understand** Using the questions, review what students know and need to find.

**Plan** Have them discuss their strategy.

**Solve** Guide students to use the make an organized list strategy to solve the problem.

- **How many children are going camping?** 4
- **How many children will sleep in each tent?** two

**Check** Have students look back at the problem to make sure that the answer fits the facts given.

- **How can you make sure that you have not counted a group too many times?** Make sure that each group of two is different.

**COMMON ERROR!**

**Exercises 6 and 9** Students may need help determining that order does not matter here. Point out that pulling out a 2 and then a 7 is the same as pulling out a 7 and then a 2 for Exercise 6. In Exercise 9, there are only 6 combinations, since taking out a quarter and a dime is the same as taking out a dime and a quarter.



# 10-3 Problem-Solving Strategy

**MAIN IDEA** I will make an organized list to solve problems.

The Burke family is going camping for the weekend. There are four children in the Burke family, Devon, Nikki, Jade, and Terrell. They will sleep in two tents, with two children in each tent. How many different combinations are possible?

**Understand**

**What facts do you know?**

- There are 4 children going camping.
- Two children will sleep in each tent.

**What do you need to find?**

- Find how many combinations are possible.

**Plan**

You can make a list of all the possible combinations. Then count the total number of different combinations.

**Solve**

First, write the name of one of the children. Then, write the name of another child by the first child's name. Continue to do this with each child. Do not repeat pairs.

| | | |
|---|---|---|
| Nikki—Jade | Jade—Terrell | Terrell—Devon |
| Nikki—Terrell | Jade—Devon | |
| Nikki—Devon | | |

There are 6 different combinations that can be in each tent.

**Check**

Look back. There are 4 children. They can each pair up with three other children. Each child's name does appear 3 times on the list. So, the answer is correct. ✓



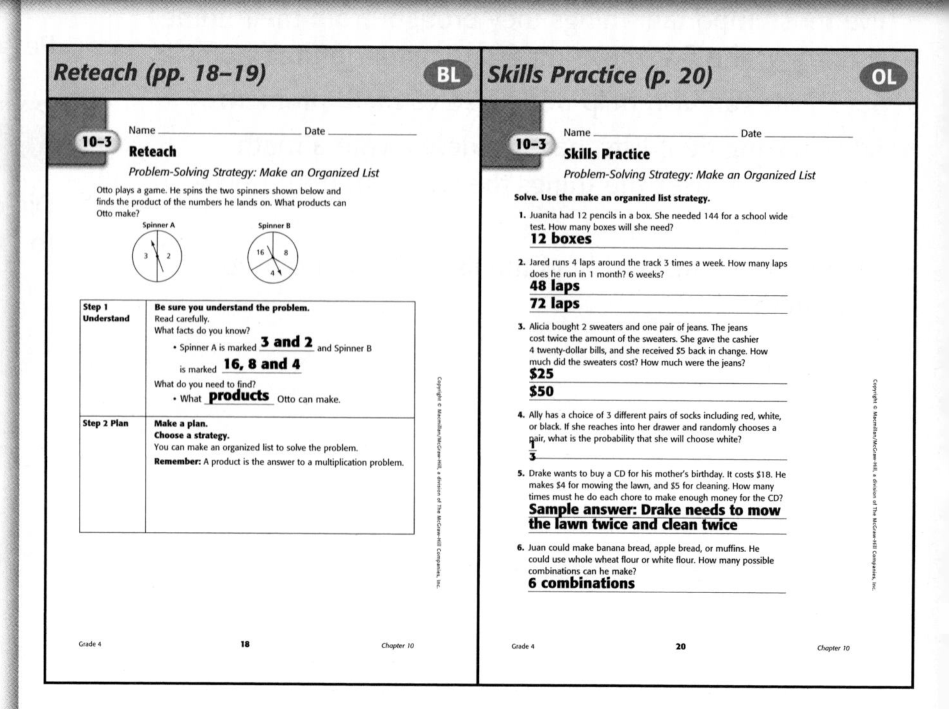

**Reteach (pp. 18–19)** BL

10-3 Name ________ Date ________

**Reteach**

*Problem-Solving Strategy: Make an Organized List*

Otto plays a game. He spins the two spinners shown below and finds the product of the numbers he lands on. What products can Otto make?

Spinner A: 3, 2 — Spinner B: 16, 8, 4

| | |
|---|---|
| **Step 1 Understand** | **Be sure you understand the problem.**<br>Read carefully.<br>What facts do you know?<br>• Spinner A is marked **3 and 2** and Spinner B is marked **16, 8 and 4**<br>What do you need to find?<br>• What **products** Otto can make. |
| **Step 2 Plan** | **Make a plan.**<br>**Choose a strategy.**<br>You can make an organized list to solve the problem.<br>**Remember:** A product is the answer to a multiplication problem. |



Grade 4 18 *Chapter 10*

**Skills Practice (p. 20)** OL

10-3 Name ________ Date ________

**Skills Practice**

*Problem-Solving Strategy: Make an Organized List*

**Solve. Use the make an organized list strategy.**

1. Juanita had 12 pencils in a box. She needed 144 for a school wide test. How many boxes will she need?
   **12 boxes**
2. Jared runs 4 laps around the track 3 times a week. How many laps does he run in 1 month? 6 weeks?
   **48 laps**
   **72 laps**
3. Alicia bought 2 sweaters and one pair of jeans. The jeans cost twice the amount of the sweaters. She gave the cashier 4 twenty-dollar bills, and she received $5 back in change. How much did the sweaters cost? How much were the jeans?
   **$25**
   **$50**
4. Ally has a choice of 3 different pairs of socks including red, white, or black. If she reaches into her drawer and randomly chooses a pair, what is the probability that she will choose white?
   $\frac{1}{3}$
5. Drake wants to buy a CD for his mother's birthday. It costs $18. He makes $4 for mowing the lawn, and $5 for cleaning. How many times must he do each chore to make enough money for the CD?
   **Sample answer: Drake needs to mow the lawn twice and clean twice**
6. Juan could make banana bread, apple bread, or muffins. He could use whole wheat flour or white flour. How many possible combinations can he make?
   **6 combinations**



Grade 4 20 *Chapter 10*

## ANALYZE the Strategy

**Refer to the problem on the previous page.**

1. Suppose one of the children brings a friend camping. How does the additional child affect the possible combinations? **Sample answer: It increases the possible outcomes by 4.**
2. Identify another way to organize all of the possible outcomes. **Sample answer: A table or diagram could be made.**
3. Suppose Nikki, Jade, and Terrell go for a hike in a single file line. Make a list to show all the possible ways they can line up. **See Ch. 10 Answer Appendix.**
4. What is the probability that Nikki will be first in line if the children line up in random order? $\frac{1}{3}$

## PRACTICE the Strategy

**Solve. Make an organized list.**

5. Richard has one blue shirt and one red shirt. He has gray pants and navy pants. How many different outfits can he wear? **4 outfits**
6. Sadie put four slips of paper into a hat. Each slip of paper has a number written on it as shown. Sadie chooses two slips of paper. How many different sums could she have? **6 sums**

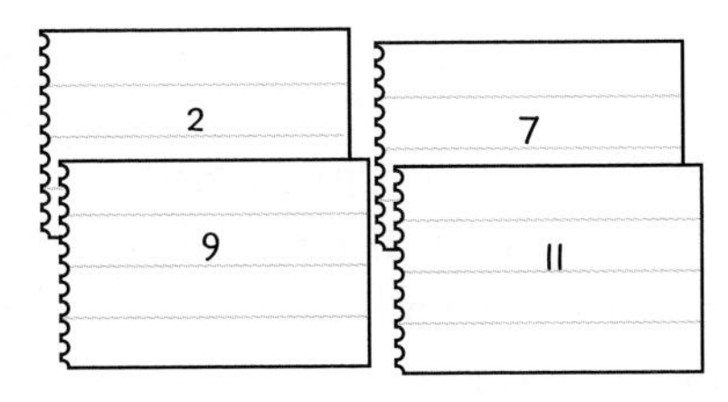


7. Yogi's mom is hanging three photographs side-by-side on a wall. How many different ways can the photographs be arranged? **6 ways**
8. Pari, Montana, Katie, and Dominic are in line for lunch. Montana is first. How many ways could the other people be arranged behind her? **6 ways**
9. Jimmy put the coins shown into a piggy bank. If he chooses 2 coins at a time, what possible combinations might he choose? **See Ch. 10 Answer Appendix.**

10. Sandra is arranging three animal-shaped pillows. One is a dog, another is a cat, and the third is a fish. How many different ways can she arrange her pillows? **6 arrangements**
11. Alexa needs to read a mystery, biography, or fantasy book. Then she must write a report, give a speech, or act out a scene from the book. How many different options are there? **9 options**
12. **WRITING IN MATH** Explain how you used the make an organized list strategy to solve Exercise 11. **See Ch. 10 Answer Appendix.**



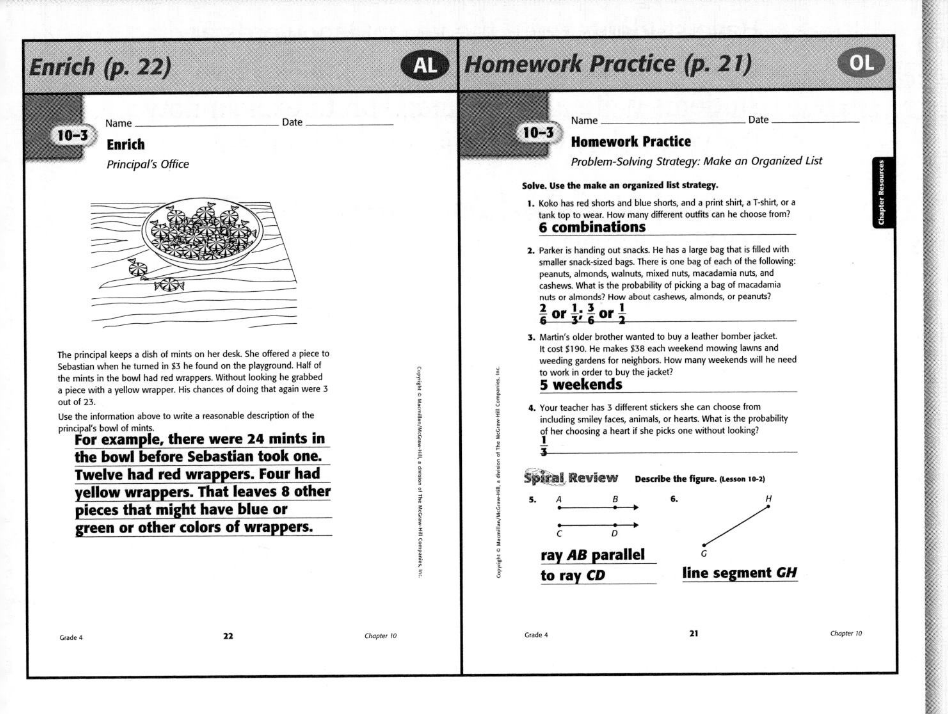

### Enrich (p. 22) AL

10-3 Name ______ Date ______

**Enrich**

*Principal's Office*

The principal keeps a dish of mints on her desk. She offered a piece to Sebastian when he turned in $3 he found on the playground. Half of the mints in the bowl had red wrappers. Without looking he grabbed a piece with a yellow wrapper. His chances of doing that again were 3 out of 23.

Use the information above to write a reasonable description of the principal's bowl of mints.

**For example, there were 24 mints in the bowl before Sebastian took one. Twelve had red wrappers. Four had yellow wrappers. That leaves 8 other pieces that might have blue or green or other colors of wrappers.**



Grade 4 22 Chapter 10

### Homework Practice (p. 21) OL

10-3 Name ______ Date ______

**Homework Practice**

*Problem-Solving Strategy: Make an Organized List*

Chapter Resources

**Solve. Use the make an organized list strategy.**

1. Koko has red shorts and blue shorts, and a print shirt, a T-shirt, or a tank top to wear. How many different outfits can he choose from? **6 combinations**
2. Parker is handing out snacks. He has a large bag that is filled with smaller snack-sized bags. There is one bag of each of the following: peanuts, almonds, walnuts, mixed nuts, macadamia nuts, and cashews. What is the probability of picking a bag of macadamia nuts or almonds? How about cashews, almonds, or peanuts? $\frac{2}{6}$ **or** $\frac{1}{3}$; $\frac{3}{6}$ **or** $\frac{1}{2}$
3. Martin's older brother wanted to buy a leather bomber jacket. It cost $190. He makes $38 each weekend mowing lawns and weeding gardens for neighbors. How many weekends will he need to work in order to buy the jacket? **5 weekends**
4. Your teacher has 3 different stickers she can choose from including smiley faces, animals, or hearts. What is the probability of her choosing a heart if she picks one without looking? $\frac{1}{3}$

**Spiral Review** **Describe the figure.** (Lesson 10-2)

5. A B C D — **ray *AB* parallel to ray *CD***
6. G H — **line segment *GH***



Grade 4 21 Chapter 10

**Analyze the Strategy** Use Exercises 1–4 to analyze and discuss the problem-solving strategy.

### BL Alternate Teaching Strategy

**If** students have trouble listing all possible outcomes…

**Then** use one of these reteach options:

1. CRM **Daily Reteach Worksheet** (pp. 18–19)
2. Show them how to use an organized list to be sure they do not leave anything out. Point out that they could also make a table, or draw a picture to help them solve these problems.

## 3 Practice

### Using the Exercises

**Exercises 5–11** Students may need help creating their organized lists. In addition, it might be helpful to draw pictures to show the possible outcomes.

**Exercise 8** You may need to point out that since Montana is always first, only the other three people need to be arranged.

## 4 Assess

### Formative Assessment

Draw a simple menu labeled Sandwich Choices. For meat, list ham and turkey, and for toppings, list lettuce, tomato, cheese, and pickles.

- **How do you determine the number of possibilities if one item is chosen from each category?** List the choices; there are 8.
- **Suppose two different toppings can be chosen with any meat. How many sandwich choices does this produce?** 12

**Quick Check** **Are students continuing to struggle with using the make an organized list strategy?**

**If Yes** → Small Group Options (p. 404B)

**If No** → Independent Work Options (p. 404B)
CRM Skills Practice Worksheet (p. 20)
CRM Enrich Worksheet (p. 22)

LESSON 10-4

# Find Points on a Grid

## Lesson Planner

### Objective

Use ordered pairs to find and name points on a grid.

### Vocabulary

**coordinate plane**, **origin**, ***x*-axis**, ***y*-axis**, **ordered pair**, **coordinates**

### Resources

**Materials:** grid paper, colored pencils or markers

**Literature Connection:** *G is for Googol: A Math Alphabet Book* by David M. Schwartz

**Teacher Technology**

TeacherWorks • Interactive Classroom • Math Songs Track #7 Lesson Plan

## Daily Routine

Use these suggestions before beginning the lesson on p. 406.

### 5-Minute Check

(Reviews Lesson 10-3)

**Solve. Make an organized list.**

Gino has $15 in bills in his pocket. How many different combinations of bills could he have in his pocket? 6

### Problem of the Day

Cecilia has 160¢. She has only quarters, dimes and nickels, and she has the same number of each of the coins. How many coins does Cecilia have? How many of each coin does she have?
12 coins; 4 of each

### Focus on Math Background

In this lesson, students are introduced to the concept of a coordinate plane (or coordinate grid). A coordinate plane provides a way to locate points in a plane. It consists of two number lines or axes that are perpendicular to each other. The axes intersect at a point called the *origin*, which has coordinates (0, 0). To find a point on the grid when an ordered pair $(a, b)$ is given:

- Start at the origin.
- Move $a$ units to the right if $a$ is positive, move $|a|$ units to the left if $a$ is negative, and do not move at all if $a$ is 0.
- Then from that point on the horizontal axis, move up $b$ units if $b$ is positive, move down $|b|$ if $b$ is negative, and do not move at all if $b$ is 0.

Note that in this lesson, only the first quadrant of the coordinate plane is examined. So only ordered pairs $(a, b)$ where $a \geq 0$ and $b \geq 0$ are presented to the students.

### Building Math Vocabulary

Write the lesson vocabulary words and their definitions on the board.

Have students write the vocabulary words and their definitions in their Math Journals. Have students write a short paragraph to explain how the vocabulary words relate to each other.

#### Visual Vocabulary Cards

Use Visual Vocabulary Cards 33, 49, and 50 to reinforce the vocabulary introduced in this lesson. (The Define/Example/Ask routine is printed on the back of each card.)

# Differentiated Instruction

## Small Group Options

LOGICAL

### Option 1 Below Level BL

**Materials:** 1″ grid paper and pencil

- Students should use the grid from Example 1 of this lesson or create new ones using 1″ grid paper.
- To help students remember how to locate points on a grid, teach them the following saying: "Always **go** to the mountain (horizontal line) and then **climb up** the mountain. **Never** begin on a mountain peak."
- Now have students practice finding points on a grid: (2, 6), (3, 4), (5, 6).
- **What happens when you start on a mountain peak?** Your answer will be backward.

VISUAL, LOGICAL

### Option 2 English Language Learners ELL

**Materials:** overhead transparency grids
**Core Vocabulary:** right and up, ordered pairs, first/second
**Common Use Verb:** go
**See Math** This strategy familiarizes students with using columns and rows on a grid.

- Draw various symbols (flower, smiley face, etc.) at different locations on a grid with zero in the middle. Also show an ordered pair.
- Say: "The **first** number indicates where to move right from the zero and the **second** tells you where to move up."
- Give students an ordered pair that will lead them to a symbol.
- Guide students by modeling and vocalizing how to move.
- Allow pairs to repeat, watching to see if each pair has landed on the correct item.
- Repeat as time permits.
- Allow students to create their own grids and ordered pairs for partners to solve as time permits.

## Independent Work Options

SPATIAL

### Option 1 Early Finishers OL AL

**Materials:** paper, pencil, grid paper

- Have students make a grid and draw objects for at least 5 points.
- On the back of the grid, students identify the ordered pair for each object.
- Have students trade grids and identify the ordered pair for each object.

### Option 2 Student Technology

Personal Tutor • Extra Examples

Math Songs, "I Draw the Line" Track #7

### Option 3 Learning Station: Social Studies (p. 392H)

Direct students to the Social Studies Learning Station for opportunities to explore and extend the lesson concept.

### Option 4 Problem-Solving Practice

Reinforce problem-solving skills and strategies with the Problem-Solving Practice worksheet.

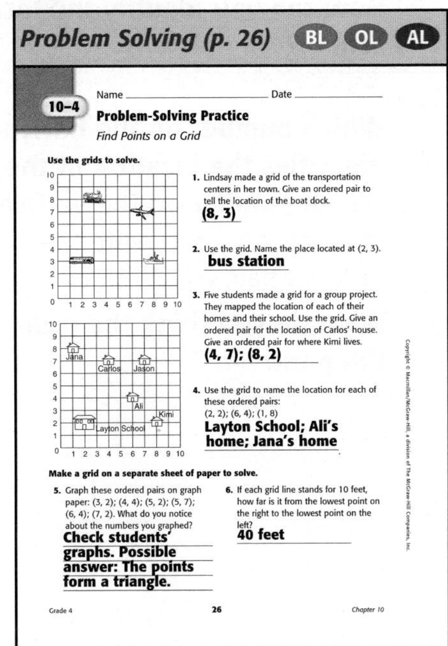

**Problem Solving (p. 26)** BL OL AL

10–4 Name ____________ Date ____________

**Problem-Solving Practice**

*Find Points on a Grid*

**Use the grids to solve.**

1. Lindsay made a grid of the transportation centers in her town. Give an ordered pair to tell the location of the boat dock.
**(8, 3)**

2. Use the grid. Name the place located at (2, 3).
**bus station**

3. Five students made a grid for a group project. They mapped the location of each of their homes and their school. Use the grid. Give an ordered pair for the location of Carlos' house. Give an ordered pair for where Kimi lives.
**(4, 7); (8, 2)**

4. Use the grid to name the location for each of these ordered pairs: (2, 2); (6, 4); (1, 8)
**Layton School; Ali's home; Jana's home**

**Make a grid on a separate sheet of paper to solve.**

5. Graph these ordered pairs on graph paper: (3, 2); (4, 4); (5, 2); (5, 7); (6, 4); (7, 2). What do you notice about the numbers you graphed?
**Check students' graphs. Possible answer: The points form a triangle.**

6. If each grid line stands for 10 feet, how far is it from the lowest point on the right to the lowest point on the left?
**40 feet**



Grade 4 26 Chapter 10

# 10-4 Find Points on a Grid

## 1 Introduce

### Activity Choice 1 • Hands-On

- Arrange students in your classroom into an array. Assign values to each vertical row of students starting with *A*. Assign a number starting with 1 to each horizontal row of students.
- One at a time, ask students at the following points to stand up: *C*2; *B*4; *A*1; *D*3.
- Select students to stand up and name their own locations.

### Activity Choice 2 • Literature

Introduce the lesson with *G is for Googol: A Math Alphabet Book* by David M. Schwartz. For a related math activity, see p. TR58.

## 2 Teach

### Scaffolding Questions

Create the following grid on the board.

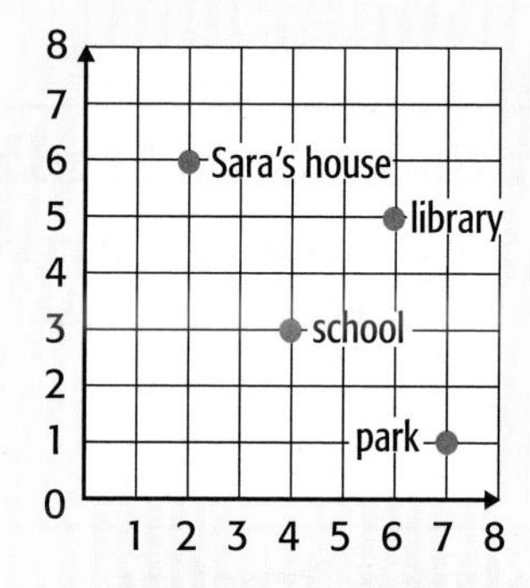


- **How can you identify the location of the school?** Sample answer: Use the horizontal and vertical numbers on the grid.
- **Which number on the horizontal axis identifies the location of the school?** 4 **Which number on the vertical axis?** 3 Tell students they can write the location as the ordered pair. (4, 3)
- **What do you think the ordered pair is for the park?** (7, 1)

# 10-4 Find Points on a Grid

**MAIN IDEA**

I will use ordered pairs to find and name points on a grid

**New Vocabulary**

**coordinate plane**
**origin**
***x*-axis**
***y*-axis**
**ordered pair**
**coordinates**

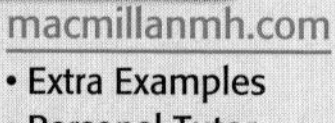


macmillanmh.com
- Extra Examples
- Personal Tutor
- Self-Check Quiz

**GET READY to Learn**

The map gives the locations of several students' homes and their school. From the location of the school at (0, 0), Dave lives 5 units right and 3 units up. This can be written as (5, 3).

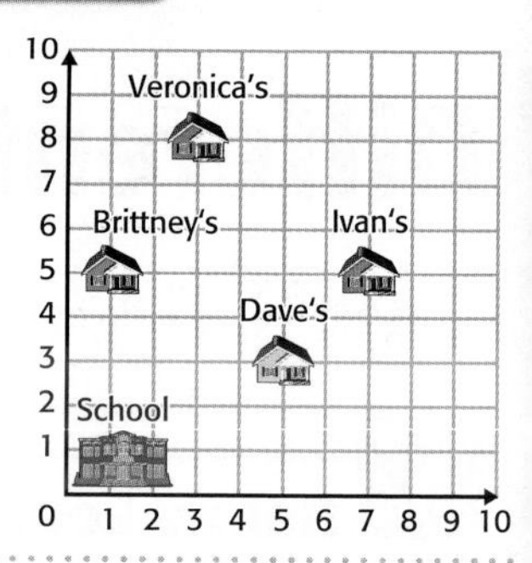


The map shown above is an example of a coordinate plane. A **coordinate plane** is formed when two number lines intersect at their zero points.

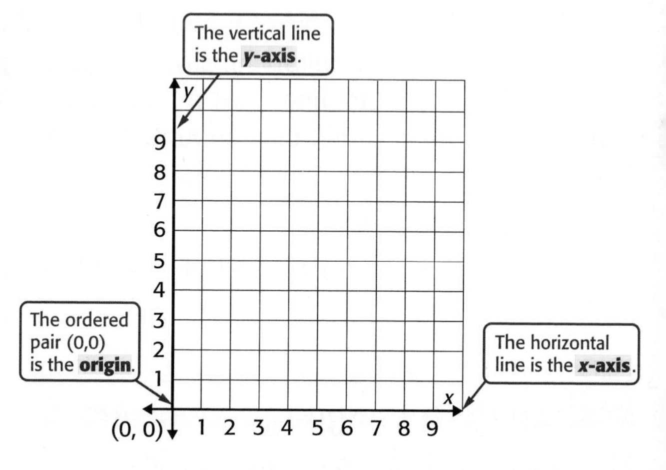


The point (5, 3) is an example of an **ordered pair**. The numbers in an ordered pair are called **coordinates**. The coordinates give the location of the point.

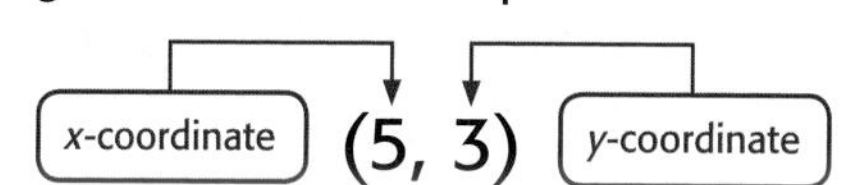




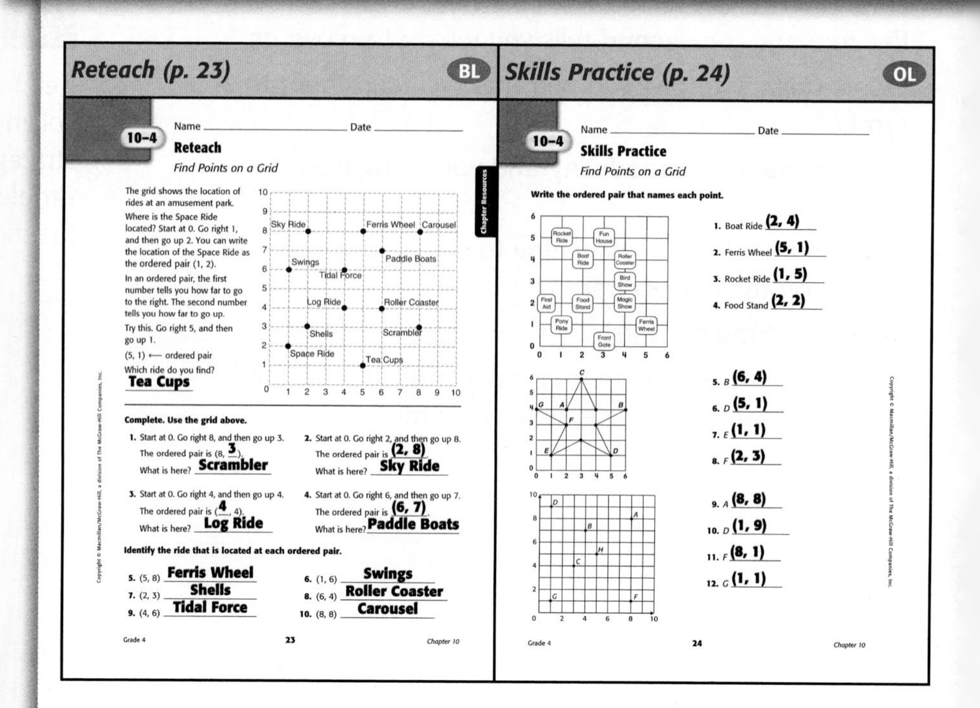

**Reteach (p. 23)** BL

10-4 Name ______ Date ______

**Reteach**

*Find Points on a Grid*

The grid shows the location of rides at an amusement park.

Where is the Space Ride located? Start at 0. Go right 1, and then go up 2. You can write the location of the Space Ride as the ordered pair (1, 2).

In an ordered pair, the first number tells you how far to go to the right. The second number tells you how far to go up.

Try this. Go right 5, and then go up 1.

(5, 1) ⟵ ordered pair

Which ride do you find? **Tea Cups**



**Complete. Use the grid above.**

1. Start at 0. Go right 8, and then go up 3. The ordered pair is (8, **3**). What is here? **Scrambler**
2. Start at 0. Go right 2, and then go up 8. The ordered pair is **(2, 8)**. What is here? **Sky Ride**
3. Start at 0. Go right 4, and then go up 4. The ordered pair is (**4**, 4). What is here? **Log Ride**
4. Start at 0. Go right 6, and then go up 7. The ordered pair is **(6, 7)**. What is here? **Paddle Boats**

**Identify the ride that is located at each ordered pair.**

5. (5, 8) **Ferris Wheel**
6. (1, 6) **Swings**
7. (2, 3) **Shells**
8. (6, 4) **Roller Coaster**
9. (4, 6) **Tidal Force**
10. (8, 8) **Carousel**

Grade 4 23 Chapter 10



**Skills Practice (p. 24)** OL

10-4 Name ______ Date ______

**Skills Practice**

*Find Points on a Grid*

**Write the ordered pair that names each point.**



1. Boat Ride **(2, 4)**
2. Ferris Wheel **(5, 1)**
3. Rocket Ride **(1, 5)**
4. Food Stand **(2, 2)**
5. *B* **(6, 4)**
6. *D* **(5, 1)**
7. *E* **(1, 1)**
8. *F* **(2, 3)**
9. *A* **(8, 8)**
10. *D* **(1, 9)**
11. *F* **(8, 1)**
12. *G* **(1, 1)**

Grade 4 24 Chapter 10

## Real-World EXAMPLE — Find Ordered Pairs

**1 ZOO A map of a zoo is shown. Identify the animal that is located at (5, 4).**

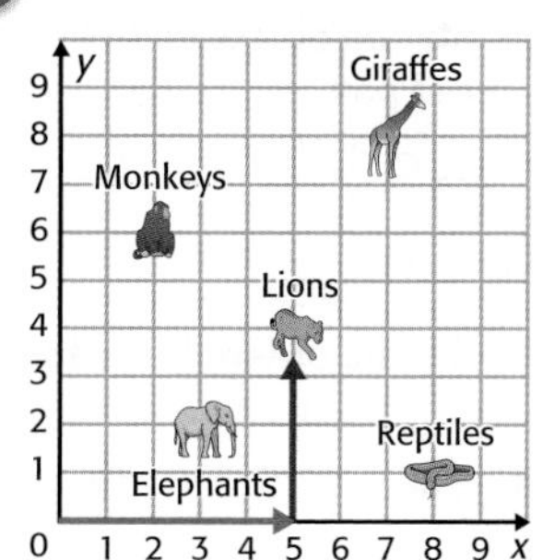


To find (**5**, **4**), start at (0, 0). Move right **5** units. Then, move up **4** units. The ordered pair (**5**, **4**) locates the lions.

## CHECK What You Know

**Identify the building that is located at each ordered pair.** See Example 1 (p. 407)

1. (6, 8) baseball stadium
2. (3, 7) library
3. (2, 4) zoo
4. (8, 6) mall

**Identify the ordered pair for each building.** See Example 1 (p. 407)

5. grocery store (1, 8)
6. hospital (9, 3)
7. bus station (9, 9)
8. town hall (5, 6)

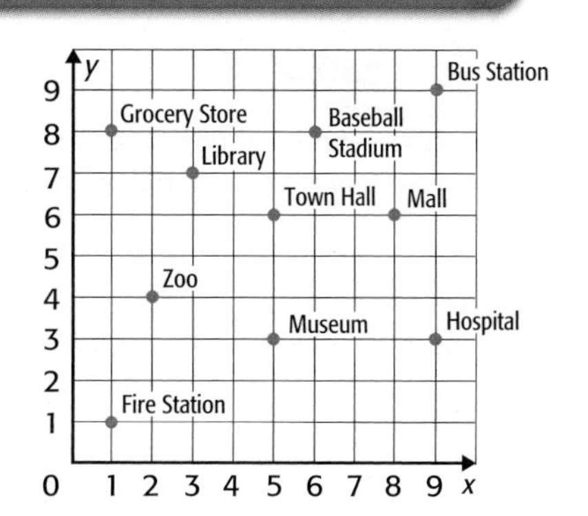


**For Exercises 9–12, use the coordinate plane above.**

9. Describe how to get from the library to the grocery store. Move 2 spaces to the left and up 1 space.
10. Describe how to get from the zoo to the museum. Move 3 spaces to the right and down 1 space.
11. Jameson is at the bus station. He needs to go to the town hall. How does he get there on the grid? Move 4 spaces left and down 3 spaces.
12. Jill is at the museum. She lives near the library. How will she get there on the grid? Move 2 spaces to the left and up 4 spaces.
13. Talk About It How does an ordered pair name a location? See Ch. 10 Answer Appendix.



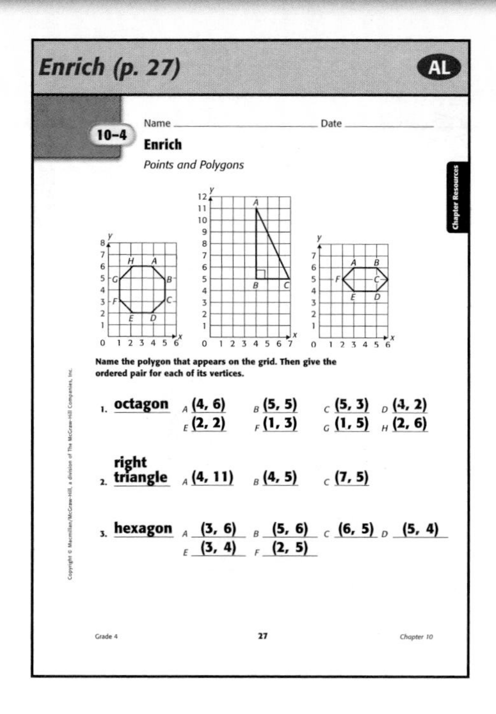

### Enrich (p. 27) AL

10–4 Name ______ Date ______

**Enrich**

*Points and Polygons*

**Name the polygon that appears on the grid. Then give the ordered pair for each of its vertices.**

1. octagon A (4, 6) B (5, 5) C (5, 3) D (4, 2) E (2, 2) F (1, 3) G (1, 5) H (2, 6)
2. right triangle A (4, 11) B (4, 5) C (7, 5)
3. hexagon A (3, 6) B (5, 6) C (6, 5) D (5, 4) E (3, 4) F (2, 5)

Chapter Resources





## GET READY to Learn

Have students open their books and read the information in **Get Ready to Learn**. Introduce **coordinate plane**, **origin**, ***x*-axis**, ***y*-axis**, **ordered pair** and **coordinates**. As a class, work through **Example 1**.

### Find Ordered Pairs

**Example 1** Be sure students understand that to find a point when given an ordered pair, start at (0, 0), move right the number of units indicated by the first number in the ordered pair, and then move up the number of units indicated by the second number in the ordered pair.

### ADDITIONAL EXAMPLE

**1** Identify what is located at point (2, 5).
post office

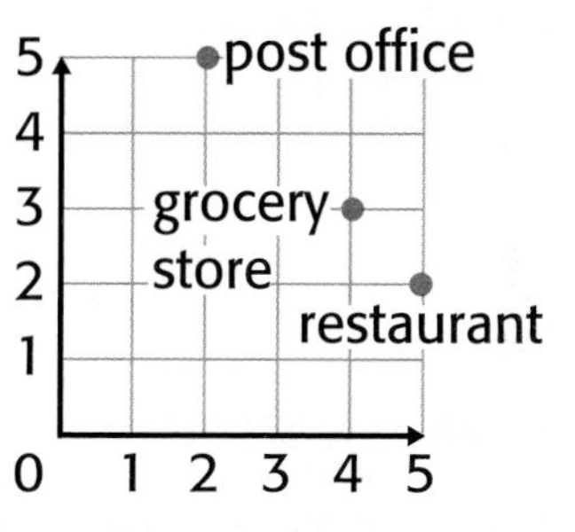


### CHECK What You Know

As a class, have students complete Exercises 1–13 in **Check What You Know** as you observe their work.

**Exercise 13** Assess student comprehension before assigning practice exercises.

## BL Alternate Teaching Strategy

**If** students have trouble using ordered pairs to find points on a coordinate plane…

**Then** use one of these reteach options:

1. CRM **Daily Reteach Worksheet** (p. 23)
2. Provide students with a $6 \times 6$ coordinate plane. Have them go over the horizontal lines with one color marker and the vertical lines with another color. Have them practice locating the point (4, 3) by first tracing over the 4 with the color of the horizontal lines and the 3 with the color of the vertical lines. Remind them to always move right and then up to locate a point.

# 3 Practice

Differentiate practice using these leveled assignments for Exercises 14–27.

| Level | Assignment |
|---|---|
| BL Below/Approaching Level | 14–15, 18–19, 22–23 |
| OL On Level | 15–17, 20–22, 24–26 |
| AL Above/Beyond Level | 15–17 odd, 27–28 |

Have students discuss and complete the Higher Order Thinking problems. For Exercise 28, encourage students to draw a grid to solve the problem. Provide them with grid paper.

**WRITING IN MATH** Have students complete Exercise 28 in their Math Journals. You may choose to use this exercise as an optional formative assessment.

# 4 Assess

## Formative Assessment

- **How do you find the ordered pair (6, 3)?** Go 6 spaces to the right of (0, 0) and 3 up.

**Quick Check** **Are students continuing to struggle with using ordered pairs to find and name points on a grid?**

**If Yes** → Small Group Options (p. 406B)

**If No** → Independent Work Options (p. 406B)
CRM Skills Practice Worksheet (p. 24)
CRM Enrich Worksheet (p. 27)

**Name the Math** Have students write a short explanation of how to locate a point on a coordinate plane when given an ordered pair.

## ! COMMON ERROR!

**Exercises 1 and 4** Students may have trouble with these points because the numbers are transposed. Tell them this tip to help them remember how to locate the coordinate pair: the A in **A**cross comes before the U in **U**p.



## Practice and Problem Solving

EXTRA PRACTICE See page R26.

**Identify the object that is located at each ordered pair.** See Example 1 (p. 407)

**14.** (9, 6) bookcase **15.** (2, 8) globe

**16.** (5, 1) teacher's desk **17.** (1, 2) pencil sharpener

**Identify the ordered pair for each object.** See Example 1 (p. 407)

**18.** coat rack (5, 9) **19.** bulletin board (1, 6)

**20.** door (0, 0) **21.** chalkboard (7, 0)

**For Exercises 22 and 23, use the coordinate plane above.**

**22.** Describe how to get from the ordered pair for the pencil sharpener to the ordered pair for the coat rack.
22, 23. See Ch.10 Answer Appendix.

**23.** Describe how to get from the ordered pair for the teacher's desk to the ordered pair for the globe.

### Data File

Latitude and longitude lines can be used to find locations on a map. These lines form a coordinate plane.

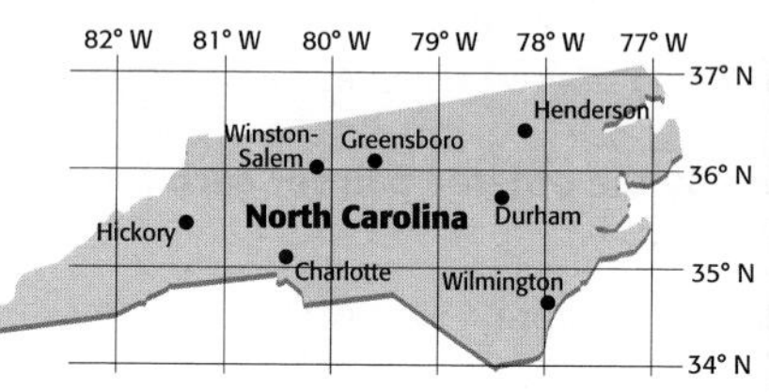


**24.** What city can be found near 36°N and 80°W? Winston-Salem, NC

**25.** What latitude and longitude lines are near Wilmington? 35° N and 78° W

**26.** Name two other cities on this map and their lines of latitude and longitude. See students' work.

### H.O.T. Problems

**27. OPEN ENDED** Draw a picture of your classroom on grid paper. Draw the location of your desk on the grid. What is the ordered pair for your location? Sample answer: (3, 5)

**28. WRITING IN MATH** How is the location of (2, 4) different from the location of (4, 2)? Explain. See Ch.10 Answer Appendix.



**Homework Practice (p. 25)** OL

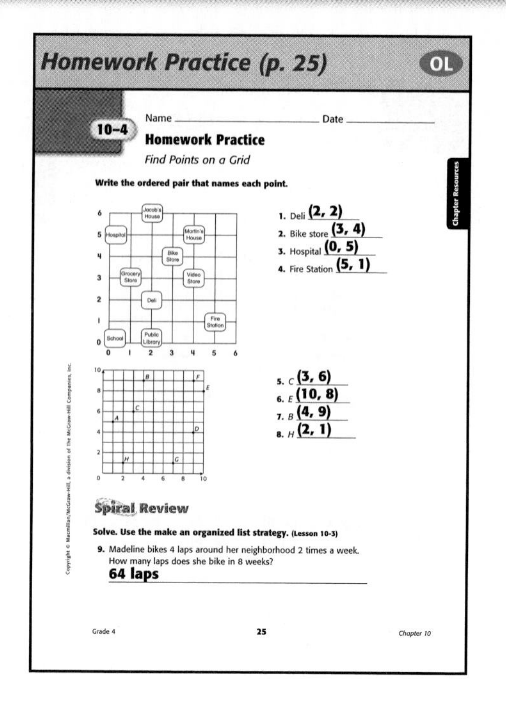

Name ________ Date ________

10–4 **Homework Practice**
*Find Points on a Grid*

**Write the ordered pair that names each point.**

1. Deli (2, 2)
2. Bike store (3, 4)
3. Hospital (0, 5)
4. Fire Station (5, 1)

5. C (3, 6)
6. E (10, 8)
7. B (4, 9)
8. H (2, 1)

**Spiral Review**

**Solve. Use the make an organized list strategy.** (Lesson 10-3)

9. Madeline bikes 4 laps around her neighborhood 2 times a week. How many laps does she bike in 8 weeks?
64 laps

Grade 4 25 Chapter 10

CHAPTER 10

# Mid-Chapter Check

Lessons 10-1 through 10-4

**Tell what number each letter on the number line represents.** (Lesson 10-1)

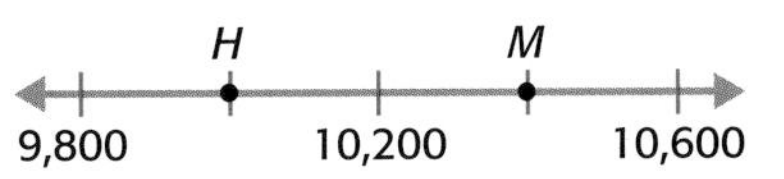


**1.** point *H* 10,000 **2.** point *M* 10,400

**3. MULTIPLE CHOICE** Which number does point *K* represent? (Lesson 10-1) D

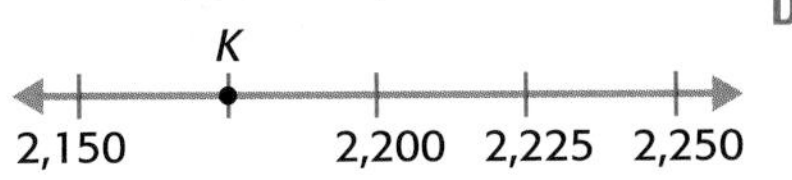


**A** 2,075 **C** 2,155

**B** 2,125 **D** 2,175

**4.** Describe the line segments formed by the top of the step stool. (Lesson 10-2)
The lines are parallel.

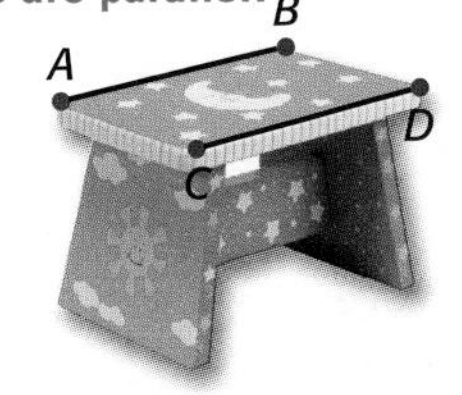


**Identify each figure.** (Lesson 10-2)

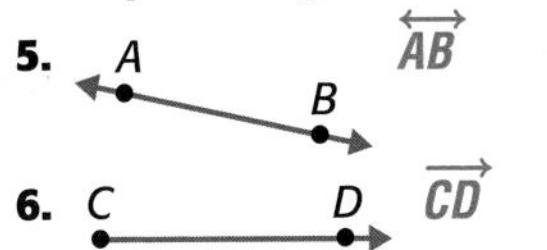


**5.** $\overleftrightarrow{AB}$

**6.** $\overrightarrow{CD}$

**7.** Serena has one red shirt and one white shirt. She has one blue skirt and one black skirt. How many different shirt-skirt outfits can she wear? (Lesson 10-3)
4 outfits

**8. MULTIPLE CHOICE** Which ordered pair is graphed? (Lesson 10-4) G

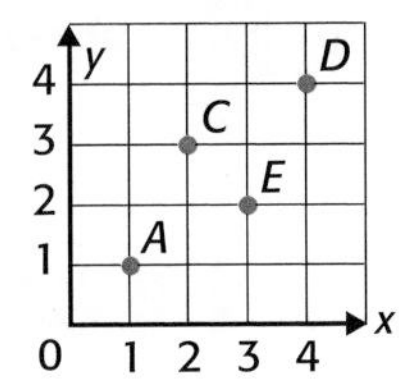


**F** (3, 4) **H** (3, 1)

**G** (2, 3) **J** (5, 2)

**Identify the letter that is located at each ordered pair.** (Lesson 10-4)

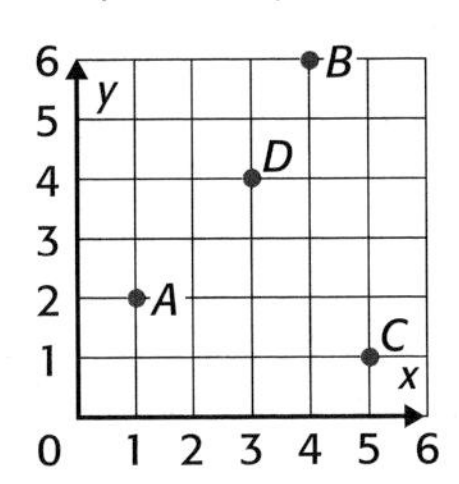


**9.** (1, 2) point *A* **10.** (4, 6) point *B*

**11.** (3, 4) point *D* **12.** (5, 1) point *C*

**13.** Refer to the coordinate plane above. Describe how to get from the ordered pair for point *A* to the ordered pair for point *B*. (Lesson 10-4)
13, 14. See Ch. 10 Answer Appendix.

**14.** WRITING IN MATH Do the ordered pairs (2, 3) and (3, 2) give the location of the same point? Explain. (Lesson 10-4)



CHAPTER 10

# Mid-Chapter Check

## Lessons 10-1 through 10-4

### Formative Assessment

Use the Mid-Chapter Check to assess students' progress in the first half of the chapter.

Customize and create multiple versions of your Mid-Chapter Check and the test answer keys.

### FOLDABLES Dinah Zike's Foldables

Use these lesson suggestions to incorporate the Foldables during the chapter.

**Lesson 10-2** Students identify, describe, and classify lines, line segments, and rays beneath the middle left tab. Vocabulary and student work can be stored in the center pocket.

**Lesson 10-4** Students use the second layer of grid paper to record information, definitions, and to plot points on a grid.

# Data-Driven Decision Making

Based on the results of the Mid-Chapter Check, use the following to review concepts that continue to present students with problems.

| Exercises | State/Local Standards | What's the Mathematics? | Error Analysis | Resources for Review |
|---|---|---|---|---|
| **1–3** Lesson 10-1 | | Locate points on a number line. | Does not identify measurement lines correctly. Does not understand "represented." | Strategic Intervention Guide (pp. 124, 126)<br>CRM Chapter 10 Resource Masters (Reteach Worksheets)<br>Math Adventures<br>My Math Zone Chapter 10<br>Math Online Extra Examples • Concepts in Motion |
| **4–6** Lesson 10-2 | | Identify parallel and intersecting lines. Define two dimensional figures. | Does not know definition of "parallel," "intersecting," "ray." Does not understand "line segment." | |
| **7** Lesson 10-3 | | Use correct problem-solving strategy. | Does not identify all choices of outfits. Does not use any strategy to solve problem. | |
| **8–12** Lesson 10-4 | | Locate points on a grid. | Does not find coordinate points in the correct order. Reverses order in writing coordinates. | |

# Explore Math Activity for 10-5

# Lesson Planner

## Objective

Demonstrate rotations, reflections, and translations using concrete models.

## Vocabulary

**transform**, **rotation**, **reflection**, **translation**

## Resources

**Manipulatives:** square pattern blocks

## 1 Introduce

- Cut a scalene triangle out of an index card and place it on the overhead. Trace around the triangle.
- Have volunteers use translations, reflections and rotations on the triangle. Ask each student to trace the triangle after his or her transformation. Point out that these transformations can be done in many directions.

## 2 Teach

**Activity 1** Give each student a square pattern block. Have students work in small groups so you can circulate and review the steps of the activity.

- For Step 2, suggest that students make a mark in one of the corners of the square they drew on their paper. A $\frac{1}{2}$ rotation will put the mark in the opposite corner.
- For Step 3, have students reflect the square over and trace around the shape.

# Explore Geometry Activity for Lesson 10-5
# Rotations, Reflections, and Translations

**MAIN IDEA**

I will explore rotations, reflections, and translations.

**You Will Need**
pattern blocks

A **transformation** is a movement of a figure. The three types of transformations are **translation** (slide), **reflection** (flip), and **rotation** (turn).

**ACTIVITY** Explore Rotations, Reflections, and Translations

**Step 1** **Trace a figure.**
Trace a square pattern block onto a piece of paper.

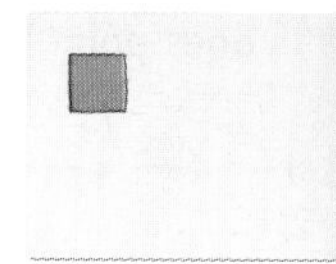

**Step 2** **Rotate (turn) a figure.**
Take the figure and turn or rotate it $\frac{1}{2}$ a turn.
Then trace it again.
This is called a rotation.

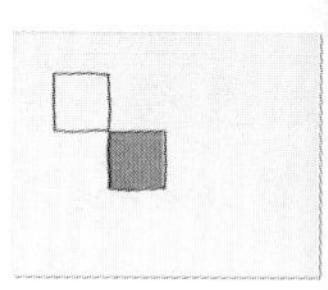

**Step 3** **Show a reflection (flip).**
Now trace the square again. Next, draw a mirror image of the square. This is called a reflection.

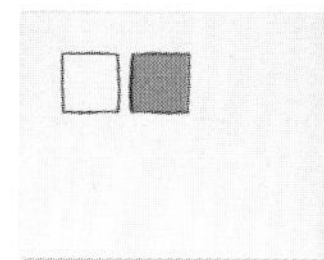

**Step 4** **Show a translation (slide).**
Trace the square one last time. Now move the square to the right (horizontally) and draw it again. Remember, do not turn it. This is called a translation.

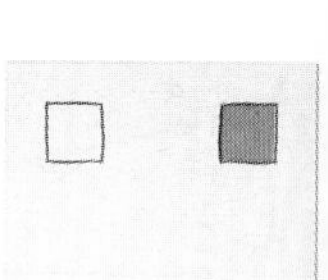

## Think About It

1. What did you do to the square to demonstrate a rotation? turned it

2. What is the difference between a rotation and a reflection? Sample answer: A rotation means the shape is turned and reflection means the shape is flipped.

3. Name two shapes that will look exactly the same after being reflected. Sample answer: circle, regular octagon

4. Describe the transformation that would move figure *A* to the location of figure *B*. translation

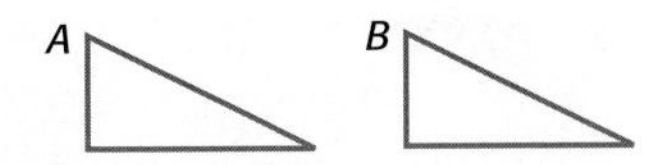

**Use each pattern block to demonstrate and draw all three transformations.**

**5.**

**6.**

**7.**

**8.**

**9.**

**10.**

5–10. See students' work.

11. Choose 3 objects from your classroom. Demonstrate one transformation with each object. Copy and complete the table. See students' work.

| Object | Transformation |
|---|---|
| Crayon | Rotation |
| ■ | Reflection |
| ■ | Translation |

12. **WRITING IN ▶MATH** In your own words, define the terms *rotation, reflection,* and *translation.*

12. Sample answer: Rotation means to turn a shape around a point. Reflection means to flip a shape over a line. Translation means to move a figure along a straight line.



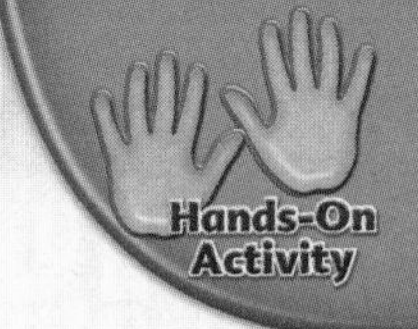


### Think About It

Assign Exercises 1–4 in the Think About It section to assess student comprehension of the concept presented in the Activity.

## 3 Assess

### Formative Assessment

Use **Check What You Know** Exercises 5–12 to assess whether students comprehend using concrete model to demonstrate rotations, reflections, and translations.

**From Concrete to Abstract** Use Exercise 12 to bridge the gap between using concrete models to transform shapes and the concept of rotations, reflections, and translations.

LESSON 10-5

# Rotations, Reflections, and Translations

## Lesson Planner

### Objective

Demonstrate rotations, reflections, and translations using concrete models.

### Vocabulary

**rotation**, **reflection**, **translation**, **transformation**

### Resources

**Materials:** dot paper, overhead projector

**Manipulatives:** rhombus pattern block

**Literature Connection:** *Tilling Shapes* by Kari Jenson Gold

**Alternate Lesson:** Use *IMPACT Mathematics:* Unit J to provide practice with transformations.

**Teacher Technology**
TeacherWorks • Interactive Classroom

## Daily Routine

Use these suggestions before beginning the lesson on p. 412.

### 5-Minute Check

(Reviews Lesson 10-4)

**Identify the object that is located at each ordered pair.**

1. (2, 3) heart
2. (3, 1) triangle
3. (5, 1) circle
4. (4, 5) diamond

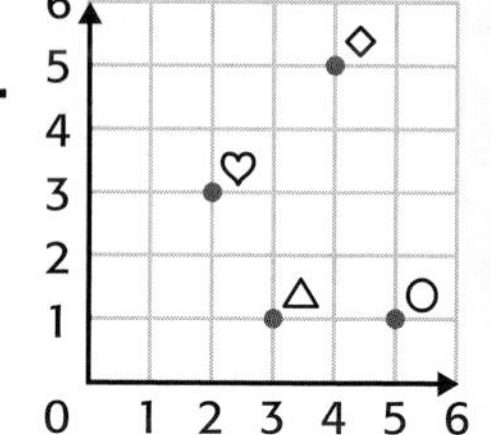


### Problem of the Day

A set of 4 chairs sells for $56, or you can buy one chair for $16. How much less is the cost of one chair if you buy the set? $2

### Focus on Math Background

This lesson considers three types of transformations, which are movements of a figure that do not change the figure's size or shape. A transformation produces a figure that is congruent to the original figure.

In a *translation*, or shift, all points on the figure move in exactly the same way, so that the figure's orientation remains the same. A *rotation* turns the figure about some point, so that each point on the figure turns through the same angle around the point of rotation. Many of the rotations in this lesson are 180° rotations. In a *reflection*, a mirror image of the figure is produced on the other side of a line of symmetry.

Note that more than one type of transformation may produce the same result.

### Building Math Vocabulary

Write the lesson vocabulary words and their definitions on the board.

Have students define transformations in their own words. Then have them draw an example of a rotation, reflection, and translation.

# Differentiated Instruction

## Small Group Options

LOGICAL, VISUAL, SPATIAL

### Option 1 Below Level BL

**Materials:** paper, scissors, pencils

- Ask students to draw a large, thick "L" and cut it out with the scissors.
- Once students have cut out their Ls, take them through the moves of rotation, reflection, and rotation using the L.
- Once they have practiced with you, have students work with a partner.
- One student moves the L and the other student identifies the movement.

KINESTHETIC

### Option 2 English Language Learners ELL

**Materials:** sets of 3 cards with 1 of the 3 core vocabulary words listed on each
**Core Vocabulary:** slide, turn, flip
**Common Use Verb:** move
**Do Math** This strategy uses kinesthetic movement to introduce vocabulary and the math concept.

- Write, then model, **slide**, **turn,** and **flip**.
- In groups of three, have students construct a "machine" that will model turns, flips, or slides with their bodies or with classroom items.
- Model doing an action in reaction to another movement. For example, one student slides to the right and touches another student. That triggers the second student to flip his or her hands over, which triggers the next movement.
- Have students demonstrate their "machine" to the class while the class holds up the word cards during the demonstrated movement. Assist groups to make a continuous loop that repeats. Discuss.
- Repeat for all groups as time permits.

## Independent Work Options

VISUAL, SPATIAL

### Option 1 Early Finishers AL

**Materials:** index cards, scissors, paper

- Have students draw a shape on an index card and cut it out.
- On a sheet of paper, have them trace around the shape. Below the shape, students use a reflection to transform the shape. Then have them trace around the transformed figure. Repeat using a translation and a rotation.
- Have students exchange papers and identify the transformations that have been drawn.

### Option 2 Student Technology

**Math Online** macmillanmh.com

Personal Tutor • Extra Examples

### Option 3 Learning Station: Art (p. 392G)

Direct students to the Art Learning Station for opportunities to explore and extend the lesson concept.

### Option 4 Problem-Solving Practice

Reinforce problem-solving skills and strategies with the Problem-Solving Practice worksheet.

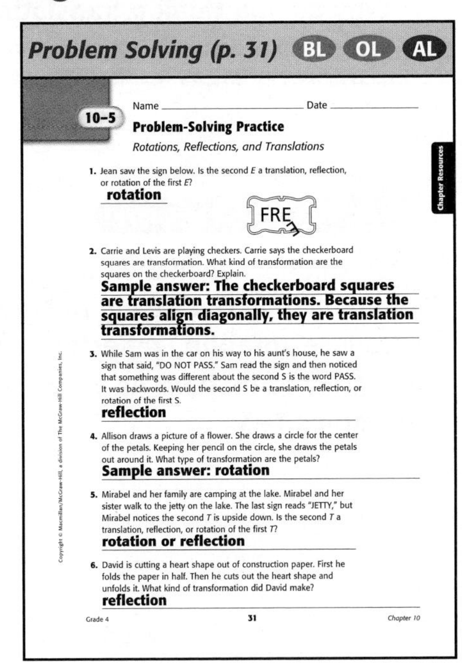

**Problem Solving (p. 31)** BL OL AL

Name ______________ Date ______________

10–5 **Problem-Solving Practice**

*Rotations, Reflections, and Translations*

Chapter Resources

1. Jean saw the sign below. Is the second *E* a translation, reflection, or rotation of the first *E*?
   **rotation**

   FRE

2. Carrie and Levis are playing checkers. Carrie says the checkerboard squares are transformation. What kind of transformation are the squares on the checkerboard? Explain.
   **Sample answer: The checkerboard squares are translation transformations. Because the squares align diagonally, they are translation transformations.**

3. While Sam was in the car on his way to his aunt's house, he saw a sign that said, "DO NOT PASS." Sam read the sign and then noticed that something was different about the second S is the word PASS. It was backwords. Would the second S be a translation, reflection, or rotation of the first S.
   **reflection**

4. Allison draws a picture of a flower. She draws a circle for the center of the petals. Keeping her pencil on the circle, she draws the petals out around it. What type of transformation are the petals?
   **Sample answer: rotation**

5. Mirabel and her family are camping at the lake. Mirabel and her sister walk to the jetty on the lake. The last sign reads "JETTY," but Mirabel notices the second *T* is upside down. Is the second *T* a translation, reflection, or rotation of the first *T*?
   **rotation or reflection**

6. David is cutting a heart shape out of construction paper. First he folds the paper in half. Then he cuts out the heart shape and unfolds it. What kind of transformation did David make?
   **reflection**



Grade 4 31 *Chapter 10*

# 10-5 Rotations, Reflections, and Translations

## 1 Introduce

**Activity Choice 1 • Hands-On** 

- Draw the following figures on the board:

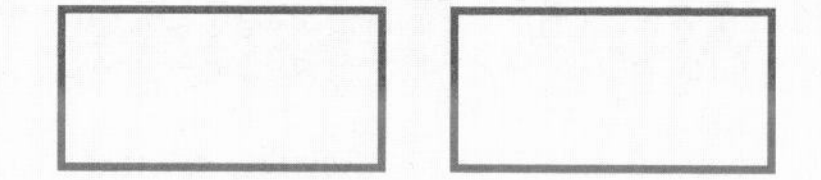

- Have students copy the figures onto paper and write out an explanation describing the transformation that took place. Answers will vary.
- Call on several students to read their explanations.

**Activity Choice 2 • Literature**

Introduce the lesson with *Tilling Shapes* by Kari Jenson Gold. For a related math activity, see p. TR58.

## 2 Teach

**Scaffolding Questions**

Draw the following on the overhead:

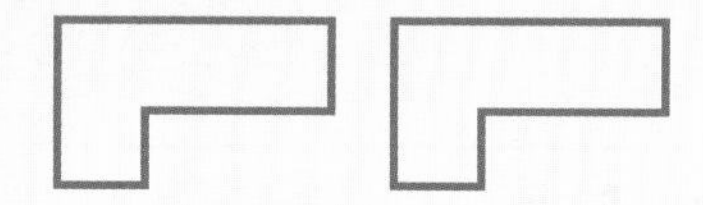

- **What kind of transformation does this show?** translation or slide
- **Could this be a reflection? Explain.** no; A reflection flips the figure over, which gives a mirror image.
- **Why do you think a translation is called a slide? Explain.** Sample answer: When you translate a figure, you slide it in a horizontal, vertical, or diagonal direction.

**GET READY to Learn**

Have students open their books and read the information in **Get Ready to Learn**. Introduce **rotation**, **reflection**, **translation** and **transformation**. As a class, work through **Examples 1–3**.



# 10-5 Rotations, Reflections, and Translations

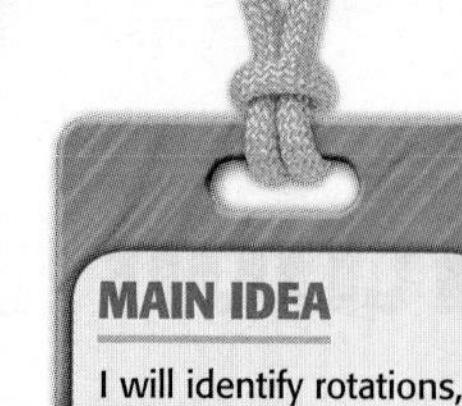

**MAIN IDEA**

I will identify rotations, reflections, and translations.

**New Vocabulary**

**transformation**
**translation**
**reflection**
**rotation**

**Math Online**

macmillanmh.com
- Extra Examples
- Personal Tutor
- Self-Check Quiz

**GET READY to Learn**

In this picture, the square pattern block has been moved. Demonstrate the movement of the square. What type of movement is shown?

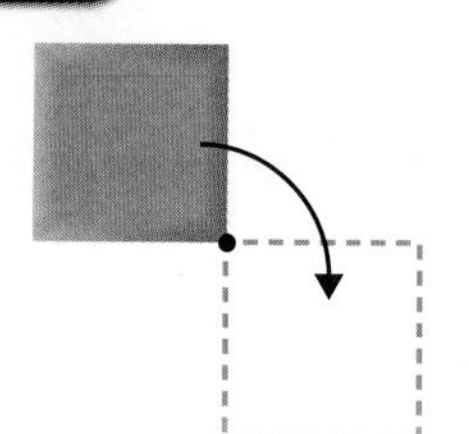

In the picture above, the square pattern block was moved or transformed. A **transformation** is a movement of a figure. The three types of transformations are **translation** (slide), **reflection** (flip), and **rotation** (turn).

**EXAMPLE** Identify Transformations

1. **Identify the transformation of the square pattern block.**

Look at the square pattern block. Notice where the pattern block started.

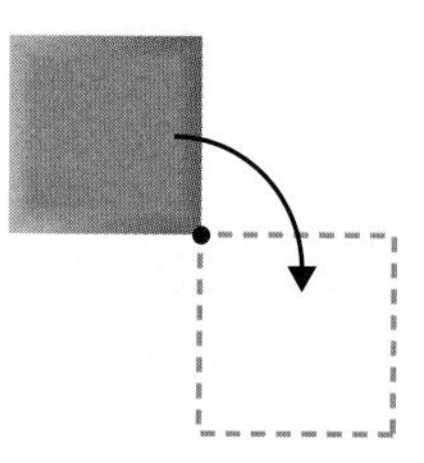

Now look at where the square pattern block ended.

The bottom right corner has not moved. It stayed on the same point. The square pattern block has been turned.

So, this is an example of rotation.



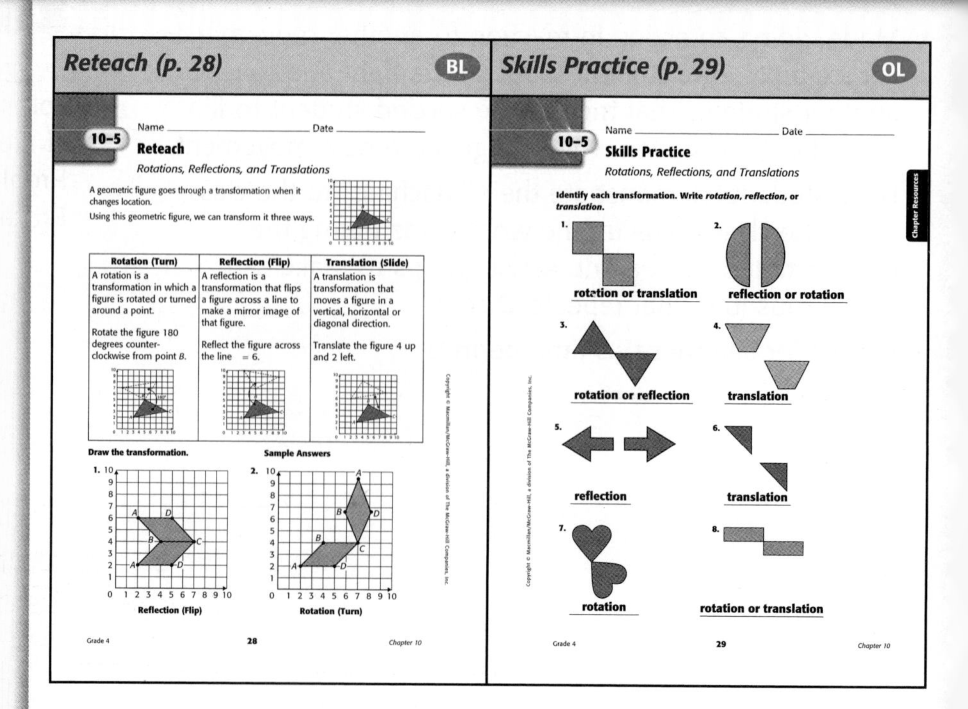

**Reteach (p. 28)** BL

10-5 Name ______ Date ______

**Reteach**

*Rotations, Reflections, and Translations*

A geometric figure goes through a transformation when it changes location.

Using this geometric figure, we can transform it three ways.

| Rotation (Turn) | Reflection (Flip) | Translation (Slide) |
|---|---|---|
| A rotation is a transformation in which a figure is rotated or turned around a point. Rotate the figure 180 degrees counter-clockwise from point *B*. | A reflection is a transformation that flips a figure across a line to make a mirror image of that figure. Reflect the figure across the line = 6. | A translation is transformation that moves a figure in a vertical, horizontal or diagonal direction. Translate the figure 4 up and 2 left. |

**Draw the transformation.** **Sample Answers**

1. Reflection (Flip)
2. Rotation (Turn)

Grade 4 28 Chapter 10



**Skills Practice (p. 29)** OL

10-5 Name ______ Date ______

**Skills Practice**

*Rotations, Reflections, and Translations*

**Identify each transformation. Write *rotation, reflection,* or *translation*.**

1. rotation or translation
2. reflection or rotation
3. rotation or reflection
4. translation
5. reflection
6. translation
7. rotation
8. rotation or translation

Grade 4 29 Chapter 10

Chapter Resources

**Vocabulary Link**
transformation
**Everyday Use** a complete change

**Math Use** a movement of a figure

## Transformations

Key Concepts

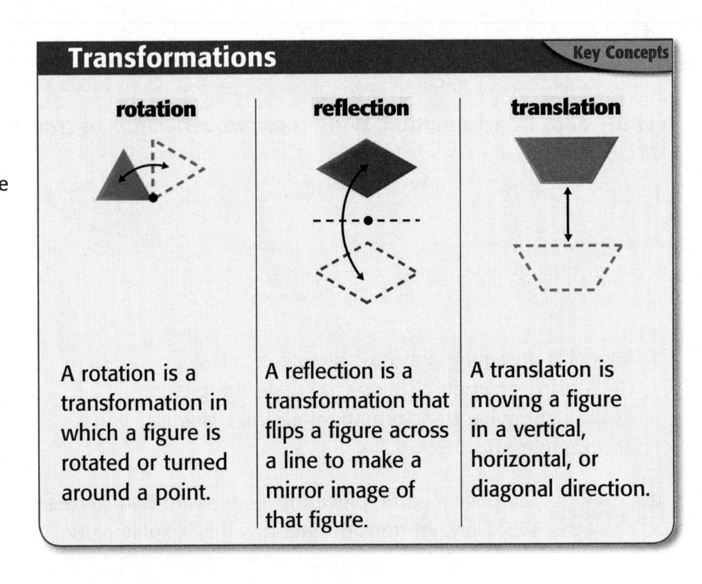


| rotation | reflection | translation |
|---|---|---|
| A rotation is a transformation in which a figure is rotated or turned around a point. | A reflection is a transformation that flips a figure across a line to make a mirror image of that figure. | A translation is moving a figure in a vertical, horizontal, or diagonal direction. |

**Real-World EXAMPLE** Identify Transformations

**2** **CLOTHING** **The T-shirt has a design of geometric shapes in a pattern. Identify the transformation of the shapes that has created this pattern.**

Notice the geometric shapes on the T-shirt.

If we fold the shirt down the middle we see that the shapes are the same, mirror images.

The shapes have been flipped. They are examples of reflections.

**EXAMPLE** Identify Transformations

**3** **Identify the transformation. Write *rotation, reflection,* or *translation.***

The triangle above moved sideways. It has not turned or flipped.

So, the transformation of the triangle is a translation.



**Enrich (p. 32)** AL

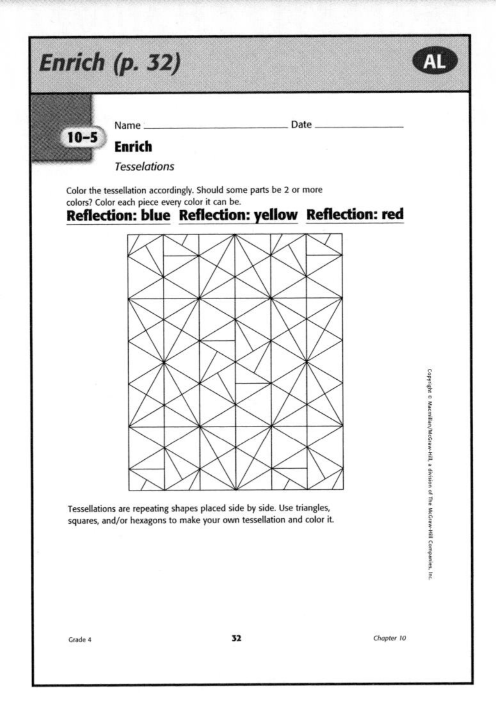
Name ______ Date ______
10-5
**Enrich**
*Tesselations*

Color the tessellation accordingly. Should some parts be 2 or more colors? Color each piece every color it can be.
**Reflection: blue** **Reflection: yellow** **Reflection: red**

Tessellations are repeating shapes placed side by side. Use triangles, squares, and/or hexagons to make your own tessellation and color it.

Grade 4 32 Chapter 10

### Demonstrate and Identify Transformations

**Example 1** Students may think that the transformation shown is a translation. Point out that a translation would move all of the corners of the square the same distance in the same direction. In this case, the corners of the square have not moved the same distance.

## ADDITIONAL EXAMPLES

**1** Identify the transformation shown.

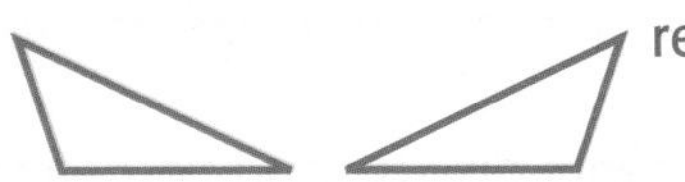

reflection

**2** Jose noticed this design on a floor. Identify the transformation of shapes that formed the design.

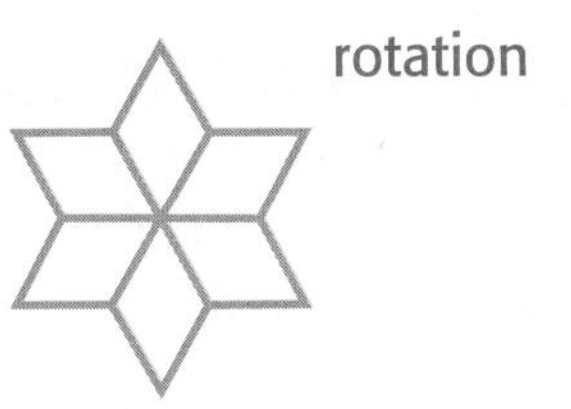

rotation

**3** Identify the transformation. Write *rotation, reflection,* or *translation.*

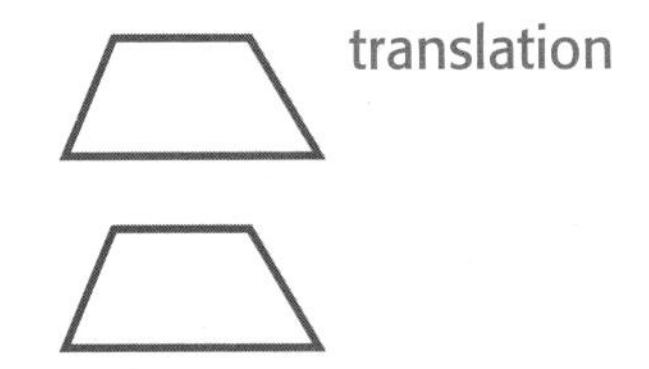

translation

**CHECK What You Know**

As a class, have students complete Exercises 1–4 in **Check What You Know** as you observe their work.

**Exercise 4** Assess student comprehension before assigning practice exercises.

## BL Alternate Teaching Strategy

**If** students have trouble identifying rotations, reflections, and translations…

**Then** use one of these reteach options:

**1** CRM **Daily Reteach Worksheet** (p. 28)

**2** Distribute dot paper and a rhombus pattern block. Have students trace around the rhombus on dot paper. Then have them practice drawing and identifying translations, reflections, and rotations.

# 3 Practice

Differentiate practice using these leveled assignments for Exercises 5–17.

| Level | Assignment |
|---|---|
| BL Below/Approaching Level | 5–7, 11–12 |
| OL On Level | 5–8, 11–12, 14–16 |
| AL Above/Beyond Level | 6–12 even, 14–16 |

Have students discuss and complete the Higher Order Thinking problems. For Exercise 14 encourage students to keep their pictures simple so the transformation will be easier to draw.

**WRITING IN ▶MATH** Have students complete Exercise 17 in their Math Journals. You may choose to use this exercise as an optional formative assessment.

### Additional Answer

**12.** Sample answer: The squares on a checkerboard will land on each other when they undergo a rotation, reflection, or translation.

**COMMON ERROR!**

Students may think that there is only one right answer to these problems. Point out that often more than one answer may be correct. For example, in Exercise 2, the top figure can be transformed into the bottom figure by reflecting it across a line (reflection) or by sliding the figure downward (translation).



## CHECK What You Know

**Identify each transformation. Write *rotation*, *reflection*, or *translation*.**

See Examples 1–3 (pp. 412–413)

**1.** 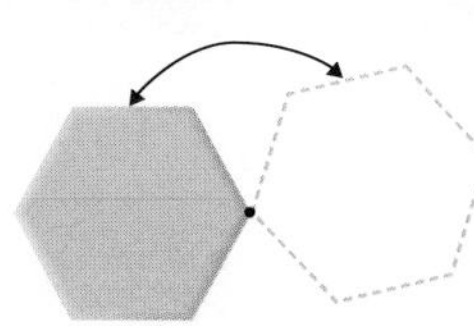 rotation

**2.** 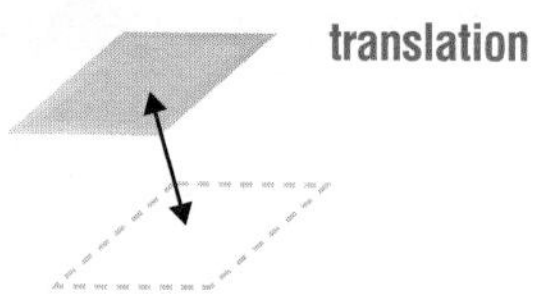 translation

**3.** Miguel is designing a mosaic picture of a tree. He is using geometric shapes to create the picture. At the right, what transformation are the triangles an example of? rotation

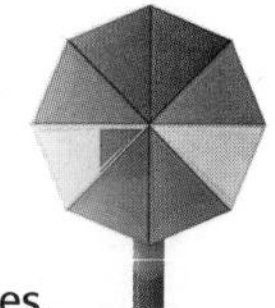

**4.** Talk About It Suppose a game piece moves forward two spaces. What kind of transformation is this? Explain your reasoning. Sample answer: translation; the game piece slid forward

## Practice and Problem Solving

EXTRA PRACTICE See page R26.

**Identify each transformation. Write *rotation*, *reflection*, or *translation*.**

See Examples 1–3 (pp. 412–413)

**5.** 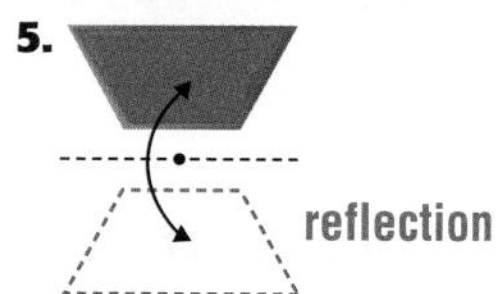 reflection

**6.** rotation

**7.** 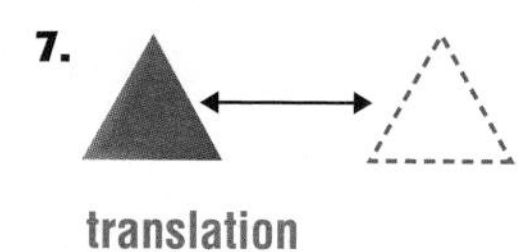 translation

**8.** translation

**9.** 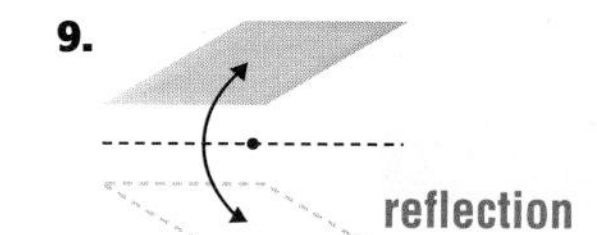 reflection

**10.** 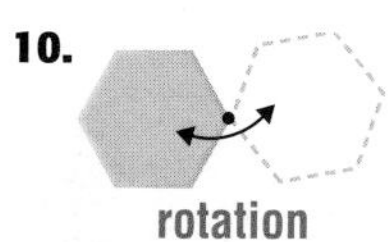 rotation

**11.** Eliza and Joey drew the picture to the right on the sidewalk with chalk. What transformations can be seen in the picture? See students' work.

**12.** Explain how the squares on a checkerboard demonstrate each transformation. See margin.

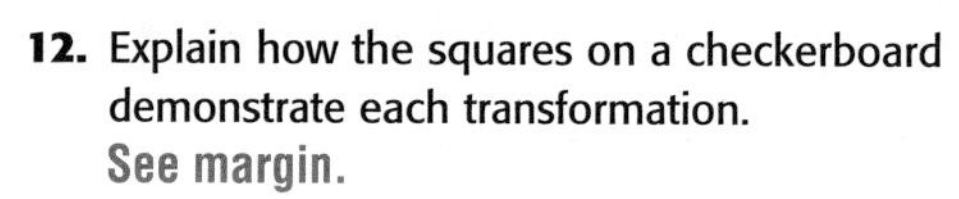

## H.O.T. Problems

**13. OPEN ENDED** Draw a picture. Then draw the picture again using a transformation. Explain what transformation you demonstrated. See students' work.

**OPEN ENDED** Using pattern blocks, draw examples of the following transformations. 14–16. See students' work.

**14.** translation **15.** rotation **16.** reflection

**17. WRITING IN MATH** Describe how a translation can also be a reflection. See Ch. 10 Answer Appendix.

## TEST Practice

**18.** Which of the following describes where point *J* is located? (Lesson 10-4) C

**A** (1, 5)
**B** (2, 7)
**C** (5, 8)
**D** (8, 5)

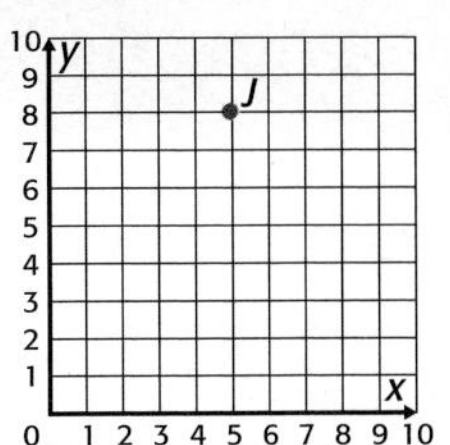

**19.** Which pair of figures does **NOT** show a rotation? (Lesson 10-5) J

**F** 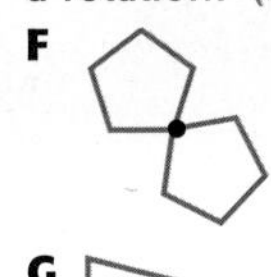

**H**

**G**

**J** 

## Spiral Review

**Identify the place that is located at each ordered pair.** (Lesson 10-4)

**20.** (5, 8) school
**21.** (8, 3) grocery store
**22.** (3, 2) fire station

**Identify the ordered pair for each building.** (Lesson 10-4)

**23.** hospital (1,6)
**24.** police station (9,9)
**25.** mall (1,1)

**26.** Dan has 85 cents. Name one combination of coins that could make up this amount. (Lesson 10-3) 8 dimes and 5 pennies

**27.** Sarah purchased 5 items. If each item was the same price and she spent $45, how much did each item cost? (Lesson 4-3) $9



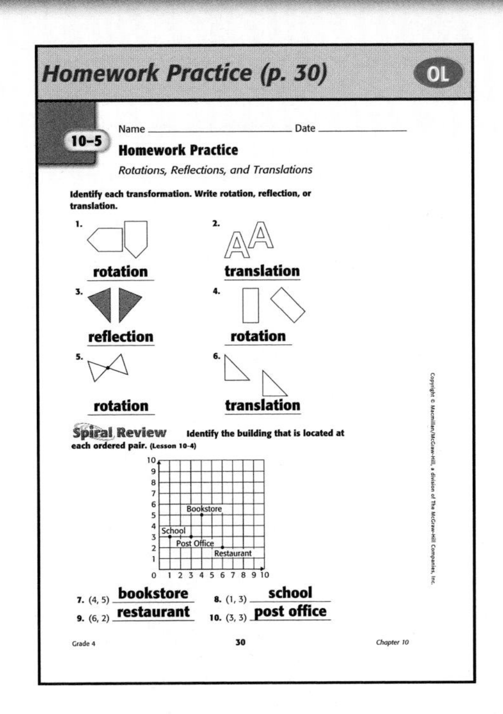

**Homework Practice (p. 30)** OL

Name ______ Date ______

10-5 **Homework Practice**
*Rotations, Reflections, and Translations*

**Identify each transformation. Write rotation, reflection, or translation.**

1. rotation
2. translation
3. reflection
4. rotation
5. rotation
6. translation

**Spiral Review** **Identify the building that is located at each ordered pair.** (Lesson 10-4)

7. (4, 5) bookstore
8. (1, 3) school
9. (6, 2) restaurant
10. (3, 3) post office

Grade 4 30 Chapter 10

# 4 Assess

### Formative Assessment

- **How can you tell that a geometric figure has undergone a transformation?** The figure has changed location.
- **How is a rotation different from a translation?** A rotation is a transformation in which a figure rotates or turns around a point, whereas a translation moves the figure in a vertical, horizontal, or diagonal direction.

**Quick Check** **Are students continuing to struggle with identifying rotations, reflections, and translations?**

**If Yes** → Small Group Options (p. 412B)
Strategic Intervention Guide (p. 126)

**If No** → Independent Work Options (p. 412B)
CRM Skills Practice Worksheet (p. 29)
CRM Enrich Worksheet (p. 32)

**Into the Future** Tell students that in a later lesson they will learn about congruent figures. Ask them to explain how they think today's lesson on rotations, reflections, and translations will help them on that lesson.

### TEST Practice

**Reviews Lessons 10-4 and 10-5**

Assign the Test Practice problems to provide daily reinforcement of test-taking skills.

### Spiral Review

**Reviews Lesson 4-3, 10-3, and 10-4**

Review and assess mastery of skills and concepts from previous chapters.

# 10-6 Problem-Solving Investigation
## Choose a Strategy

# Lesson Planner

## Objective
Choose the best strategy to solve a problem.

## Resources
**Materials:** five name tags

**Teacher Technology**
TeacherWorks • Interactive Classroom

**Real-World Problem Solving Library**
**Math and Science: *Trapped in Tar***
Use these leveled books to reinforce and extend problem-solving skills and strategies.

Leveled for:
- OL On Level
- ELL Sheltered English
- SP Spanish

For additional support, see the Real-World Problem Solving Teacher Guide.

# Daily Routine

Use these suggestions before beginning the lesson on p. 416.

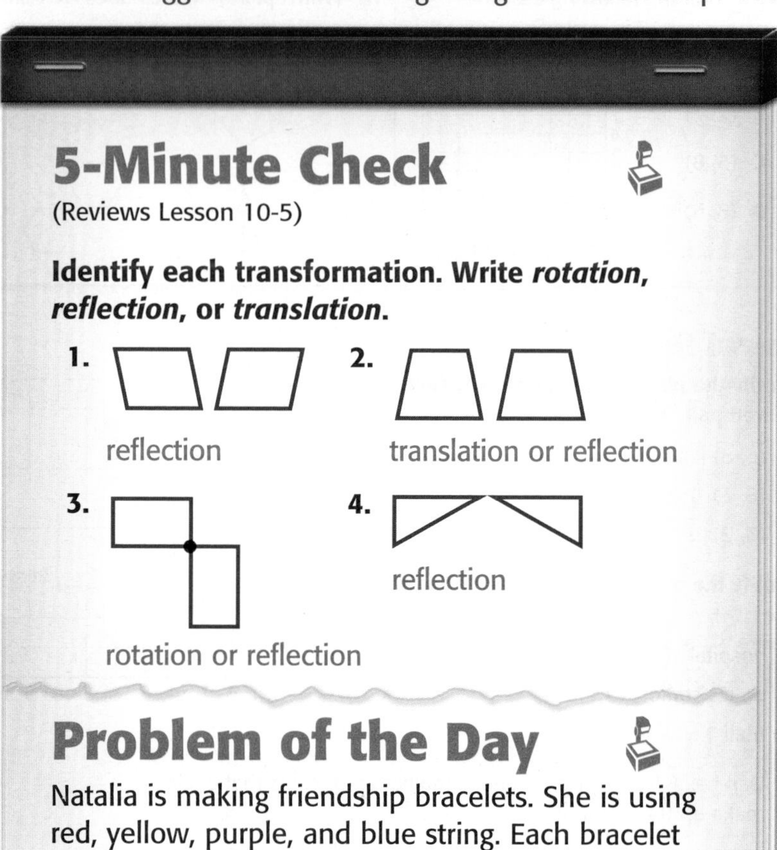

## 5-Minute Check
(Reviews Lesson 10-5)

**Identify each transformation. Write *rotation*, *reflection*, or *translation*.**

1. reflection
2. translation or reflection
3. rotation or reflection
4. reflection

## Problem of the Day
Natalia is making friendship bracelets. She is using red, yellow, purple, and blue string. Each bracelet will have two different colors. How many different color combinations can she chose from? 6

# Differentiated Instruction

## Small Group Options

LOGICAL

### Option 1 Gifted and Talented AL

**Materials:** paper and pencil

- Hand students this problem written on paper to solve:

  *Eric has a collection of books. He has 24 books total. Half of the books are fiction and 4 of the books are nonfiction. The rest of the books are reference books. Use the work backward strategy to find how many reference books are in Eric's collection.* 8 books

LINGUISTIC, INTRAPERSONAL

### Option 2 English Language Learners ELL

**Materials:** paper, pencil
**Core Vocabulary:** practice, explain, works best
**Common Use Verb:** examine

**Write Math** This strategy integrates practice of the math skill with acquired language.

- Give students a rotation problem. Ask students to examine the problem and to think about the strategies that could solve it.
- Have students discuss which strategy they think would work best to solve the problem.
- Have students write and work the problem using their strategy.
- After solving the problem, collect writings and sort them into categories. Without allowing students to see the original papers, list reasonings for each type of solution. Include all steps used, but note with a tally if the same step is used by several groups. Discuss as time permits.
- Encourage students to look for extra or unnecessary steps and explain why some steps were used by multiple groups. Repeat for other problems as time permits.

## Independent Work Options

LINGUISTIC

### Option 1 Early Finishers OL AL

- Ask each student to write a real-world problem and give it to two different students to solve. Have them explain the strategy they used.
- After solving, each student should give the problem to a third student who will check the work. Once checked, the problem should be returned to the writer.

### Option 2 Student Technology

**Math Online** macmillanmh.com

Personal Tutor • Extra Examples

### Option 3 Learning Station: Writing (p. 392G)

Direct students to the Writing Learning Station for opportunities to explore and extend the lesson concept.

## 1 Introduce

**Activity • Review**

- Present students with the following problem:
  *For a class project, Cam has to choose two partners out of five of his friends: Angie, Matt, Ming, Lily, and Patrick. How many possible groups can he make?*
- Ask for five volunteers to each wear a nametag of one of Cam's friends. Have the students act out or draw a picture of the partners Cam could work with.
- **How many groups can be made with Cam and two of his friends?** 10

## 2 Teach

Have students read the problem on Carmen's dinner. Guide them through the problem-solving steps.

**Understand** Using the questions, review what students know and need to find.

**Plan** Have them discuss their strategy.

**Solve** Guide students to use logical reasoning to solve the problem.

- **What strategy was used to solve this problem?** use logical reasoning
- **What information was given in the problem?** the cost of each item ordered and the total cost
- **How much would it cost to order one of each item?** $29
- **How much money is left?** $14
- **Which items could have been ordered with the money left?** salad, sandwich

**Check** Have students look back at the problem to make sure that the answer fits the facts given.

- **Is it possible that there could be another answer? Explain.** No, there are no other combinations that could add up to $43.

**! COMMON ERROR!**

**Exercise 8** Some students may have trouble deciding whether to multiply or divide to solve the problem. Point out that objects weigh less on the moon than on Earth.

# 10-6 Problem-Solving Investigation

**MAIN IDEA** I will choose the best strategy to solve a problem.

**P.S.I. TEAM +**

CARMEN: My family ate at a restaurant. We ordered salads for $6 each, steaks for $15 each, and sandwiches for $8 each. The total cost was $43.

YOUR MISSION: Find how many of each item was ordered.

**Understand** You know the cost of each item and the total cost of the meal. Find how many of each item was ordered.

**Plan** Use logical reasoning to solve the problem.

**Solve** At least one of each item was ordered. Add the costs.

| | |
|---|---|
| $15 | 1 steak |
| $ 6 | 1 salad |
| + $ 8 | 1 sandwich |
| $29 | |

So, the cost of the other items ordered must be $43 − $29, or $14.

Since $8 + $6 is the only combination of costs that equal $14, you know that another salad and another sandwich were ordered.

So, they ordered 1 steak, 2 salads, and 2 sandwiches.

**Check** Look back. Check your answer with addition.

$6 + $6 + $8 + $8 + $15 = $43

So, the answer is correct. ✓



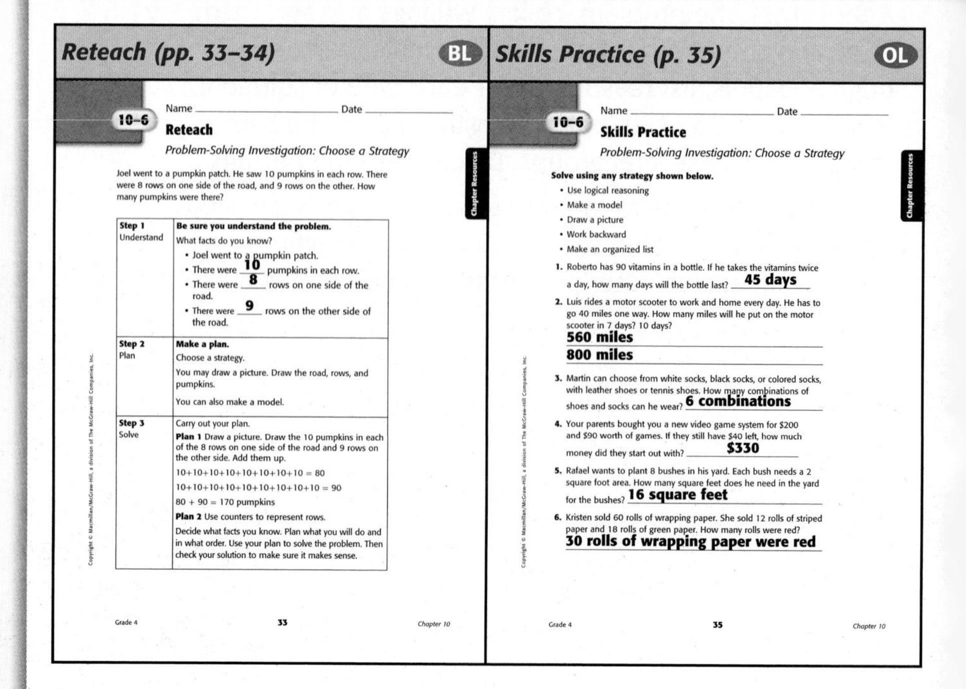

**Reteach (pp. 33–34)** BL

10-6 Name ______ Date ______

**Reteach**

*Problem-Solving Investigation: Choose a Strategy*

Joel went to a pumpkin patch. He saw 10 pumpkins in each row. There were 8 rows on one side of the road, and 9 rows on the other. How many pumpkins were there?

| | |
|---|---|
| **Step 1** Understand | **Be sure you understand the problem.** What facts do you know? • Joel went to a pumpkin patch. • There were **10** pumpkins in each row. • There were **8** rows on one side of the road. • There were **9** rows on the other side of the road. |
| **Step 2** Plan | **Make a plan.** Choose a strategy. You may draw a picture. Draw the road, rows, and pumpkins. You can also make a model. |
| **Step 3** Solve | Carry out your plan. **Plan 1** Draw a picture. Draw the 10 pumpkins in each of the 8 rows on one side of the road and 9 rows on the other side. Add them up. 10+10+10+10+10+10+10+10 = 80 10+10+10+10+10+10+10+10+10 = 90 80 + 90 = 170 pumpkins **Plan 2** Use counters to represent rows. Decide what facts you know. Plan what you will do and in what order. Use your plan to solve the problem. Then check your solution to make sure it makes sense. |

Chapter Resources



Grade 4 33 Chapter 10

**Skills Practice (p. 35)** OL

10-6 Name ______ Date ______

**Skills Practice**

*Problem-Solving Investigation: Choose a Strategy*

**Solve using any strategy shown below.**

- Use logical reasoning
- Make a model
- Draw a picture
- Work backward
- Make an organized list

1. Roberto has 90 vitamins in a bottle. If he takes the vitamins twice a day, how many days will the bottle last? **45 days**
2. Luis rides a motor scooter to work and home every day. He has to go 40 miles one way. How many miles will he put on the motor scooter in 7 days? 10 days? **560 miles** **800 miles**
3. Martin can choose from white socks, black socks, or colored socks, with leather shoes or tennis shoes. How many combinations of shoes and socks can he wear? **6 combinations**
4. Your parents bought you a new video game system for $200 and $90 worth of games. If they still have $40 left, how much money did they start out with? **$330**
5. Rafael wants to plant 8 bushes in his yard. Each bush needs a 2 square foot area. How many square feet does he need in the yard for the bushes? **16 square feet**
6. Kristen sold 60 rolls of wrapping paper. She sold 12 rolls of striped paper and 18 rolls of green paper. How many rolls were red? **30 rolls of wrapping paper were red**

Chapter Resources



Grade 4 35 Chapter 10

★ indicates multi-step problem

## Mixed Problem Solving

EXTRA PRACTICE See page R27.

**Use any strategy shown below to solve. Tell what strategy you used.**

PROBLEM-SOLVING STRATEGIES
- Use logical reasoning.
- Make a model.
- Make an organized list.
- Draw a picture.
- Work backward.

1. There are 6 wagons for the fall hayride. Each wagon needs 4 horses to pull it. How many horses will it take to pull all 6 wagons? **24 horses**

2. There are four boys and six girls in line at a movie theater. Each is carrying two food items purchased at the concession stand. How many food items do they have in all? **20 items**

★3. Curtis bought the meal shown below. He paid with a $20 bill and his change was $13. If the fruit juice cost $1, how much did each taco cost? **$2**

★4. Macie made 70 bracelets in 3 colors. She made 22 red bracelets and 18 blue bracelets. How many bracelets were yellow? **30 bracelets**

5. Carol, Irina, Yori, and Nora are on a relay team. The fastest girl will run last. The slowest girl will run second. Irina runs faster than Carol. Nora runs first. Irina runs slower than Yori. In what order does the team run? **Nora, Carol, Irina, and Yori**

6. **Algebra** Julie sold roses at a bike club fundraiser. Use the pattern in the table below to find how many roses she had left on Friday. **3 roses left**

| Day | Started with | Ended with |
|---|---|---|
| Monday | 96 | 48 |
| Tuesday | 48 | 24 |
| Wednesday | 24 | 12 |
| Thursday | 12 | 6 |
| Friday | 6 | ■ |

★7. Malik's baseball team needs $2,500 to pay for camp. They raised $310 in April and $477 in May. They already had $1,203 saved. How much do they still need to pay for camp? **$510**

8. **Measurement** An object on Earth weighs 6 times its weight on the Moon. An astronaut weighs 210 pounds on Earth. How much would he or she weigh on the Moon? **35 lb**

9. WRITING IN MATH There are three rock, five country, and two oldies CDs in Mrs. Link's car. The answer is $\frac{5}{10}$. What is the question? **See Ch. 10 Answer Appendix.**



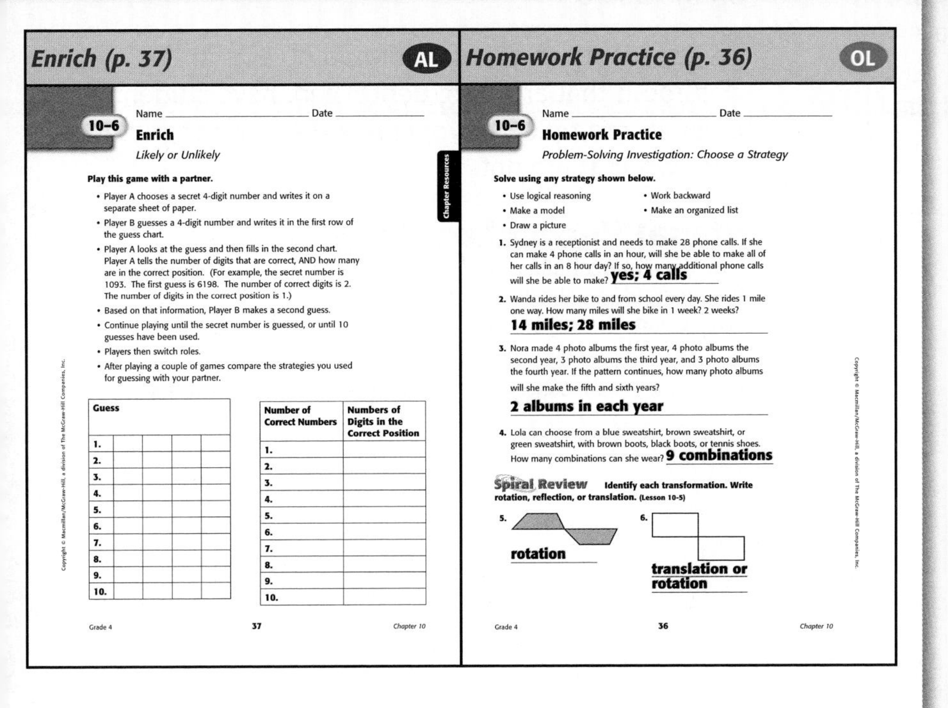

*Enrich (p. 37)* AL

10–6 Name ________ Date ________

**Enrich**

*Likely or Unlikely*

**Play this game with a partner.**

- Player A chooses a secret 4-digit number and writes it on a separate sheet of paper.
- Player B guesses a 4-digit number and writes it in the first row of the guess chart.
- Player A looks at the guess and then fills in the second chart. Player A tells the number of digits that are correct, AND how many are in the correct position. (For example, the secret number is 1093. The first guess is 6198. The number of correct digits is 2. The number of digits in the correct position is 1.)
- Based on that information, Player B makes a second guess.
- Continue playing until the secret number is guessed, or until 10 guesses have been used.
- Players then switch roles.
- After playing a couple of games compare the strategies you used for guessing with your partner.

| Guess | | | | |
|---|---|---|---|---|
| 1. | | | | |
| 2. | | | | |
| 3. | | | | |
| 4. | | | | |
| 5. | | | | |
| 6. | | | | |
| 7. | | | | |
| 8. | | | | |
| 9. | | | | |
| 10. | | | | |

| Number of Correct Numbers | Numbers of Digits in the Correct Position |
|---|---|
| 1. | |
| 2. | |
| 3. | |
| 4. | |
| 5. | |
| 6. | |
| 7. | |
| 8. | |
| 9. | |
| 10. | |

Grade 4 37 Chapter 10



*Homework Practice (p. 36)* OL

10–6 Name ________ Date ________

**Homework Practice**

*Problem-Solving Investigation: Choose a Strategy*

**Solve using any strategy shown below.**

- Use logical reasoning
- Make a model
- Draw a picture
- Work backward
- Make an organized list

1. Sydney is a receptionist and needs to make 28 phone calls. If she can make 4 phone calls in an hour, will she be able to make all of her calls in an 8 hour day? If so, how many additional phone calls will she be able to make? **yes; 4 calls**
2. Wanda rides her bike to and from school every day. She rides 1 mile one way. How many miles will she bike in 1 week? 2 weeks? **14 miles; 28 miles**
3. Nora made 4 photo albums the first year, 4 photo albums the second year, 3 photo albums the third year, and 3 photo albums the fourth year. If the pattern continues, how many photo albums will she make the fifth and sixth years? **2 albums in each year**
4. Lola can choose from a blue sweatshirt, brown sweatshirt, or green sweatshirt, with brown boots, black boots, or tennis shoes. How many combinations can she wear? **9 combinations**

**Spiral Review** **Identify each transformation. Write rotation, reflection, or translation.** (Lesson 10-5)

5. **rotation**
6. **translation or rotation**

Grade 4 36 Chapter 10



## BL Alternate Teaching Strategy

**If** students have trouble deciding which strategy is best to solve a problem…

**Then** use one of these reteach options:

1. CRM **Daily Reteach Worksheet** (pp. 33–34)
2. Help them with the understand step of the four-step plan. Have them articulate what they know and what they need to find. Often this will help them choose a strategy in the plan step of the problem-solving plan.

## 3 Practice

### Using the Exercises

**Exercises 1–8** Remind students that most of the exercises have more than one strategy that can be used to solve the problem.

**Exercise 5** Suggest students draw a picture to show the order of the girls' run.

**Exercise 6** You may need to interpret the table for students. Point out that it shows the number of roses at the beginning of the day and at the end of the day. Show them that the number at the close of Monday is the same number that she has at the opening of Tuesday and so forth.

## 4 Assess

### Formative Assessment

Present the following problem:

*If three coins are tossed, what is the probability that all three coins are heads?*

- **What strategy can you use to solve the problem?** Sample answer: make an organized list
- **What is the probability?** $\frac{1}{8}$ or 1 out of 8

**Quick Check** **Are students continuing to struggle with choosing the best strategy to solve a problem?**

**If Yes** → CRM Reteach Worksheet (pp. 33–34)

**If No** → Independent Work Options (p. 416B)
CRM Skills Practice Worksheet (p. 35)
CRM Enrich Worksheet (p. 37)

LESSON

# 10-7 Congruent Figures

## Lesson Planner

### Objective

Identify congruent figures.

### Vocabulary

**congruent**

### Resources

**Manipulatives:** pattern blocks, scissors, geomirrors

**Literature Connection:** *The Greedy Triangle* by Marilyn Burns

**Alternate Lesson:** Use *IMPACT Mathematics:* Unit J to provide practice with congruent figures.

**Teacher Technology**
TeacherWorks • Interactive Classroom • Concepts in Motion

## Daily Routine

Use these suggestions before beginning the lesson on p. 418.

### 5-Minute Check

(Reviews Lesson 10-6)

**Use any strategy to solve the problem. Tell what strategy you used.**

Cole has 4 caps. They are red, white, blue, and black. He has 2 jackets that are gray and tan. How many cap-jacket combinations are possible? 8; Sample answer: make an organized list

### Problem of the Day

Ted earned $3 raking leaves on Monday. If he doubles the previous day's amount every day this week, how much will he earn on Friday? $48

### Focus on Math Background

At the elementary school level, congruence is treated intuitively. For two figures to be congruent, they must have the same size and shape. To validate that two figures are congruent, students can trace the figures and then manipulate them by sliding, flipping, and rotating until the figures fit together. Students at this level should begin to observe that when two polygons are congruent, their corresponding angles and corresponding sides are equal in measure.

### Building Math Vocabulary

Write the lesson vocabulary word and its definition on the board.

Give students an example of two objects in the classroom that are congruent. Then, have students draw an example of two figures that are congruent and two that are not.

**Visual Vocabulary Cards**

Use Visual Vocabulary Card 7 to reinforce the vocabulary introduced in this lesson. (The Define/Example/Ask routine is printed on the back of each card.)

# Differentiated Instruction

## Small Group Options

**Option 1** LOGICAL, VISUAL, SPATIAL

### Below Level BL

**Materials:** paper, scissors

- Ask students to put 2 pieces of paper together and cut out a triangle. This produces 2 congruent triangles.
- Ask students to manipulate the triangles apart from one another.
- **Are your triangles congruent now?** yes
- Ask students to move their triangles in rotation from one another.
- **Are your triangles congruent now?** yes
- Ask students to move the triangles from one another in reflection.
- **Are your triangles congruent now?** yes

**Option 2** AUDITORY, SPATIAL, VISUAL

### English Language Learners ELL

**Materials:** construction paper, chalkboard with shapes traced

**Core Vocabulary:** congruent, useful, matching

**Common Use Verb:** goes well together

**Hear Math** This strategy introduces congruency and descriptive vocabulary.

- Ask students to think of tires on a car. Ask them if it would be useful to have one tire a lot bigger than the other three. Repeat for a square tire.
- Prompt for answers that explain why some things are the same shape and size. Provide the core vocabulary and verb to help students vocalize their explanations.
- Say, "Another word to describe something that is the same **size** and **shape** is **congruent**."
- Have students draw some things at home that goes well together.
- Have students identify them by saying, "They are **congruent**."
- Repeat as time permits.

## Independent Work Options

**Option 1** SPATIAL

### Early Finishers OL AL

**Materials:** pattern blocks

- Give each student a variety of pattern blocks. Have them create a tessellation that involves rotations, reflections or translations. Tell students that their shapes must fit together without gaps or overlaps.

**Option 2**

### Student Technology

Math Online macmillanmh.com

Personal Tutor • Extra Examples

**Option 3**

### Learning Station: Health (p. 348H)

Direct students to the Health Learning Station for opportunities to explore and extend the lesson concept.

**Option 4**

### Problem-Solving Practice

Reinforce problem-solving skills and strategies with the Problem-Solving Practice worksheet.

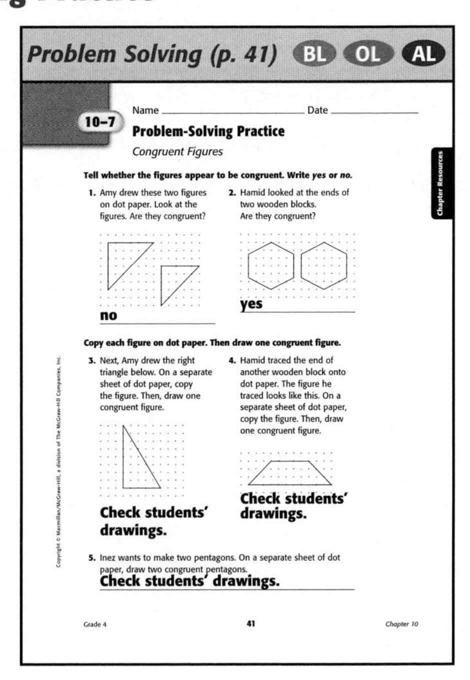

*Problem Solving (p. 41)* BL OL AL

Name ________ Date ________

10–7 **Problem-Solving Practice**

*Congruent Figures*

**Tell whether the figures appear to be congruent. Write *yes* or *no*.**

1. Amy drew these two figures on dot paper. Look at the figures. Are they congruent? **no**
2. Hamid looked at the ends of two wooden blocks. Are they congruent? **yes**

**Copy each figure on dot paper. Then draw one congruent figure.**

3. Next, Amy drew the right triangle below. On a separate sheet of dot paper, copy the figure. Then, draw one congruent figure. **Check students' drawings.**
4. Hamid traced the end of another wooden block onto dot paper. The figure he traced looks like this. On a separate sheet of dot paper, copy the figure. Then, draw one congruent figure. **Check students' drawings.**
5. Inez wants to make two pentagons. On a separate sheet of dot paper, draw two congruent pentagons. **Check students' drawings.**

Grade 4 41 Chapter 10

# Congruent Figures

## 1 Introduce

**Activity Choice 1 • Hands-On** 

- Have students fold a piece of paper in half and in half again.
- Have them trace a pattern block on the top piece of paper. Then, cut out the figure through the four layers. **How many figures are there? Are all the figures the same size and shape? How do you know?** 4; yes; They all match.

**Activity Choice 2 • Literature**

Introduce the lesson with *The Greedy Triangle* by Marilyn Burns. For a related math activity, see p. TR58.

## 2 Teach

### Scaffolding Questions

Place two congruent parallelogram pattern blocks on the overhead with the same orientation or in a simple translation.

- **Explain how the two figures are alike.** They have the same shape and same size.
- Rotate one of the blocks and ask the same question. Flip one of the pattern blocks and ask the same question.
- Tell students that they can be sure the two figures are congruent by rotating, reflecting, or translating one figure onto the other.

**GET READY to Learn**

**Hands-On Mini Activity** You can also use premade shapes and have the students trace them on the graph paper.

### Additional Answer

2. Sample answer: Figure A and Figure C; After rotating the figures, one fit exactly on top of the other one.



10-7 Congruent Figures

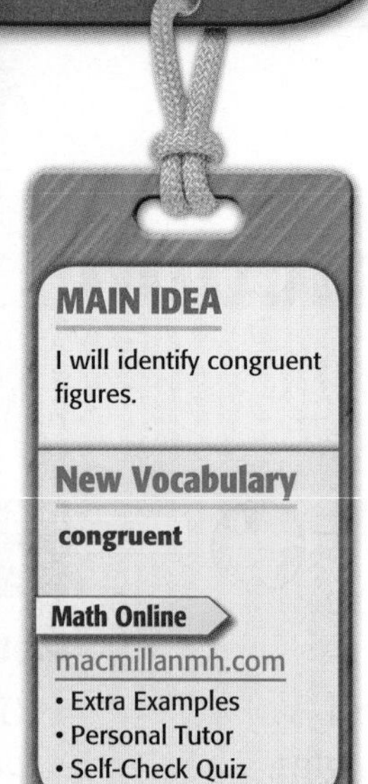

**MAIN IDEA**

I will identify congruent figures.

**New Vocabulary**

**congruent**

**Math Online**

macmillanmh.com

- Extra Examples
- Personal Tutor
- Self-Check Quiz

**GET READY to Learn**

**Hands-On Mini Activity**

**Materials:** graph paper

**Step 1** Copy figures A, B, and C on graph paper.

**Step 2** Cut out figures A, B, and C.

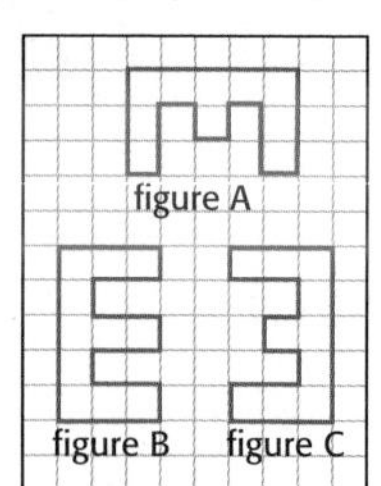


**Step 3** Place the figures on top of each other, one at a time. Use transformations if needed until one fits exactly on top of another one.

1. What transformation(s) took place to find the two figures that are the same? Sample answer: rotation and translation
2. Which two figures are the same? Explain. See margin.

When figures have the same size and shape, they are **congruent**.

**EXAMPLES** Identify Congruent Figures

**Tell whether the figures appear to be congruent. Write *yes* or *no*. If they are, describe the movements that show their congruence.**

1 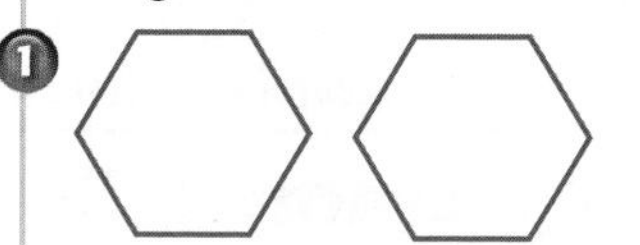

The hexagons appear to have the same size and shape. So, they are congruent. A translation took place.

2 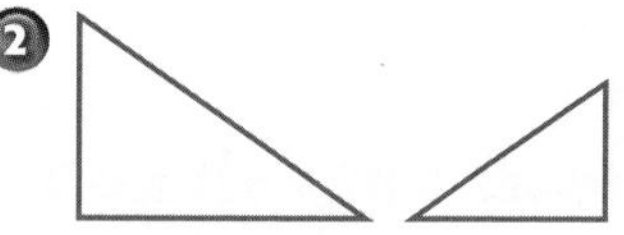

The triangles appear to have the same shape, but have a different size. So, they are not congruent.



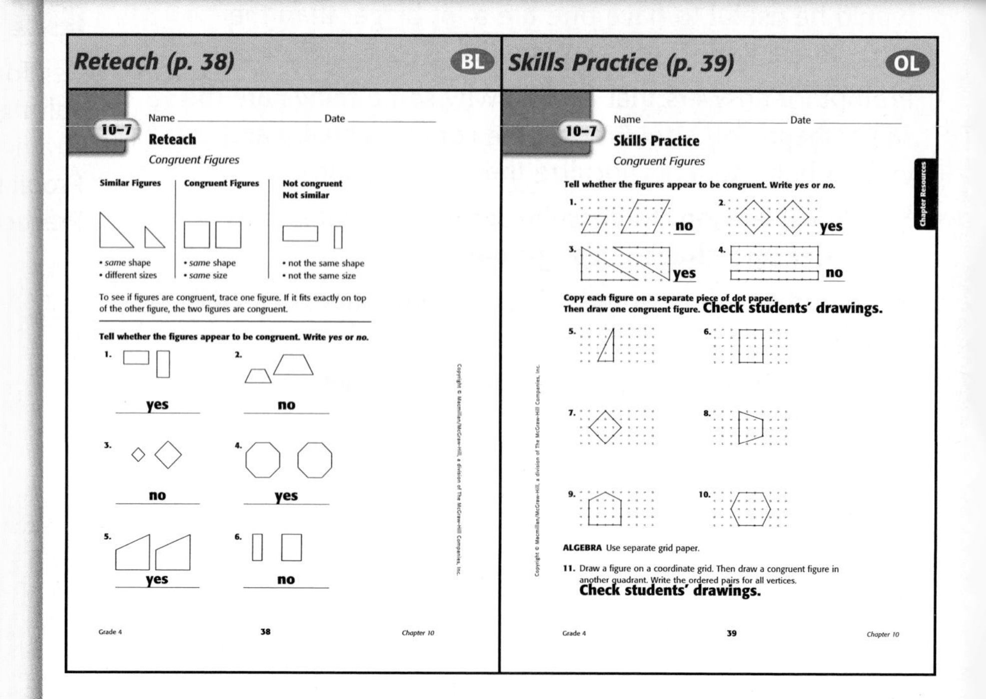

**Reteach (p. 38)** BL

10-7 Name ______ Date ______

**Reteach**

*Congruent Figures*

| Similar Figures | Congruent Figures | Not congruent Not similar |
|---|---|---|
| • *same* shape<br>• different sizes | • *same* shape<br>• *same* size | • not the same shape<br>• not the same size |

To see if figures are congruent, trace one figure. If it fits exactly on top of the other figure, the two figures are congruent.

**Tell whether the figures appear to be congruent. Write *yes* or *no*.**

1. yes
2. no
3. no
4. yes
5. yes
6. no



Grade 4 38 Chapter 10

**Skills Practice (p. 39)** OL

10-7 Name ______ Date ______

**Skills Practice**

*Congruent Figures*

Chapter Resources

**Tell whether the figures appear to be congruent. Write *yes* or *no*.**

1. no
2. yes
3. yes
4. no

**Copy each figure on a separate piece of dot paper. Then draw one congruent figure.** Check students' drawings.

5.
6.
7.
8.
9.
10.

**ALGEBRA** Use separate grid paper.

11. Draw a figure on a coordinate grid. Then draw a congruent figure in another quadrant. Write the ordered pairs for all vertices. Check students' drawings.



Grade 4 39 Chapter 10

**Identify Congruent Figures**

3 **SCHOOL The diagrams show the shapes and sizes of two classrooms. Do the two classrooms appear to be congruent? Explain.**

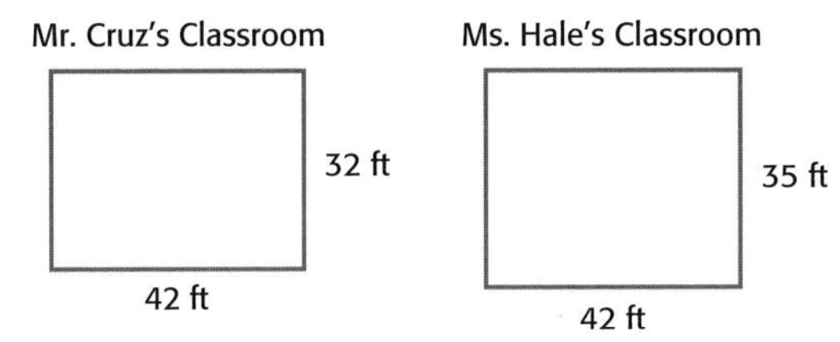


Both classrooms have the same shape. They are rectangles.

Both classrooms have the same length, but Ms. Hale's classroom has a greater width. So, they are not the same size.

Since the classrooms have different sizes, they are not congruent.

4. no; They have different sizes and shapes. So, they are not congruent

5. Sample answer: Two figures are congruent if they demonstrate a rotation, reflection, or translation.

## CHECK What You Know

**Tell whether the figures appear to be congruent. Write *yes* or *no*. If they are, describe the movements that show the congruence.** See Examples 1–3 (pp. 418–419)

1. 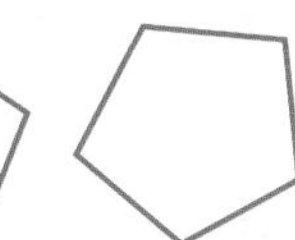 yes; rotation

2.  no

3. A ceramic tile design is shown. How many of the blue kitchen tiles appear to be congruent to the tile labeled *E*? 8

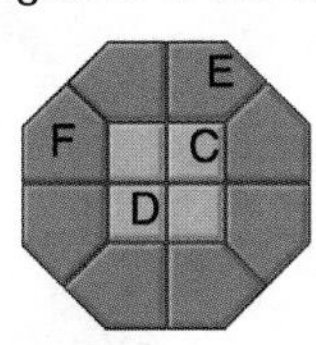


4. In the birdhouse, do the windows and door appear to be congruent? Explain.

5. Talk About It Describe the movements that can be used to check if two figures appear to be congruent.



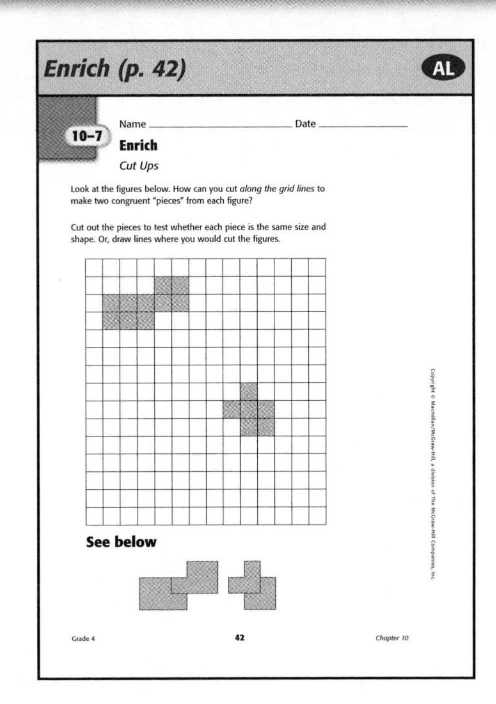

*Enrich (p. 42)* AL

10-7 Name ________ Date ________

**Enrich**

*Cut Ups*

Look at the figures below. How can you cut *along the grid lines* to make two congruent "pieces" from each figure?

Cut out the pieces to test whether each piece is the same size and shape. Or, draw lines where you would cut the figures.

**See below**



Grade 4 42 Chapter 10

### Identify Congruent Figures

**Example 1** Caution students that even if two geometric figures appear to be the same size and shape, they should use a translation, reflection, or rotation to determine congruence.

## ADDITIONAL EXAMPLES

**Tell whether the figures appear to be congruent. Write *yes* or *no*. If they are, describe the movements that show their congruence.**

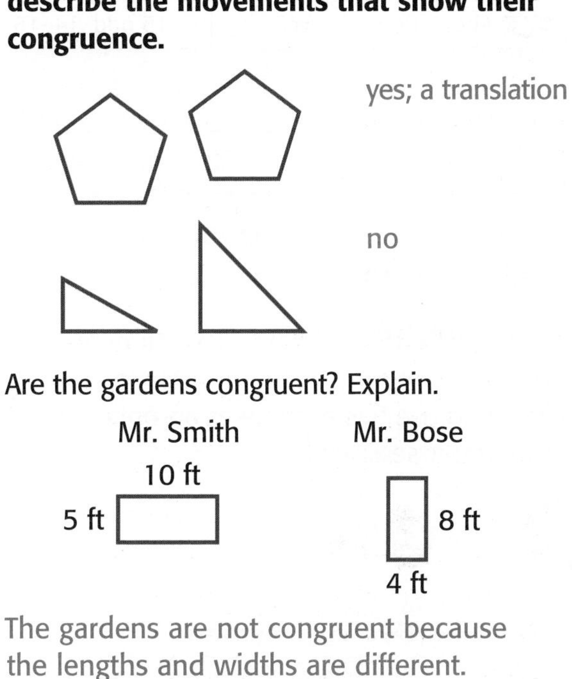

1. yes; a translation

2. no

3. Are the gardens congruent? Explain.



The gardens are not congruent because the lengths and widths are different.

### CHECK What You Know

As a class, have students complete Exercises 1–5 in **Check What You Know** as you observe their work.

**Exercise 5** Assess student comprehension before assigning practice exercises.

## BL Alternate Teaching Strategy

**If** students have trouble identifying congruent figures...

**Then** use one of these reteach options:

1 CRM **Daily Reteach Worksheet** (p. 38)

2 Have students trace one of the figures, cut it out, and superimpose it on the other, using transformations to tell whether the figures are congruent.

## COMMON ERROR!

**Exercises 10 and 11** Some students may get confused when the orientation of two figures is different. Encourage them to rotate their books so they can visualize different orientations.

# Practice

Differentiate practice using these leveled assignments for Exercises 6–16.

| Level | Assignment |
|---|---|
| BL Below/Approaching Level | 6, 9–10, 12–13 |
| OL On Level | 6–10, 12 |
| AL Above/Beyond Level | 6–15 odd, 14–16 |

Have students discuss and complete the Higher Order Thinking problems. Students may need to review the definition and properties of a square for Exercise 16. A working vocabulary is essential to all the exercises.

**WRITING IN MATH** Have students complete Exercise 16 in their Math Journals. You may choose to use this exercise as an optional formative assessment.

# 4 Assess

### Formative Assessment

- **What characteristics do congruent figures share?** same size and shape
- **How can you show that two figures are congruent?** Sample answer: You can reflect, rotate, or translate one of the figures to show that it is the same size and shape as the other.

**Quick Check** **Are students continuing to struggle with identifying congruent figures?**

**If Yes** → Small Group Options (p. 374B)

**If No** → Independent Work Options (p. 374B)
CRM Skills Practice Worksheet (p. 39)
CRM Enrich Worksheet (p. 42)

**Yesterday's News** Explain how the lesson on rotations, reflections, and translations helped you understand congruent figures.



## Practice and Problem Solving

EXTRA PRACTICE See page R27.

**Tell whether the figures appear to be congruent. Write *yes* or *no*. If they are, describe the movements that show the congruence.** See Examples 1–3 (pp. 418–419)

**6.** 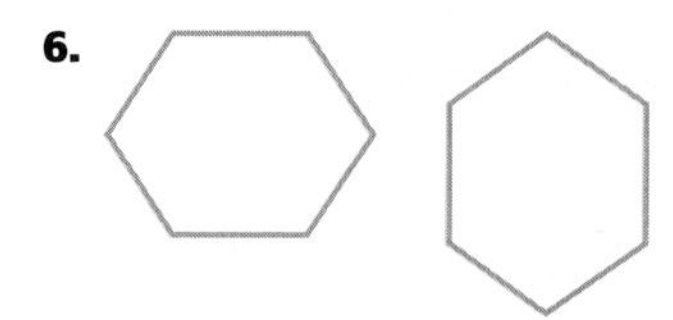 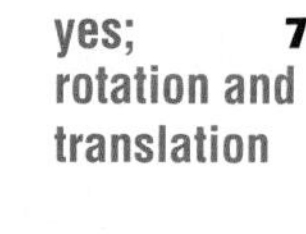 yes; rotation and translation

**7.** 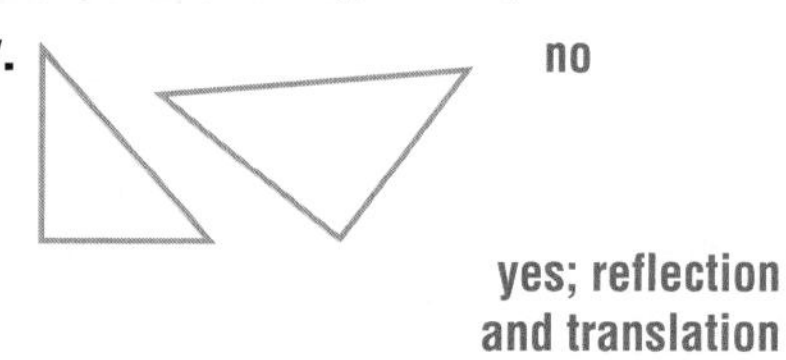 no

**8.** 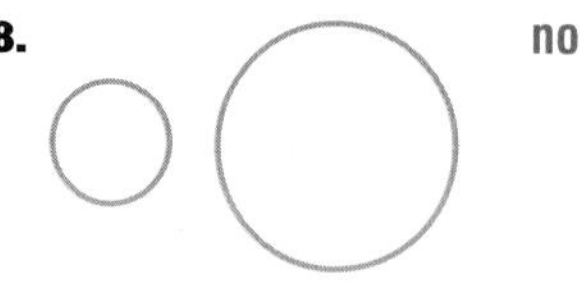 no

**9.** yes; reflection and translation

**10.** Tell whether the cells on a honeycomb appear to be congruent. yes

**11.** Which figures on a soccer ball appear to be congruent? pentagons and hexagons

**12. Measurement** The television in Lin's room is 30 inches wide and 24 inches long. His friend has the same television. If the television is 30 inches wide, how long is it? 24 in.

**13. Measurement** One of Paloma's picture frames is 5 inches wide and 7 inches long. She has another picture frame that is the same size. If it is 7 inches long, how wide is it? 5 in.

### H.O.T. Problems

**14. OPEN ENDED** Create two rectangles. Tell whether they are congruent or not congruent. Explain. 14–16. See Ch. 10 Answer Appendix.

**15. FIND THE ERROR** Tammy and Jacinto are comparing their slices of pizza. Who is correct? Explain.

**16. WRITING IN MATH** Are all squares with one side measuring 5 inches congruent? Explain your reasoning.



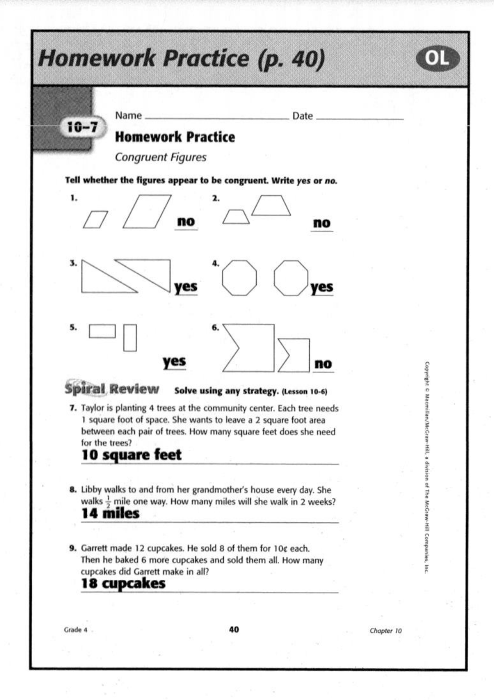

**Homework Practice (p. 40)** OL

Name ______ Date ______

10-7 **Homework Practice**

*Congruent Figures*

**Tell whether the figures appear to be congruent. Write *yes* or *no*.**

1. no
2. no
3. yes
4. yes
5. yes
6. no

**Spiral Review** **Solve using any strategy.** (Lesson 10-6)

7. Taylor is planting 4 trees at the community center. Each tree needs 1 square foot of space. She wants to leave a 2 square foot area between each pair of trees. How many square feet does she need for the trees?
**10 square feet**

8. Libby walks to and from her grandmother's house every day. She walks $\frac{1}{2}$ mile one way. How many miles will she walk in 2 weeks?
**14 miles**

9. Garrett made 12 cupcakes. He sold 8 of them for 10¢ each. Then he baked 6 more cupcakes and sold them all. How many cupcakes did Garrett make in all?
**18 cupcakes**



Grade 4 40 Chapter 10

Extend

# Technology Activity for 10-7 Congruent Figures

**MAIN IDEA**

I will use technology to explore congruent figures.

**The *Math Tool Chest* can be used to create congruent figures.**

Stamp a trapezoid. Then stamp a congruent trapezoid. Use transformations to prove both figures are congruent.

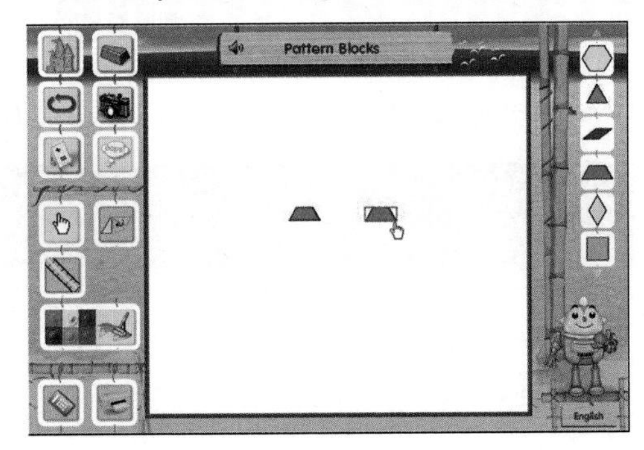


- Click on the pattern blocks tool chest.
- Click on the trapezoid pattern block.
- Stamp two trapezoids on the mat.
- Click on the move button.
- Click on one trapezoid and drag it until it is on top of the other trapezoid.

What transformation shows that the two figures are congruent?
translation

## CHECK What You Know

**Use *Math Tool Chest* to stamp each figure. Then stamp a congruent figure.**

**1.** triangle **2.** square **3.** hexagon

1–3. See students' work.

**For Exercises 4–6, use *Math Tool Chest* to solve.**

**4.** Kurt wants to create a design for a book cover. He draws congruent octagons to use in his design. Draw an example of what his design could look like. See students' work.

**5.** Two pictures in a magazine are to be outlined with congruent rectangles. Draw two rectangles that could be used to outline the pictures. Explain how you know your figures are congruent.
See students' drawings. Sample answer: They are the same size and shape.



## Using Math Tool Chest

**Geometry** The pattern blocks Tool in *Math Tool Chest* provide opportunities for students to create congruent figures quickly and easily.

- Students use the pattern blocks tools to stamp shapes in the work area.
- A figure can be manipulated by using different buttons in the work area.

Extend

# Technology Activity for 10-7

# Lesson Planner

## Objective

Use technology to explore congruent figures.

## Resources

**Math Tool Chest** *(accessible in three ways)*

- Math Online macmillanmh.com
- StudentWorks Plus
- Interactive Classroom

## Getting Started

- Share with students that this activity requires them to use *Math Tool Chest,* a computer program that allows them to explore mathematical concepts and develop math skills.
- Before class, use the Teacher Utilities to enter a list of all student names. Or, have each student enter his or her name at the Sign In screen when they begin the activity.
- Have students read the example on p. 421.
- As a class, work through the activity in the example following the instructions on the page.

LESSON 10-8

# Symmetry

## Lesson Planner

### Objective

Identify figures with symmetry.

### Vocabulary

**line symmetry**, **line of symmetry**, **bilateral symmetry**, **rotational symmetry**

### Resources

**Materials:** large regular hexagon figure on paper for all students, crayons or colored pencils, block letter bulletin board size letters, scissors, dot paper

**Manipulatives:** ruler, pattern blocks, geomirrors

**Literature Connection:** *Round Trip* by Ann Jonas

**Alternate Lesson:** Use *IMPACT Mathematics:* Unit J to provide practice with symmetry.

**Teacher Technology**

TeacherWorks • Interactive Classroom

### Focus on Math Background

There are two basic types of symmetry: line symmetry and rotational symmetry. Line symmetry is also called reflectional symmetry or mirror symmetry. Only line symmetry is presented in this lesson.

An object or figure has line symmetry if you can fold it along some line so that the points on one side of the line match exactly the points on the other side of the line. Objects with line symmetry look balanced. It is possible for figures to have more than one line of symmetry, for example, all regular polygons have more than one line of symmetry.

## Daily Routine

Use these suggestions before beginning the lesson on p. 422.

### 5-Minute Check

(Reviews Lesson 10-7)

**Tell whether the figures appear to be congruent. Write *yes* or *no*. If they are, describe the movements that show congruence.**

1. yes; translation
2. no
3. no
4. yes; reflection or translation

### Problem of the Day

There are 2 more than 3 times as many parrots as finches at the pet store. If there are 18 parrots and finches at the pet store, how many are parrots and how many are finches? 4 finches and 14 parrots

### Building Math Vocabulary

Write the lesson vocabulary words and their definitions on the board.

Have students write the new words and definitions in their Math Journals. Have them draw figures to show the different kinds of symmetry.

# Differentiated Instruction

## Small Group Options

### Option 1 Gifted and Talented (AL)

LOGICAL

**Materials:** printed circles on paper with a radius of at least 3 cm for each student, pencils, rulers, chart paper, markers

- Review the definition of line of symmetry.
- Ask students to estimate the number of lines of symmetry on their circle and record them on the chart paper.
- Once all the estimates have been recorded, ask students to draw the lines of symmetry.
- Encourage students to keep drawing until they have found all the lines of symmetry.
- As time runs out, encourage students to come to the realization that there is an infinite number of lines of symmetry.

### Option 2 English Language Learners (ELL)

VISUAL, SOCIAL

**Materials:** paper, picture of a face
**Core Vocabulary:** matching half, mine, your
**Common Use Verb:** is like
**See Math** This strategy allows students to explore the idea of symmetry.

- Draw a line down the center of the picture of a face to introduce symmetry—to look the same on both sides.
- Draw and then cut enough different colored symmetrical and non-symmetrical shapes in half so each student will have one.
- Allow students to circle the room to find their matching half.
- Taking turns in front of the class, each pair should hold up their match and say: "**Your** shape ***is like*** **mine.**"

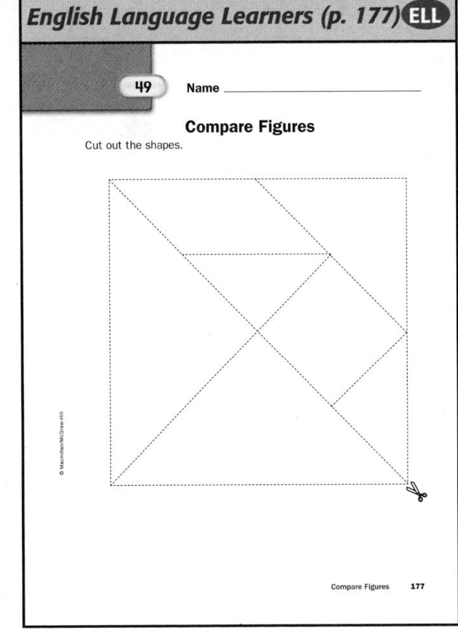

*English Language Learners (p. 177)* (ELL)

49 Name ______

**Compare Figures**

Cut out the shapes.

Compare Figures 177

*Use this worksheet to provide additional support for English Language Learners.*

## Independent Work Options

### Option 1 Early Finishers (OL) (AL)

SPATIAL

**Materials:** paper, pencil

- Students identify and list objects from the classroom that have symmetry.
- Then, students can make sketches of some symmetrical objects. Have them verify the symmetry using reflections.

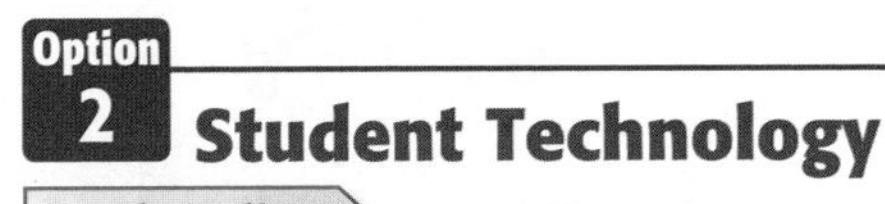

### Option 2 Student Technology

Tech Link

**Math Online** macmillanmh.com

Personal Tutor • Extra Examples

### Option 3 Learning Station: Art (p. 392G)

Direct students to the Art Learning Station for opportunities to explore and extend the lesson concept.

### Option 4 Problem-Solving Practice

Reinforce problem-solving skills and strategies with the Problem-Solving Practice worksheet.

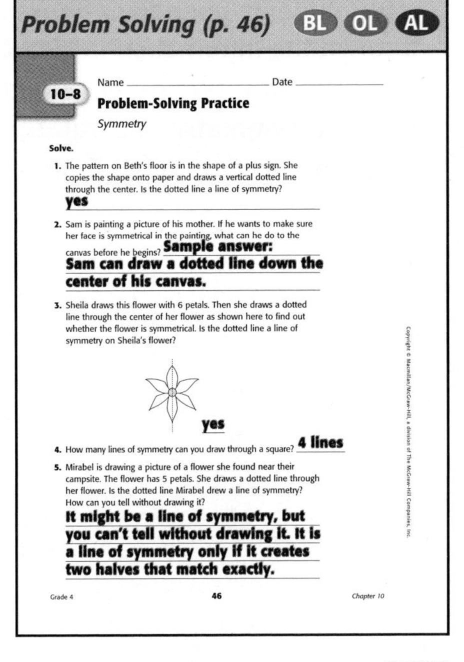

*Problem Solving (p. 46)* (BL) (OL) (AL)

10–8 Name ______ Date ______

**Problem-Solving Practice**

*Symmetry*

**Solve.**

1. The pattern on Beth's floor is in the shape of a plus sign. She copies the shape onto paper and draws a vertical dotted line through the center. Is the dotted line a line of symmetry? **yes**
2. Sam is painting a picture of his mother. If he wants to make sure her face is symmetrical in the painting, what can he do to the canvas before he begins? **Sample answer: Sam can draw a dotted line down the center of his canvas.**
3. Sheila draws this flower with 6 petals. Then she draws a dotted line through the center of her flower as shown here to find out whether the flower is symmetrical. Is the dotted line a line of symmetry on Sheila's flower? **yes**
4. How many lines of symmetry can you draw through a square? **4 lines**
5. Mirabel is drawing a picture of a flower she found near their campsite. The flower has 5 petals. She draws a dotted line through her flower. Is the dotted line Mirabel drew a line of symmetry? How can you tell without drawing it? **It might be a line of symmetry, but you can't tell without drawing it. It is a line of symmetry only if it creates two halves that match exactly.**



Grade 4 46 Chapter 10

# 10-8 Symmetry

## 1 Introduce

### Activity Choice 1 • Hands-On

- Have students cut out a regular hexagon and fold it in half. Explain that the fold is a line of symmetry and the two equal halves show that the figure has line symmetry.
- **Is there only one way to fold the hexagon in half?** no
- Have students volunteer show how they folded their hexagon in half.

### Activity Choice 2 • Literature

Introduce the lesson with *Round Trip* by Ann Jonas. For a related math activity, see p. TR58.

## 2 Teach

### Scaffolding Questions

Use block letter cut outs for the letters H, B, I, O, A, and S.

- Have volunteers use a ruler to show which letters have a line of symmetry. H, B, I, O
- **Which letters have 2 lines of symmetry?** H, I, O
- **Can a figure have more than two lines of symmetry? Explain.** yes; For example, a square has four lines of symmetry.

### GET READY to Learn

Have students open their books and read through the information in **Get Ready to Learn**. Introduce **line symmetry**, **line of symmetry**, **bilateral symmetry** and **rotational symmetry**. As a class, work through Examples 1 and 2.



# 10-8 Symmetry

**MAIN IDEA**

I will identify figures with symmetry.

**New Vocabulary**

**line symmetry**
**line of symmetry**
**bilateral symmetry**
**rotational symmetry**

**Math Online**
macmillanmh.com
- Extra Examples
- Personal Tutor
- Self-Check Quiz

### GET READY to Learn

A butterfly uses its wings to fly. Look at the left side and the right side of the butterfly. When a butterfly folds its wings in half, will the two parts match?

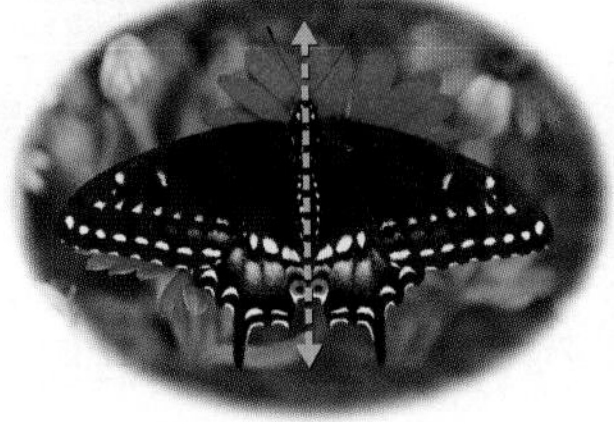

A figure has **line symmetry** if it can be folded so that the two parts of the figure match, or are congruent. The fold line is a **line of symmetry**.

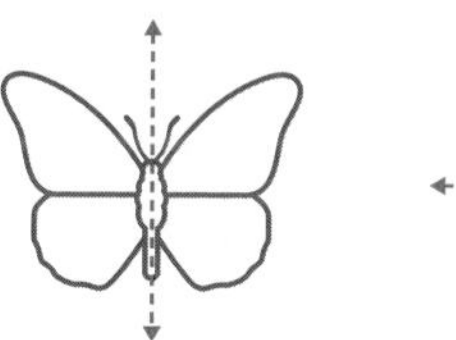

1 line of symmetry
line symmetry

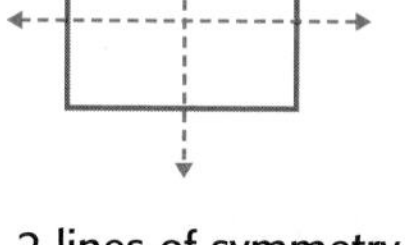

2 lines of symmetry
**bilateral symmetry**

no lines of symmetry

### EXAMPLES Identify Line Symmetry

**Tell whether each figure has line symmetry. Write *yes* or *no*. Then tell how many lines of symmetry the figure has.**

1. 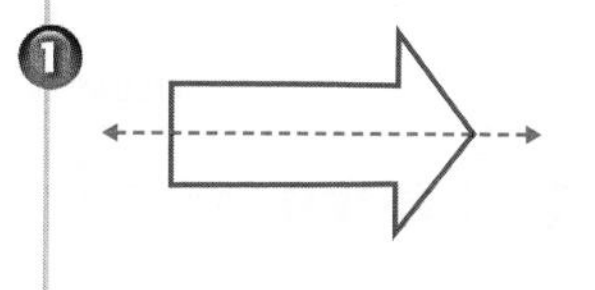

Yes; the figure has 1 line of symmetry.

2. 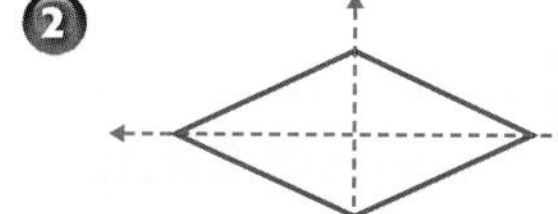

Yes; the figure has 2 lines of symmetry.



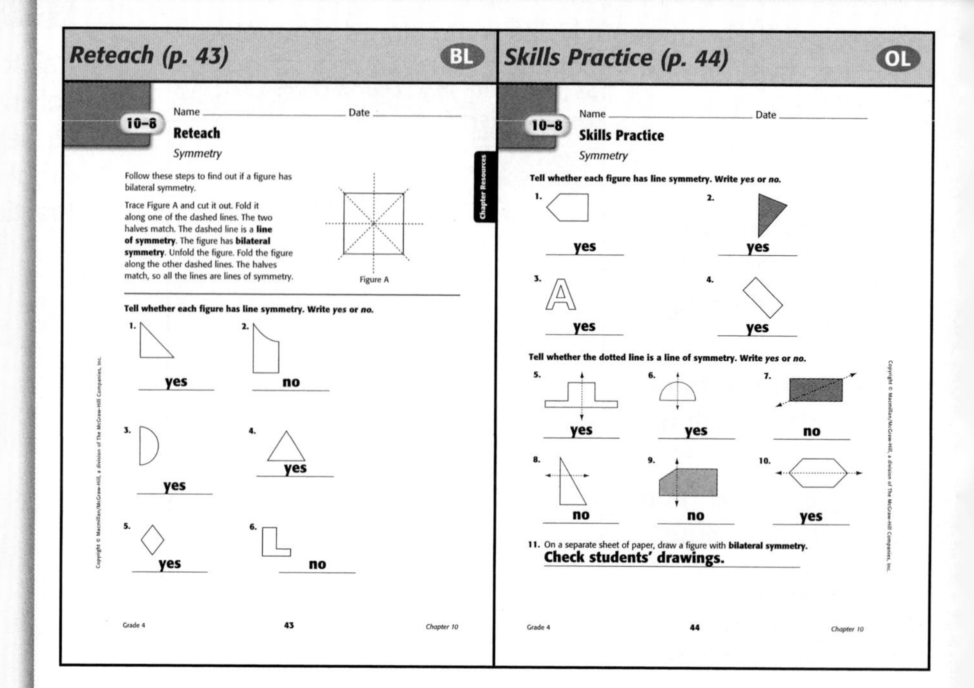

**Reteach (p. 43)** BL

10-8 Name ______ Date ______

**Reteach**

*Symmetry*

Follow these steps to find out if a figure has bilateral symmetry.

Trace Figure A and cut it out. Fold it along one of the dashed lines. The two halves match. The dashed line is a **line of symmetry**. The figure has **bilateral symmetry**. Unfold the figure. Fold the figure along the other dashed lines. The halves match, so all the lines are lines of symmetry.

Figure A

**Tell whether each figure has line symmetry. Write *yes* or *no*.**

1. yes
2. no
3. yes
4. yes
5. yes
6. no

Grade 4 43 Chapter 10

**Skills Practice (p. 44)** OL

10-8 Name ______ Date ______

**Skills Practice**

*Symmetry*

**Tell whether each figure has line symmetry. Write *yes* or *no*.**

1. yes
2. yes
3. yes
4. yes

**Tell whether the dotted line is a line of symmetry. Write *yes* or *no*.**

5. yes
6. yes
7. no
8. no
9. no
10. yes

11. On a separate sheet of paper, draw a figure with **bilateral symmetry**. **Check students' drawings.**

Grade 4 44 Chapter 10

When a figure fits exactly over itself after being rotated 180° or less, it has **rotational symmetry**.

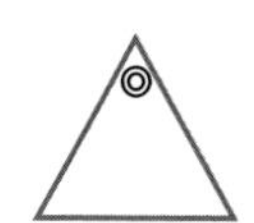 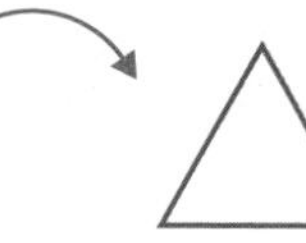 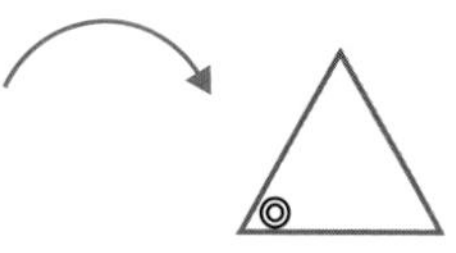

An equilateral triangle has rotational symmetry because it is the same after each rotation.

5. Sample answer: yes; It fits exactly over itself after being rotated 180° or less.

6. Sample answer: yes; The figure below has both types of symmetry.

## EXAMPLE Identify Rotational Symmetry

**3** **Tell whether the figure has rotational symmetry.**

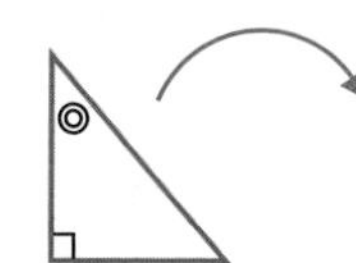 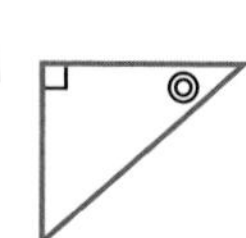 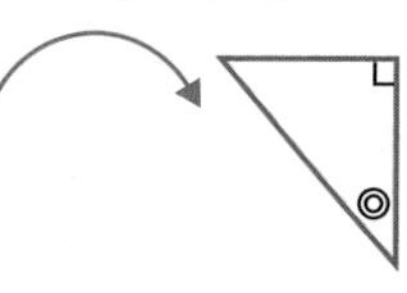

The right triangle does not look like it did before the turn. So, it does not have rotational symmetry.

## CHECK What You Know

**Tell whether each figure has line symmetry. Write *yes* or *no*. Then tell how many lines of symmetry the figure has.** See Examples 1 and 2 (p. 422)

**1.** 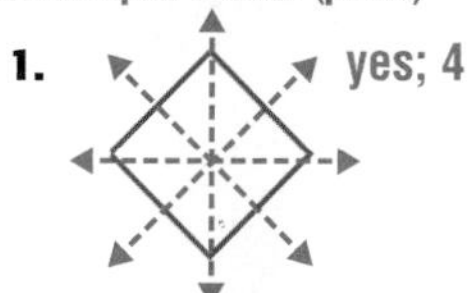 yes; 4

**2.**  no

**Tell whether the figure has rotational symmetry. Write *yes* or *no*.** See Example 3 (p. 423)

**3.** 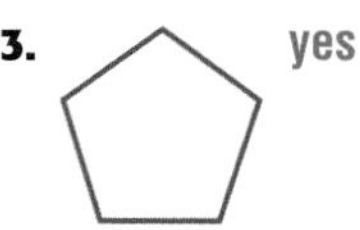 yes

**4.**  no

**5.** Tell whether the snowflake shown at the right has rotational symmetry. Explain.

**6.** Talk About It Do you think that a figure with bilateral symmetry can also have rotational symmetry? Draw a picture to explain your reasoning.



**Enrich (p. 47)** AL

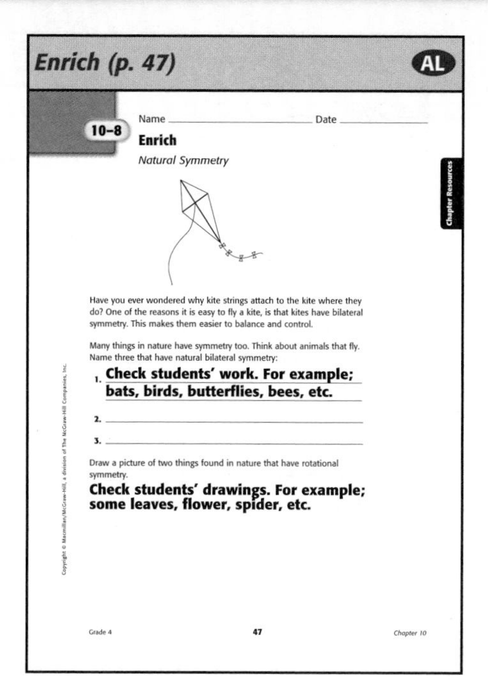

10-8 Name ______ Date ______

**Enrich**

*Natural Symmetry*

Have you ever wondered why kite strings attach to the kite where they do? One of the reasons it is easy to fly a kite, is that kites have bilateral symmetry. This makes them easier to balance and control.

Many things in nature have symmetry too. Think about animals that fly. Name three that have natural bilateral symmetry:

1. **Check students' work. For example; bats, birds, butterflies, bees, etc.**
2. ______
3. ______

Draw a picture of two things found in nature that have rotational symmetry.

**Check students' drawings. For example; some leaves, flower, spider, etc.**

Grade 4 47 Chapter 10

**Examples 1 and 2** Point out to students that it is possible for a figure to have more than two lines of symmetry.

## ADDITIONAL EXAMPLES

**Tell whether each figure has line symmetry. Write *yes* or *no*. Then tell how many lines of symmetry the figure has.**

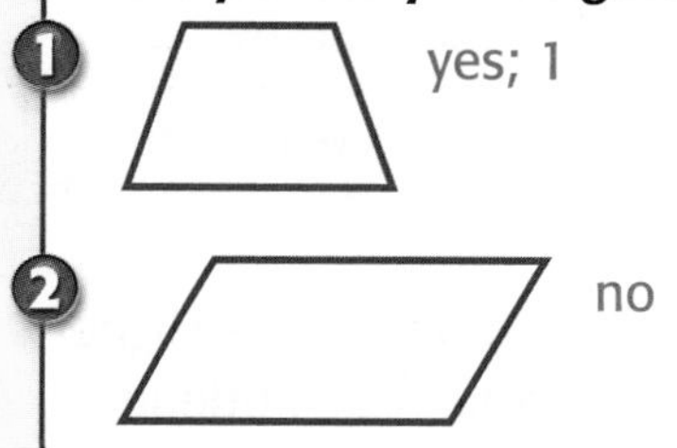

1. yes; 1
2. no

## CHECK What You Know

As a class, have students complete Exercises 1–6 in **Check What You Know** as you observe their work.

**Exercise 6** Assess student comprehension before assigning practice exercises.

## BL Alternate Teaching Strategy

**If** students struggle with identifying figures with symmetry and lines of symmetry…

**Then** use one of these reteach options:

1 CRM **Daily Reteach Worksheet** (p. 43)

2 Have students use dot paper, draw a figure, cut it out, then fold it in half. Have them work with a partner to identify the lines of symmetry in the figure.

## COMMON ERROR!

**Exercise 8** Diagonal line symmetry is more difficult for students to identify than vertical or horizontal line symmetry. Encourage students to rotate their books to get a different angle of perspective.

# 3 Practice

Differentiate practice using these leveled assignments for Exercises 5–18.

| Level | Assignment |
|---|---|
| BL Below/Approaching Level | 5–6, 9, 11, 14–15 |
| OL On Level | 8–13, 14–16 |
| AL Above/Beyond Level | 6–16 even, 17–18 |

Have students discuss and complete the Higher Order Thinking problems. Explain to students what a *plane figure* is.

**WRITING IN ▸MATH** Have students complete Exercise 20 in their Math Journals. You may choose to use this as an optional formative assessment.

# 4 Assess

## Formative Assessment

Present the following figure:

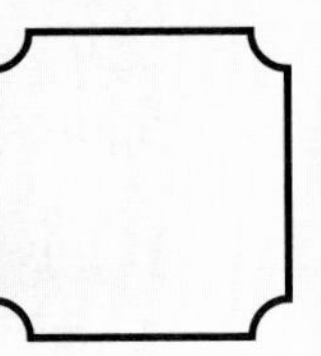

- **Explain how you know that this figure has line symmetry.**
  Sample answer: This figure has line symmetry because you can fold it into two congruent halves.

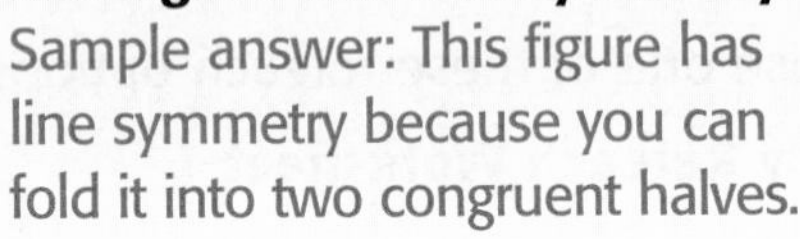

**Quick Check** **Are students continuing to struggle with identifying figures that have symmetry?**

**If Yes** → Small Group Options (p. 422B)

**If No** → Independent Work Options (p. 422B)
CRM Skills Practice Worksheet (p. 44)
CRM Enrich Worksheet (p. 47)

**Ticket Out the Door** Draw a figure on the board. On a small piece of paper, have students sketch the figure and draw in any lines of symmetry.

## Practice and Problem Solving

**Tell whether each figure has line symmetry. Write *yes* or *no*. Then tell how many lines of symmetry the figure has.**
See Examples 1 and 2 (p. 422)

7. 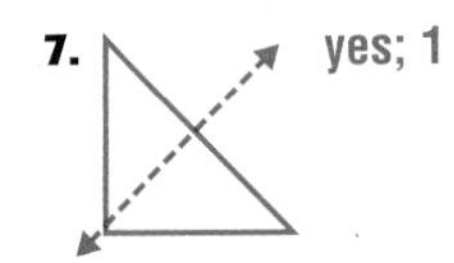 yes; 1

8.   no

9. 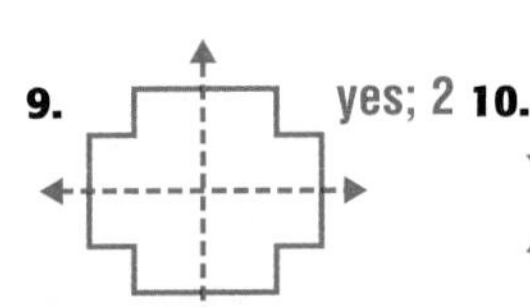 yes; 2

10. 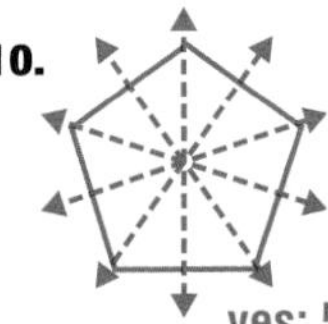 yes; 5

**Tell whether the figure has rotational symmetry. Write *yes* or *no*.** See Example 3 (p. 423)

11. 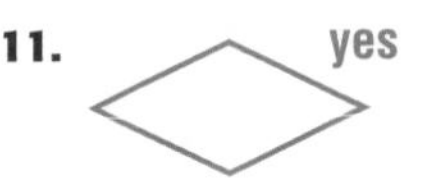 yes

12. no

13.  no

14.  yes

15. Does the letter C have symmetry? If it does, tell how many lines of symmetry the letter has. yes; 1

16. Does a square have symmetry? If is does, tell how many lines of symmetry the shape has. yes; 4

### Real-World PROBLEM SOLVING

17–19. See students' work.

**Art** Lines of symmetry can be seen in many pieces of art work such as cultural masks.

17. Sketch the mask shown and show the line of symmetry.

18. Using a sheet of grid paper, create half of a cultural mask. Then, switch papers with another student. Complete the image of the cultural mask you now have.

19. Does the cultural mask you created have rotational symmetry?

### H.O.T. Problems

20. **OPEN ENDED** Design a two-dimensional figure that has more than 3 lines of symmetry. 20, 21. See Ch. 10 Answer Appendix.

21. **WRITING IN ▸MATH** How many lines of symmetry do you think a circle has? Explain.



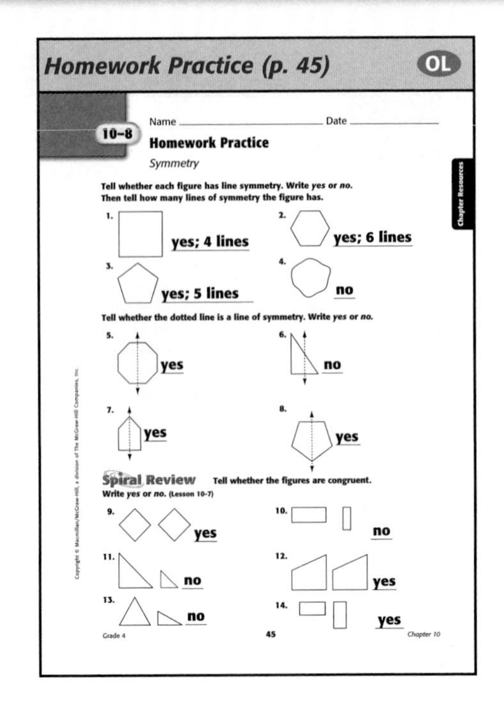

**Homework Practice (p. 45)** OL

10-8 Name ______ Date ______

**Homework Practice**

*Symmetry*

**Tell whether each figure has line symmetry. Write *yes* or *no*. Then tell how many lines of symmetry the figure has.**

1. yes; 4 lines
2. yes; 6 lines
3. yes; 5 lines
4. no

**Tell whether the dotted line is a line of symmetry. Write *yes* or *no*.**

5. yes
6. no
7. yes
8. yes

**Spiral Review** **Tell whether the figures are congruent. Write *yes* or *no*.** (Lesson 10-7)

9. yes
10. no
11. no
12. yes
13. no
14. yes

Chapter Resources



Grade 4 45 Chapter 10

424 Chapter 10 Understand and Develop Spatial Reasoning

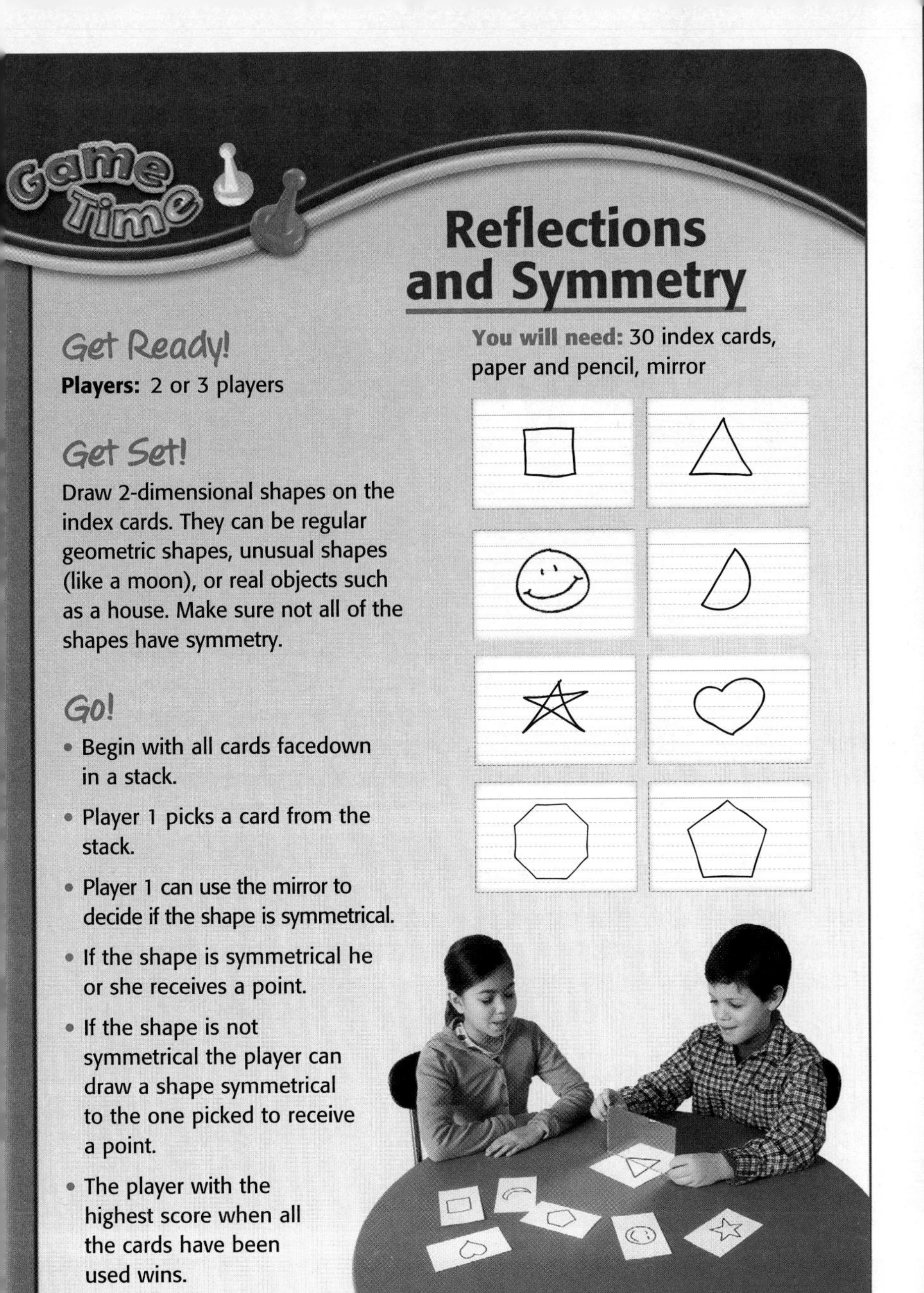

Game Time

## Reflections and Symmetry

**You will need:** 30 index cards, paper and pencil, mirror

### Get Ready!

**Players:** 2 or 3 players

### Get Set!

Draw 2-dimensional shapes on the index cards. They can be regular geometric shapes, unusual shapes (like a moon), or real objects such as a house. Make sure not all of the shapes have symmetry.

### Go!

- Begin with all cards facedown in a stack.
- Player 1 picks a card from the stack.
- Player 1 can use the mirror to decide if the shape is symmetrical.
- If the shape is symmetrical he or she receives a point.
- If the shape is not symmetrical the player can draw a shape symmetrical to the one picked to receive a point.
- The player with the highest score when all the cards have been used wins.

**Game Time** Reflections and Symmetry **425**

# Differentiated Practice

Use these leveled suggestions to differentiate the game for all learners.

| Level | Assignment |
|---|---|
| BL Below/Approaching Level | Students may work in pairs to help each other draw symmetrical shapes. |
| OL On Level | Have students play the game with the rules as written. |
| AL Above/Beyond Level | Students make cards with shapes that are all asymmetrical. |

# Reflections and Symmetry

**Math Concept: Symmetry**

**Materials:** 30 index cards, pencils, paper, mirror.

Introduce the game on p. 425 to your students to play as a class, in small groups, or at a learning workstation to review concepts introduced in this chapter.

## Instructions

- Students play in groups of 2 or 3 players. They draw 2-dimensional shapes on the index cards, making sure that some of the shapes are not symmetrical.
- Students shuffle the cards and lay the stack of cards facedown on the table.
- Player 1 chooses a card from the stack and uses the mirror to decide if the shape is symmetrical or not. If the shape is symmetrical, Player 1 receives a point. If it is not symmetrical, Player 1 tries to draw a shape using the one he or she picked, making it symmetrical, to receive one point. Players use the mirror to help them create a symmetrical shape out of one that is not symmetrical.
- Students take turns picking cards from the pile and drawing symmetrical shapes if necessary. Play continues until all the cards have been used. The player with the highest score wins.

## Extend the Game

Have students play the game using midlines instead of mirrors.

# Lesson Planner

## Objective

Interpret information and data from science to solve problems.

### National Standard 

Students should develop an understanding of the characteristics of organisms.

## Activate Prior Knowledge

Before you turn students' attention to the pages, ask them to discuss types of symmetry.

- **What items around the room have line symmetry?** Sample answer: desk

## Using the Student Page

Ask students to read the information on p. 378 and answer these questions:

- **Why do many animals have bodies with symmetry?** to help them survive
- **What other items have symmetry?** your face
- **What flowers have rotational symmetry?** daisies



# Symmetry in Nature

Symmetry can be seen in different habitats in nature. The next time you walk near a pond, you may find symmetry. A calm lake can act as a mirror and show the reflection of surrounding trees. This is an example of line symmetry.

Many animals have symmetrical bodies to help them survive. If an animal had an odd number of wings or legs, it might have a difficult time flying or walking because it would not be balanced. Think about the different parts of a plant. The petals of some flowers show rotational symmetry.

The next time you take a walk outside, take a closer look at your environment. You may discover symmetry all around you.

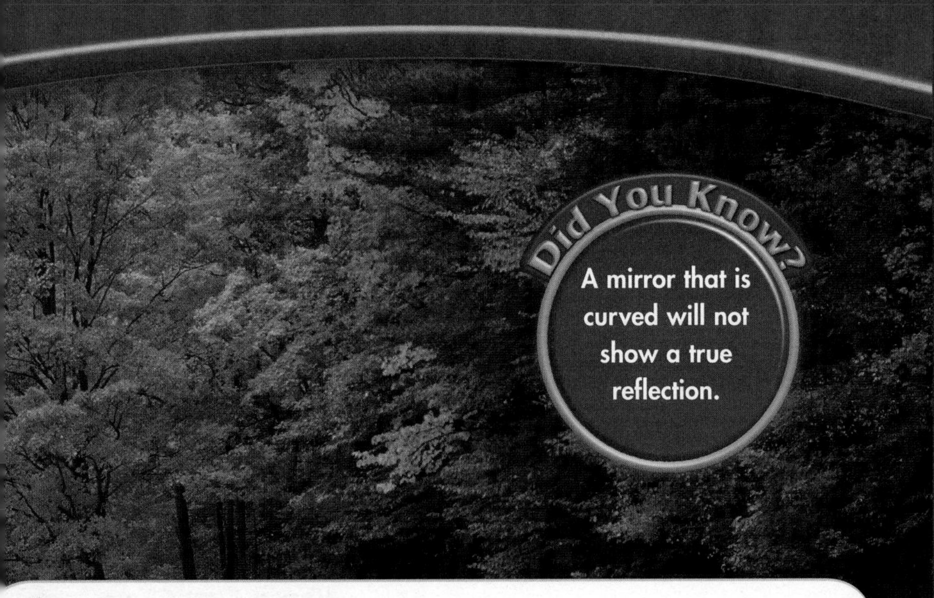

## Real-World Math

**Use the photos below to solve each problem.**

1. Identify which plants or animals above show line symmetry. all of them
2. Does the leaf have symmetry? If it does, tell how many lines of symmetry it has. yes; 1
3. Draw a picture of something in nature that shows line symmetry. Label the line of symmetry. See students' work.
4. Explain how you could test an object in nature to see if it has symmetry. 4–6. See margin.
5. Explain the difference between line symmetry and rotational symmetry.
6. What could affect the symmetry shown in the picture of the lake and trees?

## Real-World Math

Assign the exercises on p. 427. Encourage students to choose a problem-solving strategy before beginning each exercise. If necessary, review the strategies suggested in Lesson 10-6, p. 416.

**Exercise 6** Remind students that the reflection in the picture is a reflection on water.

## Extend the Activity

Have students look for other pictures of nature that show symmetry, then explain how they know.

### Additional Answers

4. Sample answer: You can look to see if one half of the object is the mirror image of the other half. You can also decide if the image would look the same after it is turned.
5. Sample answer: Line symmetry occurs when a figure can be folded so that two parts of the figure match. Rotational symmetry occurs when a figure fits exactly over itself after being rotated 180° or less.
6. Sample answer: Ripples or waves in the water.

# Chapter 10 Study Guide and Review

## Dinah Zike's Foldables

Use these lesson suggestions to incorporate the Foldables during the chapter. Students can then use their Foldables to review for the test.

**Lessons 10-7, 10-8** Have students make a Ten-tab Vocabulary Foldable using one sheet of 8.5″ × 11″ notebook paper and label as shown. Students provide definitions of the terms beneath the tabs. The Foldable can be used as a self-checking study aid to improve vocabulary recall.

## Key Vocabulary

The page references after each word denote where that term was first introduced. If students have difficulty answering Exercises 1–5, remind them they can use the page references to review the vocabulary terms.

## Vocabulary Review

Review chapter vocabulary using one of the following options.

- **Visual Vocabulary Cards** (33, 49, 50)
- **eGlossary** at macmillanmh.com



# Chapter 10 Study Guide and Review

Math Online macmillanmh.com
- STUDY TO GO
- Vocabulary Review

### FOLDABLES Study Organizer GET READY to Study

**Be sure the following Key Vocabulary words and Key Concepts are written in your Foldable.**

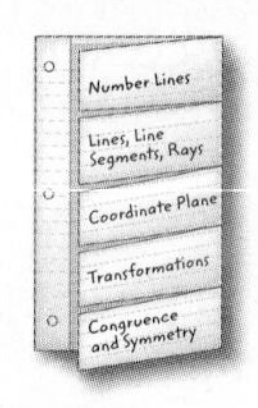


### Key Concepts

- A **number line** is a line with numbers on it in order at regular intervals. (p. 395)

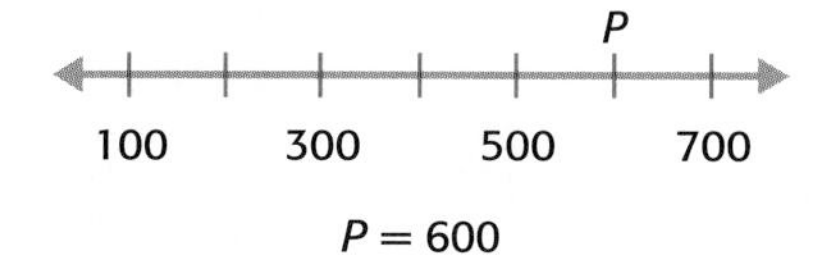


$P = 600$

- Transformations are movements of figures such as: (p. 412)

**Translation**

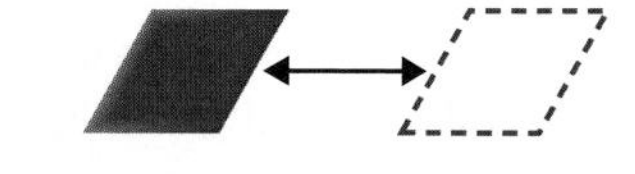

**Rotation** **Reflection**

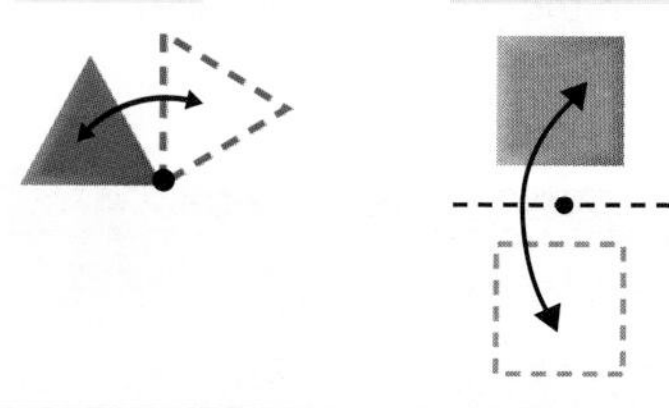

### Key Vocabulary

**coordinate plane** (p. 406)
**congruent** (p. 418)
**number line** (p. 395)
**point** (p. 395)
**transformation** (p. 412)

### Vocabulary Check

**Decide which vocabulary word best completes each sentence.**

1. A ___?___ is formed when two number lines intersect at their zero points. coordinate plane
2. A ___?___ is a movement of a figure. transformation
3. A ___?___ is an exact location in space. point
4. A ___?___ is a line with numbers on it in order at regular intervals. number line
5. Figures that are the same size and shape are ___?___. congruent



## Chapter 10 Project

### Room Redesign

Alone, in pairs, or in small groups, have students discuss the results of their completed chapter project with the class. Assess their work using the Chapter Project rubric found in Chapter 10 Resource Masters, p. 58.

## Lesson-by-Lesson Review

### 10-1 Locate Points on a Number Line (pp. 395–397)

**Example 1**
**What number is represented by point *B*?**

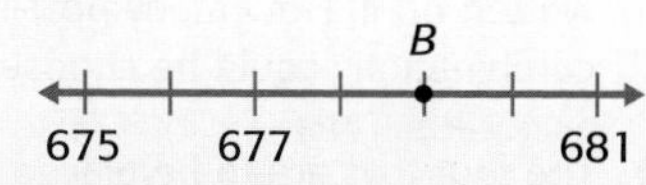


So, point *B* represents 679.

**Example 2**
**What number does point *Z* represent on the number line?**

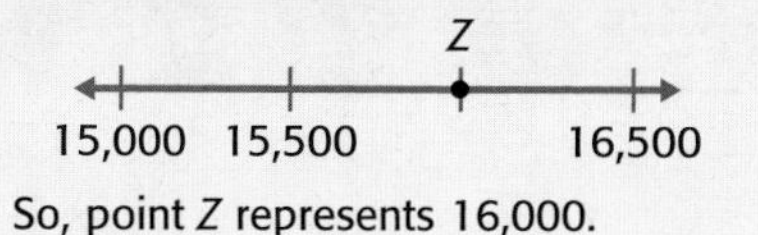


So, point *Z* represents 16,000.

**Tell what number each letter on the number line represents.**

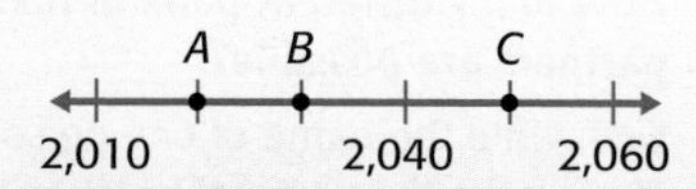


6. point *A* **2,020**
7. point *B* **2,030**
8. point *C* **2,050**
9. Tell what number point *W* represents on the number line. **16,000**

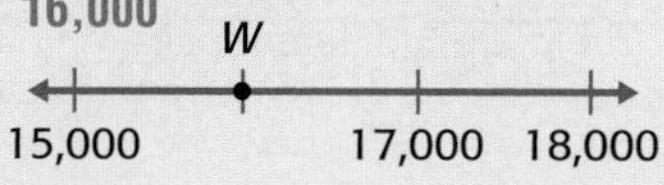


### 10-2 Lines, Line Segments, and Rays (pp. 400–403)

**Example 3**
**Describe the figure.**

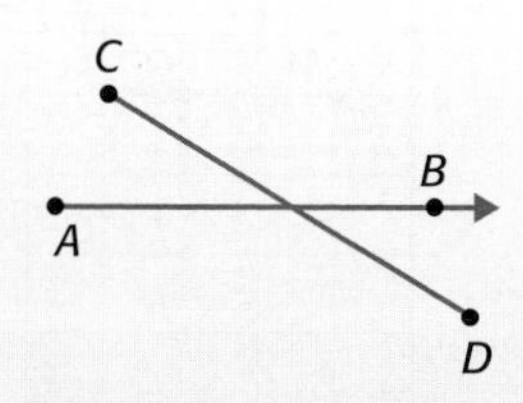


The figure shows ray *AB* and line segment *CD*. Notice that ray *AB* intersects line *CD*.

$\overrightarrow{AB}$ intersects $\overline{CD}$.

**Identify each figure.**

**10.** **11.**

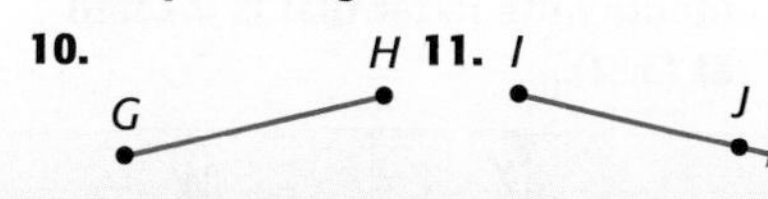


**Describe each figure.**

**12.** **13.** **14.** **15.**

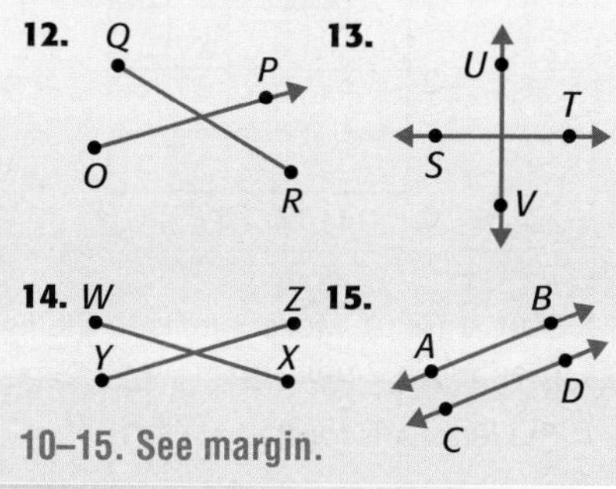


**10–15. See margin.**



# Lesson-by-Lesson Review

Have students complete the Lesson-by-Lesson Review on pp. 429–432. Then you can use Exam*View*® Assessment Suite to customize another review worksheet that practices all the objectives of this chapter or only the objectives on which your students need more help.

**Intervention** If the given examples are not sufficient to review the topics covered by the questions, use the page references next to the exercises to review that topic in the Student Edition.

### Additional Answers

10. $\overline{GH}$
11. $\overrightarrow{IJ}$
12. $\overrightarrow{OP}$ intersects $\overline{QR}$
13. $\overleftrightarrow{ST}$ intersects $\overleftrightarrow{UV}$
14. $\overline{WX}$ intersects $\overline{YZ}$
15. $\overleftrightarrow{AB}$ parallel to $\overleftrightarrow{CD}$

## 10-3 Problem-Solving Strategy: Make an Organized List (pp. 404–405)

**Example 4**
**Alfonso, Erik, Owen, and Alek are going hiking. They will hike in pairs. How many different pairs of hiking partners are possible?**

First, write the name of one person. Then, write the name of another person by the first person's name. Continue to do this without repeating pairs.

| | |
|---|---|
| Alfonso – Erik | Erik – Owen |
| Alfonso – Owen | Erik – Alek |
| Alfonso – Alek | Owen – Alek |

There are 6 different pairs.

**Solve. Use the make an organized list strategy.**

**16.** Sergio has to find a combination for his lock. It has 2, 4, and 6 written on it. How many possible combinations could he choose? 6 combinations

**17.** The four toys are to be placed on a shelf. How many different ways can the toys be arranged? 24 ways

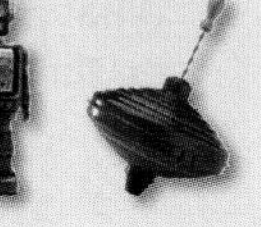

## 10-4 Find Points on a Grid (pp. 406–408)

**Example 5**
**Identify the letter that is located at (3, 2).**

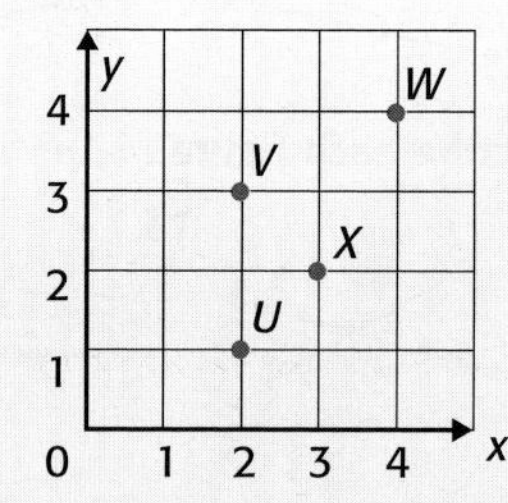


Start at (0, 0). Move 3 units to the right. Then move 2 units up.

The letter *X* is located at (3, 2).

**Identify the letter that is located at each ordered pair.**

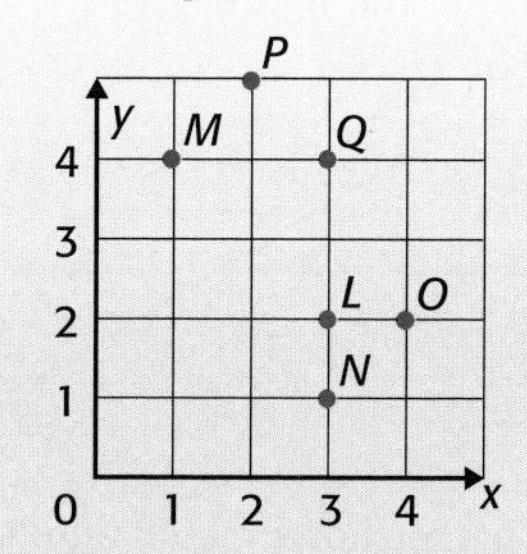


**18.** (3, 2) *L* **19.** (1, 4) *M* **20.** (2, 5) *P*

**21.** Describe how to get from *L* to *Q*. Move up two units.



430 Chapter 10 Understand and Develop Spatial Reasoning

## 10-5 Rotations, Reflections, and Translations (pp. 412–415)

**Example 6**
**Identify the transformation. Write *rotation, reflection,* or *translation.***

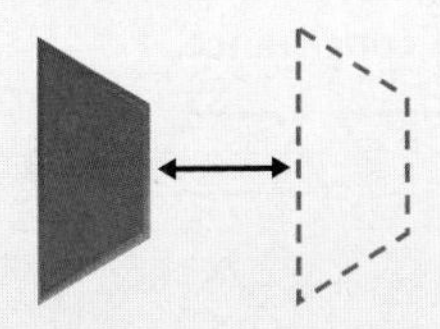

The trapezoid above has moved sideways. It has not turned or flipped.

So, the transformation of the trapezoid is a translation.

**Identify each transformation. Write *rotation, reflection,* or *translation.***

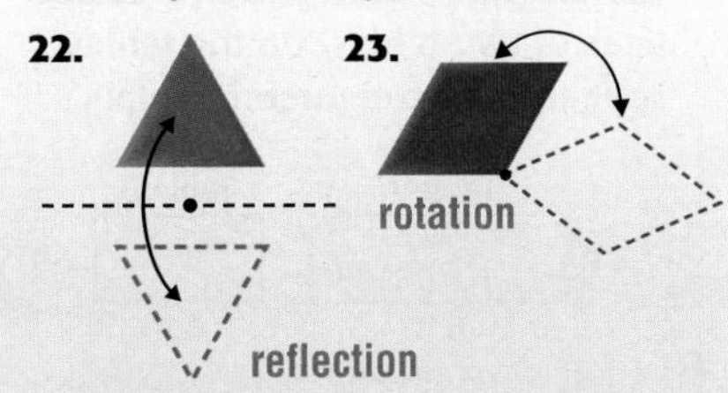


**Using pattern blocks, demonstrate the following transformations by tracing.**

**24.** reflection **25.** rotation
24, 25. See students' work.

## 10-6 Problem-Solving Investigation: Choose a Strategy (pp. 416–417)

**Example 7**
**Alberto has $5 left after buying skates for $62 and a helmet for $24. How much did he have originally?**

You can find an exact answer by using addition.

| | |
|---|---|
| $ 5 | change |
| + $62 | amount for skates |
| $67 | |
| + $24 | amount for helmet |
| $91 | |

So, Alberto had $91 originally.

**Use any strategy to solve.**

**26.** A teacher is arranging 24 desks. If she wants to group the desks in groups of 4, how many groups will she have? 6 groups

**27.** Peter can choose a ham or turkey sandwich. He can choose an apple or orange. How many different sandwich and fruit combinations can Peter choose? 4 combinations

**28.** A house has 15 rooms. One room is the kitchen, 4 rooms are bedrooms, and 2 rooms are bathrooms. How many other rooms are there? 8 rooms



Chapter 10 Study Guide and Review 431

# CHAPTER 10 Study Guide and Review



## 10-7 Congruent Figures (pp. 418–420)

**Example 8**
**The diagrams show the shapes and sizes of two tables. Do the tables appear to be congruent? Explain.**

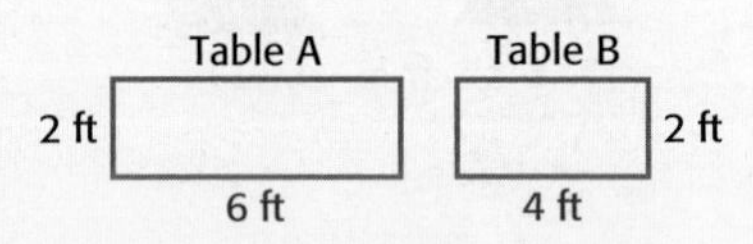


Both tables are rectangular in shape. They have the same width but do not have the same length.

Since the tables have different sizes, they do not appear to be congruent.

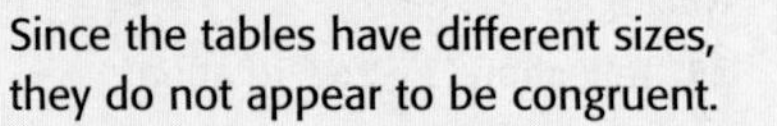

**Tell whether the figures appear to be congruent. Write *yes* or *no*. If they are, describe the movements that show the congruence.**

**29.** 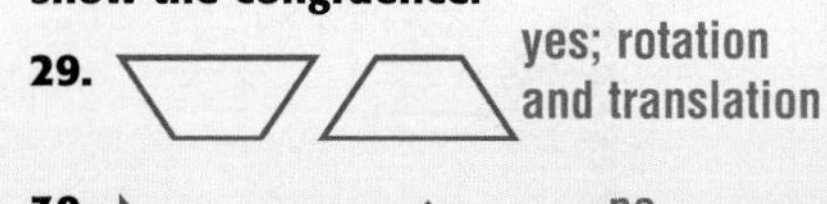 yes; rotation and translation

**30.**  no

**31.** yes; rotation and translatic

## 10-8 Symmetry (pp. 422–424)

**Example 9**
**Tell whether each figure has line symmetry. Then tell how many lines of symmetry the figure has.**

The figure has 0 lines of symmetry.

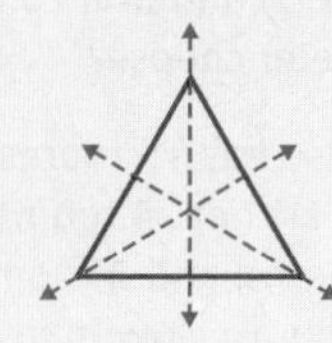

The figure has 3 lines of symmetry.

**Tell whether each figure has line symmetry. Write *yes* or *no*. Then tell how many lines of symmetry the figure has.**

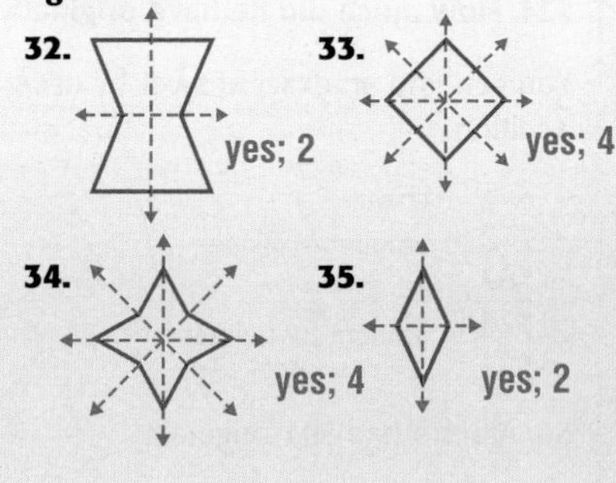

# Chapter Test

Math Online macmillanmh.com
• Chapter Test

Identify each transformation. Write *rotation, reflection,* or *translation.*

1. 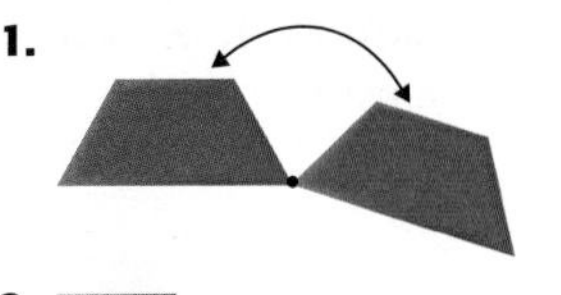 rotation

2. 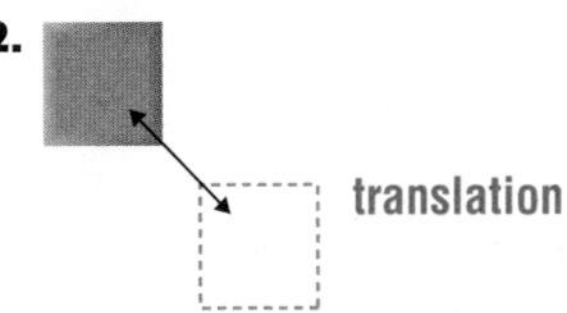 translation

3. **MULTIPLE CHOICE** Which number does point *C* represent? B

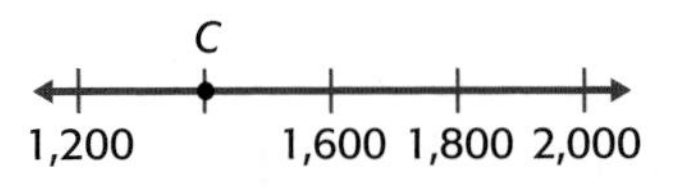


**A** 2,000 **C** 1,300

**B** 1,400 **D** 1,000

Tell what number each letter on the number line represents.

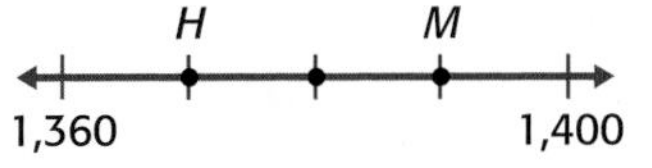


4. point *H* 1,370
5. point *M* 1,390

Identify each figure.

6. 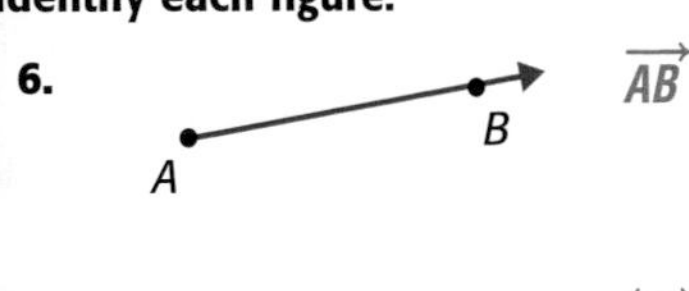

$\overrightarrow{AB}$

7. $\overleftrightarrow{JK}$

Tell whether the figures appear to be congruent. Write *yes* or *no.*

8. 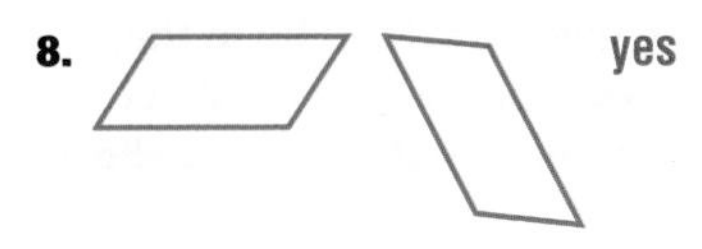 yes

9. 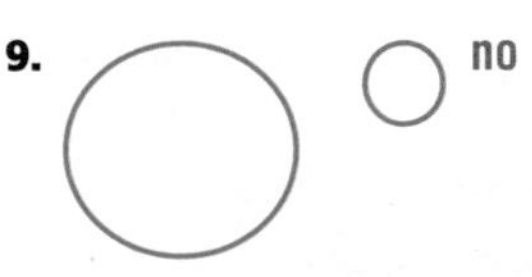 no

10. **Measurement** Tanika's swimming pool is 8 feet wide and 12 feet long. Tanika's neighbor has the same pool. If the pool is 12 feet long, how wide is it? 8 ft

Tell whether each figure has line symmetry. Write *yes* or *no.* Then tell how many lines of symmetry the figure has.

11. yes; 4
12. no; 0

13. **MULTIPLE CHOICE** How many lines of symmetry does this figure have? G

**F** 0 **H** 2

**G** 1 **J** 3

14. **WRITING IN MATH** Do all squares have the same number of lines of symmetry? Explain. See Ch. 10 Answer Appendix.

Summative Assessment 433

# Chapter 10 Chapter Test

## Summative Assessment

Use these alternate leveled chapter tests to differentiate assessment for the specific needs of your students.

| Leveled Chapter 10 Tests | | | |
|---|---|---|---|
| Form | Type | Level | CRM Pages |
| 1 | Multiple Choice | BL | 60–61 |
| 2A | Multiple Choice | OL | 62–63 |
| 2B | Multiple Choice | OL | 64–65 |
| 2C | Free Response | OL | 66–67 |
| 2D | Free Response | OL | 68–69 |
| 3 | Free Response | AL | 70–71 |

BL = below/approaching grade level
OL = on grade level
AL = above/beyond grade level

## Vocabulary Test

CRM **Chapter 10 Resource Masters** (p. 55)

ExamView Assessment Suite Customize and create multiple versions of your Chapter Test and the test answer keys.

## Data-Driven Decision Making

Based on the results of the Chapter Test, use the following to review concepts that continue to present students with problems.

| Exercises | State/Local Standards | What's the Mathematics? | Error Analysis | Resources for Review |
|---|---|---|---|---|
| 1, 2 | | Identify rotations, reflections, and translations. | Does not know "rotation," "reflection," "translation." | Strategic Intervention Guide (pp. 124, 126)<br>CRM Chapter 10 Resource Masters (Reteach)<br>Math Adventures<br>My Math Zone Chapter 10<br>Math Online Extra Examples • Concepts in Motion |
| 3–5 | | Locate points on a number line. | Does not accurately count lines and measurements to name points on a number line. | |
| 8, 9<br>11–12 | | Connect transformations to congruence and symmetry. | Does not name all lines of symmetry. Does not understand "line symmetry," "congruent." | |

# CHAPTER 10 Test Practice

## Formative Assessment

- Use Student Edition pp. 434–435 as practice and cumulative review. The questions are written in the same style as many state tests.
- You can also use these two pages to benchmark student progress, or as an alternate homework assignment.

Additional practice pages can be found in the Chapter 10 Resource Masters.

CRM **Chapter 10 Resource Masters**
Cumulative Test Practice

- Multiple Choice format (pp. 60–65)
- Free Response format (pp. 66–71)

Create practice worksheets or tests that align to your state standards.

**Math Online** Have students visit macmillanmh.com for additional practice to reinforce your state standards.

Math Online macmillanmh.com
• Test Practice

# Test Practice

Cumulative, Chapters 1–10

**PART 1 Multiple Choice**

**Read each question. Then fill in the correct answer on the answer sheet provided by your teacher or on a sheet of paper.**

**1.** Which streets appear to be parallel to each other on the map below? C

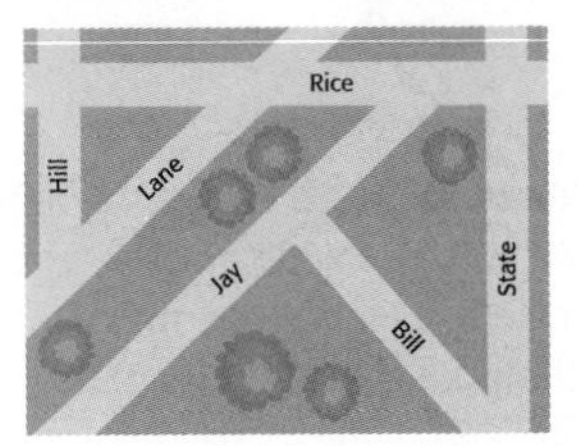


**A** Rice and Bill **C** Lane and Jay
**B** State and Lane **D** Hill and Rice

**2.** Justin practices the piano 30 minutes per day, 6 days per week. How many minutes does he practice in 10 weeks? H

**F** $6 \times 10 + 30$ **H** $6 \times 10 \times 30$
**G** $6 + 10 + 30$ **J** $30 \div 10 \times 6$

**3.** Which line, line segment, or ray is perpendicular to line *D*? D

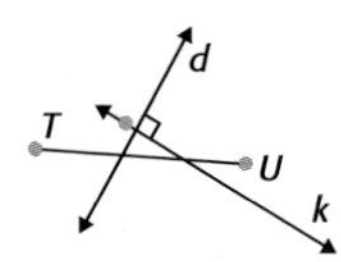


**A** Ray *Q* **C** Line *s*
**B** Line segment *TU* **D** Line *k*

**4.** Jen has 24 swimming trophies. She wants to arrange an equal number on 4 shelves of a bookcase. How many trophies will she place on each shelf? G

**F** 8 **H** 4
**G** 6 **J** 3

**5.** In the figure below, which angle appears to be obtuse? A

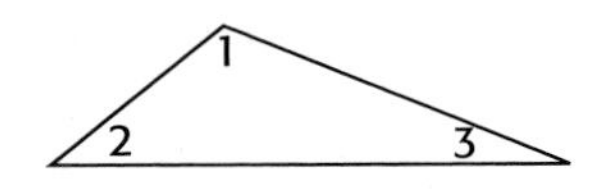


**A** 1 **C** 3
**B** 2 **D** none

**6.** Valerie has 84 beads. She wants to arrange them into 12 equal groups. How many beads will be in each group? H

**F** 5 **H** 7
**G** 6 **J** 8

**7.** A total of 8,297 visitors attended a museum on Saturday and Sunday. If 5,129 visitors attended on Saturday, how many visitors attended on Sunday? B

**A** 3,086 **C** 3,618
**B** 3,168 **D** 3,816



## Test-Taking Tip

Tell students to look at each question carefully before making a choice.

**Preparing for Standardized Tests**
For test-taking strategies and practice, see pages R42–R55.

**8.** What number on the number line does point $J$ best represent? F

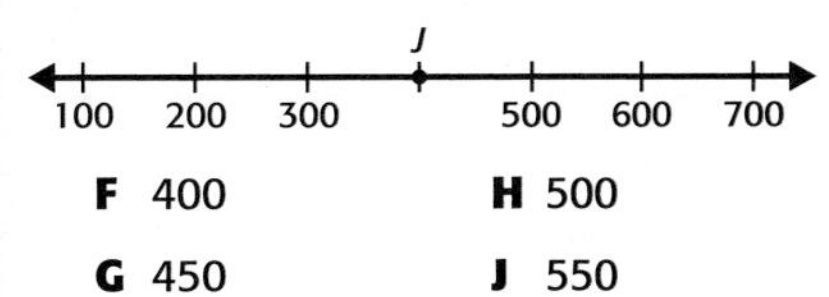


**F** 400 **H** 500

**G** 450 **J** 550

**9.** Which of these represents $9 \times 7$? D

**A** $1 \times 3 \times 7$ **C** $2 \times 9 \times 7$

**B** $2 \times 7 \times 7$ **D** $3 \times 3 \times 7$

**10.** Mira made a map of her neighborhood. Identify the building located at (7, 2). G

**Mira's Neighborhood**

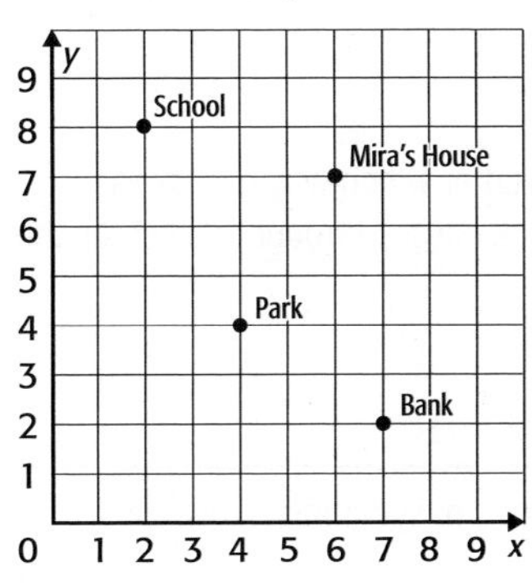


**F** Mira's house **H** Park

**G** Bank **J** School

## PART 2 Short Response

**Record your answers on the answer sheet provided by your teacher or on a sheet of paper.**

**11.** What is the value of the digit 3 in 564,327? 300

**12.** How many lines of symmetry does this shape have? 1

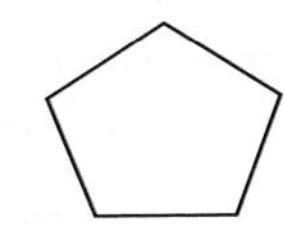

**13.** Identify two numbers that have at least one line of symmetry.
Sample answer: 3 and 8

## PART 3 Extended Response

**Record your answers on the answer sheet provided by your teacher or on a sheet of paper.**

**14.** Identify the transformation shown below. Explain. 14, 15. See margin.

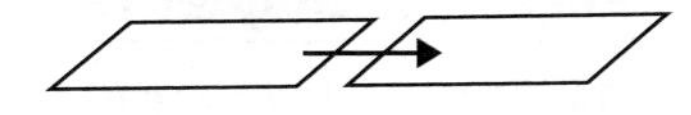

**15.** Draw two triangles to show a rotation of figures. Explain.

| NEED EXTRA HELP? | | | | | | | | | | | | | | | |
|---|---|---|---|---|---|---|---|---|---|---|---|---|---|---|---|
| If You Missed Question... | 1 | 2 | 3 | 4 | 5 | 6 | 7 | 8 | 9 | 10 | 11 | 12 | 13 | 14 | 15 |
| Go to Lesson... | 10-2 | 5-6 | 10-2 | 4-3 | 9-4 | 4-6 | 2-5 | 10-1 | 4-2 | 10-4 | 1-1 | 10-8 | 10-8 | 10-5 | 10-5 |



# Answer Sheet Practice

Have students simulate taking a state test by recording their answers on a practice recording sheet.

**Chapter 10 Resource Masters**
Student Recording Sheet (p. 76)

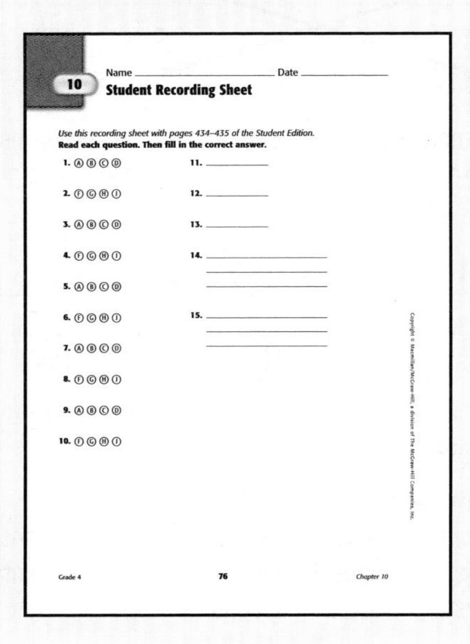
Name ________ Date ________
10 Student Recording Sheet
Use this recording sheet with pages 434–435 of the Student Edition. Read each question. Then fill in the correct answer.
1. Ⓐ Ⓑ Ⓒ Ⓓ 11. ______
2. Ⓕ Ⓖ Ⓗ Ⓙ 12. ______
3. Ⓐ Ⓑ Ⓒ Ⓓ 13. ______
4. Ⓕ Ⓖ Ⓗ Ⓙ 14. ______
5. Ⓐ Ⓑ Ⓒ Ⓓ
6. Ⓕ Ⓖ Ⓗ Ⓙ 15. ______
7. Ⓐ Ⓑ Ⓒ Ⓓ
8. Ⓕ Ⓖ Ⓗ Ⓙ
9. Ⓐ Ⓑ Ⓒ Ⓓ
10. Ⓕ Ⓖ Ⓗ Ⓙ
Grade 4 76 Chapter 10

### Additional Answers

**14.** Sample answer: translation; The figure has undergone a slide. So, the figure has undergone a translation.

**15.** Sample answer:

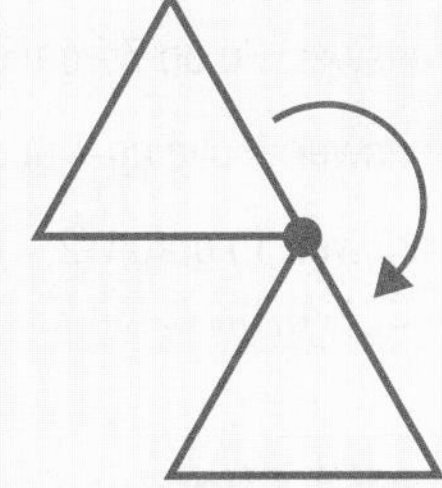

The triangle has been rotated, or turned around a point.

## Page 397, Lesson 10-1

**18.** Sample answer: Use the numbers to find intervals. Then use the intervals to find a point.

## Page 403, Lesson 10-2

**16.**

**17.**

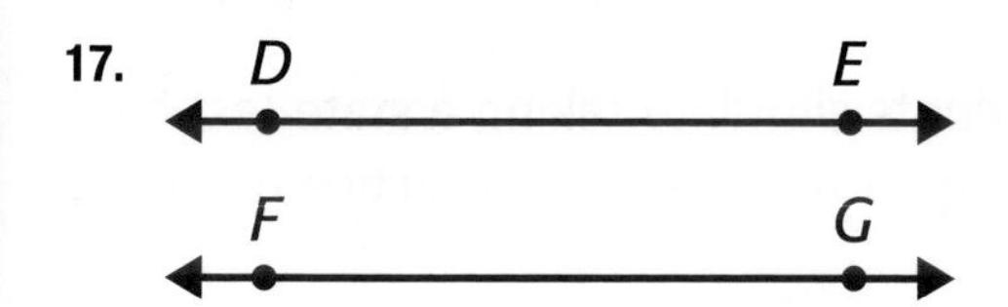


**18.**

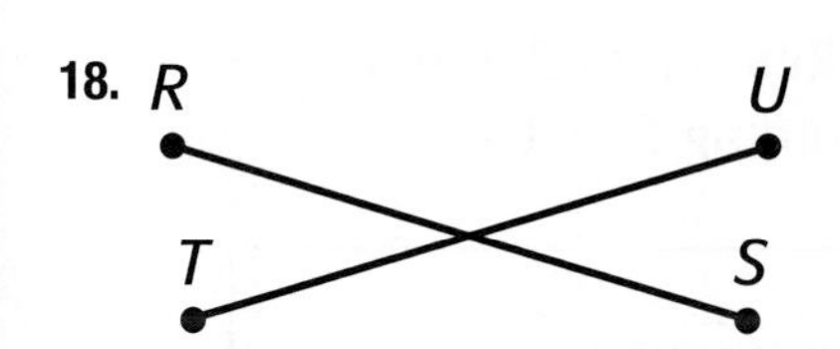


**21.** Sample answer: no; Two parallel lines never meet and perpendicular lines always meet, so two parallel lines can not be perpendicular.

## Page 405, Lesson 10-3

**3.** Nikki, Jade, Terrell; Jade, Nikki, Terrell; Terrell, Nikki, Jade; Nikki, Terrell, Jade; Jade, Terrell, Nikki; Terrell, Jade, Nikki

**9.** 2 nickels, 2 quarters, 2 dimes, 1 nickel and 1 quarter, 1 nickel and 1 dime, 1 quarter and 1 dime

**12.** Sample answer:

| | | |
|---|---|---|
| mystery—report | biography—report | fantasy—report |
| mystery—speech | biography—speech | fantasy—speech |
| mystery—act | biography—act | fantasy—act |

## Page 407, Lesson 10-4

**13.** Sample answer: An ordered pair uses numbers to name locations on a grid. The first number tells how far to move horizontally and the second number tells how far to move vertically.

**22.** Sample answer: Go up 7 from (1, 2). Then go right 4 to (5, 9).

**23.** Sample answer: Move up 7 units from (5, 1). Then go left 3 units to (2, 8).

**28.** Sample answer: To graph (2, 4), move right 2 units, then up 4 units. To graph (−2, −4), move left 2 units, then down 4 units.

## Page 409, Mid-Chapter Check

**13.** Sample answer: Move up 4 units from (1, 2). Then move right 3 units to (4, 6).

**14.** Sample answer: no; (2, 3) is 2 right and 3 up from (0, 0) and (3, 2) is 3 right, 2 up from (0, 0).

## Page 415, Lesson 10-5

**17.** Sample answer: If a square moves horizontally, the transformation that has taken place can be called a translation or a reflection.

## Page 417, Lesson 10-6

**9.** Sample answer: What is the probability that Mrs. Link will pull a country CD out of her collection in her car without looking?

## Page 420, Lesson 10-7

**14.** Sample answer: congruent; The rectangles are the same size and shape.

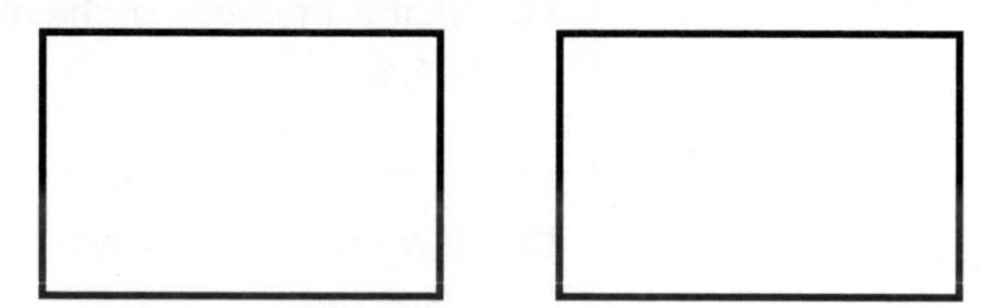

**15.** Sample answer: Jacinto; The pizza slices are the same size and shape, so they are congruent.

**16.** Sample answer: yes; A square will always have sides of equal length.

## Page 424, Lesson 10-8

**20.** Sample answer:

**21.** Sample answer: an endless number; No matter which way a circle is divided by a straight line, as long as the line passes through the center, the line will be a line of symmetry.

## Page 433, Chapter Test

**14.** Sample answer: yes; All squares have 4 lines of symmetry.

NOTES

# Chapter Overview

## Chapter-at-a-Glance

In Chapter 11, the emphasis is on measuring customary and metric units of length and measuring perimeters, areas, and temperature.

| Lesson | Math Objective | State/Local Standards |
|---|---|---|
| EXPLORE 11-1 **Estimate and Measure Lengths** (pp. 439–440) | Estimate and measure lengths to the nearest inch, $\frac{1}{2}$ inch, and $\frac{1}{4}$ inch. | |
| 11-1 **Customary Units of Length** (pp. 441–443) | Estimate and measure customary lengths. | |
| 11-2 **Convert Customary Units of Length** (pp. 444–445) | Convert customary units of length. | |
| 11-3 **Problem-Solving Strategy: Solve a Simpler Problem** (pp. 446–447) | Solve problems by solving a simpler problem. | |
| EXPLORE 11-4 **Metric Units of Length** (pp. 448–449) | Estimate and measure objects to the nearest centimeter. | |
| 11-4 **Metric Units of Length** (pp. 450–452) | Estimate and measure lengths within the metric system. | |
| 11-5 **Measure Perimeters** (pp. 456–459) | Find the perimeter of a figure. | |
| 11-6 **Measure Areas** (pp. 460–462) | Find the area of rectangles and squares. | |
| EXTEND 11-6 **Perimeters and Areas** (pp. 464–465) | Explore perimeter and area. | |
| 11-7 **Problem-Solving Investigation: Choose a Strategy** (pp. 466–467) | Choose the best strategy to solve a problem. | |
| 11-8 **Measure Temperatures** (pp. 468–471) | Measure temperature and calculate changes in temperature. | |

## Measure Length, Area, and Temperature

**BIG Idea** In third grade, students learned the basic concepts of perimeter and area. In fourth grade, students extend their knowledge by using formulas to find both perimeter and area.

**Algebra** Students work with concepts involving perimeter and area. This prepares them for algebra concepts, such as using formulas. (Lessons 11-5 and 11-6)

**G4-FP3** *Measurement:* **Developing an understanding of area and determining the areas of two-dimensional shapes**

Students recognize area as an attribute of two-dimensional regions. They learn that they can quantify area by finding the total number of same-sized units of area that cover the shape without gaps or overlaps. They understand that a square that is 1 unit on a side is the standard unit for measuring area. They select appropriate units, strategies (e.g., decomposing shapes), and tools for solving problems that involve estimating or measuring area. Students connect area measure to the area model that they have used to represent multiplication, and they use this connection to justify the formula for the area of a rectangle.

**G4-FP5C** *Geometry:* Students extend their understanding of properties of two-dimensional shapes as they find the areas of polygons. They build on their earlier work with symmetry and congruence in grade 3 to encompass transformations, including those that produce line and rotational symmetry. By using transformations to design and analyze simple tilings and tessellations, students deepen their understanding of two-dimensional space.

## Skills Trace

### Vertical Alignment

**Third Grade**

**In third grade, students learned to:**

- Measure length to the nearest half inch, inch, centimeter, and millimeter.
- Find the perimeter and area of a shape.
- Measure temperature.

**Fourth Grade**

**During this chapter, students learn to:**

- Find the perimeters and areas of polygons, and estimate and measure customary and metric units of length.
- Convert customary units of length.
- Measure temperature and calculate changes in temperature.

**After this chapter, students learn to:**

- Estimate and measure capacity, weight, and volume.

**Fifth Grade**

**In fifth grade, students learn to:**

- Convert customary and metric units of length, weight, capacity, and mass.
- Find the perimeters and areas of squares and rectangles and the volume of rectangular prisms.
- Choose appropriate temperatures in degrees Fahrenheit and Celsius.

**Backmapping and Vertical Alignment McGraw-Hill's *Math Connects*** program was conceived and developed with the final results in mind: student success in Algebra 1 and beyond. The authors, using the **NCTM Focal Points and Focal Connections** as their guide, developed this brand-new series by backmapping from Algebra 1 concepts, and vertically aligning the topics so that they build upon prior skills and concepts and serve as a foundation for future topics.

## Math Vocabulary

The following math vocabulary words for Chapter 11 are listed in the glossary of the ***Student Edition***. You can find interactive definitions in 13 languages in the ***eGlossary*** at macmillanmh.com.

**area** The number of square units needed to cover the inside of a region or plane figure. (p. 460A)

**centimeter** A metric unit for measuring length and height. 100 centimeters = 1 meter (p. 450A)

**convert** To switch or exchange for something equal in value. (p. 444A)
**Example:** $\frac{1}{2}$ for $\frac{2}{4}$

**customary** The measurement system that includes units such as foot, pound, quart, and degrees Fahrenheit. (p. 441A)

**foot** A customary unit for measuring length or height. (p. 441A)
**Example:** 1 foot = 12 inches

**inch** A customary unit for measuring length or height. (p. 441A)

**length** Measurement of the distance between two endpoints. (p. 441A)

**meter** A metric unit for measuring length or height. 1 meter = 100 centimeters (p. 450A)

**perimeter** The distance around a closed figure. (p. 456A)

**square units** A unit for measuring area. (p. 460A)

**Visual Vocabulary Cards**
Use Visual Vocabulary Cards 3, 7, and 36 to reinforce the vocabulary in this lesson. (The Define/Example/Ask routine is printed on the back of each card.)

# Chapter Planner

| Suggested Pacing | | |
|---|---|---|
| Instruction | Review & Assessment | TOTAL |
| 11 days | 1 day | **12 days** |

**Diagnostic Assessment**
Quick Check (p. 438)

| | Explore 11-1 — Pacing: 1 day | Lesson 11-1 — Pacing: 1 day | Lesson 11-2 — Pacing: 1 day |
|---|---|---|---|
| **Lesson/ Objective** | **Estimate and Measure Lengths** (pp. 439–440)<br>**Objective:** Estimate and measure lengths to the nearest inch, $\frac{1}{2}$ inch, and $\frac{1}{4}$ inch. | **Customary Units of Length** (pp. 441–443)<br>**Objective:** Estimate and measure customary lengths. | **Convert Customary Units of Length** (pp. 444–445)<br>**Objective:** Convert customary units of length. |
| **State/Local Standards** | | | |
| **Math Vocabulary** | | **foot**, **inch**, **customary**, **length**, **yard** | **convert** |
| **Lesson Resources** | **Materials**<br>notebook paper, various classroom objects less than 12 inches long<br>**Manipulatives**<br>rulers | **Materials**<br>yardsticks, tape measures, copies of rulers with different markings<br>**Manipulatives**<br>rulers<br>**Other Resources**<br>CRM Leveled Worksheets (pp. 8–12)<br>Daily Reteach • 5-Minute Check • Problem of the Day | **Manipulatives**<br>play money<br>**Other Resources**<br>CRM Leveled Worksheets (pp. 13–17)<br>Daily Reteach • 5-Minute Check • Problem of the Day |
| **Technology** | | | |
| **Math Online** | Personal Tutor | Personal Tutor | Personal Tutor |
| **Reaching All Learners** | | English Learners, p. 441B ELL<br>Below Level, p. 441B BL<br>Early Finishers, p. 441B OL AL | English Learners, p. 444B ELL<br>Gifted and Talented, p. 444B AL<br>Early Finishers, p. 444B AL |
| **Alternate Lesson** | | *IMPACT Mathematics:* Unit H | |

**KEY**

BL Below/Approaching Level | OL On Level | AL Above/Beyond Level | ELL English Learners
SE Student Edition | TE Teacher Edition | CRM Chapter 11 Resource Masters | CD-Rom
Transparency | Real-World Problem Solving Library

| | Lesson 11-3 (Pacing: 1 day) | Explore 11-4 (Pacing: 1 day) | Lesson 11-4 (Pacing: 1 day) |
|---|---|---|---|
| **Lesson/ Objective** | **Problem-Solving Strategy Solve a Simpler Problem** (pp. 446–447)<br>**Objective:** Solve problems by solving a simpler problem. | **Metric Units of Length** (pp. 448–449)<br>**Objective:** Estimate and measure objects to the nearest centimeter. | **Metric Units of Length** (pp. 450–452)<br>**Objective:** Estimate and measure lengths within the metric system. |
| **State/Local Standards** | | | |
| **Math Vocabulary** | | | **millimeter**, **centimeter**, **meter**, **kilometer** |
| **Lesson Resources** | **Other Resources**<br>CRM Leveled Worksheets (pp. 18–22)<br>Daily Reteach • 5-Minute Check • Problem of the Day<br>*Ancient Giants of the Forest* | **Materials**<br>four classroom items that can be measured in centimeters.<br>**Manipulatives**<br>metric rulers | **Materials**<br>meterstick<br>**Manipulatives**<br>rulers<br>**Other Resources**<br>CRM Leveled Worksheets (pp. 23–27)<br>Daily Reteach • 5-Minute Check • Problem of the Day |
| **Technology** | | Math Adventures | |
| **Math Online** | Personal Tutor | Personal Tutor | Personal Tutor |
| **Reaching All Learners** | English Learners, p. 446B ELL<br>Below Level, p. 446B BL<br>Early Finishers, p. 446B AL | | English Learners, p. 450B ELL<br>Below Level, p. 450B BL<br>Early Finishers, p. 450B AL |
| **Alternate Lesson** | | | *IMPACT Mathematics:* Unit H |

**Problem Solving: Science** (p. 454)

**Formative Assessment**
Mid-Chapter Check (p. 453)

# Chapter Planner

| | Lesson 11-5 (Pacing: 1 day) | Lesson 11-6 (Pacing: 1 day) | Extend 11-6 (Pacing: 1 day) |
|---|---|---|---|
| **Lesson/ Objective** | **Measure Perimeters** (pp. 456–459)<br>**Objective:** Find the perimeter of a figure. | **Measure Areas** (pp. 460–462)<br>**Objective:** Find the area of rectangles and squares. | **Perimeters and Areas** (pp. 464–465)<br>**Objective:** Explore perimeter and area. |
| **State/Local Standards** | | | |
| **Math Vocabulary** | **perimeter** | **area**, **square units** | |
| **Lesson Resources** | **Materials**<br>chenille stems (at least one per student) tape measures, rubber bands<br>**Manipulatives**<br>rulers, Geoboards<br>**Other Resources**<br>CRM Leveled Worksheets (pp. 28–32)<br>Daily Reteach • 5-Minute Check • Problem of the Day | **Materials**<br>centimeter grid paper<br>**Manipulatives**<br>base-ten blocks, rulers<br>**Other Resources**<br>CRM Leveled Worksheets (pp. 33–37)<br>Daily Reteach • 5-Minute Check • Problem of the Day | **Materials**<br>grid paper<br>**Manipulatives**<br>tiles |
| **Technology** | Math Adventures | Math Adventures | |
| **Math Online** | Personal Tutor | Personal Tutor | Concepts in Motion |
| **Reaching All Learners** | English Learners, p. 456B ELL<br>Gifted and Talented, p. 456B AL<br>Early Finishers, p. 456B OL AL | English Learners, p. 460B ELL<br>Gifted and Talented, p. 460B AL<br>Early Finishers, p. 460B OL AL | |
| **Alternate Lesson** | *IMPACT Mathematics:* Unit F | *IMPACT Mathematics:* Unit F | |

**Game Time**
Area Guess (p. 463)

| | Lesson 11-7 — Pacing: 1 day | Lesson 11-8 — Pacing: 1 day |
|---|---|---|
| **Lesson/ Objective** | **Problem-Solving Investigation**<br>**Choose a Strategy**<br>(pp. 466–467)<br>**Objective:** Choose the best strategy to solve a problem. | **Measure Temperatures**<br>(pp. 468–471)<br>**Objective:** Measure temperature and calculate changes in temperature. |
| **State/Local Standards** | | |
| **Math Vocabulary** | | **degrees**, **Fahrenheit**, **Celsius** |
| **Lesson Resources** | **Other Resources**<br>CRM Leveled Worksheets (pp. 38–42)<br>Daily Reteach • 5-Minute Check • Problem of the Day<br>*Ancient Giants of the Forest* | **Manipulatives**<br>thermometers, rulers, cups<br>**Other Resources**<br>CRM Leveled Worksheets (pp. 43–47)<br>Daily Reteach • 5-Minute Check • Problem of the Day |
| **Technology** / **Math Online** | Personal Tutor | Personal Tutor |
| **Reaching All Learners** | English Learners, p. 466B ELL<br>Gifted and Talented, p. 466B AL<br>Early Finishers, p. 466B OL AL | English Learners, p. 468B ELL<br>Below Level, p. 468B BL<br>Early Finishers, p. 468B OL |
| **Alternate Lesson** | | *IMPACT Mathematics:* Unit G |

**Summative Assessment**
- Study Guide/Review (p. 472)
- Chapter Test (p. 479)
- Test Practice (p. 480)

# Chapter Planner

## Assessment Options

### Diagnostic Assessment

- SE *Option 1:* Quick Check (p. 438)
- *Option 2:* Online Quiz macmillanmh.com
- CRM *Option 3:* Diagnostic Test (p. 49)
- CRM *Option 4:* Chapter Pretest (p. 50)

### Formative Assessment

- TE Alternate Teaching Strategies (in every lesson)
- SE Talk About It (in every lesson)
- SE Writing in Math (in every lesson)
- SE Check What You Know (in every lesson)
- TE Ticket Out the Door (p. 399)
- TE Into the Future (p. 416)
- TE Yesterday's News (p. 408)
- TE Name the Math (p. 413)
- SE Mid-Chapter Check (p. 409)
- CRM Lesson Quizzes (pp. 51–53)
- CRM Mid-Chapter Test (p. 54)

### Summative Assessment

- SE Chapter Test (p. 479)
- SE Test Practice (p. 480)
- CRM Vocabulary Test (p. 55)
- CRM Leveled Chapter Tests (pp. 60–70)
- CRM Cumulative Test Practice (pp. 73–75)
- CRM Oral Assessment (pp. 56–57)
- ExamView® Assessment Suite
- Advance Tracker

## What the Research Says . . .

Refer to these resources for more than information on teaching measurement.

- Ron Preston and Tony Thompson. "Integrating Measurement across the Curriculum." *Mathematics Teaching in the Middle School*, April 2004, Volume 9, Issue 8, p. 436.
- Kenney, P.A. and Kouba, V.L. (1997). "What do students know about measurement?" In P.A. Kenne and E. Silver (Eds.), *Results from the Sixth Mathematics Assessment of the National Assessment of Educational Progress* (pp. 141–163). Reston, VA: National Council of Teachers of Mathematics.
- Lehrer, R., Jaslow, L., & Curtis, C. (2003). "Developing Understanding of Measurement in the Elementary Grades." In D.H. Clements & G. Bright (Eds.), *Learning and Teaching Measurement. 2003 Yearbook* (pp. 100–121). Reston, VA: National Council of Teachers of Mathematics.

Targeted professional development has been articulated throughout **McGraw-Hill's *Math Connects*** program. The **McGraw-Hill Professional Development Video Library** provides short videos that support the **NCTM Focal Points and Focal Connections.** For more information visit **macmillanmh.com**.

# Teacher Notes

# Learning Stations

## Cross-Curricular Links

### Writing

**Area Travels**

Write a story about area and perimeter and see where it leads you.

- Measure the area and perimeter of your desktop.
- Imagine you are the height of your pencil and begin a short story about traveling on your desktop. Include your desktop measurements and the definitions of area and perimeter in your story.
- Now measure the area and perimeter of another polygon in the room. Finish your story to include the measurements of this polygon. Explain how your journey would be different if you would have traveled around this polygon.

**Materials:**
- rulers
- paper
- pencil

### Art

**Centimeter Art**

Create a picture made entirely of centimeters!

- Measure out one-centimeter lengths of string, yarn, and ribbons.
- Use your centimeter strips to create a picture. Outline the figures you make using your markers, or draw outlines first and fill them in with your centimeter strips.
- You can also use centimeter-long lines in your artwork.

1 cm.

**Materials:**
- string, yarn, and ribbons in various colors
- white paper, two pieces per student
- metric rulers
- glue
- markers

### Social Studies

**The Shape of Defense**

The Pentagon is the headquarters for the U.S. Department of Defense.

- If one side of the Pentagon measures 280 meters, what is the perimeter of the building? Write two formulas to show how you can find the answer.
- Draw a scale model of the Pentagon's shape. For the side measurements, replace meters with millimeters. Draw the model on a large piece of paper using a ruler. What is the perimeter in millimeters? What would it be in centimeters? Write expressions for both measurements inside your Pentagon model.

**Materials:**
- large-format art paper
- ruler
- pencil

Science

individual | LOGICAL

### Planting Rules

Marigolds must be planted 12 inches apart, so in every square foot, there can be only one marigold plant.

- Using a ruler, draw a garden plan, marked off in squares. Use inches in place of feet to draw your model. Each square inch represents one square foot. The area must equal 24 square feet. That is 24 marigolds, one per square. Use flower beads as plants.
- How many squares long is your garden? How many squares wide? Can you change the width and the length and still plant the same number of marigolds?

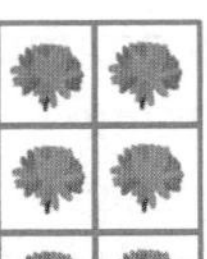

**Materials:**
- large-format art paper
- ruler
- flower beads
- pencils

Health

group | SPATIAL

### Area Relay

- Divide into teams and position one runner at each corner of the race area. The first runner of each team rolls two number cubes and uses each number as the length and width of a rectangle.
- Runners then write down the area on a piece of paper and run with the paper to the next runner, handing the paper off. Each runner does the same.
- The first team to have all runners finish and get the correct area answers wins.

*Teacher Note: This activity can be planned for recess or in gym location.*

**Materials:**
- 4 sets of 2 number cubes
- paper
- pencils

Music

pair | SPATIAL

### Musical Areas

Measuring the length and width of a room does not always have to be done using rulers or tape measures. You could use your feet, or you could use CDs.

- Take a look at a CD case. Try to estimate the length and the width of your classroom in CDs. Then measure the length and width of the room using a CD case, and see if your estimate was correct.
- Now that you have the length and the width of the room in CDs, how many CDs would it take to cover the floor of your classroom? How many of you have CD collections big enough to cover the classroom floor?

**Materials:**
- plastic CD case
- paper
- pencil

CHAPTER 11

# Introduce the Chapter

##  Real World: Room for All of Us

**Materials:** rulers

- Tell students that they are going to learn to measure length, perimeter, area, and temperature in this chapter.
- Assign partners to measure wall lengths around the classroom to the nearest foot by placing their two rulers end-to-end. Be sure to assign two sets of partners per wall, each beginning at a different corner to verify the measurements.
- Assign additional groups to measure or estimate the measurements when objects are in the way (cabinets, bookshelves, etc.).
- Sketch the shape of the classroom on the board. Ask each group to record their measurements on the sketch of the classroom.
- Use the sketch to briefly explain the concept of perimeter. Demonstrate how to find the perimeter of the classroom.

Direct students to Student Edition p. 436. Have students read the Big Idea section at the top of the page.

- **How would these people, in their jobs and careers, use the concept of perimeter: farmers, gardeners, architects, carpenters, school principals, etc.?** Accept all reasonable answers.

## WRITING IN ▸MATH

**Starting the Chapter**
Have the students make a list of when they have used area and perimeter. Ask them to choose two or three items on their list and write a short explanation of each.

**Key Vocabulary** Introduce the key vocabulary in the chapter using the routine below.

Define: Perimeter is the distance around a shape or region.
Example: A fence shows the perimeter of a yard.
Ask: How does perimeter relate to length?

**Read-Aloud Anthology** For an optional reading activity to introduce this chapter's math concepts, see the Read-Aloud Anthology on p. TR37.

CHAPTER 11

# Measure Length, Area, and Temperature

**BIG Idea** What is perimeter?

**Perimeter** is the distance around a closed figure.

**Example** Pennsylvania is home to 560,000 dairy cows. A cow pasture is a field of grass where dairy cows often graze, or eat. You can find the perimeter of the cow pasture shown by adding the lengths of the sides of the fence.

```
  225 yd
  150 yd
  225 yd
+ 150 yd
  750 yd
```

225 yd, 150 yd, 150 yd, 225 yd

So, the perimeter of the pasture is 750 yards.

### What will I learn in this chapter?

- Measure lengths in customary and metric units.
- Estimate and determine perimeters and areas.
- Relate perimeter and area.
- Measure temperatures and changes in temperature.
- Solve problems by working simpler problems.

### Key Vocabulary

**perimeter**
**area**

Math Online — Student Study Tools at macmillanmh.com



##  Chapter 11 Project

### Map Your Home

Have students create a blueprint of their homes on poster board. Solve: Find the total perimeter and area of their homes by taking two measurements in each room of the home.

- Students need to take measurements of each room in their homes.
- Students can make a sketch using grid or dot paper before drawing on the poster board.
- Students will need to use the measurements to calculate the total perimeter and area of their homes.
- Students may exhibit their poster drawings.

CRM *Refer to Chapter 11 Resource Masters, p. 58, for a rubric to assess students' progress on this project.*

**FOLDABLES Study Organizer** Make this Foldable to help you organize information about measurement. Begin with a sheet of notebook paper.

1. **Fold** a sheet of paper in half.

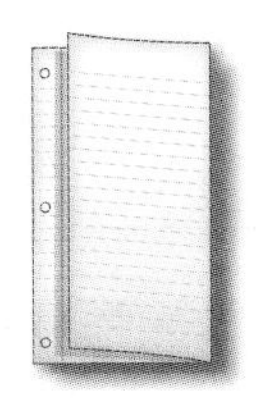

2. **Cut** every third line on one side. Ten tabs will result.

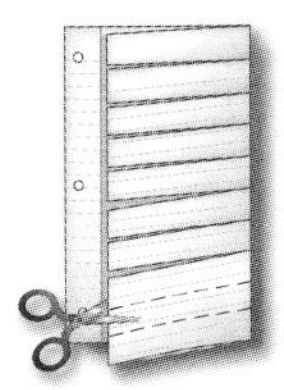

3. **Label** each tab as shown.

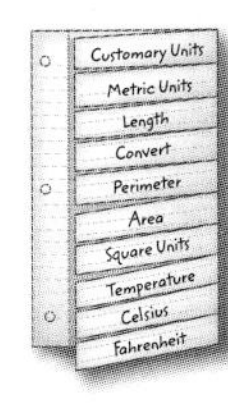




| ELL National ESL Standards Alignment for Chapter 11 | | | |
|---|---|---|---|
| Lesson, Page | ESL Standard | Modality | Level |
| 11-1, p. 441B | Goal 2, Standard 2, b | Kinesthetic, Linguistic | Intermediate |
| 11-2, p. 444B | Goal 2, Standard 2, b | Visual/Spatial, Logical | Intermediate |
| 11-3, p. 446B | Goal 2, Standard 1, h | Visual | Advanced |
| 11-4, p. 450B | Goal 1, Standard 3, g | Spatial, Auditory | Intermediate |
| 11-5, p. 456B | Goal 2, Standard 1, f | Kinesthetic, Social | Beginning |
| 11-6, p. 460B | Goal 2, Standard 3, h | Linguistic, Visual | Advanced |
| 11-7, p. 466B | Goal 2, Standard 2, c | Spatial | Advanced |
| 11-8, p. 468B | Goal 1, Standard 3, k | Linguistic, Logical | Beginning |

The National ESL Standards can be found in the Teacher Reference Handbook.

## FOLDABLES Dinah Zike's Foldables

Guide students through the directions on p. 437 to create their own Foldable graphic organizers for measurement. Students may also use their Foldables to study and review for chapter assessments.

**When to Use It** (Additional instructions for using the Foldables with these lessons are found on pp. 453 and 472.)

## Chapter 11 Literature List

| Lesson | Book Title |
|---|---|
| 11-1 | **Inchworm and a Half** Elinor J. Pinczes |
| 11-2 | **Measuring Penny** Loreen Leedy |
| 11-3 | **If You Made a Million** David M. Schwartz |
| 11-4 | **Capacity** Henry Pluckrose |
| 11-5 | **Sir Cumference and the Isle of Immeter** Cindy Neuschwander |
| 11-6 | **Spaghetti and Meatballs for All** Marilyn Burns and Gordon Silveria |
| 11-8 | **The Snowy Day** Ezra Jack Keats |
| Any | **A Cloak for the Dreamer** Aileen Friedman |

- Read the Math at Home letter found in the Chapter 11 Resource Masters, p. 4, with the class and have each student sign it. (A Spanish version is found on p. 5.)
- Send home copies of the Math at Home letter with each student.

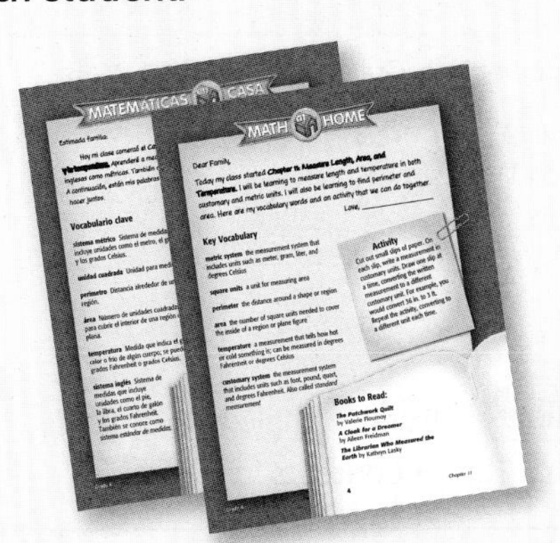

# Diagnostic Assessment

Check for students' prerequisite skills before beginning the chapter.

- **Option 1:** ***Quick Check***

  SE Student Edition, p. 438

- **Option 2:** ***Online Readiness Quiz***

  **Math Online** macmillanmh.com

- **Option 3:** ***Diagnostic Tests***

  CRM Chapter 11 Resource Masters, p. 49–50

# RTI (Response to Intervention)

**Apply the Results** Based on the results of the diagnostic assessment on Student Edition p. 438, use the chart below to address individual needs before beginning the chapter.

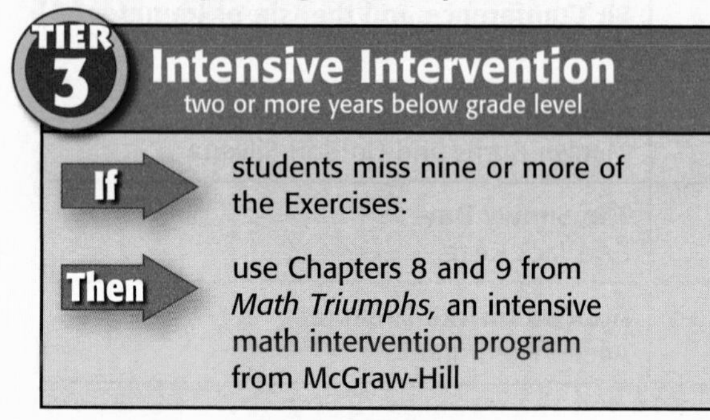

**TIER 3 Intensive Intervention**
two or more years below grade level

**If** students miss nine or more of the Exercises:

**Then** use Chapters 8 and 9 from *Math Triumphs,* an intensive math intervention program from McGraw-Hill

## ARE YOU READY for Chapter 11?

You have two ways to check prerequisite skills for this chapter.

**Option 2**

**Math Online** Take the Chapter Readiness Quiz at macmillanmh.com

**Option 1**

Complete the Quick Check below.

### QUICK Check

**Identify which figure is longer.** (Prior Grade) (Used in Lesson 11-1)

**1.** Figure A

Figure B

Figure A

**2.** 

Figure A

Figure B

Figure B

**3.** Ted is comparing his shoe to his mom's shoe. Which is longer?
Mom's shoe

Ted's shoe

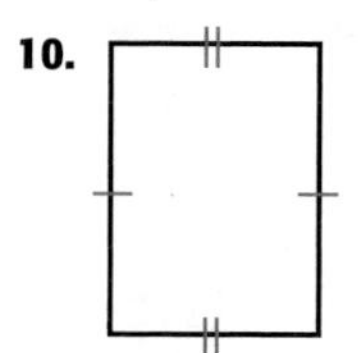

Mom's shoe

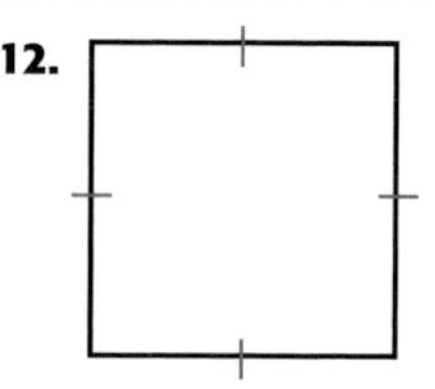

**Find the value of each expression.** (Lessons 5-1 and 5-6) (Used in Lessons 11-3 and 11-5)

**4.** $8 + 14 + 8 + 14$ 44 **5.** $9 + 16 + 9 + 16$ 50 **6.** $15 \times 7$ 105

**7.** $12 \times 6$ 72 **8.** $(2 \times 7) + (2 \times 14)$ 42 **9.** $(2 \times 13) + (2 \times 9)$ 44

**Identify which sides are the same length.** (Prior Grade) (Used in Lessons 11-5 and 11-6)

**10.** **11.** **12.**

**13. Geometry** Mercedes is making a picture frame. It will be a square. How many sides are the same length? all of the sides



| **TIER 2 Strategic Intervention** below/approaching grade level | **TIER 1 On-Level** | **Above/Beyond Level** |
|---|---|---|
| **If** students miss four to eight in: **Exercises 1–13** | **If** students miss two or three in: **Exercises 1–13** | **If** students miss one or less in: **Exercises 1–13** |
| **Then** choose a resource: | **Then** choose a resource: | **Then** choose a resource: |
| Strategic Intervention Guide (pp. 116, 118, 128)<br>CRM Chapter 9 Resource Masters Reteach Worksheets<br>**Math Online** Extra Examples • Personal Tutor • Concepts in Motion | TE Learning Stations (pp. 392I–392J)<br>TE Chapter Project (p. 392)<br>CRM Game: Convert the Number<br>Math Adventures<br>My Math Zone Chapter 10<br>**Math Online** Fact Dash | TE Learning Stations (pp. 392I–392J)<br>TE Chapter Project (p. 392)<br>Real-World Problem Solving: *Ancient Giants of the Forest*<br>My Math Zone Chapters 10 and 11<br>**Math Online** Games |

Measurement Activity for Lesson 11-1

# Estimate and Measure Lengths

In this activity, you will use a ruler to measure lengths to the nearest inch, $\frac{1}{2}$ inch, and $\frac{1}{4}$ inch.

**MAIN IDEA**

will estimate and measure lengths to the nearest inch, $\frac{1}{2}$ inch, and $\frac{1}{4}$ inch.

**You Will Need**

ruler

**ACTIVITY**

**1 Find the length of the pencil to the nearest inch, $\frac{1}{2}$ inch, and $\frac{1}{4}$ inch.**

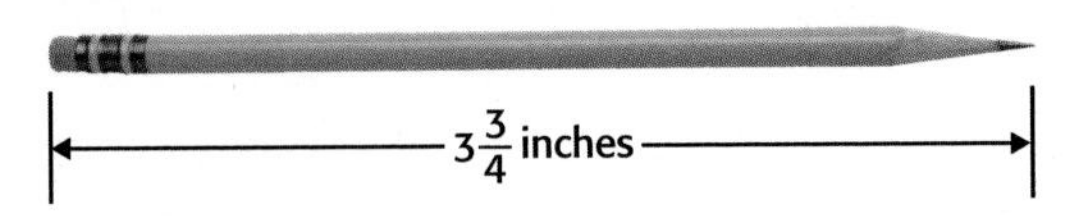


**Step 1** **Copy the table.**

| Object | Estimate | Whole Inch | $\frac{1}{2}$ Inch | $\frac{1}{4}$ Inch |
|---|---|---|---|---|
| Pencil | | | | |

**Step 2** **Estimate.**

Estimate the length of the pencil. Record your estimate in the table.

**Step 3** **Measure.**

Place the ruler against a side of the pencil so that the 0 on the ruler lines up with one end. Measure the length to the nearest inch, $\frac{1}{2}$ inch, and $\frac{1}{4}$ inch. Record the measurements in your table.

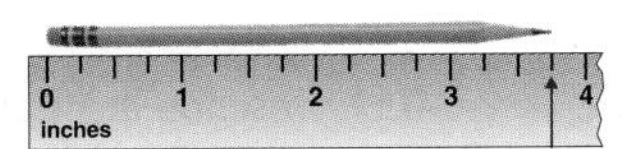

Measurement Activity for Lesson 11-1

# Lesson Planner

## Objective

Estimate and measure lengths to the nearest inch, $\frac{1}{2}$ inch, and $\frac{1}{4}$ inch.

## Resources

**Materials:** notebook paper, various classroom objects less than 12 inches long

**Manipulatives:** rulers

## 1 Introduce

- Have students estimate and measure the length of a sheet of notebook paper using uniform nonstandard units such as paperclips. **How did you estimate?** I looked at the length of one paperclip and estimated how many paperclips would go from one end of the paper to the other. **How did you measure?** I placed paperclips end-to-end along the length of the sheet of paper.
- **What other measurement tool and units might you use to measure the paper?** Sample answer: a ruler and inches
- Show students a ruler and demonstrate how to estimate and measure the paper to the nearest inch.

## 2 Teach

**Activity 1** Distribute rulers to students and point out the inch, $\frac{1}{2}$-inch, and $\frac{1}{4}$-inch marks. Have students identify different measurements on the ruler, such as $1\frac{3}{4}$ inch or $4\frac{1}{2}$ inch. Explain how to place the ruler and measure to the nearest inch, $\frac{1}{2}$ inch, and $\frac{1}{4}$ inch.

**Activity 2** Have students work in pairs or small groups to complete this activity. If necessary, help students line up their rulers with the objects to measure. Have students compare their estimates to the actual measurements.

### Think About It

Assign Exercises 1 and 2 in the **Think About It** section to assess student comprehension of the concepts presented in the Activities.

## 3 Assess

### Formative Assessment

Use **Check What You Know** Exercises 3–5 to assess whether students comprehend how to estimate and measure lengths to the nearest inch, $\frac{1}{2}$ inch, and $\frac{1}{4}$ inch.

**From Concrete to Abstract** Use Exercise 5 to bridge the gap between estimating and measuring objects using different units and making measurement decisions in real-world situations.



**ACTIVITY**

**2 Find four items in your classroom to measure to the nearest inch, $\frac{1}{2}$ inch, and $\frac{1}{4}$ inch.**

**Step 1** **Select the items.**

Find four items from your classroom that are less than 12 inches long.

**Step 2** **Estimate.**

Estimate their length in inches. Record your estimates in a table similar to the one in Activity 1.

**Step 3** **Measure.**

Measure each object's length to the nearest inch, $\frac{1}{2}$ inch, and $\frac{1}{4}$ inch. Record the measurements in your table.

### Think About It

1. Which is more accurate, measuring to the nearest inch or measuring to the nearest $\frac{1}{4}$ inch? Explain. **Measuring to the nearest $\frac{1}{4}$ inch is more accurate because it is a smaller unit.**
2. How could the length around a round object, such as a globe, be measured? **Sample answer: Wrap a piece of string around the object, mark, and measure the string.**

### CHECK What You Know

**Estimate. Then measure each to the nearest inch, $\frac{1}{2}$ inch, and $\frac{1}{4}$ inch.**

3. 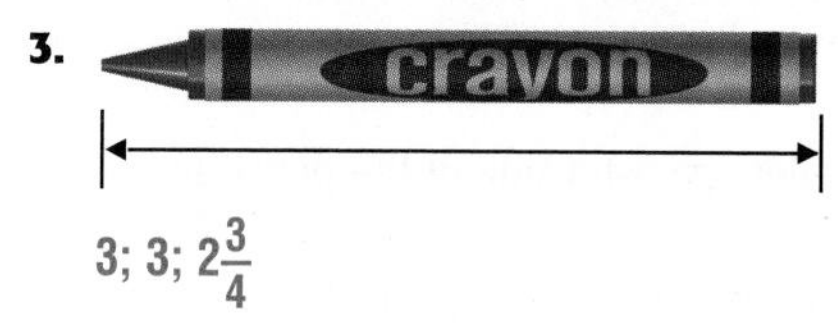


$3; 3; 2\frac{3}{4}$

4. 

$2; 1\frac{1}{2}; 1\frac{3}{4}$

5. **WRITING IN MATH** Describe a situation in which measuring to the nearest $\frac{1}{4}$ inch is necessary. **See margin.**

### Additional Answer

5. Sample answer: Measuring to the nearest $\frac{1}{4}$ inch is necessary when measuring something accurately, for example, carpet for a room or the size of wood for a project.

LESSON 11-1

# Customary Units of Length

## Lesson Planner

### Objective

Estimate and measure customary lengths.

### Vocabulary

**length**, **inch**, **foot**, **yard**, **customary**

### Resources

**Materials:** yardsticks, tape measures, copies of rulers with different markings

**Manipulatives:** rulers

**Literature Connection:** *Inchworm and a Half* by Elinor J. Pinczes

**Alternate Lesson:** Use *IMPACT Mathematics:* Unit H to provide practice with units of length.

**Teacher Technology**

TeacherWorks • Interactive Classroom

## Daily Routine

Use these suggestions before beginning the lesson on p. 441.

### 5-Minute Check

(Reviews Lesson 10-8)

**Tell whether each figure has line symmetry. Write *yes* or *no*. Then tell how many lines of symmetry the figure has. Check by using a mirror.**

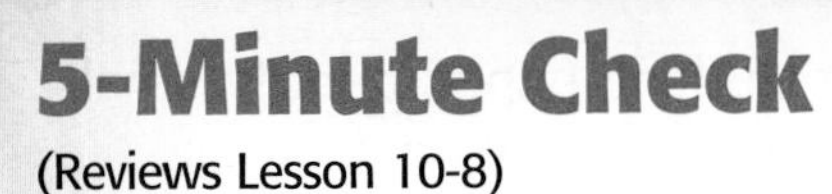

**1.** yes; 2

**2.** no

### Problem of the Day

There are 5 rectangular tables. Each table is 7 feet long. Mr. Hong sets the tables end-to-end in a straight row with 4 feet of space between each table. How long will the row be, with the spaces? 51 feet

### Focus on Math Background

Inches, feet, and yards are all units in the U.S. Customary System of units, so-called because such units are customary in the United States and in very few other places. In this lesson, students are asked to estimate lengths of objects in these units. Experience measuring ordinary objects with yardsticks is helpful, as they are marked in inches, feet, and yards. The Explore prior to this lesson has also provided experience with more precise measurements down to the nearest $\frac{1}{4}$ inch. It may be helpful to let the class discuss appropriate classroom benchmarks for an inch, foot, and yard to aid in their estimation.

### Building Math Vocabulary

Write the lesson vocabulary words and their definitions on the board.

Have students write five sentences, each containing one vocabulary word, and share them with the class.

# Differentiated Instruction

## Small Group Options

LOGICAL

### Option 1 Below Level BL

**Materials:** rulers for each student, paper, pencils, small objects to be measured

- Review the units of measure for length in the customary system.
- Ask students to estimate which part of their hand or finger is the same length as one inch.
- Distribute the rulers and ask students to check to see if they were right about their estimate.
- Once each student has established his or her own inch, ask students to measure the length of their pencils using their personal inches and then check it with the ruler.
- Repeat this process with other small objects.

KINESTHETIC, LINGUISTIC

### Option 2 English Language Learners ELL

**Materials:** rulers, yardsticks, play quarters or string, cut to inch, foot and yard
**Core Vocabulary:** feet, yards, inches
**Common Use Verb:** measure in
**Do Math** This strategy helps students choose appropriate measurement units.

- Create four posters with the boxes headed with "foot/feet," "yard/yards," and "inch/inches."
- Ask students to identify 2–3 items in the classroom that could be measured by each unit.
- Have students measure test choices by using rulers, yard-sticks, and quarters (for 1 inch).
- Draw and label items for each category and glue according to the unit on the posters. Discuss as time permits.

## Independent Work Options

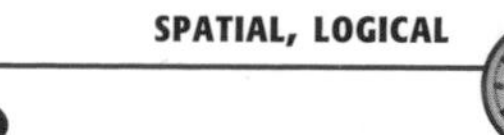


### Option 1 Early Finishers OL AL

**Materials:** rulers, yardsticks

- Write several customary measurements of length on the board, such as $\frac{1}{4}$ inch, 3 inches, $6\frac{1}{2}$ inches, 2 feet, and 3 yards.
- Have students name something in the classroom or school that they think has a measure close to each measurement given on the board.
- Have students measure the items they named and compare the actual measurements to their estimates.

### Option 2 Student Technology

Tech Link

macmillanmh.com

Personal Tutor • Extra Examples

### Option 3 Learning Station: Science (p. 436J)

Direct students to the Science Learning Station for opportunities to explore and extend the lesson concept.

### Option 4 Problem-Solving Practice

Reinforce problem-solving skills and strategies with the Problem-Solving Practice worksheet.

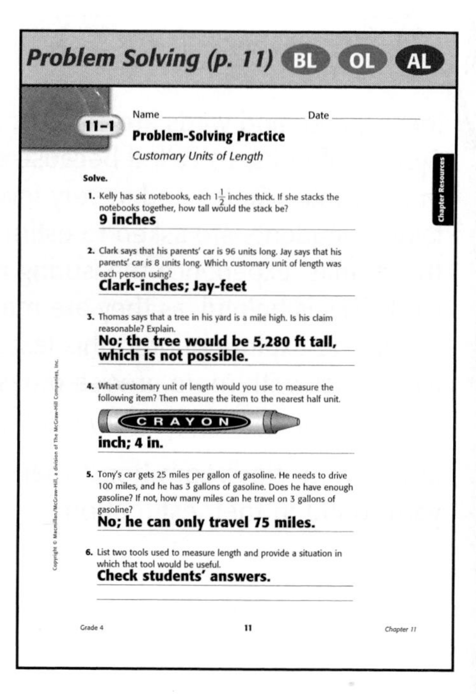

*Problem Solving (p. 11)* BL OL AL

11-1

Name ______________ Date ______________

**Problem-Solving Practice**

*Customary Units of Length*

Chapter Resources

**Solve.**

1. Kelly has six notebooks, each $1\frac{1}{2}$ inches thick. If she stacks the notebooks together, how tall would the stack be?
**9 inches**

2. Clark says that his parents' car is 96 units long. Jay says that his parents' car is 8 units long. Which customary unit of length was each person using?
**Clark-inches; Jay-feet**

3. Thomas says that a tree in his yard is a mile high. Is his claim reasonable? Explain.
**No; the tree would be 5,280 ft tall, which is not possible.**

4. What customary unit of length would you use to measure the following item? Then measure the item to the nearest half unit.
CRAYON
**inch; 4 in.**

5. Tony's car gets 25 miles per gallon of gasoline. He needs to drive 100 miles, and he has 3 gallons of gasoline. Does he have enough gasoline? If not, how many miles can he travel on 3 gallons of gasoline?
**No; he can only travel 75 miles.**

6. List two tools used to measure length and provide a situation in which that tool would be useful.
**Check students' answers.**



Grade 4 11 *Chapter 11*

# 11-1 Customary Units of Length

GET READY to Learn

The actual size of a neon damsel marine fish is shown. How long is this fish?

MAIN IDEA

will estimate and measure customary lengths.

New Vocabulary

length
customary
inch
foot
yard

Math Online

macmillanmh.com

Extra Examples
Personal Tutor
Self-Check Quiz

**Length** is the measurement of a line between two points. Inch, foot, and yard are all **customary** units of measure for length.

**Customary Measurements** — Key Concepts

| An **inch** is about the length of one paper clip. | A **foot** is about the length of a textbook. | A **yard** is about the height of a chair. |
|---|---|---|
| 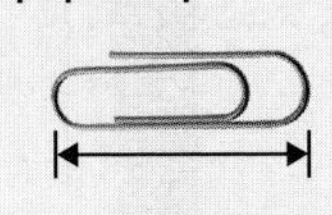 |  |  |

Real-World EXAMPLE — Estimate and Measure Length

1 **FISH Estimate. Then measure the length of the neon damsel fish to the nearest inch, $\frac{1}{2}$ inch and $\frac{1}{4}$ inch.**

| **Step 1** | **Step 2** | **Step 3** |
|---|---|---|
| **Estimate.** Compare the length to what you know about inches. | **Measure.** Using a ruler, measure the length of the fish to the nearest $\frac{1}{2}$ inch. | **Measure.** Measure the length of the fish to the nearest $\frac{1}{4}$ inch. |

So, the fish is about 2, $1\frac{1}{2}$, or $1\frac{2}{4}$ inches long.

# 11-1 Customary Units of Length

## 1 Introduce

### Activity Choice 1 • Hands-On

- Distribute rulers to pairs of students. Have students estimate the length of their partner's right shoe in inches and then use the ruler to measure it to the nearest inch.
- **Was your estimate close to the actual measure?** Answers will vary.
- Have students measure their partner's shoe to the nearest $\frac{1}{2}$ inch and $\frac{1}{4}$ inch.
- **Do you think the nearest inch, $\frac{1}{2}$ inch, or $\frac{1}{4}$ inch is the most accurate measurement? Why?** $\frac{1}{4}$ inch; Sample answer: It is closest to the actual length of the shoe.

### Activity Choice 2 • Literature

Introduce the lesson with *Inchworm and a Half* by Elinor J. Pinczes. For a related math activity, see p. TR59.

## 2 Teach

### Scaffolding Questions

- **Why are inches a good unit to use to estimate the length of a shoe?** Sample answer: A shoe is more than one inch long but less than 1 foot long.
- **How did you choose the nearest $\frac{1}{4}$-inch mark on the ruler when you measured your partner's shoe?** Sample answer: I chose the one that was closer to the end of the shoe.
- **What tool might you use to measure your partner's height in inches?** Sample answers: yardstick, tape measure **What other units on a yardstick could you use to measure each other's heights?** feet
- Extend this section by giving pairs yardsticks or tape measures and challenging them to measure each other's heights to the nearest inch.

GET READY to Learn

Have students open their books and read the information in **Get Ready to Learn**. Introduce **length**, **inch**, **foot**, **yard**, and **customary**. As a class, work through **Examples 1 and 2**.

## Estimate and Measure Length

**Example 1** Suggest that students estimate the length of the fish by comparing it to the length of a paper clip.

### ADDITIONAL EXAMPLES

1. Estimate. Then measure the length of a marker to the nearest inch, $\frac{1}{2}$ inch, and $\frac{1}{4}$ inch. Check students' work.

2. Which is the best estimate for the length of the leaf? A

   **A** 6 inches  **B** 2 feet
   **C** 3 feet  **D** 2 yards

### CHECK What You Know

As a class, have students complete Exercises 1–6 in **Check What You Know** as you observe their work.

**Exercise 5** Assess student comprehension before assigning practice exercises.

### BL Alternate Teaching Strategy

**If** students have trouble using a ruler with $\frac{1}{8}$-inch markings to measure to the nearest inch, $\frac{1}{2}$ inch, and $\frac{1}{4}$ inch…

**Then** use one of these reteach options:

1. CRM **Daily Reteach Worksheet** (p. 8)
2. Provide students with copies of three rulers: one with inch markings only, one with $\frac{1}{2}$ inch markings, and one with $\frac{1}{4}$ inch markings. Have students cut out and use the appropriate rulers to measure objects to the nearest inch, $\frac{1}{2}$ inch, and $\frac{1}{4}$ inch. Then reintroduce the ruler with $\frac{1}{8}$ inch markings.

### COMMON ERROR!

**Exercises 12–13** Students may choose the first answer choice that appears correct without checking the other choices. Remind students to consider all of the answer choices in multiple choice tests.

**Estimate Length**

2 **SCIENCE Choose the best estimate.**

Which is the best estimate for the length of the caterpillar?

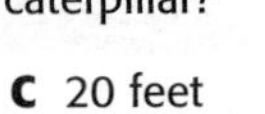

**A** 2 inches  **C** 20 feet
**B** 20 inches  **D** 2 yards

A caterpillar is small. So, estimate in inches. Since 20 inches is more than a foot and is too big, the answer is A, 2 inches.

### CHECK What You Know

**Estimate. Then measure each to the nearest inch, $\frac{1}{2}$ inch, and $\frac{1}{4}$ inch.** See Example 1 (p. 441)

1. 

3, $2\frac{1}{2}$ or 3, $2\frac{3}{4}$

2. 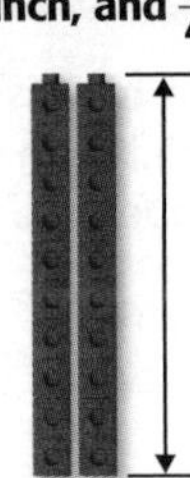

1 or 2, $1\frac{1}{2}$, $1\frac{2}{4}$

**Choose the best estimate for each length.** See Example 2 (p. 442)

3. length of a bicycle B

**A** 12 inches  **C** 12 feet
**B** 4 feet  **D** 4 yards

4. length of a paintbrush G

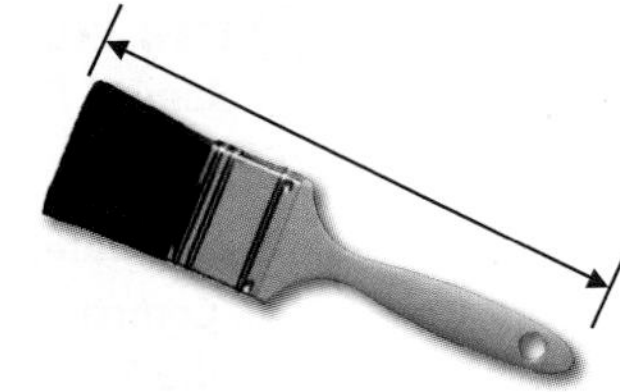

**F** 3 inches  **H** 3 feet
**G** 8 inches  **J** 8 feet

5. 

Why do you think there is more than 1 unit of measure for length? See Ch.11 Answer Appendix.



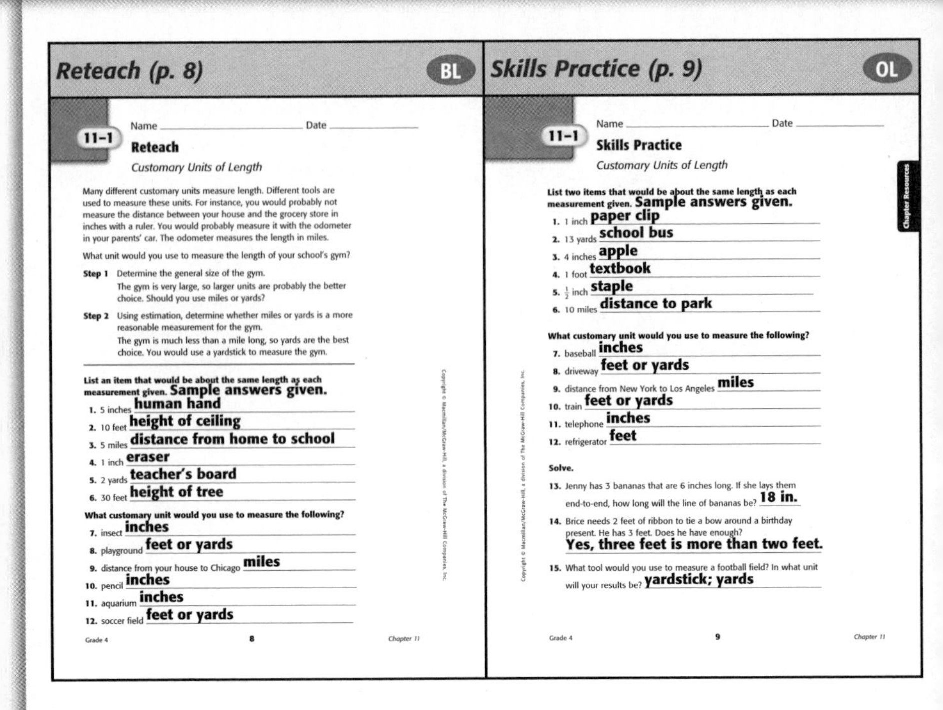

**Reteach (p. 8)** BL

11-1 Name ____________ Date ____________

**Reteach**

*Customary Units of Length*

Many different customary units measure length. Different tools are used to measure these units. For instance, you would probably not measure the distance between your house and the grocery store in inches with a ruler. You would probably measure it with the odometer in your parents' car. The odometer measures the length in miles.

What unit would you use to measure the length of your school's gym?

**Step 1** Determine the general size of the gym.
The gym is very large, so larger units are probably the better choice. Should you use miles or yards?

**Step 2** Using estimation, determine whether miles or yards is a more reasonable measurement for the gym.
The gym is much less than a mile long, so yards are the best choice. You would use a yardstick to measure the gym.

**List an item that would be about the same length as each measurement given.** Sample answers given.

1. 5 inches human hand
2. 10 feet height of ceiling
3. 5 miles distance from home to school
4. 1 inch eraser
5. 2 yards teacher's board
6. 30 feet height of tree

**What customary unit would you use to measure the following?**

7. insect inches
8. playground feet or yards
9. distance from your house to Chicago miles
10. pencil inches
11. aquarium inches
12. soccer field feet or yards

Grade 4 8 *Chapter 11*



**Skills Practice (p. 9)** OL

11-1 Name ____________ Date ____________

**Skills Practice**

*Customary Units of Length*

**List two items that would be about the same length as each measurement given.** Sample answers given.

1. 1 inch paper clip
2. 13 yards school bus
3. 4 inches apple
4. 1 foot textbook
5. $\frac{1}{2}$ inch staple
6. 10 miles distance to park

**What customary unit would you use to measure the following?**

7. baseball inches
8. driveway feet or yards
9. distance from New York to Los Angeles miles
10. train feet or yards
11. telephone inches
12. refrigerator feet

**Solve.**

13. Jenny has 3 bananas that are 6 inches long. If she lays them end-to-end, how long will the line of bananas be? 18 in.
14. Brice needs 2 feet of ribbon to tie a bow around a birthday present. He has 3 feet. Does he have enough? Yes, three feet is more than two feet.
15. What tool would you use to measure a football field? In what unit will your results be? yardstick; yards

Grade 4 9 *Chapter 11*

Chapter Resources

## Practice and Problem Solving

Estimate. Then measure each to the nearest inch, $\frac{1}{2}$ inch, and $\frac{1}{4}$ inch. See Example 1 (p. 441)

6. 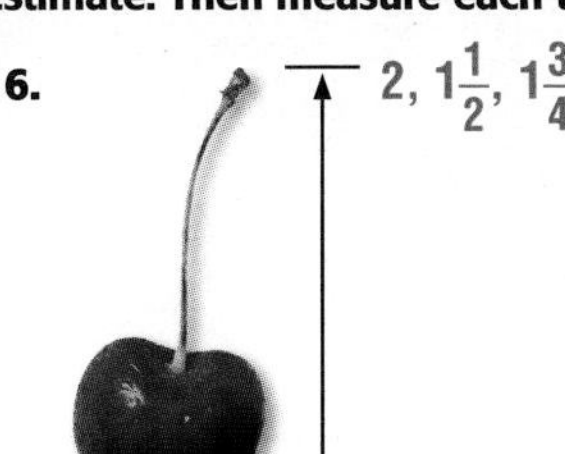 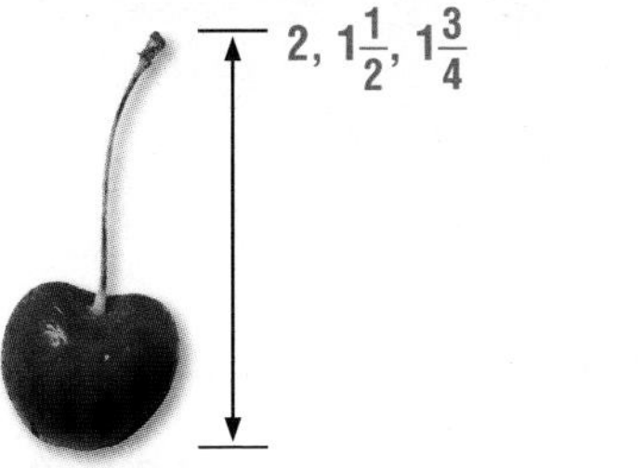 2, $1\frac{1}{2}$, $1\frac{3}{4}$

7.  2, $2\frac{1}{2}$, $2\frac{1}{4}$

8. 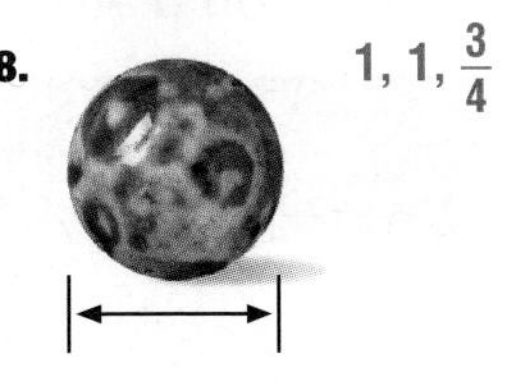 1, 1, $\frac{3}{4}$

9. 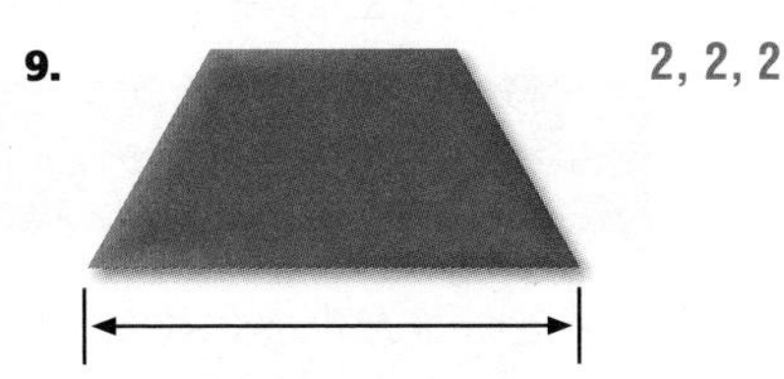 2, 2, 2

10. Patrice found a book that was $2\frac{1}{4}$ inches thick. She stacked it with another book that was the same thickness. How tall was the stack? $4\frac{1}{2}$ in.

11. Helki found a stick that was $5\frac{3}{4}$ feet long. He needed one that was about 5 feet long. Is it reasonable to say that this stick will work? Explain. Yes, because the stick is longer than what he needs.

Choose the best estimate for each length. See Example 2 (p. 442)

12. length of a whistle D
    - A 2 yards
    - B 2 feet
    - C 12 inches
    - D 2 inches

13. width of a chalkboard J 
    - F 1 foot
    - G 2 feet
    - H 1 yard
    - J 2 yards

### H.O.T. Problems

14. **OPEN ENDED** Find two objects in your home that are longer than 2 inches and shorter than 4 inches. How did you use estimation in selecting objects? 14, 15. See Ch. 11 Answer Appendix.

15. **WRITING IN MATH** List two tools used to measure length and provide a situation in which that tool would be useful.



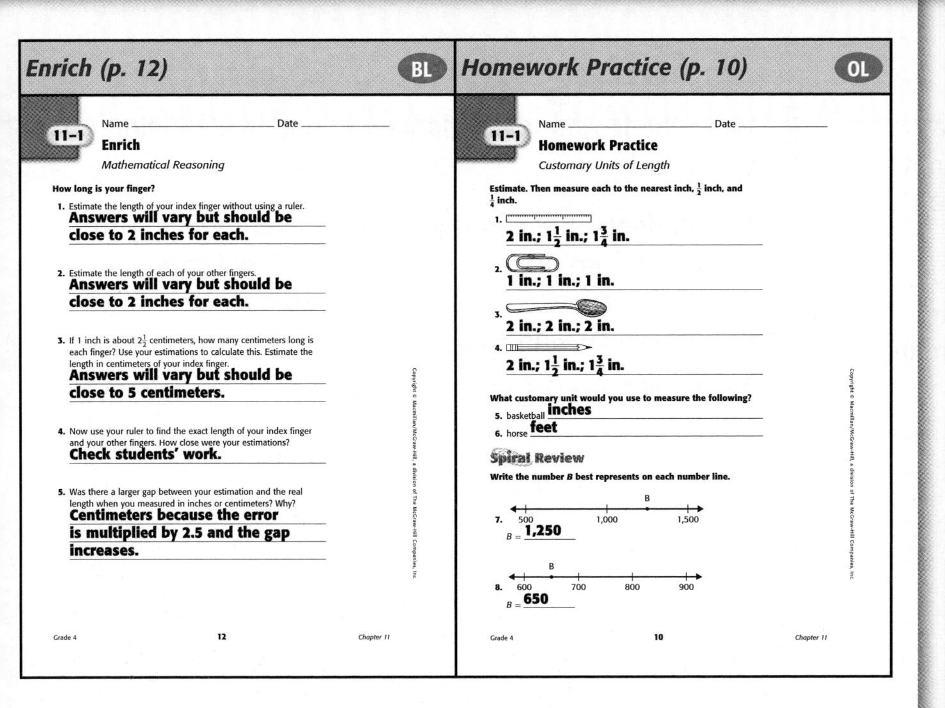

**Enrich (p. 12)** BL

11-1 Name ______ Date ______

**Enrich**

*Mathematical Reasoning*

**How long is your finger?**

1. Estimate the length of your index finger without using a ruler. **Answers will vary but should be close to 2 inches for each.**
2. Estimate the length of each of your other fingers. **Answers will vary but should be close to 2 inches for each.**
3. If 1 inch is about $2\frac{1}{2}$ centimeters, how many centimeters long is each finger? Use your estimations to calculate this. Estimate the length in centimeters of your index finger. **Answers will vary but should be close to 5 centimeters.**
4. Now use your ruler to find the exact length of your index finger and your other fingers. How close were your estimations? **Check students' work.**
5. Was there a larger gap between your estimation and the real length when you measured in inches or centimeters? Why? **Centimeters because the error is multiplied by 2.5 and the gap increases.**



Grade 4 12 *Chapter 11*

**Homework Practice (p. 10)** OL

11-1 Name ______ Date ______

**Homework Practice**

*Customary Units of Length*

**Estimate. Then measure each to the nearest inch, $\frac{1}{2}$ inch, and $\frac{1}{4}$ inch.**

1. **2 in.; $1\frac{1}{2}$ in.; $1\frac{3}{4}$ in.**
2. **1 in.; 1 in.; 1 in.**
3. **2 in.; 2 in.; 2 in.**
4. **2 in.; $1\frac{1}{2}$ in.; $1\frac{3}{4}$ in.**

**What customary unit would you use to measure the following?**

5. basketball **inches**
6. horse **feet**

**Spiral Review**

**Write the number *B* best represents on each number line.**

7. 500 1,000 B 1,500 — $B =$ **1,250**
8. 600 B 700 800 900 — $B =$ **650**



Grade 4 10 *Chapter 11*

## 3 Practice

Differentiate practice using these leveled assignments for Exercises 7–16.

| Level | Assignment |
|---|---|
| BL Below/Approaching Level | 7–8, 11, 13 |
| OL On Level | 8–10, 12–14, 16 |
| AL Above/Beyond Level | 7–13 odd, 15–16 |

Have students discuss and complete the Higher Order Thinking problems. For Exercise 15, have students measure to confirm that the objects are between the two lengths. Have them show the objects to the class.

**WRITING IN MATH** Have students complete Exercise 15 in their Math Journals. You may choose to use this exercise as an optional formative assessment.

## 4 Assess

### Formative Assessment

- **What customary unit would you use to measure the length of your math book?** inches **About how many inches long do you think the book is?** Estimates will vary.
- **What tool would you use to measure the book?** ruler
- **Measure one side of your math book. How long is it to the nearest inch? $\frac{1}{2}$ inch? $\frac{1}{4}$ inch?** Check students' measurements.

**Quick Check** **Are students continuing to struggle with estimating and measuring customary lengths?**

**If Yes** → Small Group Options (p. 441B)
Strategic Intervention Guide (p. 118)

**If No** → Independent Work Options (p. 441B)
CRM Skills Practice Worksheet (p. 9)
CRM Enrich Worksheet (p. 12)

**Ticket Out the Door** Ask students to write about a length they would measure in yards, including an estimate of the number of yards. Have them give you their papers as they leave class for the day.

LESSON 11-2

# Convert Customary Units of Length

## Lesson Planner

### Objective

Convert customary units of length.

### Vocabulary

**convert**

### Resources

**Manipulatives:** play money

**Literature Connection:** *Measuring Penny* by Loreen Leedy

**Teacher Technology**

TeacherWorks • Interactive Classroom

## Daily Routine

Use these suggestions before beginning the lesson on p. 444.

### 5-Minute Check

(Reviews Lesson 10-1)

**Estimate. Then measure each to the nearest inch, $\frac{1}{2}$ inch, and $\frac{1}{4}$ inch.** Check students' estimates and measurements.

1. a craft stick
2. your smallest finger

### Problem of the Day

Ben knows that $\frac{1}{4}$ of a foot is 3 inches. He needs at least $1\frac{1}{2}$ feet of cord to put around a box. He has 15 inches of cord. Does he have enough cord? Explain.

no; 15 inches = $1\frac{1}{4}$ feet; $1\frac{1}{4}$ feet $<$ $1\frac{1}{2}$ feet

### Focus on Math Background

Converting units means changing the measurement of a fixed length from one unit to another. The length does not change, but its measured value depends on the unit used. When converting a length measurement from a smaller to a larger unit, you must divide. And when converting from a larger unit to a smaller unit, you must multiply. Since there is no consistency among unit relationships in the customary system, a variety of conversion factors must be used:

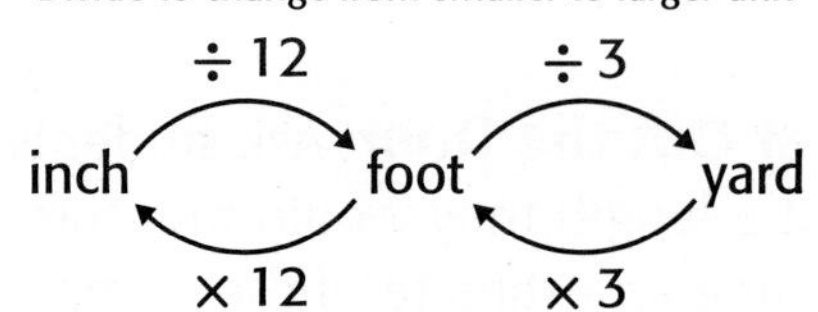


### Building Math Vocabulary

Write the lesson vocabulary word and its definition on the board.

Tell students that when you convert something, you change it from one thing to another. Have students identify and discuss various things that are converted in math, science, and everyday life.

# Differentiated Instruction

## Small Group Options

### Option 1 Gifted and Talented AL

LOGICAL

**Materials:** markers, chart paper, paper, pencils

- Copy the following problem on the chart paper: *In the frog-jumping contest, Cindy's frog jumped a total of 72 inches. Gary's frog jumped a total of 6 feet. Which frog jumped farther? Explain your answer.*
- Ask students to show their work on paper. The frogs jumped the same distance. The students should show that they know that each foot has 12 inches, so 72 inches equals 6 feet.

### Option 2 English Language Learners ELL

VISUAL/SPATIAL, LOGICAL

**Core Vocabulary:** another way, some, more accurate
**Common Use Verb:** gauge
**Talk Math** This strategy helps students estimate, measure, and convert lengths into different units.

- Post the chart from the ELL strategy from the previous lesson on Customary Units of Length. Have groups pick something in the yard column and estimate its length in feet.
- Write their estimates emphasizing target vocabulary.
- Have students divide by 3 to check their estimates.
- Have each group re-measure items in feet and write the actual dimensions in feet and inches.
- Ask: "Were **some** estimates **more accurate** than others?" Discuss possible reasons for accuracy or lack of accuracy.
- Repeat using the feet column, estimating inches as time permits.

## Independent Work Options

### Option 1 Early Finishers AL

INTRAPERSONAL

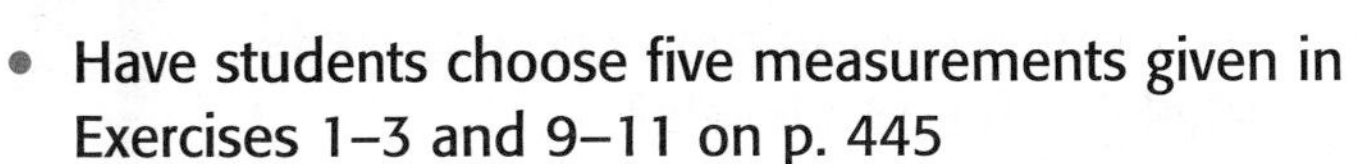

- Have students choose five measurements given in Exercises 1–3 and 9–11 on p. 445
- Challenge students to convert these measures to a different customary unit than the one asked for in the original problem. For example, they may convert 12 ft in Exercise 2 to 144 in.

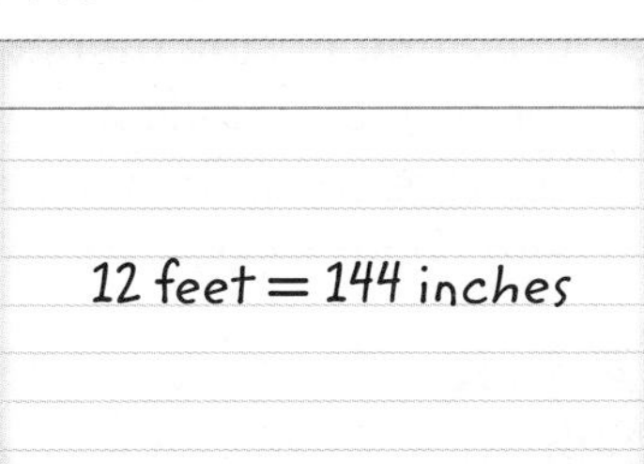


### Option 2 Student Technology

Tech Link

Math Online macmillanmh.com

Personal Tutor • Extra Examples

### Option 3 Learning Station: Music (p. 436J)

Direct students to the Music Learning Station for opportunities to explore and extend the lesson concept.

### Option 4 Problem-Solving Practice

Reinforce problem-solving skills and strategies with the Problem-Solving Practice worksheet.

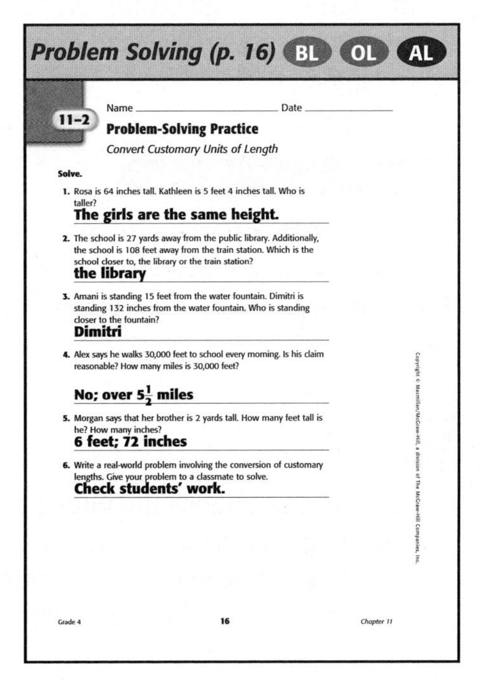

**Problem Solving (p. 16)** BL OL AL

11–2 Name ______ Date ______

**Problem-Solving Practice**

*Convert Customary Units of Length*

**Solve.**

1. Rosa is 64 inches tall. Kathleen is 5 feet 4 inches tall. Who is taller?
   **The girls are the same height.**
2. The school is 27 yards away from the public library. Additionally, the school is 108 feet away from the train station. Which is the school closer to, the library or the train station?
   **the library**
3. Amani is standing 15 feet from the water fountain. Dimitri is standing 132 inches from the water fountain. Who is standing closer to the fountain?
   **Dimitri**
4. Alex says he walks 30,000 feet to school every morning. Is his claim reasonable? How many miles is 30,000 feet?
   **No; over $5\frac{1}{2}$ miles**
5. Morgan says that her brother is 2 yards tall. How many feet tall is he? How many inches?
   **6 feet; 72 inches**
6. Write a real-world problem involving the conversion of customary lengths. Give your problem to a classmate to solve.
   **Check students' work.**



Grade 4 16 *Chapter 11*

# 11-2 Convert Customary Units of Length

## 1 Introduce

### Activity Choice 1 • Hands-On

- Provide pairs of students with play coins and bills. **How many pennies can you trade for 1 dime?** 10 **for 2 dimes?** 20 Have partners work together to make the trades described.
- Have partners make trades and answer these questions: **How many quarters can you trade for 5 nickels?** 1 **for 15 nickels?** 3
- Continue posing money conversion questions for several rounds of trades. Include conversions from smaller to larger units and larger to smaller units.

### Activity Choice 2 • Literature

Introduce the lesson with *Measuring Penny* by Loreen Leedy. For a related math activity, see p. TR59.

## 2 Teach

### Scaffolding Questions

- **Suppose you have 3 dimes. What multiplication sentence shows how many nickels you will get in exchange for the dimes?** $3 \times 2 = 6$
- **How can you use division to find the number of dimes you will get for 8 nickels?** 8 nickels $\div$ 2 = 4 dimes
- Tell students they will use multiplication and division to change customary lengths from larger units to smaller and from smaller units to larger.

### GET READY to Learn

Have students open their books and read the information in **Get Ready to Learn**. Introduce **convert**. As a class, work through **Examples 1 and 2**.

### COMMON ERROR!

Students may choose the wrong operation when converting units. Have them make a table of equivalent measures and find patterns to help them understand when to multiply and divide.



# 11-2 Convert Customary Units of Length

**MAIN IDEA**

I will convert customary units of length.

**New Vocabulary**

**convert**

**Math Online**

macmillanmh.com
- Extra Examples
- Personal Tutor
- Self-Check Quiz

### GET READY to Learn

Marla's dog, Cory, competes in big air competitions. Each dog jumps into water. Cory's longest jump is 21 feet. How many yards are in 21 feet?

To **convert** between units of measurement means to change the unit. When converting measurements, think about two things:

- The unit you are starting with and the unit you are ending with.
- Are you converting from a smaller unit to a larger unit or a larger unit to a smaller unit?

### Real-World EXAMPLE Convert to Larger Units

**1** **SPORTS** **Cory's longest jump is 21 feet. How many yards are in 21 feet?**

You know the number of feet and want to find the number of yards. Feet are a smaller unit than yards. So use division.

To convert 21 feet to yards, divide by 3.

21 ft = ■ yd
$21 \div 3 =$ ■
$21 \div 3 = 7$

← Divide by 3 because 3 feet = 1 yard.

So, there are 7 yards in 21 feet.

### EXAMPLE Convert to Smaller Units

**2** **Complete. 6 yds = ■ ft**

To convert 6 yards to feet, multiply by 3.

$6 \times 3 =$ ■
$6 \times 3 = 18$

← Multiply by 3 because 3 feet = 1 yard.

So, there are 18 feet in 6 yards.



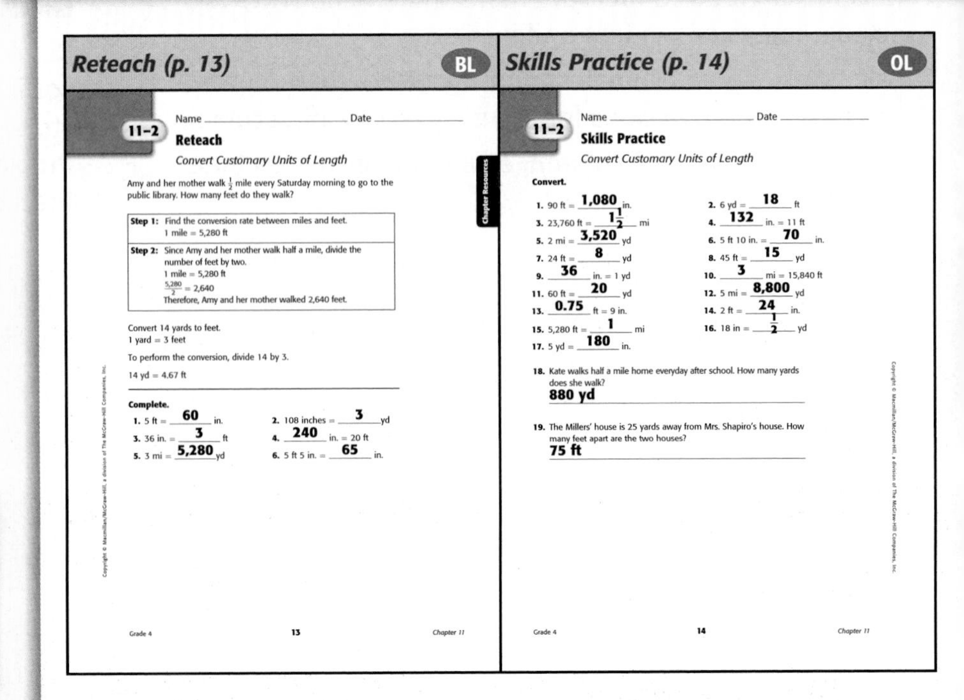

**Reteach (p. 13)** BL

11-2 Name ____________ Date ____________

**Reteach**

*Convert Customary Units of Length*

Amy and her mother walk $\frac{1}{2}$ mile every Saturday morning to go to the public library. How many feet do they walk?

| | |
|---|---|
| **Step 1:** | Find the conversion rate between miles and feet.<br>1 mile = 5,280 ft |
| **Step 2:** | Since Amy and her mother walk half a mile, divide the number of feet by two.<br>1 mile = 5,280 ft<br>$\frac{5{,}280}{2} = 2{,}640$<br>Therefore, Amy and her mother walked 2,640 feet. |

Convert 14 yards to feet.
1 yard = 3 feet

To perform the conversion, divide 14 by 3.

14 yd = 4.67 ft

**Complete.**

1. 5 ft = **60** in.
2. 108 inches = **3** yd
3. 36 in. = **3** ft
4. **240** in. = 20 ft
5. 3 mi = **5,280** yd
6. 5 ft 5 in. = **65** in.

Chapter Resources



Grade 4 13 Chapter 11

**Skills Practice (p. 14)** OL

11-2 Name ____________ Date ____________

**Skills Practice**

*Convert Customary Units of Length*

**Convert.**

1. 90 ft = **1,080** in.
2. 6 yd = **18** ft
3. 23,760 ft = **$1\frac{1}{2}$** mi
4. **132** in. = 11 ft
5. 2 mi = **3,520** yd
6. 5 ft 10 in. = **70** in.
7. 24 ft = **8** yd
8. 45 ft = **15** yd
9. **36** in. = 1 yd
10. **3** mi = 15,840 ft
11. 60 ft = **20** yd
12. 5 mi = **8,800** yd
13. **0.75** ft = 9 in.
14. 2 ft = **24** in.
15. 5,280 ft = **1** mi
16. 18 in = **$\frac{1}{2}$** yd
17. 5 yd = **180** in.

18. Kate walks half a mile home everyday after school. How many yards does she walk?
**880 yd**

19. The Millers' house is 25 yards away from Mrs. Shapiro's house. How many feet apart are the two houses?
**75 ft**



Grade 4 14 Chapter 11

## CHECK What You Know

**Complete.** See Examples 1 and 2 (p. 444)

1. 36 in. = ■ ft 3
2. 12 ft = ■ yd 4
3. 4 yd = ■ in. 144
4. 2 yd = ■ ft 6
5. ■ in. = 7 ft 84
6. 24 in. = ■ ft 2
7. The Costa family hiked a trail that was 2 miles in one direction. How many feet was the hike round-trip? 21,120
8. Talk About It Explain how to convert a smaller unit of measure to a larger unit of measure. See Ch. 11 Answer Appendix.

## Practice and Problem Solving

EXTRA PRACTICE See page R28.

**Complete.** See Examples 1 and 2 (p. 444)

9. 2 ft = ■ in. 24
10. 6 ft = ■ in. 72
11. ■ in. = 2 yd 72
12. 6 ft = ■ yd 2
13. ■ ft = 132 in. 11
14. ■ in. = 12 ft 144
15. 18 ft = ■ in. 216
16. 18 yd = ■ in. 648
17. ■ in. = 4 ft 48
18. 16 ft = ■ in. 192
19. 216 in. = ■ yd 6
20. 84 ft = ■ yd 28
21. Darin is 4 feet 10 inches tall. His brother is 68 inches tall. How many more inches taller is Darin's brother than Darin? 10 in.
22. Sumi lives 2 miles from school. Valerie lives 10,542 feet from school. Who lives closer to school? Explain your answer. See Ch.11 Answer Appendix.
23. Cassie's mom bought 16 yards of yarn. She needs 580 inches of yarn for her art project. Does she have enough? Explain. Sample answer: No; $16 \times 3 = 48$ and $48 \times 12 = 576$, which is less than 580.
24. Mr. Shank used 15 feet of tape. He bought a container of tape that was 5 yards long. Did he buy enough? Explain. Sample answer: yes, 15 ft = 5 yd.

### H.O.T. Problems

25. **OPEN ENDED** Measure two objects that are at least one foot long. Convert the measurement to a smaller unit. See students' work.
26. **CHALLENGE** Ramiro sits 5 feet from the bookshelf. Michelle sits 64 inches from the bookshelf. Who sits closer to the bookshelf? Ramiro
27. **WRITING IN MATH** Write a real-world problem involving the conversion of customary lengths. Give your problem to a classmate to solve. Sample answer: Henry kicked a soccer ball 25 yards. How many feet did he kick the ball? 75 ft



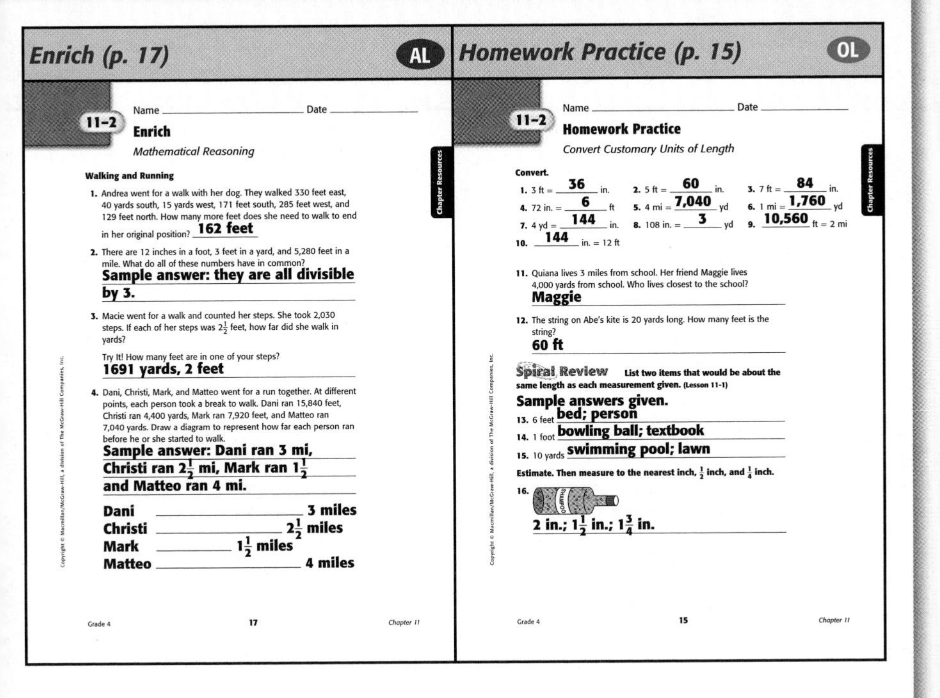

**Enrich (p. 17)** AL

11-2 Name ______ Date ______

**Enrich**

*Mathematical Reasoning*

**Walking and Running**

1. Andrea went for a walk with her dog. They walked 330 feet east, 40 yards south, 15 yards west, 171 feet south, 285 feet west, and 129 feet north. How many more feet does she need to walk to end in her original position? **162 feet**
2. There are 12 inches in a foot, 3 feet in a yard, and 5,280 feet in a mile. What do all of these numbers have in common? **Sample answer: they are all divisible by 3.**
3. Macie went for a walk and counted her steps. She took 2,030 steps. If each of her steps was $2\frac{1}{2}$ feet, how far did she walk in yards?

   Try It! How many feet are in one of your steps? **1691 yards, 2 feet**
4. Dani, Christi, Mark, and Matteo went for a run together. At different points, each person took a break to walk. Dani ran 15,840 feet, Christi ran 4,400 yards, Mark ran 7,920 feet, and Matteo ran 7,040 yards. Draw a diagram to represent how far each person ran before he or she started to walk. **Sample answer: Dani ran 3 mi, Christi ran $2\frac{1}{2}$ mi, Mark ran $1\frac{1}{2}$ and Matteo ran 4 mi.**

   Dani ______ **3 miles**
   Christi ______ **$2\frac{1}{2}$ miles**
   Mark ______ **$1\frac{1}{2}$ miles**
   Matteo ______ **4 miles**

Chapter Resources



Grade 4 17 Chapter 11

**Homework Practice (p. 15)** OL

11-2 Name ______ Date ______

**Homework Practice**

*Convert Customary Units of Length*

**Convert.**

1. 3 ft = **36** in.
2. 5 ft = **60** in.
3. 7 ft = **84** in.
4. 72 in. = **6** ft
5. 4 mi = **7,040** yd
6. 1 mi = **1,760** yd
7. 4 yd = **144** in.
8. 108 in. = **3** yd
9. **10,560** ft = 2 mi
10. **144** in. = 12 ft
11. Quiana lives 3 miles from school. Her friend Maggie lives 4,000 yards from school. Who lives closest to the school? **Maggie**
12. The string on Abe's kite is 20 yards long. How many feet is the string? **60 ft**

**Spiral Review** List two items that would be about the same length as each measurement given. (Lesson 11-1)

**Sample answers given.**

13. 6 feet **bed; person**
14. 1 foot **bowling ball; textbook**
15. 10 yards **swimming pool; lawn**

**Estimate. Then measure to the nearest inch, $\frac{1}{2}$ inch, and $\frac{1}{4}$ inch.**

16. SHAMPOO **2 in.; $1\frac{1}{2}$ in.; $1\frac{3}{4}$ in.**

Chapter Resources



Grade 4 15 Chapter 11

## CHECK What You Know

As a class, have students complete Exercises 1–8 in **Check What You Know** as you observe their work.

**Exercise 8** Assess student comprehension before assigning practice exercises.

## BL Alternate Teaching Strategy

**If** students have trouble converting units…

**Then** use one of these reteach options:

1. CRM **Daily Reteach Worksheet** (p. 13)
2. Have students draw pictures like the one below to help them convert units.
   36 in. = ■ ft

   12 in. | 12 in. | 12 in.
   1 ft | 1 ft | 1 ft

## 3 Practice

Differentiate practice using these leveled assignments for Exercises 9–27.

| Level | Assignment |
|---|---|
| BL Below/Approaching Level | 9–14, 21–22 |
| OL On Level | 12–20, 22–24, 27 |
| AL Above/Beyond Level | 10–24 even, 26–27 |

## 4 Assess

### Formative Assessment

- **What operations do you use to convert measurements?** Multiplication to convert from a larger to a smaller unit and division to convert from a smaller to a larger unit.

**Quick Check** **Are students continuing to struggle with converting customary units?**

**If Yes** → Small Group Options (p. 444B)

**If No** → Independent Work Options (p. 444B)
CRM Skills Practice Worksheet (p. 14)
CRM Enrich Worksheet (p. 17)

# 11-3 Problem-Solving Strategy
# Solve a Simpler Problem

## Lesson Planner

### Objective

Solve problems by solving a simpler problem.

### Resources

**Literature Connection:** *If You Made a Million* by David M. Schwartz

**Teacher Technology**
TeacherWorks • Interactive Classroom

**Real-World Problem Solving Library**
***Math and Science: Ancient Giants of the Forest***
Use these leveled books to reinforce and extend problem-solving skills and strategies.

Leveled for:
- OL On Level
- ELL Sheltered English
- SP Spanish

For additional support, see the Real-World Problem Solving Teacher Guide.

## Daily Routine

Use these suggestions before beginning the lesson on p. 446.

### 5-Minute Check

(Reviews Lesson 11-2)

**Complete.**

**1.** 24 in. = ■ ft 2
**2.** 5 yd = ■ ft 15
**3.** ■ in. = 4 ft 48
**4.** 12 ft = ■ yd 4
**5.** 2 yd = ■ in. 72
**6.** ■ in. = 3 yd 108

### Problem of the Day

Use the letters B, C, P, D.
Draw a horizontal line that divides each letter in half. For which letter did the line *not* form a line of symmetry? Letter P

# Differentiated Instruction

## Small Group Options

### Option 1 Below Level BL

VISUAL PAIR

**Materials:** paper and pencil

Hand each student a copy of this problem:

> The OVERNIGHT DELIVERY COMPANY charges $13 for a package up to 2 pounds with each additional pound costing $3. What is the charge for a 7-pound package?

$28

- Have each student who is participating in this exercise devise another problem using this data. Have them solve it and then share with another student to check the answer.

### Option 2 English Language Learners ELL

VISUAL

**Materials:** math book, various manipulatives
**Core Vocabulary:** add onto, start from, a problem within a problem
**Common Use Verb:** include
**See Math** This strategy helps students build small problems into larger problems so that students can visualize disassembling large problems back into smaller ones.

- Give 2 students manipulatives and say: "Work with your partner and the manipulatives to write a problem."
- Have the pair read the problem and post the solution.
- Ask a new pair of students to repeat creating and posting a problem, except they must start from the first pair's solution. Have them underline the original problem and write the total problem above the first.
- Repeat several times as time permits. Discuss.

## Independent Work Options

### Option 1 Early Finishers AL

LINGUISTIC, LOGICAL

- Challenge students to write a word problem that can be solved using the solve a simpler problem strategy.
- Have students exchange problems with a partner and solve. Or, you may have them present their problems to the class and explain how to solve it.

### Option 2 Student Technology

**Math Online**  macmillanmh.com

Personal Tutor • Extra Examples

### Option 3 Learning Station: Health (p. 436J)

Direct students to the Health Learning Station for opportunities to explore and extend the lesson concept.

# 11-3 Problem-Solving Strategy

## 1 Introduce

**Activity Choice 1 • Review**

- Pose the problem:

  *Carlos and Victor hiked for two days in Big Bend National Park. They hiked a longer distance on the second day than on the first day. If they hiked 8 miles on the first day, how much farther did they hike on second day?*
- **What information is missing?** the distance they hiked on the second day
- Provide students with a measure for how far Carlos and Victor hiked on the second day and have them solve the problem. Answers will vary.

**Activity Choice 2 • Literature**

Introduce the lesson with *If You Made a Million* by David M. Schwartz. For a related math activity, see p. TR59.

## 2 Teach

Have students read the problem on bicycling. Guide them through the problem-solving steps.

**Understand** Using the questions, review what students know and need to find.

**Plan** Have them discuss their strategy.

**Solve** Guide students to use solve a simpler problem to solve the problem.

- **Why is it easier to first find the number of blocks one time around the route?** Sample answer: It is easier to add 6 distances than 18.
- **How can you find the total blocks Pearl rides?** Add 16 + 16 + 16 or multiply 3 × 16.
- **Why do you multiply the result by 2?** It takes Pearl 2 minutes to ride one block.

**Check** Have students look back at the problem to make sure that the answer fits the facts given.

**COMMON ERROR!**

**Exercise 5** Watch for students who find the number of green tiles but then solve for one picture rather than three.

# 11-3 Problem-Solving Strategy

**MAIN IDEA** I will solve problems by solving a simpler problem.

It takes Pearl 2 minutes to ride her bike one block in her neighborhood. How long does it takes Pearl to ride the route shown in her neighborhood three times?

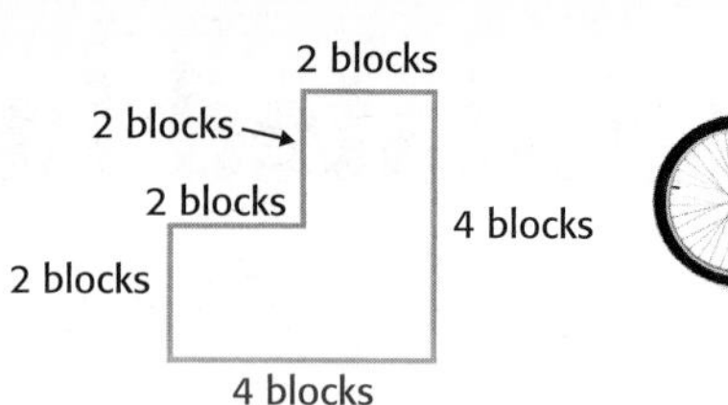

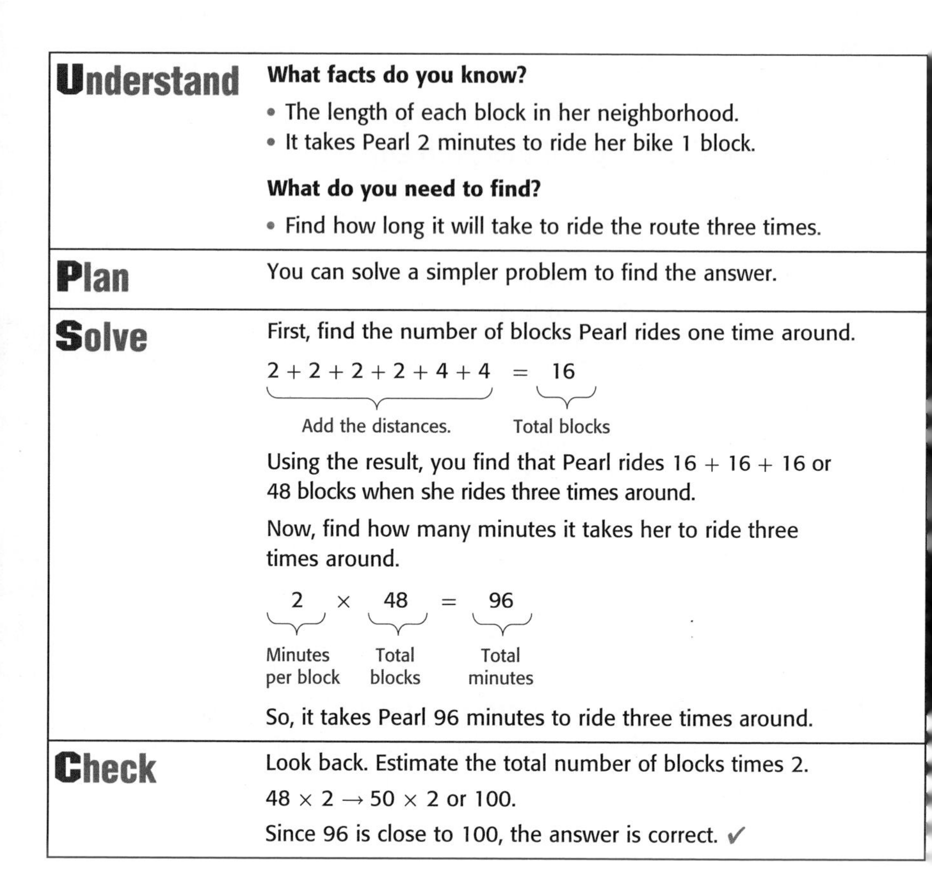

| | |
|---|---|
| **Understand** | **What facts do you know?**<br>• The length of each block in her neighborhood.<br>• It takes Pearl 2 minutes to ride her bike 1 block.<br>**What do you need to find?**<br>• Find how long it will take to ride the route three times. |
| **Plan** | You can solve a simpler problem to find the answer. |
| **Solve** | First, find the number of blocks Pearl rides one time around.<br>$\underbrace{2 + 2 + 2 + 2 + 4 + 4}_{\text{Add the distances.}} = \underbrace{16}_{\text{Total blocks}}$<br>Using the result, you find that Pearl rides 16 + 16 + 16 or 48 blocks when she rides three times around.<br>Now, find how many minutes it takes her to ride three times around.<br>$\underbrace{2}_{\text{Minutes per block}} \times \underbrace{48}_{\text{Total blocks}} = \underbrace{96}_{\text{Total minutes}}$<br>So, it takes Pearl 96 minutes to ride three times around. |
| **Check** | Look back. Estimate the total number of blocks times 2.<br>$48 \times 2 \rightarrow 50 \times 2$ or 100.<br>Since 96 is close to 100, the answer is correct. ✓ |



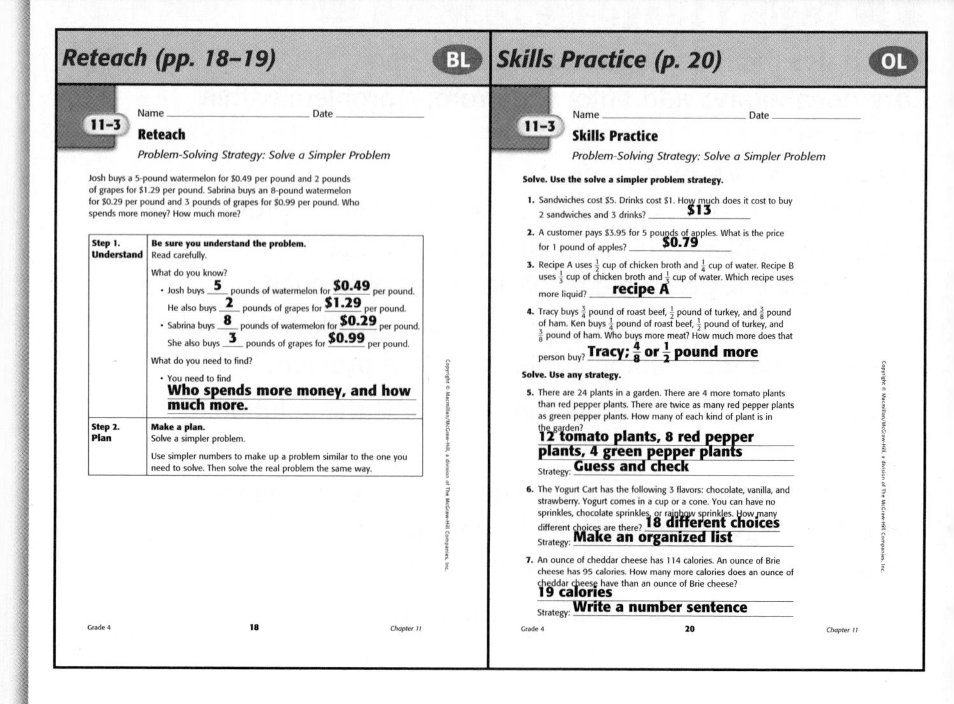

**Reteach (pp. 18–19)** BL

11-3 Name ____ Date ____

**Reteach**

*Problem-Solving Strategy: Solve a Simpler Problem*

Josh buys a 5-pound watermelon for $0.49 per pound and 2 pounds of grapes for $1.29 per pound. Sabrina buys an 8-pound watermelon for $0.29 per pound and 3 pounds of grapes for $0.99 per pound. Who spends more money? How much more?

| | |
|---|---|
| **Step 1. Understand** | **Be sure you understand the problem.**<br>Read carefully.<br>What do you know?<br>• Josh buys **5** pounds of watermelon for **$0.49** per pound.<br>He also buys **2** pounds of grapes for **$1.29** per pound.<br>• Sabrina buys **8** pounds of watermelon for **$0.29** per pound.<br>She also buys **3** pounds of grapes for **$0.99** per pound.<br>What do you need to find?<br>• You need to find **Who spends more money, and how much more.** |
| **Step 2. Plan** | **Make a plan.**<br>Solve a simpler problem.<br>Use simpler numbers to make up a problem similar to the one you need to solve. Then solve the real problem the same way. |



Grade 4 18 Chapter 11

**Skills Practice (p. 20)** OL

11-3 Name ____ Date ____

**Skills Practice**

*Problem-Solving Strategy: Solve a Simpler Problem*

**Solve. Use the solve a simpler problem strategy.**

1. Sandwiches cost $5. Drinks cost $1. How much does it cost to buy 2 sandwiches and 3 drinks? **$13**
2. A customer pays $3.95 for 5 pounds of apples. What is the price for 1 pound of apples? **$0.79**
3. Recipe A uses $\frac{1}{2}$ cup of chicken broth and $\frac{1}{4}$ cup of water. Recipe B uses $\frac{1}{3}$ cup of chicken broth and $\frac{1}{3}$ cup of water. Which recipe uses more liquid? **recipe A**
4. Tracy buys $\frac{3}{4}$ pound of roast beef, $\frac{1}{2}$ pound of turkey, and $\frac{3}{8}$ pound of ham. Ken buys $\frac{1}{4}$ pound of roast beef, $\frac{1}{2}$ pound of turkey, and $\frac{3}{8}$ pound of ham. Who buys more meat? How much more does that person buy? **Tracy; $\frac{4}{8}$ or $\frac{1}{2}$ pound more**

**Solve. Use any strategy.**

5. There are 24 plants in a garden. There are 4 more tomato plants than red pepper plants. There are twice as many red pepper plants as green pepper plants. How many of each kind of plant is in the garden? **12 tomato plants, 8 red pepper plants, 4 green pepper plants**

   Strategy: **Guess and check**
6. The Yogurt Cart has the following 3 flavors: chocolate, vanilla, and strawberry. Yogurt comes in a cup or a cone. You can have no sprinkles, chocolate sprinkles, or rainbow sprinkles. How many different choices are there? **18 different choices**

   Strategy: **Make an organized list**
7. An ounce of cheddar cheese has 114 calories. An ounce of Brie cheese has 95 calories. How many more calories does an ounce of cheddar cheese have than an ounce of Brie cheese? **19 calories**

   Strategy: **Write a number sentence**



Grade 4 20 Chapter 11

## ANALYZE the Strategy

**Refer to the problem on the previous page.**

1. Explain why $2 + 2 + 2 + 2 + 4 + 4$ was the first step in finding the answer to the problem. **To find the distance Pearl travels riding one time around.**
2. Could you have used multiplication to find the number of blocks it takes Pearl to ride the route three times? Explain. **yes; $3 \times 16 = 48$**
3. Suppose it takes Pearl 1 minute to ride her bike one block. Would it take her less than 1 hour to ride three times around her neighborhood? Explain. **yes; 48 minutes < 1 hour**
4. Look back at Exercise 3. Explain how you found the answer. **See students' work.**

★ indicates multi-step problem

## PRACTICE the Strategy

**Solve. Use the solve a simpler problem strategy.**

5. Marcos is making three tile pictures. He uses 310 green tiles to make each picture. He uses 50 less red tiles than green tiles for each picture. How many red and green tiles does he use in all? **1,710 tiles**
★6. **Measurement** Ling is putting up a wallpaper border on three walls that are 14 feet long and 12 feet tall. How many feet of wallpaper border will she use if she puts the border only at the top of the wall? **42 ft**
★7. Darius sells twice as much orange juice as lemonade. He charges $2 for each. He sold 10 cups of lemonade. How much did he earn in all? **$60**
8. A basketball coach is going to buy 16 basketballs. What will be the total cost of the basketballs? **$112**

★9. Jerome's CD has 16 songs, and each song is 3 minutes long. Ana's CD has 14 songs, and each song is 4 minutes. Whose CD plays longer and by how much? **Ana's; 8 min**
10. Five gardeners spent 260 hours in all planting trees. One of the gardeners spent 40 hours. The rest spent the same amount of time. How many hours did each spend on planting trees? **55 hr**

11. Marian is placing 72 photographs in an album. She will put the same number of photos on each of 6 pages. She can put 4 pictures in each row. How many rows will be on each page? **3 rows**
12. WRITING IN MATH Explain how you solved Exercise 11. **See Ch. 11 Answer Appendix.**



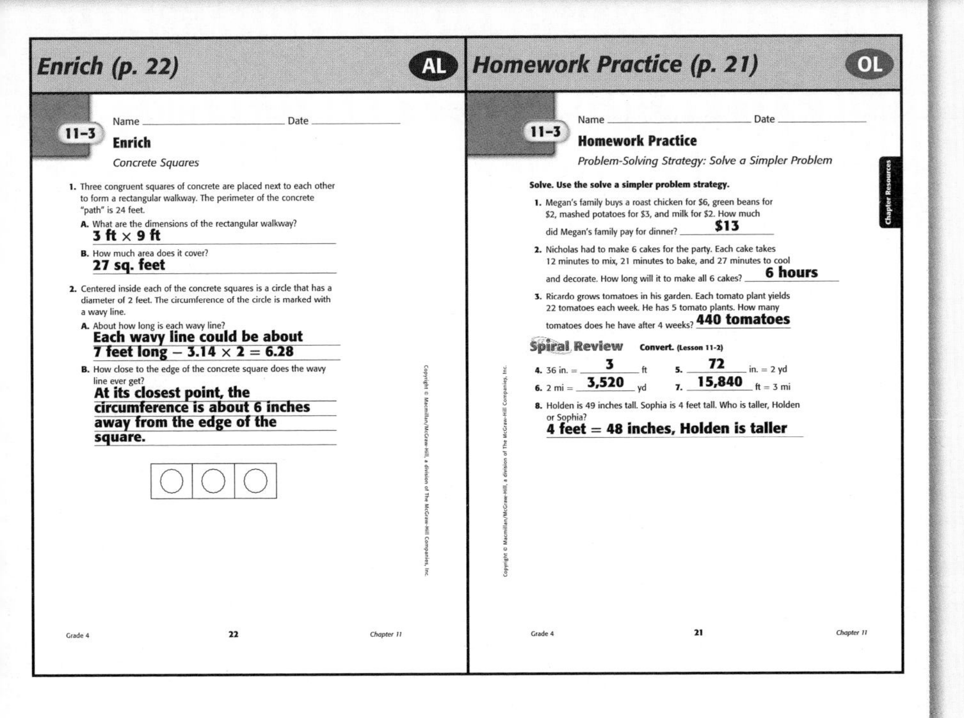

*Enrich (p. 22)* AL

Name ________ Date ________

11-3 **Enrich**

*Concrete Squares*

1. Three congruent squares of concrete are placed next to each other to form a rectangular walkway. The perimeter of the concrete "path" is 24 feet.
   A. What are the dimensions of the rectangular walkway? **3 ft × 9 ft**
   B. How much area does it cover? **27 sq. feet**
2. Centered inside each of the concrete squares is a circle that has a diameter of 2 feet. The circumference of the circle is marked with a wavy line.
   A. About how long is each wavy line? **Each wavy line could be about 7 feet long – 3.14 × 2 = 6.28**
   B. How close to the edge of the concrete square does the wavy line ever get? **At its closest point, the circumference is about 6 inches away from the edge of the square.**



Grade 4 22 Chapter 11

*Homework Practice (p. 21)* OL

Name ________ Date ________

11-3 **Homework Practice**

*Problem-Solving Strategy: Solve a Simpler Problem*

Chapter Resources

**Solve. Use the solve a simpler problem strategy.**

1. Megan's family buys a roast chicken for $6, green beans for $2, mashed potatoes for $3, and milk for $2. How much did Megan's family pay for dinner? **$13**
2. Nicholas had to make 6 cakes for the party. Each cake takes 12 minutes to mix, 21 minutes to bake, and 27 minutes to cool and decorate. How long will it to make all 6 cakes? **6 hours**
3. Ricardo grows tomatoes in his garden. Each tomato plant yields 22 tomatoes each week. He has 5 tomato plants. How many tomatoes does he have after 4 weeks? **440 tomatoes**

**Spiral Review** **Convert.** (Lesson 11-2)

4. 36 in. = **3** ft
5. **72** in. = 2 yd
6. 2 mi = **3,520** yd
7. **15,840** ft = 3 mi
8. Holden is 49 inches tall. Sophia is 4 feet tall. Who is taller, Holden or Sophia? **4 feet = 48 inches, Holden is taller**



Grade 4 21 Chapter 11

**Analyze the Strategy** Use Exercises 1–4 to analyze and discuss the problem-solving strategy.

### BL Alternate Teaching Strategy

**If** students have trouble using the solve a simpler problem strategy…

**Then** use one of these reteach options:

1. CRM **Daily Reteach Worksheet** (p. 18–19)
2. Suggest that students make a list of steps necessary for solving the problem. For example, Step 1 for the problem on p. 446 might be *use the diagram to find the number of blocks Pearl bicycles.* Encourage students to analyze the problem, list the steps, and then follow them until the problem is solved.

# 3 Practice

### Using the Exercises

**Exercises 6 and 10** Students may find it helpful to draw a picture when solving these problems.

**Exercise 11** Point out that students must first find the number of photographs per page before they can calculate the number of rows.

# 4 Assess

### Formative Assessment

Pose the following: *A deli used 360 slices of ham to make five types of sandwiches. If 80 slices were used for one type and an equal number for each of the other types, how many slices did they use for each of the other types of sandwiches?* 70

- **How can you solve a simpler problem?** Sample answer: Find the total slices used for the four types of sandwiches.
- **Solve.** 70 slices

**Quick Check** **Are students continuing to struggle with solving problems by solving a simpler problem?**

**If Yes** → Small Group Options (p. 446B)

**If No** → Independent Work Options (p. 446B)
CRM Skills Practice Worksheet (p. 20)
CRM Enrich Worksheet (p. 22)

# Lesson Planner

## Objective

Estimate and measure objects to the nearest centimeter.

## Resources

**Materials:** four classroom items that can be measured in centimeters

**Manipulatives:** metric rulers

## 1 Introduce

- Remind students of the two measurement systems widely used today. Have students name them. customary and metric
- Provide students with rulers and have them examine the side of the ruler showing customary units. **What customary unit on the ruler do we use to measure length?** inch
- Tell students to rotate the ruler to the opposite side. Explain that this side of the ruler shows metric units of length. **Which metric units are numbered on this ruler?** centimeters Have students compare and contrast the two sides of the ruler.

## 2 Teach

**Activity** Point out the centimeter marks on students' rulers. Remind them to measure to the nearest centimeter much like they would measure to the nearest inch—by lining up the 0 on the ruler with the edge of the object.

Measurement Activity for 11-4

# Metric Units of Length

**MAIN IDEA**

I will estimate and measure objects to the nearest centimeter.

**You Will Need**

metric ruler

Centimeters are **metric** units of measure for length. Each side of a base-ten unit is equal to 1 centimeter (cm).

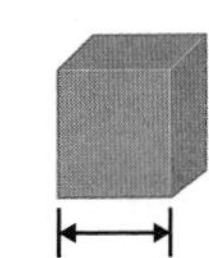


**ACTIVITY**

**1 Estimate and measure lengths.**

**Step 1 Copy the table.**

Copy the table shown.

| Object | Estimate | Length |
|---|---|---|
| | | |
| | | |
| | | |
| | | |

**Step 2 Choose four items.**

Choose four items in your classroom that can be measured in centimeters.

**Step 3 Estimate length.**

Estimate the length of each object you selected in centimeters. Record the estimates in your table.

**Step 4 Measure length.**

Place the ruler against a side of one of the objects so that 0 on the ruler lines up with the edge. Measure the object's length to the nearest centimeter.

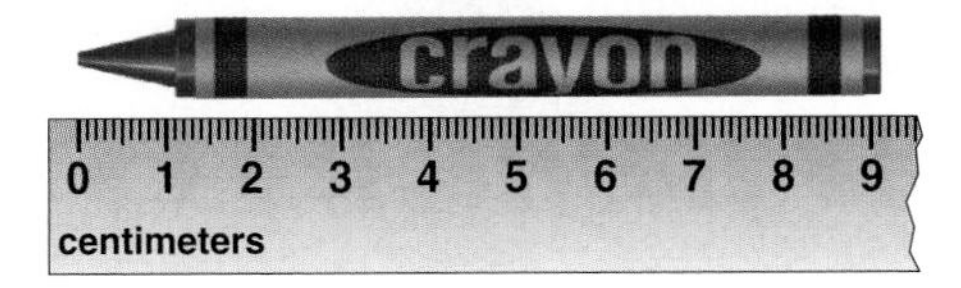

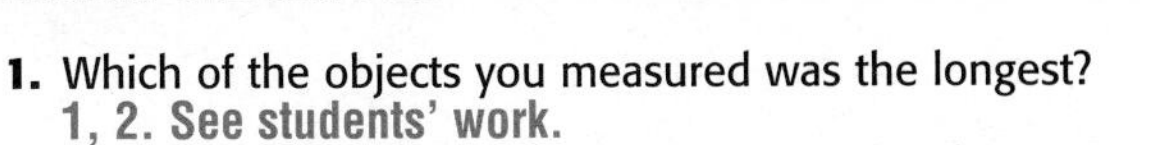

## Think About It

1. Which of the objects you measured was the longest?
   1, 2. See students' work.
2. Which of the objects you measured was the shortest?
3. How did you estimate the length of each object?
   Sample answer: Compare the length of a number of base-ten units.
4. Name two things in the room that would be about 100 centimeters long. Sample answers: window, dry erase board, bookshelf

## CHECK What You Know

**Estimate. Then measure each line segment to the nearest centimeter.**

5. 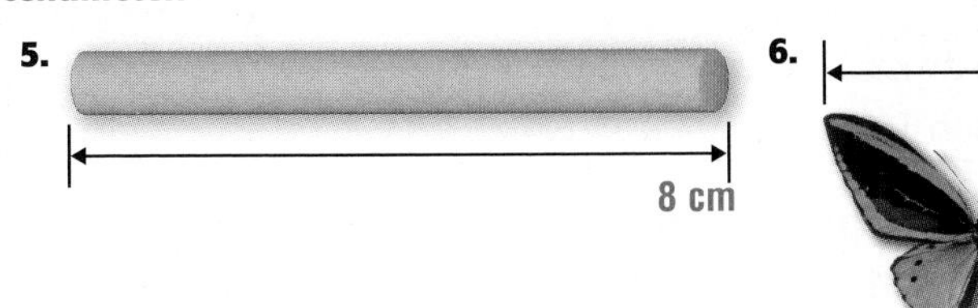
   8 cm

6. 4 cm

7. 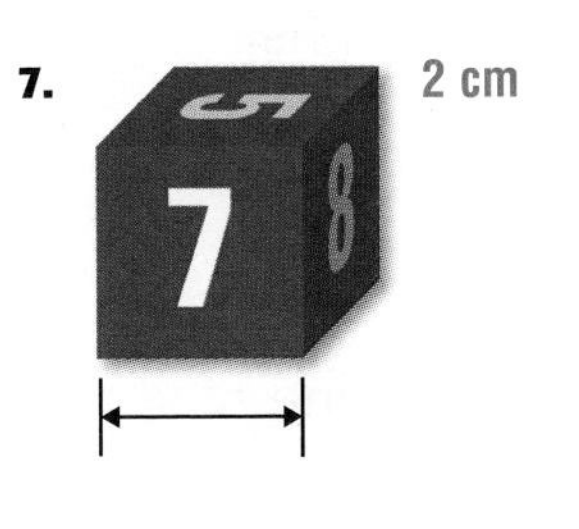
   2 cm

8. 7 cm

9. 
   2 cm

10. 1 cm
    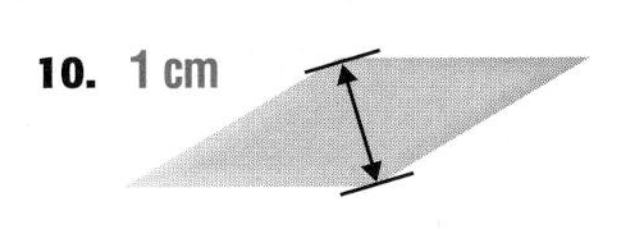

11. **WRITING IN MATH** Describe the steps in measuring the length of an object using a metric ruler. See margin.



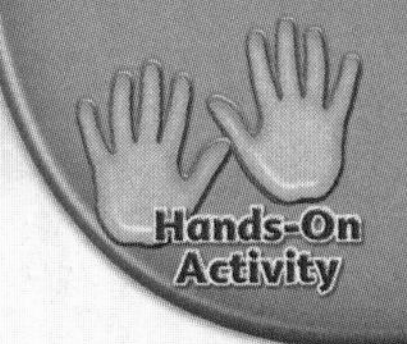


## Think About It

Assign Exercises 1–4 in the Think About It section to assess student comprehension of the concept presented in the Activity.

# 3 Assess

### Formative Assessment

Use **Check What You Know** Exercises 5–11 to assess whether students comprehend how to estimate and measure objects to the nearest centimeter.

**From Concrete to Abstract** Use Exercises 8 and 10 to bridge the gap between estimating and measuring the lengths of classroom items and estimating and measuring the lengths of line segments to the nearest centimeter.

**Extending the Concept** Challenge students to identify the smaller markings between each centimeter mark on the ruler. millimeters **How many millimeters make up one centimeter?** 10

### Additional Answer

11. Sample answer: Line up one edge of the object with 0 on the ruler. Then find the length.

LESSON 11-4

# Metric Units of Length

## Lesson Planner

### Objective

Estimate and measure lengths within the metric system.

### Vocabulary

**millimeter**, **centimeter**, **meter**, **kilometer**

### Resources

**Materials:** meterstick

**Manipulatives:** rulers

**Literature Connection:** *Ways of Measuring Then and Now* by Lisa Shulman

**Alternate Lesson:** Use *IMPACT Mathematics:* Unit H to provide practice with units of length.

**Teacher Technology**

TeacherWorks • Interactive Classroom

## Daily Routine

Use these suggestions before beginning the lesson on p. 450.

### 5-Minute Check

(Reviews Lesson 10-3)

**Solve. Use the solve a simpler problem strategy.**
Madeline owns two dogs. One dog weighs 13 pounds. The other dog weighs three times as much as the first. How much do Madeline's dogs weigh altogether? 52 pounds

### Problem of the Day

Mario arranges pieces of wood in a straight line with no gaps. The lengths of each piece are 8 inches, $\frac{1}{2}$ foot, 1 foot, and 4 inches. What is the length of the line in inches? 30 inches

### Focus on Math Background

Although customary units are in everyday use by most people in this country, even in many engineering contexts and especially in the construction industry, metric units are increasingly common. When companies do business globally, metric units are essential. Since metric units are related by powers of ten, students quickly find that conversions within the metric system are computationally easier than those within the customary system. As with customary units, it is helpful for students to establish classroom-scale benchmarks for units such as a millimeter, a centimeter, a meter, and (going beyond the classroom) a kilometer.

### Building Math Vocabulary

Write the lesson vocabulary words and their definitions on the board.

Tell students that *milli-* means *one thousandth part of, centi-* means *one hundredth part of, and kilo-* means *thousand*. Have students discuss how these meanings relate to the units *millimeter, centimeter, meter,* and *kilometer*.

# Differentiated Instruction

## Small Group Options

### Option 1 Below Level BL

SPATIAL

**Materials:** rulers for each student, pencils, small objects to measure, paper

- Ask students to look at the centimeter side of their ruler and discuss what they see. Accept any reasonable answer but you are looking for them to notice the millimeter marks and how small they are.
- Ask students if they have a fingernail that is as wide as a centimeter. For most 4th grade students, this is their index finger. For most adults, the pinky finger is one centimeter wide.
- Ask them to estimate how long their pencil is in centimeters, using their nail standard, and then measure it with their ruler. Continue with other small objects.

### Option 2 English Language Learners ELL

SPATIAL, AUDITORY

**Core Vocabulary:** shorter than, longer than, compared to
**Common Use Verb:** looks
**See Math** This strategy activates background and spatial knowledge and introduces metric units.

- Draw the following lengths and label them:
  "**cm** centimeter
  **dm** decimeter
  **m** meter
  **km** kilometer"
- Call out a metric unit and have students draw a line to that length.
- Model placing student lines next to the metric on the board. Discuss if their lines are shorter or longer than the unit called. Repeat as time permits.

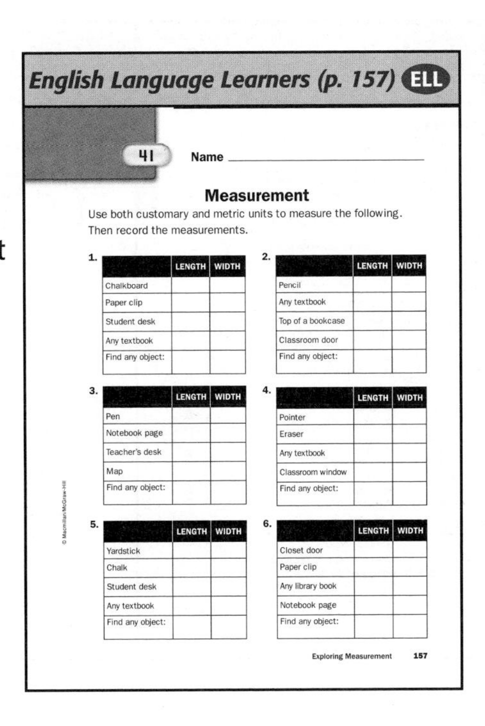

*English Language Learners (p. 157)* ELL

41 Name

**Measurement**

Use both customary and metric units to measure the following. Then record the measurements.

1.

| | LENGTH | WIDTH |
|---|---|---|
| Chalkboard | | |
| Paper clip | | |
| Student desk | | |
| Any textbook | | |
| Find any object: | | |

2.

| | LENGTH | WIDTH |
|---|---|---|
| Pencil | | |
| Any textbook | | |
| Top of a bookcase | | |
| Classroom door | | |
| Find any object: | | |

3.

| | LENGTH | WIDTH |
|---|---|---|
| Pen | | |
| Notebook page | | |
| Teacher's desk | | |
| Map | | |
| Find any object: | | |

4.

| | LENGTH | WIDTH |
|---|---|---|
| Pointer | | |
| Eraser | | |
| Any textbook | | |
| Classroom window | | |
| Find any object: | | |

5.

| | LENGTH | WIDTH |
|---|---|---|
| Yardstick | | |
| Chalk | | |
| Student desk | | |
| Any textbook | | |
| Find any object: | | |

6.

| | LENGTH | WIDTH |
|---|---|---|
| Closet door | | |
| Paper clip | | |
| Any library book | | |
| Notebook page | | |
| Find any object: | | |

Exploring Measurement 157

## Independent Work Options

### Option 1 Early Finishers AL

SPATIAL

**Materials:** ruler, three classroom objects

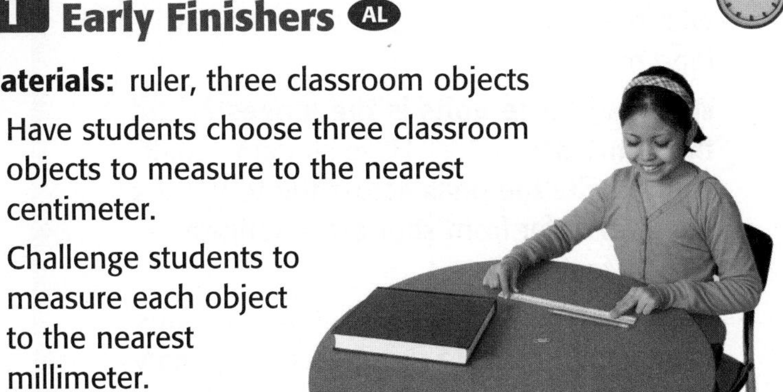

- Have students choose three classroom objects to measure to the nearest centimeter.
- Challenge students to measure each object to the nearest millimeter.

### Option 2 Student Technology

Tech Link

**Math Online** macmillanmh.com

Personal Tutor • Extra Examples

### Option 3 Learning Station: Writing (p. 436I)

Direct students to the Writing Learning Station for opportunities to explore and extend the lesson concept.

### Option 4 Problem-Solving Practice

Reinforce problem-solving skills and strategies with the Problem-Solving Practice worksheet.

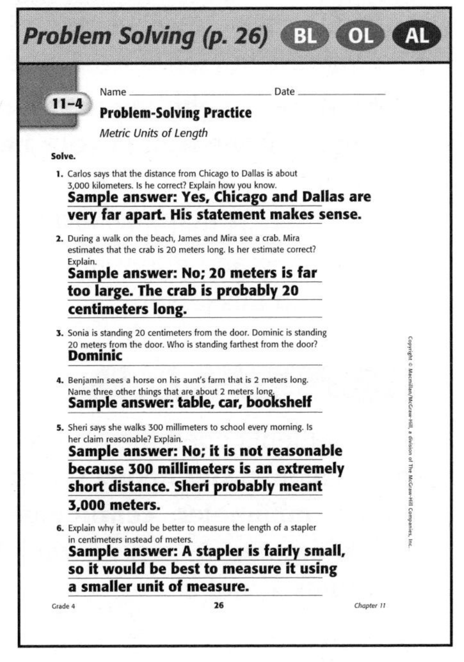

*Problem Solving (p. 26)* BL OL AL

11-4 Name Date

**Problem-Solving Practice**

*Metric Units of Length*

**Solve.**

1. Carlos says that the distance from Chicago to Dallas is about 3,000 kilometers. Is he correct? Explain how you know.
**Sample answer: Yes, Chicago and Dallas are very far apart. His statement makes sense.**
2. During a walk on the beach, James and Mira see a crab. Mira estimates that the crab is 20 meters long. Is her estimate correct? Explain.
**Sample answer: No; 20 meters is far too large. The crab is probably 20 centimeters long.**
3. Sonia is standing 20 centimeters from the door. Dominic is standing 20 meters from the door. Who is standing farthest from the door?
**Dominic**
4. Benjamin sees a horse on his aunt's farm that is 2 meters long. Name three other things that are about 2 meters long.
**Sample answer: table, car, bookshelf**
5. Sheri says she walks 300 millimeters to school every morning. Is her claim reasonable? Explain.
**Sample answer: No; it is not reasonable because 300 millimeters is an extremely short distance. Sheri probably meant 3,000 meters.**
6. Explain why it would be better to measure the length of a stapler in centimeters instead of meters.
**Sample answer: A stapler is fairly small, so it would be best to measure it using a smaller unit of measure.**

Grade 4 26 Chapter 11

# Metric Units of Length

## 1 Introduce

### Activity Choice 1 • Hands-On 

- Review customary units of length with students. **What are some customary units that we use to measure length?** inches, feet, yards Show and discuss tools for measuring with these units, such as a ruler, yardstick, and tape measure.
- **Which of these units is the longest?** yards **the shortest?** inches Have students guide you to write the units across the top of the board in order from shortest to longest: inches, feet, yards.
- Have students brainstorm different lengths they would measure using each customary unit. Write their responses under each unit heading on the board.

### Activity Choice 2 • Literature

Introduce the lesson with *Ways of Measuring Then and Now* by Lisa Shulman. For a related math activity, see p. TR59.

## 2 Teach

### Scaffolding Questions

- **What is something with a measure of about 1 inch?** Accept reasonable answers. **How could you check your estimate?** Use a ruler to measure.
- **About how long is your desk: 2 inches, 2 feet, or 2 yards? How do you know?** About 2 feet; 2 inches is too short, and 2 yards is too long.
- **What tool might you use to measure the length of one wall in your bedroom in feet?** Sample answer: yardstick
- Tell students that they will learn about estimating and measuring with metric units of length in this lesson.

### GET READY to Learn

Have students open their books and read the information in **Get Ready to Learn**. Introduce **metric**, **millimeter**, **centimeter**, **meter**, and **kilometer**. As a class, work through **Examples 1 and 2**.



# 11-4 Metric Units of Length

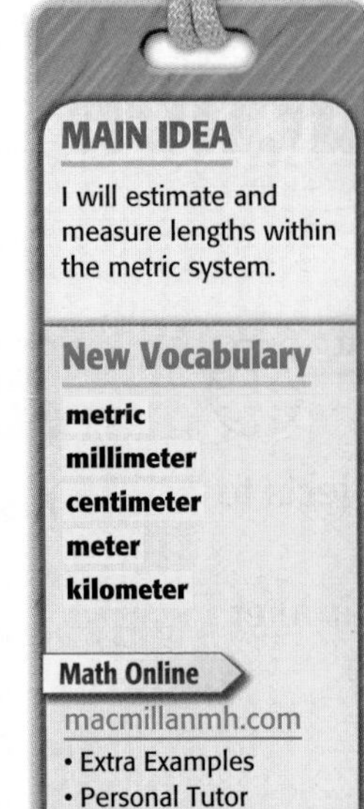


### GET READY to Learn

Doug is growing carrots in his garden. He pulled out a carrot to see if it was growing. Measure the carrot to the nearest centimeter.

A metric ruler is used to measure metric lengths. The **metric** units of length are the millimeter, centimeter, meter, and kilometer.

### Metric Measurements — Key Concepts

| A **millimeter** is about as thick as 6 sheets of notebook paper. | A **centimeter** is about the length of a ladybug. | A **meter** is about the height of a chair. | A **kilometer** is about six city blocks. |
|---|---|---|---|

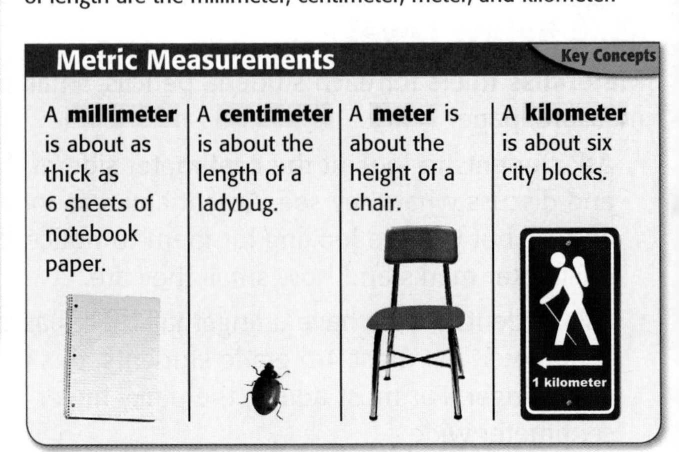


### Real-World EXAMPLE — Measure Length

**1 FOOD Measure the carrot to the nearest centimeter.**

Align the 0 on the ruler with the left side of the carrot. The carrot ends before the 13-centimeter mark. So, the carrot is almost 13 centimeters long.



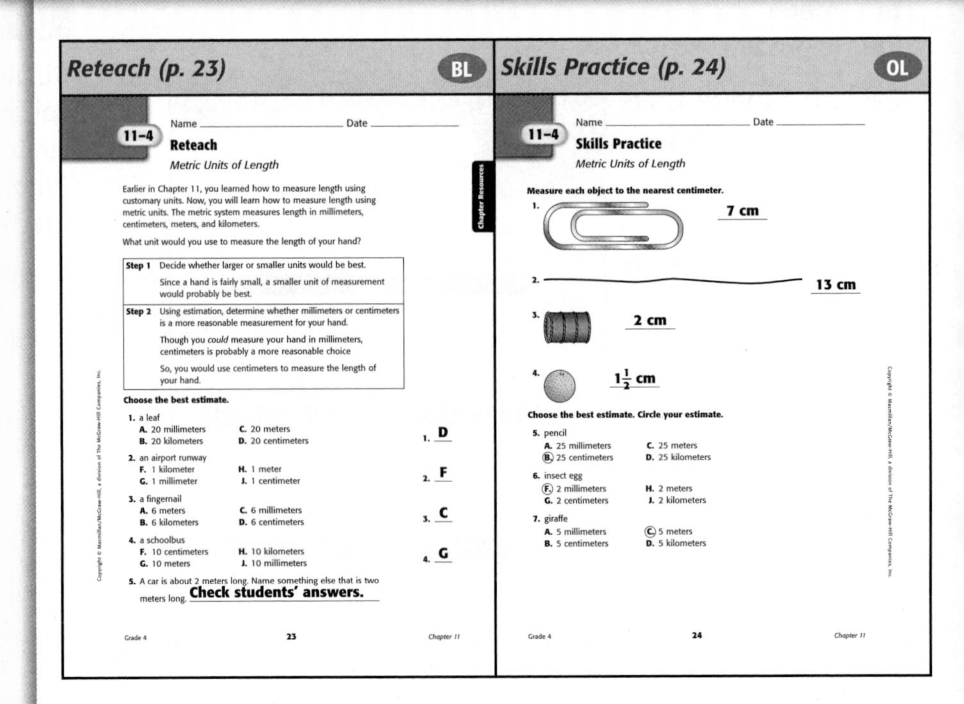

**Reteach (p. 23)** BL

11-4 Name ________ Date ________

**Reteach**

*Metric Units of Length*

Earlier in Chapter 11, you learned how to measure length using customary units. Now, you will learn how to measure length using metric units. The metric system measures length in millimeters, centimeters, meters, and kilometers.

What unit would you use to measure the length of your hand?

| | |
|---|---|
| **Step 1** | Decide whether larger or smaller units would be best. Since a hand is fairly small, a smaller unit of measurement would probably be best. |
| **Step 2** | Using estimation, determine whether millimeters or centimeters is a more reasonable measurement for your hand. Though you *could* measure your hand in millimeters, centimeters is probably a more reasonable choice. So, you would use centimeters to measure the length of your hand. |

**Choose the best estimate.**

1. a leaf
   A. 20 millimeters C. 20 meters
   B. 20 kilometers D. 20 centimeters
   1. **D**
2. an airport runway
   F. 1 kilometer H. 1 meter
   G. 1 millimeter J. 1 centimeter
   2. **F**
3. a fingernail
   A. 6 meters C. 6 millimeters
   B. 6 kilometers D. 6 centimeters
   3. **C**
4. a schoolbus
   F. 10 centimeters H. 10 kilometers
   G. 10 meters J. 10 millimeters
   4. **G**
5. A car is about 2 meters long. Name something else that is two meters long. **Check students' answers.**

Grade 4 23 Chapter 11



Chapter Resources

**Skills Practice (p. 24)** OL

11-4 Name ________ Date ________

**Skills Practice**

*Metric Units of Length*

**Measure each object to the nearest centimeter.**

1. **7 cm**
2. **13 cm**
3. **2 cm**
4. $1\frac{1}{2}$ **cm**

**Choose the best estimate. Circle your estimate.**

5. pencil
   A. 25 millimeters C. 25 meters
   (B.) 25 centimeters D. 25 kilometers
6. insect egg
   (F.) 2 millimeters H. 2 meters
   G. 2 centimeters J. 2 kilometers
7. giraffe
   A. 5 millimeters (C.) 5 meters
   B. 5 centimeters D. 5 kilometers

Grade 4 24 Chapter 11

Before measuring any object, always estimate the length to decide which unit of measurement is best to use.

**Real-World EXAMPLE** **Estimate Length**

**2 SCHOOL Which is the best estimate of the length of a student's desk?**

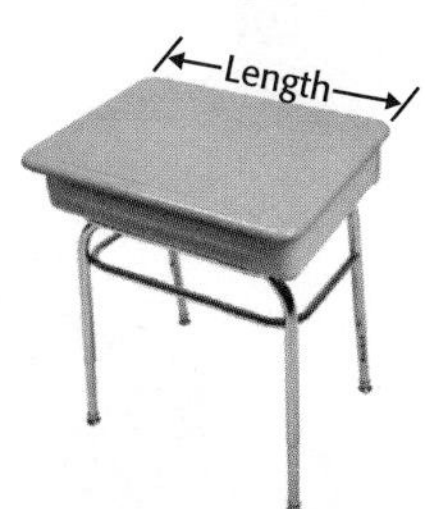


**A** 5 centimeters

**B** 5 millimeters

**C** 50 centimeters

**D** 50 millimeters

A desk has to be long enough to do work. 5 centimeters, 5 millimeters, and 50 millimeters are all too small. So, the answer must be C, 50 centimeters.

## CHECK What You Know

**Measure each object to the nearest centimeter.** See Example 1 (p. 450)

**1.** 3 cm

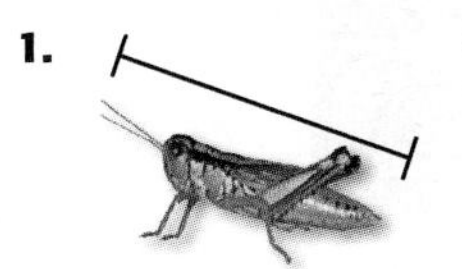

**2.** 6 cm

**Choose the best estimate.** See Example 2 (p. 451)

**3.** length of a kayak C

**A** 6 centimeters

**B** 2 meters

**C** 6 meters

**D** 2 kilometers

**4.** width of a piece of yarn F

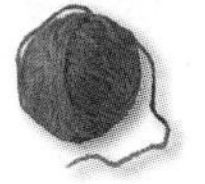

**F** 1 millimeter **H** 1 meter

**G** 1 centimeter **J** 1 kilometer

**5.** Patty said to Lina, "I'm about 150 millimeters tall." Is Patty correct? Explain why or why not.

**6.** Talk About It Describe a situation when it would be appropriate to measure an object using millimeters.

5, 6. See Ch. 11 Answer Appendix.

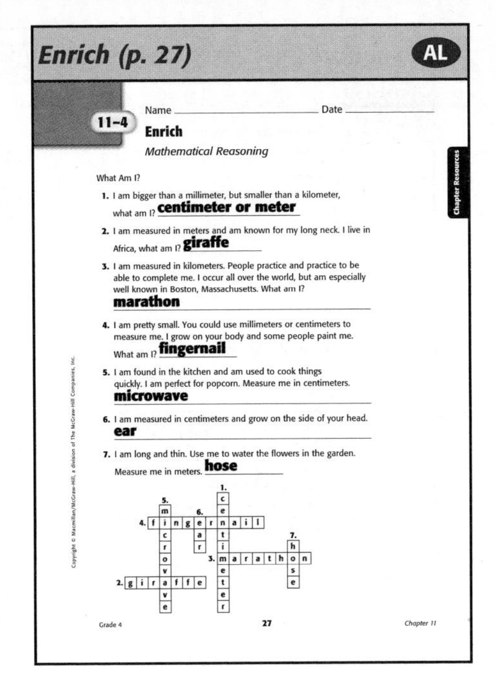

### Enrich (p. 27) AL

11-4 Name ________ Date ________

**Enrich**

*Mathematical Reasoning*

What Am I?

**1.** I am bigger than a millimeter, but smaller than a kilometer, what am I? **centimeter or meter**

**2.** I am measured in meters and am known for my long neck. I live in Africa, what am I? **giraffe**

**3.** I am measured in kilometers. People practice and practice to be able to complete me. I occur all over the world, but am especially well known in Boston, Massachusetts. What am I? **marathon**

**4.** I am pretty small. You could use millimeters or centimeters to measure me. I grow on your body and some people paint me. What am I? **fingernail**

**5.** I am found in the kitchen and am used to cook things quickly. I am perfect for popcorn. Measure me in centimeters. **microwave**

**6.** I am measured in centimeters and grow on the side of your head. **ear**

**7.** I am long and thin. Use me to water the flowers in the garden. Measure me in meters. **hose**

Chapter Resources



Grade 4 27 Chapter 11

### Measure Length

**Example 1** Make sure that students understand how to line up the ruler and measure to the nearest centimeter. Show students the millimeter markings on the ruler and have them count the number of millimeters that make up one centimeter (10). Point out the marking found halfway between each centimeter mark and explain how to use this "halfway" mark to help them round up or round down to the nearest centimeter.

### ADDITIONAL EXAMPLES

**1** Measure the length of your pencil to the nearest centimeter. Check students' work.

**2** Which is the best estimate of the length of a baseball bat? C

**A** 1 millimeter **C** 1 meter

**B** 10 centimeters **D** 10 meters

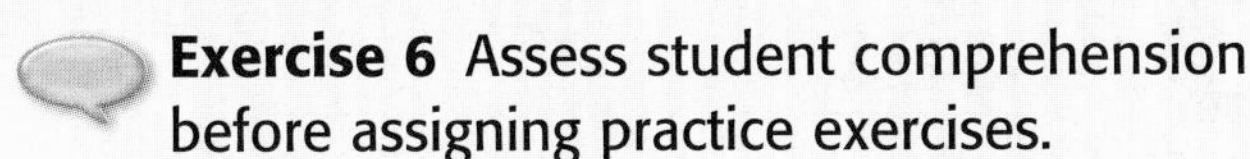

### CHECK What You Know

As a class, have students complete Exercises 1–6 in **Check What You Know** as you observe their work.

**Exercise 6** Assess student comprehension before assigning practice exercises.

### BL Alternate Teaching Strategy

**If** students have trouble estimating lengths within the metric system...

**Then** use one of these reteach options:

**1** CRM **Daily Reteach Worksheet** (p. 23)

**2** Show students a meterstick and have them identify 1 millimeter, 1 centimeter, and 1 meter on it. Use the meterstick to demonstrate that 10 millimeters make up 1 centimeter, and 100 centimeters make up 1 meter. Then tell students that 1,000 meters (or 1,000 metersticks lined up end-to-end) equals 1 kilometer. Write the equivalencies in a chart on the board and have students refer to the meterstick and chart to help them choose the best estimates.

### ! COMMON ERROR!

**Exercises 3, 9, and 10** Students may mistakenly choose estimates based on the length of the photo itself, not the object the photo represents. Tell students to think about the actual size of the object shown in each picture when choosing an estimate.

## 3 Practice

Differentiate practice using these leveled assignments for Exercises 7–14.

| Level | Assignment |
|---|---|
| BL Below/Approaching Level | 7, 9, 10 |
| OL On Level | 7–11, 13 |
| AL Above/Beyond Level | 7–11 odd, 13–14 |

Have students discuss and complete the Higher Order Thinking problems. For Exercise 13, have students use rulers or meter sticks to measure the objects and share their results with their classmates.

**WRITING IN MATH** Have students complete Exercise 15 in their Math Journals. You may choose to use this exercise as an optional formative assessment.

## 4 Assess

### Formative Assessment

- **Which metric unit would you use to measure the length of a bird house? Why?** Centimeters, because millimeters are too small, and meters and kilometers are too large.
- **Which tool would you use to measure the bird house?** metric ruler
- **How could you estimate your answer?** Sample answer: Use the width of my thumb.

**Quick Check** **Are students continuing to struggle with estimating and measuring metric lengths?**

**If Yes** → Small Group Options (p. 450B)
Strategic Intervention Guide (p. 122)

**If No** → Independent Work Options (p. 450B)
CRM Skills Practice Worksheet (p. 24)
CRM Enrich Worksheet (p. 27)

**Yesterday's News** Ask students to discuss how the lesson on measuring customary units of length helped them measure metric units of length in today's lesson.



## Practice and Problem Solving

See page R29.

**Measure each object to the nearest centimeter.** See Example 1 (p. 450)

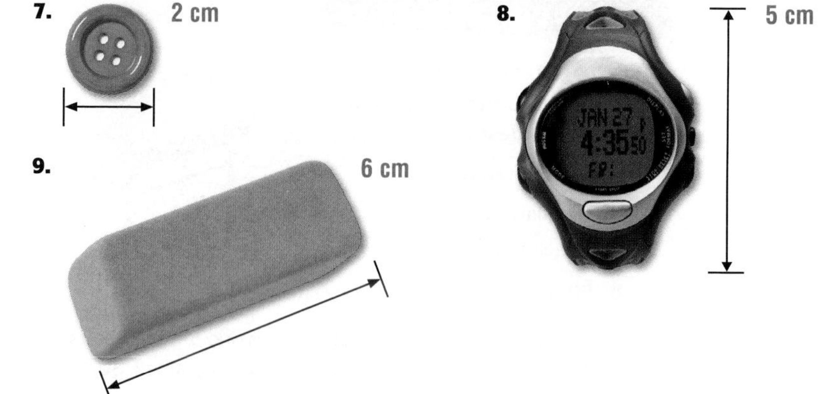


**Choose the best estimate.** See Example 2 (p. 451)

**10.** height of a cornstalk C

**A** 2 millimeters **C** 2 meters
**B** 2 centimeters **D** 2 kilometers

**11.** length of an airport runway J

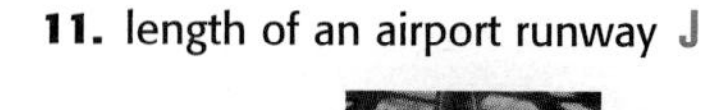

**F** 5 millimeters **H** 5 meters
**G** 50 centimeters **J** 5 kilometer

**12.** A giraffe at the zoo is 5 meters tall. Name something else that is about 5 meters tall. Sample answer: tree

**13.** Is the distance from Boston, Massachusetts, to Phoenix, Arizona, about 4,000 kilometers? Explain. See Ch. 11 Answer Appendix.

### H.O.T. Problems

**14. OPEN ENDED** Find three things in the classroom that are longer than 10 centimeters and smaller than 100 centimeters. Estimate and determine the actual measurements. See students' work.

**15. WRITING IN MATH** Explain why it would be better to measure the length of your classroom with a meter stick instead of a centimeter ruler. See Ch. 11 Answer Appendix.



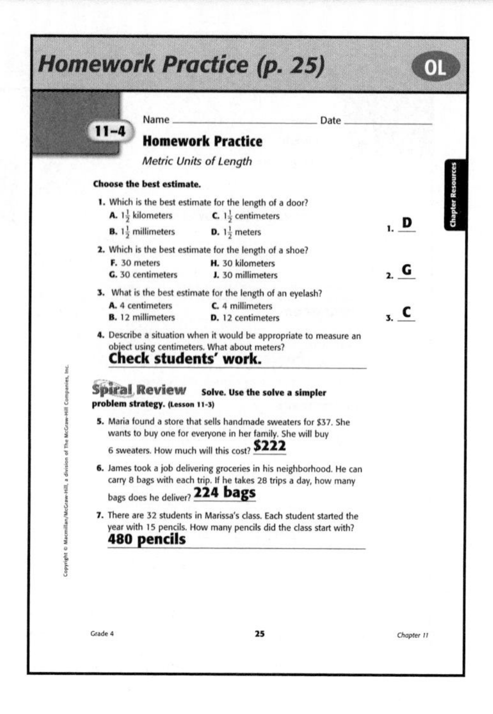

*Homework Practice (p. 25)* OL

11-4 Name ________ Date ________

**Homework Practice**

*Metric Units of Length*

**Choose the best estimate.**

1. Which is the best estimate for the length of a door?
   A. $1\frac{1}{2}$ kilometers C. $1\frac{1}{2}$ centimeters
   B. $1\frac{1}{2}$ millimeters D. $1\frac{1}{2}$ meters
   1. D
2. Which is the best estimate for the length of a shoe?
   F. 30 meters H. 30 kilometers
   G. 30 centimeters J. 30 millimeters
   2. G
3. What is the best estimate for the length of an eyelash?
   A. 4 centimeters C. 4 millimeters
   B. 12 millimeters D. 12 centimeters
   3. C
4. Describe a situation when it would be appropriate to measure an object using centimeters. What about meters?
   **Check students' work.**

**Spiral Review** **Solve. Use the solve a simpler problem strategy.** (Lesson 11-3)

5. Maria found a store that sells handmade sweaters for $37. She wants to buy one for everyone in her family. She will buy 6 sweaters. How much will this cost? **$222**
6. James took a job delivering groceries in his neighborhood. He can carry 8 bags with each trip. If he takes 28 trips a day, how many bags does he deliver? **224 bags**
7. There are 32 students in Marissa's class. Each student started the year with 15 pencils. How many pencils did the class start with? **480 pencils**

Chapter Resources

# Mid-Chapter Check

Lessons 11-1 through 11-4

**Estimate. Then measure each to the nearest inch, $\frac{1}{2}$ inch, and $\frac{1}{4}$ inch.** (Lesson 11-1)

1. 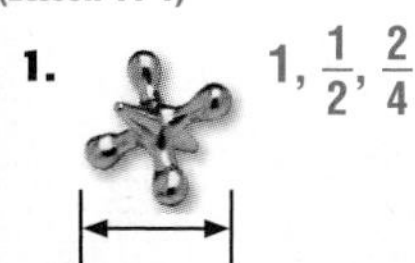 $1, 1\frac{1}{2}, 1\frac{2}{4}$

2. 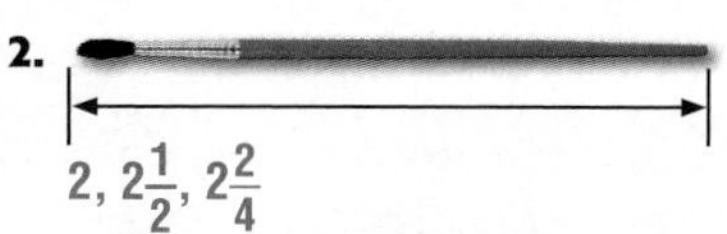 $2, 2\frac{1}{2}, 2\frac{2}{4}$

3. **MULTIPLE CHOICE** Choose the best estimate for the height of a giraffe. (Lesson 11-1) B

A 19 inches  C 19 yards

B 19 feet  D 19 miles

**Complete.** (Lesson 11-2)

4. 3 feet = ■ inches 36

5. 2 yards = ■ feet 6

6. **MULTIPLE CHOICE** Kenyi's family wants to fence in their yard. They need 80 yards of fence. How many feet of fence should they buy? (Lesson 11-2) H

F 79 feet  H 240 feet

G 96 feet  J 960 feet

7. Which measurement best describes the length of a couch, 6 feet or 6 inches? (Lesson 11-2) 6 feet

8. What is the width of the rectangle below if the length of one side of each square is 1 centimeter long? (Lesson 11-3) 8 cm

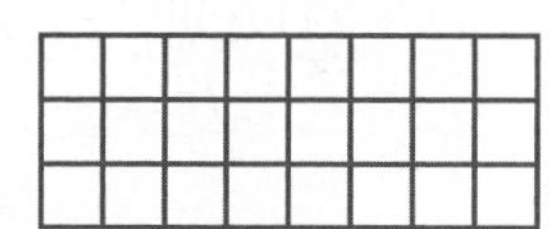

9. **MULTIPLE CHOICE** What is the length of one side of the square shown? (Lesson 11-3) B

A 2 mm  C 2 m

B 2 cm  D 2 km

10. Dexter went on a hiking trip. Which measurement best describes how far he hiked, 10 kilometers or 10 meters? (Lesson 11-4) 10 km

11. WRITING IN MATH Explain why 3 yards is equal to 108 inches. (Lesson 11-2) See margin.



# Mid-Chapter Check

## Lessons 11-1 through 11-4

### Formative Assessment

Use the Mid-Chapter Check to assess students' progress in the first half of the chapter.

**ExamView** Assessment Suite Customize and create multiple versions of your Mid-Chapter Check and the test answer keys.

### FOLDABLES Dinah Zike's Foldables

Use these lesson suggestions to incorporate the Foldable during the chapter.

If students have not completed their Foldables, guide them to create and fill in the appropriate information using the instructions on p. 453.

You may choose to use the Foldables to help students review the concepts presented in this chapter and as a tool for studying for the Mid-Chapter Check.

### Additional Answer

11. Sample answer: Since 3 yards is the same as 9 feet, you can multiply 9 and 12 to find the number of inches.

# Data-Driven Decision Making

Based on the results of the Mid-Chapter Check, use the following to review concepts that continue to present students with problems.

| Exercises | State/Local Standards | What's the Math? | Error Analysis | Resources for Review |
|---|---|---|---|---|
| **1–3** Lesson 11-1 | | Estimate and measure to the nearest half and quarter inch. Know customary units of measurement. | Does not begin at zero for measuring. Does not know how many inches are in a foot or how many feet are less in a yard. | Strategic Intervention Guide (pp. 118, 122) CRM Chapter 11 Resource Masters (Reteach) Math Adventures My Math Zone Chapter 11 Math Online Extra Examples • Concepts in Motion |
| **4–7, 11** Lesson 11-2 | | Convert customary units. | Does not know relative sizes of units. Multiplies instead of dividing. | |
| **8–9** Lesson 11-3 | | Solve problems by solving a simpler problem. | Does not understand 4-step plan. Cannot break problems into simple problems. | |
| **10** Lesson 11-4 | | Apply metric measurement concepts. | Does not begin with zero when measuring. | |

# Lesson Planner

## Objective

Interpret information and data from science to solve problems.

### National Standard 

Students should develop understanding of organisms and environments.

## Activate Prior Knowledge

Before you turn students' attention to the pages, ask them to discuss coral reefs.

- **Where are coral reefs found?** in the ocean
- **Who relies on the coral reef for food and shelter?** plants, fish

## Using the Student Page

Ask students to read the information on p. 454 and answer these questions:

- **Are all the animals in a coral reef small? Explain.** no; Sample answer: The coral reef has many animals who are over a meter long.
- **Compare the lengths of the sea cucumber, the anemone, and the soft coral. Which one can grow the longest?** soft coral

## Animals of the Coral Reef

| Animal | Range of Length |
|---|---|
| Anemone | 1 cm–50 cm |
| Dolphin | 1 m–11 m |
| Hard coral | 1 mm–50 cm |
| Jellyfish | 1 cm–2 m |
| Sea cucumber | 1 cm–60 cm |
| Sea snake | 500 cm–2 m |
| Sea turtle | 5 cm–3 m |
| Sea urchin | 1 cm–20 cm |
| Soft coral | 1 mm–1 m |
| Whale shark | 9 m–20 m |

Source: Reef Education Network

## Real-World Math

**Use the information in the table to solve each problem.**

1. Identify the two shortest animals. **hard coral and soft coral**
2. Identify the two longest animals. **whale shark and dolphin**
3. What animal can be as short as 1 centimeter and as long as 60 centimeters? **sea cucumber**
4. A sea snake can be as long as 2 meters. What other animals can be that same length? **dolphin, sea turtle, jelly fish**
5. Identify the animal that can grow to be 2,000 centimeters long. (*Hint:* 1 meter = 100 centimeters) **whale shark**
6. Suppose a dolphin is 2 meters long. What is the dolphin's length in millimeters? (*Hint:* 1 meter = 1,000 millimeters) **2,000 millimeters**
7. Draw a sea turtle that is 8 centimeters long. **See students' work.**

## Real-World Math

Assign the exercises on p. 455. Encourage students to choose a problem-solving strategy before beginning each exercise. If necessary, review the strategies suggested in Lesson 10-6, p. 416.

**Exercise 4** Remind students that it can also be longer but it must be within its size.

**Exercise 5 and 6** Hint to students to remember to convert the measures.

**WRITING IN MATH** Have students create a word problem that uses the information found in the text and in the chart on p. 454.

# Extend the Activity

Have students recreate the reef situation using different animals and amounts they determine themselves, and use verbal descriptions to describe the probabilities of seeing each animal.

LESSON **11-5**

# Measure Perimeters

## Lesson Planner

### Objective

Find the perimeter of a figure.

### Vocabulary

**perimeter**

### Resources

**Materials:** pipe cleaners (at least one per student), tape measures, rubber bands

**Manipulatives:** rulers, Geoboards

**Literature Connection:** *Sir Cumference and the Isle of Immeter* by Cindy Neuschwander

**Alternate Lesson:** Use *IMPACT Mathematics:* Unit F to provide practice with perimeter.

**Teacher Technology**
TeacherWorks • Interactive Classroom

## Daily Routine

Use these suggestions before beginning the lesson on p. 456.

### 5-Minute Check

(Reviews Lesson 11-4)

**Choose the best estimate for the length of the scissors.**

B

**A** 15 millimeters
**B** 15 centimeters
**C** 15 meters
**D** 15 kilometers

### Problem of the Day

Bobby put 11 stamps on a package. If there are 1 less than twice as many 60-cent stamps as 25-cent stamps, how many of each type of stamp are on the package? seven 60-cent stamps and four 25-cent stamps

### Focus on Math Background

The perimeter of a plane figure is the distance around the figure measured in linear units. The perimeter of any polygon can be found by adding the lengths of all of the sides of the figure. Once students are introduced to area, they often confuse area and perimeter. To help reinforce that perimeter is the distance around a figure, have students imagine an insect walking around the figure. Then ask: How many *linear units* did the insect walk? The bug walks 20 inches. So the perimeter of the rectangle is 20 inches.

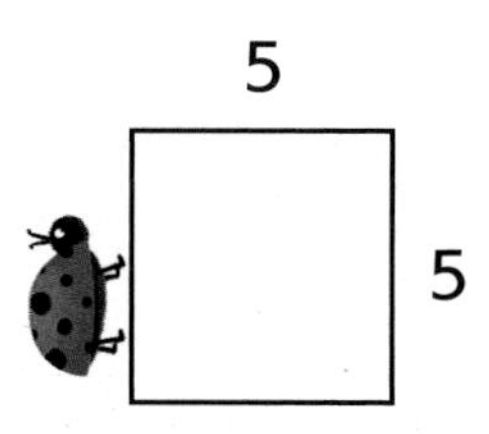


### Building Math Vocabulary

Write the lesson vocabulary word and its definition on the board.

Brainstorm examples of perimeter, such as a crust of bread, edging on a border, a picture frame, a fence, or a belt. Have a volunteer record the responses on the board. Have students explain in their own words why each of these is an example of perimeter.

**Visual Vocabulary Cards**
Use Visual Vocabulary Card 36 to reinforce the vocabulary introduced in this lesson. (The Define/Example/Ask routine is printed on the back of each card.)

# Differentiated Instruction

## Small Group Options

**Option 1** VISUAL, SPATIAL

### Gifted and Talented AL

**Materials:** grid paper and pencil

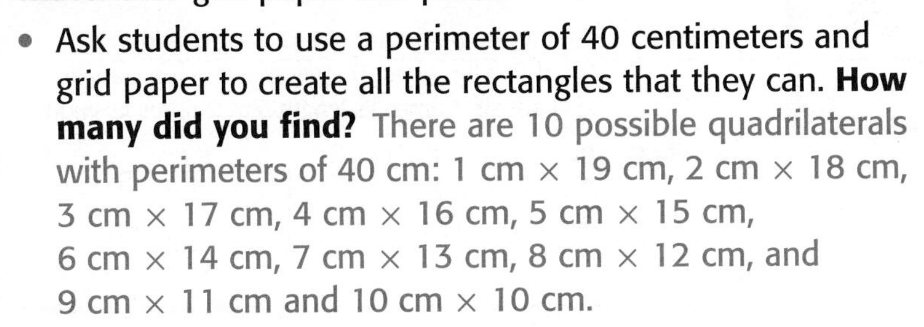

- Ask students to use a perimeter of 40 centimeters and grid paper to create all the rectangles that they can. **How many did you find?** There are 10 possible quadrilaterals with perimeters of 40 cm: 1 cm × 19 cm, 2 cm × 18 cm, 3 cm × 17 cm, 4 cm × 16 cm, 5 cm × 15 cm, 6 cm × 14 cm, 7 cm × 13 cm, 8 cm × 12 cm, and 9 cm × 11 cm and 10 cm × 10 cm.
- Use a perimeter of 18 ft and grid paper to construct triangles. Label the sides and identify. Answers will vary.

**Option 2** KINESTHETIC, SOCIAL

### English Language Learners ELL

**Materials:** string, rulers
**Core Vocabulary:** like walking, around the shape, holds
**Common Use Verb:** measure
**Do Math** This strategy allows students to explore the concept of perimeter through collaboration.

- Say: "Finding perimeter is **like walking around a shape**."
- Each group of 4–6 needs 8 pieces of one-foot long string each and a ruler.
- Assign one student to be a measurer, one a recorder, and the others to hold strings.
- Draw a shape on the board.
- Students make the shape by holding strings end to end.
- The measurer walks around students, measuring each string.
- The recorder records the measurements.
- As a group, have them add the measurements to find perimeter.

## Independent Work Options

**Option 1** LOGICAL

### Early Finishers OL AL

**Materials:** index cards, rulers

- Have students draw figures on one side of the index card and calculate the perimeter on the other side of the card.
- Students challenge classmates to find the perimeter.
- Students find the perimeter and check their solution by turning the card over.

6 in. 6 in. 6 in. 6 in. 6 in. 6 in.
6 in. × 6 = 36 in.

**Option 2**

### Student Technology

**Math Online** macmillanmh.com

Personal Tutor • Extra Examples

Math Adventures

**Option 3**

### Learning Station: Social Studies (p. 436I)

Direct students to the Social Studies Learning Station for opportunities to explore and extend the lesson concept.

**Option 4**

### Problem-Solving Practice

Reinforce problem-solving skills and strategies with the Problem-Solving Practice worksheet.

*Problem Solving (p. 31)* BL OL AL

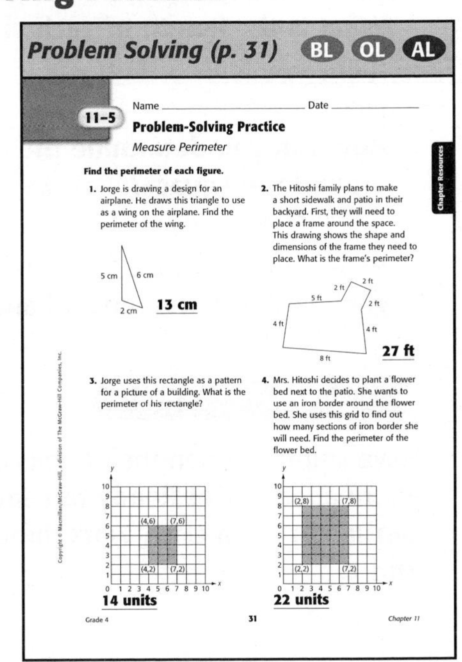
Name ________ Date ________

11-5 **Problem-Solving Practice**
*Measure Perimeter*

**Find the perimeter of each figure.**

1. Jorge is drawing a design for an airplane. He draws this triangle to use as a wing on the airplane. Find the perimeter of the wing.
**13 cm**

2. The Hitoshi family plans to make a short sidewalk and patio in their backyard. First, they will need to place a frame around the space. This drawing shows the shape and dimensions of the frame they need to place. What is the frame's perimeter?
**27 ft**

3. Jorge uses this rectangle as a pattern for a picture of a building. What is the perimeter of his rectangle?
**14 units**

4. Mrs. Hitoshi decides to plant a flower bed next to the patio. She wants to use an iron border around the flower bed. She uses this grid to find out how many sections of iron border she will need. Find the perimeter of the flower bed.
**22 units**

Grade 4 31 Chapter 11

# 11-5 Measure Perimeters

## 1 Introduce

### Activity Choice 1 • Hands-On 

**Materials:** chenille stems, ruler

- Have students work in pairs to measure and record the length of a chenille stem to the nearest inch or centimeter. **What geometric figure does the chenille stem represent?** line segment
- Have students twist the two ends of the chenille stem together. Have students make a shape or figure with the chenille stem and trace it. **How would you determine the distance around your shape?** Measure it with a ruler.
- To extend the activity, identify several different objects in the classroom. **What tools could be used to measure the distances around each object?** rulers, tape measures, meter sticks, etc.

### Activity Choice 2 • Literature

Introduce the lesson with *Sir Cumference and the Isle of Immeter* by Cindy Neuschwander. For a related math activity, see p. TR60.

## 2 Teach

### Scaffolding Questions

Have students work in pairs to create a 2 × 2 square on a geoboard with a rubber band.

- **What is the length of each side and how many sides are there?** There are 2 units on each side and 4 sides.
- **How can you determine the distance around the square?** Add 2 + 2 + 2 + 2 or multiply 4 × 2.
- Repeat the task for a 3 × 4 rectangle on the geoboard with the rubber band.

### GET READY to Learn

Have students open their books and read the information in **Get Ready to Learn**. Introduce **perimeter**. As a class, work through **Examples 1 and 2**.



# 11-5 Measure Perimeters

**MAIN IDEA**

I will find the perimeter of a figure.

**New Vocabulary**

perimeter

**Math Online**

macmillanmh.com

- Extra Examples
- Personal Tutor
- Self-Check Quiz

### GET READY to Learn

Berto is walking around a park on the path shown. How far did Berto walk?

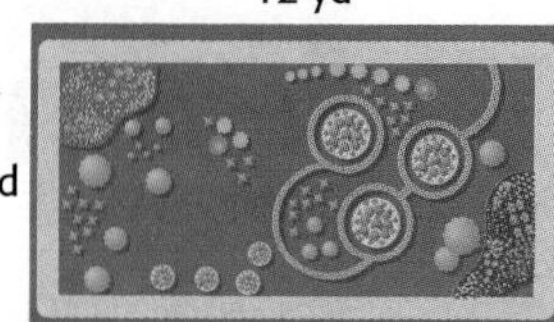

12 yd

6 yd

The distance around a closed figure is called the **perimeter**.

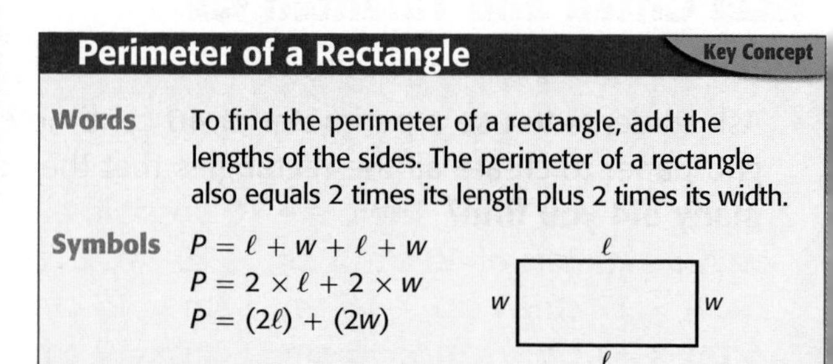

**Perimeter of a Rectangle** — Key Concept

**Words** To find the perimeter of a rectangle, add the lengths of the sides. The perimeter of a rectangle also equals 2 times its length plus 2 times its width.

**Symbols**
$P = \ell + w + \ell + w$
$P = 2 \times \ell + 2 \times w$
$P = (2\ell) + (2w)$

**Find Perimeter**

**1 DISTANCE How far did Berto walk?**

| **One Way:** Use Addition | **Another Way:** Use a Formula |
|---|---|
| Add the measures of all of the sides of the figure. | Multiply the length and the width each by 2. Then add. |
| $P = 12 + 6 + 12 + 6$<br>$P = 36$ | $P = (2\ell) + (2w)$<br>$P = (2 \times 12) + (2 \times 6)$<br>$P = 24 + 12$ or $36$ |

So, Berto walked 36 yards.



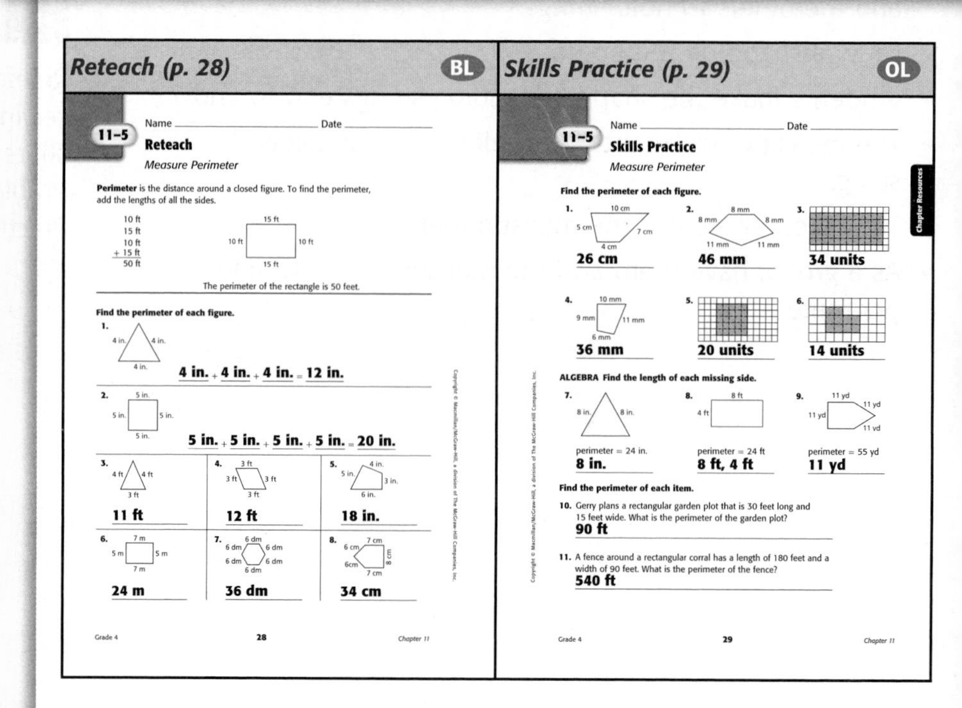

**Reteach (p. 28)** BL

11-5 Name ______ Date ______

**Reteach**

*Measure Perimeter*

**Perimeter** is the distance around a closed figure. To find the perimeter, add the lengths of all the sides.

10 ft
15 ft
10 ft
+ 15 ft
50 ft

The perimeter of the rectangle is 50 feet.

**Find the perimeter of each figure.**

1. **4 in.** + **4 in.** + **4 in.** = **12 in.**
2. **5 in.** + **5 in.** + **5 in.** + **5 in.** = **20 in.**
3. **11 ft**
4. **12 ft**
5. **18 in.**
6. **24 m**
7. **36 dm**
8. **34 cm**

Grade 4 28 Chapter 11



**Skills Practice (p. 29)** OL

11-5 Name ______ Date ______

**Skills Practice**

*Measure Perimeter*

**Find the perimeter of each figure.**

1. **26 cm**
2. **46 mm**
3. **34 units**
4. **36 mm**
5. **20 units**
6. **14 units**

**ALGEBRA Find the length of each missing side.**

7. perimeter = 24 in. **8 in.**
8. perimeter = 24 ft **8 ft, 4 ft**
9. perimeter = 55 yd **11 yd**

**Find the perimeter of each item.**

10. Gerry plans a rectangular garden plot that is 30 feet long and 15 feet wide. What is the perimeter of the garden plot? **90 ft**
11. A fence around a rectangular corral has a length of 180 feet and a width of 90 feet. What is the perimeter of the fence? **540 ft**

Grade 4 29 Chapter 11

Chapter Resources

You can estimate perimeter before finding the exact perimeter.

**EXAMPLE** Estimate and Find Perimeter

**2** **Find the perimeter of a square with side lengths of 6 inches.**

**Estimate:** 5 + 5 + 5 + 5 = 20

6 in. / 6 in. / 6 in. / 6 in.

| One Way: Use Addition | Another Way: Use a Formula |
|---|---|
| Add the measures of all of the sides of the figure. | Multiply the length of one side by 4 because there are 4 sides of equal length. |
| $P = 6 + 6 + 6 + 6$<br>$P = 24$ | $P = 4 \times$ side length<br>$P = 4 \times 6$<br>$P = 24$ |

So, the perimeter of the square is 24 inches.

**Check for Reasonableness**

The answer, 24, is close to the estimate, 20. ✓

6. To find the perimeter of a rectangle, you can use the formula. $2 \times \ell + 2 \times w = p$. To find the perimeter of a square, you can find the sum of all of the sides or use the formula $s \times 4 = p$.

## CHECK What You Know

**Estimate the perimeter. Then find the exact perimeter.**

See Examples 1 and 2 (pp. 456–457)

**1.**

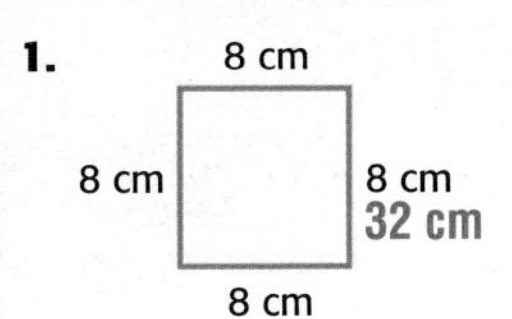


32 cm

**2.**

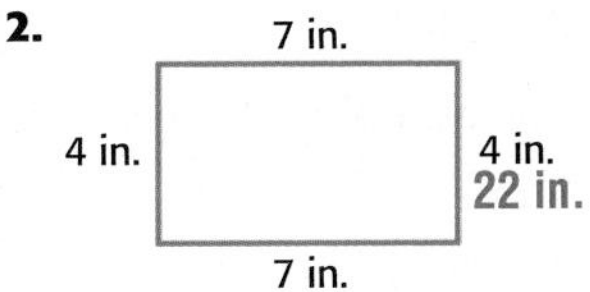


22 in.

**3.**

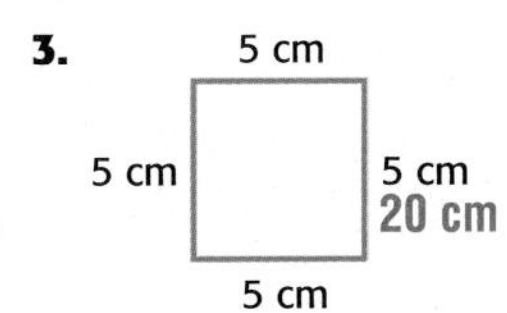


20 cm

**4.** Byron made a drawing of his room. His drawing is shown. What is the perimeter of Byron's room? 54 ft

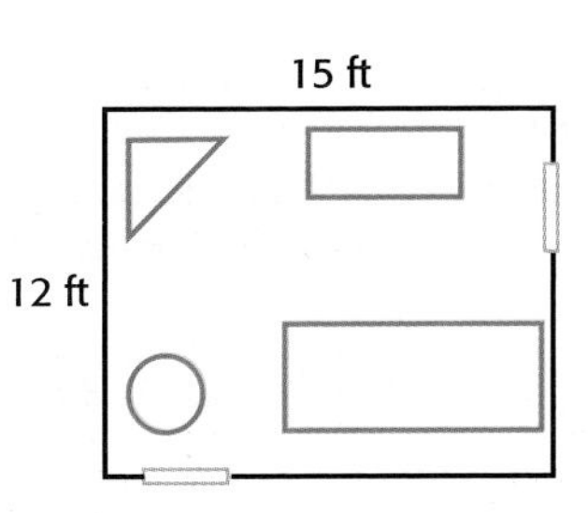


**5.** What is the perimeter of a square with side lengths of 4 inches? 16 in.

**6.** Talk About It Explain the two ways to find the perimeter of a rectangle. What are the two ways to find the perimeter of a square?



### Enrich (p. 32) AL

Name ____________ Date ____________

11-5 **Enrich**

*Perimeter Puzzles*

Each square at the right is divided into three regions. Each region has a perimeter of 8 units.

The square at the right is divided into two regions. Each region has a perimeter of 10 units.

**Divide each square below into the number of regions with the perimeter given. Try to do this in two different ways.**

1. Number of regions: 4
   Perimeter of each region: 10

2. Number of regions: 5
   Perimeter of each region: 12

3. Number of regions: 6
   Perimeter of each region: 12

**Answers will vary. Check students' work.**

Grade 4 32 Chapter 11

## Find Perimeter

**Example 2** Explain that using the formula is a more efficient way to find the perimeter of a square.

### ADDITIONAL EXAMPLES

**1** Meli is creating a pen for her puppy. The picture shows the layout for the pen. What is the perimeter of the pen?

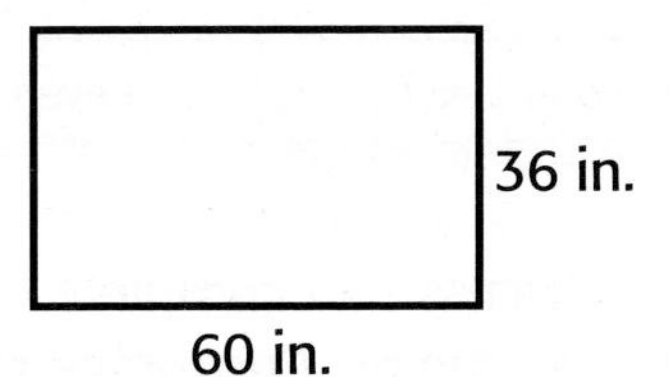


36 + 60 + 36 + 60 = 192 inches

**2** Find the perimeter of a square with side lengths of 7 centimeters. 28 cm

### CHECK What You Know

As a class, have students complete Exercises 1–6 in **Check What You Know** as you observe their work.

**Exercise 6** Assess student comprehension before assigning practice exercises.

## BL Alternate Teaching Strategy

**If** students struggle with using the formulas for perimeter…

**Then** use one of these reteach options:

1 CRM **Daily Reteach Worksheet** (p. 28)

2 Have students use tape measures to measure some rectangular and square objects in the classroom to the nearest half inch. **What are the lengths of the different sides? Are any of the sides the same length? What shortcuts could you use to determine the perimeter?** For the square, you need to measure only one side and multiply by 4. For the rectangle, you need the measures of length and width. You then can use the formula $P = 2\ell + 2w$.

# 3 Practice

Differentiate practice using these leveled assignments for Exercises 7–21.

| Level | Assignment |
|---|---|
| BL Below/Approaching Level | 1, 8, 12–15, 17 |
| OL On Level | 1–14, 17–19 |
| AL Above/Beyond Level | 8–18 even, 20–21 |

Have students discuss and complete the Higher Order Thinking problems. Encourage students to use the formulas for finding the perimeter of squares and rectangles.

**WRITING IN MATH** Have students complete Exercise 21 in their Math Journals. You may choose to use this exercise as an optional formative assessment.

### Additional Answers

20. Sample answers: Use the measurements given to find any missing side lengths. Then add up all of the side lengths.
21. Sample answer: yes; When one side of a square is doubled, all sides of the square are doubles. Therefore, the perimeter will double.

**COMMON ERROR!**

**Exercises 6–11** Watch for students who multiply $\ell \times w$ instead of using $2\ell + 2w$ when finding the perimeter of a rectangle. Have them keep this formula handy.



## Practice and Problem Solving

EXTRA PRACTICE See page R29.

**Estimate the perimeter. Then find the exact perimeter.**

See Examples 1 and 2 (pp. 456–457)

7. 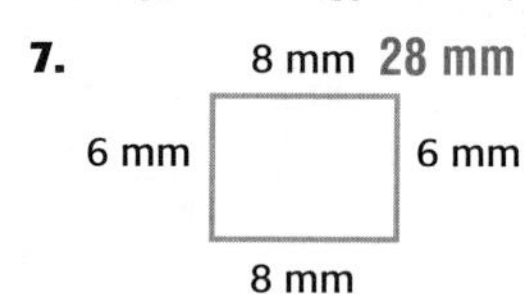

28 mm

8. 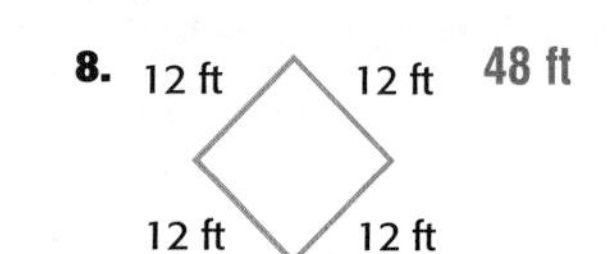

48 ft

9. 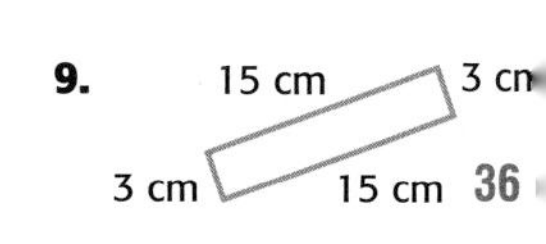

36

10. 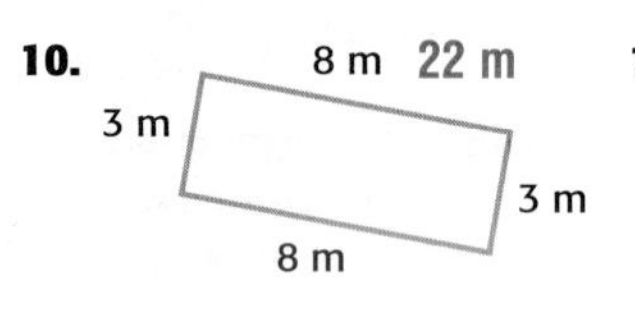

22 m

11. 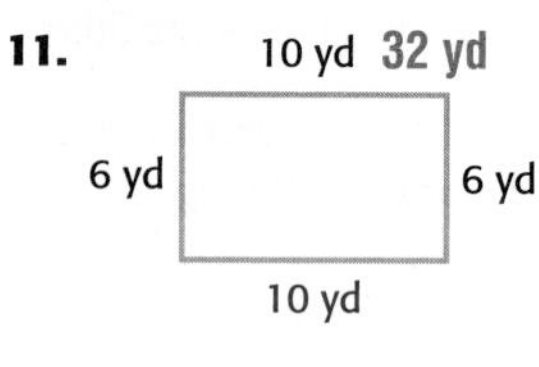

32 yd

12. 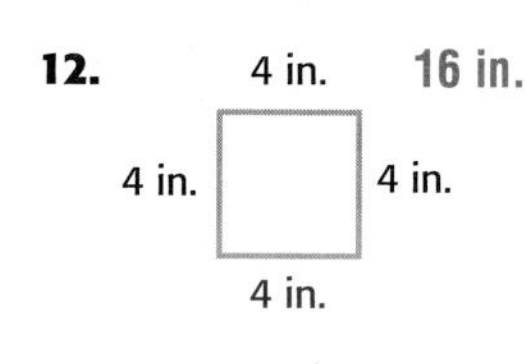

16 in.

**Estimate. Then find the perimeter of each rectangle in units.**

13. 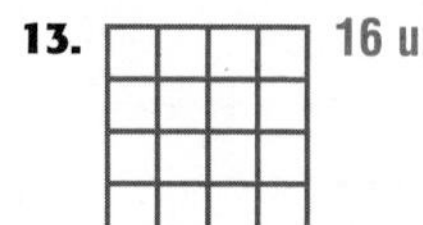 16 units

14. 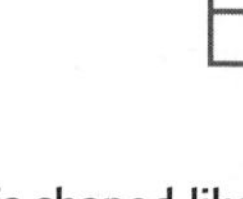 12 units

15.  20 units

16. A baseball diamond is shaped like a square. Each side is 90 feet long. What is its perimeter? 360 ft

17. A yard is 82 feet long and 45 feet wide. What is the perimeter of the yard? 254 ft

### Real-World PROBLEM SOLVING

**Social Studies** The Parthenon is an ancient building in Athens, Greece. It has a rectangular base measuring about 228 feet by 101 feet.

18. What is the perimeter of the base of the Parthenon? 658 ft
19. If you doubled the length of each side of the base, is the perimeter doubled? Show your work. 19. yes; 456 + 202 + 456 + 202 = 658 + 658.

### H.O.T. Problems

20. **OPEN ENDED** Explain how to find the perimeter of the figure shown to the right. 20, 21. See margin.

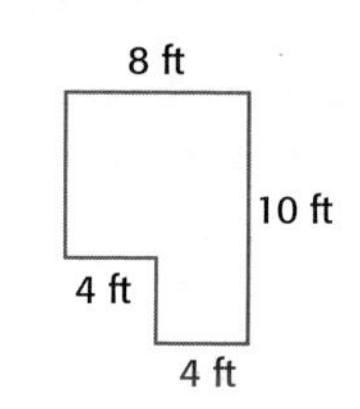


21. **WRITING IN MATH** Suppose you double the side length of a square. Will the perimeter also double? Explain.

## TEST Practice

**22.** Choose the best unit for measuring distance across the United States. (Lesson 11-4) D

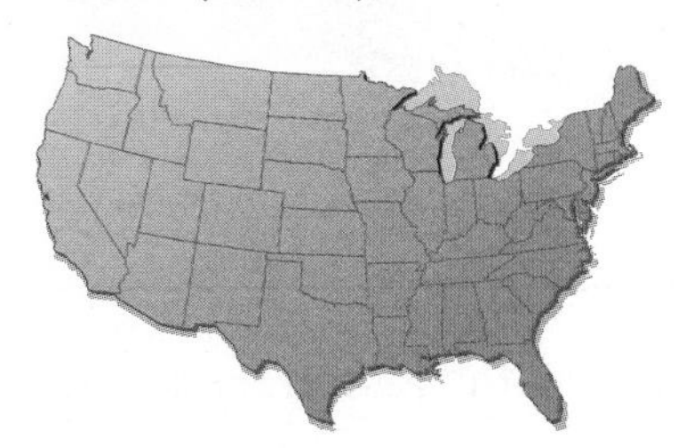

**A** centimeter

**B** meter

**C** millimeter

**D** kilometer

**23.** What is the perimeter of the figure below if the side of each block represents 1 centimeter? (Lesson 11-5) H

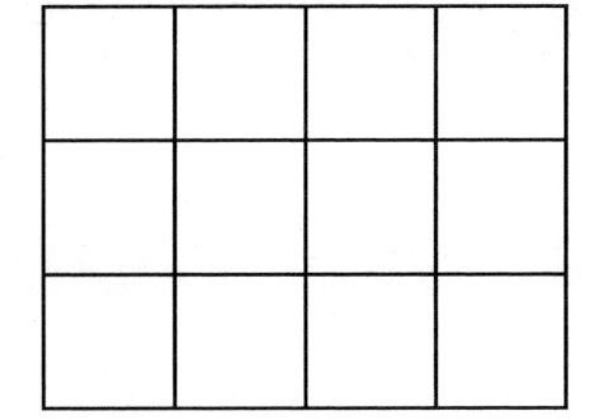

**F** 7 centimeters

**G** 12 centimeters

**H** 14 centimeters

**J** 20 centimeters

## Spiral Review

**Measure each object to the nearest centimeter.** (Lesson 11-4)

**24.** 5 cm

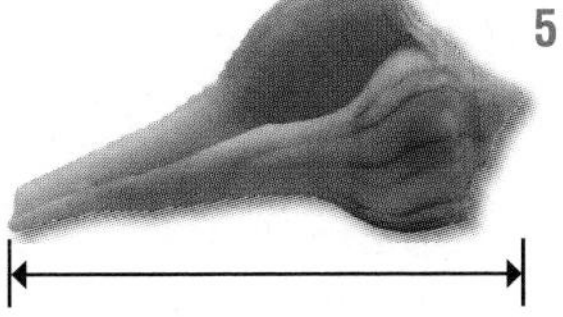

**25.** 7 cm

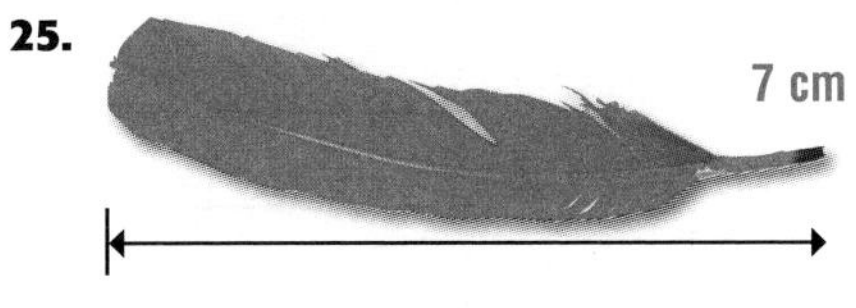

**26.** There are 15 girls in class and 13 boys in class. If 7 more girls came to class, how many students will there be in the class? (Lesson 11-3) 35

**Complete.** (Lesson 11-2)

**27.** 36 in. = ■ ft 3

**28.** 12 ft = ■ yd 4

**29.** 4 yd = ■ in. 144

**30.** **Algebra** Write an equation that describes the pattern. Then use the equation to find the next three numbers. (Lesson 5-5)
$x + 5 = y$; 20, 24, 28

| Input (x) | 3 | 7 | 11 | 15 | 19 | 23 |
|---|---|---|---|---|---|---|
| Output (y) | 8 | 12 | 16 | ■ | ■ | ■ |



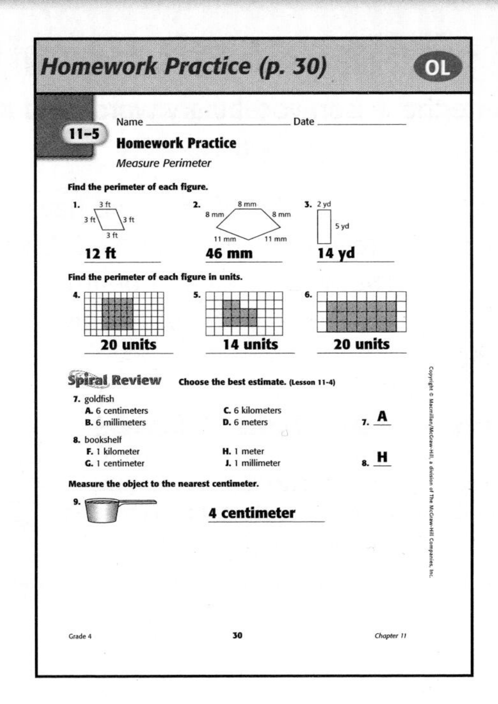
Homework Practice (p. 30) OL

11-5 Name ____ Date ____
**Homework Practice**
*Measure Perimeter*

**Find the perimeter of each figure.**

1. 12 ft
2. 46 mm
3. 14 yd

**Find the perimeter of each figure in units.**

4. 20 units
5. 14 units
6. 20 units

**Spiral Review** **Choose the best estimate.** (Lesson 11-4)

7. goldfish
A. 6 centimeters
B. 6 millimeters
C. 6 kilometers
D. 6 meters
7. A

8. bookshelf
F. 1 kilometer
G. 1 centimeter
H. 1 meter
J. 1 millimeter
8. H

**Measure the object to the nearest centimeter.**

9. 4 centimeter

Grade 4 30 Chapter 11

# 4 Assess

### Formative Assessment

- **Find the perimeter of a rectangle with width 5 meters and length 7 meters.** 24 m
- **Find the perimeter of a square with a side of 8 inches.** 32 in.

**Quick Check** **Are students continuing to struggle with finding the perimeter of a polygon?**

**If Yes** → CRM Reteach Worksheet (p. 28)

**If No** → Independent Work Options (p. 456B)
CRM Skills Practice Worksheet (p. 29)
CRM Enrich Worksheet (p. 32)

**Name the Math** Have students write the steps necessary to find the perimeter of a rectangle with length 100 cm and width 25 cm.

### Reviews Lessons 11-4 and 11-5

Assign the Test Practice problems to provide daily reinforcement of test-taking skills.

## Spiral Review

### Reviews Lessons 5-5, 11-2, 11-3, and 11-4

Review and assess mastery of skills and concepts from previous chapters.

LESSON **11-6**

# Measure Areas

## Lesson Planner

### Objective

Find the area of rectangles and squares.

### Vocabulary

**area**, **square units**

### Resources

**Materials:** centimeter grid paper

**Manipulatives:** base-ten blocks, rulers

**Literature Connection:** *Spaghetti and Meatballs for All* by Marilyn Burns and Gordon Silveria

**Alternate Lesson:** Use *IMPACT Mathematics:* Unit F to provide practice with area.

**Teacher Technology**
TeacherWorks • Interactive Classroom

## Daily Routine

Use these suggestions before beginning the lesson on p. 460.

### 5-Minute Check

(Reviews Lesson 11-5)

**Estimate the perimeter. Then find the exact perimeter.**

**1.**

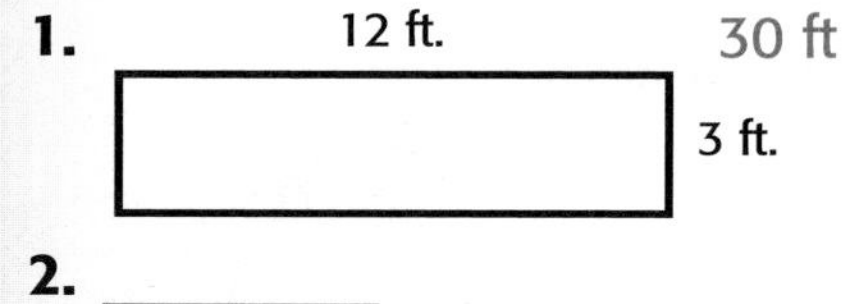


30 ft

**2.**

36 yd

### Problem of the Day

Mark has 6 square tiles, each with a side that measures 4 inches. What is the perimeter of the tiles if he places them in a row? 56 in.

### Focus on Math Background

Area gives a two-dimension measure to a region enclosed by a shape. It describes the number of square units it takes to *cover* the region and is always expressed by a numerical value and a unit of measure. Students need experience covering objects with square tiles and counting the number of squares within a figure that is drawn on grid paper. To determine the area of a region, ask: How many *square units* are there in the given region?

### Building Math Vocabulary

Write the lesson vocabulary words and their definitions on the board.

Brainstorm examples of area and have a volunteer record the responses on the board. Discuss the difference between area and perimeter and the difference between units for perimeter and square units.

**Visual Vocabulary Cards**
Use Visual Vocabulary Card 3 to reinforce the vocabulary introduced in this lesson. (The Define/Example/Ask routine is printed on the back of each card.)

# Differentiated Instruction

## Small Group Options

SPATIAL, SOCIAL

### Option 1 Gifted and Talented AL

**Materials:** seed catalogs, gardening books, paper, pencil

- Give students seed catalogs and gardening books to plan a garden.
- Tell students to consider how far apart plants must be to thrive and how tall they will grow when determining the area.

LINGUISTIC, VISUAL

### Option 2 English Language Learners ELL

**Materials:** aerial picture of a soccer field
**Core Vocabulary:** along the edge, athletes inside the area, people around the perimeter
**Common Use Verb:** watch
**Write Math** This strategy uses background knowledge and alliteration to remember and compare area and perimeter.

- Post the picture of the soccer field. Say and write: "The **Athletes are inside the Area**."
- Repeat for "The **People** who ***watch*** the game are around the **Perimeter.** They are **along the edge**."
- Have students draw their own sports field and label the athletes inside the area and the people outside along the perimeter. Encourage students to write sentences explaining how they remember area and perimeter vocabulary.

## Independent Work Options

LOGICAL

### Option 1 Early Finishers OL AL

**Materials:** centimeter grid paper

- Each student draws 5 rectangles, each with different dimensions, on centimeter grid paper.
- Students exchange papers and calculate the areas of the rectangles.
- Students return papers so that the student who draw the rectangle can check the answers.

### Option 2 Student Technology

Personal Tutor • Extra Examples

Math Adventures

### Option 3 Learning Station: Art (p. 392I)

Direct students to the Art Learning Station for opportunities to explore and extend the lesson concept.

### Option 4 Problem-Solving Practice

Reinforce problem-solving skills and strategies with the Problem-Solving Practice worksheet.

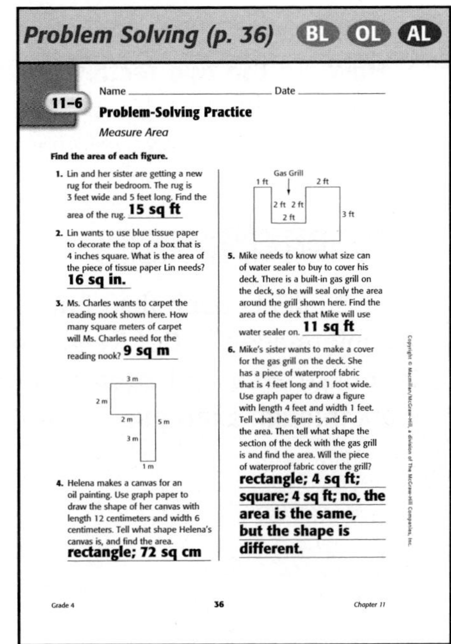

**Problem Solving (p. 36)** BL OL AL

11–6

Name ______________ Date ______________

**Problem-Solving Practice**

*Measure Area*

**Find the area of each figure.**

1. Lin and her sister are getting a new rug for their bedroom. The rug is 3 feet wide and 5 feet long. Find the area of the rug. **15 sq ft**
2. Lin wants to use blue tissue paper to decorate the top of a box that is 4 inches square. What is the area of the piece of tissue paper Lin needs? **16 sq in.**
3. Ms. Charles wants to carpet the reading nook shown here. How many square meters of carpet will Ms. Charles need for the reading nook? **9 sq m**



4. Helena makes a canvas for an oil painting. Use graph paper to draw the shape of her canvas with length 12 centimeters and width 6 centimeters. Tell what shape Helena's canvas is, and find the area. **rectangle; 72 sq cm**



5. Mike needs to know what size can of water sealer to buy to cover his deck. There is a built-in gas grill on the deck, so he will seal only the area around the grill shown here. Find the area of the deck that Mike will use water sealer on. **11 sq ft**
6. Mike's sister wants to make a cover for the gas grill on the deck. She has a piece of waterproof fabric that is 4 feet long and 1 foot wide. Use graph paper to draw a figure with length 4 feet and width 1 feet. Tell what the figure is, and find the area. Then tell what shape the section of the deck with the gas grill is and find the area. Will the piece of waterproof fabric cover the grill? **rectangle; 4 sq ft; square; 4 sq ft; no, the area is the same, but the shape is different.**



Grade 4 36 Chapter 11

# 11-6 Measure Areas

## 1 Introduce

### Activity Choice 1 • Hands-On

- Have students work in pairs to model rectangles using 16 connecting cubes.
- Model 1 row of 16 as an example. Have volunteers list all the possibilities for modeling the 16 square centimeters. Be sure students are modeling rectangles. **What lengths and widths can you use to make a rectangle with 16 squares?** 1 cm by 16 cm, 2 cm by 8 cm, and 4 cm by 4 cm
- Have them do the same for 24 square units.

### Activity Choice 2 • Literature

Introduce the lesson with *Spaghetti and Meatballs for All* by Marilyn Burns For a related math activity, see p. TR60.

## 2 Teach

### Scaffolding Questions

Use the models from the Introduce Activity 1.

- **What is the relationship between the length and width of a square cube?** They are the same measure, 1 cm.
- **Which of your models showed a square made from the 16 cubes?** the 4 cm by 4 cm
- **How is a rectangle that measures 2 cm by 8 cm the same as one that measures 8 cm by 2 cm?** They both have the same area and perimeters.
- **How are the two rectangles different?** Sample answer: On grid paper, you can show one horizontally and one vertically.

### GET READY to Learn

Have students open their books and read the information in **Get Ready to Learn**. Introduce **area** and **square units**. As a class, work through **Examples 1 and 2**.



# 11-6 Measure Areas

**MAIN IDEA**

I will find the area of rectangles and squares.

**New Vocabulary**

area
square units

**Math Online**

macmillanmh.com

- Extra Examples
- Personal Tutor
- Self-Check Quiz

### GET READY to Learn

The Perez family wants to put the sandbox shown in their backyard. What is the area of the sandbox?

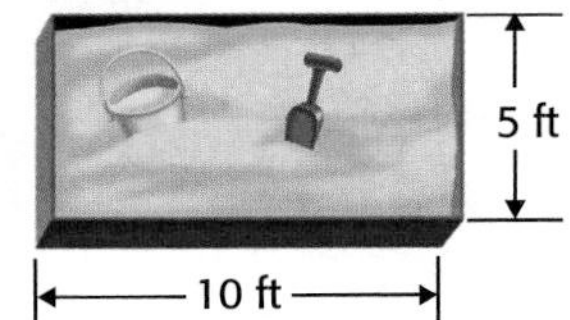


**Area** is the number of square units needed to cover a region or figure without any overlap. It is measured in **square units**.

### Real-World EXAMPLE Area of a Rectangle

**1 SANDBOX** Find the area of the sandbox.

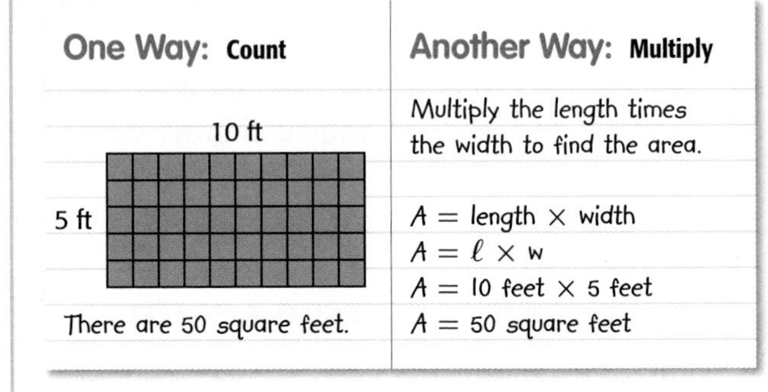

| One Way: Count | Another Way: Multiply |
|---|---|
| 10 ft / 5 ft (grid) | Multiply the length times the width to find the area. |
| | $A =$ length $\times$ width |
| | $A = \ell \times w$ |
| | $A = 10$ feet $\times$ 5 feet |
| There are 50 square feet. | $A = 50$ square feet |

So, the area of the sandbox is 50 square feet.

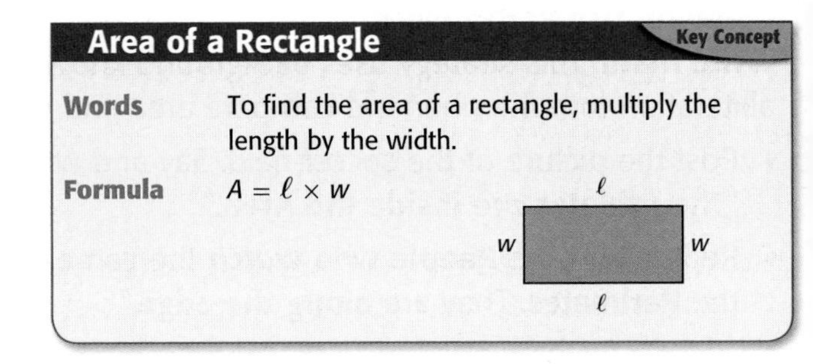

| Area of a Rectangle | Key Concept |
|---|---|
| **Words** | To find the area of a rectangle, multiply the length by the width. |
| **Formula** | $A = \ell \times w$ |





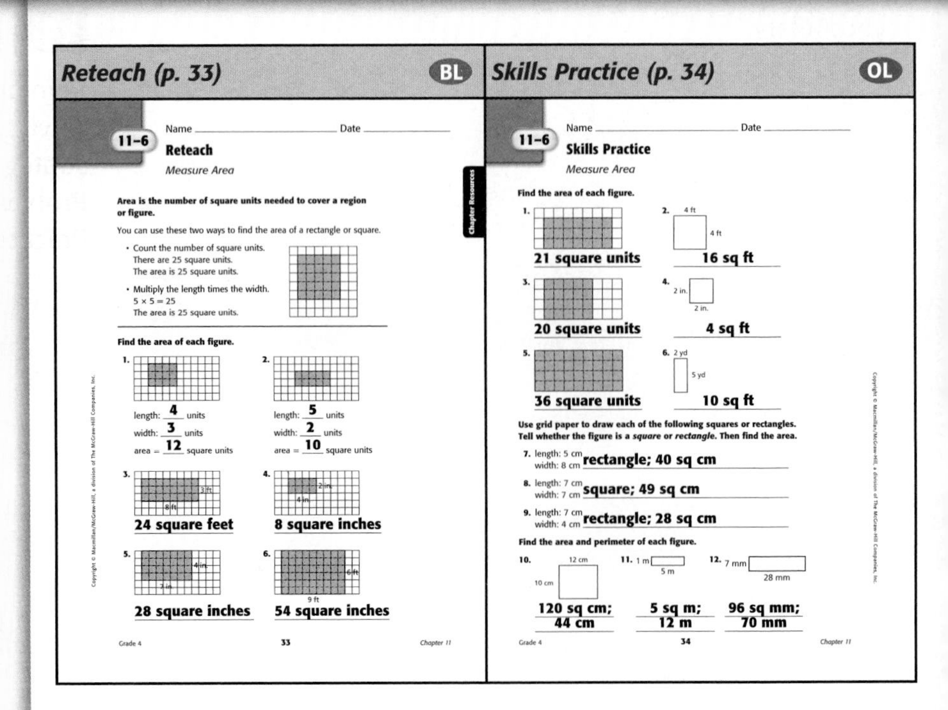

**Reteach (p. 33)** BL

11-6 Name ______ Date ______

**Reteach**

*Measure Area*

**Area is the number of square units needed to cover a region or figure.**

You can use these two ways to find the area of a rectangle or square.

- Count the number of square units.
  There are 25 square units.
  The area is 25 square units.
- Multiply the length times the width.
  $5 \times 5 = 25$
  The area is 25 square units.

**Find the area of each figure.**

1. length: **4** units
   width: **3** units
   area = **12** square units
2. length: **5** units
   width: **2** units
   area = **10** square units
3. 3 ft, 8 ft — **24 square feet**
4. 2 in., 4 in. — **8 square inches**
5. 4 in., 7 in. — **28 square inches**
6. 6 ft, 9 ft — **54 square inches**

Grade 4 33 Chapter 11



**Skills Practice (p. 34)** OL

11-6 Name ______ Date ______

**Skills Practice**

*Measure Area*

**Find the area of each figure.**

1. **21 square units**
2. 4 ft, 4 ft — **16 sq ft**
3. **20 square units**
4. 2 in., 2 in. — **4 sq ft**
5. **36 square units**
6. 2 yd, 5 yd — **10 sq ft**

**Use grid paper to draw each of the following squares or rectangles. Tell whether the figure is a *square* or *rectangle*. Then find the area.**

7. length: 5 cm, width: 8 cm — **rectangle; 40 sq cm**
8. length: 7 cm, width: 7 cm — **square; 49 sq cm**
9. length: 7 cm, width: 4 cm — **rectangle; 28 sq cm**

**Find the area and perimeter of each figure.**

10. 12 cm, 10 cm — **120 sq cm; 44 cm**
11. 1 m, 5 m — **5 sq m; 12 m**
12. 7 mm, 28 mm — **96 sq mm; 70 mm**

Grade 4 34 Chapter 11

You can also find the area of a square.

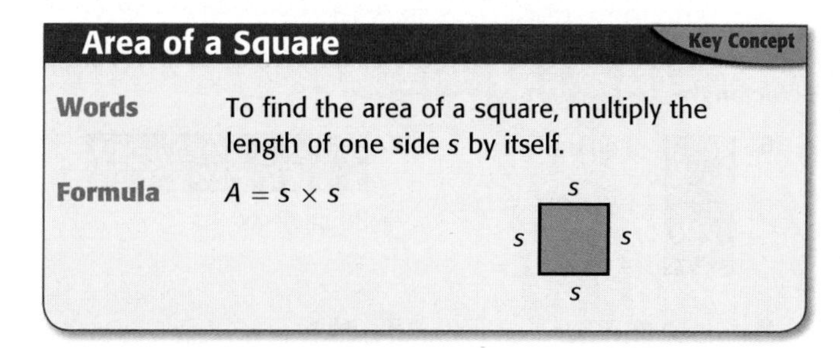

## Area of a Square

*Key Concept*

**Words** To find the area of a square, multiply the length of one side $s$ by itself.

**Formula** $A = s \times s$

**Area of a Square**

**2** **PHOTOS Find the area of the photo if its sides are 9 centimeters in length.**

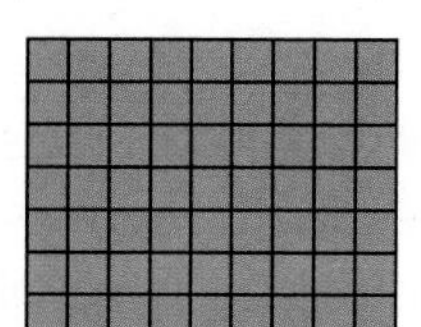


**Estimate** 9 cm × 9 cm → 10 cm × 10 cm = 100 sq cm

$A$ = side × side — Formula

$A$ = 9 cm × 9 cm — $s = 9$

$A$ = 81 square centimeters — Multiply.

The area of the photo is 81 square centimeters.

**Check for Reasonableness**

81 square centimeters is close to 100 square centimeters. ✓

5. Sample answer: To find the area of a rectangle, you can count the number of squares, or multiply length times width. To find the area of a square, you can count the number of squares, or multiply side times side.

★ indicates multi-step problem

## CHECK What You Know

**Estimate the area. Then find the exact area of each square or rectangle.**

See Examples 1 and 2 (pp. 460–461)

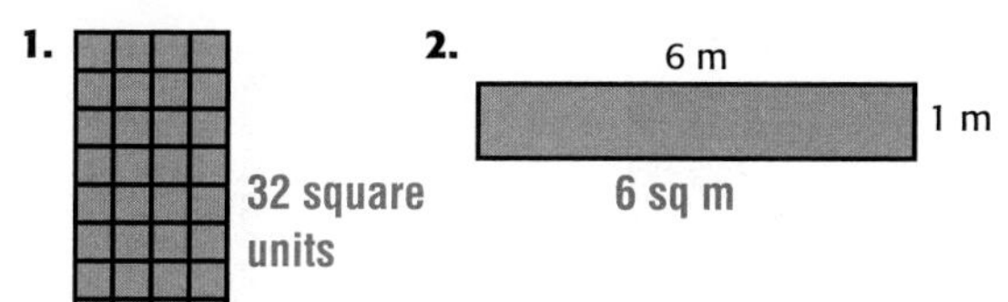

**1.** 32 square units

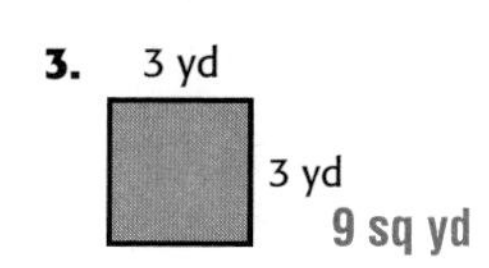

**2.** 6 m, 1 m — 6 sq m

**3.** 3 yd, 3 yd — 9 sq yd

**4.** Mr. Hart is hanging a picture on a wall. The picture frame has a length of 12 inches and a width of 9 inches. How much wall space will the picture need? 108 sq in.

**5.** Talk About It Explain two ways to find the area of a rectangle. What are two ways to find the area of a square?



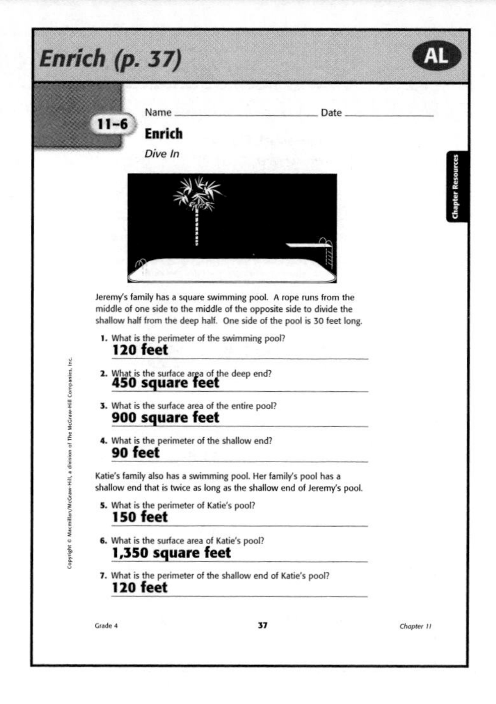

*Enrich (p. 37)* **AL**

11–6 Name ______ Date ______

**Enrich**

*Dive In*

Jeremy's family has a square swimming pool. A rope runs from the middle of one side to the middle of the opposite side to divide the shallow half from the deep half. One side of the pool is 30 feet long.

1. What is the perimeter of the swimming pool? **120 feet**
2. What is the surface area of the deep end? **450 square feet**
3. What is the surface area of the entire pool? **900 square feet**
4. What is the perimeter of the shallow end? **90 feet**

Katie's family also has a swimming pool. Her family's pool has a shallow end that is twice as long as the shallow end of Jeremy's pool.

5. What is the perimeter of Katie's pool? **150 feet**
6. What is the surface area of Katie's pool? **1,350 square feet**
7. What is the perimeter of the shallow end of Katie's pool? **120 feet**

Chapter Resources



Grade 4 — 37 — *Chapter 11*

### Area of a Square

**Example 2** Explain that you could use $\ell \times w$ to find the area of a square since a square is also a rectangle.

## Tips for New Teachers

Provide students with centimeter grid paper to use as they work through area problems.

Encourage them to draw rectangles and squares on the paper to model problems.

## ADDITIONAL EXAMPLES

**1** Find the area of the kitchen floor that is 7 feet by 9 feet. 63 square feet

**2** What is the area of a square floor tile with sides that are 6 inches in length? 36 square in.

## CHECK What You Know

As a class, have students complete Exercises 1–5 in **Check What You Know** as you observe their work.

**Exercise 5** Assess student comprehension before assigning practice exercises.

## BL Alternate Teaching Strategy

**If** students have trouble using formulas for area…

**Then** use one of these reteach options:

1. CRM **Daily Reteach Worksheet** (p. 33)
2. Have students draw a rectangle on centimeter grid paper and count the units to find the length and width. Once they have determined the length and width, have them substitute the numbers into the formula $A = \ell \times w$. To confirm, have them count the number of square units in their drawing.

# 3 Practice

Differentiate practice using these leveled assignments for Exercises 6–20.

| Level | Assignment |
|---|---|
| BL Below/Approaching Level | 6–8, 12–13 |
| OL On Level | 6–14, 17–19 |
| AL Above/Beyond Level | 7–15 odd, 16–20 |

Have students discuss and complete the Higher Order Thinking problems. Encourage students to write the formula for the area of a rectangle and then solve.

**WRITING IN ➤MATH** Have students complete Exercise 20 in their Math Journals. You may choose to use this exercise as an optional formative assessment.

# 4 Assess

### Formative Assessment

Pose the following problem to students: *There is a rectangle with length of 7 ft and width of 8 ft.*

- **What formula can you use to find the area of a rectangle?** $A = \ell \times w$
- **What is the area of the rectangle?** 56 square ft

**Quick Check** **Are students continuing to struggle with finding the area of rectangles and squares?**

**If Yes** → CRM Reteach Worksheet (p. 33)

**If No** → Independent Work Options (p. 460B)
CRM Skills Practice Worksheet (p. 34)
CRM Enrich Worksheet (p. 37)

**Into the Future** Have students discuss with a partner how using formulas to find area and perimeter will be helpful.

### COMMON ERROR!

**Exercises 6–11** Watch for students who confuse area and perimeter formulas. Have them write the area formula and then solve.



## Practice and Problem Solving

EXTRA PRACTICE See page R29.

**Estimate the area. Then find the exact area of each square or rectangle.** See Examples 1 and 2 (pp. 460–461)

6. 8 sq units
7. 20 sq units
8. 16 sq units
9. 6 m by 2 m — 12 sq m
10. 8 km by 8 km — 64 sq km
11. 10 yd by 2 yd — 20 sq yd

12. Each child in Mrs. Dixon's class has a rectangular desk that is 15 inches long and 32 inches wide. What is the area of the top of each student's desk? 480 sq in.

★13. Ricky's computer monitor is a rectangle. The length is 15 inches and the width is 12 inches. Estimate the area of the monitor. 20 in. × 10 in. = 200 sq in.

★14. A car is 15 feet long and 6 feet wide. It is parked on a rectangular driveway with an area of 112 square feet. How much of the driveway is *not* covered by the car? 22 sq ft

★15. A rectangular playground is 40 meters by 10 meters. Its area will be covered with shredded tires. Each bag of shredded tires covers 200 square meters and costs $30. Find the total cost for this project. $60

### H.O.T. Problems

16. **OPEN ENDED** Draw three rectangles that each have an area of 36 square inches, but have different perimeters. See Ch. 11 Answer Appendix.

**NUMBER SENSE The area and the measure of one side of each square or rectangle is given. Find the missing sides.**

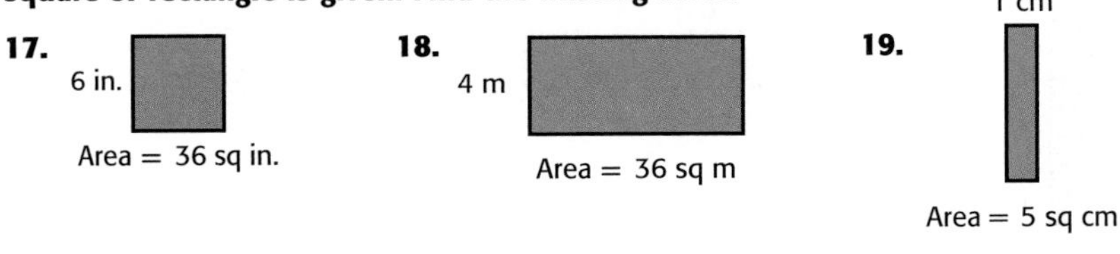


6 in., 6 in., 6 in. | 9 m, 9 m, 4 m | 5 cm, 5 cm, 1 cm

20. **WRITING IN ➤MATH** A square has sides measuring 3 feet. If the sides of a square are doubled, will the area also double? Explain. no; It will quadruple.



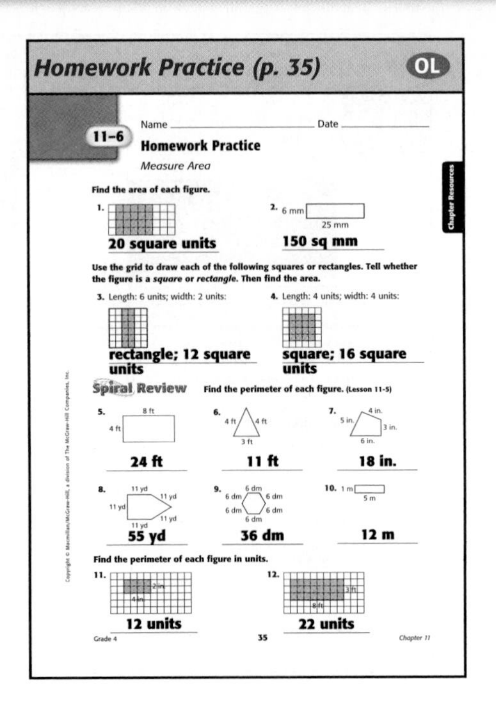
Homework Practice (p. 35) OL

11-6 Homework Practice
*Measure Area*

Find the area of each figure.

1. 20 square units
2. 6 mm, 25 mm — 150 sq mm

Use the grid to draw each of the following squares or rectangles. Tell whether the figure is a *square* or *rectangle*. Then find the area.

3. Length: 6 units; width: 2 units: rectangle; 12 square units
4. Length: 4 units; width: 4 units: square; 16 square units

Spiral Review Find the perimeter of each figure. (Lesson 11-5)

5. 24 ft
6. 11 ft
7. 18 in.
8. 55 yd
9. 36 dm
10. 12 m

Find the perimeter of each figure in units.

11. 12 units
12. 22 units

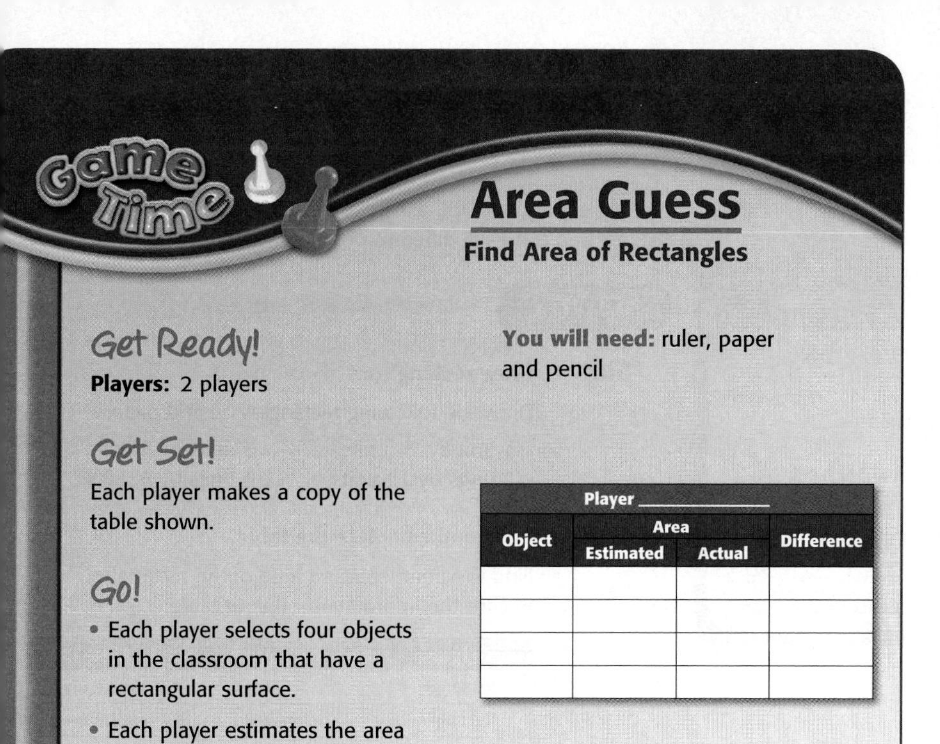

## Area Guess

**Find Area of Rectangles**

*Get Ready!*

**Players:** 2 players

**You will need:** ruler, paper and pencil

*Get Set!*

Each player makes a copy of the table shown.

| Player ________ | | | |
|---|---|---|---|
| Object | Area | | Difference |
| | Estimated | Actual | |
| | | | |
| | | | |
| | | | |
| | | | |

*Go!*

- Each player selects four objects in the classroom that have a rectangular surface.
- Each player estimates the area of the objects selected to the nearest square centimeter.
- Find the exact areas of the objects.
- Find the differences between the estimated areas and the actual areas of the objects.
- Find the sum of the four differences.
- The player who has the least difference between the estimated and actual areas wins.

**Game Time** Area Guess **463**

## Differentiated Practice

Use these leveled assignments to differentiate the game for all learners.

| Level | Assignment |
|---|---|
| BL Below/Approaching Level | Students measure the length of the figures first and estimate using the length to guide their estimates. |
| OL On Level | Have students play the game with the rules as written. |
| AL Above/Beyond Level | Students use figures that are combinations of rectangles to estimate and then measure. |

# Area Guess

### Math Concept:
### Find Area of Rectangles

**Materials:** 2 metric rulers with centimeters, paper, pencils

Introduce the game on p. 463 to your students to play as a class, in small groups, or at a learning workstation to review concepts introduced in this chapter.

## Instructions

- Students recreate the table shown on p. 463 on a sheet of notebook paper.
- Students play in pairs. They each choose four classroom objects that have a rectangular surface.
- Students estimate the area of the objects they selected to the nearest centimeter.
- Students measure the length and width of the objects together and agree on what the actual area of each object is, to the nearest centimeter.
- Players calculate the difference between their estimated areas and the actual areas. The player with the least total difference between the estimated areas and the actual areas wins.

## Extend the Game

Have students try this activity using inches instead of centimeters, and measure to the nearest inch.

# Lesson Planner

## Objective

Explore perimeter and area.

## Resources

**Materials:** grid paper

**Manipulatives:** tiles

## 1 Introduce

### Introduce the Concept

- Give each group of two students 12 square tiles and ask them to model as many rectangles as they can using all 12 of the tiles.
- **What is the area of each of your rectangles?** 12 square units
- Count the units around each of your rectangles to find the perimeter of each. **What is the perimeter of the 3 unit × 4 unit rectangle?** 14 units **Of the 1 unit × 12 unit rectangle?** 26 units
- Suppose the length of one side of a square tile is 1 inch. **What is the area of each of your rectangles?** 12 square inches

## 2 Teach

**Activity Step 2** Emphasize that area is labeled in square units, and perimeter is labeled in units.

Extend

## Measurement Activity for 11-6
# Perimeters and Areas

In this activity, you will explore whether rectangles with the same area can have different perimeters.

**ACTIVITY** Relate Perimeter and Area

**Step 1 Draw rectangles.**

Draw the following rectangles on grid paper.

- 1 unit by 24 units
- 2 units by 12 units
- 3 units by 8 units
- 4 units by 6 units

**Step 2 Copy and complete the table.**

Find the perimeter and area of the rectangles. Record the information on your table.

| Figure | Perimeter | Area |
|---|---|---|
| Rectangle 1 | 50 units | 24 square units |
| Rectangle 2 | 28 units | 24 square units |
| Rectangle 3 | 22 units | 24 square units |
| Rectangle 4 | 20 units | 24 square units |

**Step 3 Examine your table.**

What similarities and differences do you notice among the rectangles?

Is it possible for rectangles with the same area to have different perimeters?

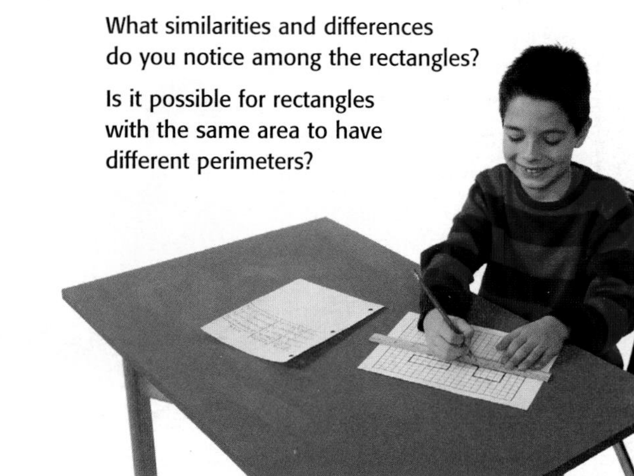

## Think About It 1–3. See margin.

1. Explain the difference between area and perimeter.
2. Is it possible to draw a rectangle that has an area of 24 square units and a perimeter of 24 units? Explain.
3. Is there a relationship between the area and the perimeter of a rectangle? Explain.
4. Look at the rectangles that you drew. What do you notice about the shape of the rectangle that has the greatest perimeter? The shape of the rectangle with the greatest perimeter was the perimeter with the smallest width.

## CHECK What You Know

**Find the perimeter and area for each square or rectangle.**

5. 16 units; 16 sq units

6. 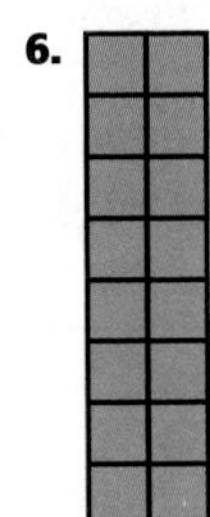 20 units; 16 sq units

7. 34 units; 16 square units

8. What do the figures in Exercises 5–7 have in common? How do these figures differ? Sample answer: These figures all have the same area, but they have different perimeters.
9. Draw two rectangles that have the same areas and the same perimeters. 9–11. See margin.
10. Can rectangles that have the same perimeter have different areas? Explain.
11. **WRITING IN MATH** If a figure has a greater perimeter than another, does it also have a greater area? Explain your thinking.



### Additional Answers

1. Area measures the number of square units that cover a figure. Perimeter measures the distance around a figure.
2. no; There are four possible length and width combinations that result in an area of 24 square units. None of these combinations result in a perimeter of 24 units.
3. no; An area can stay the same, and the perimeter can be all different sizes. Also, A perimeter can stay the same, and the area can be all different sizes.

9. 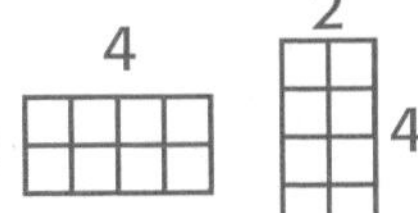

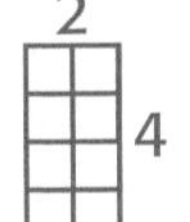


10. Sample answer: yes; A 1-by-8 rectangle has the same perimeter as a 3-by-6 rectangle, but the rectangles have different areas.
11. Sample answer: Not necessarily, the figures in problems 1–3 all have different perimeters, but their areas are the same.

## Think About It

Assign **Think About It** Exercises 1–4 to assess student comprehension of the concept presented in the Activity.

# 3 Assess

### Formative Assessment

Use the **Check What You Know** Exercises 5–10 to assess whether students understand the relationship between the perimeters and areas of rectangles.

**From Concrete to Abstract** Use Exercise 11 to bridge the gap between using manipulatives and understanding the relationship between perimeter and area.

**Extending the Concept** Have students use the perimeter of 12 units to create rectangles and generate a list of dimensions.

- **What are the dimensions for the rectangles with a perimeter of 12 units?** 1 unit by 5 units, 2 units by 4 units, and 3 units by 3 units
- **What are the areas for these rectangles?** 5, 8, and 9 square units
- **How can you describe the rectangle with the least area compared to the one with the greatest area?** Sample answer: The rectangle with the least area is longer than it is wide, and the one that has the greatest area is a square.

# 11-7 Problem-Solving Investigation
## Choose a Strategy

# Lesson Planner

## Objective

Choose the best strategy to solve a problem.

## Resources

**Teacher Technology**

TeacherWorks • Interactive Classroom

**Real-World Problem Solving Library**
**Math and Science: *Ancient Giants of the Forest***
Use these leveled books to reinforce and extend problem-solving skills and strategies.

Leveled for:

- OL On Level
- ELL Sheltered English
- SP Spanish

For additional support, see the Real-World Problem Solving Teacher Guide.

# Daily Routine

Use these suggestions before beginning the lesson on p. 466.

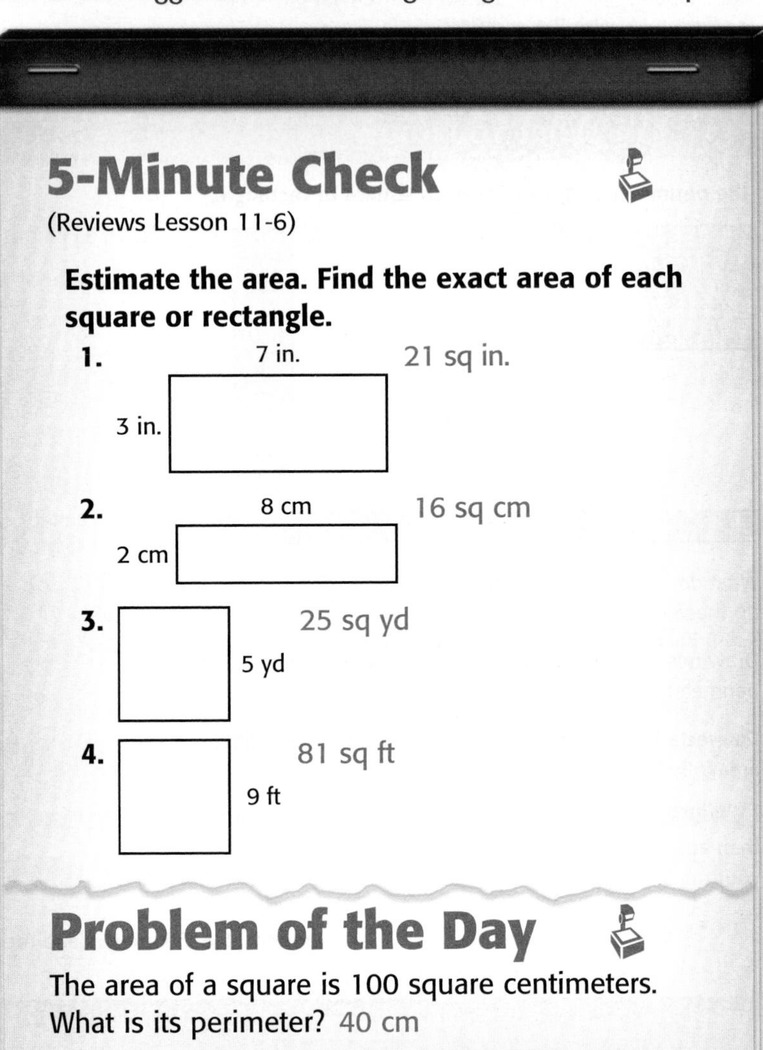

## 5-Minute Check

(Reviews Lesson 11-6)

**Estimate the area. Find the exact area of each square or rectangle.**

**1.** 7 in. by 3 in. — 21 sq in.

**2.** 8 cm by 2 cm — 16 sq cm

**3.** 5 yd — 25 sq yd

**4.** 9 ft — 81 sq ft

## Problem of the Day

The area of a square is 100 square centimeters. What is its perimeter? 40 cm

# Differentiated Instruction

## Small Group Options

LOGICAL

### Option 1 Gifted and Talented AL

**Materials:** paper and pencil

Write the following problem on the board or a piece of paper.

*Carol is trying to earn enough money for a school trip which costs $69. She babysits an hour after school each weekday, plus 3 hours on Saturday for $3 an hour. She already has $22 saved and needs the rest of the money within 2 weeks. Will she make her goal if she continues her work schedule?* yes

SPATIAL

### Option 2 English Language Learners ELL

**Materials:** per group: paper, 24 counters, 4 pieces of string or yarn at least 16 inches long

**Core Vocabulary:** separate, identify, describe

**Common Use Verb:** create

**Do Math** This strategy integrates problem-solving skills with area and perimeter applications.

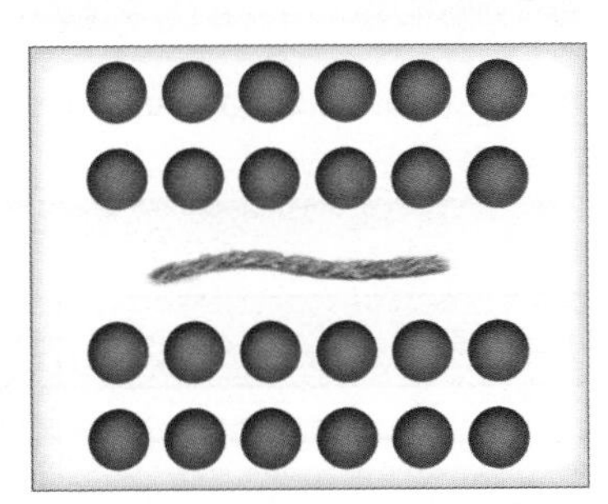

- Each group puts the counters on the paper.
- Have students use the yarn to separate the counters.
- Prompt students to identify the area and perimeter they created. Accept responses, assisting groups to write out their methods.
- Prompt students to create new area/perimeter models and describe them.
- Extend this activity by giving students an area quantity and having them show it with counters and yarn.
- Discuss different solutions as time permits.

## Independent Work Options

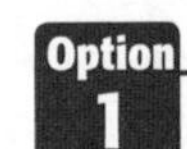

SPATIAL, LOGICAL

### Option 1 Early Finishers OL AL

**Materials:** paper and pencil

- Have students write a word problem that uses one of the strategies on p. 467. Ask them to exchange problems with other students and solve. Have students explain how the strategy they chose helped them solve the problem.

### Option 2 Student Technology

**Math Online** macmillanmh.com

Personal Tutor • Extra Examples

### Option 3 Learning Station: Science (p. 436J)

Direct students to the Science Learning Station for opportunities to explore and extend the lesson concept.

# 11-7 Problem-Solving Investigation

## 1 Introduce

**Activity • Review**

- Pose the following problem:

  *There are 7 people on the bus, and the bus picks up 4 additional people at each stop. How many stops will it take to have 31 people on the bus?*

- **What strategies could be used to solve the problem?** Sample answers: guess and check, make a table, look for a pattern, act it out
- **Could you use a combination of strategies? If so, what strategy should you start with and why?** Yes; start with act it out, so you can better understand the problem.
- **Solve the problem.** 6 stops

## 2 Teach

Have students read through the problem on painting. Guide them through the problem-solving steps.

**Understand** Using the questions, review what students know and need to find.

**Plan** Have them discuss their strategy.

**Solve** Guide students to use a model and solve a simpler problem.

- **How is finding the area of one 10-ft-by-12-ft section and then multiplying that area by 3 easier than finding the area of the entire 30-ft-by-12-ft backdrop?** Sample answer: I can use mental math to multiply $10 \times 12$ and $120 \times 3$, rather than using paper and pencil to multiply $30 \times 12$.

**Check** Have students look back at the problem to make sure it fits the facts given.

**COMMON ERROR!**

**Exercises 1–9** Watch for students who may use a strategy correctly, but make a computation error. Remind students to always check their computations.



# 11-7 Problem-Solving Investigation

**MAIN IDEA** I will choose the best strategy to solve a problem.

**P.S.I. TEAM +**

LYNN: I am painting a backdrop that is 30 feet long and 12 feet wide for the school play. The backdrop needs two coats of paint. I have two cans of paint and each covers 400 square feet.

YOUR MISSION: Determine if Lynn has enough paint to paint the backdrop.

| | |
|---|---|
| **Understand** | You know the size of the backdrop and the amount of paint Lynn has. Find if she has enough paint to paint the backdrop twice. |
| **Plan** | Use a model and solve a simpler problem. |
| **Solve** | The model shows the backdrop. Find the area of one section of the backdrop.<br>$10 \times 12 = 120$ square feet<br>[Model: Backdrop — three sections, each 10 ft by 12 ft, each labeled 120 ft]<br>Now multiply by 3 to find the area of the entire backdrop.<br>$120 \times 3 = 360$ square feet<br>Since the backdrop needs to be painted twice, you need enough paint to cover 360 + 360 or 720 square feet. Since $720 < 800$, there is enough paint. |
| **Check** | The area of the backdrop is $30 \times 12 = 360$ square feet. Two coats of paint would need to cover 720 square feet. Since Lynn has enough paint to cover 800 square feet, the answer is correct. ✓ |



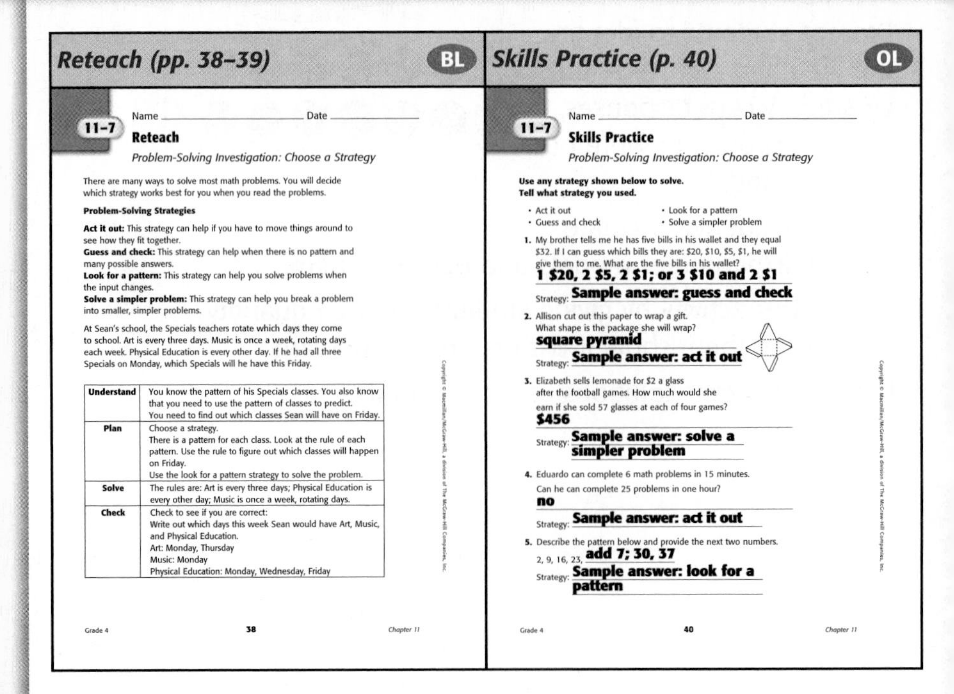

**Reteach (pp. 38–39)** BL

11-7 Name ______ Date ______

**Reteach**

*Problem-Solving Investigation: Choose a Strategy*

There are many ways to solve most math problems. You will decide which strategy works best for you when you read the problems.

**Problem-Solving Strategies**

**Act it out:** This strategy can help if you have to move things around to see how they fit together.
**Guess and check:** This strategy can help when there is no pattern and many possible answers.
**Look for a pattern:** This strategy can help you solve problems when the input changes.
**Solve a simpler problem:** This strategy can help you break a problem into smaller, simpler problems.

At Sean's school, the Specials teachers rotate which days they come to school. Art is every three days. Music is once a week, rotating days each week. Physical Education is every other day. If he had all three Specials on Monday, which Specials will he have this Friday.

| | |
|---|---|
| **Understand** | You know the pattern of his Specials classes. You also know that you need to use the pattern of classes to predict. You need to find out which classes Sean will have on Friday. |
| **Plan** | Choose a strategy. There is a pattern for each class. Look at the rule of each pattern. Use the rule to figure out which classes will happen on Friday. Use the look for a pattern strategy to solve the problem. |
| **Solve** | The rules are: Art is every three days; Physical Education is every other day; Music is once a week, rotating days. |
| **Check** | Check to see if you are correct: Write out which days this week Sean would have Art, Music, and Physical Education.<br>Art: Monday, Thursday<br>Music: Monday<br>Physical Education: Monday, Wednesday, Friday |



Grade 4 38 Chapter 11

**Skills Practice (p. 40)** OL

11-7 Name ______ Date ______

**Skills Practice**

*Problem-Solving Investigation: Choose a Strategy*

**Use any strategy shown below to solve. Tell what strategy you used.**

- Act it out
- Guess and check
- Look for a pattern
- Solve a simpler problem

1. My brother tells me he has five bills in his wallet and they equal \$32. If I can guess which bills they are: \$20, \$10, \$5, \$1, he will give them to me. What are the five bills in his wallet?
   **1 \$20, 2 \$5, 2 \$1; or 3 \$10 and 2 \$1**
   Strategy: **Sample answer: guess and check**
2. Allison cut out this paper to wrap a gift. What shape is the package she will wrap?
   **square pyramid**
   Strategy: **Sample answer: act it out**
3. Elizabeth sells lemonade for \$2 a glass after the football games. How much would she earn if she sold 57 glasses at each of four games?
   **\$456**
   Strategy: **Sample answer: solve a simpler problem**
4. Eduardo can complete 6 math problems in 15 minutes. Can he can complete 25 problems in one hour?
   **no**
   Strategy: **Sample answer: act it out**
5. Describe the pattern below and provide the next two numbers.
   2, 9, 16, 23, **add 7; 30, 37**
   Strategy: **Sample answer: look for a pattern**



Grade 4 40 Chapter 11

★ indicates multi-step problem

## Mixed Problem Solving

EXTRA PRACTICE See page R30.

**Use any of the strategies shown below to solve. Tell what strategy you used.**

PROBLEM-SOLVING STRATEGIES
- Act it out.
- Guess and check.
- Look for a pattern.
- Work a simpler problem.

1. **Measurement** One seal weighs 328 pounds. The second seal weighs 79 pounds less. How much does the second seal weigh? **249 lb**

2. **Measurement** A lion cub's weight is shown. An older lion weighs three times as much as the cub. How much do the lions weigh altogether? **104 lb**

3. Four numbers between 1 and 9 have a sum of 23. Each number is used once. What are the numbers? **Sample answer: 8, 7, 5, and 3**

4. A movie theater has 18 screens. About 212 people see a movie on each screen at the same time on Friday. About how many people are seeing movies in the theater at that time? **4,000 people**

★5. The table shows the amount of vegetables sold at a grocery store every four weeks. Is it reasonable to say that the store sells about 300 vegetables every week? **See margin.**

| Vegetable | Amount |
|---|---|
| Corn | 396 |
| Onions | 316 |
| Tomatoes | 489 |

★6. Heath brought 25 trading cards to a hobby show. He received three cards for one card in three trades. Then he gave 2 cards for one card in two trades. How many cards does Heath have now? **29 cards**

★7. Pedro bought 3 pencils for 15¢. How much would 10 pencils cost? **$10 \times 5¢ = 50¢$**

8. **Algebra** Describe the pattern below. Then find the missing number.

   20, 200, 2,000, ■, 200,000
   **Multiply by 10; 20,000**

★9. **Measurement** Clarissa has 4 pictures that are the size of the one shown. How much space will they take up in her photo album? **60 sq in.**

5 in.

3 in.

10. WRITING IN ▶MATH Explain how you solved Exercise 9. **See margin.**



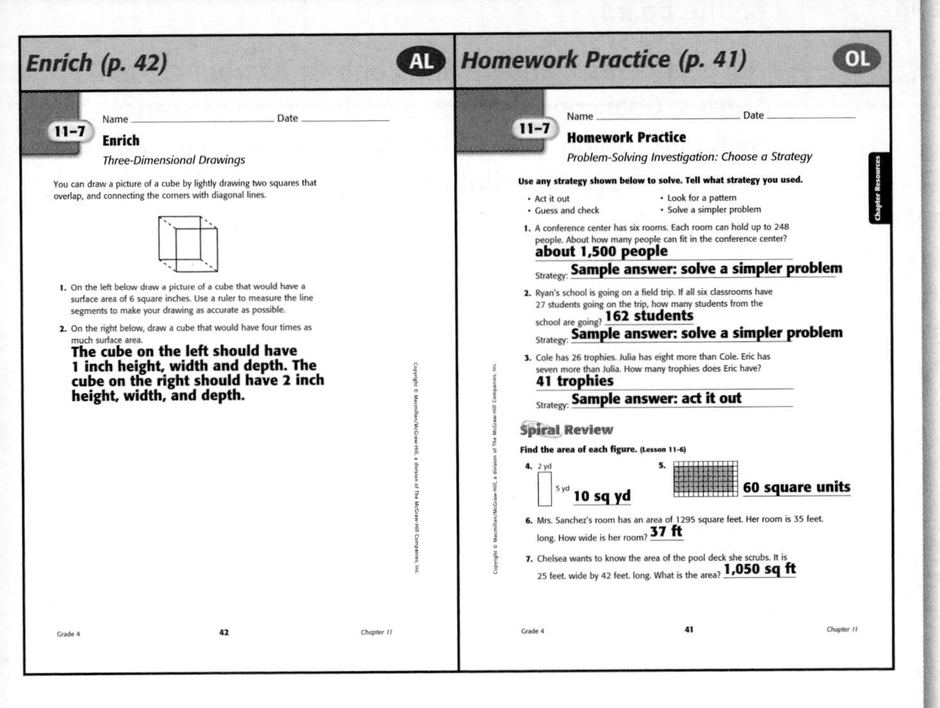

*Enrich (p. 42)* AL

11-7 Name ______ Date ______

**Enrich**

*Three-Dimensional Drawings*

You can draw a picture of a cube by lightly drawing two squares that overlap, and connecting the corners with diagonal lines.

1. On the left below draw a picture of a cube that would have a surface area of 6 square inches. Use a ruler to measure the line segments to make your drawing as accurate as possible.
2. On the right below, draw a cube that would have four times as much surface area.
   **The cube on the left should have 1 inch height, width and depth. The cube on the right should have 2 inch height, width, and depth.**



Grade 4 42 Chapter 11

*Homework Practice (p. 41)* OL

11-7 Name ______ Date ______

**Homework Practice**

*Problem-Solving Investigation: Choose a Strategy*

Chapter Resources

**Use any strategy shown below to solve. Tell what strategy you used.**
- Act it out
- Guess and check
- Look for a pattern
- Solve a simpler problem

1. A conference center has six rooms. Each room can hold up to 248 people. About how many people can fit in the conference center? **about 1,500 people**
   Strategy: **Sample answer: solve a simpler problem**
2. Ryan's school is going on a field trip. If all six classrooms have 27 students going on the trip, how many students from the school are going? **162 students**
   Strategy: **Sample answer: solve a simpler problem**
3. Cole has 26 trophies. Julia has eight more than Cole. Eric has seven more than Julia. How many trophies does Eric have? **41 trophies**
   Strategy: **Sample answer: act it out**

**Spiral Review**

**Find the area of each figure.** (Lesson 11-6)

4. 2 yd, 5 yd **10 sq yd**
5. **60 square units**
6. Mrs. Sanchez's room has an area of 1295 square feet. Her room is 35 feet. long. How wide is her room? **37 ft**
7. Chelsea wants to know the area of the pool deck she scrubs. It is 25 feet. wide by 42 feet. long. What is the area? **1,050 sq ft**



Grade 4 41 Chapter 11

## BL Alternate Teaching Strategy

**If** students have trouble choosing a strategy…

**Then** use one of these reteach options:

1. CRM **Daily Reteach Worksheet** (pp. 38–39)
2. Allow students to refer to a strategy list. Explain that there is often more than one way to solve a problem, but they should always use the four-step plan.

## 3 Practice

### Using the Exercises

**Exercises 1–9** are designed for students to use various problem-solving strategies.

**Exercises 4–5** ask students to estimate.

## 4 Assess

### Formative Assessment

Have students explain why the strategy they chose for one of the exercises is the best strategy to solve the problem. Answers will vary.

### Additional Answers

5. The grocery store sells about $400 + 300 + 500$ or about 1,200 vegetables in four weeks. Since $1,200 \div 4 = 300$, an answer of 300 is reasonable.
10. Find the area of one picture and then multiply by 4 to find the total amount of space. $5 \times 3 = 15$ and $15 \times 4 = 60$. So, 60 square inches would be used.

**Quick Check** **Are students continuing to struggle with choosing the best strategy to solve a problem?**

**If Yes** → CRM Reteach Worksheets (pp. 38–39)

**If No** → Independent Work Options (p. 420B)
CRM Skills Practice Worksheet (p. 40)
CRM Enrich Worksheet (p. 42)

LESSON 11-8

# Measure Temperatures

## Lesson Planner

### Objective

Measure temperature and calculate changes in temperature.

### Vocabulary

**degrees**, **Fahrenheit**, **Celsius**

### Resources

**Manipulatives:** thermometers, rulers, cups

**Literature Connection:** *The Snowy Day* by Ezra Jack Keats

**Teacher Technology**
TeacherWorks • Interactive Classroom

## Daily Routine

Use these suggestions before beginning the lesson on p. 468.

### 5-Minute Check

(Reviews Lesson 11-7)

**Use any strategy to solve. Tell what strategy you used.**
Caroline is covering four walls with wallpaper. Each wall is 16 feet long and 12 feet high. How many square feet of wallpaper will she use in all?
768 square feet; solve a simpler problem

### Problem of the Day

Oscar is making a square banner. Each side of the banner is 1 foot 2 inches long. How many inches of ribbon does he need to go around the border of the banner? 56 inches

### Focus on Math Background

Students have explored temperature measurement in degrees Fahrenheit in Grade 3. In this lesson, they expand their knowledge to the Celsius temperature scale. The Celsius scale was once called the Centigrade scale, as it is based on 100 divisions between the freezing and boiling points of water.

The Celsius and Fahrenheit scales have different 0 degree temperatures. The freezing point of water was defined as 0°C. 0°F is the lowest temperature to which water's freezing point can be reduced by adding salt. Both the Fahrenheit and Celsius scales register the same value at exactly one temperature, 40 degrees below zero.

### Building Math Vocabulary

Write the lesson vocabulary words and their definitions on the board.

Have students compare and contrast *Fahrenheit* and *Celsius*. Challenge them to use classroom reference materials to find out the temperatures at which water boils and freezes on both scales.

# Differentiated Instruction

## Small Group Options

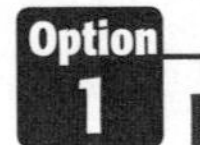

LOGICAL, SPATIAL

### Option 1 Below Level BL

**Materials:** thermometers for each student showing both °F and °C, chart paper, markers, pencils, paper

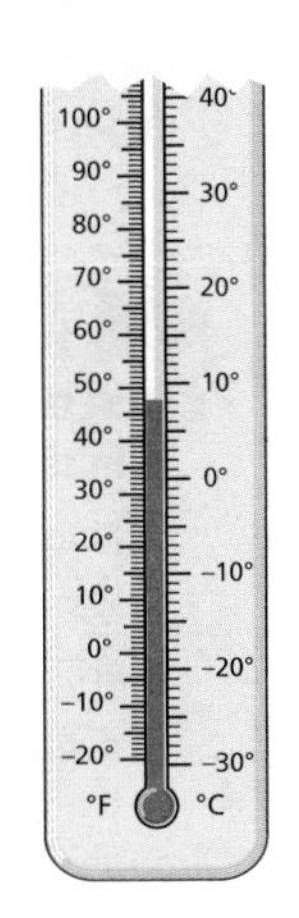


- List the following temperatures on the chart paper: 35°C, 35°F, 24°C, 24°F, 15°F, 15°C.
- Ask students to rewrite this list from the coldest temperature to the warmest temperature. 15°F, 24°F, 35°F, 15°C, 24°C, 35°C
- Ask them why the °F temps were all colder than the °C temps. Accept any reasonable answer but you are looking for something like all the temps are below or just above freezing in °F while the Celsius temps are quite warm.

LINGUISTIC, LOGICAL

### Option 2 English Language Learners ELL

**Materials:** index cards with the words: cold, hot, warm, colder, coldest, hotter, hottest
**Core Vocabulary:** hot, cold, warm
**Common Use Verb:** put in order
**Talk Math** This strategy helps students practice using terms relating to temperature.

- Have bowls of 3 different temperatures. Say, "___ is cold, ___ is warm, and ___ is hot."
- Read cards and pantomime core vocabulary. Say, "Help me put these in order from the word with lowest temperature to the one with the highest temperature."
- Students work with teacher to put cards in order, emphasizing the -er and -est suffixes.
- Allow a student to order the bowls. Have a student identify which is cold, warm, and hot.
- Repeat for as many students as time permits.

## Independent Work Options

LINGUISTIC

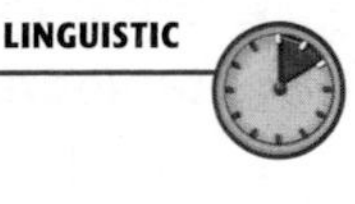

### Option 1 Early Finishers OL

- Have students use a thermometer to measure the temperature of two different items or locations in degrees Fahrenheit or Celsius, e.g., the temperature of hot and cold water and the temperatures of the classroom and the gym.
- Ask students to calculate the difference between the two temperatures.

### Option 2 Student Technology

macmillanmh.com

Personal Tutor • Extra Examples

### Option 3 Learning Station: Health (p. 436J)

Direct students to the Health Learning Station for opportunities to explore and extend the lesson concept.

### Option 4 Problem-Solving Practice

Reinforce problem-solving skills and strategies with the Problem-Solving Practice worksheet.

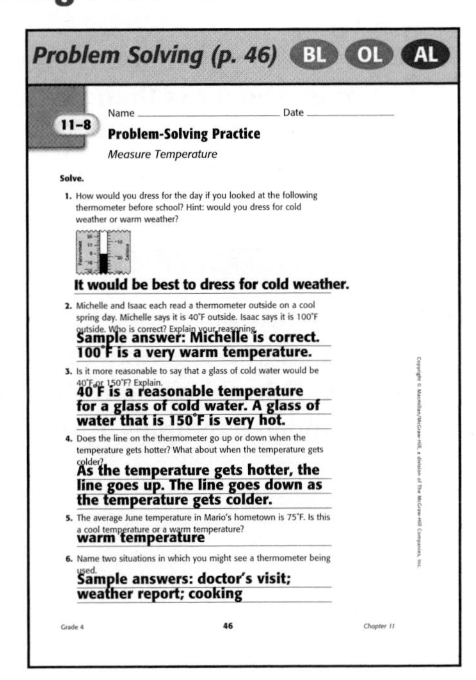

**Problem Solving (p. 46)** BL OL AL

11–8 Name ______ Date ______

**Problem-Solving Practice**

*Measure Temperature*

**Solve.**

1. How would you dress for the day if you looked at the following thermometer before school? Hint: would you dress for cold weather or warm weather?
   **It would be best to dress for cold weather.**
2. Michelle and Isaac each read a thermometer outside on a cool spring day. Michelle says it is 40°F outside. Isaac says it is 100°F outside. Who is correct? Explain your reasoning.
   **Sample answer: Michelle is correct. 100°F is a very warm temperature.**
3. Is it more reasonable to say that a glass of cold water would be 40°F or 150°F? Explain.
   **40°F is a reasonable temperature for a glass of cold water. A glass of water that is 150°F is very hot.**
4. Does the line on the thermometer go up or down when the temperature gets hotter? What about when the temperature gets colder?
   **As the temperature gets hotter, the line goes up. The line goes down as the temperature gets colder.**
5. The average June temperature in Mario's hometown is 75°F. Is this a cool temperature or a warm temperature?
   **warm temperature**
6. Name two situations in which you might see a thermometer being used.
   **Sample answers: doctor's visit; weather report; cooking**

Grade 4 46 Chapter 11

# Measure Temperatures

## 1 Introduce

### Activity Choice 1 • Hands-On

- **What measurement tells how hot or cold something is?** temperature
- **What tool do we use to measure temperature?** thermometer
- Distribute thermometers to small groups of students to examine. **What units do we use to measure temperature?** degrees

### Activity Choice 2 • Literature

Introduce the lesson with *The Snowy Day* by Ezra Jack Keats. For a related math activity, see p. TR60.

## 2 Teach

### Scaffolding Questions

Show students how to measure the room temperature in degrees Fahrenheit on the thermometer. Record the temperature.

- Place a thermometer in a cup of cold water.
- **Do you think the room temperature is warmer or colder than the water in the cup?** warmer
- Have students take the thermometer out of the cup and record the temperature in °F. **Is the air temperature warmer or colder? How do you know?** Sample answer: Warmer, because the air temperature is 67°F, the water temperature is 35°F, and 67 is greater than 35.
- **How could you find out how many degrees warmer the air is than the water?** Sample answer: Subtract 67°F − 35°F to find the difference in temperature.

### GET READY to Learn

Have students open their books and read the information in **Get Ready to Learn**. Introduce **degrees**, **Fahrenheit**, and **Celsius**. As a class, work through **Examples 1 and 2**.

## 11-8 Measure Temperatures

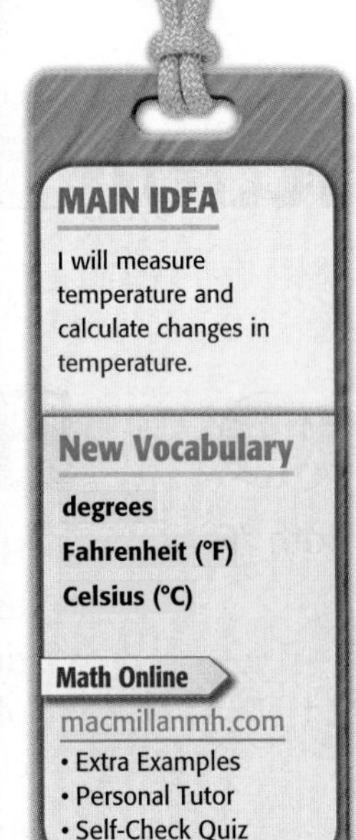


### GET READY to Learn

Ashton's teacher is measuring the temperature of the liquid being used in a science experiment. What is the temperature?

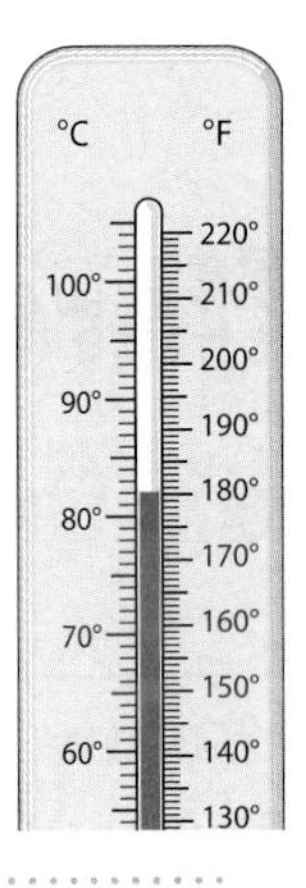


**Degrees** are the units of measurement used to describe temperature. Temperature can be measured in degrees **Celsius (°C)** or degrees **Fahrenheit (°F)**.

Read a Thermometer

1 **SCIENCE Find the temperature of the liquid being used in the experiment in degrees Celsius and Fahrenheit.**

Find the numbers next to the top of the red line.

The °C shows the temperature in degrees Celsius, and the °F shows the temperature in degrees Fahrenheit.

So, the temperature is about 82°C or 180°F.

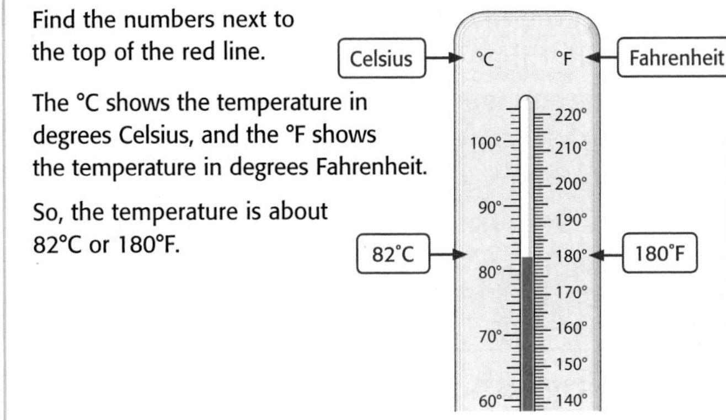




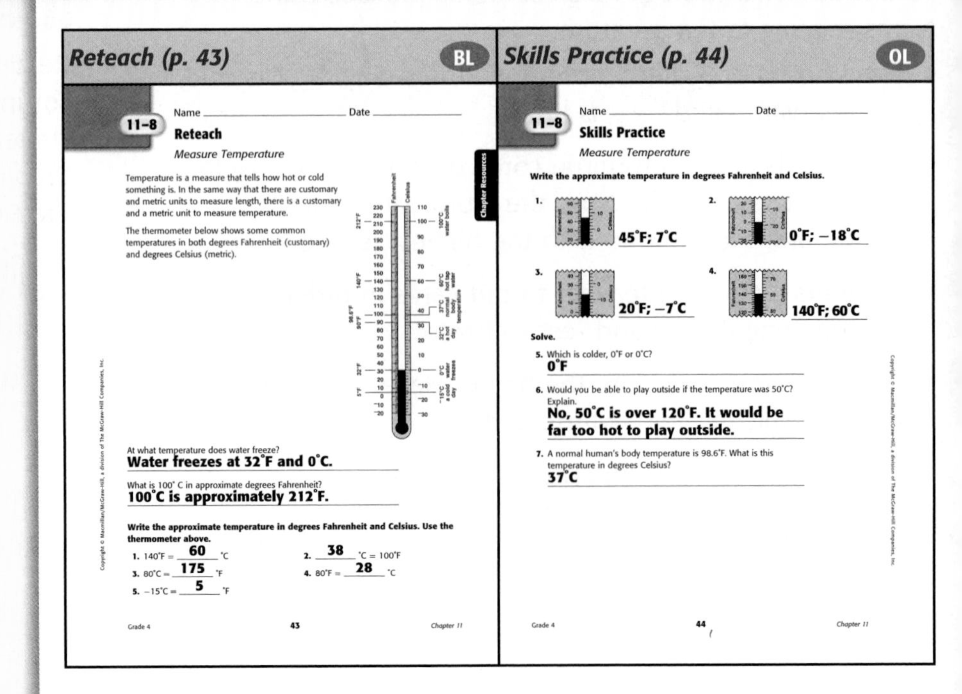

**Reteach (p. 43)** BL

11-8 Name ______ Date ______

**Reteach**

*Measure Temperature*

Temperature is a measure that tells how hot or cold something is. In the same way that there are customary and metric units to measure length, there is a customary and a metric unit to measure temperature.

The thermometer below shows some common temperatures in both degrees Fahrenheit (customary) and degrees Celsius (metric).



At what temperature does water freeze?
**Water freezes at 32°F and 0°C.**

What is 100° C in approximate degrees Fahrenheit?
**100°C is approximately 212°F.**

**Write the approximate temperature in degrees Fahrenheit and Celsius. Use the thermometer above.**

1. 140°F = **60** °C
2. **38** °C = 100°F
3. 80°C = **175** °F
4. 80°F = **28** °C
5. −15°C = **5** °F



Grade 4 43 Chapter 11

**Skills Practice (p. 44)** OL

11-8 Name ______ Date ______

**Skills Practice**

*Measure Temperature*

**Write the approximate temperature in degrees Fahrenheit and Celsius.**

1. **45°F; 7°C**
2. **0°F; −18°C**
3. **20°F; −7°C**
4. **140°F; 60°C**

**Solve.**

5. Which is colder, 0°F or 0°C?
**0°F**
6. Would you be able to play outside if the temperature was 50°C? Explain.
**No, 50°C is over 120°F. It would be far too hot to play outside.**
7. A normal human's body temperature is 98.6°F. What is this temperature in degrees Celsius?
**37°C**



Grade 4 44 Chapter 11

## ACTIVITY

### Hands-On Mini Activity

In this activity, you will measure and calculate changes in temperature.

1. Set a thermometer in the back of the classroom and another one outside.
2. At the end of math class, find the temperature indoors and outdoors.
3. How much warmer was one thermometer than the other in degrees Fahrenheit? How did you find the difference?
4. How much warmer was one thermometer than the other in degrees Celsius? How did you find the difference? **1–4. See students' work.**

Use addition or subtraction to find changes in temperatures.

### Temperature Change

**Remember**
When subtracting, you may need to regroup.

**2 Find the change in the inside and outside temperatures.**

inside thermometer

outside thermometer

84° − 68° = change in temperature

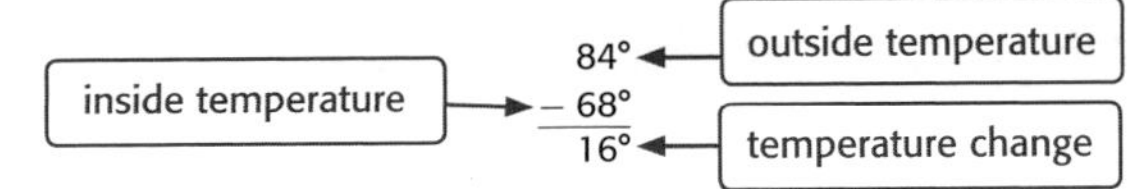


So, it is 16°F warmer outside than inside.



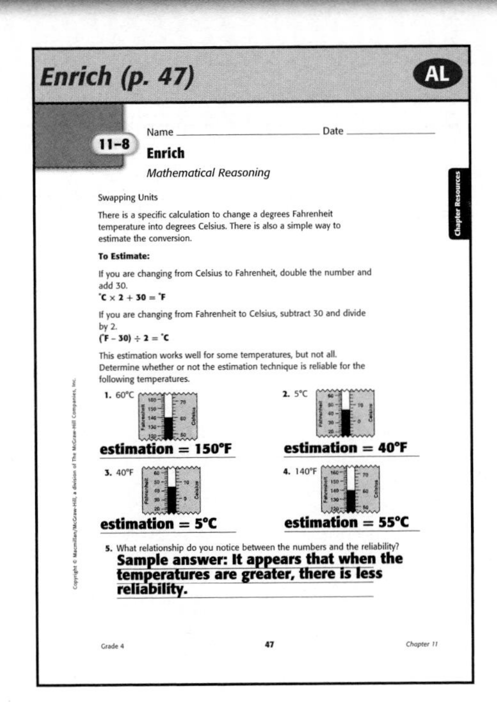

Enrich (p. 47) AL

11-8 Name ______ Date ______

**Enrich**

*Mathematical Reasoning*

Swapping Units

There is a specific calculation to change a degrees Fahrenheit temperature into degrees Celsius. There is also a simple way to estimate the conversion.

**To Estimate:**

If you are changing from Celsius to Fahrenheit, double the number and add 30.

**°C × 2 + 30 = °F**

If you are changing from Fahrenheit to Celsius, subtract 30 and divide by 2.

**(°F − 30) ÷ 2 = °C**

This estimation works well for some temperatures, but not all. Determine whether or not the estimation technique is reliable for the following temperatures.

1. 60°C **estimation = 150°F**
2. 5°C **estimation = 40°F**
3. 40°F **estimation = 5°C**
4. 140°F **estimation = 55°C**
5. What relationship do you notice between the numbers and the reliability? **Sample answer: It appears that when the temperatures are greater, there is less reliability.**

Chapter Resources

Copyright © Macmillan/McGraw-Hill, a division of The McGraw-Hill Companies, Inc.

Grade 4 47 Chapter 11

## Read a Thermometer

**Example 1** Make sure students do not confuse the readings for Fahrenheit and Celsius. You might want to point out that the numbers in degrees Fahrenheit are greater than the numbers in degrees Celsius, but that this does not mean that degrees Fahrenheit are warmer than degrees Celsius.

## ADDITIONAL EXAMPLES

**1** Write the temperature shown at the right in Fahrenheit and Celsius 65°F or about 15°C

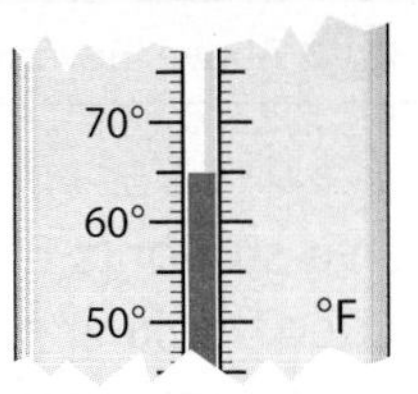


**2** Find the change in temperature from 10°F to 48°F. 38°F

## CHECK What You Know

As a class, have students complete Exercises 1–8 in **Check What You Know** as you observe their work.

**Exercise 4** Assess student comprehension before assigning practice exercises.

## BL Alternate Teaching Strategy

**If** students have trouble identifying temperatures in degrees Fahrenheit...

**Then** use one of these reteach options:

1. CRM **Daily Reteach Worksheet** (p. 43)
2. Point out the differences between the Celsius and Fahrenheit scales on a thermometer. **How many degrees does each mark represent on the Celsius scale?** 1 **How many degrees does each mark stand for on the Fahrenheit scale?** 2 Have students skip count by 2s to measure temperatures between numbers on the Fahrenheit scale.

## COMMON ERROR!

When finding the change in temperature, students may add the two temperatures or subtract the first from the second temperature or the second from the first. Remind students to subtract the smaller number from the greater number to find the change in temperature.

# 3 Practice

Differentiate practice using these leveled assignments for Exercises 9–25.

| Level | Assignment |
|---|---|
| BL Below/Approaching Level | 9–10, 13–14, 21 |
| OL On Level | 10–12, 14–16, 22, 24 |
| AL Above/Beyond Level | 10–22 even, 23–25 |

Have students discuss and complete the Higher Order Thinking problems. For Exercise 23, suggest that students find the high and low temperature in Fahrenheit and Celsius and then compare the changes in temperature.

**WRITING IN ▸MATH** Have students complete Exercise 30 in their Math Journals. You may choose to use this as an optional formative assessment.

### Additional Answer

5. Sample answer: no; She has confused 15°C and 15°F. She will not need a snowcap or mittens because it is too warm.

## CHECK What You Know

**Write the approximate temperature in degrees Fahrenheit and Celsius.** See Example 1 (p. 468)

**1.** 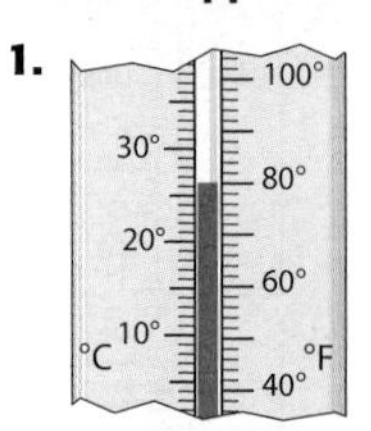

80°F; about 26°C

**2.** 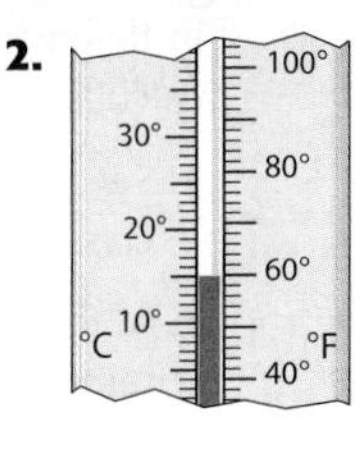

15°C; about 60°F

**Find the change in temperature.** See Example 2 (p. 469)

**3.** 16°C to 5°C 11°C

**4.** 34°F to 21°F 13°F

**5.** The thermometer reads 15°C. Vickie decides to wear her mittens and hat. Is this a good idea? Explain. See margin.

**6.** Talk About It The temperature outside is 16°F warmer than in the classroom temperature of 67°F. Write a number sentence for the outside temperature. $67 + 16 = 83$

## Practice and Problem Solving

EXTRA PRACTICE See page R30.

**Write the approximate temperature in degrees Fahrenheit and Celsius.** See Example 1 (p. 468)

**7.** 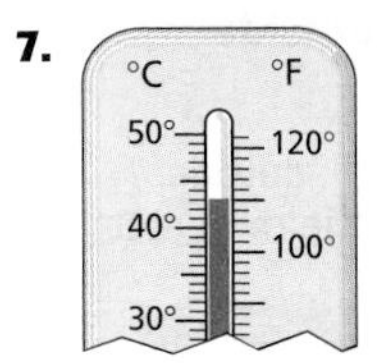

43°C; about 110°F

**8.** 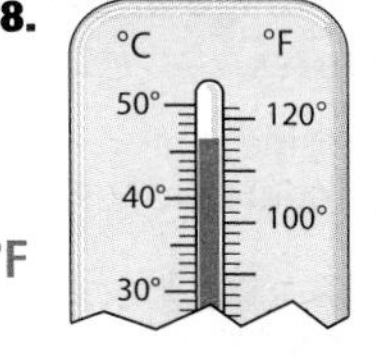

116°F; about 46°C

**9.** 

36°C; about 97°F

**10.** 91°F; about 33°C

**11.** 16°C; about 62°F

**12.** 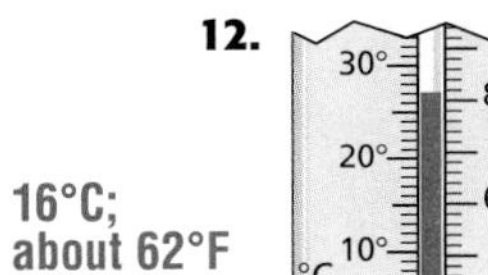

27°C; about 81°F

**Find the change in the temperature.** See Example 2 (p. 469)

**13.** 0°F to 26°F 26°F

**14.** 18°F to 6°F 12°F

**15.** 15°C to 8°C 7°C

**16.** 15°C to 31°C 16°C

**17.** 6°F to 38°F 32°F

**18.** 94°F to 59°F 35°F

**19.** 42°C to 78°C 36°C

**20.** 81°C to 13°C 68°C

**21.** 114°F to 67°F 47°F

2. Which is greater, a temperature change from 47°F to 79°F, or a temperature change from 28°F to 63°F?
**28°F to 63°F**

4. Two hamburgers are cooking on a grill. The grill's flame is 187°F. The flame needs to be 163°F hotter. At what temperature should the burgers cook?
**350°F**

**23.** Which is less, a temperature change from 17°C to 55°C, or a temperature change from 112°C to 71°C?
**17°C to 55°C**

**25.** When Neva woke up, the temperature was 20°C. By lunchtime, the temperature went up 6°C. The high temperature for the day was 31°C. How much higher did the temperature get after Neva had lunch? **5°C**

### Data File

Michigan temperatures can vary greatly between cities and during different times of day.

**26.** Identify the city and month(s) that show the least change in temperature. **Hancock, April**

**27.** Identify the city and month(s) that show a change in temperature equal to 24°F.
**Kalamazoo, May and June**

**Michigan Temperatures**

| | | April | May | June |
|---|---|---|---|---|
| Hancock Average | High | 46°F | 60°F | 68°F |
| | Low | 28°F | 40°F | 48°F |
| Kalamazoo Average | High | 60°F | 72°F | 81°F |
| | Low | 38°F | 48°F | 57°F |

**Source:** Country Studies U.S.

## H.O.T. Problems

**28. OPEN ENDED** Research the high and low temperatures from last week. Which day experienced the greatest change in temperature? **See students' work.**

**29. FIND THE ERROR** Abbie and Sashi each found the change in the temperature for today. Who is correct? Prove it. **Abbie is correct. Sashi added the temperatures together when they should have been subtracted.**

**Abbie**
"The high was 55°F and the low was 42°F. The change in temperature was 13°F."

**Sashi**
"The high was 55°F and the low was 42°F. The change in temperature was 97°F."

**30.** **WRITING IN ▸MATH** Write a real-world problem involving temperature. Have a classmate solve your problem. **See margin.**



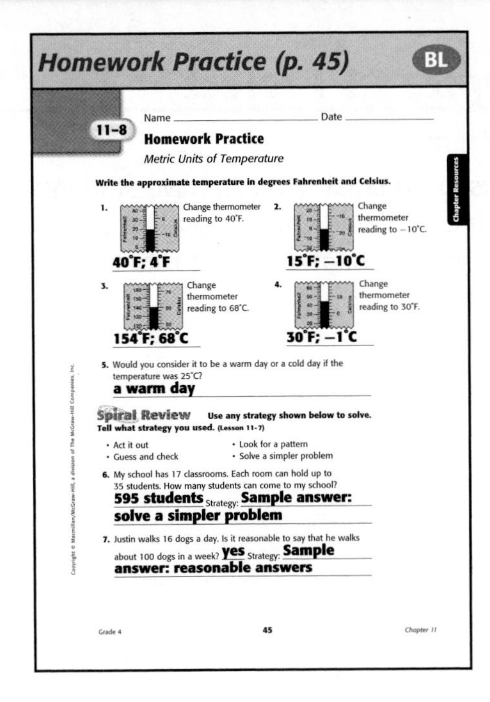

## Homework Practice (p. 45) BL

Name ______________ Date ______________

**11-8** **Homework Practice**
*Metric Units of Temperature*

**Write the approximate temperature in degrees Fahrenheit and Celsius.**

1. Change thermometer reading to 40°F.
**40°F; 4°F**

2. Change thermometer reading to −10°C.
**15°F; −10°C**

3. Change thermometer reading to 68°C.
**154°F; 68°C**

4. Change thermometer reading to 30°F.
**30°F; −1°C**

5. Would you consider it to be a warm day or a cold day if the temperature was 25°C?
**a warm day**

**Spiral Review** **Use any strategy shown below to solve. Tell what strategy you used.** (Lesson 11-7)

- Act it out
- Guess and check
- Look for a pattern
- Solve a simpler problem

6. My school has 17 classrooms. Each room can hold up to 35 students. How many students can come to my school?
**595 students** Strategy: **Sample answer: solve a simpler problem**

7. Justin walks 16 dogs a day. Is it reasonable to say that he walks about 100 dogs in a week? **yes** Strategy: **Sample answer: reasonable answers**

Chapter Resources



Grade 4 45 Chapter 11

# 4 Assess

### Formative Assessment

- **Suppose the outside temperature is 45°F and the inside temperature is 69°F. How would you find the change in temperature between the outside and inside? Explain.**
Subtract 45°F from 69°F to find the number of degrees that the temperature changed; 24°F.

**Quick Check** **Are students continuing to struggle with measuring and calculating changes in temperature?**

**If Yes** → Small Group Options (p. 422B)

**If No** → Independent Work Options (p. 422B)
CRM Skills Practice Worksheet (p. 44)
CRM Enrich Worksheet (p. 47)

**Ticket Out the Door** Have students write the change in temperature from 18°F to 39°F on a piece of paper, and have them hand it to you as they walk out the door.

### Additional Answer

**30.** Sample answer: The temperature this morning was 5°F warmer than last night. Write a number sentence where the unknown value is yesterday's high to show how to find this morning's temperature.

# CHAPTER 11 Study Guide and Review

## FOLDABLES® Dinah Zike's Foldables

Use these lesson suggestions to incorporate the Foldable during the chapter. Students can then use their Foldables to review for the test.

If students have not completed their Foldables, guide them to create and fill in the appropriate information using the instructions on pp. 438 and 453.

You may choose to use the Foldable to help students review the concepts presented in this chapter and as a tool for studying for the chapter test.

## Key Vocabulary

The page references after each word denote where that term was first introduced. If students have difficulty answering Exercises 1–5, remind them they can use the page references to review the vocabulary terms.

## Vocabulary Review

Review chapter vocabulary using one of the following options.

- **Visual Vocabulary Cards** (3, 36)
- **eGlossary** at macmillanmh.com



# CHAPTER 11 Study Guide and Review

**Be sure the following Key Vocabulary words and Key Concepts are written in your Foldable.**

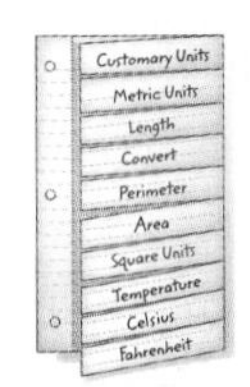


### Key Concepts

**Measure Length** (pp. 439–443 and 448–452)

- Common customary units of length are **inch**, **foot**, and **yard**.
- Metric units of length are **millimeter**, **centimeter**, **meter**, and **kilometer**.
- To measure the distance between two cities, you would use kilometers.

**Perimeter and Area** (pp. 456 and 460)

**Perimeter** is the distance around a figure.

- To find perimeter, add the lengths of the sides. $P = \ell + \ell + w + w$

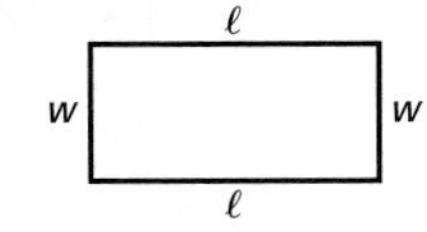


**Area** is the number of square units needed to cover a region or figure without any overlap.

- Area of a Rectangle = length × width

### Key Vocabulary

**area** (p. 460)
**convert** (p. 444)
**customary** (p. 441)
**metric** (p. 448)
**perimeter** (p. 456)

### Vocabulary Check

**Choose the vocabulary word that completes each sentence.**

1. The distance around a figure is the ___?___. perimeter
2. To find the ___?___ of a rectangle, you can multiply the length of the rectangle by its width. area
3. When you change the unit of measure, you ___?___ measurements. convert
4. ___?___ is the number of square units needed to cover a region or figure. area
5. Inch, foot, and yard are all ___?___ units of measure for length. customary

## Chapter 11 Project

### Map Your Home

Alone, in pairs, or in small groups, have students discuss the results of their completed chapter project with the class. Assess their work using the Chapter Project rubric found in Chapter 11 Resource Masters, p. 58.

## esson-by-Lesson Review

### 11-1 Customary Units of Length (pp. 441–443)

**Example 1**
**Estimate. Then measure the height of the seahorse below to the nearest inch, $\frac{1}{2}$ inch and $\frac{1}{4}$ inch.**

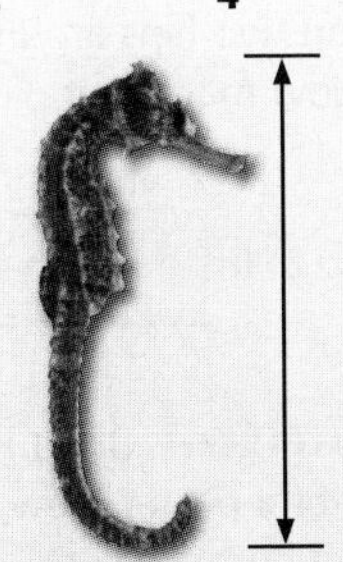

The seahorse is about 2, $1\frac{1}{2}$, or $1\frac{3}{4}$ inches long.

**Estimate. Then measure to the nearest inch, $\frac{1}{2}$ inch, and $\frac{1}{4}$ inch.**

**6.**

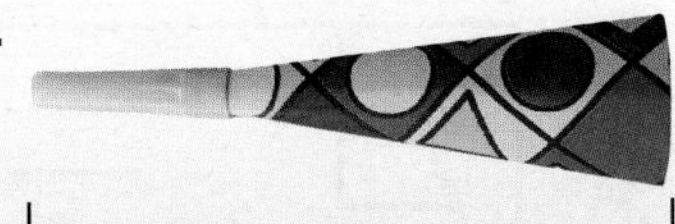

See margin.

**7.** The school supply store has index cards that are $2\frac{1}{2}$ inches wide and 3 inches long. How many inches long will four index cards be that are placed end to end? 12 in.

### 11-2 Convert Customary Units of Length (pp. 444–445)

**Example 2**
**How many feet are in 3 yards?**

You need to find the number of feet in 3 yards. Since a yard is a larger unit than a foot, use multiplication to convert.

To convert 3 yards to feet, multiply by 3.

3 yards = ■ feet

3 yards × 3 = ■ feet

Multiply by 3 since there are 3 feet in each yard.

3 × 3 = 9

So, 3 yards = 9 feet

**Complete.**

**8.** 2 ft = ■ in. 24

**9.** 6 ft = ■ in. 72

**10.** ■ in. = 2 yd 72

**11.** How many inches long is this wagon? 36 in.

**12.** John's mom needs 15 feet of fabric. She buys 4 yards of fabric. Did she buy enough? Explain. See margin.



# Lesson-by-Lesson Review

Have students complete the Lesson-by-Lesson Review on pp. 473–478. Then you can use ExamView® Assessment Suite to customize another review worksheet that practices all the objectives of this chapter or only the objectives on which your students need more help.

**Intervention** If the given examples are not sufficient to review the topics covered by the questions, use the page references next to the exercises to review that topic in the Student Edition.

### Additional Answers

**6.** 3, $2\frac{1}{2}$, $2\frac{2}{4}$

**12.** Sample answer: No; Four yards of fabric equals 4 × 3, or 12 feet of fabric. 12 < 15

# Chapter 11 Study Guide and Review

## 11-3 Problem-Solving Strategy: Solve a Simpler Problem (pp. 446–447)

**Example 3**
**Find the perimeter of the first floor of the house shown below.**

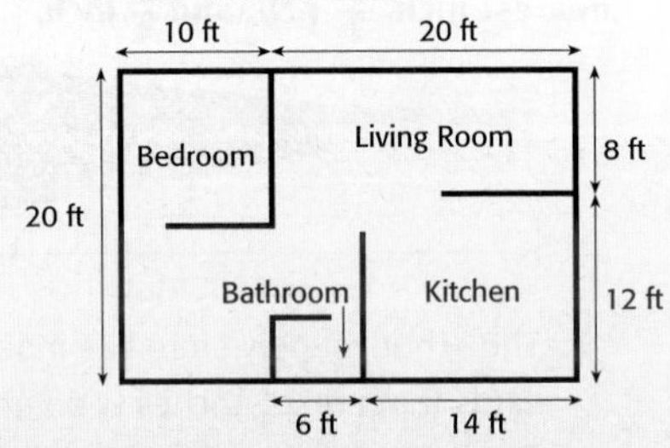


**Understand**

**What facts do you know?**

- One side measures 20 feet.
- Another side measures the sum of 10 feet and 20 feet.

**What do you need to find?**

- The perimeter of the house.

**Plan** Solve a simpler problem.

**Solve** Multiply the width by 2.

$20 \times 2 = 40$

Next, add 10 and 20. Then multiply the sum by 2.

$10 + 20 = 30$

$30 \times 2 = 60$

So, the perimeter is 40 + 60 or 100 feet.

**Check** Add all the measures

$20 + 10 + 6 + 14 + 12 + 8 + 20 + 10 = 100$

So, our answer is correct. ✓

**13. Measurement** Mr. and Mrs. Lobo are building a fence around their rectangular yard that is 16 feet long and 14 feet wide. How much fence will they need? **60 ft**

**14.** Heidi ran two laps around the track. How many feet did she run? **2,640 ft**

**15. Measurement** Oliver is buying a border for a poster. How many inches of border will Oliver need for a poster that is 44 inches long and 28 inches wide? **144 in.**

**16.** Look at this figure. What is the length of the dashed line? **7 in.**

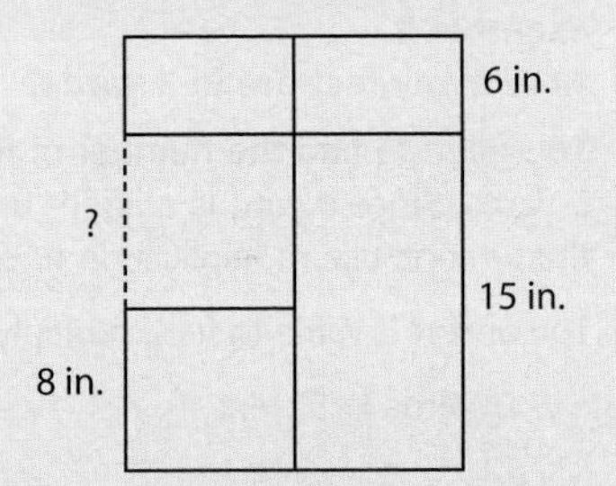


**17.** Martell had boxes he was stacking. Each was 2 feet high. If he stacks 3 boxes on top of a table that is 3 feet high, what will be the total height? **9 ft**

## 11-4 Metric Units of Length (pp. 450–452)

**Example 4**
**Measure the flower to the nearest centimeter.**

Align the 0 mark on the ruler to the left side of the flower. The flower ends at the 4-centimeter mark on the ruler.

So, the flower is 4 centimeters long.

**Measure the object to the nearest centimeter.**

**18.** 6 cm

**19.** 5 cm

## 11-5 Measure Perimeters (pp. 456–459)

**Example 5**
**Find the perimeter of the rectangle.**

12 in.
8 in. 8 in.
12 in.

$P = \ell + w + \ell + w$
$P = 12 + 8 + 12 + 8$
$P = 24 + 16$
$P = 40$ inches

**Example 6**
**Find the perimeter of the square.**

3 cm

$P = 4 \times s$
$P = 4 \times 3$
$P = 12$ centimeters

**Estimate the perimeter. Then find the exact perimeter.**

**20.** 15 cm, 3 cm — 36 cm

**21.** 6 yd, 6 yd — 24 yd

**22.** **Measurement** A poster has a length of 24 inches, and its width is 12 inches. What is the perimeter of the poster? 72 in.



**Chapter 11** Study Guide and Review **475**

Study Guide and Review

## 11-6 Measure Areas (pp. 460–462)

**Example 7**
**Find the area of a rectangle that is 7 meters long and 4 meters wide.**

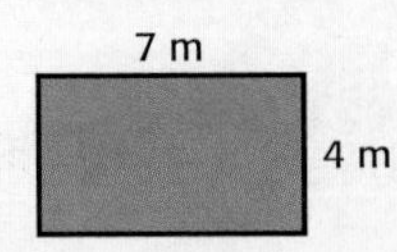


To find the area, multiply the length and the width.

$A = \ell \times w$
$A = 7$ meters $\times$ 4 meters
$A = 28$ square meters

So, the area of the rectangle is 28 square meters.

**Example 8**
**What is the area of a square with sides that are 5 inches long?**

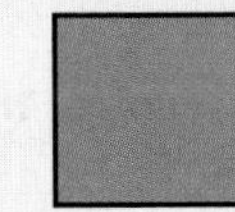


To find the area, multiply the side length by itself.

$A = s \times s$
$A = 5$ inches $\times$ 5 inches
$A = 25$ square inches

So, the area of the square is 25 square inches.

**Find the area of each square or rectangle.**

**23.** 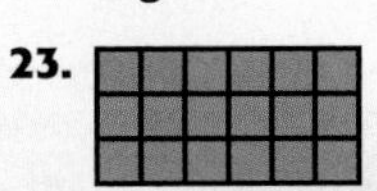 18 square units

**24.** 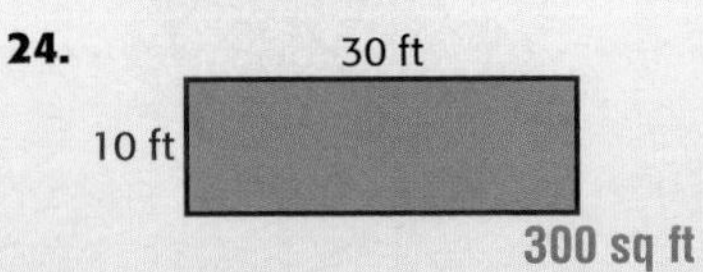

300 sq ft

**25.** 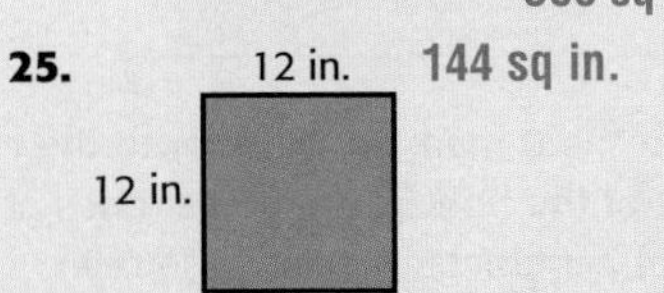

144 sq in.

**Algebra The area and the measure of one side of each square or rectangle is given. Find the measure of the missing side.**

**26.** 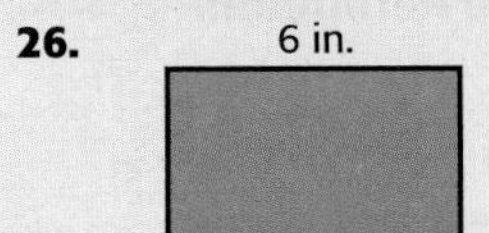


Area = 24 sq in. 4 in.

**27.** 8 ft

Area = 64 sq ft 8 ft

**28.** Rodolfo's table tennis table has an area of 45 square feet. The length is 9 feet. What is the perimeter of the table tennis table? 28 ft

476 Chapter 11 Measure Length, Area, and Temperature

## 11-7 Problem-Solving Investigation: Choose a Strategy (pp. 466–467)

**Example 9**
**Mr. Palmer is buying a cover for his pool table. Is it reasonable to say that a cover with an area of 30 square feet will be large enough to cover his pool table?**

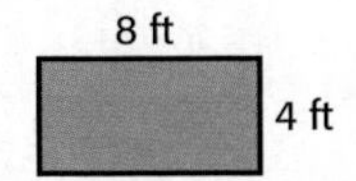


**Understand**

**What facts do you know?**

- The pool table is 8 feet by 4 feet.
- The area of the cover is 30 square feet.

**What do you need to find?**

- Is 30 square feet reasonable?

**Plan** Solve a simpler problem.

**Solve** $A = \ell \times w$

$A = 8 \text{ feet} \times 4 \text{ feet}$

$A = 32 \text{ square feet}$

The pool table has an area of 32 square feet. Since $30 < 32$, it is not reasonable to say that the cover is large enough.

**Check** $32 - 30 = 2$

So, the area of the pool table is 2 square feet larger than the cover. It is not large enough.

**Use any strategy to solve.**

**29.** Mindy is mowing the lawn. What area does she have to mow?

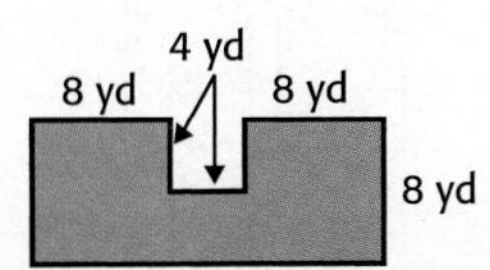


144 sq yards

**30. Measurement** What is the total area of the three squares below? 14 square units

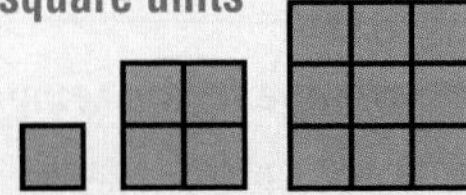

**31. Measurement** There are six tables that measure 3 feet by 6 feet. If a room measures 25 feet by 10 feet, will the tables fit in the room? See margin.

**32.** A sandbox measures 12 feet by 8 feet. The area of the playground is 200 square feet. How many square feet are not used by the sandbox? 104 sq ft

**33.** James bought lunch for $3. Then he paid his club $1. He earned $5 for mowing grass. He now has $25. How much did he start with? $24



### Addtional Answer

**31.** yes; They can be placed together in two rows of three.

CHAPTER 11 Study Guide and Review

## 11-8 Measure Temperatures (pp. 468–471)

**Example 10**
**Write the approximate temperature in degrees Fahrenheit and Celsius.**

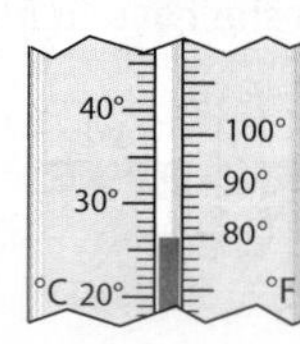


The red shows 80°F. So, it is approximately 25°C and 80°F.

**Example 11**
**Find the change in the temperatures.**

A thermometer inside reads:

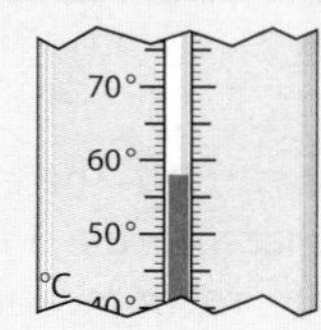


A thermometer outside reads:

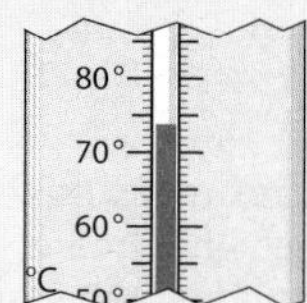


74° − 58° = change in temperature

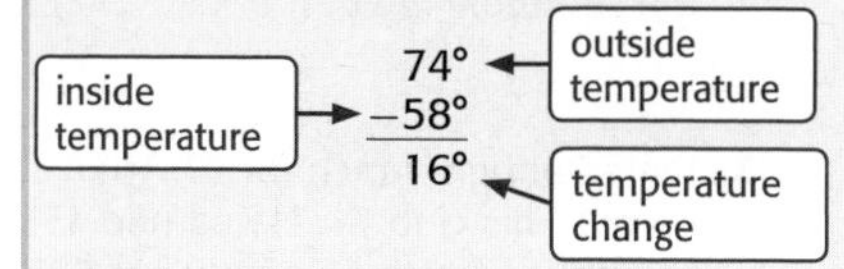


It is 16°C warmer outside than inside.

**34.** Write the approximate temperature in degrees Fahrenheit and Celsius.

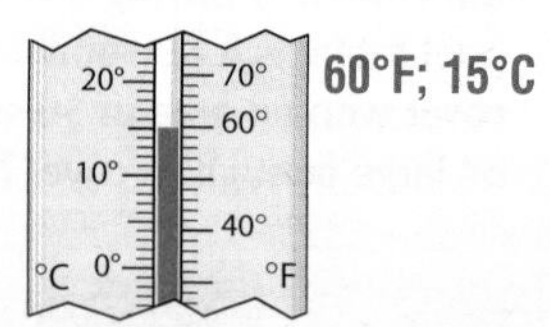


**35.** The thermometer reads 10°C. What type of clothing should be worn outside? **Sample answer: jacket**

**Find the change in temperature.**

**36.**

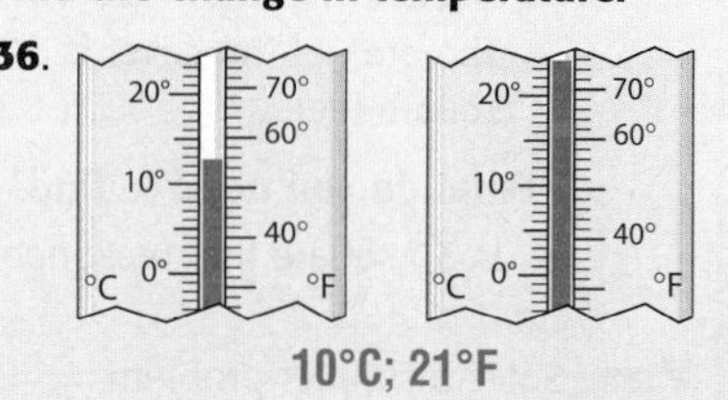


**37.**

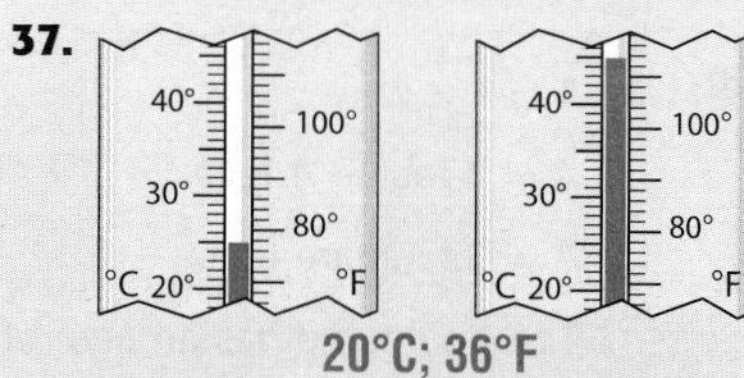


**38.** 2°F to 37°F **35°F**

**39.** 95°C to 41°C **54°C**

**40.** Elton's class is taking a field trip to the zoo. When the students arrived at school, the temperature was 80°F. When they left for the zoo, it was 95°F. How much warmer was it when they left for the zoo? **15°F**



478 Chapter 11 Measure Length, Area, and Temperature

# Chapter Test

Math Online macmillanmh.com
• Chapter Test

15. Sample answer: yes, All squares will be congruent, so they will have the same area.

**For Exercises 1 and 2, tell whether each statement is *true* or *false*.**

1. Area is the distance around a figure. false
2. To change units of measurement is to convert. true

**Choose the best estimate for each length.**

3. length of a green bean, 2 inches or 2 feet 2 in.

4. length of a sheep, 3 yards or 3 feet 3 ft

5. Tessa's swimming pool is 13 feet long. How many inches is this? 156 in.
6. A bottle of glue is about 15 centimeters tall. Name something else that has a height or width of about 15 centimeters. Sample answer: dollar bill

7. **MULTIPLE CHOICE** Which statement about the rectangle is true? C

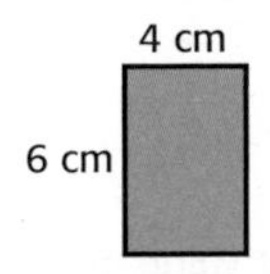


**A** The area is equal to the perimeter.
**B** The area is less than the perimeter.
**C** The perimeter is 20 centimeters.
**D** The area is 10 square centimeters.

8. Find the area of the rectangle. 8 square units

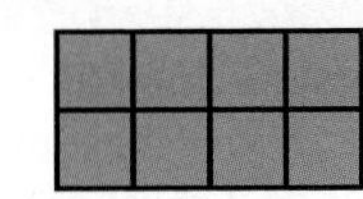

9. Brett painted 3 walls. Each wall was 9 feet tall and 12 feet long. How much wall area did he paint? 324 square ft
10. Which figure has the greater perimeter? Figure A

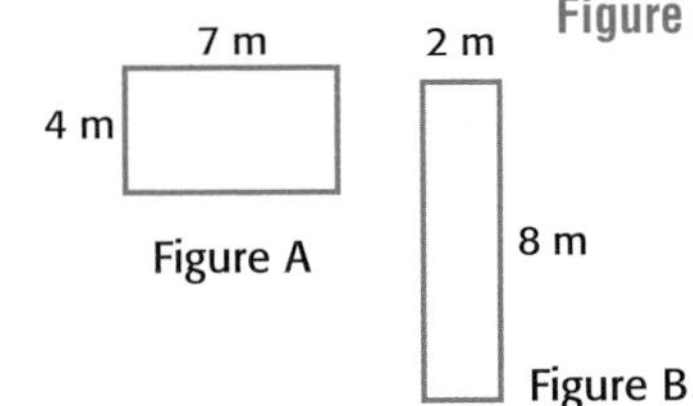


11. **Algebra** Three numbers between 1 and 8 have a sum of 20. Each number is used once. What are the numbers? 8, 7, 5

**Find the change in temperature.**

12. 25°C to 38°C 13°C
13. 70°F to 52°F 18°F
14. **MULTIPLE CHOICE** Which equation represents the area ($A$) of the square in square inches? G

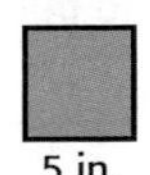


**F** $5 = A \times 5$ **H** $A = 5 + 5$
**G** $A = 5 \times 5$ **J** $A = 5 \times 4$

15. **WRITING IN MATH** Do all squares with one side of 3 inches have the same area? Explain.



# Chapter 11 Chapter Test

## Summative Assessment

Use these alternate leveled Chapter Tests to differentiate assessment for the specific needs of your students.

**Leveled Chapter 11 Tests**

| Form | Type | Level | CRM Pages |
|---|---|---|---|
| 1 | Multiple Choice | BL | 60–61 |
| 2A | Multiple Choice | OL | 62–63 |
| 2B | Multiple Choice | OL | 64–65 |
| 2C | Free Response | OL | 66–67 |
| 2D | Free Response | OL | 68–69 |
| 3 | Free Response | AL | 70–71 |

BL = below/approaching grade level
OL = on grade level
AL = above/beyond grade level

## Vocabulary Test

CRM **Chapter 11 Resource Masters** (p. 55)

ExamView Assessment Suite Customize and create multiple versions of your Chapter Test and the test answer keys.

## Data-Driven Decision Making

Based on the results of the Chapter Test, use the following to review concepts that continue to present students with problems.

| Exercises | State/Local Standards | What's the Math? | Error Analysis | Resources for Review |
|---|---|---|---|---|
| 1, 8–9, 14–15 | | Measure and solve problems involving length, width, and area. | Does not measure accurately. Does not add or multiply accurately. Does not know how to find area. | Strategic Intervention Guide (pp. 118, 122)<br>CRM Chapter 11 Resource Masters (Reteach)<br>Math Adventures<br>My Math Zone Chapter 11<br>Math Online Extra Examples • Concepts in Motion |
| 6, 10 | | Measure and solve problems involving length, width, and perimeter. | Does not measure accurately. Does not add correctly. Does not know how to find perimeter. Does not include all sides. | |
| 12–13 | | Measure temperature using a thermometer. | Does not read thermometer lines correctly. Does not subtract correctly. Adds two temperatures. | |

# CHAPTER 11 Test Practice

### Formative Assessment

- Use Student Edition pp. 480–481 as practice and cumulative review. The questions are written in the same style as many state tests.
- You can also use these two pages to benchmark student progress, or as an alternate homework assignment.

Additional practice pages can be found in the Chapter 11 Resource Masters.

CRM **Chapter 11 Resource Masters**
Cumulative Test Practice
- Multiple Choice format (pp. 65)
- Free Response format (pp. 66)

Create practice worksheets or tests that align to your state standards.

**Math Online** Have students visit macmillanmh.com for additional practice to reinforce your state standards.

## Test Practice
Cumulative, Chapters 1–11

**Math Online** macmillanmh.com
- Test Practice

**PART 1 Multiple Choice**

**Read each question. Then fill in the correct answer on the answer sheet provided by your teacher or on a sheet of paper.**

1. Which shape has bilateral symmetry? B

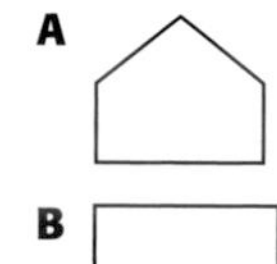

A, B, C, D

2. The numbers in the pattern decrease by the same amount each time. What are the next three numbers? G

   32, 28, 24, 20, 16, ■, ■, ■

   **F** 14, 10, 6 **H** 10, 6, 2
   **G** 12, 8, 4 **J** 9, 5, 1

3. Hannah plans to put a fence around her yard.

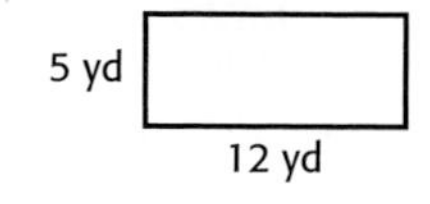


   What is the perimeter of the yard? C

   **A** 28 yards **C** 34 yards
   **B** 32 yards **D** 46 yards

4. The map shows the distance from Lora's house to school. Use a ruler to measure the line segment. What is the distance from Lora's house to school? H

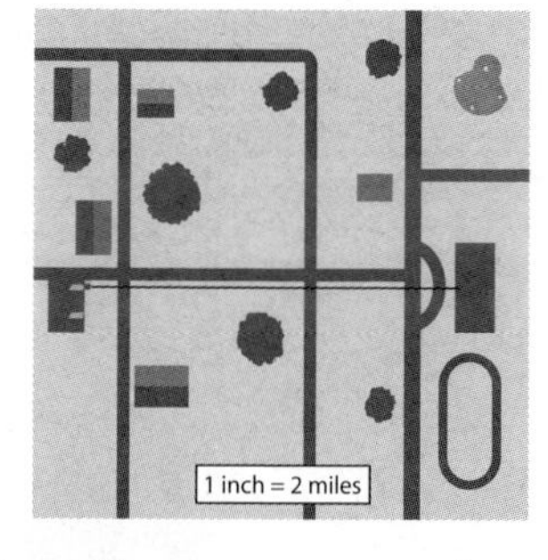


   **F** 2 miles **H** 3 miles
   **G** 2.5 miles **J** 4.5 miles

5. Nate hiked two miles. If one mile equals 5,280 feet, how many feet did he hike? D

   **A** 10,056 feet **C** 10,506 feet
   **B** 10,065 feet **D** 10,560 feet

6. What is the value of the expression below if $n = 4$? F

   $$42 \div (n + 2)$$

   **F** 7 **H** 5
   **G** 6 **J** 4



## Test-Taking Tip

Tell students that before taking the test, it is a good idea to familiarize themselves with geometry formulas.

**Preparing for Standardized Tests**
For test-taking strategies and practice, see pages R42–R55.

7. How many tiles that are 1 foot long and 1 foot wide are needed to tile the floor shown? D

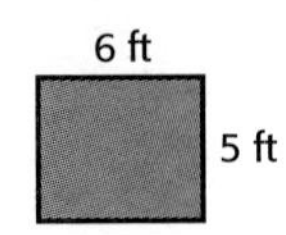


A 11 tiles
B 25 tiles
C 26 tiles
D 30 tiles

8. A rectangle has an area of 28 square units. Which of the following could not be its length and width? G

F $7 \times 4$
G $9 \times 3$
H $14 \times 2$
J $28 \times 1$

9. Which triangle appears to be congruent to the one shown at the right? C

A 
B 
C 
D 

**PART 2 Short Response**

**Record your answers on the answer sheet provided by your teacher or on a sheet of paper.**

10. Rina's bedroom is shaped like a rectangle. It is 12 feet long and 10 feet wide. What is the area, in square feet, of the room? 120 square feet

11. What is the perimeter of a square that has an area of 49 square centimeters? 28 cm

**PART 3 Extended Response**

**Record your answers on the answer sheet provided by your teacher or on a sheet of paper.**

12. Suppose the temperature on the thermometer shown below increases by 12°F. Explain how to find the new temperature. See margin.

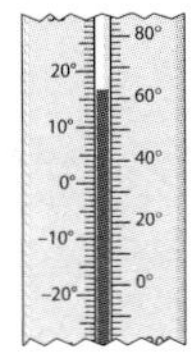


| NEED EXTRA HELP? | | | | | | | | | | | | |
|---|---|---|---|---|---|---|---|---|---|---|---|---|
| If You Missed Question... | 1 | 2 | 3 | 4 | 5 | 6 | 7 | 8 | 9 | 10 | 11 | 12 |
| Go to Lesson... | 10-8 | 5-4 | 11-5 | 11-1 | 2-4 | 5-6 | 11-6 | 11-6 | 10-7 | 11-6 | 11-6 | 11-8 |



# Answer Sheet Practice

Have students simulate taking a state test by recording their answers on a practice recording sheet.

**CRM Chapter 11 Resource Masters**
Student Recording Sheet (p. 76)

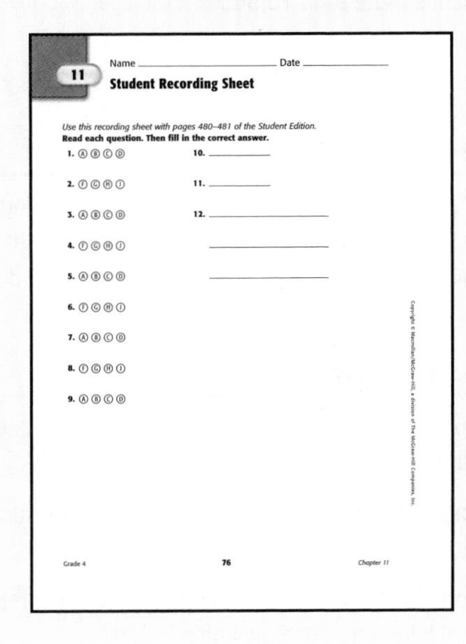
Name ______ Date ______
11 **Student Recording Sheet**

*Use this recording sheet with pages 480–481 of the Student Edition.*
**Read each question. Then fill in the correct answer.**

1. Ⓐ Ⓑ Ⓒ Ⓓ
2. Ⓕ Ⓖ Ⓗ Ⓙ
3. Ⓐ Ⓑ Ⓒ Ⓓ
4. Ⓕ Ⓖ Ⓗ Ⓙ
5. Ⓐ Ⓑ Ⓒ Ⓓ
6. Ⓕ Ⓖ Ⓗ Ⓙ
7. Ⓐ Ⓑ Ⓒ Ⓓ
8. Ⓕ Ⓖ Ⓗ Ⓙ
9. Ⓐ Ⓑ Ⓒ Ⓓ

10. ______
11. ______
12. ______

Grade 4 76 Chapter 11

## Additional Answer

12. Sample answer: The temperature shown on the thermometer is 63°F. So, an increase of 12°F would be 63°F + 12°F or 75°F.

## Page 442, Lesson 11-1

**5.** Sample answer: By having units that are larger and smaller, measurements can be more precise.

**14.** Sample answer: Pencil and calculator. Knowing things that are between 2 and 4 inches are smaller items, I avoided larger items such as textbooks, binders, and folders.

**15.** Sample answer: An odometer can be used to measure the miles from one town to the next. A measuring wheel can be used to measure the distance of the school's hallway.

## Page 445, Lesson 11-2

**8.** Sample answer: To convert smaller units to larger units, divide by the number of units in the smaller unit.

**22.** Sample answer: Valerie lives closer because 2 miles is equal to 10,560 feet, which is more than 10,542.

## Page 447, Lesson 11-3

**12.** Sample answer: First, find the number of photographs that will be placed on ech page by finding $72 \div 6 = 12$. Now, find the number of rows on each page by finding $12 \div 4 = 3$. So, there will be 3 rows on each page.

## Page 451, Lesson 11-4

**5.** Sample answer: no, 150 millimeters is too small for a person. She probably meant 150 centimeters.

**6.** Sample answer: Millimeters are good to measure small things such as bugs.

**13.** Sample answer: yes; The distance from Boston to Phoenix is very long. So, 4,000 kilometers is reasonable.

**15.** Sample answer: A meter stick is longer than a centimeter ruler. Since a classroom's length is many meters long, a meter stick would be the better measurement tool to use.

## Page 462, Lesson 11-6

**16.** $3 \times 12$; $4 \times 9$; $6 \times 6$ Sample answer:

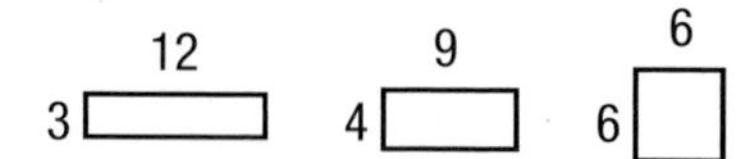

## NOTES

Chapter 11 Answer Appendix

# Chapter Overview

## Chapter-at-a-Glance

In Chapter 12, the emphasis is on measuring and estimating customary and metric units of capacity, weight, mass, and volume.

| Lesson | Math Objective | State/Local Standards |
|---|---|---|
| EXPLORE 12-1 **Estimate and Measure Capacity** (p. 485) | Estimate and measure capacity. | |
| 12-1 **Customary Units of Capacity** (pp. 486–489) | Estimate and measure customary capacities. | |
| 12-2 **Convert Customary Units of Capacity** (pp. 490–491) | Convert customary units of capacity. | |
| 12-3 **Metric Units of Capacity** (pp. 492–495) | Estimate and measure metric capacities. | |
| EXPLORE 12-4 **Estimate and Measure Weight** (pp. 496–497) | Estimate and measure weight. | |
| 12-4 **Customary Units of Weight** (pp. 498–500) | Estimate and measure customary units of weight. | |
| 12-5 **Problem-Solving Strategy: Use Logical Reasoning** (pp. 502–503) | Solve problems using logical reasoning. | |
| 12-6 **Convert Customary Units of Weight** (pp. 504–507) | Convert customary units of weight. | |
| 12-7 **Metric Units of Mass** (pp. 508–510) | Estimate and measure mass and learn the difference between weight and mass. | |
| 12-8 **Estimate and Measure Volume** (pp. 512–515) | Estimate and measure volume in cubic units. | |
| 12-9 **Problem-Solving Investigation: Choosing the Best Strategy** (pp. 518–519) | Choose the best strategy to solve a problem. | |
| 12-10 **Elapsed Time** (pp. 520–523) | Solve problems about elapsed time. | |

## Measure Capacity, Weight, and Volume

**BIG Idea** In Grade 3, students identified and used concrete models that approximate standard units of weight, mass, capacity, and volume to measure various items. In Chapter 12, students transition from using models to approximate measurements to using measurement tools. Students are also introduced to conversions within the customary measurement system. These prerequisite skills will be further developed in Grade 5, when students connect models with formulas. In Lesson 12-10, students expand upon their foundation of telling time to the minute to solving problems that involve elapsed time.

**G4-FP3** *Measurement:* **Developing an understanding of area and determining the areas of two-dimensional shapes**

Students recognize area as an attribute of two-dimensional regions. They learn that they can quantify area by finding the total number of same-sized units of area that cover the shape without gaps or overlaps. They understand that a square that is 1 unit on a side is the standard unit for measuring area. They select appropriate units, strategies (e.g., decomposing shapes), and tools for solving problems that involve estimating or measuring area. Students connect area measure to the area model that they have used to represent multiplication, and they use this connection to justify the formula for the area of a rectangle.

**G4-FP5C** *Geometry:* Students extend their understanding of properties of two-dimensional shapes as they find the areas of polygons. They build on their earlier work with symmetry and congruence in grade 3 to encompass transformations, including those that produce line and rotational symmetry. By using transformations to design and analyze simple tilings and tessellations, students deepen their understanding of two-dimensional space.

## Skills Trace

**Vertical Alignment**

### Third Grade

**In third grade, students learned to:**

- Measure and choose customary and metric units of capacity, weight, and mass.
- Use models to measure volume.
- Tell time.

### Fourth Grade

**During this chapter, students learn to:**

- Estimate and measure capacity, weight, mass, and volume.
- Convert customary units of capacity and weight.
- Explain the difference between weight and mass.
- Solve problems about elapsed time.

**After this chapter, students learn to:**

- Find equivalent fractions.

### Fifth Grade

**In fifth grade, students learn to:**

- Convert customary and metric units of capacity, weight, mass, and time.
- Add and subtract measures of elapsed time.

**Backmapping and Vertical Alignment** **McGraw-Hill's *Math Connects*** program was conceived and developed with the final results in mind: student success in Algebra 1 and beyond. The authors, using the **NCTM Focal Points and Focal Connections** as their guide, developed this brand-new series by backmapping from Algebra 1 concepts, and vertically aligning the topics so that they build upon prior skills and concepts and serve as a foundation for future topics.

## Math Vocabulary

The following math vocabulary words for Chapter 12 are listed in the glossary of the ***Student Edition.*** You can find interactive definitions in 13 languages in the ***eGlossary*** at macmillanmh.com.

**capacity** The amount a container can hold, measured in units of dry or liquid measure. (p. 486A)

**cubic units** A unit for measuring volume, such as a cubic inch or a cubic centimeter. (p. 512A)

**cup • pint** Customary units for measuring capacity. 2 cups = 1 pint, 16 cups = 1 gallon (p. 486A)

**elapsed time** The amount of time between the beginning and end of an activity. (p. 520A)

**gallon • quart** Customary units for measuring capacity for liquids. 1 gallon = 4 quarts (p. 486A)

**gram • kilogram** Metric units for measuring mass. (p. 508A)

**liter • milliliter** Metric units for measuring volume or capacity. 1 liter = 1000 milliliters (p. 492A)

**mass** The amount of matter in an object. (p. 508A)

**pound • ounce** Customary units for measuring weight. 1 pound = 16 ounces (p. 498A)

**ton** A customary unit to measure weight. 1 ton = 2000 pounds (p. 498A)

**volume** The number of cubic units needed to fill a 3-dimensional figure or solid figure. (p. 512A)

**weight** A measurement that tells how heavy or light an object is. (p. 498A)

# Chapter Planner

| Suggested Pacing | | |
|---|---|---|
| Instruction | Review & Assessment | TOTAL |
| 12 days | 1 day | **13 days** |

**Diagnostic Assessment**
Quick Check (p. 484)

| | Explore 12-1 (Pacing: 1 day) | Lesson 12-1 (Pacing: 1 day) | Lesson 12-2 (Pacing: 1 day) |
|---|---|---|---|
| **Lesson/ Objective** | **Estimate and Measure Capacity** (p. 485)<br><br>**Objective:** Estimate and measure capacity. | **Customary Units of Capacity** (pp. 486–489)<br><br>**Objective:** Estimate and measure customary capacities. | **Convert Customary Units of Capacity** (pp. 490–491)<br><br>**Objective:** Convert customary units of capacity. |
| **State/Local Standards** | | | |
| **Math Vocabulary** | | **capacity**, **fluid ounce**, **cup**, **pint**, **quart**, **gallon** | |
| **Lesson Resources** | **Materials**<br>water, food coloring<br><br>**Manipulatives**<br>capacity containers (cup, pint, quart, and gallon) | **Materials**<br>water, pictures of containers<br><br>**Manipulatives**<br>capacity containers<br><br>**Other Resources**<br>CRM Leveled Worksheets (pp. 8–12)<br>Daily Reteach • 5-Minute Check • Problem of the Day | **Materials**<br>two pots (or bowls), sand (rice or water)<br><br>**Manipulatives**<br>standard containers for measuring capacity<br><br>**Other Resources**<br>CRM Leveled Worksheets (pp. 13–17)<br>Daily Reteach • 5-Minute Check • Problem of the Day |
| **Technology** | | | Math Adventures |
| **Math Online** | | Personal Tutor | Personal Tutor |
| **Reaching All Learners** | | English Learners, p. 486B ELL<br>Gifted and Talented, p. 486B AL<br>Early Finishers, p. 486B AL | English Learners, p. 490B ELL<br>Below Level, p. 490B BL<br>Early Finishers, p. 490B AL |
| **Alternate Lesson** | | *IMPACT Mathematics:* Unit H | |

**KEY**

BL Below/Approaching Level · OL On Level · AL Above/Beyond Level · ELL English Learners
SE Student Edition · TE Teacher Edition · CRM Chapter 12 Resource Masters · CD-Rom
Transparency · Real-World Problem Solving Library

| | Lesson 12-3 (Pacing: 1 day) | Explore 12-4 (Pacing: 1 day) | Lesson 12-4 (Pacing: 1 day) |
|---|---|---|---|
| **Lesson/ Objective** | **Metric Units of Capacity** (pp. 492–495)<br>**Objective:** Estimate and measure metric capacities. | **Estimate and Measure Weight** (pp. 496–497)<br>**Objective:** Estimate and measure weight. | **Customary Units of Weight** (pp. 498–500)<br>**Objective:** Estimate and measure customary units of weight. |
| **State/Local Standards** | | | |
| **Math Vocabulary** | **liter**, **milliliter** | | **weight**, **ounce**, **pound**, **ton** |
| **Lesson Resources** | **Materials**<br>vase, pitcher or other objects that hold liquid, everyday objects whose content are measured in L or mL<br>**Manipulatives**<br>capacity containers<br>**Other Resources**<br>CRM Leveled Worksheets (pp. 18–22)<br>Daily Reteach • 5-Minute Check • Problem of the Day | **Materials**<br>chalkboard eraser, glue bottle<br>**Manipulatives**<br>balance scale, ounce and pound weights | **Manipulatives**<br>balance scale, weights<br>**Other Resources**<br>CRM Leveled Worksheets (pp. 23–27)<br>Daily Reteach • 5-Minute Check • Problem of the Day |
| **Technology** / Math Online | Concepts in Motion • Personal Tutor | | Personal Tutor |
| **Reaching All Learners** | English Learners, p. 492B ELL<br>Below Level, p. 492B BL<br>Early Finishers, p. 492B AL | | English Learners, p. 498B ELL<br>Below Level, p. 498B BL<br>Early Finishers, p. 498B AL |
| **Alternate Lesson** | *IMPACT Mathematics:* Unit H | | |

**Formative Assessment**
Mid-Chapter Check (p. 501)

# Chapter Planner

| | Lesson 12-5 (Pacing: 1 day) | Lesson 12-6 (Pacing: 1 day) | Lesson 12-7 (Pacing: 1 day) |
|---|---|---|---|
| **Lesson/ Objective** | **Problem-Solving Strategy Using Logical Reasoning** (pp. 502–503)<br>**Objective:** Solve problems using logical reasoning. | **Convert Customary Units of Weight** (pp. 504–507)<br>**Objective:** Convert customary units of weight. | **Metric Units of Mass** (pp. 508–510)<br>**Objective:** Estimate and measure mass and learn the difference between weight and mass. |
| **State/Local Standards** | | | |
| **Math Vocabulary** | | | **mass**, **gram**, **kilogram** |
| **Lesson Resources** | **Other Resources**<br>CRM Leveled Worksheets (pp. 28–32)<br>Daily Reteach • 5-Minute Check • Problem of the Day<br>*Strange but True* | **Manipulatives**<br>pan balance<br>**Other Resources**<br>CRM Leveled Worksheets (pp. 33–37)<br>Daily Reteach • 5-Minute Check • Problem of the Day | **Materials**<br>small objects to be weighed, packages marked in grams or kilograms<br>**Manipulatives**<br>pan balance<br>**Other Resources**<br>CRM Leveled Worksheets (pp. 38–42)<br>Daily Reteach • 5-Minute Check • Problem of the Day |
| **Technology**<br>Math Online | Personal Tutor | Personal Tutor | Personal Tutor |
| **Reaching All Learners** | English Learners, p. 502B ELL<br>Below Level, p. 502B BL<br>Early Finishers, p. 502B OL AL | English Learners, p. 504B ELL<br>Below Level, p. 504B BL<br>Early Finishers, p. 504B AL | English Learners, p. 508B ELL<br>Below Level, p. 508B BL<br>Early Finishers, p. 508B AL |
| **Alternate Lesson** | | | |

**Game Time**
Massive Estimates (p. 511)

| | Lesson 12-8 (Pacing: 1 day) | Lesson 12-9 (Pacing: 1 day) | Lesson 12-10 (Pacing: 1 day) |
|---|---|---|---|
| **Lesson/Objective** | **Estimate and Measure Volume** (pp. 512–515)<br>**Objective:** Estimate and measure volume in cubic units. | **Problem-Solving Investigation Choosing the Best Strategy** (pp. 518–519)<br>**Objective:** Choose the best strategy to solve a problem. | **Elapsed Time** (pp. 520–523)<br>**Objective:** Solve problems about elapsed time. |
| **State/Local Standards** | | | |
| **Math Vocabulary** | **volume**, **cubic units**, **cubic centimeter** | | **elapsed time** |
| **Lesson Resources** | **Manipulatives**<br>rectangular prism and cube from the set of geometric solids, centimeter cubes<br>**Other Resources**<br>CRM Leveled Worksheets (pp. 43–47)<br>Daily Reteach • 5-Minute Check • Problem of the Day | **Other Resources**<br>CRM Leveled Worksheets (pp. 48–52)<br>Daily Reteach • 5-Minute Check • Problem of the Day<br>*Strange but True* | **Materials**<br>stopwatch<br>**Manipulatives**<br>clocks<br>**Other Resources**<br>CRM Leveled Worksheets (pp. 53–57)<br>Daily Reteach • 5-Minute Check • Problem of the Day |
| **Technology** | Math Adventures | | Math Adventures |
| **Math Online** | Personal Tutor | Personal Tutor | Personal Tutor |
| **Reaching All Learners** | English Learners, p. 512B ELL<br>Gifted and Talented, p. 512B AL<br>Early Finishers, p. 512B AL | English Learners, p. 518B ELL<br>Gifted and Talented, p. 518B AL<br>Below Level, p. 518B OL AL | English Learners, p. 520B ELL<br>Gifted and Talented, p. 520B AL<br>Early Finishers, p. 520B AL |
| **Alternate Lesson** | *IMPACT Mathematics:* Unit H | | *IMPACT Mathematics:* Unit G |

**Problem Solving in Science** (p. 516)

**Summative Assessment**
- Study Guide/Review (p. 524)
- Chapter Test (p. 531)
- Test Practice (p. 532)

# Chapter Overview

## Assessment Options

### Diagnostic Assessment

- SE *Option 1:* Quick Check (p. 484)
- *Option 2:* Online Quiz macmillanmh.com
- CRM *Option 3:* Diagnostic Test (p. 59)
- CRM *Option 4:* Chapter Pretest (p. 60)

### Formative Assessment

- TE Alternate Teaching Strategy (in every lesson)
- SE Talk About It (in every lesson)
- SE Writing in Math (in every lesson)
- SE Check What You Know (in every lesson)
- TE Ticket Out the Door (pp. 495, 510, 529)
- TE Into the Future (p. 489)
- TE Yesterday's News (p. 507)
- TE Name the Math (pp. 500, 515)
- SE Mid-Chapter Check (p. 501)
- CRM Lesson Quizzes (pp. 61–63)
- CRM Mid-Chapter Test (p. 64)

### Summative Assessment

- SE Chapter Test (p. 531)
- SE Test Practice (pp. 532–533)
- CRM Vocabulary Test (p. 65)
- CRM Leveled Chapter Tests (pp. 70–81)
- CRM Cumulative Test Practice (pp. 84–86)
- CRM Oral Assessment (p. 66–67)
- ExamView® Assessment Suite
- Advance Tracker

## Assessment Tips

Measurement concepts can be difficult for students to grasp, so be very clear regarding the objectives you want them to master.

- Come up with four or five specific objectives you want to observe during this chapter.
- Create a class checklist, which includes these four or five objectives.
- When students master a specific objective, check it off.
- Add comments where appropriate.

## Professional Development

Targeted professional development has been articulated throughout **McGraw-Hill's *Math Connects*** program. The **McGraw-Hill Professional Development Video Library** provides short videos that support the **NCTM Focal Points and Focal Connections.** For more information visit **macmillanmh.com**.

# Teacher Notes

# Learning Stations

## Cross-Curricular Links

### Writing

individual | LINGUISTIC

**Clock Journal**

Write a journal entry that tells how you spend your time.

- Write a fictional entry in your journal that tells about your day. Next to each event you describe, draw two clocks: one with the starting time for that event and one with the end time. Then, under the clocks, write the elapsed time.
- At the end of your journal entry, write about the activity that took you the longest that day. Was it an activity you enjoyed? Explain in your journal.

My Day, Minute by Minute

**Materials:**
- lined paper
- pencil

### Art

pair | VISUAL

**Rainbow Paint**

Measure and swirl together paints to make a rainbow.

- You and your partner each choose a different paint color and measure four ounces of each color. Put both into one bowl, one color at a time. Gently swirl with a stirrer. Make sure you do not overmix.
- How many cups of paint do you have in your bowl? Paint your first stripe of your rainbows with your swirled paint.
- Repeat the process with two other paint colors. Label your paintings with the number of ounces of paint you mixed. How many cups is that?

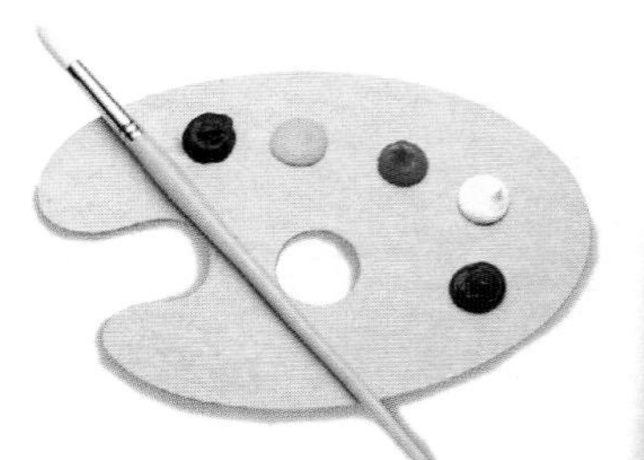

**Materials:**
- paper
- tempera paints
- liquid measuring cups
- plastic bowls that will hold at least one cup of paint each
- paintbrushes
- water for rinsing

### Health

individual | LOGICAL

**Serving Reality Check**

To stay healthy, you need to keep a close watch on portion sizes. Food measurements are everywhere, so check your labels.

- Look at the label on the back of a juice bottle. How many ounces does the bottle contain? How many servings does the label say you can get from the bottle? How many ounces is one serving?
- Measure out servings and put them into plastic cups. How many servings did you get? Is the label right about the number of servings in the bottle?

**Materials:**
- paper
- pencils
- bottles of juice
- measuring cup with ounces marked
- plastic cups

## Science

pair | SPATIAL

### Measuring Minerals

Sometimes estimating mass by looks can be deceiving.

- Look at the different minerals and stones that your teacher has provided. See if you and your partner can agree on an estimate of their mass based on how big they each look.
- Now, weigh each item, using the balance scale and gram weights, to find the actual mass of each mineral or stone. Which one is the heaviest? the lightest?

**Materials:**
- similar sizes of different types of stones or minerals
- balance and gram weights
- paper
- pencils

## Music

pair | LOGICAL

### Listening Time

- Look at the list of song times on a CD with your partner. If you and your partner each listened to half of the songs on the CD, who would be listening longer?
- Which is the longest song on the CD? the shortest?
- Have a race with your partner to see who can rearrange the songs on the list in order from shortest to longest first. Time yourselves to see how long you each take to rearrange the list! What is the difference between your time and that of your partner?

CD with Song 1 = 3:11 min

CD with Song 2 = 4:26 min

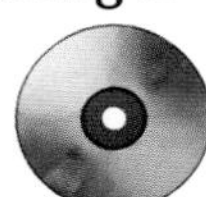
CD with Song 3 = 2:35 min

**Materials:**
- lists of songs from CDs, with the time for each song marked on the list
- stopwatch or timer
- paper
- pencils

## Social Studies

pair | LOGICAL

### Little by Little

If everyone conserves fuel a little at a time, it adds up.

- Take turns rolling the number cube with your partner. Each time you roll the cube, that number is the number of quarts of fuel you conserve. For each round of rolling, the person who rolls the highest amount wins the round. Keep track of how many quarts you conserve for each round.
- There may be a winner for each round, but who wins the conservation game in the end? Add up the number of quarts you each conserved, and convert those amounts to gallons. Who has conserved the greatest number of gallons of fuel overall?

**Materials:**
- number cube
- paper
- pencils

# Introduce the Chapter

## Real World: In the Supermarket

**Materials:** grocery ads, scissors, bulletin board

Share with students that in this chapter they will learn how to estimate, measure, and convert units of capacity, volume, weight, and mass, and learn how to find elapsed time.

Start a bulletin board by displaying the heads Capacity, Weight, and Mass. Include a list of customary and metric units under each head.

- Assign groups of four. Give students grocery ads and have them find items that are sold by capacity, weight, or mass.
- Have students cut out the ads and pin them under the appropriate head on the bulletin board.
- Refer students to this bulletin board while they work through this chapter.

Direct students to Student Edition p. 482. Have students read the information at the top of the page.

- **Which operation would you use to convert pounds to ounces?** multiplication
- **Which operation would you use to convert ounces to pounds?** division

## WRITING IN MATH

**Starting the Chapter**

Have students describe in their Math Journals two real-life situations in which they have estimated, measured, or used units of capacity, weight, mass, or elapsed time.

**Key Vocabulary** Introduce the key vocabulary in the chapter using the routine below.

Define: Capacity is the amount a container can hold, measured in units of dry or liquid measure.
Example: The capacity of a water bottle is 1 liter.
Ask: What are some examples of capacity that you know?



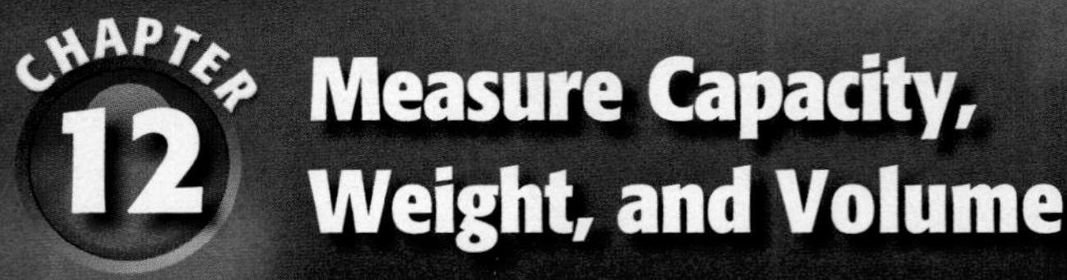


## BIG Idea How do you convert units of weight?

To convert a larger unit to a smaller unit, you multiply. To convert a smaller unit to a larger unit, you divide.

**Example** Suppose the total birth weight of eight pandas is 32 ounces. To find the total birth weight in pounds, divide 32 by 16 since there are 16 ounces in 1 pound.

$$\begin{array}{r} 2 \\ 16\overline{)32} \\ -32 \\ \hline 0 \end{array}$$

16 ounces = 1 pound
Divide 32 by 16 to find the birth weight in pounds.

So, the total birth weight of 8 pandas is 2 pounds.

### What will I learn in this chapter?

- Use customary units of capacity and weight.
- Use metric units of capacity and mass.
- Solve problems using logical reasoning.
- Measure and estimate volume.
- Solve problems about elapsed time.

### Key Vocabulary

**capacity**
**weight**
**mass**
**weight**
**elapsed time**

**Math Online** Student Study Tools at macmillanmh.com

## Chapter 12 Project

### Fruit Salad

Students use grocery circulars to figure out how much they will have to spend to make a fruit salad for the whole class.

- Each student pair comes up with a recipe for fruit salad, including any fruits they want that appear in grocery circulars provided for them. They estimate how much of each fruit they will need, how much each quantity of fruit will weigh, and figure out the total cost for each quantity of fruit.
- They make a poster showing their fruit salad recipe with the weight quantities for each fruit, how many people they plan to serve, and the approximate cost for each quantity of fruit. They can use the circular they are given to decorate their poster.

*Refer to Chapter 12 Resource Masters, p. 68, for a rubric to assess students' progress on this project.*

**FOLDABLES® Study Organizer**

Make this Foldable to help you organize information about capacity, weight, and volume. Begin with 5 sheets of $8\frac{1}{2}'' \times 11''$ paper.

1. **Stack** 5 sheets of paper so they are $\frac{3}{4}$ inch apart.

2. **Roll** up the edge, so all tabs are the same size.

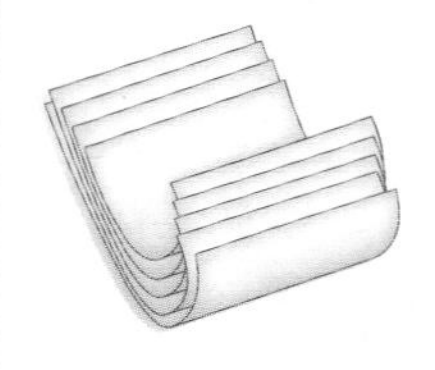

3. **Crease** and staple along the fold.

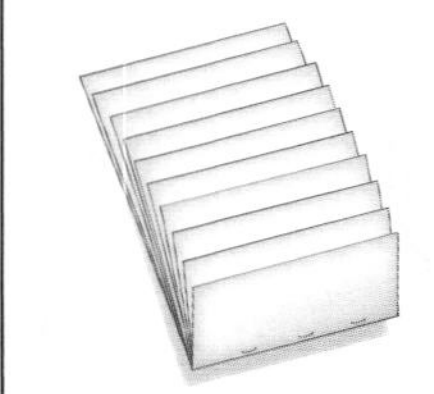

4. **Label** the tabs with the topics from each lesson.

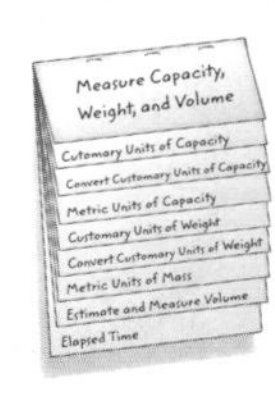




## ELL National ESL Standards Alignment for Chapter 12

| Lesson, Page | ESL Standard | Modality | Level |
|---|---|---|---|
| 12-1, p. 486B | Goal 1, Standard 3, k | Kinesthetic, Auditory | Beginning |
| 12-2, p. 490B | Goal 2, Standard 1, c | Logical, Spatial | Intermediate |
| 12-3, p. 492B | Goal 2, Standard 2, g | Kinesthetic, Visual | Intermediate |
| 12-4, p. 498B | Goal 2, Standard 2, l | Social, Linguistic | Advanced |
| 12-5, p. 502B | Goal 2, Standard 1, h | Logical, Visual | Advanced |
| 12-6, p. 504B | Goal 2, Standard 2, a | Kinesthetic, Logical | Intermediate |
| 12-7, p. 508B | Goal 2, Standard 2, b | Linguistic, Logical | Intermediate |
| 12-8, p. 512B | Goal 1, Standard 3, c | Visual, Auditory | Intermediate |
| 12-9, p. 518B | Goal 2, Standard 1, h | Visual | Advanced |
| 12-10, p. 520B | Goal 1, Standard 2, c | Auditory, Linguistic | Advanced |

The National ESL Standards can be found in the Teacher Reference Handbook.

## FOLDABLES® Dinah Zike's Foldables

**Teach** Guide students through the directions on p. 483 to create their own Foldable graphic organizers. Students may use their Foldables to study and review chapter assessments.

**When to Use It** Lessons 12-1, 12-3, 12-4, 12-7, and 12-10. (Additional instructions on pp. 501 and 524.)

## Chapter 12 Literature List

| Lesson | Book Title |
|---|---|
| 12-1 | **Pigs in a Pantry**<br>Amy Axelrod |
| 12-2 | **Mole Bakes Bread**<br>Carolyn Green |
| 12-3 | **Capacity**<br>Henry Pluckrose |
| 12-4 | **How Much, How Many, How Far, How Heavy, How Long, How Tall is 1,000?**<br>Helen Nolan |
| 12-5 | **Math Curse**<br>Jon Scieszka |
| 12-6 | **Is a Blue Whale the Biggest Thing There is?**<br>Robert E. Wells |
| 12-7 | **Who Sank the Boat?**<br>Pamela Allen |
| 12-8 | **Room for Ripley**<br>Stuart J. Murphy |
| 12-10 | **"Something Furry in the Garage at 6:30 A.M." from *Math Poetry***<br>Betsy Franco |

- Read the Math at Home letter found in the Chapter 12 Resource Masters, p. 4, with the class and have each student sign it. (A Spanish version is found on p. 5)
- Send home copies of the Math at Home letter with each student.

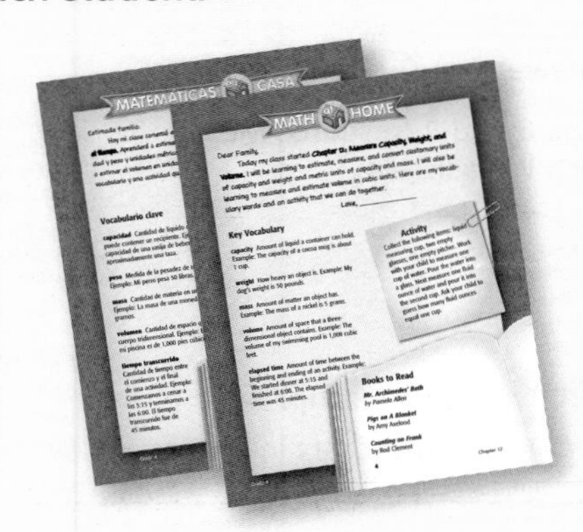

## Diagnose

Check for students' prerequisite skills before beginning the chapter.

- **Option 1:** ***Quick Check***
  SE Student Edition, p. 484
- **Option 2:** ***Online Assessment***
  **Math Online** macmillanmh.com
- **Option 3:** ***Diagnostic Tests***
  CRM Chapter 12 Resource Masters, pp. 59–60

# ARE YOU READY for Chapter 12?

You have two ways to check prerequisite skills for this chapter.

**Option 2**

**Math Online** Take the Chapter Readiness Quiz at macmillanmh.com.

**Option 1**

Complete the Quick Check below.

### QUICK Check

**Multiply or divide.** (Lesson 4-5) (Used in Lessons 12-2, 12-6, and 12-8)

**1.** $2 \times 8$ 16 **2.** $4 \times 16$ 64 **3.** $8 \times 24$ 192 **4.** $9 \times 36$ 324

**5.** $4 \div 2$ 2 **6.** $12 \div 4$ 3 **7.** $36 \div 6$ 6 **8.** $64 \div 8$ 8

**9.** Dan shared his markers equally with three friends. How many markers did each person get? 3 markers

**Compare. Use $>$, $<$, or $=$.** (Lesson 1-4) (Used in Lesson 12-2)

**10.** 12 ● 21 $<$ **11.** 64 ● 36 $>$ **12.** 128 ● 182 $<$

**13.** The table shows the number of cans collected by two fourth grade classes at Franklin Elementary School. Which class collected more cans? Miss Davis' class

| Cans Collected | |
|---|---|
| **Class** | **Number of Cans Collected** |
| Mr. Santos | 236 |
| Miss Davis | 263 |

**Write the time shown on each clock.** (Prior Grade) (Used in Lesson 12-10)

**14.**

3:00

**15.** 4:15

**16.**

5:45

484 **Chapter 12** Measure Capacity, Weight, and Volume

## RTI (Response to Intervention)

**Apply the Results** Based on the results of the diagnostic assessment on Student Edition p. 484, use the chart below to address individual needs before beginning the chapter.

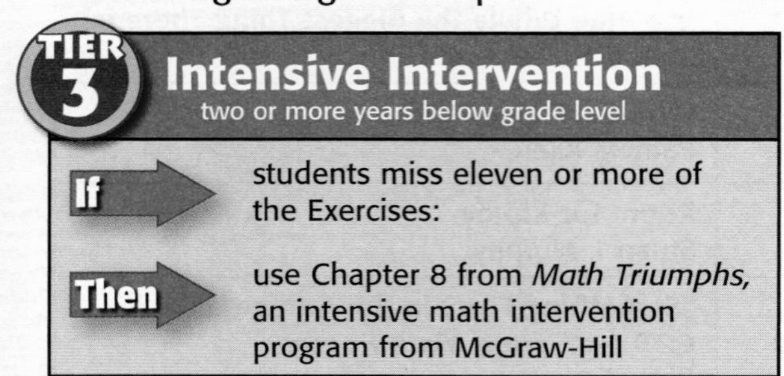

**TIER 3 Intensive Intervention**
two or more years below grade level

**If** students miss eleven or more of the Exercises:

**Then** use Chapter 8 from *Math Triumphs*, an intensive math intervention program from McGraw-Hill

| TIER 2 Strategic Intervention (below/approaching grade level) | TIER 1 On-Level | Above/Beyond Level |
|---|---|---|
| **If** students miss five to ten in: **Exercises 1–16** | **If** students miss three or four in: **Exercises 1–16** | **If** students miss two or less in: **Exercises 1–16** |
| **Then** choose a resource: | **Then** choose a resource: | **Then** choose a resource: |
| Strategic Intervention Guide (p. 122)<br>CRM Chapters 6 and 7 Resource Masters (Reteach Worksheets)<br>**Math Online** Extra Examples • Personal Tutor • Concepts in Motion | Learning Stations (pp. 438I–438J)<br>TE Chapter Project (p. 438)<br>CRM Game: Measurement Match<br>Math Adventures<br>My Math Zone Chapter 11<br>**Math Online** Fact Dash | Learning Stations (pp. 438I–438J)<br>TE Chapter Project (p. 438)<br>Real-World Problem Solving: *Strange but True*<br>My Math Zone Chapters 11 and 12<br>**Math Online** Games |

Measurement Activity for 12-1

# Estimate and Measure Capacity

**MAIN IDEA**

I will estimate and measure capacity.

**You Will Need**
cup, pint, quart, and gallon measuring tools
water

**Capacity** is the amount of liquid a container can hold.

1 cup

1 pint

1 quart

1 gallon

**ACTIVITY** Measure Capacity

**Step 1** **Measure.**
Fill the cup with water and pour its contents into the pint. Repeat until the pint is full. It takes 2 cups to fill the pint. So, there are 2 cups in a pint.

**Step 2** **Copy and complete the table.**
Estimate. Then use water to find the exact measures.

| Container | Estimate | Actual |
|---|---|---|
| Pint | ■ cups | ■ cups |
| Quart | ■ pints | ■ pints |
| Gallon | ■ quarts | ■ quarts |

## Think About It

1. How many cups are in one pint? 2 cups
2. How many quarts are in one gallon? 4 quarts

3. ■ cups = 3 pints 6 cups
4. ■ pints = 4 gallons 32 pints
5. WRITING IN MATH Is it faster to water two large flower pots using a one-cup pitcher or a one-quart pitcher? Explain. See margin.

Measurement Activity for 12-1

# Lesson Planner

## Objective

Estimate and measure capacity.

## Resources

**Materials:** water, food coloring

**Manipulatives:** capacity containers (cup, pint, quart, and gallon)

## 1 Introduce

- Display containers (with no labels) for a cup, a pint, a quart, and a gallon. **Which container holds the least amount of liquid? the greatest?** Have students point out the proper containers. Have a volunteer label the containers and then order them from the smallest to the largest.

## 2 Teach

**Activity 1** Emphasize that the material in the cup container must be level before it is poured into the pint container. Help students fill containers properly.

## 3 Assess

### Formative Assessment

Use **Check What You Know** Exercises 3–5 to assess whether students comprehend how to estimate and measure capacity.

### Additional Answer

5. Sample answer: It would be faster to use the pitcher that holds one quart because its capacity is greater.

LESSON 12-1

# Customary Units of Capacity

## Lesson Planner

### Objective

Estimate and measure customary capacities.

### Vocabulary

**capacity**, **fluid ounce**, **cup**, **pint**, **quart**, **gallon**

### Resources

**Materials:** water, pictures of containers

**Manipulatives:** capacity containers

**Literature Connection:** *Pigs in a Pantry* by Amy Axelrod

**Alternate Lesson:** Use *IMPACT Mathematics:* Unit H to provide practice with capacity.

**Teacher Technology**

TeacherWorks • Interactive Classroom

## Daily Routine

Use these suggestions before beginning the lesson on p. 486.

### 5-Minute Check

(Reviews Lesson 11–8)

**Find the change in the temperatures.**

1. 12°C to 17°C 5°C
2. 21°C to 13°C 8°C
3. 112°F to 85°F 27°F
4. 2°F to 79°F 77°F
5. 85°F to 45°F 40°F

### Problem of the Day

Mr. Chandra drives to and from work each weekday. His trip is 15 miles one way. How many miles does he drive to and from work each week? 150 miles

### Focus on Math Background

Capacity as used here describes liquid volume. Historically, units for measuring liquid volume and solid volume developed separately, although both types of unit measure the three-dimensional space occupied by an object or substance. For example, there are about $7\frac{1}{2}$ gallons in a cubic foot.

The *U.S. Customary System* is a relatively new name for the system of measurement that originated in England hundreds of years ago. It was referred to as the British System until recently, but is now rarely used outside the United States. The basic unit of measure for capacity is cups.

### Building Math Vocabulary

Write the lesson vocabulary words and their definitions on the board.

Have students write the words and their definitions in their Math Journals. Brainstorm products that are sold by the fluid ounce, cup, pint, quart, or gallon. Have a volunteer list the responses on the board. Students should include an example for each customary unit in their notebooks.

# Differentiated Instruction

## Small Group Options

### Option 1 Gifted and Talented AL

SPATIAL

**Materials:** clear plastic measuring cups (1 or 2 cup sizes), several rocks (student's fist size), water

- Discuss the volume and capacity of a rock and how you might discover its actual volume.
- Have students estimate one of the rocks you provide.
- Now put rock in the measuring cup and fill with water to the one cup line (eye-level measurement).
- Have students carefully remove the rock from the cup without losing more than a drop of water.
- Now look at the amount of water left in the cup.
- Students will then be able to add the amount of water + the rock = one cup.
- Repeat this process with the other rocks provided.
- Ask students if they have ever seen anyone measure like this. Some people may measure solid shortening in this manner.
- Tell students that the actual name for this process is displacement.

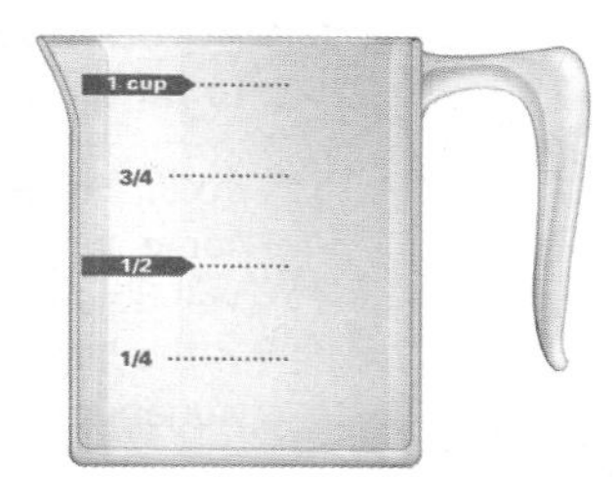


### Option 2 English Language Learners ELL

KINESTHETIC, AUDITORY

**Materials:** water, containers
**Core Vocabulary:** rim, almost full, too much/overflowed
**Common Use Verb:** fill up
**Do Math** This strategy teaches students vocabulary of capacity by pouring and comparing the capacity of various containers.

- Model filling a cup with water, emphasizing the rim. Say: "This is the **rim**. I am ***filling*** the cup ***up***. It is **almost full**." Repeat to the rim, saying: "The cup is full."
- Repeat, overflowing the cup, saying: "There is **too much** for the cup to hold. The cup **overflowed**."
- Have students repeat filling containers. Prompt students to use vocabulary, restating student language as needed.
- Repeat the procedure with other containers, allowing students to compare relative capacities.

## Independent Work Options

### Option 1 Early Finishers AL

VISUAL, LOGIC

**Materials:** grocery ads, scissors

- Students use the grocery ads to find and cut out products that are sold in containers, such as orange juice in half-gallon cartons or yogurt in one-cup containers.
- Have students write problems like Exercises 7–12 on p. 488.
- Students place the problems in a problem bank for other students to solve.

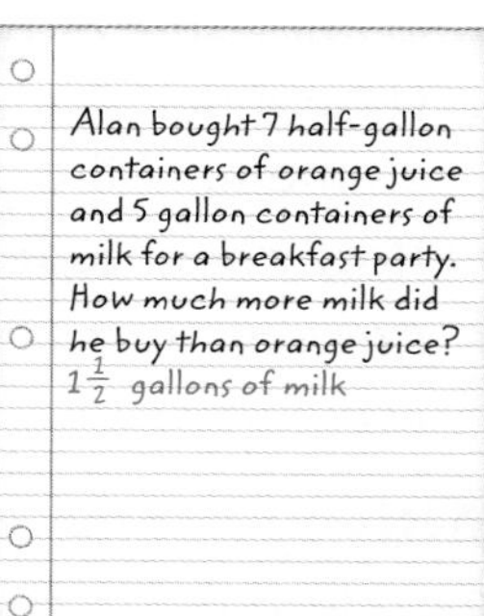


### Option 2 Student Technology

**Math Online** macmillanmh.com

Personal Tutor • Extra Examples

### Option 3 Learning Station: Health (p. 482I)

Direct students to the Health Learning Station for opportunities to explore and extend the lesson concept.

### Option 4 Problem-Solving Practice

Reinforce problem-solving skills and strategies with the Problem-Solving Practice worksheet.

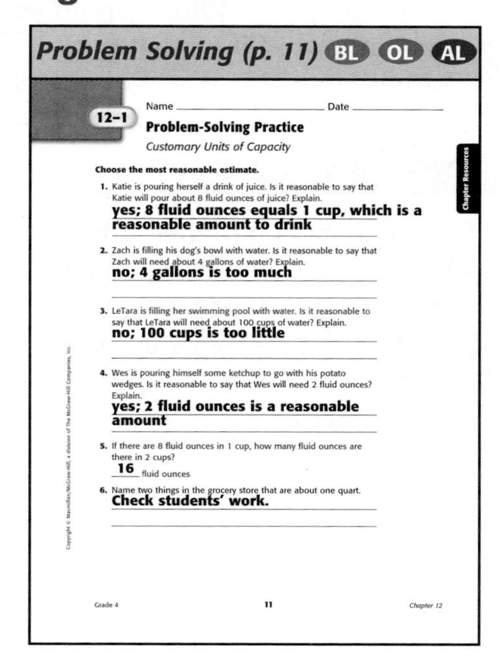

**Problem Solving (p. 11) BL OL AL**

12–1 Name ____________ Date ____________

**Problem-Solving Practice**

*Customary Units of Capacity*

Chapter Resources

**Choose the most reasonable estimate.**

1. Katie is pouring herself a drink of juice. Is it reasonable to say that Katie will pour about 8 fluid ounces of juice? Explain.
   **yes; 8 fluid ounces equals 1 cup, which is a reasonable amount to drink**
2. Zach is filling his dog's bowl with water. Is it reasonable to say that Zach will need about 4 gallons of water? Explain.
   **no; 4 gallons is too much**
3. LeTara is filling her swimming pool with water. Is it reasonable to say that LeTara will need about 100 cups of water? Explain.
   **no; 100 cups is too little**
4. Wes is pouring himself some ketchup to go with his potato wedges. Is it reasonable to say that Wes will need 2 fluid ounces? Explain.
   **yes; 2 fluid ounces is a reasonable amount**
5. If there are 8 fluid ounces in 1 cup, how many fluid ounces are there in 2 cups?
   **16** fluid ounces
6. Name two things in the grocery store that are about one quart.
   **Check students' work.**

Copyright © Macmillan/McGraw-Hill, a division of The McGraw-Hill Companies, Inc.

Grade 4 11 Chapter 12

# 12-1 Customary Units of Capacity

## 1 Introduce

**Activity Choice 1 • Hands-On** 

- Pose this problem: *Tina bought a quart of frozen yogurt for a party. She will scoop one cup of yogurt into each cone. How many cones do you think she can fill?* List the estimates.
- Have a volunteer measure out a quart of water, sand, or rice into a large container. Have other volunteers measure out one cup at a time until the quart is used up.
- **How many cones can Tina fill?** 4 cones
- Compare the responses on the board with the actual measurement.

**Activity Choice 2 • Literature**

Introduce the lesson with *Pigs in a Pantry* by Amy Axelrod. For a related math activity, see p. TR60.

## 2 Teach

### Scaffolding Questions

Display containers for a cup, a pint, a quart, and a gallon. Show students pictures of objects such as a sandbox, a coffee mug, a sink, etc.

- **Which container would you use to fill each object?** Answers will vary depending on the pictures shown.
- **When would you use a gallon container to fill something?** Sample answer: when it has a large capacity **When would you use a cup container to fill something?** Sample answer: when the object does not hold very much

**GET READY to Learn**

Have students open their books and read the information in **Get Ready to Learn.** Introduce **capacity**, **fluid ounce**, **cup**, **pint**, **quart**, and **gallon**. As a class, work through **Examples 1 and 2**.



# 12-1 Customary Units of Capacity

**MAIN IDEA**

I will estimate and measure customary capacities.

**New Vocabulary**

capacity
fluid ounce
cup
pint
quart
gallon

**Math Online**

macmillanmh.com
- Extra Examples
- Personal Tutor
- Self-Check Quiz

**GET READY to Learn**

Jorge is filling an aquarium. He went to the kitchen to find a container to fill the aquarium. Which container should Jorge use to fill his aquarium most quickly?

1 cup 1 quart 1 gallon

The amount a container can hold is its **capacity**. Different containers measure different capacities. A cup contains 8 **fluid ounces**.

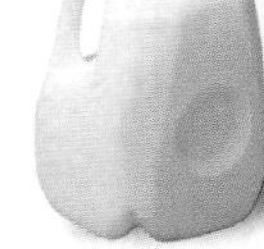

1 **fl oz** 1 **cup** 1 **pint** 1 **quart** 1 **gallon**

**Real-World EXAMPLE** Estimate Capacity

**1 AQUARIUMS Which container should Jorge use to fill the aquarium most quickly?**

To fill the aquarium most quickly, Jorge should use the container that will hold the most liquid. The gallon is the largest unit. It will fill the aquarium most quickly.



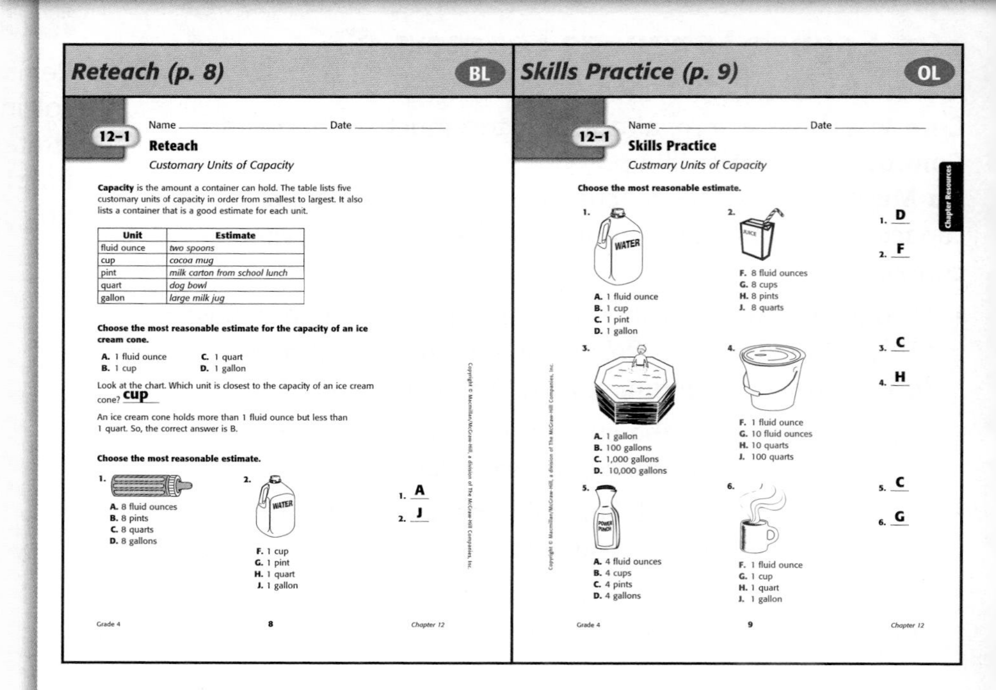

**Reteach (p. 8)** BL

12-1 Name ________ Date ________

**Reteach**

*Customary Units of Capacity*

**Capacity** is the amount a container can hold. The table lists five customary units of capacity in order from smallest to largest. It also lists a container that is a good estimate for each unit.

| Unit | Estimate |
|---|---|
| fluid ounce | *two spoons* |
| cup | *cocoa mug* |
| pint | *milk carton from school lunch* |
| quart | *dog bowl* |
| gallon | *large milk jug* |

**Choose the most reasonable estimate for the capacity of an ice cream cone.**

A. 1 fluid ounce C. 1 quart
B. 1 cup D. 1 gallon

Look at the chart. Which unit is closest to the capacity of an ice cream cone? cup

An ice cream cone holds more than 1 fluid ounce but less than 1 quart. So, the correct answer is B.

**Choose the most reasonable estimate.**

1. A. 8 fluid ounces B. 8 pints C. 8 quarts D. 8 gallons
2. (WATER) F. 1 cup G. 1 pint H. 1 quart J. 1 gallon

1. A
2. J



Grade 4 8 Chapter 12

**Skills Practice (p. 9)** OL

12-1 Name ________ Date ________

**Skills Practice**

*Custmary Units of Capacity*

**Choose the most reasonable estimate.**

1. (WATER) A. 1 fluid ounce B. 1 cup C. 1 pint D. 1 gallon
2. (JUICE) F. 8 fluid ounces G. 8 cups H. 8 pints J. 8 quarts
3. A. 1 gallon B. 100 gallons C. 1,000 gallons D. 10,000 gallons
4. F. 1 fluid ounce G. 10 fluid ounces H. 10 quarts J. 100 quarts
5. (POWER PUNCH) A. 4 fluid ounces B. 4 cups C. 4 pints D. 4 gallons
6. F. 1 fluid ounce G. 1 cup H. 1 quart J. 1 gallon

1. D
2. F
3. C
4. H
5. C
6. G

Chapter Resources



Grade 4 9 Chapter 12

## Real-World EXAMPLES Estimate Capacity

**2** **FOOD Nita is pouring salsa into a small bowl. Is the most reasonable estimate for the capacity of the bowl 8 fluid ounces, 8 cups, 8 quarts, or 8 gallons?**

The salsa is a small amount. So, 8 gallons, 8 quarts, and 8 cups are too much. The most reasonable estimate for the capacity of the bowl is 8 fluid ounces.

**3** **Is the most reasonable estimate for the capacity of the bathtub 20 fluid ounces, 20 cups, 20 quarts, or 20 gallons?**

The bathtub can hold a large amount of water. So, 20 fluid ounces, 20 cups, and 20 quarts are too small. The most reasonable estimate for the capacity of the bathtub is 20 gallons.

## CHECK What You Know

**Choose the most reasonable estimate for each capacity.** See Examples 1–3 (pp. 486–487)

**1.**

**A** 1 fluid ounce
**B** 1 pint
**C** 1 quart
**D** 100 quarts C

**2.**

**F** 4 fluid ounces
**G** 4 cups
**H** 40 cups
**J** 4 gallons G

**3.**

**A** 1 fluid ounce
**B** 1 cup
**C** 1 pint
**D** 1 gallon D

**4.** Talk About It Is it possible for both of the containers shown to have a capacity of 1 pint? Explain why or why not. Sample answer: Yes, because one is tall and thinner than the other, which is wider and shorter.

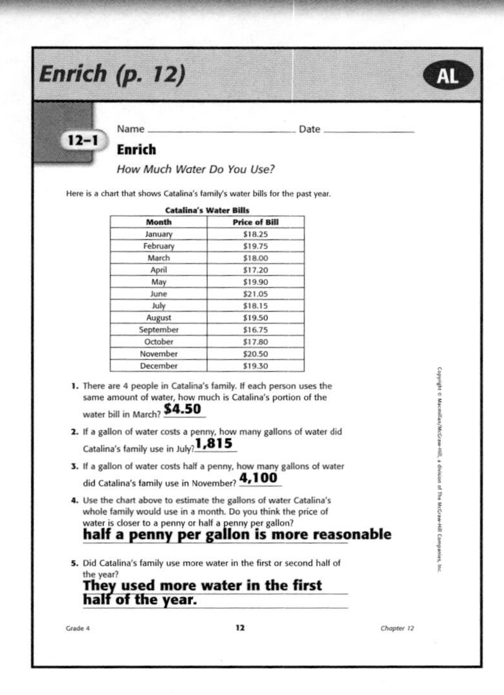

**Enrich (p. 12)** AL

12–1

Name ______________ Date ______________

**Enrich**

*How Much Water Do You Use?*

Here is a chart that shows Catalina's family's water bills for the past year.

**Catalina's Water Bills**

| Month | Price of Bill |
|---|---|
| January | $18.25 |
| February | $19.75 |
| March | $18.00 |
| April | $17.20 |
| May | $19.90 |
| June | $21.05 |
| July | $18.15 |
| August | $19.50 |
| September | $16.75 |
| October | $17.80 |
| November | $20.50 |
| December | $19.30 |

1. There are 4 people in Catalina's family. If each person uses the same amount of water, how much is Catalina's portion of the water bill in March? **$4.50**
2. If a gallon of water costs a penny, how many gallons of water did Catalina's family use in July? **1,815**
3. If a gallon of water costs half a penny, how many gallons of water did Catalina's family use in November? **4,100**
4. Use the chart above to estimate the gallons of water Catalina's whole family would use in a month. Do you think the price of water is closer to a penny or half a penny per gallon? **half a penny per gallon is more reasonable**
5. Did Catalina's family use more water in the first or second half of the year? **They used more water in the first half of the year.**



Grade 4 12 Chapter 12

## Estimate Capacity

**Example 2** Call attention to the fact that "fluid ounces" are used to measure capacity, whereas "ounces" are used to measure weight.

### ADDITIONAL EXAMPLES

**1** Mark is filling his baby brother's bottle with milk. Which is the most reasonable estimate for the capacity of the baby's bottle: a cup, a quart, or a gallon? a cup

**2** Lara is filling her canteen with water to take on a hike. Is the most reasonable capacity of the canteen 2 fluid ounces, 2 cups, 2 quarts, or 2 gallons? 2 cups

### CHECK What You Know

As a class, have students complete Exercises 1–4 in **Check What You Know** as you observe their work.

**Exercise 4** Assess student comprehension before assigning practice exercises.

## BL Alternate Teaching Strategy

**If** students have trouble using customary units to estimate and measure capacities…

**Then** use one of these reteach options:

1. CRM **Daily Reteach Worksheet** (p. 8)
2. Provide actual containers, instead of pictures, for cup, quart, and gallon. Then have students test and adjust their estimates by using the containers to measure the estimates.
   - After students test their estimates, have them give examples of when it is useful to use gallon, quart, or cup containers.

# 3 Practice

Differentiate practice using these leveled assignments for Exercises 5–7.

| Level | Assignment |
|---|---|
| BL Below/Approaching Level | 5–7, 11–12, 4 |
| OL On Level | 7–10, 2–3, 5, 6 |
| AL Above/Beyond Level | 6–16 even, 17–18 |

Have students discuss and complete the Higher Order Thinking problems. For Exercise 16, have students estimate the capacity of the items they chose.

**WRITING IN MATH** Have students complete Exercise 18 in their Math Journals. You may choose to use this as an optional formative assessment.

### Additional Answers

**14.** Sample answer: yes; The average person uses up to 30 gallons of water each day. So, using this much water for 7 days equals 30 × 7 or 210 gallons.

**15.** Sample answer: no; The least amount of water used per brushing is 1 gallon which is larger than 1 cup. So, it is not reasonable to say that Callie uses 2 cups of water when brushing her teeth three times.

**16.** Sample answer: yes; Callie can save up to 11 gallons of water with each washing. 11 + 11 + 11 = 33

### COMMON ERROR!

**Exercises 5–10** Some students may have difficulty determining the reasonableness of an estimate. Show students a cup, quart, and gallon container.



## Practice and Problem Solving

See page R30.

**Choose the most reasonable estimate for each capacity.** See Examples 1–3 (pp. 486–487)

**5.** 

**F** 12,000 fluid ounces
**G** 12,000 pints
**H** 12,000 quarts
**J** 12,000 gallons J

**6.** 

**A** 2 fluid ounces
**B** 2 cups
**C** 2 pints
**D** 2 gallons D

**7.** 

**F** 1 fluid ounce
**G** 1 cup
**H** 1 quart
**J** 1 gallon F

**8.**

**A** 8 fluid ounces
**B** 8 cups
**C** 8 pints
**D** 8 gallons A

**9.**

**F** 1 quart
**G** 10 quarts
**H** 100 quarts
**J** 1,000 quarts F

**10.**  

**A** 16 gallons
**B** 16 quarts
**C** 16 fluid ounces
**D** 16 cups C

**Estimate and then measure the capacity of each object.**

**11.** water bottle

**12.** juice box

**13.** sink

11–13. See students' work.

### Real-World PROBLEM SOLVING

**Water** Some household activities and the amount of water they consume are listed in the table. 14–16. See margin.

**Water Consumption**

| Activity | Water Used (gallons) |
|---|---|
| Take shower | 15–30 |
| Brush teeth (water running) | 1–2 |
| Wash dishes (by hand) | 20 |
| Wash dishes (in dishwasher) | 9–12 |
| Flush toilet | 5–7 |

**Source:** California Urban Water Conservation Council

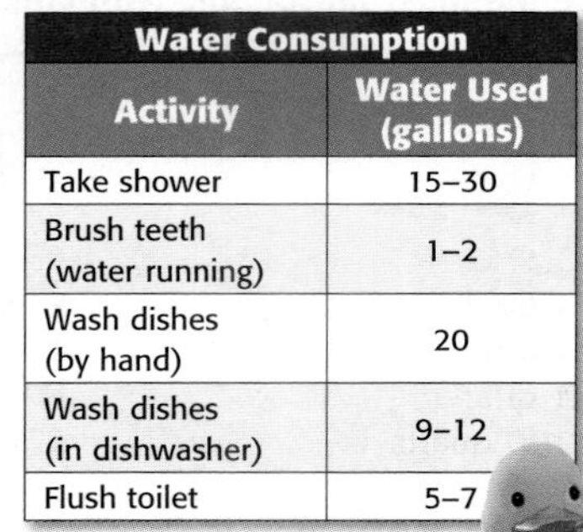

**14.** If Callie takes one shower each day, is it reasonable to say that she could use 210 gallons of water in one week? Explain.

**15.** Callie brushes her teeth three times each day. Is it reasonable to say that she uses 2 cups of water in one day? Explain.

**16.** Callie washes dishes three times each week. Is it reasonable to say that she could save 30 gallons of water in a week by washing the dishes in a dishwasher instead of by hand? Explain.

## H.O.T. Problems

**17. OPEN ENDED** Name two things in your classroom that would hold more than one cup. **Sample answer: backpack and sink**

**18. WRITING IN MATH** A set of twins is sharing 1 pint of ice cream. Their friend, Shannon, is eating 1 cup of ice cream. Who is eating the most ice cream? Explain. **Sample answer: Everyone is eating an equal amount of ice cream because 2 cups = 1 pint.**

## TEST Practice

**19.** At bedtime the temperature was 45°F. In the morning it was 15°F cooler. What was the temperature in the morning? (Lesson 11-8) **C**

**A** 75°F

**B** 60°F

**C** 30°F

**D** 15°F

**20.** Which of the following holds about 1 quart of water? (Lesson 12-1) **H**

F

H

G

J

## Spiral Review

**Find the change in the temperatures.** (Lesson 11-8)

**21.** 75°F to 34°F **41°F** **22.** 35°C to 50°C **15°C** **23.** 85°F to 68°F **17°F**

**Write the approximate temperature in degrees Fahrenheit and Celsius.** (Lesson 11-8)

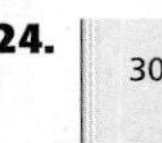

**24.**
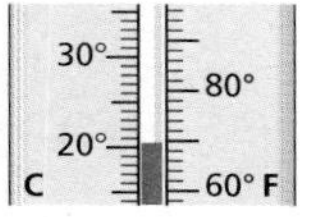

**70°F; 20°C**

**25.**

**80°F; 26°C**

**26.** Tonya got money for her birthday. She got $8 from her friends, $16 from her parents, and $5 from her sister. She now has $48. How much did she have originally? (Lesson 11-7) **$19**

**Estimate. Then measure each to the nearest inch, $\frac{1}{2}$ inch, and $\frac{1}{4}$ inch.** (Lesson 11-1)

**27.**
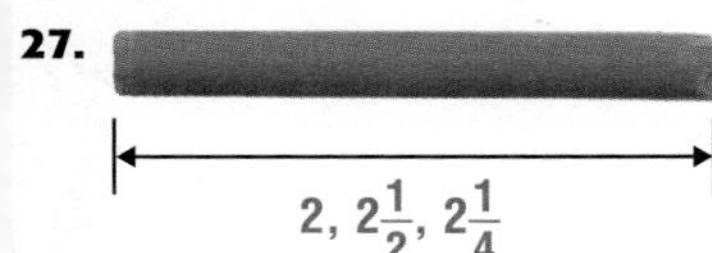
**2, $2\frac{1}{2}$, $2\frac{1}{4}$**

**28.**

**2, $1\frac{1}{2}$, $1\frac{1}{4}$**



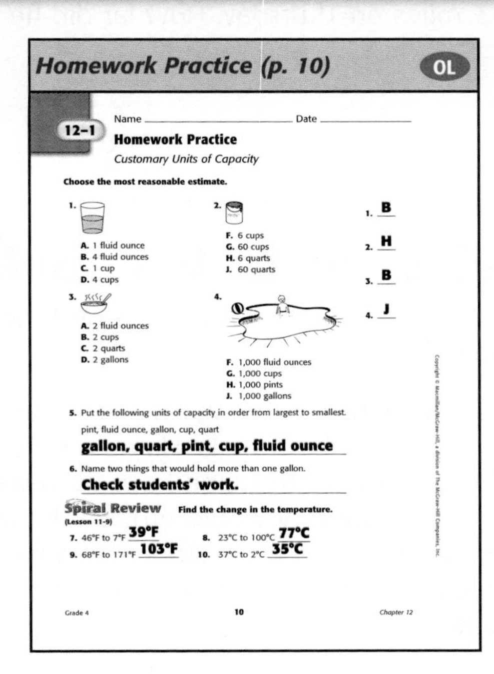

**Homework Practice (p. 10)** OL

Name ____________ Date ____________

**12-1 Homework Practice**
*Customary Units of Capacity*

**Choose the most reasonable estimate.**

1. A. 1 fluid ounce B. 4 fluid ounces C. 1 cup D. 4 cups — 1. **B**

2. F. 6 cups G. 60 cups H. 6 quarts J. 60 quarts — 2. **H**

3. A. 2 fluid ounces B. 2 cups C. 2 quarts D. 2 gallons — 3. **B**

4. F. 1,000 fluid ounces G. 1,000 cups H. 1,000 pints J. 1,000 gallons — 4. **J**

5. Put the following units of capacity in order from largest to smallest.
pint, fluid ounce, gallon, cup, quart
**gallon, quart, pint, cup, fluid ounce**

6. Name two things that would hold more than one gallon.
**Check students' work.**

**Spiral Review** (Lesson 11-9) **Find the change in the temperature.**

7. 46°F to 7°F **39°F** 8. 23°C to 100°C **77°C**
9. 68°F to 171°F **103°F** 10. 37°C to 2°C **35°C**

Grade 4 10 Chapter 12

# 4 Assess

## Formative Assessment

Which is a reasonable estimate for the capacity of a bathtub? D

**A** 45 fluid ounces

**B** 45 cups

**C** 45 quarts

**D** 45 gallons

**Quick Check** **Are students continuing to struggle with using customary units to measure capacity?**

**If Yes** → Strategic Intervention Guide (p. 122)

**If No** → Independent Work Options (p. 486B)
CRM Skills Practice Worksheet (p. 9)
CRM Enrich Worksheet (p. 12)

**Into the Future** Tell students that today they learned about customary units of capacity. Ask them how they think what they learned today will help them with the next lesson on converting customary units of capacity.

## TEST Practice

**Reviews Lessons 11-8 and 12-1**

Assign the Test Practice problems to provide daily reinforcement of test-taking skills.

## Spiral Review

**Reviews Lessons 11-1, 11-7, and 11-8**

Review and assess mastery of skills and concepts from previous chapters.

LESSON 12-2

# Convert Customary Units of Capacity

## Lesson Planner

### Objective

Convert customary units of capacity.

### Review Vocabulary

**capacity, fluid ounce**

### Resources

**Materials:** two pots (or bowls), sand (rice or water)

**Manipulatives:** standard containers for measuring capacity

**Literature Connection:** *Mole Bakes Bread* by Carolyn Green

**Teacher Technology**

TeacherWorks • Interactive Classroom

### Focus on Math Background

A given amount of liquid contains more small units than it does large units. So conversion from a measurement based on small units to one based on large units involves division. Conversely, conversion from large units to small units involves multiplication.

## Daily Routine

Use these suggestions before beginning the lesson on p. 490

### 5-Minute Check 

(Reviews Lesson 12-1)

**Choose the more reasonable estimate for the amount of water in the pool.** A

**A** 15 gallons
**B** 15 quarts
**C** 15 pints
**D** 15 cups

### Problem of the Day 

Farid biked 25 miles over 5 days. He rode 8 miles on Monday, 2 miles on Tuesday, 5 miles on Wednesday, and 3 miles on Thursday. How far did he bike on Friday? 7 miles

### Review Math Vocabulary

Write the review vocabulary words and their definitions on the board.

Have students review the vocabulary words in their notebooks or Math Journals. Name a container, such as a bathtub or a juice box, and have volunteers tell which unit of capacity would provide the most reasonable measure. Have students name another unit that might also be used to determine the capacity of the container.

# Differentiated Instruction

## Small Group Options

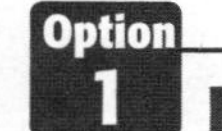

### Option 1 Below Level (BL)

LOGICAL

**Materials:** paper and pencil

- Provide students with the following problem:
- *Mrs. Alvarez has been asked to bring the punch for a family party. She expects 18 adults and 15 children. Directions for the punch say you should make 3 cups for each adult and 2 cups for each child. How many cups of punch will she need to make?* 84 cups
- How many gallons is this? about 5 gallons

### Option 2 English Language Learners (ELL)

LOGICAL, VISUAL, SPATIAL

**Materials:** empty milk gallon, measuring cup, overhead 3 × 3 grid, overhead pictures of large and small containers (like a bathtub, water bottle, bowl of soup, big fish tank, etc.), magazines, paste, index cards

**Core Vocabulary**: cup, gallon, to fill

**Common Use Verb:** would use

**See Math** This strategy helps students visualize a gallon and a cup.

- Show the cup and the gallon. Divide the room in half, assigning either cup or gallon to each group. Pair off students.
- Have a pair make a 3 × 3 grid.
- Model holding up a bowl and the "cup" partner putting an X in one of the grid squares. Repeat for bathtub picture, putting an O in the grid.
- Continue until one student has three in a row.
- Confirm answers. Say: "Yes, you ***would use*** a **cup** to fill a bowl." or "Yes, you would use a gallon to fill a bathtub."
- Allow pairs to cut out examples of their unit (cups or gallons) from magazines. Have them paste pictures on index cards and use to repeat strategy in pairs.

## Independent Work Options

### Option 1 Early Finishers (AL)

LOGICAL

**Materials:** paper, pencil, index cards

- Have each student list 5 measures of capacity, such as 14 gallons, on an index card.
- Have each student exchange his or her list with another student. For each measure listed, the student writes as many conversions as possible. For example, for 14 gallons, the student writes 56 quarts, 112 pints, 224 cups, and 1,792 fl oz.

14 gallons
56 quarts
112 pints
224 cups
1,792 fl oz.

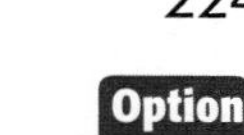

### Option 2 Student Technology

**Math Online** macmillanmh.com

Personal Tutor • Extra Examples

 Math Adventures

### Option 3 Learning Station: Social Studies (p. 482J)

Direct students to the Social Studies Learning Station for opportunities to explore and extend the lesson concept.

### Option 4 Problem-Solving Practice

Reinforce problem-solving skills and strategies with the Problem-Solving Practice worksheet.

***Problem Solving (p. 16)*** BL OL AL

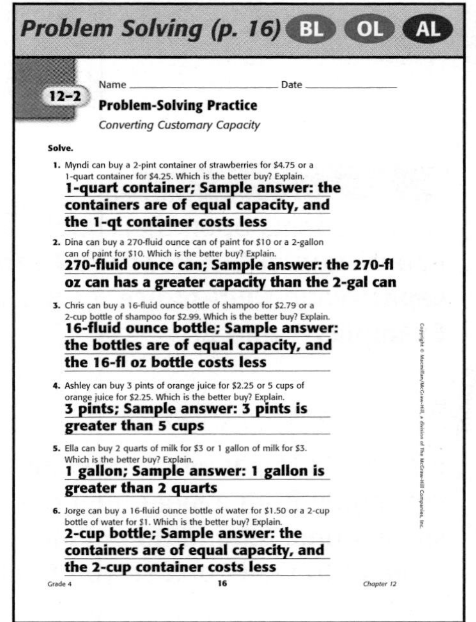

Name _______________ Date _______

12–2 **Problem-Solving Practice**

*Converting Customary Capacity*

**Solve.**

1. Myndi can buy a 2-pint container of strawberries for $4.75 or a 1-quart container for $4.25. Which is the better buy? Explain.
**1-quart container; Sample answer: the containers are of equal capacity, and the 1-qt container costs less**
2. Dina can buy a 270-fluid ounce can of paint for $10 or a 2-gallon can of paint for $10. Which is the better buy? Explain.
**270-fluid ounce can; Sample answer: the 270-fl oz can has a greater capacity than the 2-gal can**
3. Chris can buy a 16-fluid ounce bottle of shampoo for $2.79 or a 2-cup bottle of shampoo for $2.99. Which is the better buy? Explain.
**16-fluid ounce bottle; Sample answer: the bottles are of equal capacity, and the 16-fl oz bottle costs less**
4. Ashley can buy 3 pints of orange juice for $2.25 or 5 cups of orange juice for $2.25. Which is the better buy? Explain.
**3 pints; Sample answer: 3 pints is greater than 5 cups**
5. Ella can buy 2 quarts of milk for $3 or 1 gallon of milk for $3. Which is the better buy? Explain.
**1 gallon; Sample answer: 1 gallon is greater than 2 quarts**
6. Jorge can buy a 16-fluid ounce bottle of water for $1.50 or a 2-cup bottle of water for $1. Which is the better buy? Explain.
**2-cup bottle; Sample answer: the containers are of equal capacity, and the 2-cup container costs less**

Grade 4 16 Chapter 12

# 12-2 Convert Customary Units of Capacity

## 1 Introduce

### Activity Choice 1 • Hands-On

- Display two large bowls and various standard containers for measuring capacity. Provide sand, rice, or water for measuring.
- Have a volunteer fill a bowl with sand.
- Have another volunteer scoop a few handfuls of sand into the second bowl. **Which unit of capacity should you use to describe the amount of sand in the second bowl?** Answers will vary.
- Estimate the amount of sand in the second bowl. List the estimates on the board.
- Have a volunteer measure the sand in the second bowl. Discuss how the estimates compared with the actual measure.

### Activity Choice 2 • Literature

Introduce the lesson with *Mole Bakes Bread* by Carolyn Green. For a related math activity, see p. TR61.

## 2 Teach

### Scaffolding Questions

On the board, draw and label standard containers: gallon, quart, pint, cup.

- **How else can you label the cup?** 8 fl oz
- **How can you use the cup container to find how many fluid ounces are in a quart?** Sample answer: Fill the quart container with water; pour the water into a cup and empty it until all the water from the quart container is gone. Record the number of times the cup was filled and emptied. Then multiply the number of cups by 8 to find the total number of fluid ounces in a quart.

### GET READY to Learn

Have students open their books and read the information in **Get Ready to Learn**. Review **capacity**and **fluid ounce**. As a class, work through **Examples 1 and 2**.

### COMMON ERROR!

If students forget which operation to use when converting from a larger unit of measure to a smaller unit, remind them that there will be more of the new unit so you multiply.

# 12-2 Convert Customary Units of Capacity

## GET READY to Learn

Marcus has a 2-gallon container of laundry detergent. How many quarts of laundry detergent does he have?

**MAIN IDEA**

I will convert customary units of capacity.

**Math Online**

macmillanmh.com

- Extra Examples
- Personal Tutor
- Self-Check Quiz

You can use multiplication and division to convert units.

- To change from a larger unit to a smaller unit, multiply.
- To change from a smaller unit to a larger unit, divide.

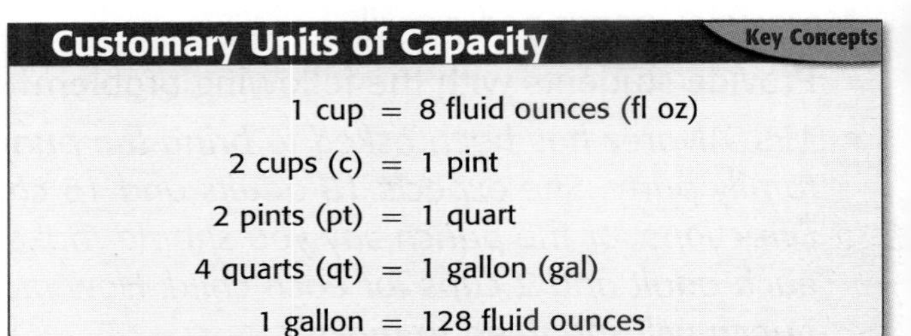

**Customary Units of Capacity** — Key Concepts

| | | |
|---|---|---|
| 1 cup | = | 8 fluid ounces (fl oz) |
| 2 cups (c) | = | 1 pint |
| 2 pints (pt) | = | 1 quart |
| 4 quarts (qt) | = | 1 gallon (gal) |
| 1 gallon | = | 128 fluid ounces |

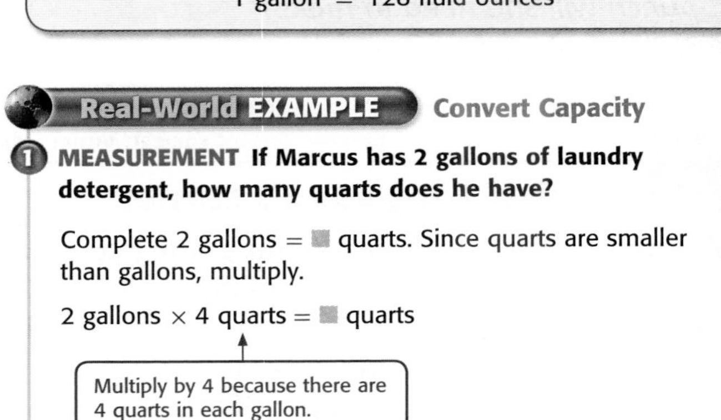

**Real-World EXAMPLE** Convert Capacity

**1 MEASUREMENT If Marcus has 2 gallons of laundry detergent, how many quarts does he have?**

Complete 2 gallons = ■ quarts. Since quarts are smaller than gallons, multiply.

2 gallons × 4 quarts = ■ quarts



2 gallons × 4 quarts = 8 quarts

So, there are 8 quarts in 2 gallons.



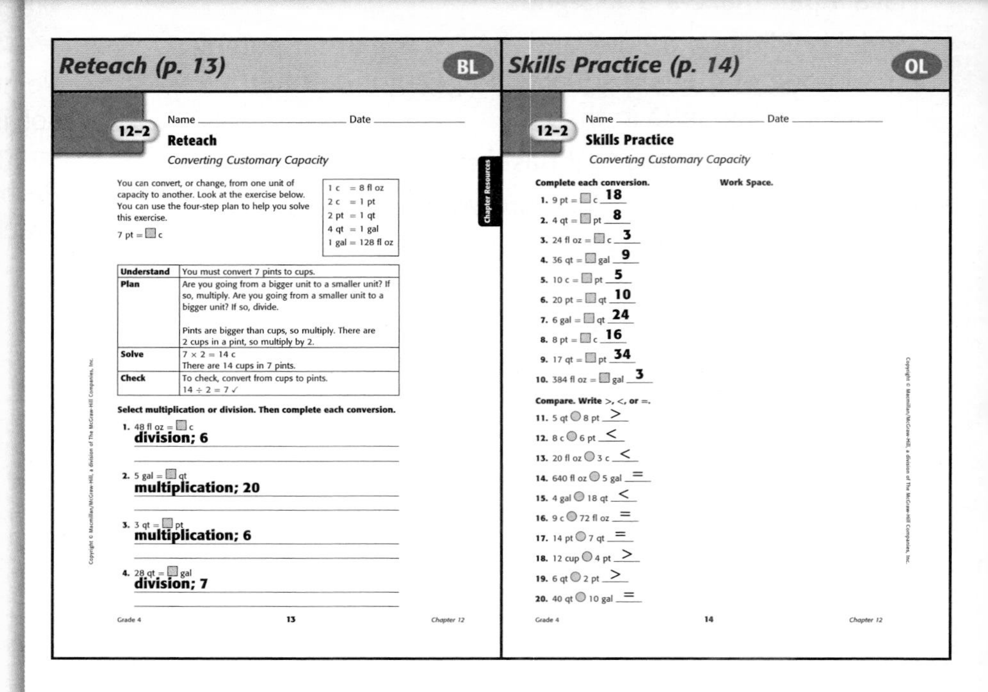

**Reteach (p. 13)** BL

12-2 Name ______ Date ______

**Reteach**

*Converting Customary Capacity*

You can convert, or change, from one unit of capacity to another. Look at the exercise below. You can use the four-step plan to help you solve this exercise.

7 pt = ☐ c

| | | |
|---|---|---|
| 1 c | = | 8 fl oz |
| 2 c | = | 1 pt |
| 2 pt | = | 1 qt |
| 4 qt | = | 1 gal |
| 1 gal | = | 128 fl oz |

| | |
|---|---|
| **Understand** | You must convert 7 pints to cups. |
| **Plan** | Are you going from a bigger unit to a smaller unit? If so, multiply. Are you going from a smaller unit to a bigger unit? If so, divide. Pints are bigger than cups, so multiply. There are 2 cups in a pint, so multiply by 2. |
| **Solve** | 7 × 2 = 14 c There are 14 cups in 7 pints. |
| **Check** | To check, convert from cups to pints. 14 ÷ 2 = 7 ✓ |

**Select multiplication or division. Then complete each conversion.**

1. 48 fl oz = ☐ c **division; 6**
2. 5 gal = ☐ qt **multiplication; 20**
3. 3 qt = ☐ pt **multiplication; 6**
4. 28 qt = ☐ gal **division; 7**

Grade 4 13 Chapter 12

Chapter Resources



**Skills Practice (p. 14)** OL

12-2 Name ______ Date ______

**Skills Practice**

*Converting Customary Capacity*

**Complete each conversion.** **Work Space.**

1. 9 pt = ☐ c **18**
2. 4 qt = ☐ pt **8**
3. 24 fl oz = ☐ c **3**
4. 36 qt = ☐ gal **9**
5. 10 c = ☐ pt **5**
6. 20 pt = ☐ qt **10**
7. 6 gal = ☐ qt **24**
8. 8 pt = ☐ c **16**
9. 17 qt = ☐ pt **34**
10. 384 fl oz = ☐ gal **3**

**Compare. Write >, <, or =.**

11. 5 qt ○ 8 pt **>**
12. 8 c ○ 6 pt **<**
13. 20 fl oz ○ 3 c **<**
14. 640 fl oz ○ 5 gal **=**
15. 4 gal ○ 18 qt **<**
16. 9 c ○ 72 fl oz **=**
17. 14 pt ○ 7 qt **=**
18. 12 cup ○ 4 pt **>**
19. 6 qt ○ 2 pt **>**
20. 40 qt ○ 10 gal **=**

Grade 4 14 Chapter 12

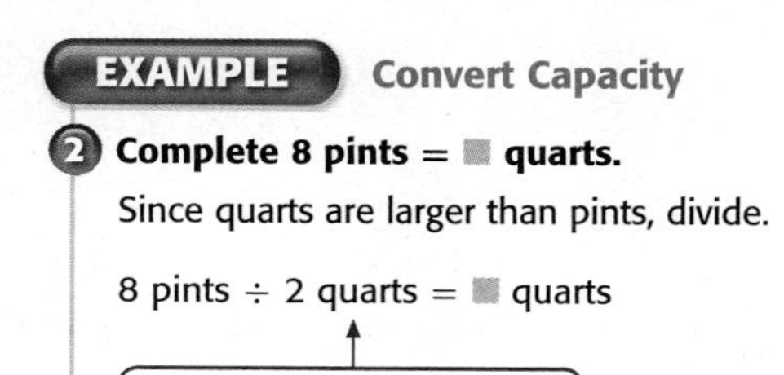

**EXAMPLE** Convert Capacity

**2** **Complete 8 pints = ■ quarts.**

Since quarts are larger than pints, divide.

8 pints ÷ 2 quarts = ■ quarts

Divide by 2 because there are 2 pints in each quart.

8 pints ÷ 2 quarts = 4 quarts

So, 8 pints = 4 quarts.

5. Multiply 6 by 2 because 2 cups are equal to 1 pint.

## CHECK What You Know

**Complete.** See Examples 1 and 2 (pp. 490–491)

**1.** 20 pt = ■ qt 10
**2.** 3 c = ■ fl oz 24
**3.** 4 qt = ■ pt 8

**4.** Gwenith has 3 gallons of milk. How many quarts of milk does she have? 12 quarts

**5.** Talk About It Explain how to convert 6 pints to cups.

## Practice and Problem Solving

EXTRA PRACTICE See page R31.

**Complete.** See Examples 1 and 2 (pp. 490–491)

**6.** 64 fl oz = ■ c 8
**7.** 6 gal = ■ qt 24
**8.** ■ gal = 20 qt 5
**9.** 5 c = ■ fl oz 40
**10.** ■ pt = 30 c 15
**11.** ■ c = 128 fl oz 16

**Compare. Use >, <, or =.**

**12.** 4 qt ● 10 pt <
**13.** 10 gal ● 1,280 fl oz =
**14.** 1 qt ● 2 c >

**15.** Tomas is buying a 16-fluid ounce container of liquid dish soap. How many cups of dish soap is he buying? 2 cups

**16.** Karen is buying 4 gallons of orange juice. How many quarts of orange juice is she buying? 16 quarts

### H.O.T. Problem

**17.** WRITING IN MATH Write a rule for converting capacities measured in customary units. Sample answer: When converting from a larger unit to a smaller unit use multiplication.



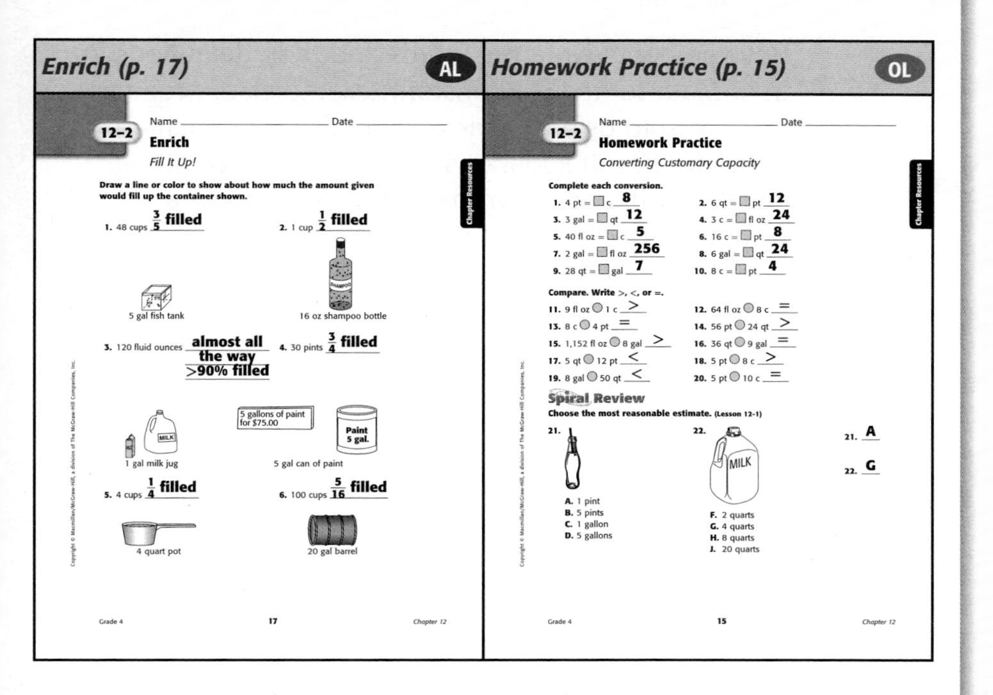

*Enrich (p. 17)* AL

12-2 Name ________ Date ________
**Enrich**
*Fill It Up!*

Draw a line or color to show about how much the amount given would fill up the container shown.

1. 48 cups 3/5 filled — 5 gal fish tank
2. 1 cup 1/2 filled — 16 oz shampoo bottle
3. 120 fluid ounces almost all the way >90% filled — 1 gal milk jug
4. 30 pints 3/4 filled — 5 gal can of paint (5 gallons of paint for $75.00)
5. 4 cups 1/4 filled — 4 quart pot
6. 100 cups 5/16 filled — 20 gal barrel

Grade 4 17 Chapter 12

*Homework Practice (p. 15)* OL

12-2 Name ________ Date ________
**Homework Practice**
*Converting Customary Capacity*

Complete each conversion.

1. 4 pt = ■ c 8
2. 6 qt = ■ pt 12
3. 3 gal = ■ qt 12
4. 3 c = ■ fl oz 24
5. 40 fl oz = ■ c 5
6. 16 c = ■ pt 8
7. 2 gal = ■ fl oz 256
8. 6 gal = ■ qt 24
9. 28 qt = ■ gal 7
10. 8 c = ■ pt 4

Compare. Write >, <, or =.

11. 9 fl oz ○ 1 c >
12. 64 fl oz ○ 8 c =
13. 8 c ○ 4 pt =
14. 56 pt ○ 24 qt >
15. 1,152 fl oz ○ 8 gal >
16. 36 qt ○ 9 gal =
17. 5 qt ○ 12 pt <
18. 5 pt ○ 8 c >
19. 8 gal ○ 50 qt <
20. 5 pt ○ 10 c =

**Spiral Review**
Choose the most reasonable estimate. (Lesson 12-1)

21. A. 1 pint B. 5 pints C. 1 gallon D. 5 gallons — 21. A
22. F. 2 quarts G. 4 quarts H. 8 quarts J. 20 quarts — 22. G

Grade 4 15 Chapter 12

## CHECK What You Know

As a class, have students complete Exercises 1–5 in **Check What You Know** as you observe their work.

**Exercise 5** Assess student comprehension before assigning practice exercises.

## BL Alternate Teaching Strategy

**If** students have trouble converting customary capacity units...

**Then** use one of these reteach options:

1 CRM **Daily Reteach Worksheet** (p. 13)

2 Allow students to use standard containers as manipulatives to determine conversions. **How can you use the containers to determine conversions?** Answers will vary.

# 3 Practice

Differentiate practice using these leveled assignments for Exercises 6–17.

| Level | Assignment |
|---|---|
| BL Below/Approaching Level | 6–8, 12–14 |
| OL On Level | 8–11, 13–16 |
| AL Above/Beyond Level | 7–15 odd, 17 |

# 4 Assess

### Formative Assessment

- **Which operation do you use to convert from a smaller unit of measure to a larger unit?** division **a larger unit of measure to a smaller unit?** multiplication

**Quick Check** **Are students continuing to struggle with converting customary units of capacity?**

**If Yes** → Small Group Options (p. 490B)

**If No** → Independent Work Options (p. 490B)
CRM Skills Practice Worksheet (p. 14)
CRM Enrich Worksheet (p. 17)

LESSON 12-3

# Metric Units of Capacity

## Lesson Planner

### Objective

Estimate and measure metric capacities.

### Vocabulary

**liter**, **milliliter**

### Resources

**Materials:** vase, pitcher or other objects that hold liquid, everyday objects whose contents are measured in L or mL

**Manipulatives:** capacity containers

**Literature Connection:** *Capacity* by Henry Pluckrose

**Alternate Lesson:** Use *IMPACT Mathematics:* Unit H to provide practice with capacity.

**Teacher Technology**

TeacherWorks • Interactive Classroom • Concepts in Motion

## Daily Routine

Use these suggestions before beginning the lesson on p. 492.

### 5-Minute Check

(Reviews Lesson 12-2)

**Complete.**

1. 3 gal = ■ qt 12
2. 32 fl oz = ■ c 4

**Compare. Use >, <, or =.**

3. 3 qt ● 6 pt =
4. 1 gal ● 2 qt >

### Problem of the Day

Josh and five friends bought tickets to a soccer game. Each ticket cost $15. How much did the group spend for tickets? $90

### Focus on Math Background

The basic metric unit for liquid volume is the liter. A milliliter is one-thousandth of a liter. Many kinds of drinks sold in the U.S. are packaged in containers measured in liters or milliliters. Other products, like ice cream, often list both customary and metric units.

A liter is equivalent to about 34 fluid ounces, or slightly more than a quart. And a milliliter is exactly the same size as a cubic centimeter.

In science and medicine, measurement of capacity is almost always done with metric units.

### Building Math Vocabulary

Write the lesson vocabulary words and their definitions on the board.

Have students write the words and their definitions in their Math Journals. Brainstorm examples of products that are sold using metric units of capacity, such as 2-liter bottles of soda, or small bottles of eye drops, cough syrup, and other medicines (mL). Have a volunteer list the responses on the board.

# Differentiated Instruction

## Small Group Options

LOGICAL

### Option 1 Below Level BL

**Materials:** paper and pencil

- Convey to students:

> Mia needs $7\frac{1}{2}$ liters of soda for the class picnic. She can buy liter containers for \$2 or 2-liter containers for \$3. Which is the best buy for the picnic?
>
> Eight liters for \$16 or four 2-liter bottles for \$12; four 2-liter bottles is the best buy.

KINESTHETIC, VISUAL

### Option 2 English Language Learners ELL

**Materials:** droppers, cups, funnel
**Core Vocabulary:** funnel, dropper, liter bottle
**Common Use Verb:** take/took

**Write Math** This strategy helps students understand metric units of capacity.

- Post a liter bottle with a funnel. Model using a dropper ten times into a cup and pouring it into the liter bottle.
- Give each student a dropper and cup.
- Have students repeat, pouring 10 drops into the funnel each time.
- Tally the number of cups poured.
- After the liter bottle is full, have students write out how many milliliters drops it took to fill a liter bottle.
- Have students present their findings and discuss.

## Independent Work Options

VISUAL, LOGICAL

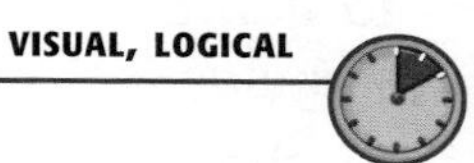

### Option 1 Early Finishers AL

**Materials:** newspapers, store and drug store flyers

- Provide print materials for students.
- Students search the print media for examples of products that are sold in liter or milliliter containers.
- Allow students to cut out and make a display of these products. If the print materials cannot be cut, have students copy or describe the products.
- Allow students to share their information with the class.

### Option 2 Student Technology

**Math Online** macmillanmh.com

Personal Tutor • Extra Examples

### Option 3 Learning Station: Science (p. 482J)

Direct students to the Science Learning Station for opportunities to explore and extend the lesson concept.

### Option 4 Problem-Solving Practice

Reinforce problem-solving skills and strategies with the Problem-Solving Practice worksheet.

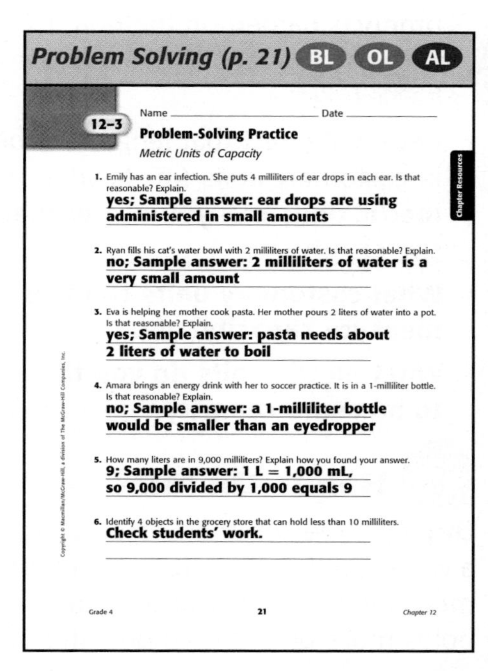

*Problem Solving (p. 21)* BL OL AL

12-3

Name ______________ Date ______________

**Problem-Solving Practice**

*Metric Units of Capacity*

Chapter Resources

1. Emily has an ear infection. She puts 4 milliliters of ear drops in each ear. Is that reasonable? Explain.
**yes; Sample answer: ear drops are using administered in small amounts**

2. Ryan fills his cat's water bowl with 2 milliliters of water. Is that reasonable? Explain.
**no; Sample answer: 2 milliliters of water is a very small amount**

3. Eva is helping her mother cook pasta. Her mother pours 2 liters of water into a pot. Is that reasonable? Explain.
**yes; Sample answer: pasta needs about 2 liters of water to boil**

4. Amara brings an energy drink with her to soccer practice. It is in a 1-milliliter bottle. Is that reasonable? Explain.
**no; Sample answer: a 1-milliliter bottle would be smaller than an eyedropper**

5. How many liters are in 9,000 milliliters? Explain how you found your answer.
**9; Sample answer: 1 L = 1,000 mL, so 9,000 divided by 1,000 equals 9**

6. Identify 4 objects in the grocery store that can hold less than 10 milliliters.
**Check students' work.**



Grade 4 21 Chapter 12

# Metric Units of Capacity

## 1 Introduce

### Activity Choice 1 • Hands-On

- On a transparency, write exercises, such as 5 gal = ■ qt. **How do you convert 5 gallons to quarts?** Multiply 5 × 4 because there are 4 quarts in 1 gallon.
- On the transparency, write *x* eyedroppers = 1 medicine cup.
- Using a 2-mL eyedropper fill a 30 mL medicine cup. **How many eyedroppers did it take to fill the cup?** 15
- **How would you find the number of eyedroppers it takes to fill 3 medicine cups?** 3 × 15 = 45
- **What operation do you use to convert smaller units of measure to larger units?** division
- **What operation do you use to convert larger units of measure to smaller units?** multiplication

### Activity Choice 2 • Literature

Introduce the lesson with *Capacity* by Henry Pluckrose. For a related math activity, see p. TR61.

## 2 Teach

### Scaffolding Questions

Write liter and milliliter on the board.

- **On what products have you seen these words used?** Have a volunteer list the products named on the board. Sample answer: beverage containers and medicine bottles
- Review the fact that length can be measured in customary units (in., ft, yd, mi). **What metric units can you use to measure length?** cm, m, km
- **What customary units can you use to measure capacity?** fl oz, c, qt, gal
- **What metric units do you think we can use to measure capacity?** liter, milliliter

### Hands-On Mini Activity

Display three common objects such as a vase, a water bottle, or a pitcher. Then use a one-liter measuring container to determine whether each holds more or less than one liter of liquid.



# 12-3 Metric Units of Capacity

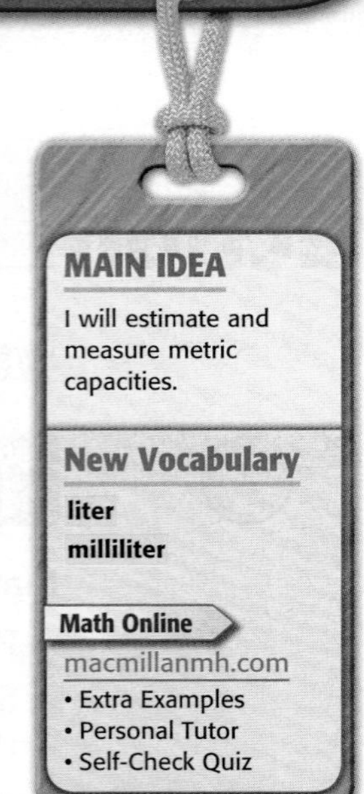

**MAIN IDEA**

I will estimate and measure metric capacities.

**New Vocabulary**

**liter**

**milliliter**

**Math Online**

macmillanmh.com

- Extra Examples
- Personal Tutor
- Self-Check Quiz

## GET READY to Learn

**Hands-On Mini Activity**

A liter is a metric unit of capacity. This container holds a liter.

**Materials:** 3 different containers, liter measuring tool

**Step 1 Copy the table.**

| Object | Estimate | Actual |
|---|---|---|
| | | |
| | | |
| | | |

**Step 2 Estimate.**

Select three containers. Choose one and estimate whether it has a capacity that is greater than, less than, or equal to 1 liter. Record the estimate.

**Step 3 Measure.**

Fill a liter measuring tool with water. Pour the water into each of the containers. Tell whether each container is greater than, less than, or equal to 1 liter. Record the results.

In the metric system, the **liter** and **milliliter** are often used as units of measurement for capacity.

liter (L)

A bottle about this size can hold a liter.

milliliter (mL)

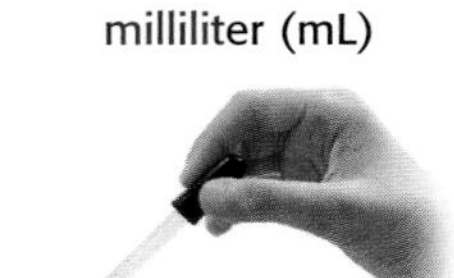

A milliliter is less than half of an eyedropper.



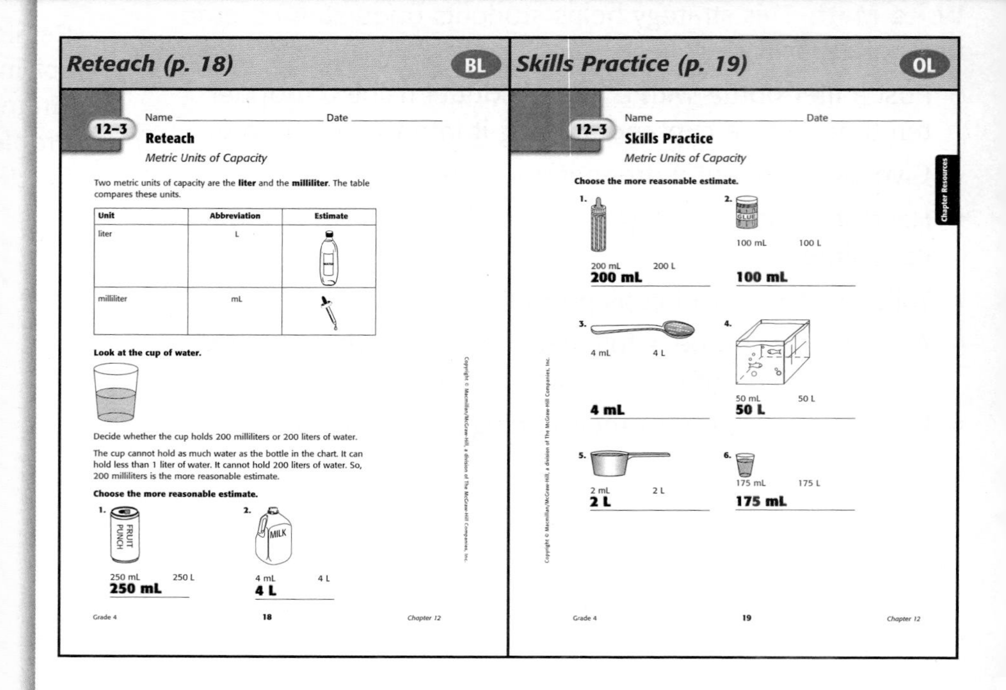

**Reteach (p. 18)** BL

12-3 Name ______ Date ______

**Reteach**

*Metric Units of Capacity*

Two metric units of capacity are the **liter** and the **milliliter**. The table compares these units.

| Unit | Abbreviation | Estimate |
|---|---|---|
| liter | L | |
| milliliter | mL | |

**Look at the cup of water.**

Decide whether the cup holds 200 milliliters or 200 liters of water.

The cup cannot hold as much water as the bottle in the chart. It can hold less than 1 liter of water. It cannot hold 200 liters of water. So, 200 milliliters is the more reasonable estimate.

**Choose the more reasonable estimate.**

1. FRUIT PUNCH — 250 mL 250 L — **250 mL**
2. MILK — 4 mL 4 L — **4 L**

Grade 4 18 Chapter 12



**Skills Practice (p. 19)** OL

12-3 Name ______ Date ______

**Skills Practice**

*Metric Units of Capacity*

**Choose the more reasonable estimate.**

1. 200 mL 200 L — **200 mL**
2. GLUE — 100 mL 100 L — **100 mL**
3. 4 mL 4 L — **4 mL**
4. 50 mL 50 L — **50 L**
5. 2 mL 2 L — **2 L**
6. 175 mL 175 L — **175 mL**

Grade 4 19 Chapter 12

Chapter Resources

## Real-World EXAMPLES Convert Capacity

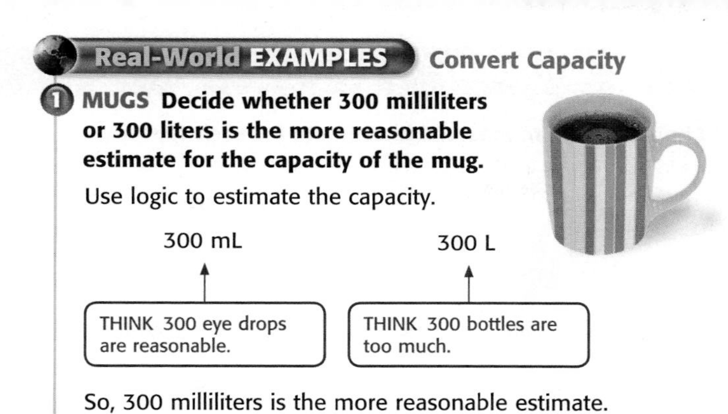

**1 MUGS Decide whether 300 milliliters or 300 liters is the more reasonable estimate for the capacity of the mug.**

Use logic to estimate the capacity.

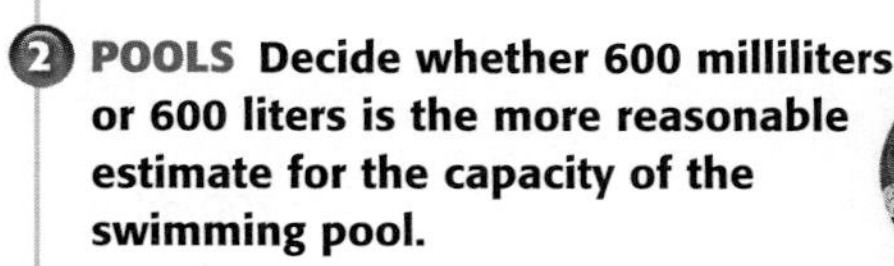


So, 300 milliliters is the more reasonable estimate.

**2 POOLS Decide whether 600 milliliters or 600 liters is the more reasonable estimate for the capacity of the swimming pool.**

Use logic to estimate the capacity.

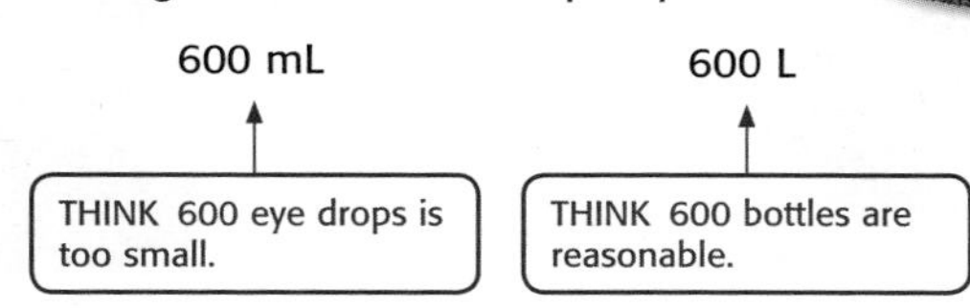


So, 600 milliliters is the more reasonable estimate.

4. Sample answer: no; 3 liters of water is equal to about 12 glasses of water, which is too much for a person at one time.

5. Sample answer: Since medicine is usually given in a small amount, the milliliter would be the appropriate unit.

## CHECK What You Know

**Choose the more reasonable estimate for each capacity.** See Examples 1 and 2 (p. 493)

**1.** 1 mL or 1 L **1 L**

**2.** 220 mL or 220 L **220 mL**

**3.**

135 mL or 135 L **135 L**

**4.** Jonah said he drank 3 liters of water after his soccer game. Is this a reasonable statement? Explain.

**5.** Talk About It Describe the unit of capacity you would use to measure the capacity of a bottle of medicine.



### Enrich (p. 22) AL

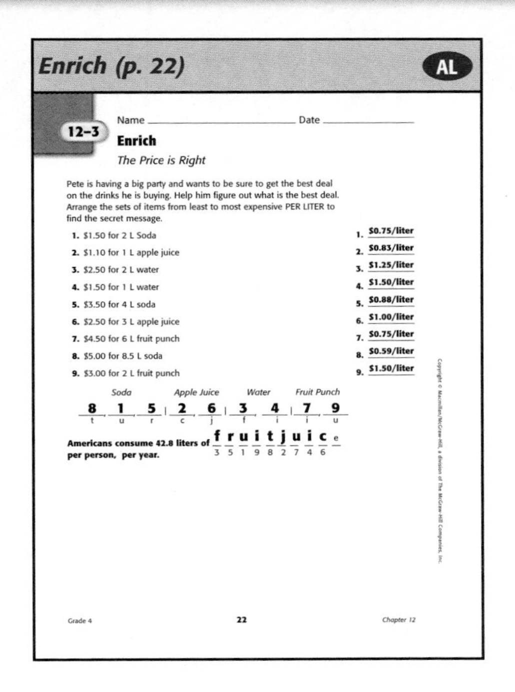

12–3

Name ______________________ Date ____________

**Enrich**

*The Price is Right*

Pete is having a big party and wants to be sure to get the best deal on the drinks he is buying. Help him figure out what is the best deal. Arrange the sets of items from least to most expensive PER LITER to find the secret message.

1. $1.50 for 2 L Soda — 1. $0.75/liter
2. $1.10 for 1 L apple juice — 2. $0.83/liter
3. $2.50 for 2 L water — 3. $1.25/liter
4. $1.50 for 1 L water — 4. $1.50/liter
5. $3.50 for 4 L soda — 5. $0.88/liter
6. $2.50 for 3 L apple juice — 6. $1.00/liter
7. $4.50 for 6 L fruit punch — 7. $0.75/liter
8. $5.00 for 8.5 L soda — 8. $0.59/liter
9. $3.00 for 2 L fruit punch — 9. $1.50/liter

| Soda | | | Apple Juice | | Water | | Fruit Punch | |
|---|---|---|---|---|---|---|---|---|
| 8 | 1 | 5 | 2 | 6 | 3 | 4 | 7 | 9 |
| t | u | r | c | j | f | i | i | u |

**Americans consume 42.8 liters of** f r u i t j u i c e **per person, per year.**

3 5 1 9 8 2 7 4 6





### Estimate Capacity

**Example 1** Avoid comparing customary units of capacity with these metric units. Help students think in metric terms.

#### ADDITIONAL EXAMPLE

**1** Decide whether 2 mL or 2 L is the more reasonable estimate for the capacity of a watering can. 2 L

#### CHECK What You Know

As a class, have students complete Exercises 1–5 in **Check What You Know** as you observe their work.

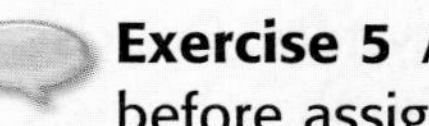

**Exercise 5** Assess student comprehension before assigning practice exercises.

### BL Alternate Teaching Strategy

**If** students have trouble estimating capacity within the metric system…

**Then** use one of these reteach options:

1 CRM **Daily Reteach Worksheet** (p. 18)

2 Display a 1-liter or 1.5-liter container and a mL product, such as contact rewetting drops. **What products do you think would be sold in 1-liter containers? in milliliter packaging?** Accept all reasonable answers.

Encourage students to think and speak in metric terms. Avoid comparing metric measures to customary measures.

#### COMMON ERROR!

If students fail to comprehend the relative size of the metric units milliliter and liter, it might be helpful to point out that an object with a capacity of one liter is 1,000 times the size of an object with a capacity of one milliliter.

# 3 Practice

Differentiate practice using these leveled assignments for Exercises 6–16.

| Level | Assignment |
|---|---|
| BL Below/Approaching Level | 6–9, 12–13 |
| OL On Level | 6–10, 12–13, 14 |
| AL Above/Beyond Level | 7–13 even, 14–16 |

Have students discuss and complete the Higher Order Thinking problems. Point out that metric units are based on multiples of 10: 1,000 mL = 1L. Encourage students to use mental math when working with the metric system. Exercise 14 asks students about objects in their homes.

**WRITING IN ➤MATH** Have students complete Exercise 16 in their Math Journals. You may choose to use this as an optional formative assessment.

### Additional Answers

**15.** Fill the 7-liter bucket with water. Fill the 4-liter bucket with the water from the 7-liter bucket. The water leftover in the 7-liter bucket is equal to 3 liters.

**16.** Sample answer: There would be 15,000 milliliters in a liter. You find this answer by using multiplication, since you are going from a larger to a smaller unit.

## Practice and Problem Solving

See page R31.

**Choose the more reasonable estimate for each capacity.**

See Examples 1 and 2 (p. 493)

**6.** 

150 mL or 150 L **150 mL**

**7.** 

120 mL or 120 L **120 mL**

**8.** 

500 mL or 500 L **500 mL**

**9.** 

700 mL or 700 L **700 mL**

**10.** 1 mL or 1 L **1 L**

**11.** 

30 mL or 30 L **30 L**

**12.** Jenna said that she took 4 milliliters of medicine for her cold. Is this a reasonable statement? Explain.
**Sample answer: yes, Medicine is usually taken in small amounts.**

**13.** Select three containers. Estimate and then measure whether each container has a capacity that is greater than, less than, or equal to 1 liter.
**See students' work.**

| Object | Estimate | Actual |
|---|---|---|
| | | |
| | | |
| | | |

### H.O.T. Problems

**14. OPEN ENDED** Identify four objects in your house that can hold more than 1 liter. **Sample answer: kitchen sink; bath tub; washing machine; pool**

**15. CHALLENGE** Suppose you have a 4-liter bucket and a 7-liter bucket. You need 3 liters of water for an aquarium. Explain how to get 3 liters of water if neither bucket is marked. **15, 16. See margin.**

**16. WRITING IN ➤MATH** How many milliliters are in 15 liters? Explain.

17. Theo drank 64 fluid ounces of water in one day. Which of the following is equal to the amount of water Theo drank? (Lesson 12-2) B

A 4 cups  C 4 quarts

B 4 pints  D 4 gallons

18. Which is the best estimate of the capacity of a glass of iced tea? (Lesson 12-3) G

F 250 L  H 250 lb

G 250 mL  J 250 fl oz

## Spiral Review

**Complete.** (Lesson 12-2)

19. 12 gal = ■ qt 48  20. 32 fl oz = ■ c 4  21. ■ pt = 18 c 9

**Choose the most reasonable estimate for each capacity.** (Lesson 12-1)

22.

A 2 fl oz  C 2 qt

B 2 c  D 2 gal B

23.

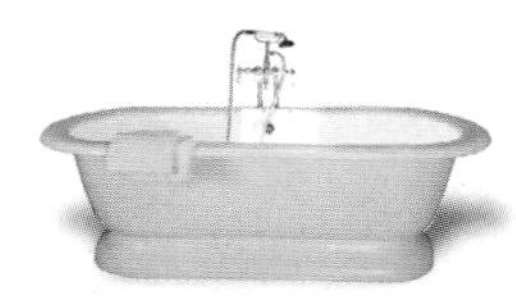

F 78 fl oz  H 78 qt

G 78 c  J 78 gal J

**Tell whether the figures appear to be congruent. Write *yes* or *no*. If they are, describe the movements that show the congruence.** (Lesson 10-7)

24.

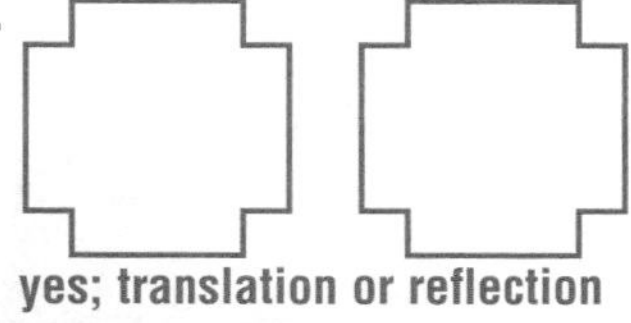

yes; translation or reflection

25.

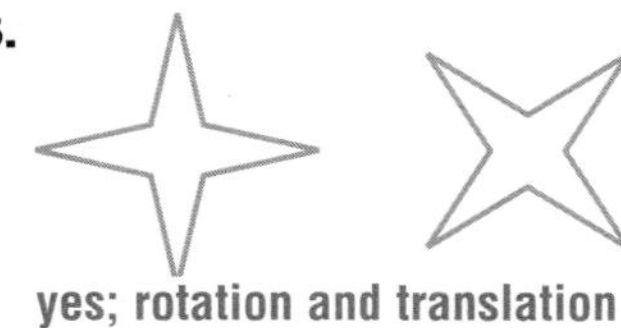

yes; rotation and translation

**Multiply. Check for reasonableness.** (Lesson 6-6)

26. $218 \times 3$ = 654  27. $896 \times 5$ = 4,480  28. $2,731 \times 7$ = 19,117

29. Matt drank 22 fluid ounces of grape juice in one day. Is it reasonable to say that he drank more than 3 cups of grape juice that day? Explain. (Lesson 6-2) See margin.



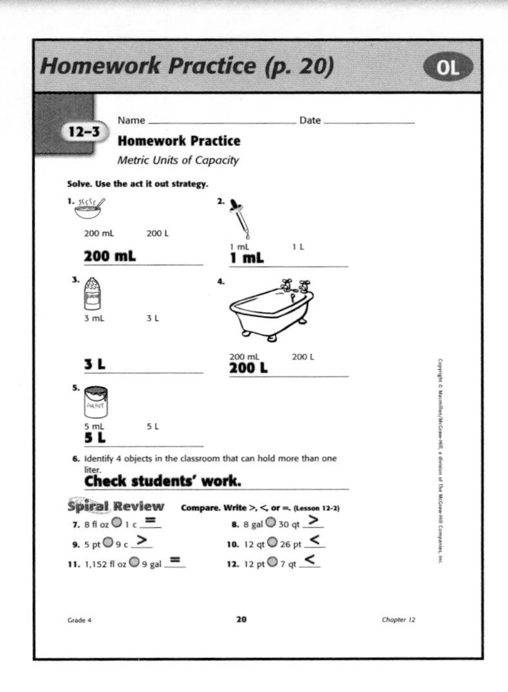
Homework Practice (p. 20) OL

12-3 Homework Practice
Metric Units of Capacity

Solve. Use the act it out strategy.

1. 200 mL  200 L — 200 mL
2. 1 mL  1 L — 1 mL
3. 3 mL  3 L — 3 L
4. 200 mL  200 L — 200 L
5. 5 mL  5 L — 5 L
6. Identify 4 objects in the classroom that can hold more than one liter. Check students' work.

Spiral Review Compare. Write >, <, or =. (Lesson 12-2)

7. 8 fl oz ○ 1 c =  8. 8 gal ○ 30 qt >
9. 5 pt ○ 9 c >  10. 12 qt ○ 26 pt <
11. 1,152 fl oz ○ 9 gal =  12. 12 pt ○ 7 qt <

# 4 Assess

## Formative Assessment

- **What are two metric units of capacity?** L, mL
- **Which metric unit would you use to estimate the capacity of a large punch bowl?** L
- **Which metric unit would you use to estimate the capacity of a travel-size bottle of shampoo?** mL

**Quick Check** **Are students continuing to struggle with estimating and measuring capacity within the metric system?**

**If Yes** → Small Group Options (p. 492B)

**If No** → Independent Work Options (p. 492B)
CRM Skills Practice Worksheet (p. 19)
CRM Enrich Worksheet (p. 22)

**Ticket Out the Door** List the metric units of measure you know for length and capacity.

### Reviews Lessons 12-2 and 12-3

Assign the Test Practice problems to provide daily reinforcement of test-taking skills.

## Spiral Review

### Reviews Lessons 6-2, 6-6, 10-7, 12-1, and 12-2

Review and assess mastery of skills and concepts from previous chapters.

### Additional Answer

29. Sample answer: no; 3 cups = 24 fluid ounces. Since 22 < 24, it is not reasonable to say Matt drank more than 3 cups of grape juice.

Explore

# Measurement Activity for 12-4

# Lesson Planner

## Objective

Estimate and measure weight.

## Resources

**Materials:** chalkboard eraser, glue bottle

**Manipulatives:** balance scale, ounce and pound weights

## 1 Introduce

- **How do you weigh something?** Sample answer: Put it on a scale.
- **When you weigh yourself on a scale, what unit of measure do you use to tell a friend how much you weigh?** pound
- **What other units do you know for measuring weight?** Sample answers: ton, ounce

## 2 Teach

**Activity** Have a volunteer place the eraser on one side of the balance scale and a pound weight on the other side.

- **If the side with the pound weight is lower than the side with the eraser, what does that mean?** Sample answer: The eraser does not weigh as much as a pound.
- **What do you have to do to weigh the eraser now?** Sample answer: Take off the pound weight and use ounce weights until the scale is balanced.



Explore

Measurement Activity for 12-4

# Estimate and Measure Weight

**MAIN IDEA**

I will estimate and measure weight.

**You Will Need**
chalkboard eraser
balance scale
glue bottle

In this activity, you will measure the weight of objects. The **weight** of an object is how heavy it is.

**ACTIVITY** Measure Weight

**Step 1** **Copy the table.**

| Object | Estimate | Actual |
|---|---|---|
| Eraser | | |
| Glue bottle | | |
| Math book | | |
| Object of your choice | | |

**Step 2** **Estimate.**

Estimate the weight of a chalkboard eraser. Record the estimate.

**Step 3** **Measure.**

Place the eraser on one side of a balance scale. Set ounce or pound weights on the other side until the sides are balanced. Record the actual weight. Repeat Steps 2 and 3 for the other objects.

## Think About It

1. Order the four objects you weighed in the activity from greatest to least weight. See students' work.
2. Use the weights of the objects you found to estimate the weight of two other objects in your classroom. Weigh the objects. Were your estimations close? See students' work.
3. Is the total weight of the four objects you measured greater than 2 pounds? Explain. Sample answer: Yes, I found the answer by adding the weights together.

## CHECK What You Know

4. How many 1-ounce weights are needed to balance the scale when a 1-pound weight is in the other pan? 16
5. How many ounces are in two pounds? 32 ounces
6. How many ounces are in four pounds? 64 ounces

**Compare. Use >, <, or =.**

7. 46 ounces ● 3 pounds <
8. 5 pounds ● 78 ounces >
9. 96 ounces ● 6 pounds =
10. 7 pounds ● 110 ounces >
11. 130 ounces ● 8 pounds >
12. 9 pounds ● 145 ounces <
13. Identify three objects in your classroom that weigh more than an eraser and less than your math book. Estimate each object's weight. Then weigh each object and record the exact weight in a table like the one shown below. See students' work.

| Object | Estimate | Actual |
|---|---|---|
| | | |
| | | |
| | | |

14. WRITING IN MATH Write a sentence that describes the relationship that is usually found between an object's size and weight. See margin.



### Additional Answer

**14.** Sample answer: The larger an object is, the more it weighs.

## Think About It

Assign Exercises 1–3 in the **Think About It** section to assess student comprehension of the concept presented in the Activity.

# 3 Assess

### Formative Assessment

Use **Check What You Know** Exercises 4–14 to assess whether students comprehend how to estimate and measure customary weights.

**From Concrete to Abstract** Use Exercise 13 to bridge the gap between using a scale to weigh objects and using objects that you know the weight of to estimate the weights of other objects.

### Extending the Concept

- **What can you say about the relationship of pounds and ounces?** 1 pound = 16 ounces

LESSON 12-4

# Customary Units of Weight

## Lesson Planner

### Objective

Estimate and measure customary units of weight.

### Vocabulary

**weight**, **ounce**, **pound**, **ton**

### Resources

**Manipulatives:** balance scale, weights

**Literature Connection:** *How Much, How Many, How Far, How Heavy, How Long, How Tall is 1000?* by Helen Nolan

**Teacher Technology**

TeacherWorks • Interactive Classroom

## Daily Routine

Use these suggestions before beginning the lesson on p. 498.

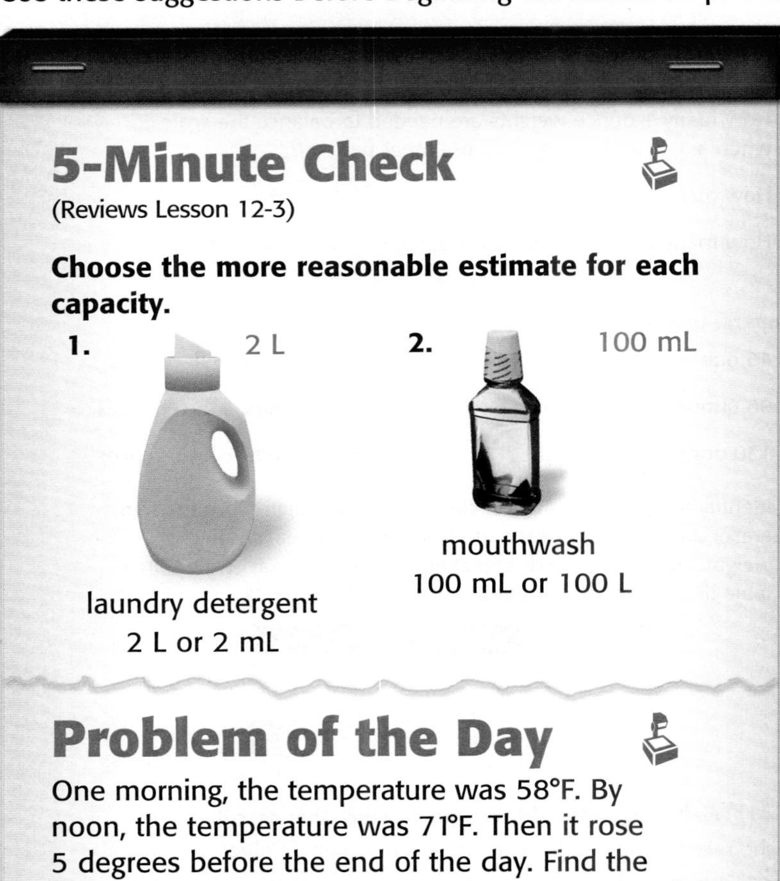

### 5-Minute Check

(Reviews Lesson 12-3)

**Choose the more reasonable estimate for each capacity.**

**1.** laundry detergent 2 L or 2 mL 2 L

**2.** mouthwash 100 mL or 100 L 100 mL

### Problem of the Day

One morning, the temperature was 58°F. By noon, the temperature was 71°F. Then it rose 5 degrees before the end of the day. Find the change in temperature from morning to the end of the day. 18°F

### Focus on Math Background

The basic metric unit for liquid volume is the *liter*. A *milliliter* is one-thousandth of a liter. Many kinds of drinks sold in the United States are packaged in containers measured in liters or milliliters. Other products, like ice cream, often list both customary and metric units.

A liter is equivalent to about 34 fluid ounces, or slightly more than a quart. And a milliliter is exactly the same size as a cubic centimeter.

In science and medicine, measurement of capacity is almost always done with metric units.

### Building Math Vocabulary

Write the lesson vocabulary words and their definitions on the board.

Have students write the words and their definitions in their Math Journals. Brainstorm objects that can be reasonably weighed in ounces. Have a volunteer list the responses on the board. Then brainstorm objects that can be weighed in pounds and weighed in tons.

# Differentiated Instruction

## Small Group Options

LOGICAL

### Option 1 Below Level BL

**Materials:** pencil and paper plus four classroom objects of students' choice

- Have students choose four objects from the classroom such as a book, desk, etc.
- Figure the weight of each object.
- Write the problem using the same numeral but differing weights, for instance, a dog.

**A** 15 ounces
**B** 15 pounds
**C** 15 tons

- Have students exchange problems with a classmate and see if they can answer correctly. Answers will vary depending on objects chosen.

SOCIAL, LINGUISTIC

### Option 2 English Language Learners ELL

**Materials:** approximate 1-pound items, classroom objects
**Core Vocabulary:** with both hands, weighs more than/less than a pound, opinions
**Common Use Verb:** pass
**Talk Math** This strategy applies estimating weight to help students vocalize their estimations.

- Write: **"____ weighs less than a pound. ____ weighs more than a pound"**.
- Pass around 1-pound objects as students sit in a circle.
- Have every other student choose a classroom item and sit between remaining students.
- Model passing the object with both hands, saying the correct scaffold while the receiving student listens. The receiving student repeats, passing to the next student.
- Repeat for all objects.
- Discuss if other students agreed with them, and why there might be differences of opinions.

## Independent Work Options

TACTILE, LOGICAL

### Option 1 Early Finishers AL

**Materials:** balance scale, scale bathroom

- Have partners take turns naming objects and estimating weights.
- One student names an object in the classroom that can be weighed in ounces or pounds. The partner records an estimate of the weight of the object.
- Together, the partners weigh the object and discuss how close to the estimate the actual weight is.
- For small objects, students use the balance scale. For heavier objects, students use a weight scale such as a bathroom scale

### Option 2 Student Technology

**Math Online** macmillanmh.com

Personal Tutor • Extra Examples

### Option 3 Learning Station: Science (p. 486J)

Direct students to the Science Learning Station for opportunities to explore and extend the lesson concept.

### Option 4 Problem-Solving Practice

Reinforce problem-solving skills and strategies with the Problem-Solving Practice worksheet.

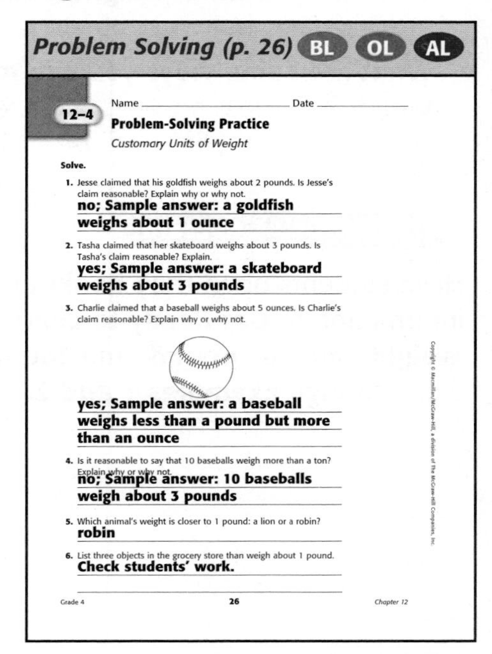

*Problem Solving (p. 26)* BL OL AL

12–4 Name ____________ Date ____________

**Problem-Solving Practice**

*Customary Units of Weight*

**Solve.**

1. Jesse claimed that his goldfish weighs about 2 pounds. Is Jesse's claim reasonable? Explain why or why not.
**no; Sample answer: a goldfish weighs about 1 ounce**

2. Tasha claimed that her skateboard weighs about 3 pounds. Is Tasha's claim reasonable? Explain.
**yes; Sample answer: a skateboard weighs about 3 pounds**

3. Charlie claimed that a baseball weighs about 5 ounces. Is Charlie's claim reasonable? Explain why or why not.
**yes; Sample answer: a baseball weighs less than a pound but more than an ounce**

4. Is it reasonable to say that 10 baseballs weigh more than a ton? Explain why or why not.
**no; Sample answer: 10 baseballs weigh about 3 pounds**

5. Which animal's weight is closer to 1 pound: a lion or a robin?
**robin**

6. List three objects in the grocery store than weigh about 1 pound.
**Check students' work.**

Grade 4 26 Chapter 12

# 12-4 Customary Units of Weight

## 1 Introduce

### Activity Choice 1 • Hands-On

- Provide a balance scale. Have a volunteer place three 1-pound weights on one side.
- **What objects in the classroom do you think weigh less than 3 pounds?** Accept and list five responses.
- Have volunteers place the named objects, one at a time, on the other side of the scale.
- Discuss the findings, comparing the estimates to the actual weights.

### Activity Choice 2 • Literature

Introduce the lesson with *How Much, How Many, How Far, How Heavy, How Long, How Tall is 1000?* by Helen Nolan. For a related math activity, see p. TR61.

## 2 Teach

### Scaffolding Questions

Write cup, quart, and gallon on the board.

- **How are these units related?** Sample answers: These customary units are used to measure capacity.
- **What do you think is the relationship among ounce, pound, and ton?** Sample answer: These customary units are used to measure weight.
- **What do you think weight means?** Sample answer: how heavy an object is
- **What are some ways you can measure weight?** Sample answer: Use a scale; compare an object to an object whose weight is known.

### GET READY to Learn

Have students open their books and read the information in **Get Ready to Learn**. Introduce **weight**, **ounce**, **pound**, and **ton**. As a class, work through **Examples 1 and 2**.

# 12-4 Customary Units of Weight

**MAIN IDEA**

I will estimate and measure customary units of weight.

**New Vocabulary**

weight
ounce
pound
ton

**Math Online**

macmillanmh.com
- Extra Examples
- Personal Tutor
- Self-Check Quiz

### GET READY to Learn

Suzie's father went to the store to buy some sugar for their favorite recipe. Suzie wondered how much the bag of sugar weighed.

The **weight** of an object is how heavy it is. The customary units of weight are **ounce (oz)**, **pound (lb)**, and **ton (T)**.

1 ounce 1 pound 1 ton

### Real-World EXAMPLE Estimate Weight

**1** **FOOD Which is a more reasonable unit to use for the weight of a bag of sugar, ounces or pounds?**

A small packet of sugar would be weighed in ounces.

A bag of sugar is much larger and would be weighed in pounds.



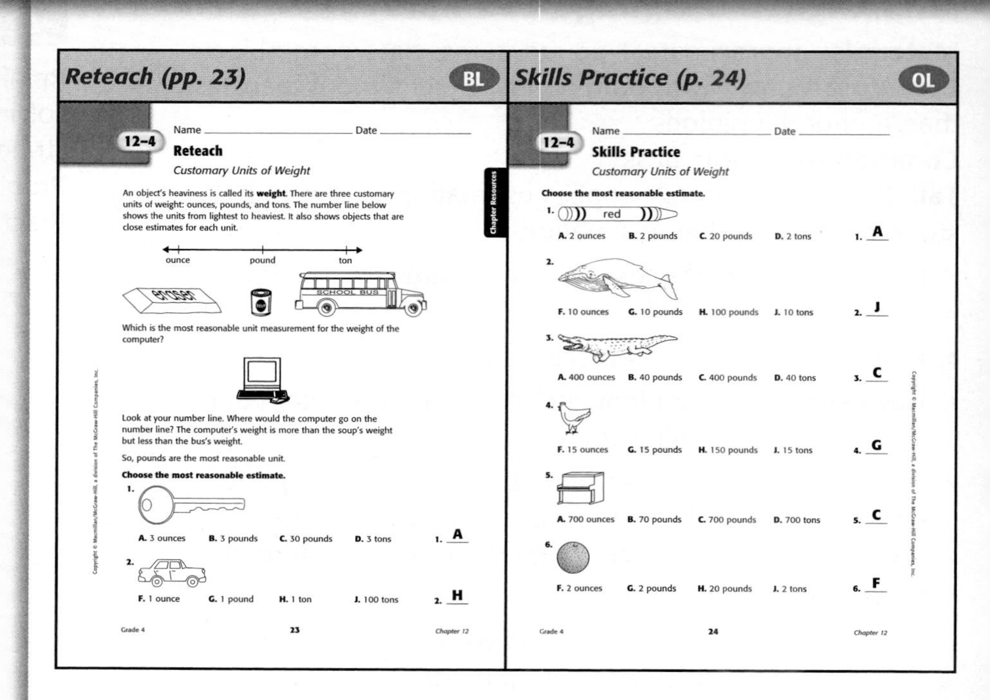

**Reteach (pp. 23)** BL

12-4 Name ______ Date ______

**Reteach**

*Customary Units of Weight*

An object's heaviness is called its **weight**. There are three customary units of weight: ounces, pounds, and tons. The number line below shows the units from lightest to heaviest. It also shows objects that are close estimates for each unit.

ounce pound ton

Which is the most reasonable unit measurement for the weight of the computer?

Look at your number line. Where would the computer go on the number line? The computer's weight is more than the soup's weight but less than the bus's weight.

So, pounds are the most reasonable unit.

**Choose the most reasonable estimate.**

1. **A.** 3 ounces **B.** 3 pounds **C.** 30 pounds **D.** 3 tons 1. A
2. **F.** 1 ounce **G.** 1 pound **H.** 1 ton **J.** 100 tons 2. H

Grade 4 23 *Chapter 12*



**Skills Practice (p. 24)** OL

12-4 Name ______ Date ______

**Skills Practice**

*Customary Units of Weight*

**Choose the most reasonable estimate.**

1. **A.** 2 ounces **B.** 2 pounds **C.** 20 pounds **D.** 2 tons 1. A
2. **F.** 10 ounces **G.** 10 pounds **H.** 100 pounds **J.** 10 tons 2. J
3. **A.** 400 ounces **B.** 40 pounds **C.** 400 pounds **D.** 40 tons 3. C
4. **F.** 15 ounces **G.** 15 pounds **H.** 150 pounds **J.** 15 tons 4. G
5. **A.** 700 ounces **B.** 70 pounds **C.** 700 pounds **D.** 700 tons 5. C
6. **F.** 2 ounces **G.** 2 pounds **H.** 20 pounds **J.** 2 tons 6. F

Grade 4 24 *Chapter 12*

**Estimate Weight**

**2 PLANTS Which is the most reasonable estimate for the weight of a leaf: 1 ounce, 1 pound, 1 ton, or 10 tons?**

Compare the weight of a leaf to the weight of objects that you know. A leaf weighs less than a pineapple or one pound.

Objects that weigh less than one pound are weighed in ounces. The only option that contains ounces is 1 ounce.

5. Sample answer: 56 pounds; 56 ounces is too light and 5 tons is too heavy.

6. Sample answer: No; a large cardboard box full of feathers would weigh less than an aquarium that is full of water and smaller in size.

## CHECK What You Know

**Choose the most reasonable estimate for the weight of each object.**
See Examples 1 and 2 (pp. 498–499)

**1.** paper airplane

**A** 4 ounces **C** 4 pounds
**B** 40 ounces **D** 4 tons A

**2.** helicopter

**F** 5 ounces **H** 5 tons
**G** 500 ounces **J** 500 tons H

**3.** rabbit

**A** 4 ounces **C** 40 pounds
**B** 4 pounds **D** 4 tons B

**4.** chair

**F** 5 ounces **H** 50 tons
**G** 50 pounds **J** 500 tons G

**5.** Is it more reasonable to say that a fourth grade student weighs 56 ounces, 56 pounds, or 5 tons? Explain.

**6.** Talk About It Does an object that is small always weigh less than an object that is large? Explain.



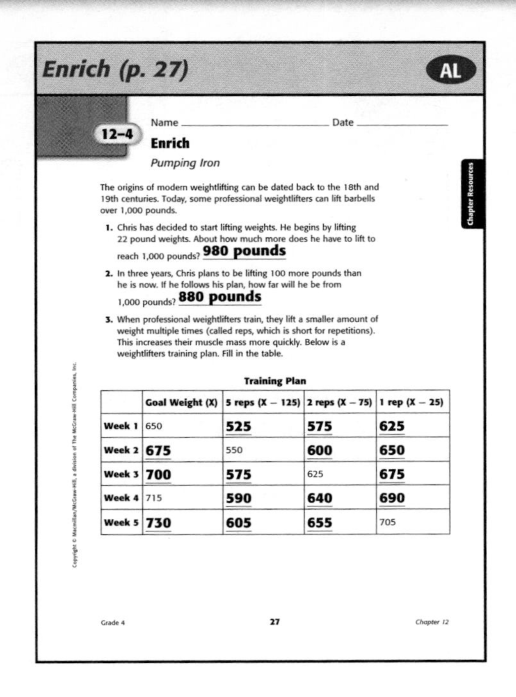

*Enrich (p. 27)* AL

12–4 Name ______ Date ______

**Enrich**

*Pumping Iron*

The origins of modern weightlifting can be dated back to the 18th and 19th centuries. Today, some professional weightlifters can lift barbells over 1,000 pounds.

1. Chris has decided to start lifting weights. He begins by lifting 22 pound weights. About how much more does he have to lift to reach 1,000 pounds? **980 pounds**

2. In three years, Chris plans to be lifting 100 more pounds than he is now. If he follows his plan, how far will he be from 1,000 pounds? **880 pounds**

3. When professional weightlifters train, they lift a smaller amount of weight multiple times (called reps, which is short for repetitions). This increases their muscle mass more quickly. Below is a weightlifters training plan. Fill in the table.

**Training Plan**

| | Goal Weight (X) | 5 reps (X – 125) | 2 reps (X – 75) | 1 rep (X – 25) |
|---|---|---|---|---|
| Week 1 | 650 | **525** | **575** | **625** |
| Week 2 | **675** | 550 | **600** | **650** |
| Week 3 | **700** | **575** | 625 | **675** |
| Week 4 | 715 | **590** | **640** | **690** |
| Week 5 | **730** | **605** | **655** | 705 |

Chapter Resources



Grade 4 27 Chapter 12

## Estimate Weight

**Example 2** Suggest that students ask themselves: Is the weight of a colored pencil closer to the weight of 6 strawberries, 6 pineapples, 6 cars, or 10 cars?

### ADDITIONAL EXAMPLES

1. Which is a more reasonable unit of measurement for the weight of a large cat, ounces or pounds? pounds

2. Which is the most reasonable estimate for the weight of an adult elephant: 5 ounces, 5 pounds, or 5 tons? 5 tons

### CHECK What You Know

As a class, have students complete Exercises 1–6 in **Check What You Know** as you observe their work.

**Exercise 6** Assess student comprehension before assigning practice exercises.

## BL Alternate Teaching Strategy

**If** students have trouble estimating weights in customary units...

**Then** use one of these reteach options:

1 CRM **Daily Reteach Worksheet** (p. 23)

2 Provide a balance scale. Choose an object in the classroom that weighs about 5 pounds. Have students estimate the weight of the object.

- **Do you think this object weighs 5 ounces, 5 pounds, or 5 tons?** 5 pounds
- Have students weigh the object to compare their estimates to the actual weight.

### COMMON ERROR!

**Exercises 7–12** If students consistently choose incorrect estimates, remind them of the benchmarks for 1 ounce, 1 pound, and 1 ton that are shown on the first page of this lesson.

# 3 Practice

Differentiate practice using these leveled assignments for Exercises 7–15.

| Level | Assignment |
|---|---|
| BL Below/Approaching Level | 9, 13 |
| OL On Level | 8–12, 14, 15 |
| AL Above/Beyond Level | 7–15 odd, 16 |

Have students discuss and complete the Higher Order Thinking problem. Before they answer Exercise 16, have students compare the object to a benchmark weight.

# 4 Assess

## Formative Assessment

On the board, sketch an automobile, a person, and a marker.

- **Which unit would be most reasonable to determine the weight of the person?** pound **of the automobile?** ton **of the marker?** ounce

**Quick Check** **Are students continuing to struggle with using customary units to estimate and measure weight?**

**If Yes** → Small Group Options (p. 498B)

**If No** → Independent Work Options (p. 498B)
CRM Skills Practice Worksheet (p. 24)
CRM Enrich Worksheet (p. 27)

**Name the Math** Have students explain how they would estimate the weight of an object.

### Additional Answers

**13.** Sample answer: yes; 1 ounce and 1 pound would weigh too little.

**14.** Sample answer: If 2 horses weigh 1 ton, then 4 horses would weigh 2 tons.

**15.** Sample answer: no; If 2 horses weigh 1 ton, then 8 horses weigh 4 tons.

## Practice and Problem Solving

See page R31.

**Choose the most reasonable estimate for the weight of each object.**

See Examples 1 and 2 (pp. 498–499)

**7.** acorn

A 1 ounce
B 11 ounces
C 1 pound
D 1 ton A

**8.** bed

F 20 ounces
G 20 pounds
H 200 pounds
J 20 tons H

**9.** shell

A 4 ounces
B 4 pounds
C 400 pounds
D 4 tons B

**10.** camper

F 3 ounces
G 3 pounds
H 300 pounds
J 3 tons J

**11.** goldfish

A 2 ounces
B 2 pounds
C 20 pounds
D 2 tons A

**12.** desk

F 18 ounces
G 18 pounds
H 180 pounds
J 1 ton G

### Data File

The thoroughbred horse is the state horse of Maryland.

**13.** Is it reasonable to say that two thoroughbred horses weigh one ton? Explain.
13–15. See margin.

**14.** What is a reasonable estimate for the weight of four thoroughbred horses? Explain.

**15.** Is it reasonable to say that a herd of eight thoroughbred horses weighs 2 tons? Explain.

### H.O.T. Problem

**16. NUMBER SENSE** Estimate the weight of three objects in your desk. Then weigh. Order the objects from greatest to least weight. See students' work.



**Homework Practice (p. 25)** OL

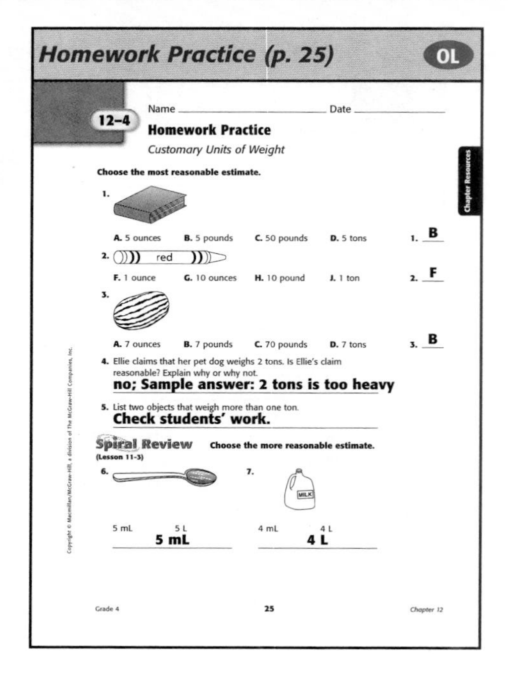
Name ______ Date ______
12–4 **Homework Practice**
*Customary Units of Weight*
Chapter Resources
**Choose the most reasonable estimate.**
1. A. 5 ounces B. 5 pounds C. 50 pounds D. 5 tons 1. B
2. F. 1 ounce G. 10 ounces H. 10 pound J. 1 ton 2. F
3. A. 7 ounces B. 7 pounds C. 70 pounds D. 7 tons 3. B
4. Ellie claims that her pet dog weighs 2 tons. Is Ellie's claim reasonable? Explain why or why not.
no; Sample answer: 2 tons is too heavy
5. List two objects that weigh more than one ton.
Check students' work.
**Spiral Review** (Lesson 11-3) **Choose the more reasonable estimate.**
6. 5 mL 5 L **5 mL**
7. 4 mL 4 L **4 L**
Grade 4 25 Chapter 12

## CHAPTER 12 Mid-Chapter Check

Lessons 12-1 through 12-4

**Choose the most reasonable estimate for each capacity.** (Lesson 12-1)

**1.**

A 5 pints
B 5 gallons
C 5 fluid ounces
D 5 cups B

**2.**

F 16 fluid ounces
G 16 cups
H 16 pints
J 16 gallons F

**3.** Wendy is washing her mother's car. Is it reasonable to say that she will need about 16 pints of water? Explain.
No, 16 pints is too little.

**4.** Adamo is filling his cat's water bowl. Is it reasonable to say that he will need about 8 fluid ounces of water? Explain.
Yes, 8 fluid ounces is enough.

**Complete.** (Lesson 12-2)

**5.** 6 c = ■ fl oz
48 fl oz

**6.** ■ gal = 8 qt
2 gal

**7.** ■ pt = 30 c
15 pt

**8.** 20 pt = ■ qt
10 qt

**Compare. Use >, <, or =.** (Lesson 12-2)

**9.** 5 pt ● 3 qt
<

**10.** 1 c ● 7 fl oz
>

**11. MULTIPLE CHOICE** Which of the comparisons is true? (Lesson 12-2) D

A 4 qt > 10 pt
B 6 pt < 11 c
C 1 gal > 5 qt
D 16 oz < 2 gal

**12. MULTIPLE CHOICE** Which of the following is a reasonable estimate? (Lesson 12-3) J

F A glass of water can hold about 10 milliliters of water.
G A swimming pool can hold about 15 liters of water.
H A bottle of juice has a capacity of 100 milliliters.
J A bucket can hold about 5 liters of water.

**Choose the more reasonable estimate for each capacity.** (Lesson 12-3)

**13.**

600 L or 600 mL
600 mL

**14.**

3 mL or 3 L
3 L

**15.** Choose the most reasonable estimate for the weight of a guinea pig. (Lesson 12-4)

A 2 pounds
B 12 pounds
C 120 pounds
D 2 tons A

**16.** WRITING IN MATH Explain how metric units of capacity are related. (Lesson 12-3) See Ch. 12 Answer Appendix.



## CHAPTER 12 Mid-Chapter Check

### Lessons 12-1 through 12-4

### Formative Assessment

Use the Mid-Chapter check to assess students' progress in the first half of the chapter.

Customize and create multiple versions of your Mid-Chapter Check and the test answer keys.

### FOLDABLES Dinah Zike's Foldables

Use these lesson suggestions to incorporate the Foldables during the chapter.

**Lesson 12-1** Under the first tab of the Foldable, students include the following vocabulary: capacity, pint, quart, gallon.

**Lesson 12-3** Under the second tab of the Foldable, students review the definition of "capacity" and relate it to metric measurement. Students give examples of how they estimate and measure capacity. Have students record the terms liter and milliliter.

**Lesson 12-4** Have students include the following vocabulary under the appropriate tab on the Foldable: weight, pound, ounces.

# Data-Driven Decision Making

Based on the results of the Mid-Chapter Check, use the following to review concepts that continue to present students with problems.

| Exercises | State/Local Standards | What's the Mathematics? | Error Analysis | Resources for Review |
|---|---|---|---|---|
| **1–4** Lesson 12-1 | | Estimate and measure customary capacities. | Confuses units of measure. | Strategic Intervention Guide (p. 122)<br>CRM Chapter 12 Resource Masters (Reteach)<br>Math Adventures My Math Zone Chapter 12<br>Math Online Extra Examples • Concepts in Motion |
| **5–11** Lesson 12-2 | | Convert customary units of capacity. | Chooses wrong operation to convert. Does not understand relationship between units. | |
| **12–14** Lesson 12-3 | | Estimate and measure capacity within the metric system. | Confuses metric and customary units. Does not know meaning of metric prefixes. | |
| **15–16** Lesson 12-4 | | Estimate and measure customary units of weight. | Does not know practical meaning of "pound," "ounce," or "ton." | |

# 12-5 Problem-Solving Strategy
# Using Logical Reasoning

## Lesson Planner

### Objective

Solve problems using logical reasoning.

### Resources

**Literature Connection:** *Math Curse* by Jon Scieszka

**Teacher Technology**

TeacherWorks • Interactive Classroom

**Real-World Problem Solving Library**
**Math and Science: *Strange but True***
Use these leveled books to reinforce and extend problem-solving skills and strategies.

Leveled for:

- OL On Level
- ELL Sheltered English
- SP Spanish

For additional support, see the Real-World Problem Solving Teacher Guide.

## Daily Routine

Use these suggestions before beginning the lesson on p. 502.

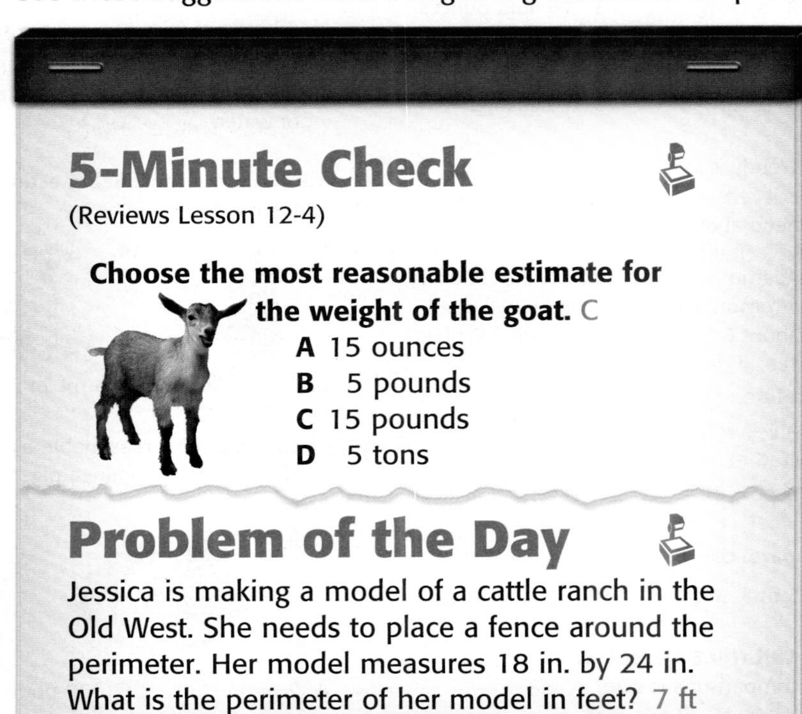

### 5-Minute Check

(Reviews Lesson 12-4)

**Choose the most reasonable estimate for the weight of the goat.** C

**A** 15 ounces
**B** 5 pounds
**C** 15 pounds
**D** 5 tons

### Problem of the Day

Jessica is making a model of a cattle ranch in the Old West. She needs to place a fence around the perimeter. Her model measures 18 in. by 24 in. What is the perimeter of her model in feet? 7 ft

# Differentiated Instruction

## Small Group Options

### Option 1 Below Level BL

VISUAL, PAIR

**Materials:** paper and pencil

Hand the following problem to pairs of students:

Jack, Ana, and Linda join the library book club. Their reading totals are 5 books, 6 books, and 8 books. Ana reads the least amount of books because she has a job. The girl with the longest name reads the most. Place the number of books for the book club with the correct person so the librarian can record the results.

Ana reads 5 books, Jack reads 6 books, and Linda reads 8 books.

- **What strategies did you use to find the answer?** Answers will vary.

### Option 2 English Language Learners ELL

LOGICAL, VISUAL

**Materials:** chart, scissors, glue
**Core Vocabulary:** identify, sort logically, cut and paste
**Common Use Verb:** select

**See Math** This strategy provides practice with metric and customary units of capacity in real-world application using logical reasoning.

- Post a chart listing customary and metric units in increasing order with space underneath to paste pictures.
- Have students select a picture from a magazine or flyer for each unit. Cut and paste selections onto chart.
- Have a volunteer look at one of the pictures. Using logical reasoning, explain why or why not that picture should be with that size of unit. (Students may not use their own example.)
- Repeat as time permits.

## Independent Work Options

### Option 1 Early Finishers OL AL

LOGICAL

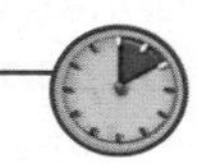

**Materials:** index cards, pencil

- On one side of an index card, students write a word problem involving measurement that can be solved by logical reasoning.
- On the other side of the card, the student writes the answer to the problem and explains how the strategy was used to solve the problem.
- Have students contribute their cards to a problem bank.

### Option 2 Student Technology

Math Online macmillanmh.com

Personal Tutor • Extra Examples

### Option 3 Learning Station: Art (p. 482I)

Direct students to the Art Learning Station for opportunities to explore and extend the lesson concept.

# 12-5 Problem-Solving Strategy

## 1 Introduce

**Activity • Review**

Pose this situation: *Tim, Javier, and Carter spent $30 at the movies for their tickets, popcorn, and drinks. The tickets cost $7 each. The three drinks cost $1 each. How much did they spend for popcorn?* $6

- **What information do you have?** Sample answer: how many people went to the movies and how much they spent for tickets and drinks
- **What do you need to find?** how much they spent on popcorn
- **What strategy can you use to solve the problem?** Sample answer: work backward

**Activity • Literature**

Introduce the lesson with *Math Curse* by Jon Scieszka. For a related math activity, see p. TR61.

## 2 Teach

Have students read the problem on animals. Guide them through the problem-solving steps.

**Understand** Using the questions, review what students know and need to find.

**Plan** Have them discuss their strategy.

**Solve** Guide students to use logical reasoning to solve the problem.

- **Which animal do you think weighs the most?** elephant **the least?** monkey
- **Which measure of capacity would you use to weigh an elephant?** ton **a monkey?** pounds

**Check** Have students look back at the problem to make sure that the answer fits the facts given.

- **Does the answer fit the facts given in the problem?** Accept all reasonable answers.

**! COMMON ERROR!**

**Exercises 4–10** Some students may have trouble getting started because they are not reading the problems carefully. Have them read each problem silently, then have them verbalize what they know and need to find.

# Problem-Solving Strategy

**MAIN IDEA** I will solve problems using logical reasoning.

Adina, Tonisha, and Carl are each writing a report. The reports are about elephants, lions, and monkeys. Adina is writing about an animal whose weight is measured in tons. Carl is writing about an animal whose average weight is 375 pounds. Which animal is each student writing a report about?

**Understand**

**What facts do you know?**

- Adina is writing about an animal whose weight is in tons.
- Carl is writing about an animal whose weight is 375 pounds.

**What do you need to find?**

- The animal each student is writing about.

**Plan**

You can make a table and use logical reasoning to solve.

**Solve**

Place an X in the boxes that you know cannot be correct.

- Adina must be writing about elephants because the other two animals' weights are in pounds.
- Carl must be writing about lions because monkeys weigh much less than 300 pounds.

| | Elephant | Lion | Monkey |
|---|---|---|---|
| Adina | yes | X | X |
| Tonisha | X | X | yes |
| Carl | X | yes | X |

So, Adina is writing about elephants, Tonisha is writing about monkeys, and Carl is writing about lions.

**Check**

Look back. The answer makes sense for the facts given in the problem. So, the answer is correct. ✓



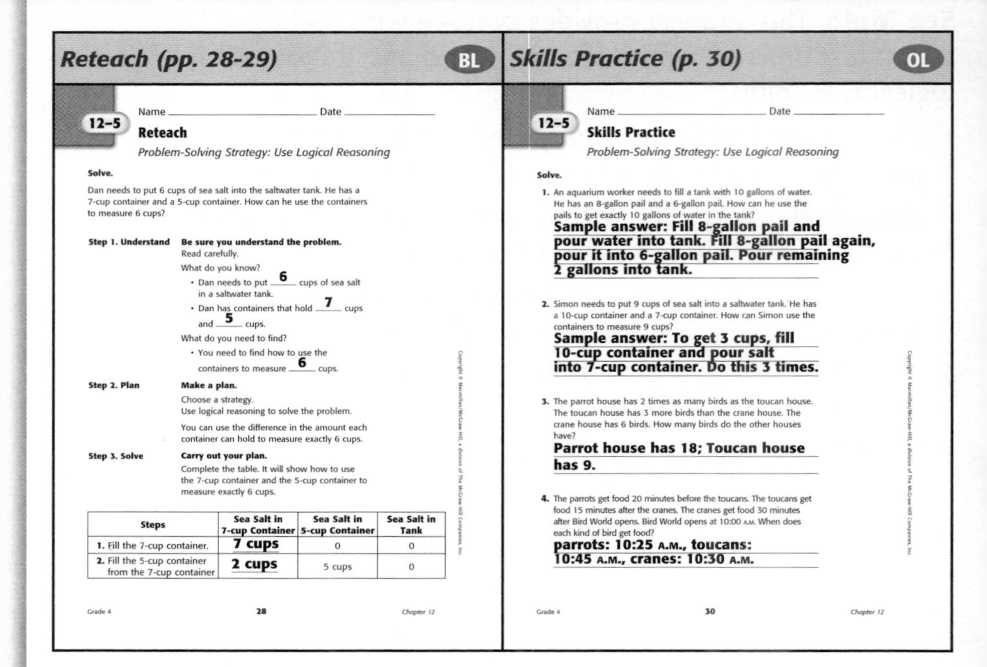

**Reteach (pp. 28-29)** BL

12–5 Name ______ Date ______

**Reteach**

*Problem-Solving Strategy: Use Logical Reasoning*

**Solve.**

Dan needs to put 6 cups of sea salt into the saltwater tank. He has a 7-cup container and a 5-cup container. How can he use the containers to measure 6 cups?

**Step 1. Understand** **Be sure you understand the problem.**
Read carefully.
What do you know?
- Dan needs to put **6** cups of sea salt in a saltwater tank.
- Dan has containers that hold **7** cups and **5** cups.

What do you need to find?
- You need to find how to use the containers to measure **6** cups.

**Step 2. Plan** **Make a plan.**
Choose a strategy.
Use logical reasoning to solve the problem.
You can use the difference in the amount each container can hold to measure exactly 6 cups.

**Step 3. Solve** **Carry out your plan.**
Complete the table. It will show how to use the 7-cup container and the 5-cup container to measure exactly 6 cups.

| Steps | Sea Salt in 7-cup Container | Sea Salt in 5-cup Container | Sea Salt in Tank |
|---|---|---|---|
| 1. Fill the 7-cup container. | **7 cups** | 0 | 0 |
| 2. Fill the 5-cup container from the 7-cup container | **2 cups** | 5 cups | 0 |

Grade 4 28 Chapter 12



**Skills Practice (p. 30)** OL

12–5 Name ______ Date ______

**Skills Practice**

*Problem-Solving Strategy: Use Logical Reasoning*

**Solve.**

1. An aquarium worker needs to fill a tank with 10 gallons of water. He has an 8-gallon pail and a 6-gallon pail. How can he use the pails to get exactly 10 gallons of water in the tank?
**Sample answer: Fill 8-gallon pail and pour water into tank. Fill 8-gallon pail again, pour it into 6-gallon pail. Pour remaining 2 gallons into tank.**

2. Simon needs to put 9 cups of sea salt into a saltwater tank. He has a 10-cup container and a 7-cup container. How can Simon use the containers to measure 9 cups?
**Sample answer: To get 3 cups, fill 10-cup container and pour salt into 7-cup container. Do this 3 times.**

3. The parrot house has 2 times as many birds as the toucan house. The toucan house has 3 more birds than the crane house. The crane house has 6 birds. How many birds do the other houses have?
**Parrot house has 18; Toucan house has 9.**

4. The parrots get food 20 minutes before the toucans. The toucans get food 15 minutes after the cranes. The cranes get food 30 minutes after Bird World opens. Bird World opens at 10:00 A.M. When does each kind of bird get food?
**parrots: 10:25 A.M., toucans: 10:45 A.M., cranes: 10:30 A.M.**

Grade 4 30 Chapter 12

★ indicates multi-step problem

## ANALYZE the Strategy

**Refer to the problem on the previous page.** 1–3. See Ch. 12 Answer Appendix.

1. Explain how logical reasoning helped to solve the problem.
2. Why do you think a table was used in solving the problem?
3. Suppose a rhinoceros is being written about instead of a monkey. Would it be possible to determine which animal each person is writing about?

## PRACTICE the Strategy

**Solve. Use logical reasoning.**

4. Three dogs are named Max, Sam, and Rufus. One is a collie, one is a spaniel, and one is a pug. Sam is not the collie. The spaniel's name is the longest. What are the names of each dog?
   4, 5. See Ch. 12 Answer Appendix.

5. Hector arranges the cards in a row. The 2 is between the two odd numbered cards. The 4 has no card to its left. The 3 has cards on both sides. What is the order?

6. There are 4 people in a line. Tiernon is at the end. Juan is second in line. Moses is in front of Tiernon. Amy is first. What is the order of the people? Amy, Juan, Moses, Tiernon

7. Manuella, Danny, and Tyson are wearing red, blue, and yellow T-shirts. Manuella is wearing red, and Danny is not wearing blue. What color T-shirt is each person wearing?
   See Ch. 12 Answer Appendix.

8. Jesse, Kata, Romeo, and Sheldon play basketball. Their numbers are 5, 7, 9, and 12. Jesse's number equals the number of letters in his name. Kata's is a two-digit number, while Romeo's number is not a prime number. What is Sheldon's number? 7

★9. Lizzy has dogs, birds, and fish. She has twice as many dogs as birds. She has three more fish than dogs. She has two birds. How many dogs and fish does she have? 4 dogs, 7 fish

10. Copy and complete the table below. Use the digits 1, 2, 3, and 4 so that each row and column has each digit listed one time.

| 2 | 3 | 4 | 1 |
|---|---|---|---|
| 1 | 4 | 3 | 2 |
| 3 | 1 | 2 | 4 |
| 4 | 2 | 1 | 3 |

11. WRITING IN MATH Explain what it means to use logical reasoning.
    See Ch. 12 Answer Appendix.



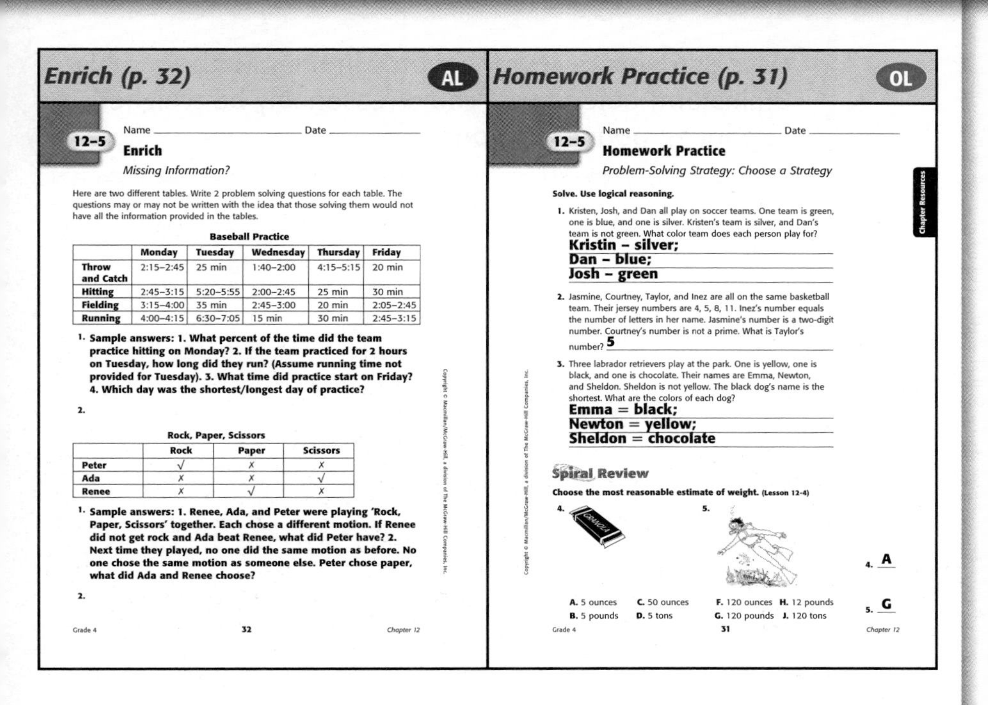

### Enrich (p. 32) AL

12–5 Name ______ Date ______

**Enrich**

*Missing Information?*

Here are two different tables. Write 2 problem solving questions for each table. The questions may or may not be written with the idea that those solving them would not have all the information provided in the tables.

**Baseball Practice**

| | Monday | Tuesday | Wednesday | Thursday | Friday |
|---|---|---|---|---|---|
| Throw and Catch | 2:15–2:45 | 25 min | 1:40–2:00 | 4:15–5:15 | 20 min |
| Hitting | 2:45–3:15 | 5:20–5:55 | 2:00–2:45 | 25 min | 30 min |
| Fielding | 3:15–4:00 | 35 min | 2:45–3:00 | 20 min | 2:05–2:45 |
| Running | 4:00–4:15 | 6:30–7:05 | 15 min | 30 min | 2:45–3:15 |

1. **Sample answers: 1. What percent of the time did the team practice hitting on Monday? 2. If the team practiced for 2 hours on Tuesday, how long did they run? (Assume running time not provided for Tuesday). 3. What time did practice start on Friday? 4. Which day was the shortest/longest day of practice?**

2.

**Rock, Paper, Scissors**

| | Rock | Paper | Scissors |
|---|---|---|---|
| Peter | √ | ✗ | ✗ |
| Ada | ✗ | ✗ | √ |
| Renee | ✗ | √ | ✗ |

1. **Sample answers: 1. Renee, Ada, and Peter were playing 'Rock, Paper, Scissors' together. Each chose a different motion. If Renee did not get rock and Ada beat Renee, what did Peter have? 2. Next time they played, no one did the same motion as before. No one chose the same motion as someone else. Peter chose paper, what did Ada and Renee choose?**

2.

Grade 4 32 Chapter 12



### Homework Practice (p. 31) OL

12–5 Name ______ Date ______

**Homework Practice**

*Problem-Solving Strategy: Choose a Strategy*

Chapter Resources

**Solve. Use logical reasoning.**

1. Kristen, Josh, and Dan all play on soccer teams. One team is green, one is blue, and one is silver. Kristen's team is silver, and Dan's team is not green. What color team does each person play for?
   **Kristin – silver; Dan – blue; Josh – green**
2. Jasmine, Courtney, Taylor, and Inez are all on the same basketball team. Their jersey numbers are 4, 5, 8, 11. Inez's number equals the number of letters in her name. Jasmine's number is a two-digit number. Courtney's number is not a prime. What is Taylor's number? **5**
3. Three labrador retrievers play at the park. One is yellow, one is black, and one is chocolate. Their names are Emma, Newton, and Sheldon. Sheldon is not yellow. The black dog's name is the shortest. What are the colors of each dog?
   **Emma = black; Newton = yellow; Sheldon = chocolate**

**Spiral Review**

**Choose the most reasonable estimate of weight.** (Lesson 12-4)

4. GRANOLA
   A. 5 ounces B. 5 pounds C. 50 ounces D. 5 tons
   4. **A**
5. F. 120 ounces G. 120 pounds H. 12 pounds J. 120 tons
   5. **G**

Grade 4 31 Chapter 12



**Analyze the Strategy** Use Exercises 1–3 to analyze and discuss the problem-solving strategy.

## BL Alternate Teaching Strategy

**If** students have trouble using logical reasoning to solve problems…

**Then** use one of these reteach options:

1. CRM **Daily Reteach Worksheet** (pp. 28–29)
2. Guide students to set up a table.

- **How many columns and rows do you need in the table? Explain.** 3 columns and 3 rows since there are 3 animals and 3 students writing reports.
- **What headings can you use for the columns and rows? Explain.** Sample answer: Use all animal names for the columns: Elephant, Lion, Monkey, and all student names for the rows: Adina, Tonisha, Carl.

# 3 Practice

### Using the Exercises

**Exercises 4, 7, 8, and 10** can be solved by using a table and logical reasoning.

**Exercises 5 and 6** can be solved by drawing a diagram and using logical reasoning.

# 4 Assess

### Formative Assessment

Pose this situation:

*Maria is taller than Julie but shorter than Tali. Julie is taller than Saki. Who is the shortest in the group?* Saki

- **What strategy can you use to solve the problem?** Sample answer: draw a picture and use logical reasoning

**Quick Check** **Are students continuing to struggle with using logical reasoning?**

**If Yes** → Small Group Options (p. 492B)
Strategic Intervention Guide (p. 122)

**If No** → Independent Work Options (p. 492B)
CRM Skills Practice Worksheet (p. 30)
CRM Enrich Worksheet (p. 32)

LESSON 12-6

# Convert Customary Units of Weight

## Lesson Planner

### Objective

Convert customary units of weight.

### Review Vocabulary

**ounce, pound, ton**

### Resources

**Manipulatives:** pan balance

**Literature Connection:** *Is a Blue Whale the Biggest Thing There is?* by Robert E. Wells

**Teacher Technology**

TeacherWorks • Interactive Classroom

## Daily Routine

Use these suggestions before beginning the lesson on p. 504.

### 5-Minute Check

(Reviews Lesson 12-5)

**Solve. Use logical reasoning.**

Ela and her two friends chose their fruit. The fruits are oranges, strawberries, and cherries. Meg's favorite is not red. Leigh's favorite does not grow on a tree. Which fruit is each person's favorite? Meg, oranges; Ela, cherries; Leigh, strawberries

### Problem of the Day

Luis, Carlo, and Ken bought movie tickets. Each ticket cost the same amount. The three tickets cost $21. How much did Carlo pay for his ticket? $7

### Focus on Math Background

As with conversions of capacity, you divide when changing from smaller units to larger units and multiply for the reverse:

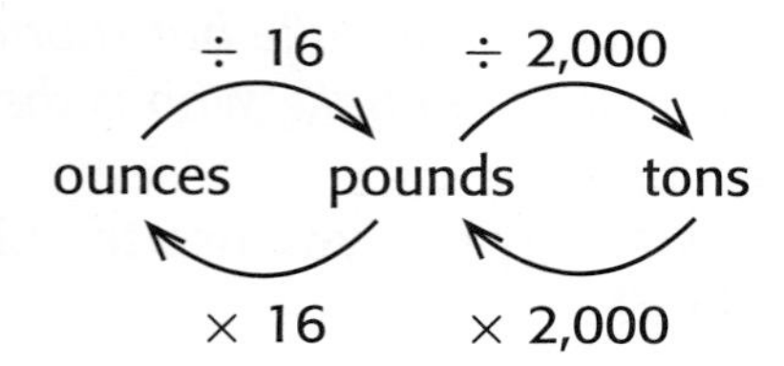


The abbreviation for pound, lb, may seem unusual. It is derived from the Latin word *libra*, which means "scales" or "balance." The symbol # is also sometimes used as an abbreviation for the pound.

### Review Math Vocabulary

Write the review vocabulary words and their definitions on the board.

Have students review the words in their Math Journals. Brainstorm objects that could reasonably be weighed in ounces, pounds, or tons.

# Differentiated Instruction

## Small Group Options

### Option 1 Below Level BL

INTRAPERSONAL

**Materials:** weight scale from nurse's office, paper and pencil

- Have students solve the following problem:

Mom buys a 10 pound sack of potatoes. She counts the potatoes and finds there are 20 in the sack. About how much does each potato weigh?

### Option 2 English Language Learners ELL

KINESTHETIC, LOGICAL

**Materials:** index cards, "is the same as" chart with 7 pound intervals marked in the right column
**Core Vocabulary:** make it true, on, between
**Common Use Verb:** flip

**Do Math** This strategy helps students visualize and convert customary measurements of weight.

- Have students write cards with any number up to 99 and "ounce/s" after it.
- Write: "16 ounces, 32 ounces," etc. to the left of the "is the same as" column. Opposite the ounces on the right side, write: "1 pound, 2 pounds," etc., to 7 pounds.
- Have a student read his or her card and place on or between the appropriate pounds.
- Repeat for all students. Discuss results.
- Extend the strategy by having students estimate how many pounds would equal ounces numbering in the 100s.

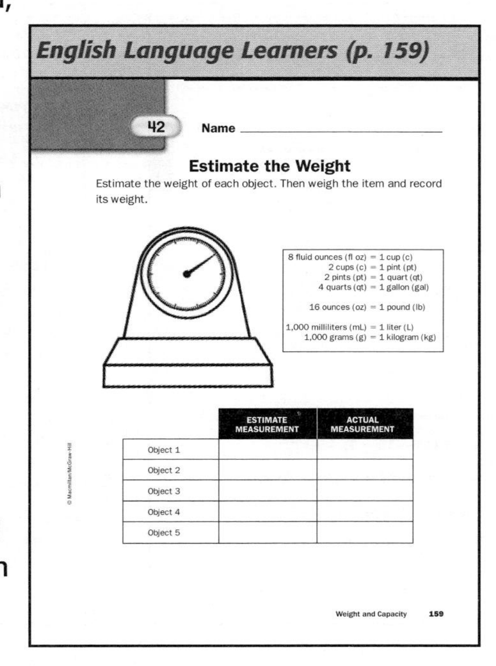

*English Language Learners (p. 159)*

42 Name ______

**Estimate the Weight**

Estimate the weight of each object. Then weigh the item and record its weight.

8 fluid ounces (fl oz) = 1 cup (c)
2 cups (c) = 1 pint (pt)
2 pints (pt) = 1 quart (qt)
4 quarts (qt) = 1 gallon (gal)
16 ounces (oz) = 1 pound (lb)
1,000 milliliters (mL) = 1 liter (L)
1,000 grams (g) = 1 kilogram (kg)

| | ESTIMATE MEASUREMENT | ACTUAL MEASUREMENT |
|---|---|---|
| Object 1 | | |
| Object 2 | | |
| Object 3 | | |
| Object 4 | | |
| Object 5 | | |

Weight and Capacity 159

## Independent Work Options

### Option 1 Early Finishers AL

LOGICAL

**Materials:** paper, pencil

- Assign pairs. One student names a range of weights, such as greater than 5 pounds but less than 100 pounds. The partner names an object that would fit that range and estimates the weight.
- Together the partners convert the estimated weight into ounces.
- Partners record their ranges, estimates, and conversions.

### Option 2 Student Technology

Math Online macmillanmh.com

Personal Tutor • Extra Examples

### Option 3 Learning Station: Science (p. 482J)

Direct students to the Science Learning Station for opportunities to explore and extend the lesson concept.

### Option 4 Problem-Solving Practice

Reinforce problem-solving skills and strategies with the Problem-Solving Practice worksheet.

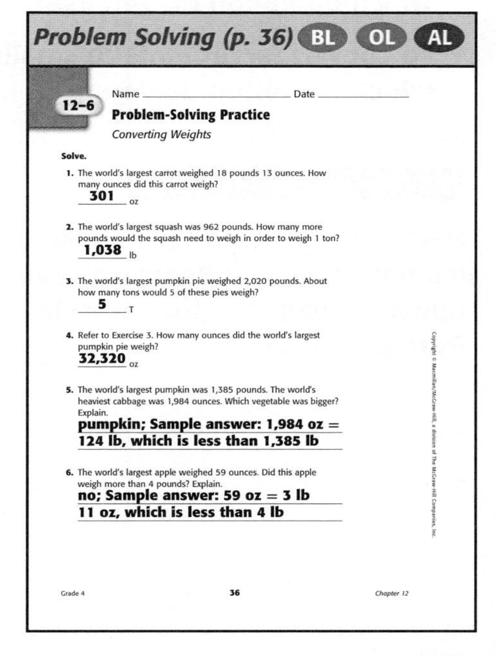

*Problem Solving (p. 36)* BL OL AL

Name ______ Date ______

12–6 **Problem-Solving Practice**
*Converting Weights*

**Solve.**

1. The world's largest carrot weighed 18 pounds 13 ounces. How many ounces did this carrot weigh?
   **301** oz
2. The world's largest squash was 962 pounds. How many more pounds would the squash need to weigh in order to weigh 1 ton?
   **1,038** lb
3. The world's largest pumpkin pie weighed 2,020 pounds. About how many tons would 5 of these pies weigh?
   **5** T
4. Refer to Exercise 3. How many ounces did the world's largest pumpkin pie weigh?
   **32,320** oz
5. The world's largest pumpkin was 1,385 pounds. The world's heaviest cabbage was 1,984 ounces. Which vegetable was bigger? Explain.
   **pumpkin; Sample answer: 1,984 oz = 124 lb, which is less than 1,385 lb**
6. The world's largest apple weighed 59 ounces. Did this apple weigh more than 4 pounds? Explain.
   **no; Sample answer: 59 oz = 3 lb 11 oz, which is less than 4 lb**

Grade 4 36 Chapter 12

# Convert Customary Units of Weight

## 1 Introduce

### Activity Choice 1 • Hands-On

- Provide a balance scale.
- Have a volunteer place a 1-pound weight on one side of the scale.
- Have other volunteers place 1-ounce weights on the other side of the scale, one at a time, until the scale is balanced.
- **How many 1-ounce weights does it take to balance the scale with 1 pound?** 16
- **How many ounces do you think are in 1 pound?** 16

### Activity Choice 2 • Literature

Introduce the lesson with *Is a Blue Whale the Biggest Thing There Is?* by Robert E. Wells. For a related math activity, see p. TR62.

## 2 Teach

### Scaffolding Questions

On the board, write 16 ounces = 1 pound and 2,000 pounds = 1 ton.

- **To convert a weight from ounces to pounds, which operation do you use?** division
- **To convert a weight from pounds to ounces, which operation do you use?** multiplication
- **To convert smaller units to larger units, which operation do you use?** division
- **To convert larger units to smaller units, which operation do you use?** multiplication

### GET READY to Learn

Have students open their books and read the information in **Get Ready to Learn**. Review **ounce, pound,** and **ton.** As a class, work through **Examples 1 and 2**.



# 12-6 Convert Customary Units of Weight

**MAIN IDEA**

I will convert customary units of weight.

**Math Online**
macmillanmh.com
- Extra Examples
- Personal Tutor
- Self-Check Quiz

### GET READY to Learn

Leigh needs to buy 2 pounds of hamburger for dinner. The package she found was 32 ounces. Does 32 ounces equal 2 pounds?

Recall that to convert from a larger unit to a smaller unit, multiply. To convert from a smaller unit to a larger unit, divide.

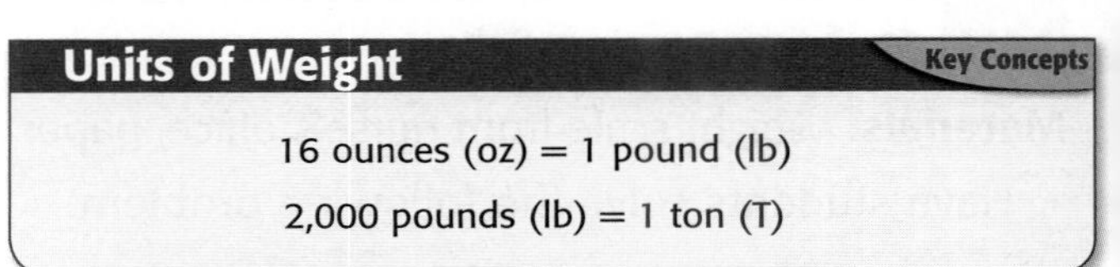


### Real-World EXAMPLE Convert Customary Weights

**1 FOOD Is 32 ounces of hamburger equal to 2 pounds of hamburger?**

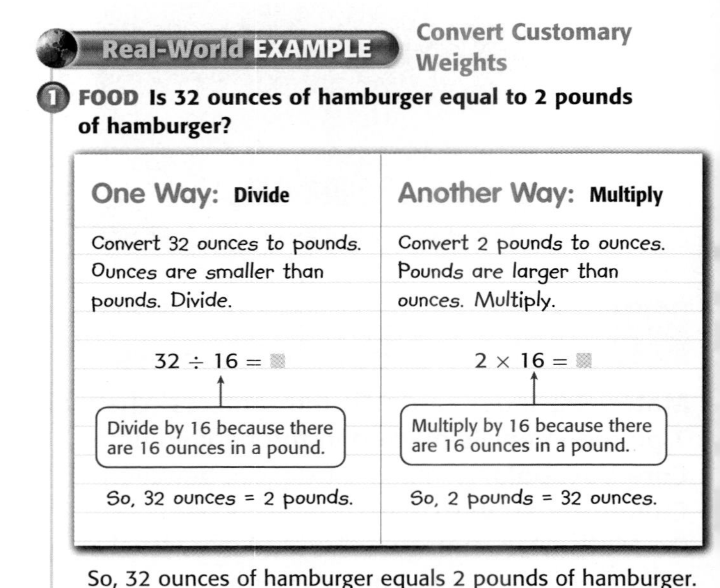


So, 32 ounces of hamburger equals 2 pounds of hamburger.

504 **Chapter 12** Measure Capacity, Weight, and Volume

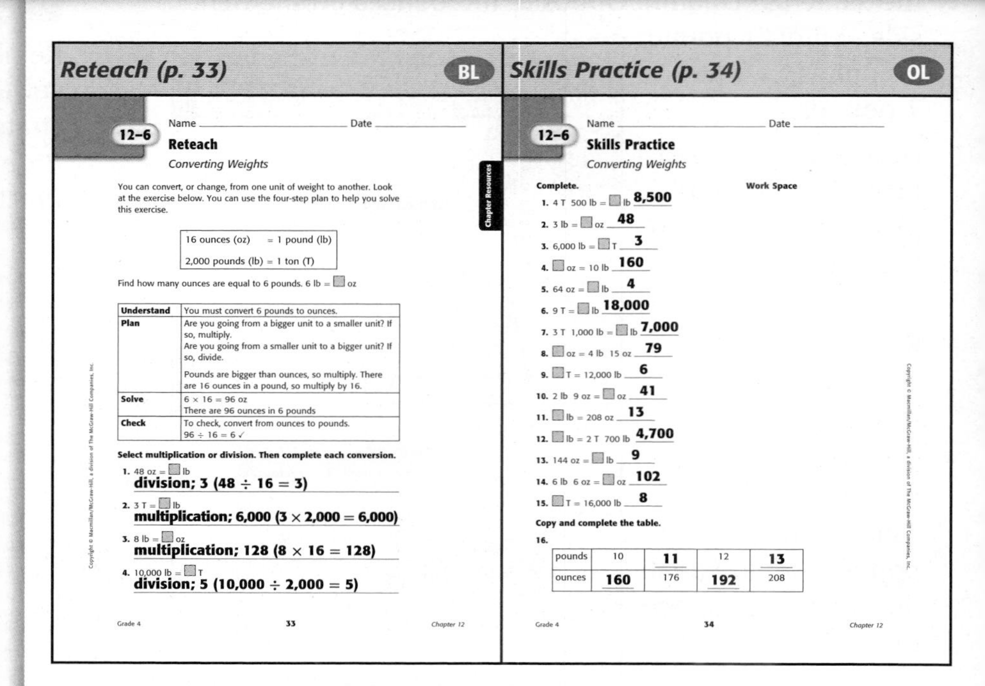

**Reteach (p. 33)** BL

12-6 Name ______ Date ______

**Reteach**

*Converting Weights*

You can convert, or change, from one unit of weight to another. Look at the exercise below. You can use the four-step plan to help you solve this exercise.

| 16 ounces (oz) | = 1 pound (lb) |
|---|---|
| 2,000 pounds (lb) | = 1 ton (T) |

Find how many ounces are equal to 6 pounds. 6 lb = ■ oz

| **Understand** | You must convert 6 pounds to ounces. |
|---|---|
| **Plan** | Are you going from a bigger unit to a smaller unit? If so, multiply. Are you going from a smaller unit to a bigger unit? If so, divide. Pounds are bigger than ounces, so multiply. There are 16 ounces in a pound, so multiply by 16. |
| **Solve** | 6 × 16 = 96 oz There are 96 ounces in 6 pounds |
| **Check** | To check, convert from ounces to pounds. 96 ÷ 16 = 6 ✓ |

**Select multiplication or division. Then complete each conversion.**

1. 48 oz = ■ lb **division; 3 (48 ÷ 16 = 3)**
2. 3 T = ■ lb **multiplication; 6,000 (3 × 2,000 = 6,000)**
3. 8 lb = ■ oz **multiplication; 128 (8 × 16 = 128)**
4. 10,000 lb = ■ T **division; 5 (10,000 ÷ 2,000 = 5)**

Grade 4 33 Chapter 12

Chapter Resources

Copyright © Macmillan/McGraw-Hill, a division of The McGraw-Hill Companies, Inc.

**Skills Practice (p. 34)** OL

12-6 Name ______ Date ______

**Skills Practice**

*Converting Weights*

**Complete.** **Work Space**

1. 4 T 500 lb = ■ lb **8,500**
2. 3 lb = ■ oz **48**
3. 6,000 lb = ■ T **3**
4. ■ oz = 10 lb **160**
5. 64 oz = ■ lb **4**
6. 9 T = ■ lb **18,000**
7. 3 T 1,000 lb = ■ lb **7,000**
8. ■ oz = 4 lb 15 oz **79**
9. ■ T = 12,000 lb **6**
10. 2 lb 9 oz = ■ oz **41**
11. ■ lb = 208 oz **13**
12. ■ lb = 2 T 700 lb **4,700**
13. 144 oz = ■ lb **9**
14. 6 lb 6 oz = ■ oz **102**
15. ■ T = 16,000 lb **8**

**Copy and complete the table.**

16.

| pounds | 10 | **11** | 12 | **13** |
|---|---|---|---|---|
| ounces | **160** | 176 | **192** | 208 |

Grade 4 34 Chapter 12

Copyright © Macmillan/McGraw-Hill, a division of The McGraw-Hill Companies, Inc.

A ton is a very heavy unit of measurement. Recall that there are 2,000 pounds in one ton.

**Real-World EXAMPLE** Convert Customary Weights

**2** **DINOSAURS** **Use the table to find how many pounds a Stegosaurus weighed.**

| Dinosaur Weights | |
|---|---|
| **Dinosaur** | **Weight (tons)** |
| Allosaurus | 2 |
| Megalosaurus | 1 |
| Stegasaurus | 3 |
| Supersaurus | 60 |
| Tyrannosaurus | 8 |

**Source:** Arts & Letters Corporation

To find the weight of a Stegosaurus in pounds, multiply the number of tons by 2,000.

$3 \times 2{,}000 = \blacksquare$

$3 \times 2{,}000 = 6{,}000$

THINK $3 \times 2 = 6$
$3 \times 20 = 60$
$3 \times 200 = 600$
So, $3 \times 2{,}000 = 6{,}000$.

So, a Stegosaurus weighed 6,000 pounds.

## CHECK What You Know

**Complete.** See Examples 1 and 2 (pp. 504–505)

**1.** 4 lb = ■ oz **64**

**2.** 48 oz = ■ lb **3**

**3.** 4,000 lb = ■ T **2**

**4.** ■ T = 6,000 lb **3**

**5.** ■ oz = 1 lb 4 oz **20**

**6.** ■ lb = 4 T and 100 lb **8,100**

**7.** A hippopotamus eats 100 pounds of food a day. How many days would it take the hippo to eat one ton of food? **20 days**

**8.** An ostrich egg weighs 64 ounces. Is the weight of the ostrich egg greater than 5 pounds? Explain.

**8, 9. See margin.**

**9.** Talk About It Explain why you multiply to convert a larger unit of measure to a smaller unit of measure.



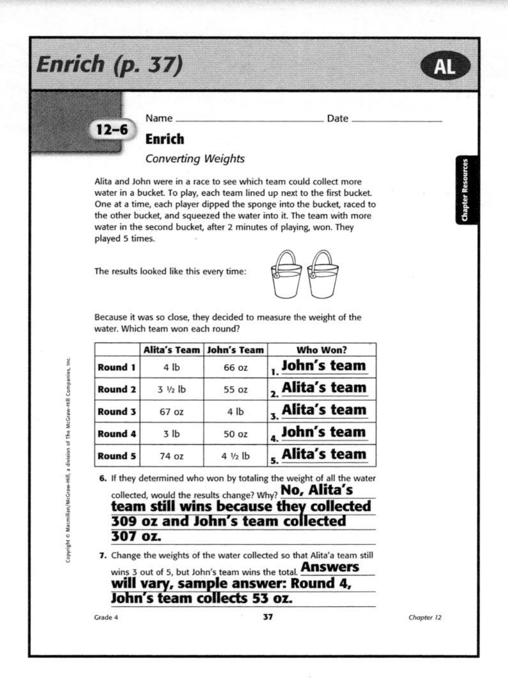

*Enrich (p. 37)* **AL**

12–6 Name ________ Date ________

**Enrich**

*Converting Weights*

Alita and John were in a race to see which team could collect more water in a bucket. To play, each team lined up next to the first bucket. One at a time, each player dipped the sponge into the bucket, raced to the other bucket, and squeezed the water into it. The team with more water in the second bucket, after 2 minutes of playing, won. They played 5 times.

The results looked like this every time:

Because it was so close, they decided to measure the weight of the water. Which team won each round?

| | Alita's Team | John's Team | Who Won? |
|---|---|---|---|
| **Round 1** | 4 lb | 66 oz | 1. **John's team** |
| **Round 2** | 3 ½ lb | 55 oz | 2. **Alita's team** |
| **Round 3** | 67 oz | 4 lb | 3. **Alita's team** |
| **Round 4** | 3 lb | 50 oz | 4. **John's team** |
| **Round 5** | 74 oz | 4 ½ lb | 5. **Alita's team** |

**6.** If they determined who won by totaling the weight of all the water collected, would the results change? Why? **No, Alita's team still wins because they collected 309 oz and John's team collected 307 oz.**

**7.** Change the weights of the water collected so that Alita'a team still wins 3 out of 5, but John's team wins the total. **Answers will vary, sample answer: Round 4, John's team collects 53 oz.**

Grade 4 37 *Chapter 12*

Chapter Resources



### Convert Customary Weights

**Example 1** Tell students that in problems such as this one, you can convert either measurement. In this problem, you can convert 32 ounces to pounds or 2 pounds to ounces. Point out that often times one conversion is easier than the other.

## ADDITIONAL EXAMPLES

**1** Does 8,000 pounds equal 2 tons? No, 8,000 pounds equals 4 tons.

**2** Use the table on p. 505 to find how many pounds a Tyrannosaurus weighed.
$2{,}000 \times 8 = 16{,}000$ pounds

## CHECK What You Know

As a class, have students complete Exercises 1–9 in **Check What You Know** as you observe their work.

**Exercise 9** Assess student comprehension before assigning practice exercises.

## BL Alternate Teaching Strategy

**If** students have trouble converting customary units of weight…

**Then** use one of these reteach options:

1 CRM **Daily Reteach Worksheet** (p. 33)

2 Have students make conversion charts they can keep handy for reference. Suggestions include the following:

- Make it a two-column chart: Large Units to Smaller and Small Units to Larger.
- Indicate whether multiplication or division is used to convert from one unit to the other.
- Give at least one example in each column to use as a model for future conversions.

### Additional Answers

**8.** Sample answer: no; An ostrich egg weighs 64 ounces or 4 pounds, which is less than 5 pounds.

**9.** Sample answer: There is more of the smaller unit than the larger unit in the same amount of weight. Therefore, to get to the higher number you must multiply.

**Lesson 12-6** Convert Customary Units of Weight **505**

# 3 Practice

Differentiate practice using these leveled assignments for Exercises 10–24.

| Level | Assignment |
|---|---|
| BL Below/Approaching Level | 10–12, 17, 19 |
| OL On Level | 10–16, 18, 19–21, 23 |
| AL Above/Beyond Level | 10–21 even, 22–24 |

Have students discuss and complete the Higher Order Thinking problems. For Exercise 22, suggest that students estimate the weight of each object.

**WRITING IN MATH** Have students complete Exercise 24 in their Math Journals. You may choose to use this as an optional formative assessment.

### Additional Answers

**22.** Sample answer: Two objects that can be measured in tons are a truck and an airplane. Two objects that cannot be measured in tons are a grain of rice and a piece of paper.

**24.** Sample answer: To find the answer, convert 2 tons to 4,000 pounds. Then add 1,265 pounds to 4,000. The answer is 5,265 pounds.

**COMMON ERROR!**

**Exercise 10** Watch for students who answer 8 oz, as they may be confusing 8 fl oz in 1 cup with 16 oz in 1 lb. Allow students to use conversion tables.



## Practice and Problem Solving

See page R32.

**Complete.** See Examples 1 and 2 (pp. 504–505)

**10.** 1 lb = ■ oz 16

**11.** 160 oz = ■ lb 10

**12.** ■ T = 8,000 lb 4

**13.** 5 lb = ■ oz 80

**14.** ■ lb = 3 T and 600 lb 6,600

**15.** ■ oz = 3 lb and 6 oz 54

**16.** **Algebra** Copy and complete the table below.

| Pounds | 6 | ■ 7 | 8 | ■ 9 |
|---|---|---|---|---|
| Ounces | ■ 96 | 112 | ■ 128 | 144 |

**17.** A baby blue whale weighs about 3,000 pounds and can gain about 200 pounds each day. About how many days would it take a baby blue whale to gain 1 ton of weight? about 10 days

**18.** The weight capacity of a bridge is 3 tons. Three trucks need to cross the bridge at the same time. If each truck weighs 1,800 pounds, can they safely cross at the same time? Explain. yes; 1,800 × 3 or 5,400 is less than 6 tons

### Real-World PROBLEM SOLVING

**Animals** Baby animals weigh different amounts at birth.

| Animal | Birth Weight |
|---|---|
| Alligator | 2 ounces |
| Giraffe | 100–150 pounds |
| Giant panda | 3 to 5 ounces |
| Walrus | 100–160 pounds |

**Source:** San Diego Zoo

**19.** What is the fewest number of baby walruses whose weight would equal about 1 ton? 12 baby walruses

**20.** What is the greatest number of giant pandas whose weight would equal about 3 pounds? 16

**21.** An alligator nest usually contains about 30 eggs. What will the total weight of the babies be in pounds after all 30 eggs hatch? 3 pounds and 12 ounces

### H.O.T. Problems

**22.** **OPEN ENDED** Give two examples of objects that can be measured in tons and two examples of objects that cannot be measured in tons. See margin.

**23.** **CHALLENGE** Tiffany weighed 7 pounds 12 ounces when she was born. Her weight doubled after four months. How much did Tiffany weigh after four months? 15 pounds 8 ounces

**24.** **WRITING IN MATH** Explain how to convert 2 tons 1,265 pounds to pounds. See margin.

## TEST Practice

**25.** Which is the most reasonable measurement for a can of green beans? (Lesson 12-4) **A**

- **A** 13 ounces
- **B** 130 ounces
- **C** 13 pounds
- **D** 13 tons

**26.** Russ paid $10 for dog food that costs $1.25 per pound. Which is the most reasonable estimate for the amount of dog food Russ bought? (Lesson 12-4) **G**

- **F** 8 ounces
- **G** 8 pounds
- **H** 80 pounds
- **J** 8 tons

**27.** Which table represents the relationship between pounds and ounces? (Lesson 12-6) **A**

**A**

| Pounds | 1 | 2 | 3 | 4 |
|---|---|---|---|---|
| Ounces | 16 | 32 | 48 | 64 |

**B**

| Pounds | 1 | 2 | 3 | 4 |
|---|---|---|---|---|
| Ounces | 8 | 16 | 24 | 32 |

**C**

| Pounds | 1 | 2 | 3 | 4 |
|---|---|---|---|---|
| Ounces | 16 | 24 | 32 | 40 |

**D**

| Pounds | 16 | 32 | 48 | 64 |
|---|---|---|---|---|
| Ounces | 1 | 2 | 3 | 4 |

## Spiral Review

**28.** Greg, Liza, Erina, and Julius each play a sport. The sports they play are baseball, soccer, tennis, and volleyball. Liza uses a racquet. Julius does not play volleyball. Greg uses a mitt. Which sport does each student play? (Lesson 12-5) See margin.

**Choose the more reasonable estimate for the weight of each object.** (Lesson 12-4)

**29.**

10 ounces or 10 pounds **10 ounces**

**30.**

50 ounces or 50 pounds **50 pounds**

**Choose the more reasonable estimate for each capacity.** (Lesson 12-3)

**31.** 225 mL or 225L **225mL**

**32.**

2 mL or 2L **2L**



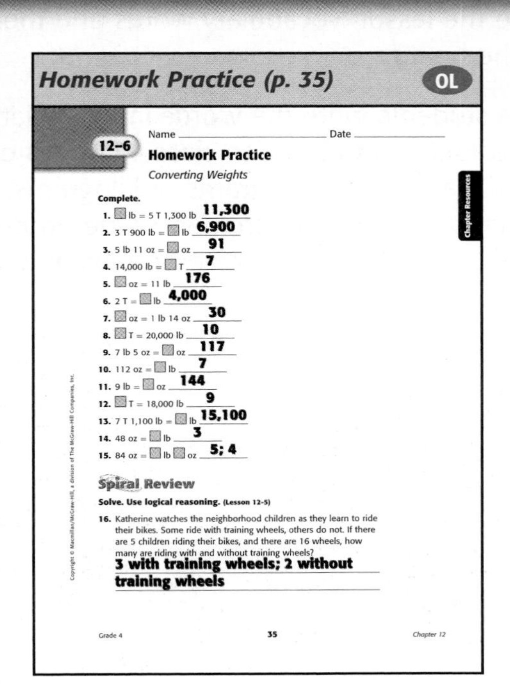

Homework Practice (p. 35) OL

Name ________ Date ________

12-6 **Homework Practice**

*Converting Weights*

**Complete.**

1. ☐ lb = 5 T 1,300 lb **11,300**
2. 3 T 900 lb = ☐ lb **6,900**
3. 5 lb 11 oz = ☐ oz **91**
4. 14,000 lb = ☐ T **7**
5. ☐ oz = 11 lb **176**
6. 2 T = ☐ lb **4,000**
7. ☐ oz = 1 lb 14 oz **30**
8. ☐ T = 20,000 lb **10**
9. 7 lb 5 oz = ☐ oz **117**
10. 112 oz = ☐ lb **7**
11. 9 lb = ☐ oz **144**
12. ☐ T = 18,000 lb **9**
13. 7 T 1,100 lb = ☐ lb **15,100**
14. 48 oz = ☐ lb **3**
15. 84 oz = ☐ lb ☐ oz **5; 4**

Spiral Review

**Solve. Use logical reasoning.** (Lesson 12-5)

16. Katherine watches the neighborhood children as they learn to ride their bikes. Some ride with training wheels, others do not. If there are 5 children riding their bikes, and there are 16 wheels, how many are riding with and without training wheels? **3 with training wheels; 2 without training wheels**

Chapter Resources



Grade 4 35 Chapter 12

# 4 Assess

## Formative Assessment

- **How do you convert 5 pounds to ounces?** Multiply 16 × 5; 90 oz
- **How do you convert 80 ounces to pounds?** Divide 80 by 16; 5 lb

**Quick Check** **Are students continuing to struggle with converting customary units of weight?**

**If Yes** → Small Group Options (p. 504B)

**If No** → Independent Work Options (p. 504B)
CRM Skills Practice Worksheet (p. 34)
CRM Enrich Worksheet (p. 37)

**Yesterday's News** Have students write about how they think that the lesson, Customary Units of Weight, helped them with today's lesson on converting customary units of weight.

## TEST Practice

### Reviews Lessons 12-4 and 12-6

Assign the Test Practice problems to provide daily reinforcement of test-taking skills.

## Spiral Review

### Reviews Lessons 12-3, 12-4, and 12-5

Review and assess mastery of skills and concepts from previous chapters.

### Additional Answer

**28.** Liza plays tennis, Greg plays baseball, Julius plays soccer, and Erina plays volleyball.

LESSON

# 12-7 Metric Units of Mass

## Lesson Planner

### Objective

Estimate and measure mass and learn the difference between weight and mass.

### Vocabulary

**mass**, **gram**, **kilogram**

### Resources

**Materials:** small objects to be weighed, packages marked in grams or kilograms

**Manipulatives:** pan balance

**Literature Connection:** *Who Sank the Boat?* by Pamela Allen

**Teacher Technology**
TeacherWorks • Interactive Classroom

## Daily Routine

Use these suggestions before beginning the lesson on p. 508.

### 5-Minute Check

(Reviews Lessons 12-6)

**Complete.**

1. 3 lb = ■ oz 48
2. 64 oz = ■ lb 4
3. ■ T = 14,000 lb 7
4. 1 lb 8 oz = ■ oz 24
5. ■ lb = 2 T 4,000

### Problem of the Day

Franklin School has a total of 226 students and teachers in the middle grades. If there are 10 teachers and there are 27 students in each class, how many classes are there? 8 classes

### Focus on Math Background

Whereas an object's weight varies with position, its mass remains constant. Mass is a direct measure of quantity of matter.

A gram is a relatively small unit. But in medical, scientific, and industrial applications, much smaller units like the milligram (one-thousandth of a gram) and microgram (one-millionth of a gram) are commonly used. Larger quantities, such as the mass of a person, are measured in kilograms. A kilogram is equal to 1,000 grams, and is actually the international standard mass unit.

### Building Math Vocabulary

Write the lesson vocabulary words and their definitions on the board.

Have students write the words in their Math Journals. Ask volunteers to bring to class packages or labels that show mass marked in grams or kilograms. Suggest that students include a description of the products and their masses in their journals as examples of gram and kilogram.

# Differentiated Instruction

## Small Group Options

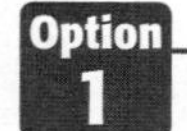

SPATIAL

### Option 1 Below Level BL

**Materials:** 5 nickels, 1 quarter, 4 dimes, school balance, paper and pencil

- Say to students:

  **A nickel's mass is about 5 grams. How many nickels equal the mass of a quarter?** Answers will vary. However, two nickels is a good choice.
- **How many dimes equal the mass of a nickel?** Answers will vary. However, 3 dimes is a good choice.
- Answers can be checked with a school balance scale.

LINGUISTIC, LOGICAL

### Option 2 English Language Learners ELL

**Materials:** unlined index cards with ">" on one side and "=" on the other

**Core Vocabulary:** mass, measure, true/untrue

**Common Use Verb:** flip

**Talk Math** This strategy helps students recognize mass units of real objects.

- Take a symbol card and place < between a pencil and a dollar bill. Ask: "Is the sentence **true**? Does a pencil have less **mass** than a dollar?" Accept answers. Measure items on a scale. Repeat, flipping to the = sign and the greater than sign until the sentence is true.
- Model and write: "This sentence is true/untrue."
- Have students form and read "sentences" that illustrate the relationship between items. If the sentence is untrue, allow them to experiment to find the answer.

## Independent Work Options

TACTILE/LOGICAL

### Option 1 Early Finishers AL

**Materials:** balance scale

- Assign partners. Partners take turns estimating, recording, and determining the mass of several small classroom objects.
- One student chooses a classroom object and records an estimate of mass.
- Together the partners weigh the object to determine its mass.
- Partners discuss how closely the estimate and actual measurement compare.

### Option 2 Student Technology

**Math Online** macmillanmh.com

Personal Tutor • Extra Examples

### Option 3 Learning Station: Social Studies (p. 482J)

Direct students to the Social Studies Learning Station for opportunities to explore and extend the lesson concept.

### Option 4 Problem-Solving Practice

Reinforce problem-solving skills and strategies with the Problem-Solving Practice worksheet.

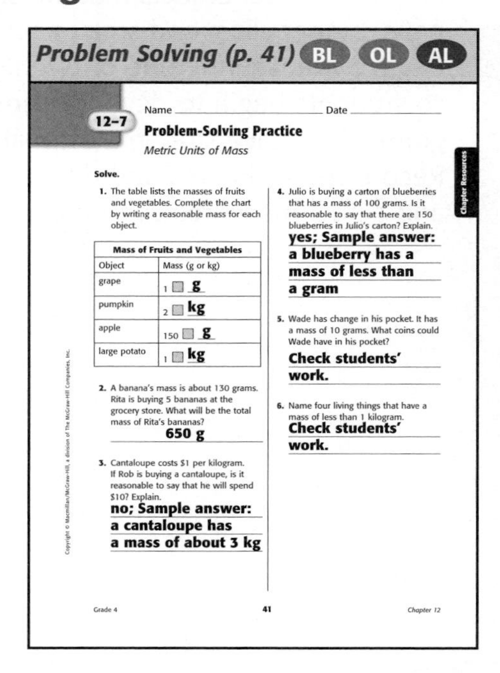

**Problem Solving (p. 41)** BL OL AL

12–7 Name ______ Date ______

**Problem-Solving Practice**

*Metric Units of Mass*

**Solve.**

1. The table lists the masses of fruits and vegetables. Complete the chart by writing a reasonable mass for each object.

| Mass of Fruits and Vegetables | |
|---|---|
| Object | Mass (g or kg) |
| grape | 1 **g** |
| pumpkin | 2 **kg** |
| apple | 150 **g** |
| large potato | 1 **kg** |

2. A banana's mass is about 130 grams. Rita is buying 5 bananas at the grocery store. What will be the total mass of Rita's bananas?
**650 g**

3. Cantaloupe costs $1 per kilogram. If Rob is buying a cantaloupe, is it reasonable to say that he will spend $10? Explain.
**no; Sample answer: a cantaloupe has a mass of about 3 kg**

4. Julio is buying a carton of blueberries that has a mass of 100 grams. Is it reasonable to say that there are 150 blueberries in Julio's carton? Explain.
**yes; Sample answer: a blueberry has a mass of less than a gram**

5. Wade has change in his pocket. It has a mass of 10 grams. What coins could Wade have in his pocket?
**Check students' work.**

6. Name four living things that have a mass of less than 1 kilogram.
**Check students' work.**

Chapter Resources



Grade 4 41 Chapter 12

# Metric Units of Mass

## 1 Introduce

### Activity Choice 1 • Hands-On

- Allow students to examine packages and labels that are marked with metric units of mass: gram and kilogram.
- **Why do you think the information on the label is given in both customary units and metric units?** Accept all reasonable answers.
- Tell students that in this lesson they will learn the difference between weight (oz and lb) and mass (g and kg).

### Activity Choice 2 • Literature

Introduce the lesson with *Who Sank the Boat?* by Pamela Allen. For a related math activity, see p. TR62.

## 2 Teach

### Scaffolding Questions

- **What is the basic metric unit of measure for length?** meter
- **What is the basic metric unit of measure for capacity?** liter
- **In this lesson, you will learn about *gram* and *kilogram*. What do you think the basic metric unit of mass is?** gram

### Hands-On Mini Activity

Since the mass of the objects is to be measured in grams, select objects that are small, such as pens, binder clips, and small pads of paper. Begin by measuring one or two items as a class so students begin to develop benchmarks for a gram. Then have students estimate the mass. Record the estimates and discuss how estimates and actual measures compare.



# 12-7 Metric Units of Mass

**MAIN IDEA**

I will estimate and measure mass and learn the difference between weight and mass.

**New Vocabulary**

**mass**
**gram**
**kilogram**

**Math Online**

macmillanmh.com

- Extra Examples
- Personal Tutor
- Self-Check Quiz

## GET READY to Learn

### Hands-On Mini Activity

You can use a balance scale to find the mass of objects.

**Materials:** balance scale, four different objects, gram weights

**Step 1 Copy the table.**

| Object | Estimate | Mass (grams) |
|---|---|---|
| | | |
| | | |
| | | |
| | | |

**Step 2 Estimate.**

Select four objects that will fit on one side of the balance scale. Choose one and estimate its mass in grams. Record the estimate.

**Step 3 Measure.**

Set the object on one side of the balance scale. On the other side, set gram weights until both sides are balanced. Record the actual mass. Repeat Steps 2 and 3 for the other objects.

1. Did the larger objects have a greater mass than the smaller objects? See students' work.
2. Explain how a larger object can have less mass than a smaller object. Sample answer: A larger object can have less matter than a smaller object.



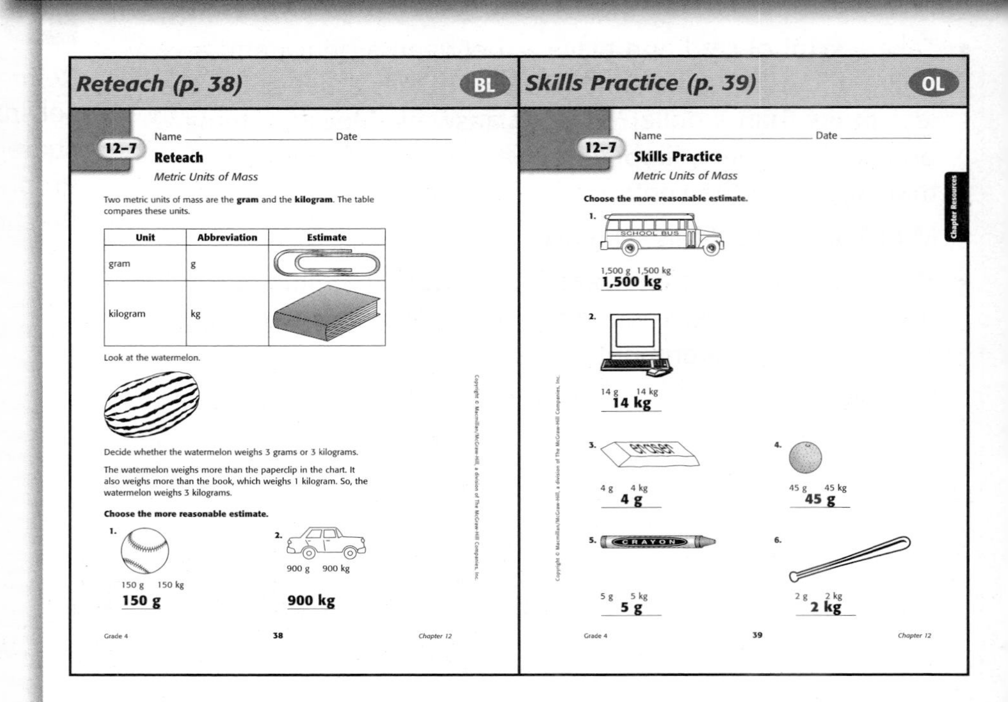

**Reteach (p. 38)** BL

12-7 Name ______ Date ______

**Reteach**

*Metric Units of Mass*

Two metric units of mass are the **gram** and the **kilogram**. The table compares these units.

| Unit | Abbreviation | Estimate |
|---|---|---|
| gram | g | |
| kilogram | kg | |

Look at the watermelon.

Decide whether the watermelon weighs 3 grams or 3 kilograms.

The watermelon weighs more than the paperclip in the chart. It also weighs more than the book, which weighs 1 kilogram. So, the watermelon weighs 3 kilograms.

**Choose the more reasonable estimate.**

1. 150 g 150 kg **150 g**
2. 900 g 900 kg **900 kg**

Grade 4 38 Chapter 12



**Skills Practice (p. 39)** OL

12-7 Name ______ Date ______

**Skills Practice**

*Metric Units of Mass*

**Choose the more reasonable estimate.**

1. 1,500 g 1,500 kg **1,500 kg**
2. 14 g 14 kg **14 kg**
3. 4 g 4 kg **4 g**
4. 45 g 45 kg **45 g**
5. 5 g 5 kg **5 g**
6. 2 g 2 kg **2 kg**

Grade 4 39 Chapter 12

**Mass** is the amount of matter an object has. The mass of an object is not affected by gravity. In contrast, an object's weight differs depending on gravity.

**Remember**

You would weigh less on the Moon than you do on Earth. However, your mass is the same on Earth as it is on the Moon.

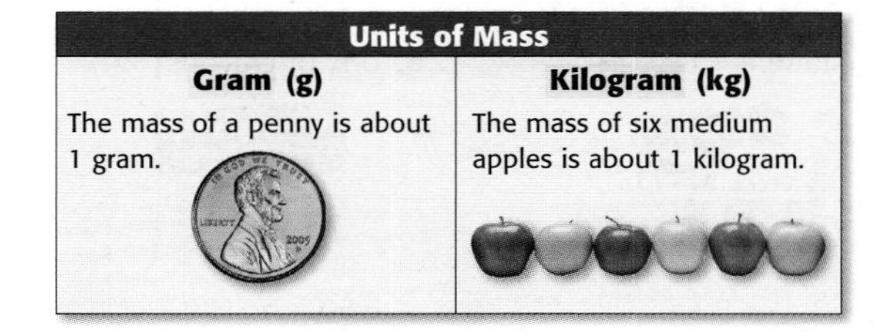

| Units of Mass | |
|---|---|
| **Gram (g)** | **Kilogram (kg)** |
| The mass of a penny is about 1 gram. | The mass of six medium apples is about 1 kilogram. |

You can use what you know about the gram and kilogram to estimate mass.

**Estimate Mass**

**1 TECHNOLOGY Which is the more reasonable estimate for the mass of the laptop, 2 grams or 2 kilograms?**

If the laptop has a mass of 2 grams, it would have the same mass as 2 pennies. This is not a reasonable estimate.
So, a reasonable estimate is 2 kilograms.

4. Sample answer: Weight is affected by gravity whereas mass is not.

## CHECK What You Know

**Choose the more reasonable estimate for the mass of each object.**

See Example 1 (p. 509)

1. ball cap

25 g or 25 kg **25 g**

2. polar bear

450 g or 450 kg **450 kg**

3. Is it more reasonable to say that Cheryl lifts dumbbells that have a mass of 30 grams or 30 kilograms? Explain. **See margin.**

4. Talk About It Explain the difference between weight and mass. Look back at Explore 11-4 if needed.



### Estimate Mass

**Example 1** Tell students to use the benchmarks provided in the Units of Mass table. Ask them if the mass of a laptop is closer to the mass of 2 pennies or 12 (2 × 6) apples.

### ADDITIONAL EXAMPLES

1. Which is the more reasonable estimate for the mass of a penguin, 4 g or 4 kg? 4 kg

### CHECK What You Know

As a class, have students complete Exercises 1–4 in **Check What You Know** as you observe their work.

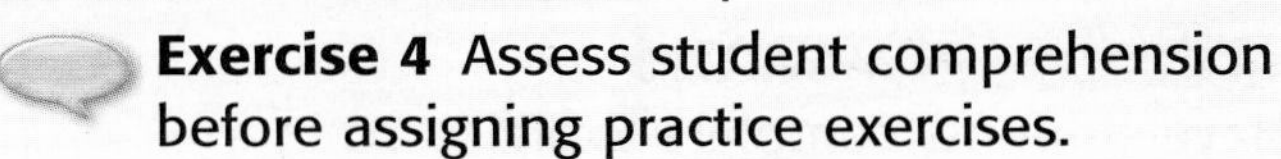

**Exercise 4** Assess student comprehension before assigning practice exercises.

### BL Alternate Teaching Strategy

**If** students have trouble estimating and measuring the mass of objects...

**Then** use one of these reteach options:

1. CRM **Daily Reteach Worksheet** (p. 38)
2. Provide items that can be used as benchmarks for 1 gram and 1 kilogram. **If you need to measure something light, which SI unit would you use?** gram **If you need to measure something heavy, which SI unit would you use?** kilogram

   Allow students to handle benchmark models so they can differentiate the measures.

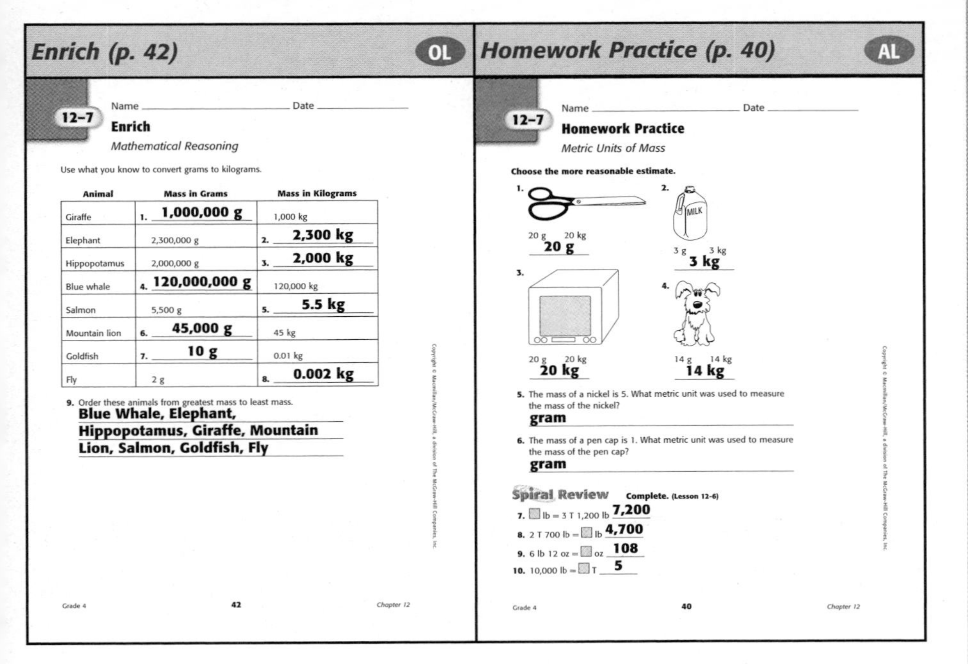

**Enrich (p. 42)** OL

12-7 Name ________ Date ________

**Enrich**

*Mathematical Reasoning*

Use what you know to convert grams to kilograms.

| Animal | Mass in Grams | Mass in Kilograms |
|---|---|---|
| Giraffe | 1. **1,000,000 g** | 1,000 kg |
| Elephant | 2,300,000 g | 2. **2,300 kg** |
| Hippopotamus | 2,000,000 g | 3. **2,000 kg** |
| Blue whale | 4. **120,000,000 g** | 120,000 kg |
| Salmon | 5,500 g | 5. **5.5 kg** |
| Mountain lion | 6. **45,000 g** | 45 kg |
| Goldfish | 7. **10 g** | 0.01 kg |
| Fly | 2 g | 8. **0.002 kg** |

9. Order these animals from greatest mass to least mass. **Blue Whale, Elephant, Hippopotamus, Giraffe, Mountain Lion, Salmon, Goldfish, Fly**

Grade 4 42 Chapter 12

**Homework Practice (p. 40)** AL

12-7 Name ________ Date ________

**Homework Practice**

*Metric Units of Mass*

**Choose the more reasonable estimate.**

1. 20 g 20 kg **20 g**
2. 3 g 3 kg **3 kg**
3. 20 g 20 kg **20 kg**
4. 14 g 14 kg **14 kg**
5. The mass of a nickel is 5. What metric unit was used to measure the mass of the nickel? **gram**
6. The mass of a pen cap is 1. What metric unit was used to measure the mass of the pen cap? **gram**

**Spiral Review** Complete. (Lesson 12-6)

7. ☐ lb = 3 T 1,200 lb **7,200**
8. 2 T 700 lb = ☐ lb **4,700**
9. 6 lb 12 oz = ☐ oz **108**
10. 10,000 lb = ☐ T **5**

Grade 4 40 Chapter 12

### Additional Answers

3. Sample answer: It is more reasonable to say that Cheryl lifts weights that are 30 kilograms because 30 grams would equal 30 pennies, which does not have enough mass to exercise with.

### COMMON ERROR!

Students often confuse mass and weight. Remind them that the mass of an object does not change with the location of the object. So, the mass of a person is the same on Earth as it is on the Moon. This is not true for the weight of an object, as weight is influenced by the force of gravity.

# 3 Practice

Differentiate practice using these leveled assignments for Exercises 5–16.

| Level | Assignment |
|---|---|
| BL Below/Approaching Level | 5–8, 11 |
| OL On Level | 5–8, 11, 12, 14 |
| AL Above/Beyond Level | 5–13, odd, 14–16 |

Have students discuss and complete the Higher Order Thinking problems. Remind students that six apples have the mass of about 1 kilogram.

Have students complete Exercise 16 in their Math Journals. You may choose to use this exercise as an optional formative assessment.

# 4 Assess

## Formative Assessment

**Explain why 5 g or 5 kg is the more reasonable estimate for the dog.** 5 kg; Sample answer: A penny is about a gram and 6 medium apples are about a kilogram, so the mass of a dog is closer to 30 apples than 5 pennies.

**Quick Check** **Are students continuing to struggle with estimating and measuring the mass of an object?**

**If Yes** → Small Group Options (p. 508B)

**If No** → Independent Work Options (p. 508B)
CRM Skills Practice Worksheet (p. 39)
CRM Enrich Worksheet (p. 42)

**Ticket Out the Door** Ask students to choose the more reasonable estimate for the mass of their textbook: 3 g or 3 kg.

## Practice and Problem Solving

EXTRA PRACTICE See page R32.

**Choose the more reasonable estimate for the mass of each object.**
See Example 1 (p. 509)

5. stamps

8 g

8 g or 8 kg

6. box of crayons

100 g

100 g or 100 kg

7. cooler

25 kg

25 g or 25 kg

8. ball

20 g

20 g or 20 kg

9. tool box

30 kg

30 g or 30 kg

10. trampoline

50 kg

50 g or 50 kg

11. The table lists items that can be found in a classroom. Estimate and then measure the mass of each object. Copy and complete the table. Sample answers are given.

**Mass of Classroom Objects**

| Object | Estimate | Actual |
|---|---|---|
| Glue bottle (20 g) | ■ | ■ |
| Paper clip (1 g) | ■ | ■ |
| Pencil (12 g) | ■ | ■ |
| Stapler (200 g) | ■ | ■ |

12. Tyler bought a large bag of peanuts at a baseball game. Is it more reasonable to say that the mass of the peanuts is 1 gram or 1 kilogram? 1 kilogram

13. Alicia is buying 6 oranges that cost $1 per kilogram. Is it reasonable to say that the cost of the oranges will be greater than $6? Explain. See margin.

### H.O.T. Problems

14. **OPEN ENDED** Name five classroom objects that have a mass greater than 1 kilogram. Sample answer: backpack filled with textbooks, desk, student, television, and door

15. **CHALLENGE** Which weighs more, an astronaut on Earth or the same astronaut on the Moon? Explain. 15, 16. See margin.

16.  WRITING IN MATH Write about a real-world situation in which you would have to decide which metric unit to use to measure an object's mass.



13. Sample answer: no; The mass of the oranges would be less than 4 kg. Since 4 kg would cost $6, the cost of 6 oranges would be less than $6.

15. The astronaut weighs more on Earth than in space because the gravitational force is less on the Moon than on the Earth.

16. Sample answer: Buying fruit from a grocery store where the fruit must be weighed to determine its cost.

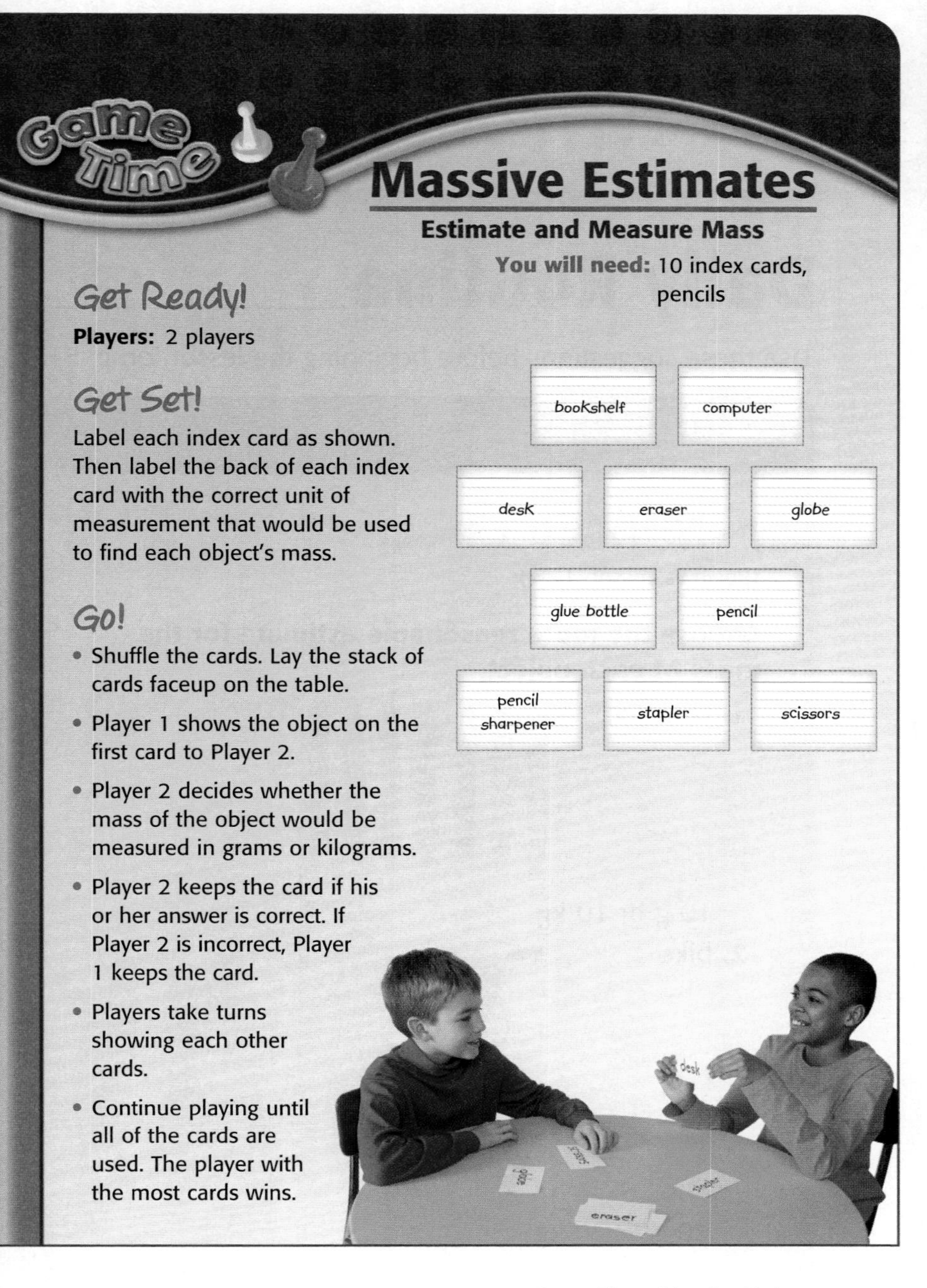

Massive Estimates

Estimate and Measure Mass

**You will need:** 10 index cards, pencils

*Get Ready!*

**Players:** 2 players

*Get Set!*

Label each index card as shown. Then label the back of each index card with the correct unit of measurement that would be used to find each object's mass.

bookshelf | computer | desk | eraser | globe | glue bottle | pencil | pencil sharpener | stapler | scissors

*Go!*

- Shuffle the cards. Lay the stack of cards faceup on the table.
- Player 1 shows the object on the first card to Player 2.
- Player 2 decides whether the mass of the object would be measured in grams or kilograms.
- Player 2 keeps the card if his or her answer is correct. If Player 2 is incorrect, Player 1 keeps the card.
- Players take turns showing each other cards.
- Continue playing until all of the cards are used. The player with the most cards wins.

**Game Time** Massive Estimates 511

## Differentiated Practice

Use these leveled suggestions to differentiate the game for all learners.

| Level | Assignment |
|---|---|
| BL Below/Approaching Level | Students may use a conversion chart to show which units of measure are smaller. |
| OL On Level | Have students play the game with the rules as written. |
| AL Above/Beyond Level | Students estimate the actual mass of the object on the card. |

# Massive Estimates

**Math Concept:**
**Estimate and Measure Mass**

**Materials:** 10 index cards, pencils

Introduce the game on p. 511 to your students to play as a class, in small groups, or at a learning workstation to review concepts introduced in this chapter.

## Instructions

- Students label each index card with the words shown on page 511. Then, they label the back of each card with the correct unit of measurement that would be used to find each object's mass.
- Students shuffle the cards and lay the stack of cards faceup on the table, with the object name on the first card showing.
- Player 1 shows the object on the first card to Player 2. Player 2 decides if the object's mass should be measured in grams or kilograms.
- If Player 2's answer is correct, he or she keeps the card. If Player 2's answer is incorrect, Player 1 keeps the card.
- Players take turns showing each other cards until all of the cards are used. The player with the most cards wins the game.

## Extend the Game

Have students make the game using object names they choose themselves.

LESSON 12-8

# Estimate and Measure Volume

## Lesson Planner

### Objective

Estimate and measure volume in cubic units.

### Vocabulary

**volume**, **cubic units**, **cubic centimeter**

### Resources

**Manipulatives:** rectangular prism and cube from the set of geometric solids, centimeter cubes

**Literature Connection:** *Room for Ripley* by Stuart J. Murphy

**Alternate Lesson:** Use *IMPACT Mathematics:* Unit H to provide practice with volume.

**Teacher Technology**
TeacherWorks • Interactive Classroom

## Daily Routine

Use these suggestions before beginning the lesson on p. 512.

### 5-Minute Check

(Reviews Lesson 12-7)

**Choose the more reasonable estimate for the mass of each object.**

**1.** crayons 10 g

10 g or 10 kg

**2.** bike 20 g

20 g or 20 kg

### Problem of the Day

Kiko bought a sandwich for $4, a juice drink for $2, and an ice cream for $2. He gave the clerk $10. How much change did he receive? $2

### Focus on Math Background

Students learned in Grade 3 that volume is a measure of how much space an object occupies. Volume can be found by filling an empty three-dimensional object with cubic units, or by building a model with cubes. Now students will estimate as well as find the volume of three-dimensional objects.

### Building Math Vocabulary

Write the lesson vocabulary words and their definition on the board.

Have students write the new terms in their Math Journals.
**What is the definition of a cube?** A rectangular prism whose faces are all square.
Brainstorm and list items that are cubes, such as number cubes and some tissue boxes.

# Differentiated Instruction

## Small Group Options

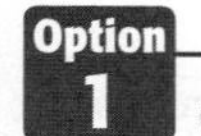

### Option 1 Gifted and Talented AL

SPATIAL

**Materials:** centimeter cubes – 24 per student, colored paper, pencil, scissors, and glue

- Provide this problem to students:

> You have just gone to work for a candy company as their designer of new candy boxes. A new candy mint, which is the same size and shape as a centimeter cube is to be sold in stores very soon. The company wants to put 24 mints in the container. Your job is to design a box that allows the mints to fit securely and looks great to customers, too.

Answers will vary. Accept all that meet the description requirements.

### Option 2 English Language Learners ELL

VISUAL, AUDITORY

**Materials:** cubes
**Core Vocabulary:** deep/depth, wide/width, long/length
**Common Use Verb:** has

**See Math** This strategy helps students recognize the relationship between depth, width, and length.

- Write *width* and *wide* on the board.
- Point to the words on the board as you say: "This ***has*** a width of 2 units. How **wide** is it?" 2 cubic units wide
- Repeat this procedure with *deep/depth* and *long/length*.
- Post the scaffolds deep/depth, long/length, and wide/width. If appropriate, also have students practice "This has a _____ of _____ cubic units. It is _____ units _____."
- Have students use cubes to create a cube and write sentences that describe it.

## Independent Work Options

### Option 1 Early Finishers AL

TACTILE, LOGICAL

**Materials:** centimeter cubes

- Have students estimate the volume in cubic centimeters of classroom objects, such as a lunch box or a crayon box.
- Then students use centimeter cubes to determine the volume of the object.
- Have students record their estimates and measurements to share with the class.

### Option 2 Student Technology

**Math Online** macmillanmh.com

Personal Tutor • Extra Examples

 Math Adventures

### Option 3 Learning Station: Music (p. 482J)

Direct students to the Music Learning Station for opportunities to explore and extend the lesson concept.

### Option 4 Problem-Solving Practice

Reinforce problem-solving skills and strategies with the Problem-Solving Practice worksheet.

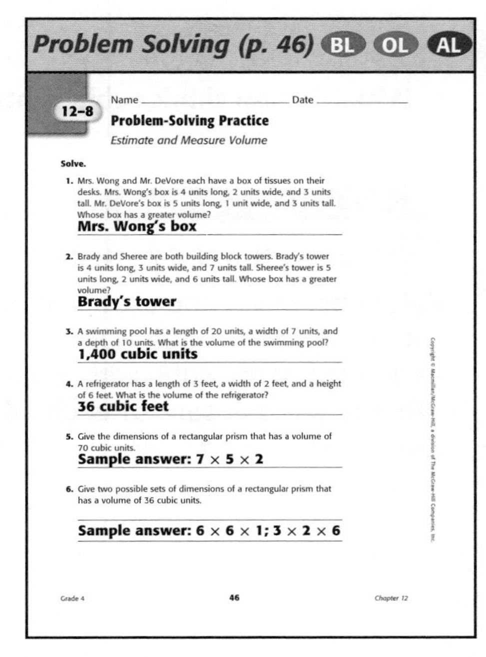

**Problem Solving (p. 46) BL OL AL**

12–8 Name _____ Date _____

**Problem-Solving Practice**
*Estimate and Measure Volume*

**Solve.**

1. Mrs. Wong and Mr. DeVore each have a box of tissues on their desks. Mrs. Wong's box is 4 units long, 2 units wide, and 3 units tall. Mr. DeVore's box is 5 units long, 1 unit wide, and 3 units tall. Whose box has a greater volume?
**Mrs. Wong's box**
2. Brady and Sheree are both building block towers. Brady's tower is 4 units long, 3 units wide, and 7 units tall. Sheree's tower is 5 units long, 2 units wide, and 6 units tall. Whose box has a greater volume?
**Brady's tower**
3. A swimming pool has a length of 20 units, a width of 7 units, and a depth of 10 units. What is the volume of the swimming pool?
**1,400 cubic units**
4. A refrigerator has a length of 3 feet, a width of 2 feet, and a height of 6 feet. What is the volume of the refrigerator?
**36 cubic feet**
5. Give the dimensions of a rectangular prism that has a volume of 70 cubic units.
**Sample answer: $7 \times 5 \times 2$**
6. Give two possible sets of dimensions of a rectangular prism that has a volume of 36 cubic units.
**Sample answer: $6 \times 6 \times 1$; $3 \times 2 \times 6$**



Grade 4 46 Chapter 12

# 12-8 Estimate and Measure Volume

## 1 Introduce

### Activity Choice 1 • Hands-On

- Provide students with centimeter cubes.
- Have each student draw a square on a piece of paper and estimate how many centimeter cubes will fit in one layer on the square.
- Then have students place a layer of cubes on their squares.
- **How close was your estimate to the actual number of cubes you used?** Answers will vary.

### Activity Choice 2 • Literature

Introduce the lesson with *Room for Ripley* by Stuart J. Murphy. For a related math activity, see p. TR62.

## 2 Teach

### Scaffolding Questions

Draw and label a 4 cm-by-6 cm rectangle on an overhead transparency.

- **How do you find the perimeter of this rectangle?** Find the sum of the measures of the sides.
- **How do you find the area of this rectangle?** Multiply its length times its width.
- **What is the area of this rectangle?** 24 $cm^2$
- **What does square centimeter mean?** Sample answer: It means a square that measures 1 cm in length and 1 cm in width.
- **What do you think cubic centimeter means?** Accept all reasonable answers.

### GET READY to Learn

**Hands-On Mini Activity**

Before beginning the activity, provide students with centimeter cubes. Have volunteers measure each edge of the cube with a metric ruler. **What is the measure of each edge of the cube?** 1 cm



# 12-8 Estimate and Measure Volume

**MAIN IDEA**

I will estimate and measure volume in cubic units.

**New Vocabulary**

volume
cubic units
cubic centimeter

**Math Online** macmillanmh.com
- Extra Examples
- Personal Tutor
- Self-Check Quiz

### GET READY to Learn

**Volume** is the amount of space a three-dimensional figure contains. It is measured in **cubic units**. Each side of a centimeter cube has a length of 1 centimeter. So, the volume for a rectangular prism is measured in **cubic centimeters**.

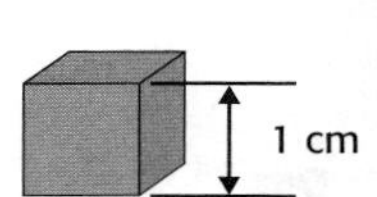


**Hands-On Mini Activity**

**Materials:** cube and rectangular prism, centimeter cubes

Find the volume of each three-dimensional figure.

**Step 1 Estimate.**
Estimate how many centimeter cubes it will take to fill the cube.

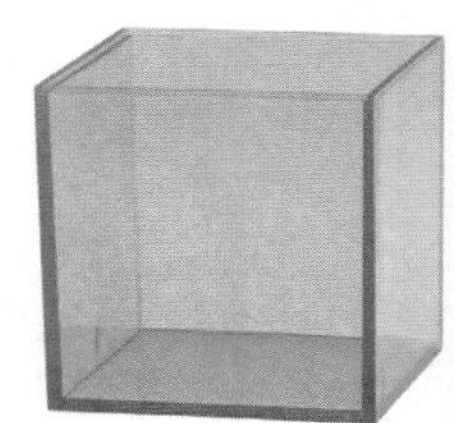

**Step 2 Measure.**
Place centimeter cubes inside the cube. When it is full, count the centimeter cubes. The number of centimeter cubes that the cube will hold is the volume of the cube. Compare this with your estimate.

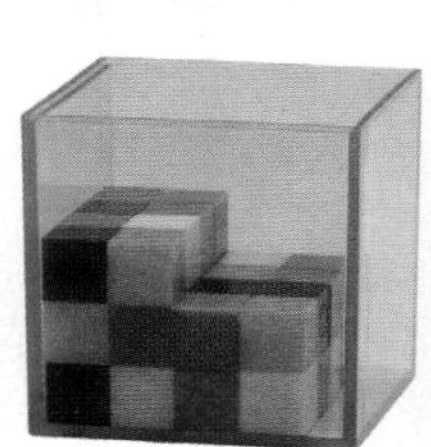

**Step 3 Apply.**
Repeat Steps 1 and 2 for the rectangular prism.

1. What is the volume of the rectangular prism? 60 cubic units
2. Which has a greater volume, the prism or the cube? how much greater? cube; 65 cubic units



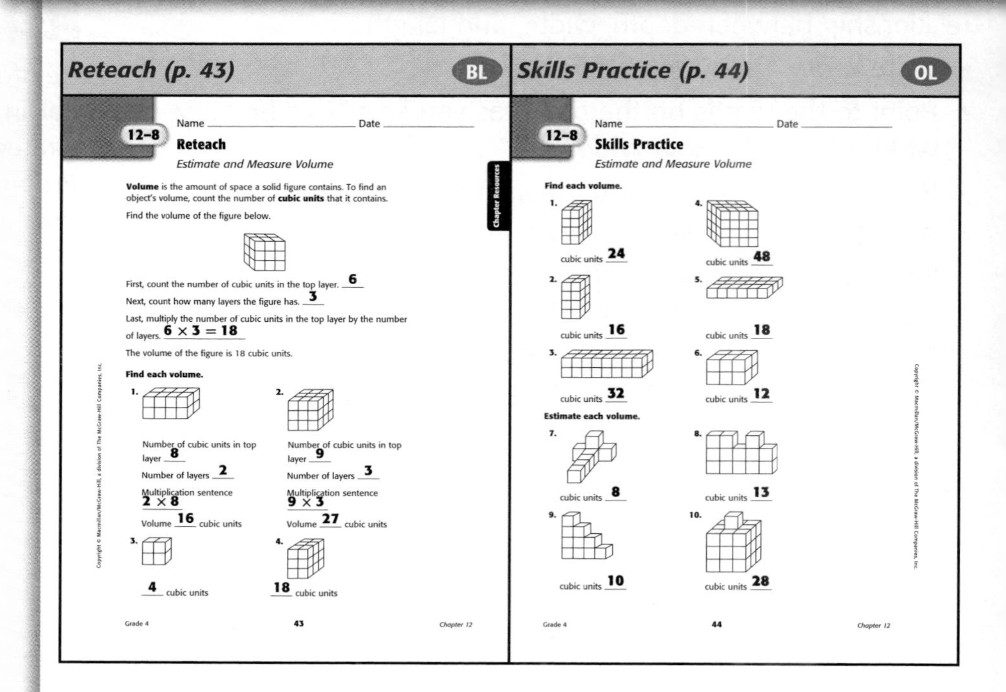

**Reteach (p. 43)** BL

12-8 Name ____ Date ____

**Reteach**

*Estimate and Measure Volume*

**Volume** is the amount of space a solid figure contains. To find an object's volume, count the number of **cubic units** that it contains.

Find the volume of the figure below.

First, count the number of cubic units in the top layer. 6

Next, count how many layers the figure has. 3

Last, multiply the number of cubic units in the top layer by the number of layers. $6 \times 3 = 18$

The volume of the figure is 18 cubic units.

**Find each volume.**

1. Number of cubic units in top layer 8
   Number of layers 2
   Multiplication sentence $2 \times 8$
   Volume 16 cubic units
2. Number of cubic units in top layer 9
   Number of layers 3
   Multiplication sentence $9 \times 3$
   Volume 27 cubic units
3. 4 cubic units
4. 18 cubic units

Grade 4 43 Chapter 12



**Skills Practice (p. 44)** OL

12-8 Name ____ Date ____

**Skills Practice**

*Estimate and Measure Volume*

**Find each volume.**

1. cubic units 24
2. cubic units 16
3. cubic units 32
4. cubic units 48
5. cubic units 18
6. cubic units 12

**Estimate each volume.**

7. cubic units 8
8. cubic units 13
9. cubic units 10
10. cubic units 28

Grade 4 44 Chapter 12

To find the volume of a figure, count the number of cubic units needed to fill the figure.

**Volume** — Key Concept

Volume is the number of cubic units needed to fill a three-dimensional figure.

**Remember**
To help you determine volume, you can build a model using base-ten blocks.

**EXAMPLE** Find Volume

**1 Find the volume of the cube shown.**

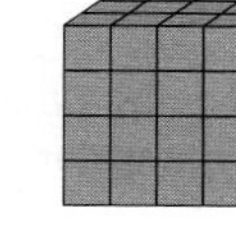

Count the number of cubes it takes to make the object.

The cube shown has 4 layers. Each layer has 16 cubes.

one layer

16 cubes

four layers

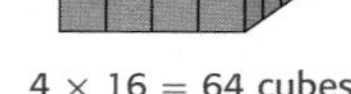

$4 \times 16 = 64$ cubes

So, the volume of the cube is 64 cubic units.

You can estimate to find the volume of a three-dimensional figure that has different numbers of cubes in each layer.

**EXAMPLE** Estimate Volume

**2 Estimate the volume of the figure shown.**

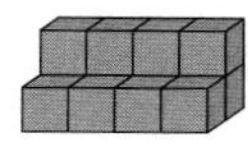

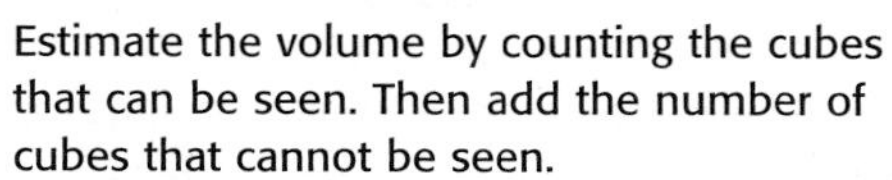

Estimate the volume by counting the cubes that can be seen. Then add the number of cubes that cannot be seen.

Four cubes can be seen in the top layer.

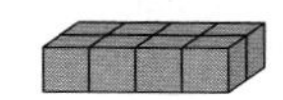

Five cubes can be seen in the bottom layer and three cubes are hidden.

So, the volume of the figure is $4 + 8$ or 12 cubic units.



**Enrich (p. 47)** AL

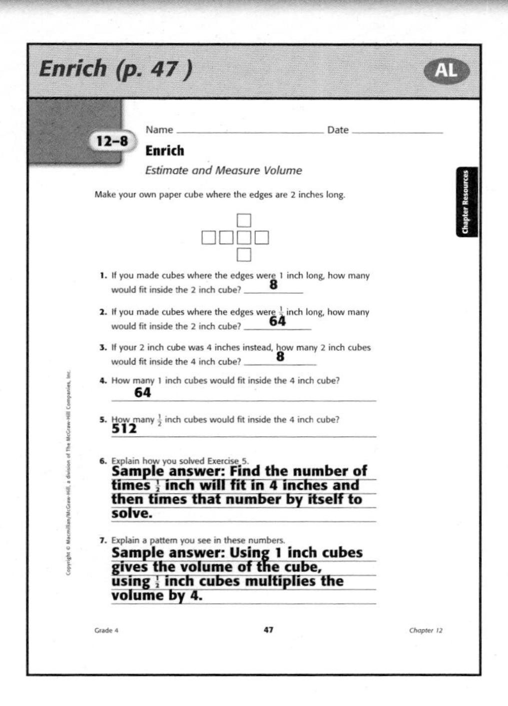

12-8 Name ______ Date ______

**Enrich**

*Estimate and Measure Volume*

Make your own paper cube where the edges are 2 inches long.

1. If you made cubes where the edges were 1 inch long, how many would fit inside the 2 inch cube? **8**
2. If you made cubes where the edges were $\frac{1}{2}$ inch long, how many would fit inside the 2 inch cube? **64**
3. If your 2 inch cube was 4 inches instead, how many 2 inch cubes would fit inside the 4 inch cube? **8**
4. How many 1 inch cubes would fit inside the 4 inch cube? **64**
5. How many $\frac{1}{2}$ inch cubes would fit inside the 4 inch cube? **512**
6. Explain how you solved Exercise 5. **Sample answer: Find the number of times $\frac{1}{2}$ inch will fit in 4 inches and then times that number by itself to solve.**
7. Explain a pattern you see in these numbers. **Sample answer: Using 1 inch cubes gives the volume of the cube, using $\frac{1}{2}$ inch cubes multiplies the volume by 4.**

Grade 4 47 Chapter 12

Chapter Resources

## Estimate Volume

**Example 2** Watch for students who cannot visualize the models. Encourage students to use manipulatives to model the examples.

**ADDITIONAL EXAMPLES**

1. Find the volume of the cube. 27 cubic units

2. Estimate the volume of the figure. 14 cubic units

**CHECK What You Know**

As a class, have students complete Exercises 1–6 in **Check What You Know** as you observe their work.

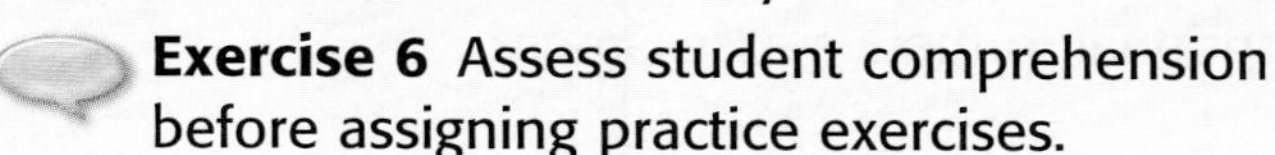

**Exercise 6** Assess student comprehension before assigning practice exercises.

## BL Alternate Teaching Strategy

**If** students have trouble estimating and measuring volume...

**Then** use one of these reteach options:

1 CRM **Daily Reteach Worksheet** (p. 43)

2 Use centimeter cubes to build the model layer by layer. Then have students examine the model from different perspectives to help visualize hidden cubes. Encourage students to draw a picture of their models to reinforce the ability to visualize hidden cubes.

**COMMON ERROR!**

**Exercise 16** Some students may be confused by the height of 1 unit, not realizing that is the height of one cube. Have them use base-ten cubes to model the problem.

# 3 Practice

Differentiate practice using these leveled assignments for Exercises 7–19.

| Level | Assignment |
|---|---|
| BL Below/Approaching Level | 7–9, 10–12, 13 |
| OL On Level | 7–9, 10–12, 13–16, 17, 19 |
| AL Above/Beyond Level | 7–16 even, 17–19 |

Have students discuss and complete the Higher Order Thinking problems. Encourage students to use mental math. Most exercises require multiplying three basic factors.

**WRITING IN MATH** Have students complete Exercise 19 in their Math Journals. You may choose to use this exercise as an optional formative assessment.

## Additional Answers

**5.** Sample answers: length = 2, width = 3, and height = 2; or length = 4, width = 3, and height = 1

**6.** Sample answer: 2, since the figure is a cube I know that the length, height, and width all have the same dimension. A cube that has dimensions of $2 \times 2 \times 2 = 8$ cubic units.

**15.** Sample answer: Toby's box; the volume of Toby's box is $8 \times 4 \times 1$ or 32 cubic units and the volume of Javier's box is $5 \times 7 \times 1$ or 35 cubic units.

**16.** Sample answer: 33 cubic units. The answer can be found by finding the volume of both towers and subtracting to find the difference.

**Find the volume of each figure.** See Example 1 (p. 513)

**1.** 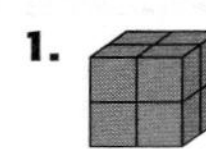 8 cubic units

**2.** 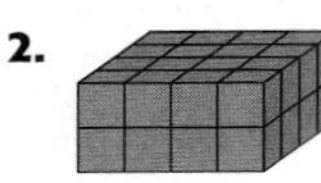 32 cubic units

**Estimate the volume of each figure.** See Example 2 (p. 513)

**3.** 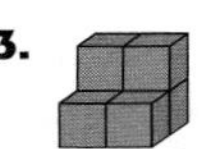 6 cubic units

**4.** 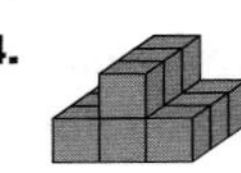 12 cubic units

**5.** Rona has 12 cubes. Model and describe a rectangular prism she could create that has a volume of 12 cubic units.
5, 6. See margin.

**6.** Talk About It The volume of a cube is 8 cubic units. What is the height of the cube? Explain.

## Practice and Problem Solving

**Find the volume of each figure.** See Example 1 (p. 513)

**7.** 27 cubic units

**8.** 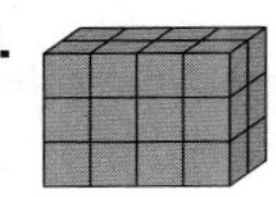 24 cubic units

**9.** 105 cubic units

**Estimate the volume of each figure.** See Example 2 (p. 513)

**10.** 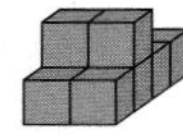 10 cubic units

**11.**  15 cubic units

**12.** 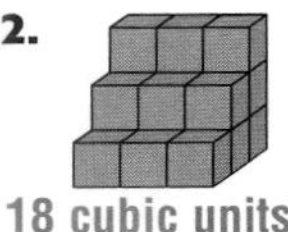 18 cubic units

**13.** A book is 9 units long, 5 units wide, and 2 units high. Use models to find the volume. 90 cubic units

**14.** A shoe box is 10 units long, 6 units wide, and 4 units high. Use models to find the volume. 240 cubic units

**15.** Toby and Lena each have a box. Toby's box is 8 units long, 4 units wide, and 1 unit tall. Lena's box is 5 units long, 7 units wide, and 1 unit tall. Whose box has a volume of 32 cubic units? Explain.
15, 16. See margin.

**16.** Vijay is making a tower 3 units long, 4 units wide, and 5 units tall. So far, the tower is 3 units long, 3 units wide, and 3 units tall. Find the volume that is left to be added to the tower. Explain.

## H.O.T. Problems

**17. OPEN ENDED** Give the dimensions of a rectangular prism that has a volume greater than 50 cubic units. $5 \times 5 \times 4$

**18. WHICH ONE DOESN'T BELONG?** Identify the figure that does not belong with the other three. Explain. **18, 19. See margin.**

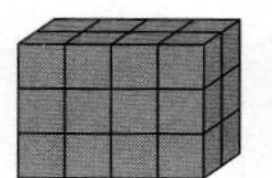
figure A

figure B

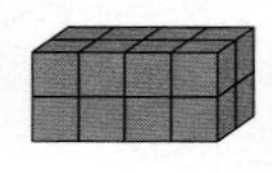
figure C

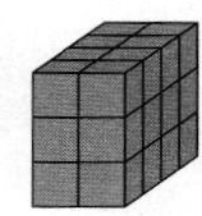
figure D

**19. WRITING IN MATH** Explain the difference between area and volume.

## TEST Practice

**20.** Which of these units would best measure the mass of a watermelon? (Lesson 12-7) **C**

**A** cups

**B** grams

**C** kilograms

**D** meters

**21.** Which is the best estimate for the volume of the prism? (Lesson 12-8) **J**

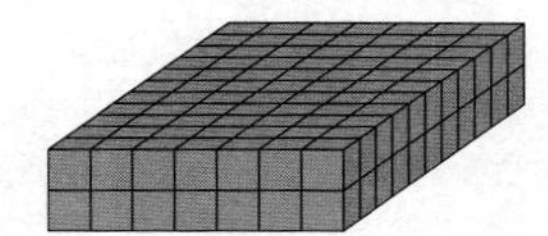

**F** 14 cubic units

**G** 22 cubic units

**H** 77 cubic units

**J** 154 cubic units

## Spiral Review

**Choose the more reasonable estimate for the mass of each object.** (Lesson 12-7)

**22.** cherry

5 g or 5 kg **5 g**

**23.** wagon

15 g or 15 kg **15 kg**

**Complete.** (Lesson 12-6)

**24.** 1 lb = ■ oz **16**

**25.** 80 oz = ■ lb **5**

**26.** 8,000 lb = ■ T **4**

**27.** Alex's smoothie is 32 ounces. Minda's smoothie is half the size of Alex's smoothie. Tyrell's smoothie is 8 ounces less than Alex's smoothie. How many ounces is each person's smoothie? (Lesson 12-5)
**Alex's smoothie is 32 oz, Minda's smoothie is 16 oz, Tyrell's smoothie = 24 oz**



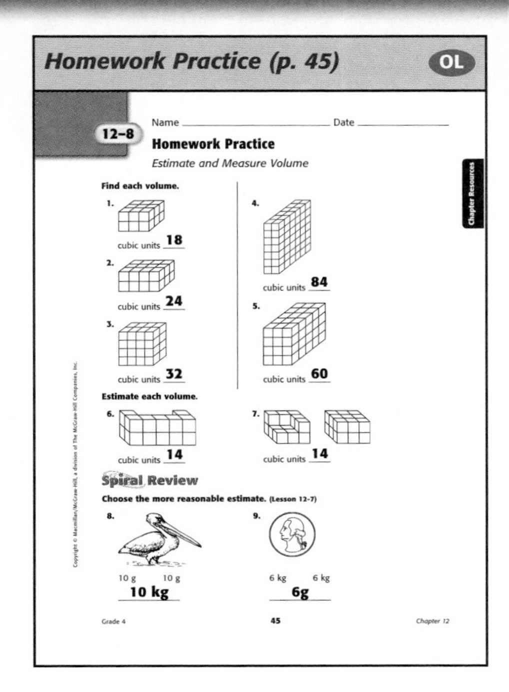

**Homework Practice (p. 45)** OL

12-8 Name ______ Date ______

**Homework Practice**

*Estimate and Measure Volume*

**Find each volume.**

1. cubic units **18**
2. cubic units **24**
3. cubic units **32**
4. cubic units **84**
5. cubic units **60**

**Estimate each volume.**

6. cubic units **14**
7. cubic units **14**

**Spiral Review**

**Choose the more reasonable estimate.** (Lesson 12-7)

8. 10 g 10 kg **10 kg**
9. 6 kg 6 kg **6g**

Grade 4 45 Chapter 12

# 4 Assess

### Formative Assessment

Draw and label a 5-cm by 4-cm by 2-cm rectangular prism on the board.

- **What is the volume of this prism?** 40 cubic centimeters
- Draw and label a 4-cm by 6-cm by 2-cm rectangular prism on the board. **Which three-dimensional figure has the greater volume?** This prism has a volume of 48 cubic centimeters. So, the volume of this prism is greater than the volume of the other prism.

**Quick Check** **Are students continuing to struggle with estimating and measuring volume?**

**If Yes** → CRM Reteach Worksheet (p. 43)

**If No** → Independent Work Options (p. 512B)
CRM Skills Practice Worksheet (p. 44)
CRM Enrich Worksheet (p. 47)

**Name the Math** Have students explain how to find the volume of a rectangular prism that is 5 units long, 2 units wide, and 8 units tall.

### TEST Practice

**Reviews Lessons 12-7 and 12-8**

Assign the Test Practice problems to provide daily reinforcement of test-taking skills.

### Spiral Review

**Reviews Lessons 12-5, 12-6, and 12-7**

Review and assess mastery of skills and concepts from previous chapters.

### Additional Answers

**18.** Sample answer: The rectangular prism that has dimensions that are $4 \times 2 \times 2$ does not belong because its volume is 16 cubic units and the volume of the other is 24 cubic units.

**19.** Sample answer: Area measures the number of units need to over a 2 dimensional object. Where as volume measures the number of units a 3-dimensional object can hold.

# Lesson Planner

## Objective

Interpret information and data from science to solve problems.

### National Standard 

Students should develop understanding of organisms and environments.

## Activate Prior Knowledge

Before you turn students' attention to the pages, ask them to discuss tide pools and creatures found in an aquarium.

- **Name some creatures you know who live in tide pools.** starfish, crabs, mussels
- **Name a sea plant that appears in tide pools.** kelp

## Using the Student Page

Ask students to read the information on p. 516 and answer these questions:

- **How many quarts of water would you need to fill the 30-gallon aquarium?** 120 quarts
- **How many more times would you have to use a quart container to fill a 30-gallon aquarium than you would for a 25-gallon aquarium?** 20 more times

**Aquariums**

| Capacity (gal) | Length (in.) | Width (in.) |
| --- | --- | --- |
| 20 | 24 | 12 |
| 25 | 30 | 12 |
| 30 | 36 | 18 |
| 40 | 48 | 12 |

## Real-World Math

**Use the information above to solve each problem.**

1. Elias has decided to buy a 20-gallon aquarium. He will use a one-quart container to fill the aquarium. How many times will Elias use the one-quart container to fill the 20-gallon aquarium? **80 times**
2. Suppose Elias decided to get the 25-gallon aquarium instead. How many times will he need to use his one-quart container to fill the aquarium? **100 times**
3. How many more times would Elias have to use a quart container to fill a 40-gallon aquarium than you would for a 30-gallon aquarium? **40 times**
4. If Elias buys the 20-gallon aquarium, what would the length and width of the aquarium be in feet? **length = 2 feet, width = 1 foot**
5. If Elias buys the 40-gallon aquarium, what would the length and width of the aquarium be in feet? **length = 4 feet, width = 1 foot**
6. Elias is also buying the gravel to place in the bottom of his 20-gallon aquarium. He needs one pound of gravel for every gallon of water. How many ounces of gravel will he need for the 20-gallon aquarium? **320 ounces**
7. If Elias buys the 25-gallon aquarium, how many ounces of gravel will he need? **400 ounces**

## Real-World Math

Assign the exercises on p. 517. Encourage students to choose a problem-solving strategy before beginning each exercise. If necessary, review the strategies suggested in Lesson 11-7, p. 466.

**Exercise 1** Remind students that there are four quarts in a gallon.

**Exercise 4** Remind students that there are 12 inches in a foot.

**WRITING IN MATH** Have students create a word problem that uses the information found in the text and in the picture on pp. 516–517.

## Extend the Activity

Have students calculate gravel amounts for a larger-capacity aquarium and add this information to the chart on p. 517.

# Lesson Planner

## Objective

Choose the best strategy to solve a problem.

## Resources

**Teacher Technology**

TeacherWorks • Interactive Classroom

**Real-World Problem Solving**
**Math and Science: *Strange but True***
Use these leveled books to reinforce and extend problem-solving skills and strategies.

Leveled for:

- OL On Level
- ELL Sheltered English
- SP Spanish

For additional support, see the Real-World Problem Solving Teacher Guide.

# Daily Routine

Use these suggestions before beginning the lesson on p. 518.

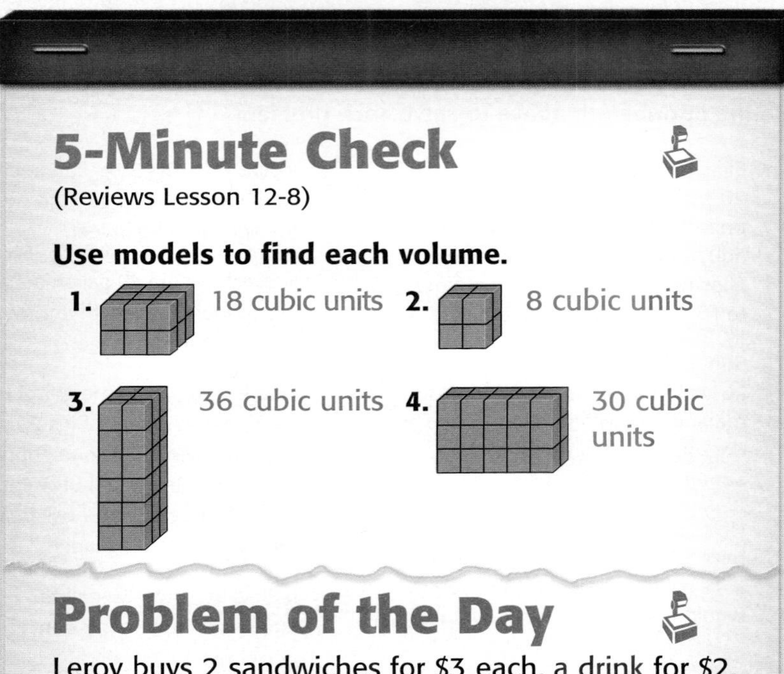

## 5-Minute Check

(Reviews Lesson 12-8)

**Use models to find each volume.**

**1.** 18 cubic units **2.** 8 cubic units

**3.** 36 cubic units **4.** 30 cubic units

## Problem of the Day

Leroy buys 2 sandwiches for $3 each, a drink for $2, and an ice cream cone for $1. He pays with a $20 bill. What is the least and greatest number of bills he could receive in change? Explain. Since his change is $11, the least number of bills would be 2: a ten-dollar bill and a one-dollar bill; the greatest number of bills would be 11: 11 one-dollar bills.

# Differentiated Instruction

## Small Group Options

LOGICAL

### Option 1 Gifted and Talented AL

**Materials:** paper and pencil

Pose the following problem to students:

Miguel is helping his club wash cars to raise money for a charity. They charge $6 for small cars and $8 for large cars or vans. When Miguel counts the money at the end of the morning, he announces they have made $106.

- **How many small cars and large vehicles did they wash?** 3 small cars and 11 large cars or vans

VISUAL

### Option 2 English Language Learners ELL

**Materials:** small bag with three manipulatives, index cards, pocket chart

**Core Vocabulary:** what's, when, my rule

**Common Use Verb:** raise

**See Math** This strategy uses the guess and check method to deepen understanding of math skills.

- Say, "I have a rule for adding. When you know **my rule**, raise your hand."
- Underline the 11-inch side of a sheet of paper in one color. Using a 1-inch strip, extend the line 1 inch in a second color. Write: "11 inches + ____ = 12 inches."
- Repeat for several sequential units ("10 inches + ____ = 11 inches, etc.) items until several students have raised their hands.
- Ask: **"What's my rule?"**
- Have students with the right rule create their own measurement rule and repeat in small groups.

## Independent Work Options

VISUAL, LOGICAL

### Option 1 Early Finishers OL AL

**Materials:** newspapers, store flyers, index card, pencil

- Provide students with access to print materials that have ads for product sales, such as electronic store flyers, discount store circulars, and so on.
- On one side of the index card, the student uses information found in the ads to write a word problem.
- On the other side of the card, the student writes the answer and identifies a strategy that can be used to solve the problem.
- Have students contribute their cards to a problem bank.

### Option 2 Student Technology

**Math Online** macmillanmh.com

Personal Tutor • Extra Examples

### Option 3 Learning Station: Health (p. 482I)

Direct students to the Health Learning Station for opportunities to explore and extend the lesson concept.

# 1 Introduce

**Activity • Review**

- Pose this situation:
  *A particular snail can crawl 2 feet every 10 minutes. If it crawled 12 feet, how long did it take?*
- **How can you use act it out to help solve this problem?** Sample answer: Mark 12 feet on the floor with masking tape; step off 2 feet repeatedly and record the number of steps on the board. Then multiply the number of steps by 10.
- **How many hours did it take the snail to crawl 12 feet?** 1 hour or 60 min

# 2 Teach

Have students read the problem on video games. Guide them through the problem-solving steps.

**Understand** Using the questions, review what students know and need to find.

**Plan** Have them discuss their strategy.

**Solve** Guide students to use the make a table strategy to solve the problem.

- **Who will be able to buy the most games? Explain.** Felice; her games cost less.
- **Why does one table show an increase by 20 and the other an increase by 15?** Sample answers: The tables represent the cost of a game for each game system.

**Check** Have students look back at the problem to make sure that the answer fits the facts given.

## COMMON ERROR!

**Exercise 7** After seeing the pattern 32 and 64 and 96 (32 + 64 = 96) some students may jump to the conclusion that you add the last two sums to find a new sum. Explain that the pattern shown in the table is add 32 tokens for each 2 guests.





**MAIN IDEA** I will solve problems by choosing the best strategy.

## P.S.I. TEAM +

AIDEN: I have a video game system. Games cost $20. Felice has a different video game system. Her games cost $15. How many video games can we each buy if we each have $60?

YOUR MISSION: Find how many games each person can buy.

**Understand** Games for Aiden's game system cost $20. Games for Felice's game system cost $15. Each has $60 to spend on video games. Find how many games each person can buy.

**Plan** Organize the data to show the number of games and the total amount of money spent.

**Solve**

| Aiden | |
|---|---|
| Rule: $t = 20g$ | |
| Games | Total ($) |
| 1 | 20 |
| 2 | 40 |
| 3 | 60 |

| Felice | |
|---|---|
| Rule: $t = 15g$ | |
| Games | Total ($) |
| 1 | 15 |
| 2 | 30 |
| 3 | 45 |
| 4 | 60 |

Since Aiden's games cost more, he can buy only 3. Felice can buy 4.

**Check** Look back. Since $20 \times 3 = 60$ and $15 \times 4 = 60$, you know that the answer is correct. ✓



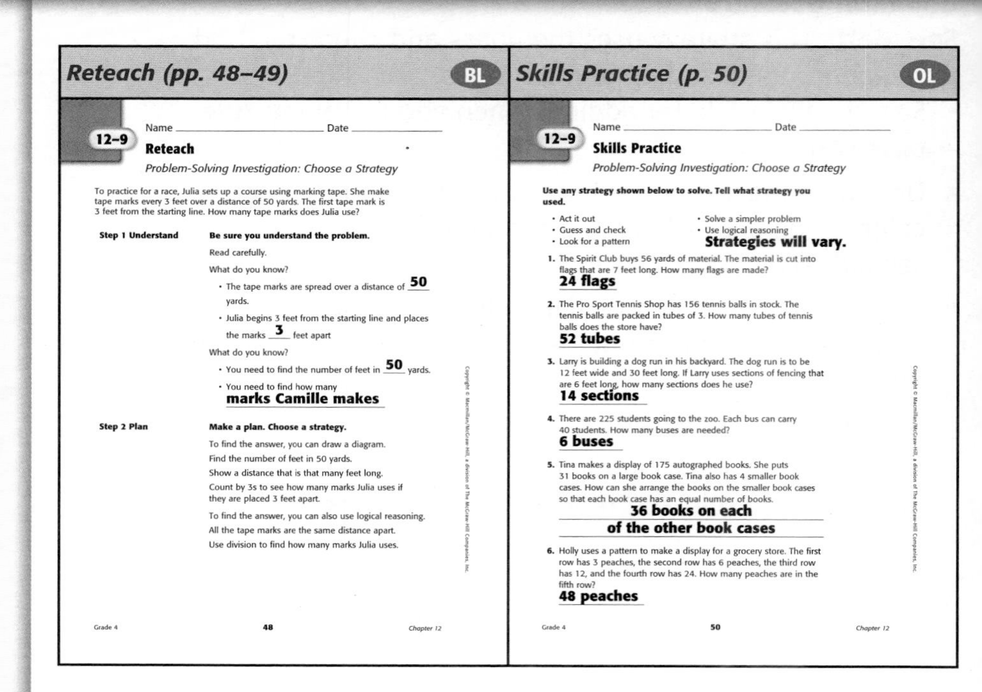

**Reteach (pp. 48–49)** BL

12–9 Name ______ Date ______

**Reteach**

*Problem-Solving Investigation: Choose a Strategy*

To practice for a race, Julia sets up a course using marking tape. She make tape marks every 3 feet over a distance of 50 yards. The first tape mark is 3 feet from the starting line. How many tape marks does Julia use?

**Step 1 Understand** **Be sure you understand the problem.**

Read carefully.

What do you know?

- The tape marks are spread over a distance of **50** yards.
- Julia begins 3 feet from the starting line and places the marks **3** feet apart

What do you know?

- You need to find the number of feet in **50** yards.
- You need to find how many **marks Camille makes**

**Step 2 Plan** **Make a plan. Choose a strategy.**

To find the answer, you can draw a diagram.
Find the number of feet in 50 yards.
Show a distance that is that many feet long.
Count by 3s to see how many marks Julia uses if they are placed 3 feet apart.

To find the answer, you can also use logical reasoning.
All the tape marks are the same distance apart.
Use division to find how many marks Julia uses.



Grade 4 48 Chapter 12

**Skills Practice (p. 50)** OL

12–9 Name ______ Date ______

**Skills Practice**

*Problem-Solving Investigation: Choose a Strategy*

**Use any strategy shown below to solve. Tell what strategy you used.**

- Act it out
- Guess and check
- Look for a pattern
- Solve a simpler problem
- Use logical reasoning

**Strategies will vary.**

1. The Spirit Club buys 56 yards of material. The material is cut into flags that are 7 feet long. How many flags are made?
   **24 flags**
2. The Pro Sport Tennis Shop has 156 tennis balls in stock. The tennis balls are packed in tubes of 3. How many tubes of tennis balls does the store have?
   **52 tubes**
3. Larry is building a dog run in his backyard. The dog run is to be 12 feet wide and 30 feet long. If Larry uses sections of fencing that are 6 feet long, how many sections does he use?
   **14 sections**
4. There are 225 students going to the zoo. Each bus can carry 40 students. How many buses are needed?
   **6 buses**
5. Tina makes a display of 175 autographed books. She puts 31 books on a large book case. Tina also has 4 smaller book cases. How can she arrange the books on the smaller book cases so that each book case has an equal number of books.
   **36 books on each of the other book cases**
6. Holly uses a pattern to make a display for a grocery store. The first row has 3 peaches, the second row has 6 peaches, the third row has 12, and the fourth row has 24. How many peaches are in the fifth row?
   **48 peaches**



Grade 4 50 Chapter 12

★ indicates multi-step problem

## Mixed Problem Solving

EXTRA PRACTICE See page R33.

**Use any strategy shown below to solve. Tell what strategy you used.**

PROBLEM-SOLVING STRATEGIES
- Act it out.
- Guess and check.
- Look for a pattern.
- Work a simpler problem.
- Use logical reasoning.

★**1. Measurement** Keisha and Andy went hiking from 9:30 A.M. until 12:00 P.M. After lunch, they hiked for another hour and 40 minutes. How many minutes did they spend hiking? **4 hrs 10 min**

**2.** For every day at school that no students are absent, a teacher put 3 marbles in a jar. If the jar holds 426 marbles, how many days of no absences will it take to fill the jar? **142 days**

★**3.** A family spends $22 on tickets for a community play. If there are two adults, how many children are with them? **4 children**

Community Play
–TICKETS–
CHILDREN $3 ADULTS $5

★**4. Measurement** A roller coaster car carries 32 people every 10 minutes. There are 572 people in line in front of Ruben. About how long will it take for him to ride the roller coaster? **180 min**

★**5.** Dora took 8 photos with her camera. She takes 2 more photos each day for a week. How many more days does she need to take photos to have 30? **4 days**

★**6.** Sally gave a cashier $25 for two CDs. They cost the same amount. She got $3 back. How much did each CD cost? **$11**

**7. Algebra** April's party is being held at an arcade. Each guest will be given 16 tokens to play games. Copy and complete the table to find how many tokens are needed for 12 guests.

| Guests | Tokens |
|---|---|
| 2 | 32 |
| 4 | 64 |
| 6 | 96 |
| 8 | 128 |
| 10 | **160** ■ |
| 12 | **192** ■ |

**8.** A concert hall has 13 rows of seats. The hall has a total of 221 seats. Write a number sentence that could be used to find the number of seats in each row. **$221 \div 13 = \blacksquare$**

★**9.** Myron has 2 red marbles for every one green marble. He has three times as many blue marbles as red marbles. Myron has four red marbles. How many green and blue marbles does he have? **2 green and 12 blue marbles**

**10.** WRITING IN MATH Identify the problem-solving strategy you used to find the answer to Exercise 9. Explain how you found the answer. **See Ch. 12 Answer Appendix.**



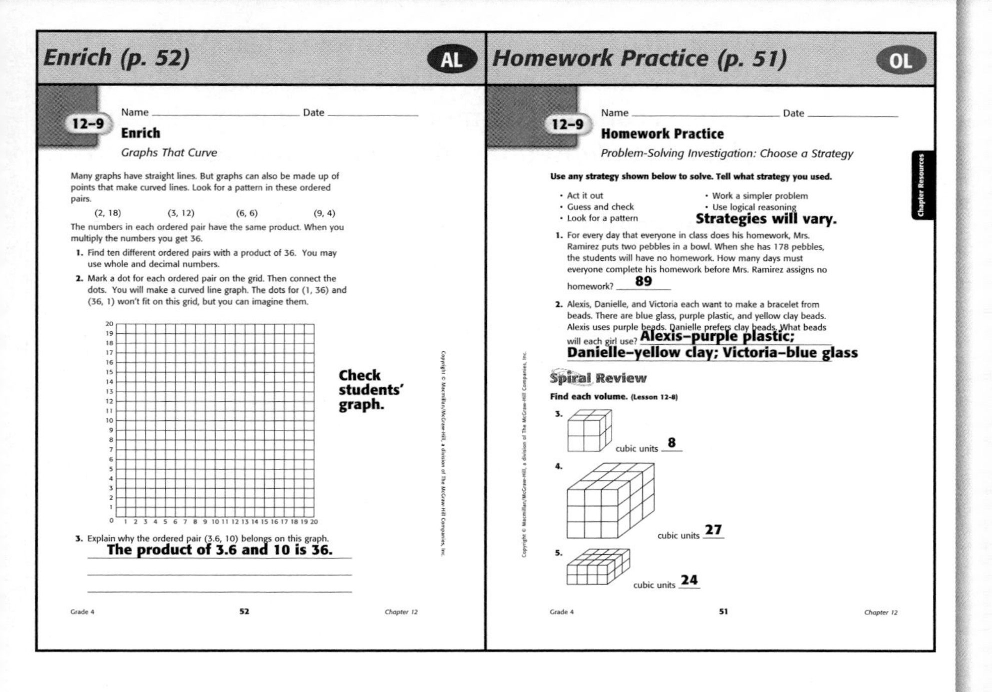
**Enrich (p. 52)** AL

12–9 Name ______ Date ______

**Enrich**

*Graphs That Curve*

Many graphs have straight lines. But graphs can also be made up of points that make curved lines. Look for a pattern in these ordered pairs.

(2, 18) (3, 12) (6, 6) (9, 4)

The numbers in each ordered pair have the same product. When you multiply the numbers you get 36.

1. Find ten different ordered pairs with a product of 36. You may use whole and decimal numbers.
2. Mark a dot for each ordered pair on the grid. Then connect the dots. You will make a curved line graph. The dots for (1, 36) and (36, 1) won't fit on this grid, but you can imagine them.

**Check students' graph.**

3. Explain why the ordered pair (3.6, 10) belongs on this graph. **The product of 3.6 and 10 is 36.**

Grade 4 52 Chapter 12

**Homework Practice (p. 51)** OL

12–9 Name ______ Date ______

**Homework Practice**

*Problem-Solving Investigation: Choose a Strategy*

**Use any strategy shown below to solve. Tell what strategy you used.**

- Act it out
- Guess and check
- Look for a pattern
- Work a simpler problem
- Use logical reasoning

**Strategies will vary.**

1. For every day that everyone in class does his homework, Mrs. Ramirez puts two pebbles in a bowl. When she has 178 pebbles, the students will have no homework. How many days must everyone complete his homework before Mrs. Ramirez assigns no homework? **89**
2. Alexis, Danielle, and Victoria each want to make a bracelet from beads. There are blue glass, purple plastic, and yellow clay beads. Alexis uses purple beads. Danielle prefers clay beads. What beads will each girl use? **Alexis–purple plastic; Danielle–yellow clay; Victoria–blue glass**

**Spiral Review**

**Find each volume.** (Lesson 12-8)

3. cubic units **8**
4. cubic units **27**
5. cubic units **24**

Grade 4 51 Chapter 12



## BL Alternate Teaching Strategy

**If** students have trouble choosing the best strategy...

**Then** use one of these reteach options:

1 CRM **Daily Reteach Worksheet** (pp. 48–49)

2 Emphasize that most problems can be solved by more than one strategy, and that they should choose the strategy with which they are most comfortable.

- **What other strategies could you use to solve the problems on p. 474?** Sample answers: look for a pattern, act it out, guess and check

## 3 Practice

### Using the Exercises

**Exercise 5** may be a challenge for students. Point out that the question is asking for the number of the *first* day on which Dora takes *at least* 30 photos. Help students get started by creating a table on the board and helping them fill in the first row: Day 1, 11 photos.

**Exercise 8** asks students to write a number sentence using a symbol.

## 4 Assess

### Formative Assessment

*In a basketball game, each field goal basket is worth 2 points and each free throw is worth 1 point. Hakeem scored 27 points in a basketball game. If he made 9 baskets, how many free throws did he make?*

- **What strategy can you use to solve this problem?** Sample answer: act it out
- **How do you find the number of free throws?** Subtract 27 – 18. **How many free throws did he make?** 9 free throws

**Quick Check** **Are students continuing to struggle with choosing the best strategy?**

**If Yes** → CRM Reteach Worksheet (pp. 48–49)

**If No** → Independent Work Options (p. 518B)
CRM Skills Practice Worksheet (p. 50)
CRM Enrich Worksheet (p. 52)

LESSON

# 12-10 Elapsed Time

## Lesson Planner

### Objective

Solve problems about elapsed time.

### Vocabulary

**elapsed time**

### Resources

**Materials:** stopwatch

**Manipulatives:** clocks

**Literature Connection:** "Something Furry in the Garage at 6:30 A.M." from *Math Poetry* by Betsy Franco

**Alternate Lesson:** Use *IMPACT Mathematics:* Unit G to provide practice with time.

**Teacher Technology**
TeacherWorks • Interactive Classroom

## Daily Routine

Use these suggestions before beginning the lesson on p. 520

### 5-Minute Check

(Reviews Lessons 12-9)

**Use any strategy to solve. Tell what strategy you used.**

Sam has a board that is 72 inches long. He cut the board into 3 equal pieces and then cut each of the pieces in half. How long is each piece? 12 inches; draw a picture

### Problem of the Day

The top of a rectangular picnic table measures 2 m by 4 m. What is the perimeter of the tabletop? 12 m What is the area of the tabletop? 8 meters$^2$

### Focus on Math Background

*Elapsed time* refers to the measure of a *time interval*, and implies a starting time and an ending time. So while the time on a clock is measured from midnight or noon, elapsed time is found by subtracting clock times:

Elapsed time = (time activity ends) − (time activity begins)

Just as with subtraction of whole numbers, regrouping may be necessary when clock times are subtracted. Units for time (seconds, minutes, hours, etc.) are identical in both customary and metric systems of measurement.

### Building Math Vocabulary

Write the lesson vocabulary word and its definition on the board.

Have students write the new term in their Math Journals. Brainstorm the ways time is measured: hour, minute, second, week, month, year, century, and so on. Explain that *elapsed* means the time that has passed.

- **How many hours elapse between the time you go to bed and the time you get up?** Answers will vary.

# Differentiated Instruction

## Small Group Options

LOGICAL

### Option 1 Gifted and Talented AL

- Hand this problem to students written on paper:

  *Kia wants to bake brownies. They take 10 minutes to prepare the mix and 30 minutes to bake. If she gathers the ingredients and begins to mix at 9:10, will the brownies be done at 10:00? Show your work with clock faces.* Yes, Kia will have 10 minutes to spare.

AUDITORY, LINGUISTIC

### Option 2 English Language Learners ELL

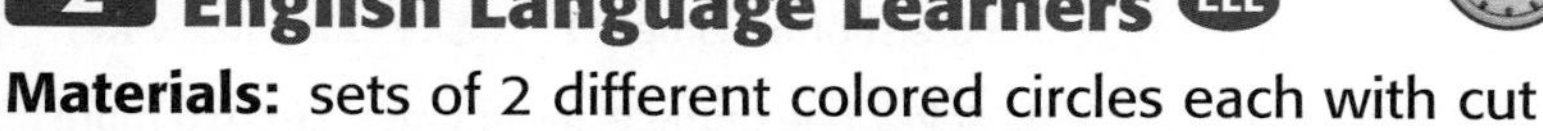

**Materials:** sets of 2 different colored circles each with cut radiuses and one numbered like a clock for each student, pictures of various activities that take an hour or less

**Core Vocabulary:** for, minutes, how long

**Common Use Verb:** would want (+ infinitive)

**Hear Math** This strategy teaches students to understand elapsed time and sharpen their listening skills.

- Show a picture of a student swimming. Say: "How long would you want to swim?" Model showing the percentage of time with the circles. Use the numbered disk to show elapsed time. Discuss your answer.
- Give each student a set of circles and repeat with another picture.
- Sort students by elapsed time. Allow groups to explain their reasoning.
- Have groups listen and restate the reasoning of the first group.
- Continue for all groups.
- Repeat for other pictures as time permits.

## Independent Work Options

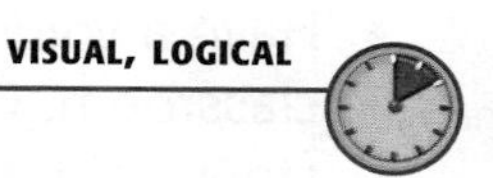

VISUAL, LOGICAL

### Option 1 Early Finishers AL

- Have students make up schedules, such as bus schedules, theater schedules, or game schedules. Each schedule should have four or more starting times.
- Then have students write two or three questions that can be solved using their schedule. They can use Exercises 10–11 as a model.
- Students can exchange and solve each other's problems.

### Option 2 Student Technology

**Math Online** macmillanmh.com

Personal Tutor • Extra Examples

 Math Adventures

### Option 3 Learning Station: Writing (p. 482I)

Direct students to the Writing Learning Station for opportunities to explore and extend the lesson concept.

### Option 4 Problem-Solving Practice

Reinforce problem-solving skills and strategies with the Problem-Solving Practice worksheet.

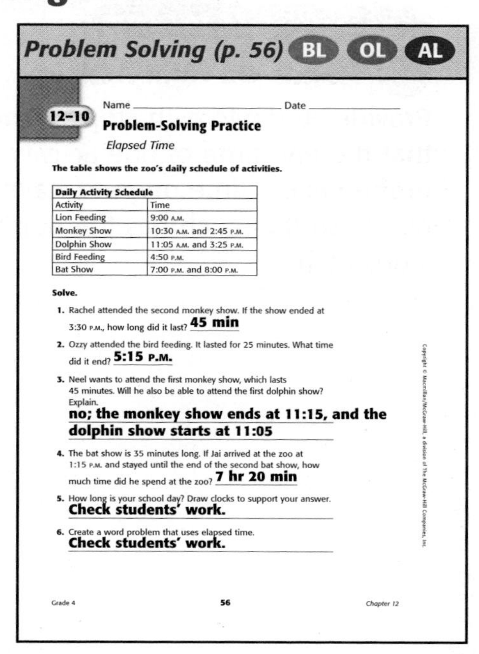

**Problem Solving (p. 56)** BL OL AL

12–10

Name ______________ Date ______________

**Problem-Solving Practice**

*Elapsed Time*

**The table shows the zoo's daily schedule of activities.**

| Daily Activity Schedule | |
|---|---|
| Activity | Time |
| Lion Feeding | 9:00 A.M. |
| Monkey Show | 10:30 A.M. and 2:45 P.M. |
| Dolphin Show | 11:05 A.M. and 3:25 P.M. |
| Bird Feeding | 4:50 P.M. |
| Bat Show | 7:00 P.M. and 8:00 P.M. |

**Solve.**

1. Rachel attended the second monkey show. If the show ended at 3:30 P.M., how long did it last? **45 min**
2. Ozzy attended the bird feeding. It lasted for 25 minutes. What time did it end? **5:15 P.M.**
3. Neel wants to attend the first monkey show, which lasts 45 minutes. Will he also be able to attend the first dolphin show? Explain.
   **no; the monkey show ends at 11:15, and the dolphin show starts at 11:05**
4. The bat show is 35 minutes long. If Jai arrived at the zoo at 1:15 P.M. and stayed until the end of the second bat show, how much time did he spend at the zoo? **7 hr 20 min**
5. How long is your school day? Draw clocks to support your answer.
   **Check students' work.**
6. Create a word problem that uses elapsed time.
   **Check students' work.**



Grade 4 56 Chapter 12

# 12-10 Elapsed Time

## 1 Introduce

### Activity Choice 1 • Hands-On

- Provide a volunteer with a stopwatch and discuss how a stopwatch works.
- Have a volunteer walk the perimeter of the classroom. Clock the elapsed time with the stopwatch. **How long did the walk take?** Answers will vary.
- Have another volunteer touch his or her toes ten times. Clock the elapsed time. **How long did this task take?** Answers will vary.

### Activity Choice 2 • Literature

Introduce the lesson with "Something Furry in the Garage at 6:30 A.M." from *Math Poetry* by Betsy Franco. For a related math activity, see p. TR62.

## 2 Teach

### Scaffolding Questions

- **What is the smallest unit of time we regularly use?** second
- **How many seconds are in a minute?** 60 seconds
- **What unit is equal to 60 minutes?** 1 hour
- **What other units of time do we use? Explain what the unit means.** Sample answer: a year is 365 or 366 days, or 52 weeks, or 12 months

### GET READY to Learn

**Hands-On Mini Activity**

Provide students with stopwatches. Point out that the end time of one activity is the start time of the next. If time permits, have students switch places so that each has the opportunity to use a stopwatch.



# 12-10 Elapsed Time

**MAIN IDEA**

I will solve problems about elapsed time.

**New Vocabulary**

**elapsed time**

**Math Online**

macmillanmh.com

- Extra Examples
- Personal Tutor
- Self-Check Quiz

### GET READY to Learn

**Hands-On Mini Activity**

**Materials:** stopwatch

You can use a stopwatch to find elapsed time.

**Step 1** **Copy the table.**

| Activity | Start Time | End Time | Elapsed Time |
|---|---|---|---|
| Write alphabet | ■ | ■ | ■ |
| Name 10 states | ■ | ■ | ■ |
| Jump 20 times | ■ | ■ | ■ |

**Step 2** **Measure.**

Write the alphabet while your partner uses a stopwatch to time you. Record the start and end times. Complete the next two activities while your partner times you. Do not reset the stopwatch between the activities. Record the start and end times.

**Step 3** **Copy and complete the table.**

To find the elapsed times, subtract the start times from the end times. Find the elapsed time between each event. Record the results.

1. Which event took the longest time? the shortest time? **1, 2. See students' work.**
2. Select one of the elapsed times. List two more activities that might take that long.

The last column of your table gives examples of elapsed time. **Elapsed time** is the amount of time between the beginning and ending of an activity.



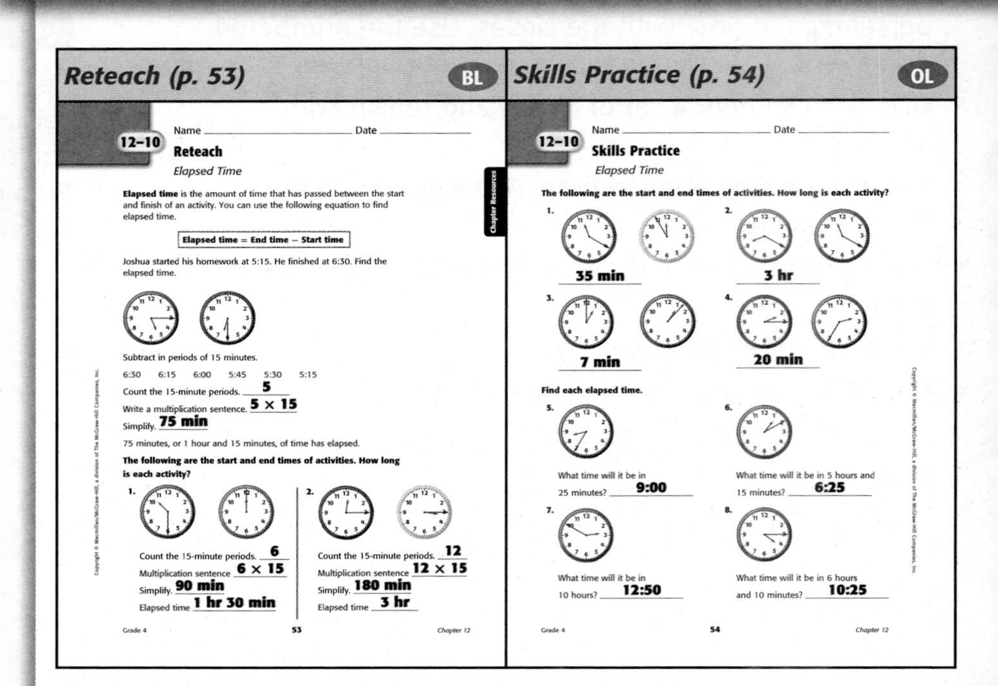

***Reteach (p. 53)*** BL

12-10 Name ______ Date ______

**Reteach**

*Elapsed Time*

**Elapsed time** is the amount of time that has passed between the start and finish of an activity. You can use the following equation to find elapsed time.

**Elapsed time = End time − Start time**

Joshua started his homework at 5:15. He finished at 6:30. Find the elapsed time.

Subtract in periods of 15 minutes.

6:30 6:15 6:00 5:45 5:30 5:15

Count the 15-minute periods. **5**

Write a multiplication sentence. **5 × 15**

Simplify. **75 min**

75 minutes, or 1 hour and 15 minutes, of time has elapsed.

**The following are the start and end times of activities. How long is each activity?**

1. Count the 15-minute periods. **6**
   Multiplication sentence **6 × 15**
   Simplify. **90 min**
   Elapsed time **1 hr 30 min**
2. Count the 15-minute periods. **12**
   Multiplication sentence **12 × 15**
   Simplify. **180 min**
   Elapsed time **3 hr**

Grade 4 53 *Chapter 12*

Chapter Resources



***Skills Practice (p. 54)*** OL

12-10 Name ______ Date ______

**Skills Practice**

*Elapsed Time*

**The following are the start and end times of activities. How long is each activity?**

1. **35 min**
2. **3 hr**
3. **7 min**
4. **20 min**

**Find each elapsed time.**

5. What time will it be in 25 minutes? **9:00**
6. What time will it be in 5 hours and 15 minutes? **6:25**
7. What time will it be in 10 hours? **12:50**
8. What time will it be in 6 hours and 10 minutes? **10:25**

Grade 4 54 *Chapter 12*

## Real-World EXAMPLES Elapsed Time

**1 TRAVEL It takes Louisa one hour and 30 minutes to travel to her aunt's house. If she leaves at 4:00 P.M., what time will she get to her aunt's house?**

Add 1 hour and 30 minutes to 4:00 P.M.

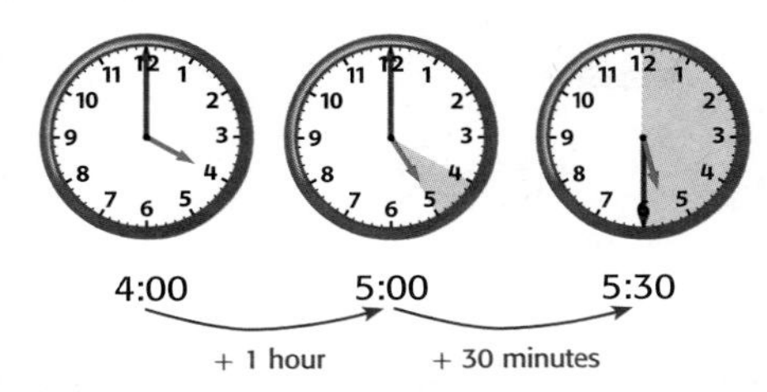

4:00 → 5:00 → 5:30

+ 1 hour + 30 minutes

So, Louisa will get to her aunt's house at 5:30 P.M.

**2 The clock shows the time Justin's soccer practice started. It ends at 5:30 P.M. Find the elapsed time.**

Find the elapsed time between 3:15 P.M. and 5:30 P.M.

1 hour + 1 hour + 15 minutes = 2 hours 15 minutes

So, the elapsed time is 2 hours 15 minutes.

4. Sample answer: Count the number of hours and minutes that pass between 9:15 P.M. and 6:30 A.M.

## CHECK What You Know

**The following are movie times. Find the length of each movie.** See Examples 1 and 2 (p. 521)

**1.** Start Time End Time

1 hour 30 minutes

**2.** Start Time End Time

1 hour 45 minutes

**3.** Julian's family went to the library at the time shown at the right. How much time has elapsed if they stay until 4:00? See Example 1 (p. 521) 40 minutes

**4.** Kayla went to sleep at the time shown at the right and awoke at 6:30 A.M. Explain how to find how long Kayla slept. See Example 2 (p. 521)

9:15



## Elapsed Time

**Example 1** Be sure students know how to read time properly and understand a 12-hour clock.

### ADDITIONAL EXAMPLE

**1** It takes Marisa 15 minutes to bike to the gym. If she leaves her home at 4:55 P.M., what time will she arrive at the gym? 5:10 P.M.

### CHECK What You Know

As a class, have students complete Exercises 1–5 in **Check What You Know** as you observe their work.

**Exercise 5** Assess student comprehension before assigning practice exercises.

### BL Alternate Teaching Strategy

**If** students have trouble solving problems about elapsed time…

**Then** use one of these reteach options:

1 CRM **Daily Reteach Worksheet** (p. 53)

2 Have students make and label a clock with moveable hands that shows 60 minutes.

**Model the time from 50 minutes past 3 to 10 minutes past four. How many minutes elapsed?** 20 minutes

- Allow students to use the clock as a model to determine elapsed time.

### Enrich (p. 57) AL

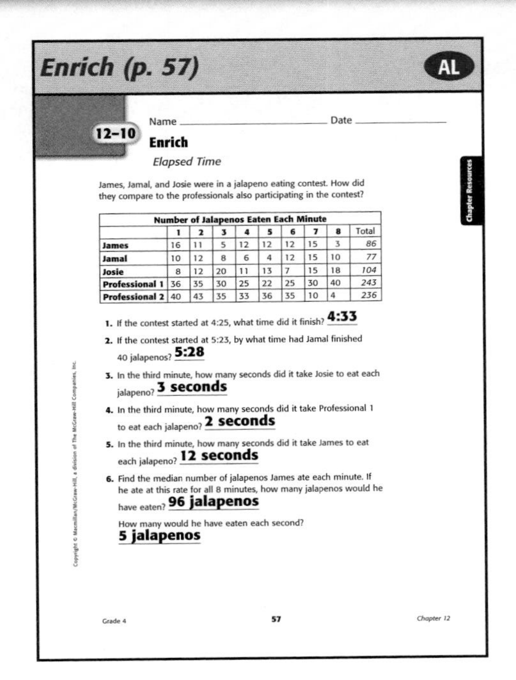

12-10

Name ______ Date ______

**Enrich**

*Elapsed Time*

James, Jamal, and Josie were in a jalapeno eating contest. How did they compare to the professionals also participating in the contest?

| Number of Jalapenos Eaten Each Minute | | | | | | | | | |
|---|---|---|---|---|---|---|---|---|---|
| | **1** | **2** | **3** | **4** | **5** | **6** | **7** | **8** | Total |
| **James** | 16 | 11 | 5 | 12 | 12 | 12 | 15 | 3 | *86* |
| **Jamal** | 10 | 12 | 8 | 6 | 4 | 12 | 15 | 10 | *77* |
| **Josie** | 8 | 12 | 20 | 11 | 13 | 7 | 15 | 18 | *104* |
| **Professional 1** | 36 | 35 | 30 | 25 | 22 | 25 | 30 | 40 | *243* |
| **Professional 2** | 40 | 43 | 35 | 33 | 36 | 35 | 10 | 4 | *236* |

1. If the contest started at 4:25, what time did it finish? **4:33**
2. If the contest started at 5:23, by what time had Jamal finished 40 jalapenos? **5:28**
3. In the third minute, how many seconds did it take Josie to eat each jalapeno? **3 seconds**
4. In the third minute, how many seconds did it take Professional 1 to eat each jalapeno? **2 seconds**
5. In the third minute, how many seconds did it take James to eat each jalapeno? **12 seconds**
6. Find the median number of jalapenos James ate each minute. If he ate at this rate for all 8 minutes, how many jalapenos would he have eaten? **96 jalapenos**

   How many would he have eaten each second? **5 jalapenos**



Grade 4 57 Chapter 12

### COMMON ERROR!

**Exercise 12** Some students might use the first presentation in the schedule to solve the problem. Point out that the 4 P.M. presentation applies, since the last presentation Albert attended ended at 3:45 P.M.

# 3 Practice

Differentiate practice using these leveled assignments for Exercises 6–18.

| Level | Assignment |
|---|---|
| BL Below/Approaching Level | 5–6, 9–10, 11 |
| OL On Level | 6–10, 12, 13 |
| AL Above/Beyond Level | 6–13 odd, 14–16 |

Have students discuss and complete the Higher Order Thinking problems. Exercise 14 is a multi-step problem. Remind students to consider the problem-solving strategies they have learned.

## Practice and Problem Solving

See page R33.

**The following are times of baseball games. Find the length of each game.** See Examples 1 and 2 (p. 521)

**5.** Start Time End Time

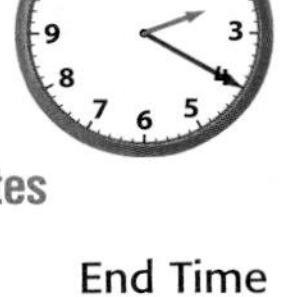

2 hours 5 minutes

**6.** Start Time End Time

2 hours 55 minutes

**7.** Start Time End Time

2:20

2 hours 45 minutes

**8.** Start Time End Time

2 hours 55 minutes

**Find each elapsed time.** See Examples 1 and 2 (p. 521)

**9.** The clock shows when Helen began reading her book. It is 12:50 when she stops.
35 minutes

**10.** The clock shows when Chris went to the park. He stays until 5:15 P.M.
1 hour 5 minutes

### Real-World PROBLEM SOLVING

*Science* The table shows the schedule of an aquarium's daily presentations.

| Daily Presentations Schedule | |
|---|---|
| **Presentation** | **Time** |
| Amazon Creature Feature | 1:30 P.M. |
| Diver in the Water | 11:30 A.M. and 1:30 P.M. |
| Dolphin Training Lesson | 11 A.M. and 1 P.M. |
| Reptile Report | 3 P.M. |
| You "Otter" Know This | 10 A.M. and 4 P.M. |

**11.** Albert attended the Amazon Creature Feature, which ended at 2:45 P.M. How long did it last?
1 hour and 15 minutes

**12.** Next, Albert attended the Reptile Report. It ended at 3:45 P.M. How long was this presentation?
45 minutes

**13.** Albert attended You "Otter" Know This last. It lasted 1 hour and 30 minutes. If it takes Albert 20 minutes to get home, did he make it home in time to eat at 6 P.M.? Explain. See margin.

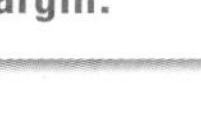



### Additional Answer

**13.** Sample answer: yes; watching the presentation and getting home took 1 hour and 30 minutes + 20 minutes or 1 hour and 50 minutes. This means Albert got home at 5:50 P.M.

## H.O.T. Problems

**14. CHALLENGE** Dennis earns $5 for each hour he works. One day he worked from 8:00 A.M. until 12:00 P.M., had lunch, and then worked for 3 more hours. How much money did he earn that day? $35; $(4 + 3) \times 5 = 35$

**15. FIND THE ERROR** Haley and Hidalgo are finding elapsed time. Who is correct? Explain your reasoning. See margin.

**Haley**
It's 10:30 a.m. In 1 hour and 45 minutes, it will be 12:15 p.m.

**Hidalgo**
It's 10:45 a.m. In 30 minutes it will be 11:45 p.m.

## TEST Practice

**16.** A pencil box is 6 units long, 3 units wide and 2 units high. What is its volume? (Lesson 12-8) C

A 32 cubic units  C 36 cubic units

B 34 cubic units  D 38 cubic units

**17.** Gretchen downloaded music for 45 minutes. She began at 11:45 A.M. What time did she finish? (Lesson 12-10) G

F 11:00 A.M.  H 11:00 P.M.

G 12:30 P.M.  J 12:30 A.M.

## Spiral Review

**18.** Airports have limits on luggage weight. Is it more reasonable to say that an airport's weight limit is 35 grams or 35 kilograms? Explain. (Lesson 12-9) See margin.

**Find the volume of each figure.** (Lesson 12-8)

**19.** 24 cubic units

**20.** 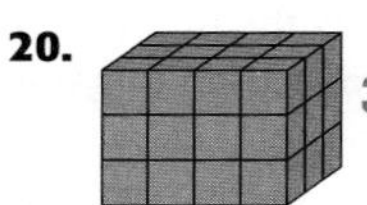 36 cubic units

**Choose the more reasonable estimate for the mass of each object.** (Lesson 12-7)

**21.** dog

40g or 40 kg 40kg

**22.** hamster

500 g or 500 kg 500 g



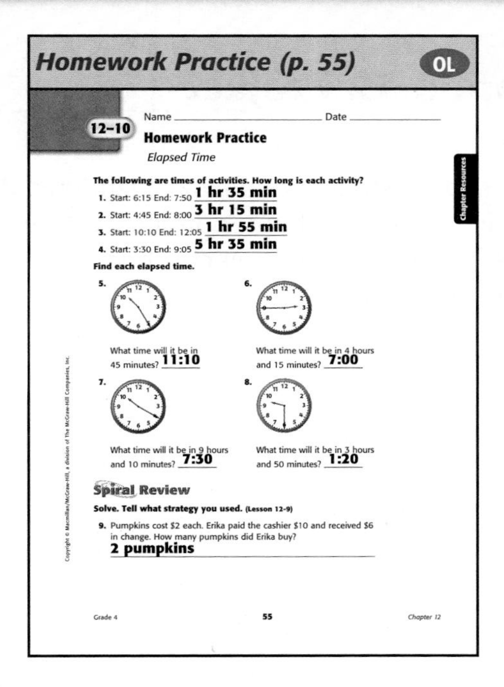

**Homework Practice (p. 55)** OL

Name ______ Date ______

12–10 **Homework Practice**
*Elapsed Time*

**The following are times of activities. How long is each activity?**

1. Start: 6:15 End: 7:50 **1 hr 35 min**
2. Start: 4:45 End: 8:00 **3 hr 15 min**
3. Start: 10:10 End: 12:05 **1 hr 55 min**
4. Start: 3:30 End: 9:05 **5 hr 35 min**

**Find each elapsed time.**

5. What time will it be in 45 minutes? **11:10**
6. What time will it be in 4 hours and 15 minutes? **7:00**
7. What time will it be in 9 hours and 10 minutes? **7:30**
8. What time will it be in 3 hours and 50 minutes? **1:20**

**Spiral Review**

**Solve. Tell what strategy you used.** (Lesson 12-9)

9. Pumpkins cost $2 each. Erika paid the cashier $10 and received $6 in change. How many pumpkins did Erika buy?
**2 pumpkins**

Grade 4  55  Chapter 12

# 4 Assess

## Formative Assessment

Pose this problem: *Diego has to be at a soccer game at 10:00 A.M. Saturday. It takes him 20 minutes to get to the field.*

- **What time does Diego have to leave his house to get to the field on time?** 9:40 A.M.

**Quick Check** **Are students continuing to struggle with solving problems about elapsed time?**

**If Yes** → CRM Reteach Worksheet (p. 53)

**If No** → Independent Work Options (p. 520B)
CRM Skills Practice Worksheet (p. 54)
CRM Enrich Worksheet (p. 57)

**Ticket Out the Door** Have students determine the elapsed time between the time they arrive at school on a normal day and the time they leave. Have them hand the information to you on a piece of paper as they leave your class.

## TEST Practice

### Reviews Lessons 12-8 and 12-10

Assign the Test Practice problems to provide daily reinforcement of test-taking skills.

## Spiral Review

### Reviews Lessons 12-7, 12-8, and 12-9

Review and assess mastery of skills and concepts from previous chapters.

### Additional Answers

**15.** Sample answer: Haley; 30 minutes after 10:45 A.M. is 11:15 A.M., not 11:45 A.M.

**18.** Sample answer: 35 kilograms; 35 grams is equal to the weight of 35 paper clips, so 35 grams is too light for a luggage weight limit.

# Chapter 12 Study Guide and Review

## Dinah Zike's Foldables

Use these lesson suggestions to incorporate the Foldables during the chapter. Students can then use their Foldables to review for the test.

**Lesson 12-7** Instruct students to define the term mass under the appropriate tab on their Foldables. Help them differentiate between the terms mass and weight in their definition. Students should record what they learn about estimating and measuring mass.

**Lesson 12-10** Have students include the following vocabulary terms and definitions in the Time section of their Foldables: hour, minute, second. Students might list ways in which they estimate elapsed time based upon their own experiences with given amounts of time: 30-minute television show, two-hour movie, 15-minute recess, others.

## Key Vocabulary

The page references after each word denote where that term was first introduced. If students have difficulty answering Exercises 1–7, remind them they can use the page references to review the vocabulary terms.

## Vocabulary Review

Review chapter vocabulary using one of the following options.

- **eGlossary** at macmillanmh.com



# Chapter 12 Study Guide and Review

**Be sure the following Key Vocabulary words and Key Concepts are written in your Foldable.**

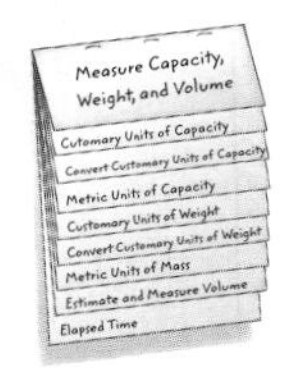


### Key Concepts

- **Capacity** is the amount of liquid a container holds. The customary units of capacity are fluid ounces, cups, pints, gallons, and quarts. The metric units of capacity are liter and milliliter. (p. 486)
- The **weight** of an object is how heavy it is. Weight is measured in ounces, pounds, and tons. (p. 498)
- The **mass** of an object is the amount of matter it has. Mass is measured in grams and kilograms. (p. 509)
- **Volume** is the amount of space a three-dimensional figure contains. It is measured in cubic units. (p. 512)

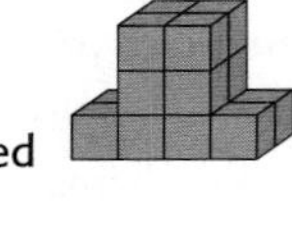

- **Elapsed time** is the amount of time between the beginning and ending of an activity. (p. 520)

### Key Vocabulary

**capacity** (p. 486)
**elapsed time** (p. 520)
**mass** (p. 509)
**volume** (p. 512)
**weight** (p. 498)

### Vocabulary Check

**Complete each sentence with the correct vocabulary word.**

1. ___?___ is the amount of matter an object has. mass
2. The ___?___ of an object is how heavy it is. weight
3. ___?___ is the amount of time between the beginning and end of an activity. elapsed time
4. ___?___ is measured in grams and kilograms. mass
5. ___?___ is the amount of space that a three-dimensional figure contains. volume
6. ___?___ is measured in ounces, pounds, and tons. weight
7. The amount of liquid a container holds is its ___?___. capacity

## Chapter 12 Project

### Fruit Salad

Alone, in pairs, or in small groups, have students discuss the results of their completed chapter project with the class. Assess their work using the Chapter Project rubric found in Chapter 12 Resource Masters, p. 68.

## Lesson-by-Lesson Review

### 12-1 Customary Units of Capacity (pp. 486–489)

**Example 1**
**Carrie is pouring fruit juice into a punch bowl. Is the most reasonable estimate for the capacity of the bowl 2 fluid ounces, 2 cups, 2 quarts, or 2 gallons?**

The punch is a large amount. So, 2 fluid ounces, 2 cups, and 2 quarts are too small. The most reasonable estimate for the capacity of the punch bowl is 2 gallons.

**Choose the most reasonable estimate for each capacity.**

8. **A** 4 fluid ounces
   **B** 4 cups
   **C** 4 quarts
   **D** 4 gallons D

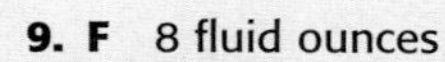

9. **F** 8 fluid ounces
   **G** 8 cups
   **H** 8 quarts
   **J** 8 gallons F

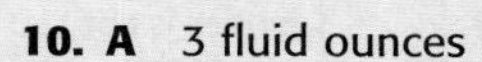

10. **A** 3 fluid ounces
    **B** 3 cups
    **C** 3 quarts
    **D** 3 gallons C

### 12-2 Convert Customary Units of Capacity (pp. 490–491)

**Example 2**
**Complete the conversion 3 c = ■ fl oz.**

Since fluid ounces are smaller than cups, multiply.

3 cups × 8 fluid ounces = ■

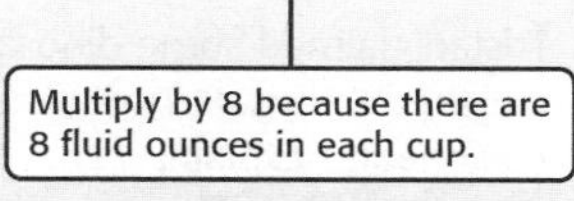
Multiply by 8 because there are 8 fluid ounces in each cup.

$3 \times 8 = 24$

So, there are 24 fluid ounces in 3 cups.

**Complete.**

11. 16 fl oz = ■ c 2
12. 2 gal = ■ qt 8
13. ■ pt = 12 qt 24
14. ■ pt = 18 c 9

**Compare. Use >, <, or =.**

15. 5 qt ● 10 pt =
16. 2 cups ● 18 fl oz <
17. Chen is buying a 16-fluid ounce container of spaghetti sauce. How many cups of spaghetti sauce is he buying? 2 cups



# Lesson-by-Lesson Review

Have students complete the Lesson-by-Lesson Review on pp. 525–530. Then you can use Exam*View*® Assessment Suite to customize another review worksheet that practices all the objectives of this chapter or only the objectives on which your students need more help.

**Intervention** If the given examples are not sufficient to review the topics covered by the questions, use the page references next to the exercises to review that topic in the Student Edition.

# Chapter 12 Study Guide and Review

### Additional Answers

**21.** Sample answer: no; 200 L is too much.

**23.** Sample answer: yes; Dinosaurs were very large.

**24.** Sample answer: no; 50 pounds is too heavy for basketball.





## 12-3 Metric Units of Capacity (pp. 492–495)

**Example 3**
**Decide whether 700 mL or 700 L is the more reasonable estimate for the capacity of a bottle of salad dressing.**

Use logic to estimate the capacity of the bottle of salad dressing.

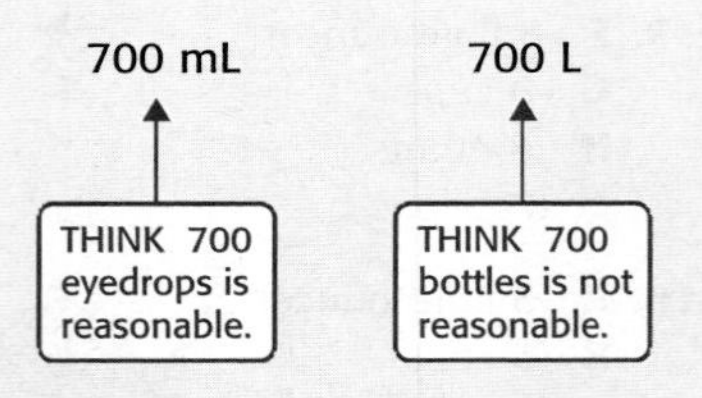


So, 700 mL is a more reasonable estimate.

**Choose the more reasonable estimate for each capacity.**

**18.** 

265 mL or 265 L **265 mL**

**19.** 

6 mL or 6 L **6 L**

**20.** 

800 mL or 800 L **800 mL**

**21.** Carina said that her father's car's gas tank holds 200 liters of gas. Is that reasonable? Explain. **See margin.**

## 12-4 Customary Units of Weight (pp. 498–500)

**Example 4**
**Which is the most reasonable estimate for the weight of a pencil case: 1 ounce, 1 pound, 10 pounds, or 10 tons?**

A pencil case weighs more than a strawberry or 1 ounce. A pencil case weighs less than 10 pineapples or 10 pounds. Tons weigh more than pounds, so the answer is 1 pound.

**22.** Choose the most reasonable estimate for the weight of the table.

**A** 8 ounces
**B** 80 pounds
**C** 800 pounds
**D** 8 tons **B**

**23.** Tristan claimed some dinosaurs weighed 3 tons. Is Tristan's claim reasonable? Explain.

**23, 24. See margin.**

**24.** Annie claims her basketball weighs 50 lbs. Is Annie's claim reasonable?

## 12-5 Problem-Solving Strategy: Use Logical Reasoning (pp. 502–503)

**Example 5**

**Jed, Sayra, Mark, and Ebony competed in a race. Jed came in third place. Ebony was faster than Mark. Sayra won the race. Which order did they finish the race?**

**Understand** Jed came in third place. Ebony was faster than Mark. Sayra won the race. Find the order they finished the race.

**Plan** Use logical reasoning to solve.

**Solve** Since Sayra won the race, she came in first place.

Jed came in third place.

Since Ebony was faster than Mark, she came in second place. Mark came in fourth place.

| | 1st Place | 2nd Place | 3rd Place | 4th Place |
|---|---|---|---|---|
| Jed | X | X | yes | X |
| Sayra | yes | X | X | X |
| Mark | X | X | X | yes |
| Ebony | X | yes | X | X |

The order was Sayra, Ebony, Jed, and Mark.

**Check** Look back. The answer makes sense for the facts given in the problem. ✓

**25.** The Ruiz family is on a bike ride. Each person is riding either a bicycle or a tricycle. There are 5 members in the family and 11 wheels. The number of bicycles is four times the number of tricycles. How many tricycles and bicycles are there?
**1 tricycle and 4 bicycle**

**26.** Felix, Laura, and Suki packed lunches with a peanut butter sandwich, a turkey sandwich, and a bologna sandwich. Laura's sandwich is shown. Suki's sandwich had bologna on it. Which sandwich did each person get in their lunch? **26–28. See margin.**

**27.** Rhonda, Jordan, and Mala were born in September, December, and June. Jordan's birthday is in the winter. The number of letters in Mala's name matches the number of letters in her birth month. In what month was each person born?

**28.** Bella has a brother named Ricardo and a sister named Rosa. The ages of the three children are 3, 5, and 10. Bella is twice as old as Ricardo. What are the ages of the children?



### Additional Answers

**26.** Laura = peanut butter and jelly, Suki = bologna, Felix = turkey

**27.** Rhonda = September, Jordan = December, Mala = June

**28.** Bella = 10, Ricardo = 5, Rosa = 3

# Study Guide and Review

## Study Guide and Review

### 12-6 Convert Customary Units of Weight (pp. 504–507)

**Example 6**
**Shawn is holding a 5 pound bag of flour. How many ounces is this?**

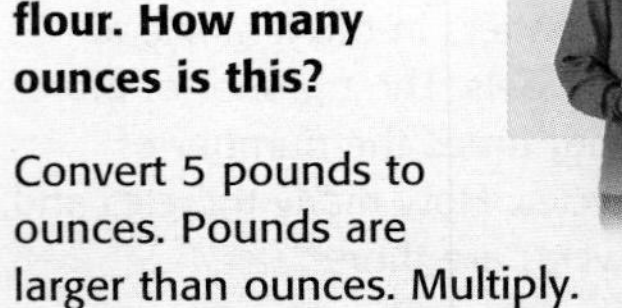

Convert 5 pounds to ounces. Pounds are larger than ounces. Multiply.

$5 \times 16 = 80$

Multiply by 16 because there are 16 ounces in a pound.

So, 5 pounds equals 80 ounces.

**Complete.**

29. 2,000 lb = ■ T 1
30. 32 oz = ■ lb 2
31. 16 oz and 1 lb = ■ lb 2
32. 1 lb = ■ oz 16
33. ■ lb = 3 T 6,000
34. ■ lb = 2 T and 2 lb 4,002
35. Benton uses 7 ounces of clay to make a vase. How many pounds of clay will he need to make 4 vases? 1 pound 12 ounces
36. A sandwich shop uses 2 ounces of ham on a sandwich. If 20 sandwiches are made in one day, how many pounds of ham will be used? 2 pounds 8 ounces

### 12-7 Metric Units of Mass (pp. 508–510)

**Example 7**
**Which is the more reasonable estimate for the mass of the dog: 20 grams or 20 kilograms?**

If the dog has a mass of 20 grams, it would have the same mass as 20 pennies. This is not a reasonable estimate.

So, a reasonable estimate for the mass of the dog is 20 kg.

**Choose the more reasonable estimate for the mass of each object.**

37. pencil 4 g
4 g or 4 kg
38. chair 15 kg
15 g or 15 kg
39. Is it more reasonable to say that the mass of a pair of scissors is 50 grams or 50 kilograms? 50 grams

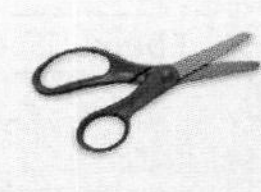

40. Is it more reasonable to say that the mass of a medium tub of popcorn is 1 gram or 1 kilogram? 1 kilogram

528 Chapter 12 Measure Capacity, Weight, and Volume

## 12-8 Estimate and Measure Volume (pp. 512–515)

**Example 8**
**Use models to find the volume of the cube shown to the right.**

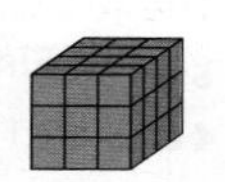

The cube shown has 3 layers. Each layer has 9 cubes.

one layer | three layers

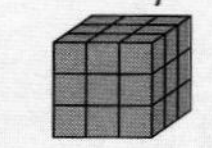

9 cubes | $9 \times 3 = 27$ cubes

So, the volume is 27 cubic units.

**Find the volume of each figure.**

**41.** 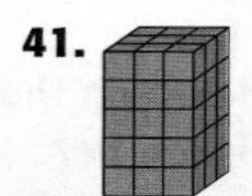 45 cubic units

**42.** 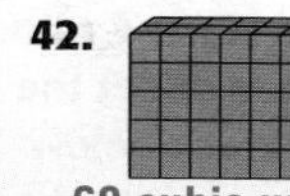 60 cubic units

**Estimate the volume of each figure.**

**43.**  18 cubic units

**44.** 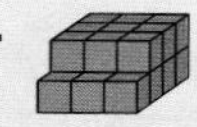 21 cubic units

## 12-9 Problem-Solving Investigation: Choose a Strategy (pp. 518–519)

**Example 9**
**Jamal's school is going to see a play. There are 230 seats in the theater. If every class has 25 students, how many classes can see the play at the same time?**

There are 230 seats in the theater and 25 students in each class. Find how many classes can see the play at the same time.

Divide the number of seats in the theater by the number of students in each class.

seats in theater ÷ students per class

$230 \div 25 = 9 \text{ R}5$

So, 9 classes can see the play at the same time.

Adding 25 nine times equals 225. So, the answer is correct.

**Use any strategy to solve.**

**45.** Kelsey has a week to catch 30 insects for science class. Yesterday she caught 3. The insects she caught today are shown below. If she catches 5 more each day for 4 days, how many more will she need to catch to have 30? 5

**46.** Bobby went to the grocery store on Tuesday and tomatoes were $1 each. Jessica went to the store on Wednesday and the price of tomatoes had increased to $2 each. If both spend $12 on tomatoes, how many did each buy? See margin.



### Additional Answer

**46.** Bobby = 12; Jessica = 6

# CHAPTER 12 Study Guide and Review

## 12-10 Elapsed Time (pp. 520–523)

**Example 10**
**Lana started working on her homework at the time shown on the first clock below. She finished her homework at the time shown on the second clock below. How long did it take Lana to complete her homework?**

You can find the elapsed time by counting the hours and minutes between 4:45 P.M. and 6:00 P.M.

So, it took Lana 1 hour and 15 minutes to complete her homework.

**Example 11**
**What time will it be in 3 hours and 45 minutes?**

Add 3 hours and 45 minutes to 12:15.

12:15 → 1:15 → 2:15 → 3:15 → 4:00

+ 1 hour + 1 hour + 1 hour + 45 minutes

So, in 3 hours and 45 minutes it will be 4:00.

**The following are times of football games. Find the length of each game.**

**47.** Start Time End Time

3 hours and 25 minutes

**48.** Start Time End Time

4 hours and 30 minutes

**Find each elapsed time.**

**49.** Franklin walked in the park from 2:10 P.M. until the time shown on the clock. 55 min

**50.** Delia left the store at 7:05 P.M. The clock shows when she arrived home. 20 min

**51.** A school play started at 5:30 P.M. and ended at 7:25 P.M. How long was the play? 1 hour 55 minutes



530 Chapter 12 Measure Capacity, Weight, and Volume

# Chapter Test

Math Online macmillanmh.com
• Chapter Test

For Exercises 1 and 2, tell whether each statement is ***true*** or ***false***.

**1.** Weight is the amount of matter an object has. false

**2.** You can use a stopwatch to find elapsed time. true

**Choose the most reasonable estimate for each capacity.**

**3.** 

**A** 6 fluid ounces
**B** 6 cups
**C** 6 quarts
**D** 6 gallons A

**4.** 

**F** 1 fluid ounce
**G** 1 cup
**H** 1 pint
**J** 1 quart J

**Choose the most reasonable estimate for the weight of each object.**

**5.** microscope

**A** 7 tons
**B** 70 pounds
**C** 7 pounds
**D** 7 ounces C

**6.** bald eagle

**F** 8 ounces
**G** 8 pounds
**H** 80 pounds
**J** 8 tons G

**7. MULTIPLE CHOICE** Which of the comparisons is false? D

**A** 3 qt > 2 pt
**C** 2 gal > 6 qt
**B** 10 pt < 25 c
**D** 16 oz < 2 c

**8.** Pete, Tia, and Paz are playing soccer. Their jersey numbers are 4, 3, and 13. Tia's number equals the number of letters in her name. Pete's is a two-digit number. Find Paz's number. 4

**Complete.**

**9.** ■ lb = 4 T 8,000 lb

**10.** 80 oz = ■ lb 5 lb

**Choose the more reasonable estimate for the mass of each object.**

**11.** ruler

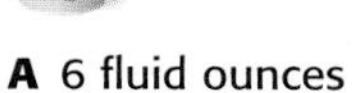

20 g or 20 kg 20 g

**12.** picture

10 g or 10 kg 10 kg

**Find the volume of each figure.**

**13.** 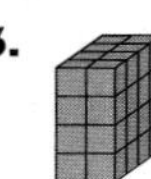

32 cubic units

**14.** 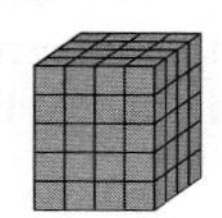

80 cubic units

**15. MULTIPLE CHOICE** How much time passes from 4:15 p.m. to 5:30 p.m.? G

**F** 1 hour
**G** 1 hour 15 minutes
**H** 1 hour 30 minutes
**J** 1 hour 45 minutes

**16.** Find the elapsed time. What time will it be in 4 hours and 40 minutes? 3:05

**17.** WRITING IN MATH Explain how to find elapsed time. See Ch. 12 Answer Appendix.



# Chapter 12 Chapter Test

## Summative Assessment

Use these alternate leveled chapter tests to differentiate assessment for the specific needs of your students.

| Leveled Chapter 12 Tests | | | |
|---|---|---|---|
| **Form** | **Type** | **Level** | **CRM Pages** |
| 1 | Multiple Choice | BL | 70–71 |
| 2A | Multiple Choice | OL | 72–73 |
| 2B | Multiple Choice | OL | 74–75 |
| 2C | Free Response | OL | 76–77 |
| 2D | Free Response | OL | 78–79 |
| 3 | Free Response | AL | 80–81 |

BL = below/approaching grade level
OL = on grade level
AL = above/beyond grade level

## Vocabulary Test

CRM **Chapter 12 Resource Masters** (p. 65)

ExamView Assessment Suite Customize and create multiple versions of your Chapter Test and the test answer keys.

# Data-Driven Decision Making

Based on the results of the Chapter Test, use the following to review concepts that continue to present students with problems.

| Exercises | State/Local Standards | What's the Mathematics? | Error Analysis | Resources for Review |
|---|---|---|---|---|
| **5–6, 9–10** | | Estimate and measure customary units of weight. | Does not know "pound," "ounce," or "ton." | Strategic Intervention Guide (p. 122)<br>CRM Chapter 12 Resource Master (Reteach)<br>Math Adventures<br>My Math Zone Chapter 12<br>Math Online Extra Examples • Concepts in Motion |
| **13–14** | | Measure volume. | Does not accurately count blocks. Does not multiply correctly. | |
| **15–17** | | Measure elapsed time. | Cannot count from A.M. to P.M. | |
| **13–14** | | Estimate and measure mass. | Confuses weight and mass. Does not know "gram." | |

# CHAPTER 12 Test Practice

## Formative Assessment

- Use Student Edition pp. 532–533 as practice and cumulative review. The questions are written in the same style as many state tests.
- You can also use these two pages to benchmark student progress, or as an alternate homework assignment.

Additional practice pages can be found in the Chapter 12 Resource Masters.

CRM **Chapter 12 Resource Masters**
Cumulative Test Practice
- Multiple Choice format (pp. 70–75)
- Free Response format (pp. 76–81)

Create practice worksheets or tests that align to your state standards.

**Math Online** Have students visit macmillanmh.com for additional practice to reinforce your state standards.

**Math Online** macmillanmh.com
- Test Practice

## CHAPTER 12 Test Practice
Cumulative, Chapters 1–12

**PART 1 Multiple Choice**

**Read each question. Then fill in the correct answer on the answer sheet provided by your teacher or on a sheet of paper.**

**1.** Which unit of measure would be most reasonable to use when finding the capacity of a thermos? B

**A** fluid ounces **C** quarts
**B** cups **D** gallons

**2.** Percy is flying to his grandparents' house. It takes 25 minutes to drive to the airport. He needs to arrive at least 1 hour before his plane leaves. What other information is needed for Percy to arrive at the airport on time? F

**F** the time the plane leaves
**G** how fast he drives
**H** the distance he will fly
**J** the amount of time he will fly

**3.** How many lines of symmetry does the figure have? B

**A** 0
**B** 1
**C** 2
**D** 4

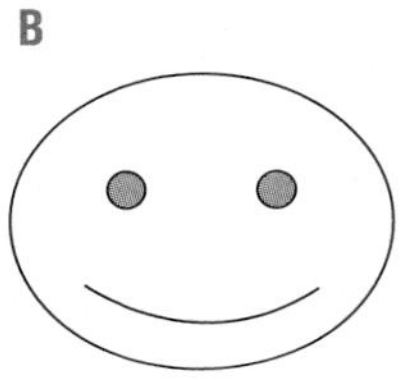

**4.** Which rule best describes the pattern of numbers below? H

4, 7, 10, 13, 16, 19, 22

**F** Subtract 3. **H** Add 3.
**G** Subtract 4. **J** Add 4.

**5.** Which term best describes the picture below? C

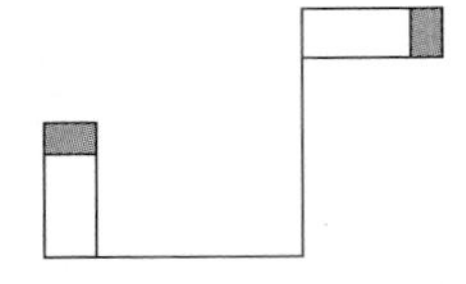

**A** dilation **C** rotation
**B** reflection **D** translation

**6.** Isabel exercises every three days. If she exercised on Monday and Thursday, what are the next two days she will exercise? G

**F** Sunday and Tuesday
**G** Sunday and Wednesday
**H** Friday and Monday
**J** Saturday and Monday

**7.** Rigo has $2,008 in his bank account. If he buys a laptop for $1,299, how much money will he have left? D

**A** $1,819 **C** $819
**B** $1,291 **D** $709



## Test-Taking Tip

Remind students to always be sure they are answering the question being asked.

**Preparing for Standardized Tests**
For test-taking strategies and practice, see pages R42–R55.

**8.** Which unit of measure would be most reasonable to use when finding the capacity of cleaning solution a contact lens holds? J

**F** gram
**G** kilogram
**H** liter
**J** milliliter

**9.** A vegetable garden is 8 yards long and 55 yards wide. What is the area, in square yards, of the garden? A

**A** 440 square yards
**B** 430 square yards
**C** 425 square yards
**D** 420 square yards

**10.** The weight of a small puppy is best measured in what units? H

**F** milligrams
**G** grams
**H** pounds
**J** ounces

**PART 2 Short Response**

**Record your answers on the answer sheet provided by your teacher or on a sheet of paper.**

**11.** How many cups equal 24 fluid ounces? 3

**12.** A landscaper orders 3 tons of mulch. How many pounds are there in 3 tons? **6,000 pounds**

**13.** Compare 4 lb ● 48 oz. Use >, <, or =.
>

**PART 3 Extended Response**

**Record your answers on the answer sheet provided by your teacher or on a sheet of paper.**

**14.** Which unit of measure would be most reasonable to use when finding the capacity of bubble solution that a bottle of bubbles holds: fluid ounces, cups, pints, or quarts? Explain. **14,15. See margin.**

**15.** Is it reasonable to say that the capacity of the bottle of bubbles shown above is 48 fluid ounces? Explain.

| NEED EXTRA HELP? | | | | | | | | | | | | | | | |
|---|---|---|---|---|---|---|---|---|---|---|---|---|---|---|---|
| If You Missed Question... | 1 | 2 | 3 | 4 | 5 | 6 | 7 | 8 | 9 | 10 | 11 | 12 | 13 | 14 | 15 |
| Go to Lesson... | 12-1 | 12-10 | 10-8 | 5-4 | 10-5 | 5-4 | 2-7 | 12-3 | 11-6 | 12-4 | 12-2 | 12-6 | 12-6 | 12-1 | 12-2 |



# Answer Sheet Practice

Have students simulate taking a state test by recording their answers on a practice recording sheet.

CRM **Chapter 12 Resource Masters**
Student Recording Sheet (p. 86)

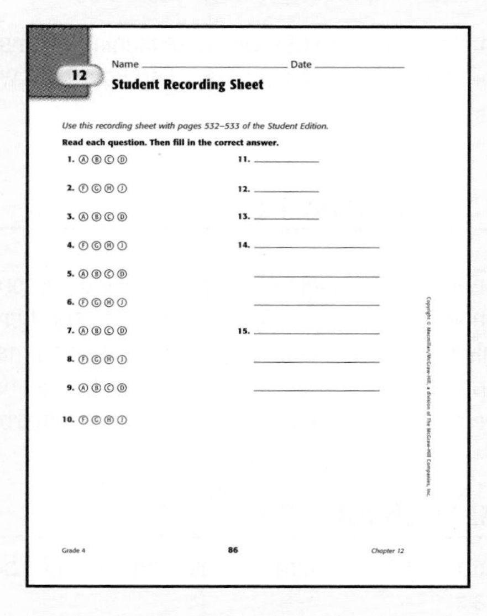
Name ______ Date ______
12 **Student Recording Sheet**
*Use this recording sheet with pages 532–533 of the Student Edition.*
**Read each question. Then fill in the correct answer.**
1. Ⓐ Ⓑ Ⓒ Ⓓ
2. Ⓕ Ⓖ Ⓗ Ⓙ
3. Ⓐ Ⓑ Ⓒ Ⓓ
4. Ⓕ Ⓖ Ⓗ Ⓙ
5. Ⓐ Ⓑ Ⓒ Ⓓ
6. Ⓕ Ⓖ Ⓗ Ⓙ
7. Ⓐ Ⓑ Ⓒ Ⓓ
8. Ⓕ Ⓖ Ⓗ Ⓙ
9. Ⓐ Ⓑ Ⓒ Ⓓ
10. Ⓕ Ⓖ Ⓗ Ⓙ
11. ______
12. ______
13. ______
14. ______
15. ______
Grade 4 86 Chapter 12

## Additional Answers

**14.** Sample answer: fluid ounces; The bubble solution is a small amount. So, cups, pints, and quarts are too much.

**15.** Sample answer: no; The capacity of the bottle of bubbles is small. So, 48 fluid ounces or 6 cups are too much.

## Pages 501, Mid-Chapter Check

16. Sample answer: The units of capacity are milliliter and liter. There are 1,000 milliliters in a liter.

## Pages 503, Lesson 12-5

1. Sample answer: By eliminating wrong answers, the correct answer was left as the only possible option.
2. Sample answer: The table is an easy way to organize the information.
3. Sample answer: no; There would be two animals whose weight can be measured in tons, so it is not possible to determine which person is writing about these animals.
4. Rufus is the spaniel; Max is the collie; and Sam is the pug.
5. From left to right 4, 3, 2, and 5
7. Manuella, red; Danny, yellow; Tyson, blue
11. Sample answer: To use logical reasoning means to use what you know about the context of a situation and figure out what is possible and impossible.

## Pages 519, Lesson 12-9

10. Sample answer: logical reasoning; Use the information given to find the number of green and blue marbles. The number of red marbles Myron has is given, which is four. He has three times as many blue marbles as red marbles, or $3 \times 4 = 12$ blue marbles. He has two red marbles for every green marble, so he has $4 \div 2 = 2$ green marbles.

## Page 531, Chapter Test

17. Sample answer: Count the hours and minutes between the start and end times.

**NOTES**

# Chapter Overview

## Chapter-at-a-Glance

In Chapter 13, the emphasis is on concepts with fractions, including identifying equivalent fractions, and comparing fractions.

| Lesson | Math Objective | State/Local Standards |
|---|---|---|
| **13-1 Parts of a Whole** (pp. 537–539) | Identify, write, and read fractions for parts of a whole. | |
| **13-2 Parts of a Set** (pp. 540–543) | Identify, write, read, and model fractions for parts of a set. | |
| **13-3 Problem-Solving Strategy: Draw a Picture** (pp. 544–545) | Solve problems by drawing a picture. | |
| **EXPLORE 13-4 Equivalent Fractions** (pp. 546–547) | Identify equivalent fractions. | |
| **13-4 Equivalent Fractions** (pp. 548–551) | Find equivalent fractions. | |
| **13-5 Compare and Order Fractions** (pp. 554–557) | Compare and order simple fractions. | |
| **13-6 Mixed Numbers** (pp. 560–563) | Write mixed numbers and improper fractions. | |
| **13-7 Problem-Solving Investigation: Choose a Strategy** (pp. 564–565) | Choose the best strategy to solve a problem. | |

## Describe and Compare Fractions

**BIG Idea** Throughout this chapter, students are presented with many real-word examples to illuminate the relationship fractions have with other numbers. In addition, the concepts in this chapter will prepare students for adding and subtracting fractions with unlike denominators—a critical fifth-grade skill.

**Algebra** Students compare fractions and find fraction equivalents. These concepts help prepare them for algebra concepts, such as writing equations and inequalities.
(Lessons 13-4 and 13-5)

**G4-FP2** *Number and Operations:* **Developing an understanding of decimals, including the connections between fractions and decimals**

Students understand decimal notation as an extension of the base-ten system of writing whole numbers that is useful for representing more numbers, including numbers between 0 and 1, between 1 and 2, and so on. Students relate their understanding of fractions to reading and writing decimals that are greater than or less than 1, identifying equivalent decimals, comparing and ordering decimals, and estimating decimal or fractional amounts in problem solving. They connect equivalent fractions and decimals by comparing models to symbols and locating equivalent symbols on the number line.

**G4-FP8C** *Number and Operations:* Building on their work in grade 3, students extend their understanding of place value and ways of representing numbers to 100,000 in various contexts. They use estimation in determining the relative sizes of amounts or distances. Students develop understandings of strategies for multidigit division by using models that represent division as the inverse of multiplication, as partitioning, or as successive subtraction. By working with decimals, students extend their ability to recognize equivalent fractions. Students' earlier work in grade 3 with models of fractions and multiplication and division facts supports their understanding of techniques for generating equivalent fractions and simplifying fractions.

## Skills Trace

### Vertical Alignment

#### Third Grade

**In third grade, students learned to:**

- Construct concrete models of fractions.
- Compare and describe fraction parts of whole objects and sets.
- Model equivalent fractions.

#### Fourth Grade

**During this chapter, students learn to:**

- Identify, read, write, and model fractions and equivalent fractions.
- Write mixed numbers and improper fractions.
- Compare and order simple fractions.

**After this chapter, students learn to:**

- Understand the relationship between fractions and decimals.

#### Fifth Grade

**In fifth grade, students learn to:**

- Write mixed numbers as improper fractions and vice versa.
- Compare fractions.
- Write fractions as decimals and visa versa.
- Add, subtract, and simplify fractions.

**Backmapping and Vertical Alignment** **McGraw-Hill's *Math Connects*** program was conceived and developed with the final results in mind: student success in Algebra 1 and beyond. The authors, using the **NCTM Focal Points and Focal Connections** as their guide, developed this brand-new series by backmapping from Algebra 1 concepts, and vertically aligning the topics so that they build upon prior skills and concepts and serve as a foundation for future topics.

## Math Vocabulary

The following math vocabulary words for Chapter 13 are listed in the glossary of the ***Student Edition***. You can find interactive definitions in 13 languages in the ***eGlossary*** at macmillanmh.com.

**denominator** The bottom number in a fraction. (p. 537A)

**equivalent fractions** Fractions that represent the same number. (p. 548A)

**fraction** A number that represents part of a whole or part of a set. (p. 557A)

**improper fraction** A fraction with a numerator that is greater than or equal to the denominator. (p. 560A)

**mixed number** A number that has a whole number part and a fraction part. (p. 560A)

**numerator** The number above the bar in a fraction; the part of the fraction that tells how many of the equal parts are being used. (p. 537A)

**Visual Vocabulary Cards**
Use Visual Vocabulary Cards 10, 19, 20, 25, and 30 to reinforce the vocabulary in this lesson. (The Define/Example/Ask routine is printed on the back of each card.)

denominator

# Chapter Planner

| Suggested Pacing | | |
|---|---|---|
| Instruction | Review & Assessment | TOTAL |
| 8 days | 1 day | **9 days** |

**Diagnostic Assessment**
Quick Check (p. 536)

| | Lesson 13-1 (Pacing: 1 day) | Lesson 13-2 (Pacing: 1 day) | Lesson 13-3 (Pacing: 1 day) |
|---|---|---|---|
| **Lesson/ Objective** | **Parts of a Whole** (pp. 537–539)<br>**Objective:** Identify, write, and read fractions for parts of a whole. | **Parts of a Set** (pp. 540–543)<br>**Objective:** Identify, write, read, and model fractions for parts of a set. | **Problem-Solving Strategy Draw a Picture** (pp. 544–545)<br>**Objective:** Solve problems by drawing a picture. |
| **State/Local Standards** | | | |
| **Math Vocabulary** | **fraction**, **numerator**, **denominator** | | |
| **Lesson Resources** | **Materials**<br>paper plates, markers/paints/etc., large zip-close plastic baggies<br>**Manipulatives**<br>fraction models<br>**Other Resources**<br>CRM Leveled Worksheets (pp. 8–12)<br>Daily Reteach • 5-Minute Check • Problem of the Day | **Manipulatives**<br>counters<br>**Other Resources**<br>CRM Leveled Worksheets (pp. 13–17)<br>Daily Reteach • 5-Minute Check • Problem of the Day | **Manipulatives**<br>counters<br>**Other Resources**<br>CRM Leveled Worksheets (pp. 18–22)<br>Daily Reteach • 5-Minute Check • Problem of the Day<br>*Life in the United States* |
| **Technology** | Math Tool Chest<br>Math Adventures | Math Adventures | |
| **Math Online** | Personal Tutor | Personal Tutor | Personal Tutor |
| **Reaching All Learners** | English Learners, p. 537B ELL<br>Below Level, p. 537B BL<br>Early Finishers, p. 537B OL AL | English Learners, p. 540B ELL<br>Gifted and Talented, p. 540B AL<br>Early Finishers, p. 540B OL AL | English Learners, p. 544B ELL<br>Gifted and Talented, p. 544B AL<br>Early Finishers, p. 544B OL AL |
| **Alternate Lesson** | | | |

**KEY**

BL Below/Approaching Level · OL On Level · AL Above/Beyond Level · ELL English Learners
SE Student Edition · TE Teacher Edition · CRM Chapter 13 Resource Masters · CD-Rom
Transparency · Real-World Problem Solving Library

| | Explore 13-4 (Pacing: 1 day) | Lesson 13-4 (Pacing: 1 day) | Lesson 13-5 (Pacing: 1 day) |
|---|---|---|---|
| **Lesson/ Objective** | **Equivalent Fractions** (pp. 546–547)<br>**Objective:** Identify equivalent fractions. | **Equivalent Fractions** (pp. 548–551)<br>**Objective:** Find equivalent fractions. | **Compare and Order Fractions** (pp. 554–557)<br>**Objective:** Compare and order simple fractions. |
| **State/Local Standards** | | | |
| **Math Vocabulary** | | **equivalent fractions** | |
| **Lesson Resources** | **Materials**<br>grid paper, rules<br>**Manipulatives**<br>fraction models | **Materials**<br>colored paper, grid paper<br>**Other Resources**<br>CRM Leveled Worksheets (pp. 23–27)<br>Daily Reteach • 5-Minute Check • Problem of the Day | **Manipulatives**<br>fraction models<br>**Other Resources**<br>CRM Leveled Worksheets (pp. 28–32)<br>Daily Reteach • 5-Minute Check • Problem of the Day |
| **Technology** | | Math Adventures | Math Adventures |
| **Math Online** | Concepts in Motion | Personal Tutor | Personal Tutor |
| **Reaching All Learners** | | English Learners, p. 548B ELL<br>Below Level, p. 548B BL<br>Early Finishers, p. 548B OL AL | English Learners, p. 554B ELL<br>Below Level, p. 554B AL<br>Early Finishers, p. 554B OL AL |
| **Alternate Lesson** | | *IMPACT Mathematics:* Unit D | *IMPACT Mathematics:* Unit D |

**Game Time**
Fractions Made Equal (p. 562)

**Formative Assessment**
Mid-Chapter Check (p. 563)

**Problem Solving in Science**
(p. 558)

# Chapter Planner

| | Lesson 13-6 (Pacing: 1 day) | Lesson 13-7 (Pacing: 1 day) |
|---|---|---|
| **Lesson/ Objective** | **Mixed Numbers** (pp. 560–563)<br>**Objective:** Write mixed numbers and improper fractions. | **Problem-Solving Investigation: Choose a Strategy** (pp. 564–565)<br>**Objective:** Choose the best strategy to solve a problem. |
| **State/Local Standards** | | |
| **Math Vocabulary** | **mixed number**, **improper fraction** | |
| **Lesson Resources** | **Materials**<br>the paper plate fraction pieces made in Activity Choice 1 from Lesson 13-1<br>**Other Resources**<br>CRM Leveled Worksheets (pp. 33–37)<br>Daily Reteach • 5-Minute Check • Problem of the Day | **Manipulatives**<br>counters<br>**Other Resources**<br>CRM Leveled Worksheets (pp. 38–42)<br>Daily Reteach • 5-Minute Check • Problem of the Day<br>*Life in the United States* |
| **Technology** | Math Adventures | |
| **Math Online** | Personal Tutor | Personal Tutor |
| **Reaching All Learners** | English Learners, p. 560B ELL<br>Gifted and Talented, p. 560B BL<br>Early Finishers, p. 560B OL AL | English Learners, p. 564B ELL<br>Below Level, p. 564B BL<br>Early Finishers, p. 564B OL AL |
| **Alternate Lesson** | *IMPACT Mathematics:* Unit D | |

**Summative Assessment**
- Study Guide/Review (p. 566)
- Chapter Test (p. 571)
- Test Practice (p. 572)

## Assessment Options

### Diagnostic Assessment

- SE *Option 1:* Quick Check (p. 492)
- *Option 2:* Online Quiz macmillanmh.com
- CRM *Option 3:* Diagnostic Test (p. 44)
- CRM *Option 4:* Chapter Pretest (p. 45)

### Formative Assessment

- TE Alternate Teaching Strategies (in every lesson)
- SE Talk About It (in every lesson)
- SE Writing in Math (in every lesson)
- SE Check What You Know (in every lesson)
- TE Ticket Out the Door (p. 557)
- TE Into the Future (p. 539)
- TE Name the Math (pp. 551, 563)
- SE Mid-Chapter Check (p. 553)
- CRM Lesson Quizzes (pp. 46–48)
- CRM Mid-Chapter Test (p. 49)

### Summative Assessment

- SE Chapter Test (p. 571)
- SE Test Practice (p. 572)
- CRM Vocabulary Test (p. 50)
- CRM Leveled Chapter Tests (pp. 55–66)
- CRM Cumulative Test Practice (pp. 69–71)
- CRM Oral Assessment (pp. 51–52)
- ExamView® Assessment Suite
- Advance Tracker

## McGraw Hill Professional Development

Targeted professional development has been articulated throughout **McGraw-Hill's *Math Connects*** program. The **McGraw-Hill Professional Development Video Library** provides short videos that support the **NCTM Focal Points and Focal Connections.** For more information visit macmillanmh.com.

Model Lessons

Instructional Strategies

## Assessment Tips

As students work on describing and comparing fractions, take time to observe their understanding of these concepts.

- Record individual student observations on an address label.
- Make sure address labels are dated.
- Paste the label on the inside cover of a student's file folder. You will be able to chart progress over time.

## Teacher Notes

# Learning Stations

## Cross-Curricular Links

### Writing

**Now You Are Cooking**

If you have ever looked at a recipe, you know that fractions are often used when measuring ingredients.

- Explain how you might use fractions to follow a recipe. Where do you usually find fractions in recipes? What measurements do cooks use that are divided into fractions? What are the most common fractions used on measuring cups and spoons?
- Say whether you have ever followed a recipe or measured in cooking. Describe how you used fractions.

Ingredients:
$\frac{1}{4}$ pound of butter
$\frac{1}{2}$ cup dark-brown sugar
$\frac{1}{2}$ cup granulated sugar
1 egg
1 teaspoon vanilla
$1\frac{1}{8}$ cups flour
$\frac{1}{2}$ teaspoon salt
$\frac{1}{2}$ teaspoon baking soda
$\frac{1}{2}$ cup chopped nuts
6 ounces semi-sweet chocolate chips (1 cup)

**Materials:**

- paper
- pencil

### Art

**Fraction Puzzles**

Create a fraction puzzle using your artwork.

- Each partner folds one piece of cardboard in half four times, making lines to cut for 16 rectangles.
- Each partner draws a picture or creates a collage picture, gluing it to the cardboard and completely covering one side of the cardboard. Allow to dry for a few minutes, and then cut along the lines on the back of the cardboard. Switch puzzles.
- Model a fraction for your partner with the puzzle pieces. Write the fraction down and see if your partner can write an equivalent fraction.

**Materials:**

- 8.5 × 11 inch cardboard
- construction paper
- art or nature magazines for clip art
- glue
- scissors
- rulers

### Social Studies

**What is Your Opinion?**

Opinion polls are used in government and in business. The results can be written as fractions.

- Design an opinion poll. With your group, think of a topic you want to ask fellow students about, and write one question for your poll. Give four possible answers for your question.
- Have your classmates answer the poll question. Then tally the data. What is the fraction for each answer? (*Hint:* The number of answers for one option is the numerator, and the total number of students in the class is the denominator.)

$\frac{4}{24}$ of students like basketball, $\frac{3}{24}$ of students like tennis, $\frac{8}{24}$ of students like football, $\frac{1}{24}$ students don't like sports.

**Materials:**

- markers
- paper
- pencils

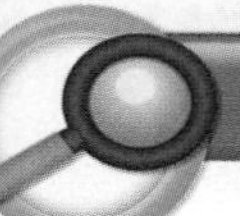

## Science

group LOGICAL

### How Low Can You Grow?

Measure several plants and express their heights in fractions.

- Each person in the group measures at least one plant in inches. Record the heights of your plants in the first column of a two-column chart. Label this first column Plant Measurements.
- Each group member writes his or her plant measurement as a fraction of a yard in the second column of the chart next to the plant measurement. Remember that a yard equals 36 inches. Express the fraction in its simplest form by reducing it.
- Whose plant measured the largest fraction of a yard? Whose measured the smallest fraction of a yard?

**Materials:**
- several plants of varying heights, at least one per student in each group
- yardstick
- paper
- pencils

## Music

### Equivalent Sounds

In music notation, notes represent a fraction of a measure. A quarter note is a quarter of a 4-beat measure. An eighth note is a half of a quarter note, or an eighth of a measure. A sixteenth note is a sixteenth of a measure. Four sixteenth notes equal a quarter note.

- Make a spinner with 2, 4, 6, 8, 10, 12, 14, and 16 to give you a numerator, or number of notes. Toss a coin to give you the denominator, or type of note: heads is eighth notes, tails is sixteenth notes.
- One person spins, tosses, and writes down the notes. The other person writes equivalent notes. Take turns spinning and writing.

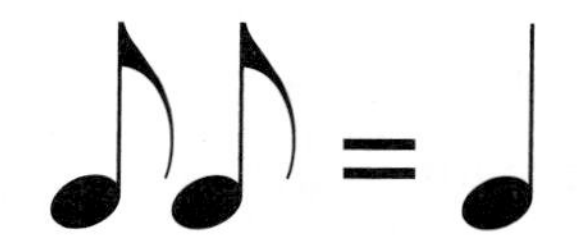

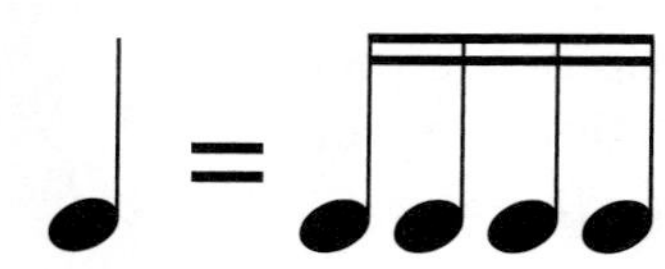

**Materials:**
- spinner
- pencils
- paper

## Health

### Portion Fractions

Do you know what a portion of rice looks like? How about pasta?

- Serve what you think is a serving of pasta onto your plate. Then serve what you think is a serving of rice.
- On another paper plate, measure out a half-cup of pasta and a quarter cup of rice.
- Use the measuring cups to measure the first servings you gave yourself. How many half-cups of pasta do you have? How many quarter-cups of rice? Compare your fractions to the fractions used for the actual portions. How much bigger or smaller are your portions?

**Materials:**
- cooked short pasta such as rotini
- cooked rice
- dry-measure measuring cups
- pencils
- paper plates

CHAPTER 13

# Introduce the Chapter

##  Real World: Pizza Party

**Materials:** large cardboard circles, available from many pizza parlors; various art supplies to represent toppings

Share with students that they will be learning about fractions in this chapter.

- Explain that a fraction is a number that names a part of a whole or a part of a set.
- Write $\frac{1}{2}$, $\frac{1}{3}$, and $\frac{5}{7}$ on the board and explain that they are fractions.

Students will work in groups of four to decorate cardboard pizzas. Tell them they first need to draw lines to cut the pizza into 8 slices, and then each member of the group can decorate two slices any way they want.

Display the decorated pizza rounds at the front of the class. Choose 1 pizza, display it on the bulletin board, and label it "1." Hold it up in front of the class and ask, "How much is $\frac{1}{2}$ of this pizza?" Cut this pizza in half and display it on a bulletin board. Label it "$\frac{1}{2}$." Repeat the same process with $\frac{1}{4}$, $\frac{1}{8}$, and $\frac{3}{4}$.

Direct students to Student Edition p. 534. Have students read the paragraph at the top of the page.

- **What are some examples of fractions in our everyday lives?** pieces of pie or pizza, measuring cup, money, etc.

## WRITING IN MATH

**Starting the Chapter**

Ask students to think about when they have seen or used fractions. Have them write about some of these times and explain what the fractions show. Encourage them to use examples.

**Key Vocabulary** Introduce the key vocabulary in the chapter using the routine below.

Define: A fraction is a number that represents part of a whole.

Example: The recipe calls for $\frac{1}{2}$ cup of sugar.

Ask: How do fractions help when following a recipe?

**Read-Aloud Anthology** For an optional reading activity to introduce this chapter's math concepts, see the Read-Aloud Anthology on p. TR38.



# CHAPTER 13 Describe and Compare Fractions

**BIG Idea** What is a fraction?

A **fraction** is a number that names part of a whole or part of a set.

**Example** If you have a pizza that is cut into eight pieces, each piece would be *one eighth* or *one of eight* pieces.

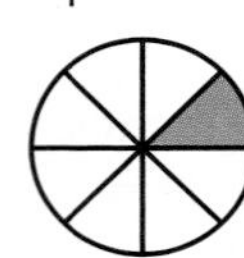 or 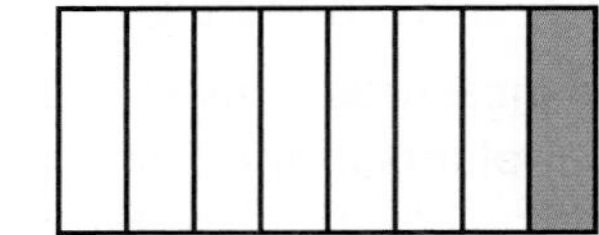

**What will I learn in this chapter?**

- Identify, read, and write fractions.
- Identify and find equivalent fractions.
- Compare and order fractions.
- Solve problems by drawing a picture.

**Key Vocabulary**

**fraction**
**numerator**
**denominator**
**equivalent fractions**
**mixed number**

Student Study Tools at macmillanmh.com



##  Chapter 13 Project

**Fraction Party**

Students plan a party with foods that must be divided from one whole into fractions.

- Students make a list of party foods that come in whole form and must be divided up. Examples include pizza, pies, and cakes.
- Students decide how many pieces each food item should be divided into. They count how many portions they need for the whole class and express it as a mixed number if necessary. They round up the mixed number in order to make a list of how many whole items they need for each type of food.
- Challenge students to express as fractions how many portions of each food would be left if they bought the items on the list, and each student ate one portion of each food.

CRM *Refer to Chapter 13 Resource Masters, p. 53, for a rubric to assess students' progress on this project.*

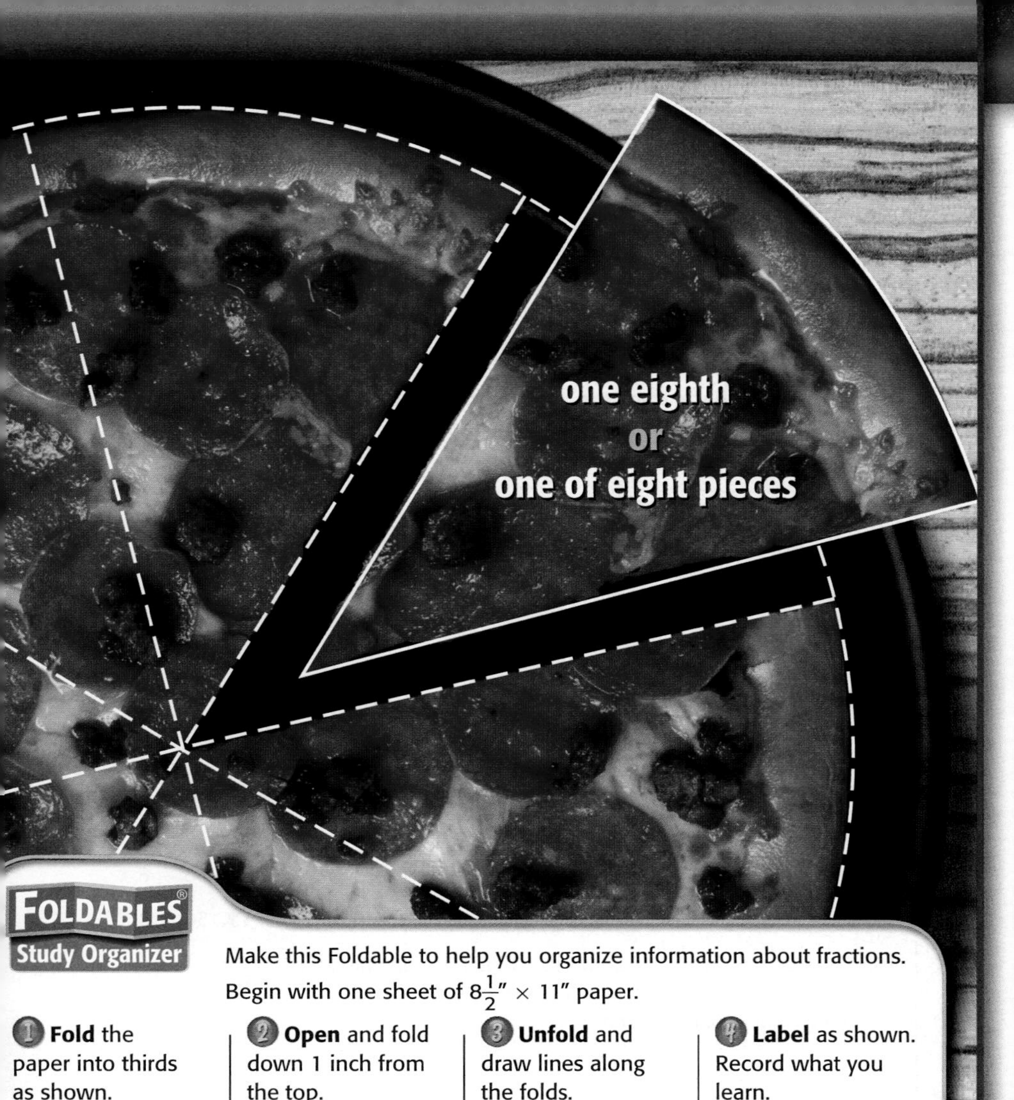


**FOLDABLES Study Organizer**

Make this Foldable to help you organize information about fractions. Begin with one sheet of $8\frac{1}{2}$" × 11" paper.

1. **Fold** the paper into thirds as shown.
2. **Open** and fold down 1 inch from the top.
3. **Unfold** and draw lines along the folds.
4. **Label** as shown. Record what you learn.

Fractions | Equivalent Fractions | Mixed Numbers



## ELL National ESL Standards Alignment for Chapter 13

| Lesson, Page | ESL Standard | Modality | Level |
|---|---|---|---|
| 13-1, p. 537B | Goal 3, Standard 3, b | Auditory | Beginning |
| 13-2, p. 540B | Goal 2, Standard 2, i | Visual | Intermediate |
| 13-3, p. 544B | Goal 2, Standard 2, f | Intrapersonal | Advanced |
| 13-4, p. 548B | Goal 2, Standard 1, b | Visual, Logical | Intermediate |
| 13-5, p. 554B | Goal 1, Standard 3, b | Logical, Social | Beginning |
| 13-6, p. 560B | Goal 2, Standard 3, h | Interpersonal, Linguistic | Intermediate |
| 13-7, p. 564B | Goal 3, Standard 2, c | Linguistic | Intermediate |

The National ESL Standards can be found in the Teacher Reference Handbook.

## FOLDABLES Dinah Zike's Foldables

Guide students through the directions on p. 435 to create their own Foldable graphic organizers for fractions. Students may also use their Foldables to study and review for chapter assessments.

**When to Use It** Lessons 13-1, 13-2, 13-4, 13-5, and 13-6. (Additional instructions for using the Foldables with these lessons are found on pp. 563 and 566.)

## Chapter 12 Literature List

| Lesson | Book Title |
|---|---|
| 13-1 | **Gator Pie**<br>Louise Mathews |
| 13-2 | **Each Orange Had 8 Slices**<br>Paul Giganti, Jr. |
| 13-3 | **Inchworm and a Half**<br>Elinor J. Pinczes |
| 13-4 | **Fraction Fun**<br>David A. Adler |
| 13-5 | **Inchworm and a Half**<br>Elinor J. Pinczes |
| 13-6 | **Fraction Action**<br>Loreen Leedy |
| Any | **Math Man**<br>Teri Daniels |
| Any | **Sir Cumference and the First Round Table: A Math Adventure**<br>Cindy Neuschwander |

- Read the Math at Home letter found in the Chapter 13 Resource Masters, p. 4, with the class and have each student sign it. (A Spanish version is found on p. 5.)
- Send home copies of the Math at Home letter with each student.

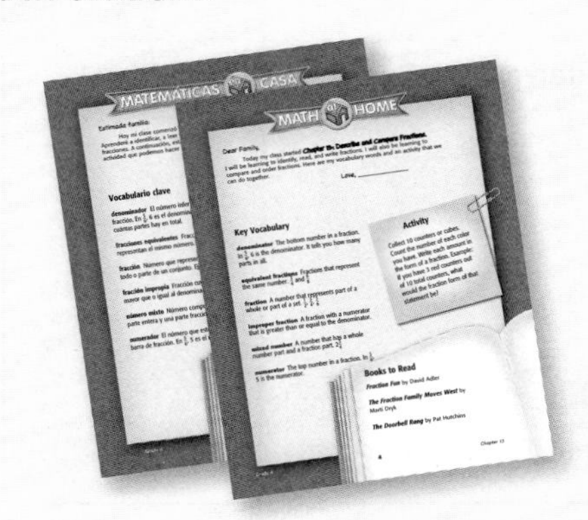

# Diagnostic Assessment

Check for students' prerequisite skills before beginning the chapter.

- **Option 1:** ***Quick Check***

  SE Student Edition, p. 536

- **Option 2:** ***Online Assessment***

  **Math Online** macmillanmh.com

- **Option 3:** ***Diagnostic Tests***

  CRM Chapter 13 Resource Masters, p. 44–45

# RTI (Response to Intervention)

**Apply the Results** Based on the results of the diagnostic assessment on Student Edition p. 536, use the chart below to address individual needs before beginning the chapter.

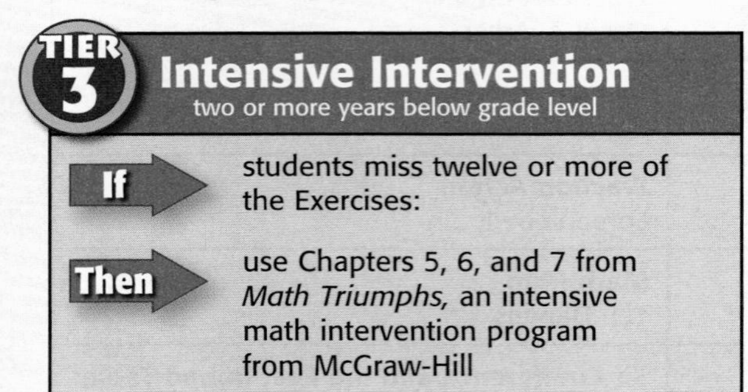

**TIER 3 Intensive Intervention**
two or more years below grade level

**If** students miss twelve or more of the Exercises:

**Then** use Chapters 5, 6, and 7 from *Math Triumphs,* an intensive math intervention program from McGraw-Hill

# ARE YOU READY for Chapter 13?

You have two ways to check prerequisite skills for this chapter.

**Option 2**

**Math Online** Take the Chapter Readiness Quiz at macmillanmh.com.

**Option 1**

Complete the Quick Check below.

## QUICK Check

**Write the word that names the equal parts in each whole. Write *halves, thirds, fourths,* or *fifths.***
(Prior Grade) (Used in Lesson 13-1)

**1.** thirds

**2.** fifths

**3.** halves

**4.** fourths

**Divide.** (Lesson 4-5) (Used in Lessons 13-4 and 13-5)

**5.** 16 ÷ 4 4 **6.** 48 ÷ 8 6 **7.** 24 ÷ 3 8 **8.** 36 ÷ 6 6

**9.** 72 ÷ 9 8 **10.** 64 ÷ 8 8 **11.** 42 ÷ 6 7 **12.** 56 ÷ 8 7

**13.** Tyree downloaded 120 songs in 10 days. He downloaded the same number of songs each day. How many songs did he download each day? 12

**List the factors of each number.** (Lesson 4-9) (Used in Lesson 13-5)

**14.** 12 1, 2, 3, 4, 6, 12 **15.** 30 1, 2, 3, 5, 6, 10, 15, 30 **16.** 45 1, 3, 5, 9, 15, 45 **17.** 21 1, 3, 7, 21

**18.** Write the factor of 36 that is missing from the list 1, 2, 3, 4, 6, ■, 12, 18, 36. 9



| **TIER 2 Strategic Intervention** below/approaching grade level | **TIER 1 On-Level** | **Above/Beyond Level** |
|---|---|---|
| **If** students miss six to eleven in: **Exercises 1–18** | **If** students miss three to five in: **Exercises 1–18** | **If** students miss two or less in: **Exercises 1–18** |
| **Then** choose a resource: | **Then** choose a resource: | **Then** choose a resource: |
| Strategic Intervention Guide (pp. 22, 24, 26, 28, 92, 93, 94, 95, 98)<br>**Math Online** Extra Examples • Personal Tutor • Concepts in Motion | TE Learning Stations (pp. 534G–534H)<br>TE Chapter Project (p. 534)<br>CRM Game: Fractions Pairs<br>Math Adventures<br>My Math Zone Chapter 12<br>**Math Online** Fact Dash | TE Learning Stations (pp. 534G–534H)<br>TE Chapter Project (p. 534)<br>Real-World Problem Solving: *Life in the United States*<br>My Math Zone Chapters 12 and 13<br>**Math Online** Games |

LESSON 13-1

# Parts of a Whole

## Lesson Planner

### Objective

Identify, write, and read fractions for parts of a whole.

### Vocabulary

**fraction**, **numerator**, **denominator**

### Resources

**Materials:** paper plates (3 per student), markers/paints/etc. for decorating them, large zip-close plastic bags (1 per student)

**Manipulatives:** fraction models

**Literature Connection:** *Gator Pie* by Louise Mathews

**Teacher Technology**

TeacherWorks • Interactive Classroom • Math Tool Chest

## Daily Routine

Use these suggestions before beginning the lesson on p. 537.

### 5-Minute Check

(Reviews Lesson 12-10)

**Find each elapsed time. Use a clock if needed.**

1. What time will it be in 3 hours and 10 minutes? 5:15
2. What time will it be in 1 hour and 40 minutes? 6:10

4:30

### Problem of the Day

Two glitter stickers trade for one scratch-n-sniff sticker, and three scratch-n-sniff stickers trade for two gel stickers. How many glitter stickers does Syrah need to trade for two gel stickers? 6

### Focus on Math Background

In the previous grade, students learned the names of fractional parts halves, thirds, and fourths. In this chapter, students will build on this background. In this lesson, students explore using fractions to name a part of a whole and in the next lesson, they will use fractions to describe a part of a set or group. The numerator of a fraction "enumerates," or counts, *equal*-size parts. The number of parts is "named" by the denominator, with the name coming from the total number of equal parts contained in the whole. Parts of a whole can be shown

- in words, such as "three-fourths";
- as a symbol, such as $\frac{3}{4}$;
- as the quotient of two numbers, such as 3 divided by 4; and
- as a figure, such as the one shown on p. 537.

### Building Math Vocabulary

Write the lesson vocabulary words and their definitions on the board.

Have students write three different fractions. Have them label the numerator and denominator of each. Then ask them to draw a picture to represent each fraction they wrote.

#### Visual Vocabulary Cards

Use Visual Vocabulary Cards 10, 19 and 30 to reinforce the vocabulary introduced in this lesson. (The Define/Example/Ask routine is printed on the back of each card.)

# Differentiated Instruction

## Small Group Options

### Option 1 Below Level BL

VISUAL, SPATIAL

**Materials:** pattern blocks for each student, chart paper

- Give each student a yellow hexagon pattern block.
- Ask students to use other pattern blocks to cover the yellow completely. The rule is that they can only use one color to cover it. 6 green triangles, 3 blue parallelograms, 2 red trapezoids
- When one color is discovered, ask students to take one of them away. **What is the fraction of blocks covering the yellow now? What is the fraction of blocks not covering the yellow?** Answers will vary.
- Encourage students to discover all the possibilities and discuss as many of the fractions involved as possible.

### Option 2 English Language Learners ELL

AUDITORY

**Materials:** picture of a round cake
**Core Vocabulary:** equal pieces called fractions, piece of cake, easy
**Common Use Verb:** cut

**Hear Math** This strategy uses background knowledge to introduce the concept of fractions and the idiom "a piece of cake."

- Show the picture. Have students show how it was cut.
- Ask students why the cake is not cut in a grid, to solicit the idea of equal pieces.
- Relate the idea of how the cake was cut to the concept of dividing a whole into equal pieces
- Say: "***Cutting*** cake into equal pieces is **easy**, just like dividing. The **equal pieces** are **called fractions**."
- Model cutting equal pieces on the diameters and say: "It is a '**piece of cake**' to divide cake into equal fractions."

## Independent Work Options

### Option 1 Early Finishers OL AL

VISUAL, SPATIAL

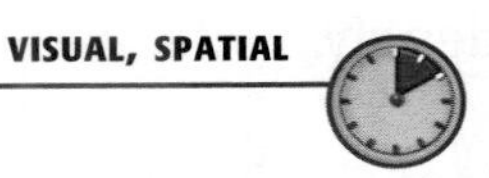

**Materials:** paper plates made in Activity Choice 1, plus three extra plates per student

- Have students decorate and then divide and cut paper plates into fifths, sixths, and eighths.

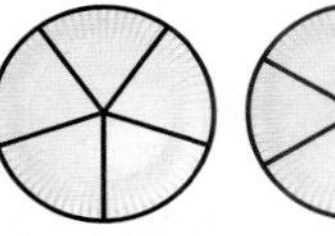
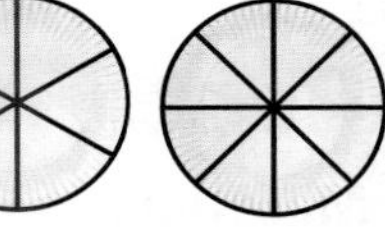

- **Which is larger, $\frac{1}{2}$ or $\frac{1}{6}$?** $\frac{1}{2}$
- **How many $\frac{1}{8}$ pieces equal a $\frac{1}{2}$ piece?** 4
- **If four different students each have $\frac{1}{5}$ of pie, how much of the pie do they have altogether?** $\frac{4}{5}$

### Option 2 Student Technology

Math Online macmillanmh.com

Math Tool Chest Fractions
Personal Tutor • Extra Examples
Math Adventures

### Option 3 Learning Station: Music (p. 534H)

Direct students to the Music Learning Station for opportunities to explore and extend the lesson concept.

### Option 4 Problem-Solving Practice

Reinforce problem-solving skills and strategies with the Problem-Solving Practice worksheet.

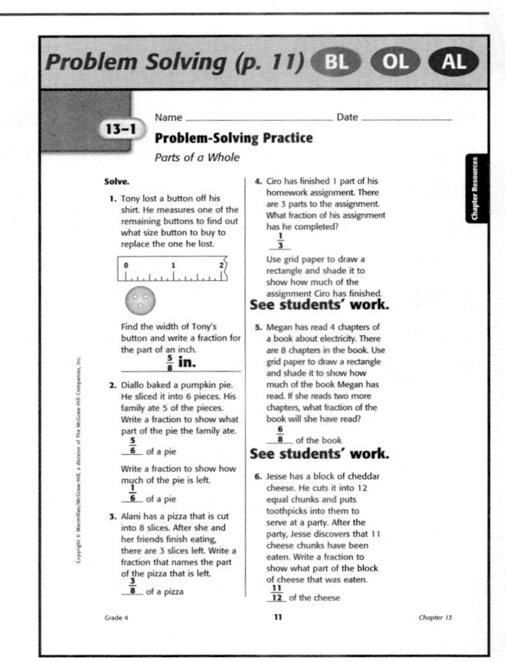

Problem Solving (p. 11) BL OL AL

13–1 Name ______ Date ______

**Problem-Solving Practice**

*Parts of a Whole*

Chapter Resources

**Solve.**

1. Tony lost a button off his shirt. He measures one of the remaining buttons to find out what size button to buy to replace the one he lost.

   Find the width of Tony's button and write a fraction for the part of an inch.
   $\frac{5}{8}$ **in.**

2. Diallo baked a pumpkin pie. He sliced it into 6 pieces. His family ate 5 of the pieces. Write a fraction to show what part of the pie the family ate.
   $\frac{5}{6}$ of a pie

   Write a fraction to show how much of the pie is left.
   $\frac{1}{6}$ of a pie

3. Alani has a pizza that is cut into 8 slices. After she and her friends finish eating, there are 3 slices left. Write a fraction that names the part of the pizza that is left.
   $\frac{3}{8}$ of a pizza

4. Ciro has finished 1 part of his homework assignment. There are 3 parts to the assignment. What fraction of his assignment has he completed?
   $\frac{1}{3}$

   Use grid paper to draw a rectangle and shade it to show how much of the assignment Ciro has finished.
   **See students' work.**

5. Megan has read 4 chapters of a book about electricity. There are 8 chapters in the book. Use grid paper to draw a rectangle and shade it to show how much of the book Megan has read. If she reads two more chapters, what fraction of the book will she have read?
   $\frac{6}{8}$ of the book
   **See students' work.**

6. Jesse has a block of cheddar cheese. He cuts it into 12 equal chunks and puts toothpicks into them to serve at a party. After the party, Jesse discovers that 11 cheese chunks have been eaten. Write a fraction to show what part of the block of cheese that was eaten.
   $\frac{11}{12}$ of the cheese



Grade 4 11 Chapter 13

# 13-1 Parts of a Whole

Some of the pieces of pizza have pepperoni. Some have just cheese. You can use a fraction to describe the pizza and the toppings.

**MAIN IDEA**

I will identify, write, and read fractions for parts of a whole.

**New Vocabulary**

**fraction**
**numerator**
**denominator**

**Math Online**

macmillanmh.com
- Extra Examples
- Personal Tutor
- Self-Check Quiz

A **fraction** is a number that names part of a whole or part of a set. In a fraction, the **numerator** tells the number of equal parts. The **denominator** tells the number of equal parts in all.

pieces with pepperoni ⟶ 3 ⟵ numerator
total number of pieces ⟶ 4 ⟵ denominator

**1** **FOOD** **Suppose Molly and her mom made the pizza shown. What fraction of the pizza is pepperoni?**

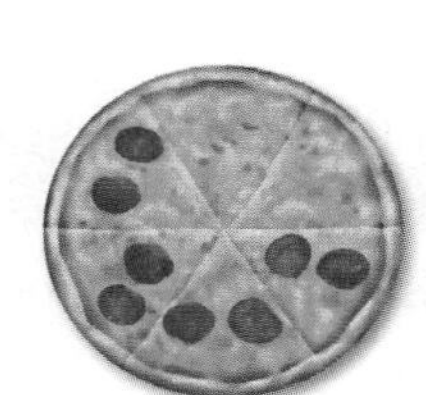

**Write** pepperoni slices ⟶ 4 / total slices in all ⟶ 6 ($\frac{4}{6}$)

**Read** *four sixths* or *four divided by six*

So, $\frac{4}{6}$ of the whole pizza is pepperoni.

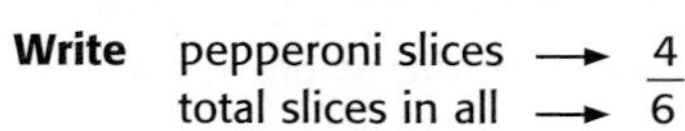

**Write and Read Fractions**

**2** **What fraction of the figure is shaded?**

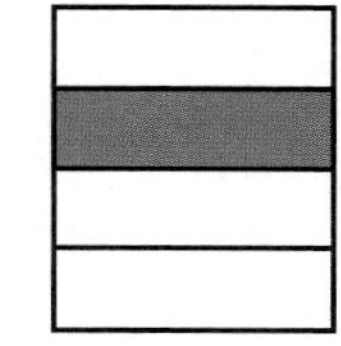

**Write** parts shaded ⟶ 1 / total equal parts in all ⟶ 4 ($\frac{1}{4}$)

**Read** *one fourth* or *one divided by four*

So, $\frac{1}{4}$ of the whole figure is shaded.



# 13-1 Parts of a Whole

## 1 Introduce

### Activity Choice 1 • Hands-On

- Each student will need three paper plates. Each plate will represent a different kind of pie. If time allows, they can color and decorate these before the fraction lesson begins.
- Help students divide their "pies" by folding them into halves, thirds, and fourths.
- **How many halves make a whole pie?** 2
- **If there were only one of these large pieces, what fraction of the pie is left?** $\frac{1}{2}$
- Allow students time to become familiar with these common fractions. Using several students' plates, count by halves, then thirds and fourths. Provide large plastic bags for students to keep their pieces. They will use them in 13-6.

### Activity Choice 2 • Literature

Introduce the lesson with *Gator Pie* by Louise Mathews. For a related math activity, see p. TR63.

## 2 Teach

### Scaffolding Questions

Ask students to get out their paper plate fractions, or use fraction models.

- **How many thirds are needed to make up a whole pie?** 3
- **How many fourths are needed to make up a whole pie?** 4
- **Can you predict how many fifths would be needed to make a whole pie?** 5
- Help students make the connection between the name of the fraction and the number of pieces the corresponding pie would be cut into.
- **Order the pie pieces from least to greatest.** $\frac{1}{5}, \frac{1}{4}, \frac{1}{3}$

### GET READY to Learn

Have students open their books and read the information in **Get Ready to Learn**. Introduce **fraction**, **numerator**, and **denominator**. As a class, work through **Examples 1–3**.

## Real-World Example

**Example 1** Remind students that the denominator represents the total number of equal pieces. It should always be written on the bottom of the fraction.

### ADDITIONAL EXAMPLES

1. What fraction of the circle is blue? $\frac{5}{8}$

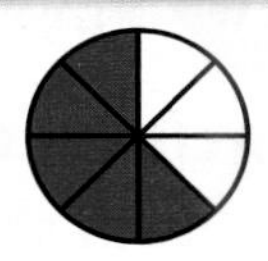

2. What fraction of the figure is shaded? $\frac{3}{6}$ (or $\frac{1}{2}$)

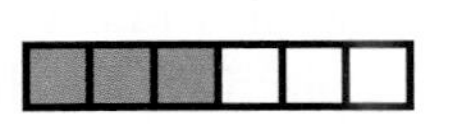

3. Gina is decorating a card for her mother's birthday. She decides to put glitter on $\frac{2}{3}$ of the card. Draw a picture to show this fraction.

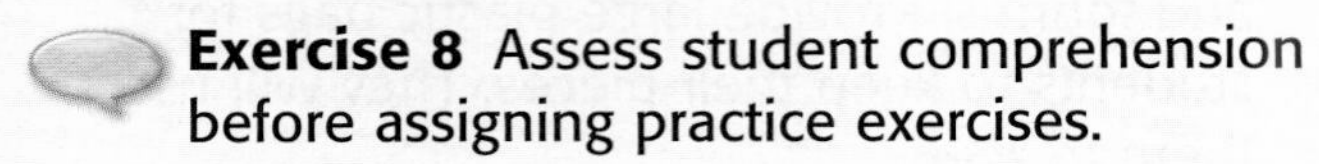


As a class, have students complete Exercises 1–8 in **Check What You Know** as you observe their work.

**Exercise 8** Assess student comprehension before assigning practice exercises.

## BL Alternate Teaching Strategy

**If** students have trouble identifying, writing, and reading fractions for parts of a whole...

**Then** use one of these reteach options:

1 CRM **Daily Reteach Worksheet** (p. 8)

2 Review the meaning of the numerator and denominator. **What does the denominator of a fraction represent?** the total number of equal parts **What does the numerator represent?** the number of parts being counted Give the students several circles and rectangles divided into 2, 3, 4, 5, or 6 equal parts. Ask them to shade in $\frac{1}{2}, \frac{2}{3}, \frac{3}{4}, \frac{4}{5}$ and $\frac{5}{6}$ on the appropriate circle or rectangle.

3 Have students use Math Tool Chest to help complete the problem-solving exercises.

### ! COMMON ERROR!

**Exercise 25** Students may correctly find that peanuts are $\frac{1}{8}$ of the mix and raisins are $\frac{2}{8}$ of the mix, but not know what to do next. Suggest they add the cups of peanuts and raisins first, then find the fraction this represents.



You can use different pictures to show the same part of a whole.

**Remember**
The denominator is always the bottom number in a fraction. Remember that **d** in **d**enominator could stand for **d**own.

### Real-World EXAMPLE — Draw a Fraction Model

3 **GARDENS The students at Watson Elementary School are making a garden. They will plant vegetables in $\frac{1}{3}$ of the whole garden. Draw a picture to show this fraction.**

| One Way: Use a Rectangle | Another Way: Use a Circle |
|---|---|
| vegetables / other / other | vegetables / other / other |
| Divide a rectangle into 3 equal parts. Shade one part to show one third. | Divide a circle into 3 equal parts. Shade one part to show one third. |

### CHECK What You Know

**Write the fraction that names part of the whole.** See Examples 1 and 2 (p. 537)

1. part left $\frac{3}{4}$
2. part shaded $\frac{3}{4}$
3. part not shaded $\frac{5}{6}$

4–6. See Ch. 13 Answer Appendix.

**Draw a picture and shade part of it to show the fraction.** See Example 3 (p. 538)

4. $\frac{1}{4}$
5. $\frac{2}{3}$
6. $\frac{5}{8}$

7. A birthday cake is cut into 8 equal pieces. Arnaldo ate one piece. The guests ate the remaining pieces. What fraction of the whole cake did the guests eat? $\frac{7}{8}$

8. **Talk About It** What part of a fraction is the denominator? What does the denominator mean? Sample answer: The denominator is the bottom number; it means the total number of pieces.



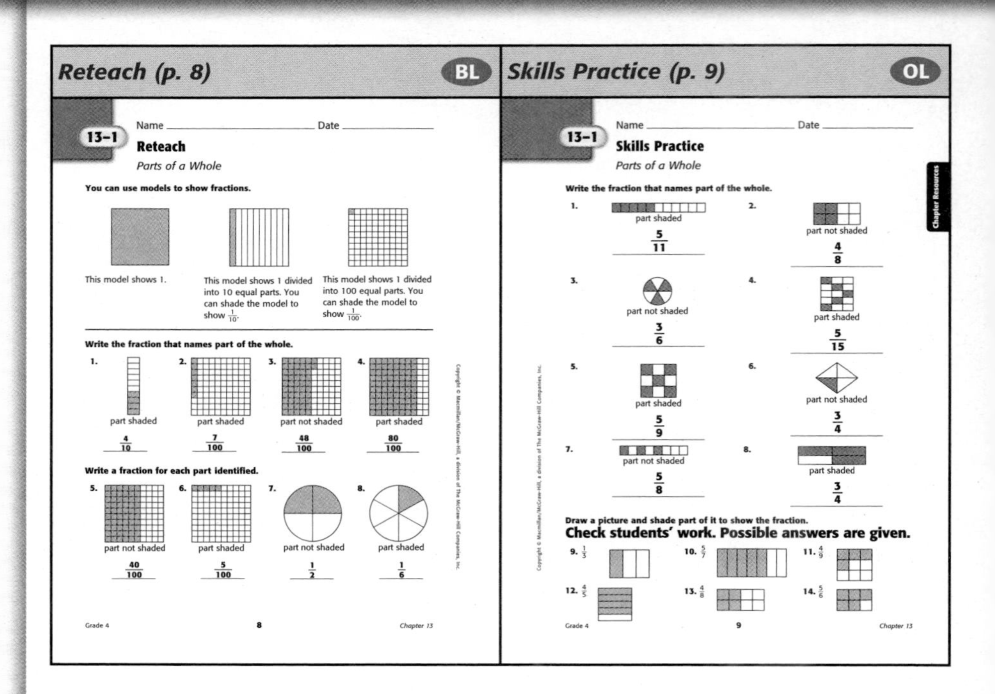
**Reteach (p. 8)** BL

13-1 Name ________ Date ________
**Reteach**
*Parts of a Whole*

**You can use models to show fractions.**

This model shows 1. This model shows 1 divided into 10 equal parts. You can shade the model to show $\frac{1}{10}$. This model shows 1 divided into 100 equal parts. You can shade the model to show $\frac{1}{100}$.

**Write the fraction that names part of the whole.**

1. part shaded $\frac{4}{10}$
2. part shaded $\frac{7}{100}$
3. part not shaded $\frac{48}{100}$
4. part shaded $\frac{80}{100}$

**Write a fraction for each part identified.**

5. part not shaded $\frac{40}{100}$
6. part shaded $\frac{5}{100}$
7. part not shaded $\frac{1}{2}$
8. part shaded $\frac{1}{6}$

Grade 4 8 Chapter 13

**Skills Practice (p. 9)** OL

13-1 Name ________ Date ________
**Skills Practice**
*Parts of a Whole*

**Write the fraction that names part of the whole.**

1. part shaded $\frac{5}{11}$
2. part not shaded $\frac{4}{8}$
3. part not shaded $\frac{3}{6}$
4. part shaded $\frac{5}{15}$
5. part shaded $\frac{5}{9}$
6. part not shaded $\frac{3}{4}$
7. part not shaded $\frac{5}{8}$
8. part shaded $\frac{3}{4}$

**Draw a picture and shade part of it to show the fraction.**
**Check students' work. Possible answers are given.**

9. $\frac{1}{3}$ 10. $\frac{5}{7}$ 11. $\frac{4}{9}$ 12. $\frac{4}{5}$ 13. $\frac{4}{6}$ 14. $\frac{5}{8}$

Grade 4 9 Chapter 13

# Practice and Problem Solving

See page R34.

**Write the fraction that names part of the whole.** See Examples 1 and 2 (p. 537)

**9.**  $\frac{7}{12}$

part left

**10.**  $\frac{1}{2}$

part filled

**11.**  $\frac{3}{4}$

part filled

**12.** $\frac{4}{5}$

part shaded

**13.** $\frac{5}{8}$

part not shaded

**14.**  $\frac{1}{8}$

part not shaded

15–18. See Ch. 13 Answer Appendix.

**Draw a picture and shade part of it to show the fraction.** See Example 3 (p. 538)

**15.** $\frac{3}{5}$ **16.** $\frac{3}{6}$ **17.** $\frac{7}{8}$ **18.** $\frac{4}{10}$

**Alphabet flags are used by ships at sea to send short messages. Write the fraction for the part of each flag that is blue.**

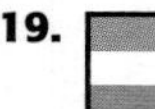

**19.**  $\frac{2}{5}$

Letter C

**20.** 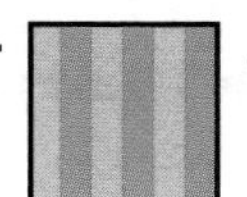 $\frac{3}{6}$

Letter G

**21.**  $\frac{8}{16}$

Letter N

**22.** 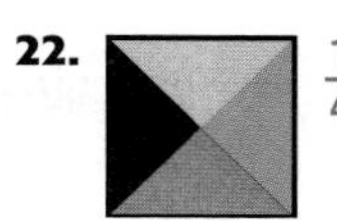 $\frac{1}{4}$

Letter Z

**For Exercises 23–25, use the recipe shown.**

Recipe for: Party Mix
1 cup peanuts
3 cups rice cereal
2 cups pretzels
2 cups raisins
Makes: one batch

**23.** What is the total number of cups of ingredients needed to make one batch of the party mix? 8

**24.** What fraction of the ingredients is pretzels? $\frac{2}{8}$

**25.** What fraction of the ingredients is peanuts and raisins? $\frac{3}{8}$

## H.O.T. Problems

**26. OPEN ENDED** Name two different real-world items that can show the fraction $\frac{2}{3}$. Sample answer: Two of the three tennis balls are yellow; $\frac{2}{3}$ of a measuring cup is full.

**27. WRITING IN ▶MATH** If the denominator of $\frac{2}{5}$ was increased from 5 to 10, would it be greater or less than $\frac{2}{5}$? Explain. See Ch. 13 Answer Appendix.



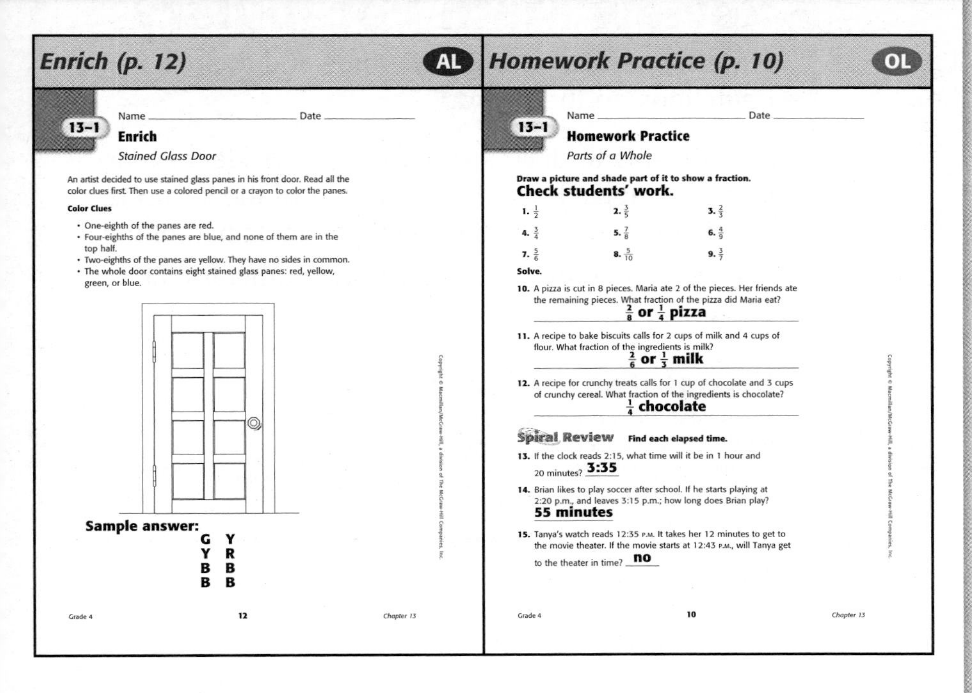

**Enrich (p. 12)** AL

13–1 Name ______ Date ______

**Enrich**

*Stained Glass Door*

An artist decided to use stained glass panes in his front door. Read all the color clues first. Then use a colored pencil or a crayon to color the panes.

**Color Clues**

- One-eighth of the panes are red.
- Four-eighths of the panes are blue, and none of them are in the top half.
- Two-eighths of the panes are yellow. They have no sides in common.
- The whole door contains eight stained glass panes: red, yellow, green, or blue.

**Sample answer:**

G Y
Y R
B B
B B

Grade 4 12 *Chapter 13*



**Homework Practice (p. 10)** OL

13–1 Name ______ Date ______

**Homework Practice**

*Parts of a Whole*

**Draw a picture and shade part of it to show a fraction.**
**Check students' work.**

1. $\frac{1}{2}$ 2. $\frac{3}{5}$ 3. $\frac{2}{3}$
4. $\frac{3}{4}$ 5. $\frac{7}{8}$ 6. $\frac{4}{9}$
7. $\frac{5}{6}$ 8. $\frac{5}{10}$ 9. $\frac{3}{7}$

**Solve.**

**10.** A pizza is cut in 8 pieces. Maria ate 2 of the pieces. Her friends ate the remaining pieces. What fraction of the pizza did Maria eat? **$\frac{2}{8}$ or $\frac{1}{4}$ pizza**

**11.** A recipe to bake biscuits calls for 2 cups of milk and 4 cups of flour. What fraction of the ingredients is milk? **$\frac{2}{6}$ or $\frac{1}{3}$ milk**

**12.** A recipe for crunchy treats calls for 1 cup of chocolate and 3 cups of crunchy cereal. What fraction of the ingredients is chocolate? **$\frac{1}{4}$ chocolate**

**Spiral Review** **Find each elapsed time.**

**13.** If the clock reads 2:15, what time will it be in 1 hour and 20 minutes? **3:35**

**14.** Brian likes to play soccer after school. If he starts playing at 2:20 p.m., and leaves 3:15 p.m.; how long does Brian play? **55 minutes**

**15.** Tanya's watch reads 12:35 P.M. It takes her 12 minutes to get to the movie theater. If the movie starts at 12:43 P.M., will Tanya get to the theater in time? **no**

Grade 4 10 *Chapter 13*



# 3 Practice

Differentiate practice using these leveled assignments for Exercises 9–27.

| Level | Assignment |
|---|---|
| BL Below/Approaching Level | 9, 12–13, 15–17, 21–23 |
| OL On Level | 11–13, 16–21, 23–25, 26 |
| AL Above/Beyond Level | 10–24 even, 26–27 |

Have students discuss and complete the Higher Order Thinking problems. For Exercise 27, encourage students to draw pictures to represent the fractions.

**WRITING IN ▶MATH** Have students complete Exercise 27 in their Math Journals. You may choose to use this exercise as an optional formative assessment.

# 4 Assess

## Formative Assessment

- **Draw a picture to represent $\frac{2}{5}$.** Answers will vary.
- **Explain how to determine the fraction represented by the shaded part of this figure.**

Sample answer: First count the 8 equal pieces the circle is divided into–this is the denominator. Then count the 3 pieces shaded–this is the numerator.
- **What does the denominator of a fraction represent?** the total number of equal pieces

**Quick Check** **Are students continuing to struggle with identifying, writing, and reading fractions for parts of a whole?**

**If Yes** → Small Group Options (p. 537B)
Strategic Intervention Guide (p. 22)

**If No** → Independent Work Options (p. 537B)
CRM Skills Practice Worksheet (p. 9)
CRM Enrich Worksheet (p. 12)

**Into the Future** Explain to students that the next lesson is on parts of a set. Ask them to write how they think today's lesson on parts of a whole will help them with tomorrow's lesson.

LESSON 13-2

# Parts of a Set

## Lesson Planner

### Objective

Identify, write, read, and model fractions for parts a set.

### Review Vocabulary

**numerator, denominator**

### Resources

**Manipulatives:** counters

**Literature Connection:** *Each Orange Had 8 Slices* by Paul Giganti, Jr.

**Teacher Technology**
TeacherWorks • Interactive Classroom

## Daily Routine

Use these suggestions before beginning the lesson on p. 540.

### 5-Minute Check

(Reviews Lesson 12-1)

**Write the fraction that names part of the whole.**

1. $\frac{3}{4}$
2. $\frac{2}{3}$

**Draw a picture and shade part of it to show the fraction.**

3. $\frac{2}{5}$ Answers will vary.
4. $\frac{5}{6}$ Answers will vary.

### Problem of the Day

Maria is half as old as her cousin Geno, and in five years their ages will total 34. How old are Maria and Geno now? Maria is 8; Geno is 16.

### Focus on Math Background

In the previous section, students used fractions to model parts of a whole. In this section, they use them to model a part of a set or group. For example, if a pizza is cut into six slices, five of the slices can be thought of as $\frac{5}{6}$ of a whole pizza or as $\frac{5}{6}$ of a set of 6 slices. Sorting objects according to their characteristics helps students understand the concept of parts of a set, and asking them to identify the fraction of a set *not* having a given characteristic lays the groundwork for the study of logic and the concept of complement as it is used in probability.

In this lesson, the word "model" is used to describe the use of a diagram to represent a fraction.

### Review Math Vocabulary

Write the review vocabulary words and their definitions on the board.

Ask students to draw a rectangle and divide it evenly into 5 sections. Have them shade 4 of the sections. Ask them to write the fraction that names part of the whole. $\frac{4}{5}$ Then have them label the numerator and denominator.

**Visual Vocabulary Cards**

Use Visual Vocabulary Cards 10 and 30 to reinforce the vocabulary reviewed in this lesson. (The Define/Example/Ask routine is printed on the back of each card.)

# Differentiated Instruction

## Small Group Options

**Option 1** LOGICAL, INTRAPERSONAL 

### Gifted and Talented AL

Have students find fractions of larger numbers:

1. $\frac{5}{8}$ of 64 40
2. $\frac{3}{4}$ of 56 42
3. $\frac{2}{3}$ of 72 48
4. $\frac{4}{6}$ of 126 84

**Option 2** VISUAL 

### English Language Learners ELL

**Materials:** colored pencils, picture of group of boys and girls

**Core Vocabulary:** all, sets within the whole, top/bottom

**Common Use Verb:** stands for

**See Math** This strategy uses colors to allow students to visually see fractions as sets within all of something.

- Give each student two different colored pencils.
- Show the picture and have students count all the children.
- Write this number and put a line above it in black. Say: "The **bottom** number ***stands for*** **all** of the children."
- Say: "Some of the children have red clothes. Count them."
- Write that number in red on the top. Say: "The red number ***stands for*** the children wearing red. They are a **set within the whole** of **all** the children."
- Repeat with different colors as time permits.

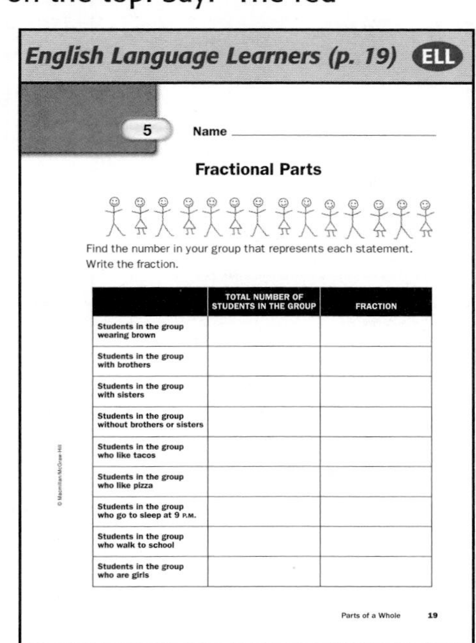

*English Language Learners (p. 19)* ELL

5 Name ____________

**Fractional Parts**

Find the number in your group that represents each statement. Write the fraction.

| | TOTAL NUMBER OF STUDENTS IN THE GROUP | FRACTION |
|---|---|---|
| Students in the group wearing brown | | |
| Students in the group with brothers | | |
| Students in the group with sisters | | |
| Students in the group without brothers or sisters | | |
| Students in the group who like tacos | | |
| Students in the group who like pizza | | |
| Students in the group who go to sleep at 9 P.M. | | |
| Students in the group who walk to school | | |
| Students in the group who are girls | | |



Parts of a Whole 19

*Use this worksheet to provide additional support for English Language Learners.*

## Independent Work Options

**Option 1** LINGUISTIC, SPATIAL 

### Early Finishers OL AL

**Materials:** tissue paper, green pipe cleaners, glue

- Have students make paper flowers by bunching tissue paper and gluing it on a green pipe cleaner stem. Ask each student to make 6 red, 4 yellow, 4 blue, and 4 purple flowers.
- Have each student create a bouquet using some of the flowers. Switch bouquets with a partner. Instruct each student to write the fractions that represent each color.

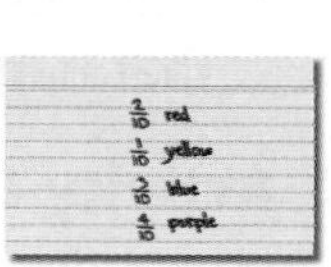

**Option 2** Tech Link

### Student Technology

macmillanmh.com

Personal Tutor • Extra Examples

Math Adventures

**Option 3**

### Learning Station: Health (p. 534H)

Direct students to the Health Learning Station for opportunities to explore and extend the lesson concept.

**Option 4**

### Problem-Solving Practice

Reinforce problem-solving skills and strategies with the Problem-Solving Practice worksheet.

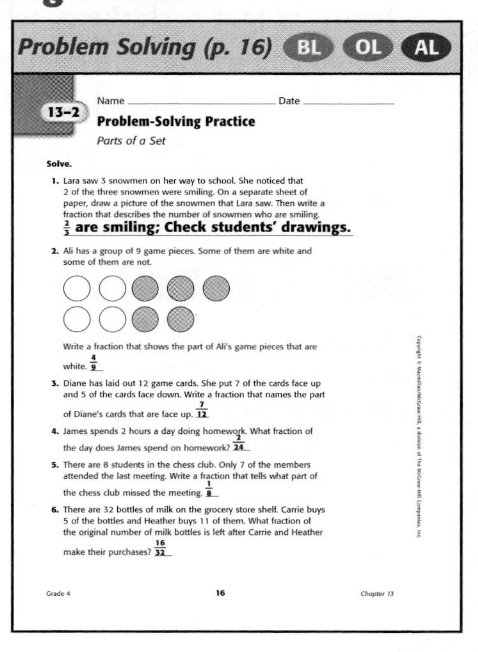

*Problem Solving (p. 16)* BL OL AL

13–2 Name ____________ Date ____________

**Problem-Solving Practice**

*Parts of a Set*

**Solve.**

1. Lara saw 3 snowmen on her way to school. She noticed that 2 of the three snowmen were smiling. On a separate sheet of paper, draw a picture of the snowmen that Lara saw. Then write a fraction that describes the number of snowmen who are smiling. **$\frac{2}{3}$ are smiling; Check students' drawings.**
2. Ali has a group of 9 game pieces. Some of them are white and some of them are not.

   Write a fraction that shows the part of Ali's game pieces that are white. $\frac{4}{9}$
3. Diane has laid out 12 game cards. She put 7 of the cards face up and 5 of the cards face down. Write a fraction that names the part of Diane's cards that are face up. $\frac{7}{12}$
4. James spends 2 hours a day doing homework. What fraction of the day does James spend on homework? $\frac{2}{24}$
5. There are 8 students in the chess club. Only 7 of the members attended the last meeting. Write a fraction that tells what part of the chess club missed the meeting. $\frac{1}{8}$
6. There are 32 bottles of milk on the grocery store shelf. Carrie buys 5 of the bottles and Heather buys 11 of them. What fraction of the original number of milk bottles is left after Carrie and Heather make their purchases? $\frac{16}{32}$



Grade 4 16 Chapter 13

# 13-2 Parts of a Set

## 1 Introduce

### Activity Choice 1 • Hands-On 

- Observe your students. Choose a group of students to stand up at the front of the class and make fractions based on the color or style of their hair or clothes. **How many students are in the group? How many are wearing a red shirt? (have brown hair, etc.)?** Answers will vary. Tell students the fraction of students wearing red shirts.
- **What does the numerator of the fraction tell you?** the number of students wearing red shirts **the denominator?** the number of students
- Tell students they will learn about fractions that name sets in this lesson.

### Activity Choice 2 • Literature

Introduce the lesson with *Each Orange Had 8 Slices* by Paul Giganti, Jr. For a related math activity, see p. TR63.

## 2 Teach

### Scaffolding Questions

Use characters from a current book read in class or any other appropriate group. As a sample, ask students to consider a barnyard with 3 cows, 4 sheep, 2 goats, 3 pigs, and 6 chickens.

- **How many animals are in the barnyard?** 18 **How many are chickens?** 6
- **If you write a fraction for the part of the barnyard that is chickens, which number would you use for the denominator? Explain.** 18 because that is the total number of animals.
- **What fraction of the animals in the barnyard are chickens?** $\frac{6}{18}$

### GET READY to Learn

Have students open their books and read the information in **Get Ready to Learn**. Review **numerator** and **denominator**. As a class, work through **Examples 1–3**.

# 13-2 Parts of a Set

**MAIN IDEA**

I will identify, write, read, and model fractions for parts of a set.

**Math Online**

macmillanmh.com
- Extra Examples
- Personal Tutor
- Self-Check Quiz

### GET READY to Learn

A set of toy cars has two red cars, one green car, and one blue car. What fraction of the set of cars is green?

A set is a group of objects. In Lesson 13-1, you learned to use a fraction to name part of a whole. Fractions can also be used to name part of a set.

**Real-World EXAMPLE**

**1 CARS What fraction of the set of cars is green?**

**Write** green cars → $\frac{1}{4}$ ← numerator
total cars → ← denominator

**Read** *one fourth* or *one divided by four*

So, $\frac{1}{4}$ of the set of cars is green.

**EXAMPLE** Write and Read Fractions

**2 What fraction of the set of stars is *not* green?**

**Write** stars *not* green → $\frac{2}{5}$
total stars →

**Read** *two fifths* or *two divided by five*

So, $\frac{2}{5}$ of the set of stars are *not* green.

540 Chapter 13 Describe and Compare Fractions

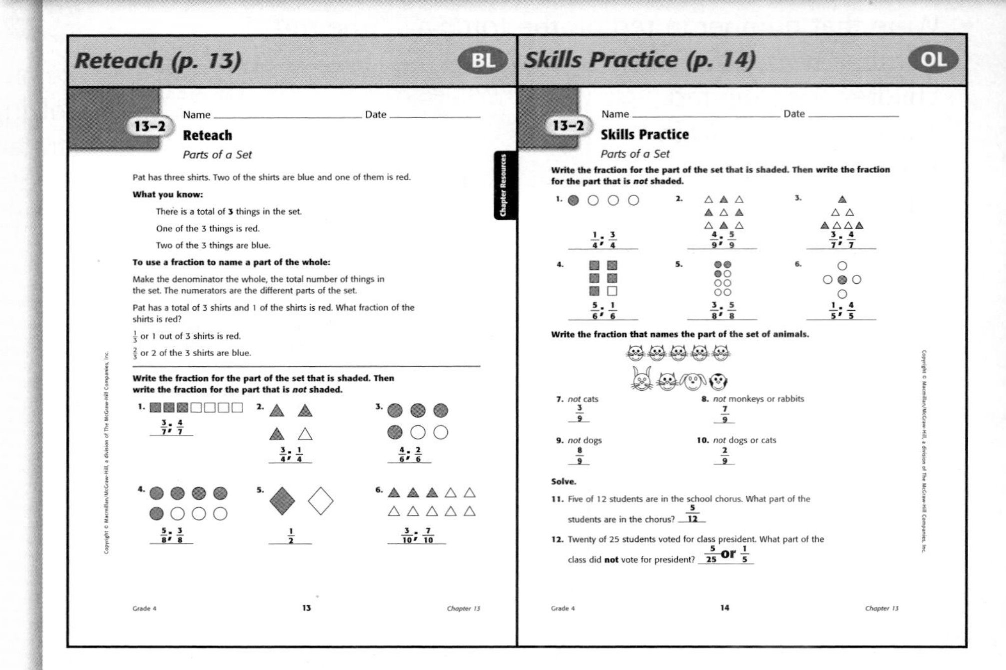

**Reteach (p. 13)** BL

13-2 Name ______ Date ______
**Reteach**
*Parts of a Set*

Pat has three shirts. Two of the shirts are blue and one of them is red.

**What you know:**

There is a total of **3** things in the set.
One of the 3 things is red.
Two of the 3 things are blue.

**To use a fraction to name a part of the whole:**

Make the denominator the whole, the total number of things in the set. The numerators are the different parts of the set.

Pat has a total of 3 shirts and 1 of the shirts is red. What fraction of the shirts is red?

$\frac{1}{3}$ or 1 out of 3 shirts is red.
$\frac{2}{3}$ or 2 of the 3 shirts are blue.

**Write the fraction for the part of the set that is shaded. Then write the fraction for the part that is *not* shaded.**

1. $\frac{3}{7}$; $\frac{4}{7}$
2. $\frac{3}{4}$; $\frac{1}{4}$
3. $\frac{4}{6}$; $\frac{2}{6}$
4. $\frac{5}{8}$; $\frac{3}{8}$
5. $\frac{1}{2}$
6. $\frac{3}{10}$; $\frac{7}{10}$

Grade 4 13 Chapter 13



**Skills Practice (p. 14)** OL

13-2 Name ______ Date ______
**Skills Practice**
*Parts of a Set*

**Write the fraction for the part of the set that is shaded. Then write the fraction for the part that is *not* shaded.**

1. $\frac{1}{4}$; $\frac{3}{4}$
2. $\frac{4}{9}$; $\frac{5}{9}$
3. $\frac{3}{7}$; $\frac{4}{7}$
4. $\frac{5}{6}$; $\frac{1}{6}$
5. $\frac{3}{8}$; $\frac{5}{8}$
6. $\frac{1}{5}$; $\frac{4}{5}$

**Write the fraction that names the part of the set of animals.**

7. *not* cats $\frac{3}{9}$
8. *not* monkeys or rabbits $\frac{7}{9}$
9. *not* dogs $\frac{8}{9}$
10. *not* dogs or cats $\frac{2}{9}$

**Solve.**

11. Five of 12 students are in the school chorus. What part of the students are in the chorus? $\frac{5}{12}$
12. Twenty of 25 students voted for class president. What part of the class did **not** vote for president? $\frac{5}{25}$ or $\frac{1}{5}$

Grade 4 14 Chapter 13

You have learned that fractions can be used to name part of a whole and part of a set. Another way of looking at fractions is as division of whole numbers by whole numbers.

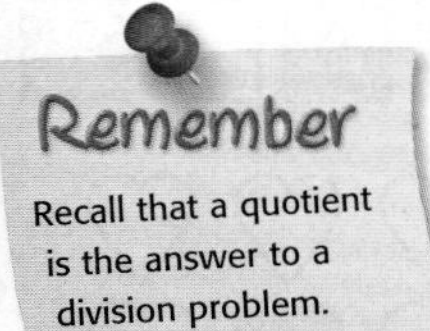

**Remember**

Recall that a quotient is the answer to a division problem.

## Real-World EXAMPLE — Fraction as a Quotient

**3** **FOOD Tammy and three friends went to a pancake breakfast. They ordered and shared three pancakes equally. What part of the pancakes did each receive?**

Draw a picture to show the division.

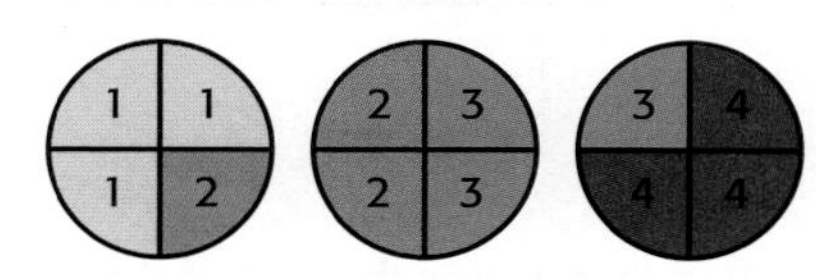


Three pancakes are divided among 4 people. So, each person receives 3 divided by 4 or $\frac{3}{4}$ of the pancakes.

★ indicates multi-step problem

## CHECK What You Know

**Write the fraction for the part of the set that is yellow. Then write the fraction for the part that is *not* yellow.** See Examples 1 and 2 (p. 540)

**1.**  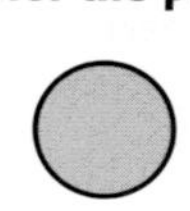 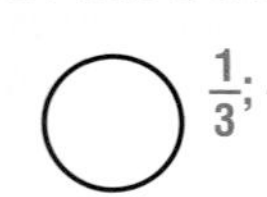 $\frac{1}{3}, \frac{2}{3}$

**2.** 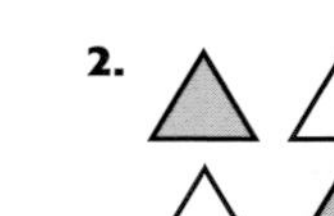 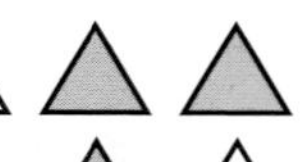 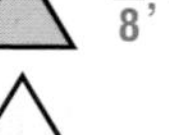 $\frac{5}{8}, \frac{3}{8}$

**Write the fraction that names the part of the set of vegetables.**
See Examples 1 and 2 (p. 540)

**3.** *not* red peppers $\frac{4}{7}$

**4.** *not* corn $\frac{5}{7}$

**5.** *not* green peppers $\frac{5}{7}$

**6.** Five chimpanzees are sharing four bananas equally. What part of the bananas does each receive? See Example 3 (p. 541) $\frac{4}{5}$

**7.** Talk About It — Explain what the following sentence means. *Three-fifths of a set of animals are dogs.*
Sample answer: This means that there could be a total of 5 animals, 3 of which are dogs.



**Enrich (p. 17)** AL

13–2 Name ______ Date ______

**Enrich**

*Name That Part*

**Write the fraction represented by each idea below. For example, two stars on the American flag is $\frac{2}{50}$ or $\frac{1}{25}$.**

1. One day a week $\frac{1}{7}$
2. Three months in a year $\frac{3}{12}$
3. Eight toes on two feet $\frac{8}{10}$
4. Two legs on a spider $\frac{2}{8}$
5. Ten minutes in an hour $\frac{10}{60}$
6. The left shoe of a pair $\frac{1}{2}$
7. One flat tire on a car $\frac{1}{4}$
8. Twelve inches of a yard $\frac{12}{36}$
9. Three arms on an octopus $\frac{3}{8}$
10. The color yellow on a traffic light $\frac{1}{3}$

Grade 4 17 Chapter 13



Chapter Resources

### Fraction as a Quotient

**Example 3** Point out that the pancakes are divided into 4 equal parts because there are 4 people (Tammy and 3 other people) who went to breakfast. Then each person gets three of the twelve equal parts, or $\frac{3}{4}$ of a pancake.

### ADDITIONAL EXAMPLES

**1** What fraction of the set of bicycles is red? $\frac{3}{5}$

**2** What fraction of the helmets is *not* black? $\frac{5}{7}$

**3** Rafiq pops two bags of popcorn. If he shares the popcorn equally with six friends, what part of the bags of popcorn does each person receive? $\frac{2}{7}$

### CHECK What You Know

As a class, have students complete Exercises 1–7 in **Check What You Know** as you observe their work.

**Exercise 7** Assess student comprehension before assigning practice exercises.

## BL Alternate Teaching Strategy

**If** students have trouble identifying, reading, writing, and modeling fractions for parts a set…

**Then** use one of these reteach options:

1. CRM **Daily Reteach Worksheet** (p. 13)
2. Provide counters or other manipulatives for students to use to model various sets. Allow them to use these manipulatives as they work through the exercises to find the fractions for the parts of the sets.

# 3 Practice

Differentiate practice using these leveled assignments for Exercises 8–24.

| Level | Assignment |
|---|---|
| BL Below/Approaching Level | 8–10, 12–14, 18–19, 20 |
| OL On Level | 9–11, 13–16, 20–21, 23 |
| AL Above/Beyond Level | 9–21 odd, 22–24 |

Have students discuss and complete the Higher Order Thinking problems. Remind students to draw pictures of the sets and shade or color to represent the fractions.

**WRITING IN MATH** Have students complete Exercise 24 in their Math Journals. You may choose to use this exercise as an optional formative assessment.

**COMMON ERROR!**

**Exercise 12–17** Students may fail to notice the word *not* in these exercises. Point out that "not circles" means to write a fraction that names the part of the set that is triangles and squares.



## Practice and Problem Solving

EXTRA PRACTICE See page R34.

**Write the fraction for the part of the set that is blue. Then write the fraction for the part that is *not* blue.** See Examples 1 and 2 (p. 540)

**8.**  $\frac{3}{4}, \frac{1}{4}$

**9.** 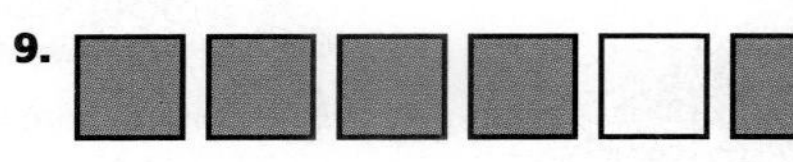 $\frac{5}{6}, \frac{1}{6}$

**10.** 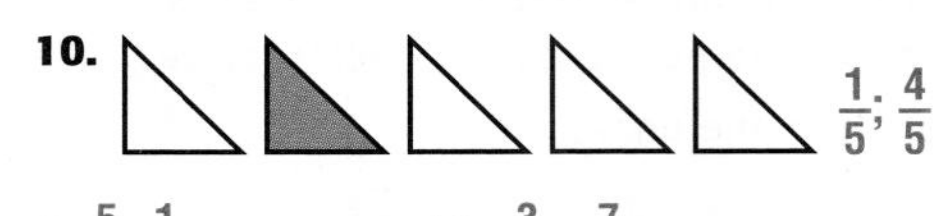 $\frac{1}{5}, \frac{4}{5}$

**11.**  $\frac{3}{10}, \frac{7}{10}$

**Write the fraction that names the part of the set of shapes.** See Example 2 (p. 540)

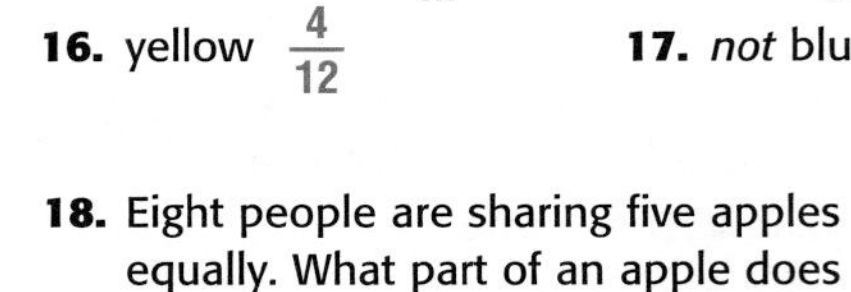

**12.** circles $\frac{5}{12}$

**13.** *not* squares $\frac{7}{12}$

**14.** *not* triangles $\frac{10}{12}$

**15.** red $\frac{2}{12}$

**16.** yellow $\frac{4}{12}$

**17.** *not* blue $\frac{9}{12}$

**18.** Eight people are sharing five apples equally. What part of an apple does each receive? See Example 3 (p. 541) $\frac{5}{8}$

**19.** Twelve elephants are sharing nine bales of hay equally. What part of a bale of hay does each receive? See Example 3 (p. 541) $\frac{9}{12}$

### Data File

The state mammal of Alabama is the black bear. Black bears usually have 1 to 5 cubs. Cubs measure 8 inches in length and weigh 8 to 12 ounces at birth.

**20.** ★ Suppose 10 black bears are traveling together. If 4 of them are adult females and 3 are cubs, what fraction is adult males? $\frac{3}{10}$

**21.** A black bear has 3 cubs. If one of the cubs is male, what fraction of the cubs is female? $\frac{2}{3}$

## H.O.T. Problems

**22. OPEN ENDED** Draw a set of objects that shows the fraction $\frac{3}{5}$. See Ch. 13 Answer Appendix.

**23. FIND THE ERROR** Three eighths of a set of fruit are oranges. What part is *not* oranges? Who is correct, Sonja or Jairo?

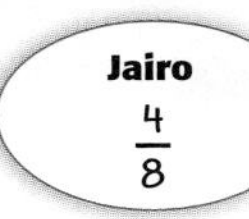

Sonja: $\frac{5}{8}$

Jairo: $\frac{4}{8}$

Sample answer: Sonja; The fraction $\frac{3}{8}$ means 3 out of 8. So, 8 − 3 or 5 pieces are not oranges. Thus, $\frac{5}{8}$ are not oranges.

**24. WRITING IN MATH** Write a problem that involves identifying a fraction that describes part of a group. See Ch. 13 Answer Appendix.

## TEST Practice

**25.** Which figure shows $\frac{2}{5}$? (Lesson 13-1) B

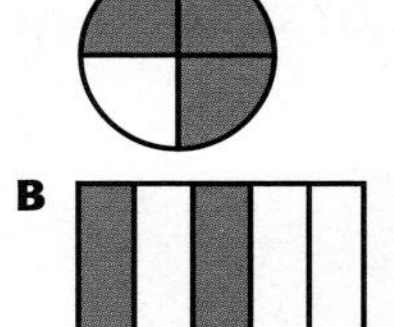

A C B D

**26.** Stephen walks his dog 4 days each week. His brother walks the dog the other days. What fraction names the part of a week Stephen's brother walks the dog? (Lesson 13-2) F

F $\frac{3}{7}$ H $\frac{4}{7}$

G $\frac{1}{2}$ J $\frac{3}{4}$

## Spiral Review

**Draw a picture and shade part of it to show the fraction.** (Lesson 13-1) 27–29. See Ch. 13 Answer Appendix.

**27.** $\frac{2}{5}$ **28.** $\frac{1}{6}$ **29.** $\frac{4}{10}$

**30. Measurement** Maurice left for school at 8:30 A.M. He arrived at 9:05 A.M. How long did it take him to get to school? Use a clock if needed. (Lesson 12-10) 35 min

**31. Measurement** Estimate and measure the weight of two objects in your bookbag. (Lesson 12-4) See students' work.



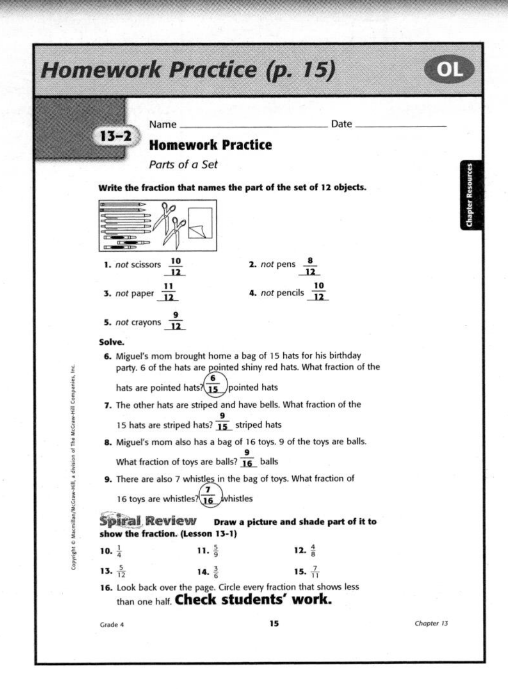

### Homework Practice (p. 15) OL

13-2 Name ______ Date ______

**Homework Practice**

*Parts of a Set*

**Write the fraction that names the part of the set of 12 objects.**

1. *not* scissors $\frac{10}{12}$
2. *not* pens $\frac{8}{12}$
3. *not* paper $\frac{11}{12}$
4. *not* pencils $\frac{10}{12}$
5. *not* crayons $\frac{9}{12}$

**Solve.**

6. Miguel's mom brought home a bag of 15 hats for his birthday party. 6 of the hats are pointed shiny red hats. What fraction of the hats are pointed hats? $\frac{6}{15}$ pointed hats
7. The other hats are striped and have bells. What fraction of the 15 hats are striped hats? $\frac{9}{15}$ striped hats
8. Miguel's mom also has a bag of 16 toys. 9 of the toys are balls. What fraction of toys are balls? $\frac{9}{16}$ balls
9. There are also 7 whistles in the bag of toys. What fraction of 16 toys are whistles? $\frac{7}{16}$ whistles

**Spiral Review** **Draw a picture and shade part of it to show the fraction. (Lesson 13-1)**

10. $\frac{1}{4}$ 11. $\frac{5}{9}$ 12. $\frac{4}{8}$

13. $\frac{5}{12}$ 14. $\frac{3}{6}$ 15. $\frac{7}{11}$

16. Look back over the page. Circle every fraction that shows less than one half. **Check students' work.**

Grade 4 15 Chapter 13



Chapter Resources

# 4 Assess

## Formative Assessment

Draw a dozen stars on the board. Make 6 with stripes, 3 with polka dots, 1 shaded, and 2 plain.

- **What part of the stars is shaded?** $\frac{1}{12}$
- **What part has polka dots?** $\frac{3}{12}$
- **What part of the stars is not striped?** $\frac{6}{12}$

**Quick Check** **Are students continuing to struggle with identifying, reading, writing, and modeling fractions for parts of a set?**

**If Yes** → Strategic Intervention Guide (p. 26)

**If No** → Independent Work Options (p. 540B)
CRM Skills Practice Worksheet (p. 14)
CRM Enrich Worksheet (p. 17)

**Yesterday's News** Ask students to explain how yesterday's lesson on parts of a whole helped them with today's lesson on parts of a set.

## TEST Practice

### Reviews Lessons 13-1 and 13-2

Assign the Test Practice problems to provide daily reinforcement of test-taking skills.

## Spiral Review

### Reviews Lessons 12-4, 12-10, and 13-1

Review and assess mastery of skills and concepts from previous chapters.

# Problem-Solving Strategy
# Draw a Picture

## Lesson Planner

### Objective

Solve problems by drawing a picture.

### Resources

**Manipulatives:** counters

**Literature Connection:** *Inchworm and a Half* by Elinor J. Pinczes

**Teacher Technology**
TeacherWorks • Interactive Classroom

**Real-World Problem Solving Library**
**Math and Social Studies:** ***Life in the United States***
Use these leveled books to reinforce and extend problem-solving skills and strategies.

Leveled for:
- OL On Level
- ELL Sheltered English
- SP Spanish

For additional support, see the Real-World Problem Solving Teacher Guide.

## Daily Routine

Use these suggestions before beginning the lesson on p. 544.

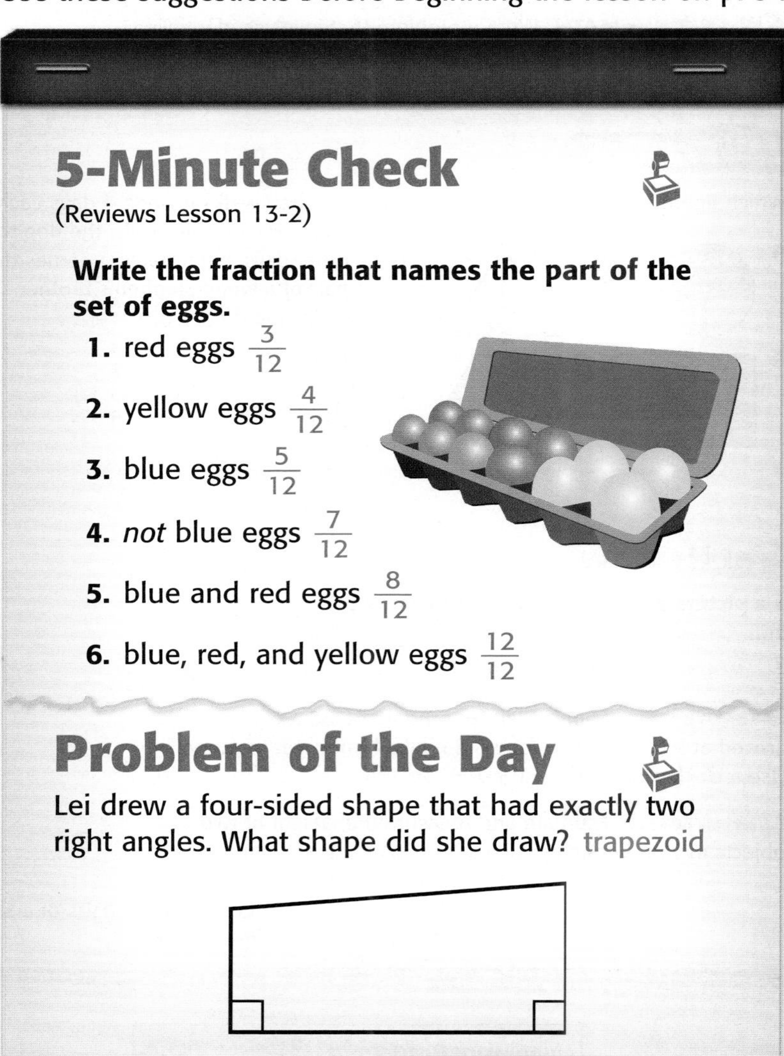

### 5-Minute Check
(Reviews Lesson 13-2)

**Write the fraction that names the part of the set of eggs.**

1. red eggs $\frac{3}{12}$
2. yellow eggs $\frac{4}{12}$
3. blue eggs $\frac{5}{12}$
4. *not* blue eggs $\frac{7}{12}$
5. blue and red eggs $\frac{8}{12}$
6. blue, red, and yellow eggs $\frac{12}{12}$

### Problem of the Day

Lei drew a four-sided shape that had exactly two right angles. What shape did she draw? trapezoid

# Differentiated Instruction

## Small Group Options

**Option 1** LINGUISTIC, LOGICAL

### Gifted and Talented AL

**Materials:** visual access to an analog clock, chart paper

- Write the following problem on the chart paper: *Erica spent $\frac{2}{3}$ of an hour practicing the piano. Tim spent $\frac{3}{4}$ of an hour practicing the violin. Who spent more time and by how many minutes?*
- Encourage students to draw two clocks, dividing each into the fractional parts indicated.
- How many minutes in $\frac{1}{4}$ of an hour? 15 minutes
- How many minutes in $\frac{1}{3}$ of an hour? 20 minutes

- Encourage students to shade in the fractions indicated to help them figure the answer.
- Some students may tell you that Tim practiced longer. Encourage them to go back to the problem to find the answer to the second question. 5 minutes
- If Tim practiced for $\frac{1}{2}$ an hour and Erica practiced for $\frac{2}{4}$ of an hour, who practiced more then? $\frac{1}{2}$ and $\frac{2}{4}$ are equivalent; They practiced the same amount.

**Option 2** INTRAPERSONAL

### English Language Learners ELL

**Core Vocabulary:** clap, hop, translate movement into parts of a whole
**Common Use Verb:** copy
**Do Math** This strategy uses kinesthetic and patterning skills to teach transitions of kinesthetic fractions into visual representations.

- Model the 3-step action: hop, hop, hop/clap (hop and clap simultaneously). Repeat until students can copy you.
- Write the actions as a fraction: $\frac{\text{clap}}{\text{hop hop hop}}$ $\frac{1}{3}$
- Have students draw a picture that translates the same 1 of 3 information.
- Repeat as time permits, allowing students to come up with their own pattern and with the rest of their group drawing it out.

## Independent Work Options

**Option 1** SPATIAL, LINGUISTIC

### Early Finishers OL AL

**Materials:** pencils, paper

- Draw a picture that could represent the answer to a problem-solving problem. Trade the picture with another student. Then ask each student to make up a problem to go with the picture.
- Discuss the pictures and problems to be sure they accurately represent each other.

**Option 2**

### Student Technology

**Math Online** macmillanmh.com

Personal Tutor • Extra Examples

**Option 3**

### Learning Station: Art (p. 534G)

Direct students to the Art Learning Station for opportunities to explore and extend the lesson concept.

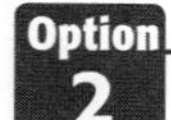

# 13-3 Problem-Solving Strategy

## 1 Introduce

**Activity Choice 1 • Review**

- Pose the following problem to students:

  *Rocky is helping plan his little sister's birthday party. He wants to get 3 party favors for each of the 8 guests. How many favors should Rocky buy?*
- **Which problem-solving strategy could you use to solve this problem?** Sample answer: make a table
- **Solve the problem.** 24

**Activity Choice 2 • Literature**

Introduce the lesson with *Inchworm and a Half* by Elinor J. Pinczes. For a related math activity, see p. TR63.

## 2 Teach

Have students read the problem on reptiles. Guide them through the problem-solving steps.

**Understand** Using the questions, review what students know and need to find.

**Plan** Have them discuss their strategy.

**Solve** Guide students to use the draw a picture strategy to solve the problem.

- **How many circles will you need to draw to represent the total number of reptiles?** 15
- **How many circles will you shade to represent $\frac{1}{3}$ of the circles? Explain.** 5; $\frac{1}{3}$ of 15 is 5.

**Check** Have students look back at the problem to make sure that the answer fits the facts given.

- **Add 5 turtles + 2 snakes + 8 lizards. Does that equal 15?** yes

### COMMON ERROR!

Students often do not know where to begin to solve problems with multiple steps. Suggest they first draw a picture, and then work backward to solve.



# 13-3 Problem-Solving Strategy

**MAIN IDEA** I will solve problems by drawing a picture.

Brandi and her mom are at a pet store. The pet store has 15 reptiles. One third of the reptiles are turtles. Two are snakes, and the rest are lizards. How many of each reptile are there?

| | |
|---|---|
| **Understand** | **What facts do you know?**<br>• There are 15 reptiles at the store.<br>• One third are turtles.<br>• Two are snakes.<br>• The rest are lizards.<br><br>**What do you need to find?**<br>• Find the number of each reptile. |
| **Plan** | Draw a picture to solve the problem. |
| **Solve** | • Draw 15 circles. Since the fraction $\frac{1}{3}$ is used, place the circles in 3 equal groups.<br>• To show the turtles, shade $\frac{1}{3}$ of the circles. That is, one of the three equal groups. So, there are 5 turtles. There are 2 snakes, so shade 2 circles to show the snakes.<br>• There are 8 circles not shaded. This is the number of lizards.<br><br>So, there are 5 turtles, 2 snakes, and 8 lizards at the pet store.<br><br>turtles<br>snakes |
| **Check** | Look back. 5 turtles + 2 snakes + 8 lizards = 15 reptiles. The pet store has 15 reptiles. So, the answer is correct. |

544 Chapter 13 Describe and Compare Fractions

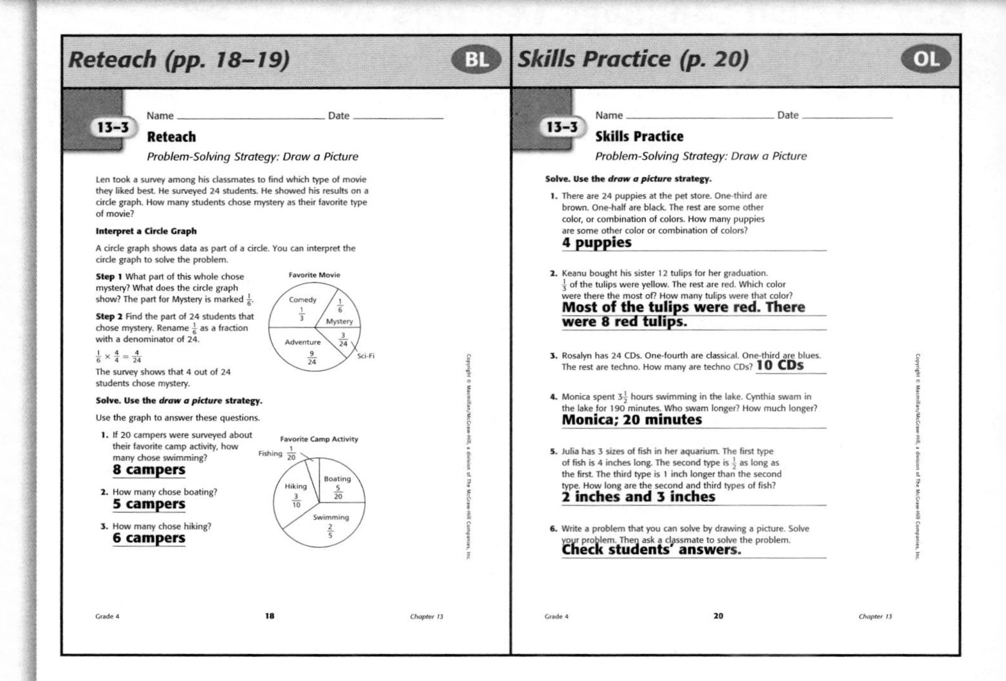

**Reteach (pp. 18–19)** BL

13-3 Name ______ Date ______

**Reteach**

*Problem-Solving Strategy: Draw a Picture*

Len took a survey among his classmates to find which type of movie they liked best. He surveyed 24 students. He showed his results on a circle graph. How many students chose mystery as their favorite type of movie?

**Interpret a Circle Graph**

A circle graph shows data as part of a circle. You can interpret the circle graph to solve the problem.

**Step 1** What part of this whole chose mystery? What does the circle graph show? The part for Mystery is marked $\frac{1}{6}$.

**Step 2** Find the part of 24 students that chose mystery. Rename $\frac{1}{6}$ as a fraction with a denominator of 24.

$\frac{1}{6} \times \frac{4}{4} = \frac{4}{24}$

The survey shows that 4 out of 24 students chose mystery.



**Solve. Use the *draw a picture* strategy.**

Use the graph to answer these questions.

1. If 20 campers were surveyed about their favorite camp activity, how many chose swimming? **8 campers**
2. How many chose boating? **5 campers**
3. How many chose hiking? **6 campers**





Grade 4 18 Chapter 13

**Skills Practice (p. 20)** OL

13-3 Name ______ Date ______

**Skills Practice**

*Problem-Solving Strategy: Draw a Picture*

**Solve. Use the *draw a picture* strategy.**

1. There are 24 puppies at the pet store. One-third are brown. One-half are black. The rest are some other color, or combination of colors. How many puppies are some other color or combination of colors? **4 puppies**
2. Keanu bought his sister 12 tulips for her graduation. $\frac{1}{3}$ of the tulips were yellow. The rest are red. Which color were there the most of? How many tulips were that color? **Most of the tulips were red. There were 8 red tulips.**
3. Rosalyn has 24 CDs. One-fourth are classical. One-third are blues. The rest are techno. How many are techno CDs? **10 CDs**
4. Monica spent $3\frac{1}{2}$ hours swimming in the lake. Cynthia swam in the lake for 190 minutes. Who swam longer? How much longer? **Monica; 20 minutes**
5. Julia has 3 sizes of fish in her aquarium. The first type of fish is 4 inches long. The second type is $\frac{1}{2}$ as long as the first. The third type is 1 inch longer than the second type. How long are the second and third types of fish? **2 inches and 3 inches**
6. Write a problem that you can solve by drawing a picture. Solve your problem. Then ask a classmate to solve the problem. **Check students' answers.**



Grade 4 20 Chapter 13

★ indicates multi-step problem

## ANALYZE the Strategy

2, 4. See Ch. 13 Answer Appendix.

**Refer to the problem on the previous page.**

1. Explain why you used 15 circles. 1. Sample answer: There are 15 reptiles and each circle represents 1 reptile.
2. You know that $\frac{1}{3}$ of the reptiles are turtles. Explain why 5 circles were shaded to show the number of turtles.
3. ★ If the pet store had 24 reptiles, how many of the reptiles would be lizards? 14 lizards
4. Check your answer to Exercise 3. How do you know that it is correct?

## PRACTICE the Strategy

EXTRA PRACTICE See page R34.

**Solve. Use the draw a picture strategy.**

★5. **Measurement** There are three trees in a backyard. The second tree is half as tall as the first. The third tree is taller than the second tree and shorter than the first tree. The total height of the trees is 24 feet. What is the height of each tree? 10 ft, 5 ft, 9 ft

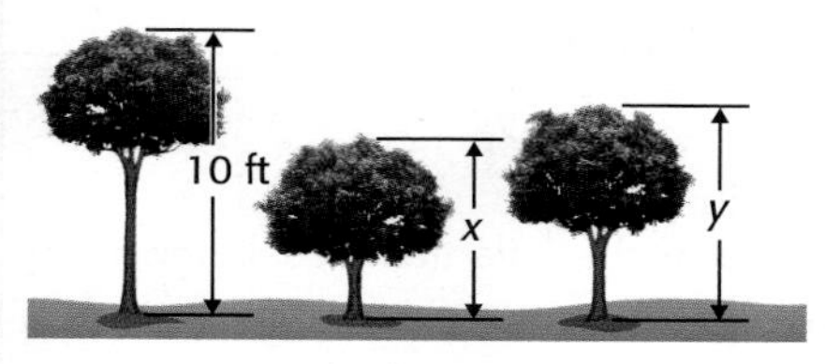


6. Pam and three other students are waiting in a line. Lakita is ahead of Pam. Sanjay is third in line. Rob is behind Sanjay. In what order are the students standing? Lakita, Pam, Sanjay, then Rob

7. Emil bought his mom a dozen roses. Some of the roses are shown below. The rest are white. Which color were there the most of? How many roses were that color? red; 6

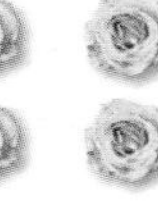

★8. There are 22 students in Ms. Lane's class. Half of them packed their lunches. Eight students are buying pizza. The rest are buying salads. How many students are buying salads? 3 students

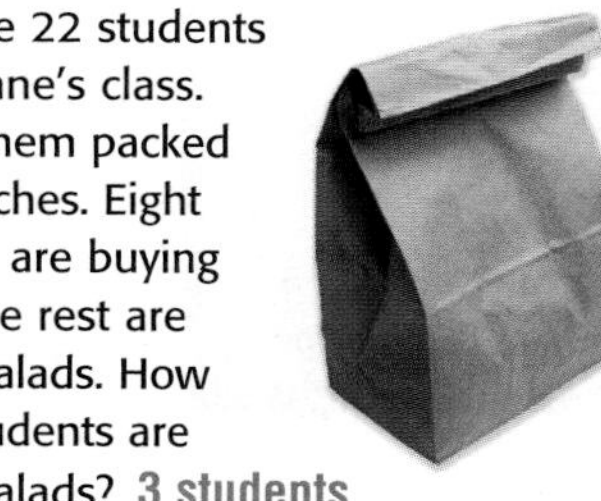

9. **Measurement** The table shows how long Adam and Kenya rode their bikes. Who biked more minutes? How many more minutes? Adam; 5 min

| Biking Schedule | |
|---|---|
| **Name** | **Time Spent Biking** |
| Adam | $\frac{1}{3}$ of an hour |
| Kenya | 15 minutes |

10. ★ There are 16 books on a shelf. One-fourth of the books are about animals. Two are adventure. The rest are mystery. How many are mystery books? 10

11. **WRITING IN MATH** Look back at Exercise 10. Explain how you used the draw a picture strategy to solve the problem. See Ch. 13 Answer Appendix.



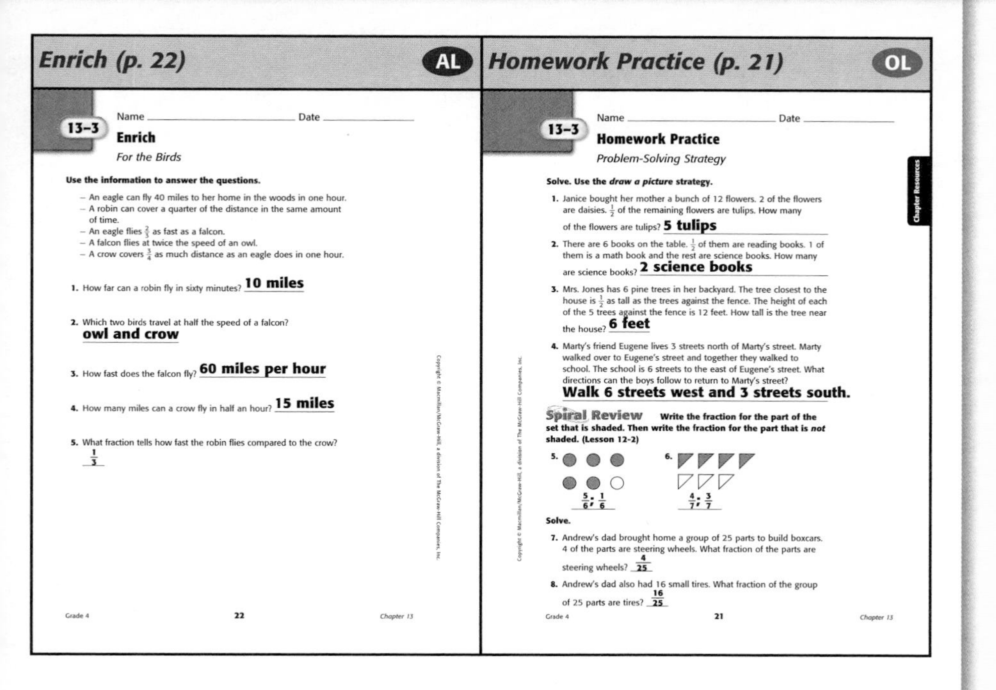

**Enrich (p. 22)** AL

13-3 Name ________ Date ________

**Enrich**

*For the Birds*

**Use the information to answer the questions.**

- An eagle can fly 40 miles to her home in the woods in one hour.
- A robin can cover a quarter of the distance in the same amount of time.
- An eagle flies $\frac{2}{3}$ as fast as a falcon.
- A falcon flies at twice the speed of an owl.
- A crow covers $\frac{3}{4}$ as much distance as an eagle does in one hour.

1. How far can a robin fly in sixty minutes? **10 miles**
2. Which two birds travel at half the speed of a falcon? **owl and crow**
3. How fast does the falcon fly? **60 miles per hour**
4. How many miles can a crow fly in half an hour? **15 miles**
5. What fraction tells how fast the robin flies compared to the crow? $\frac{1}{3}$



Grade 4 22 Chapter 13

**Homework Practice (p. 21)** OL

13-3 Name ________ Date ________

**Homework Practice**

*Problem-Solving Strategy*

Chapter Resources

**Solve. Use the *draw a picture* strategy.**

1. Janice bought her mother a bunch of 12 flowers. 2 of the flowers are daisies. $\frac{1}{2}$ of the remaining flowers are tulips. How many of the flowers are tulips? **5 tulips**
2. There are 6 books on the table. $\frac{1}{2}$ of them are reading books. 1 of them is a math book and the rest are science books. How many are science books? **2 science books**
3. Mrs. Jones has 6 pine trees in her backyard. The tree closest to the house is $\frac{1}{2}$ as tall as the trees against the fence. The height of each of the 5 trees against the fence is 12 feet. How tall is the tree near the house? **6 feet**
4. Marty's friend Eugene lives 3 streets north of Marty's street. Marty walked over to Eugene's street and together they walked to school. The school is 6 streets to the east of Eugene's street. What directions can the boys follow to return to Marty's street? **Walk 6 streets west and 3 streets south.**

**Spiral Review** **Write the fraction for the part of the set that is shaded. Then write the fraction for the part that is *not* shaded. (Lesson 12-2)**

5. $\frac{5}{6}$, $\frac{1}{6}$
6. $\frac{4}{7}$, $\frac{3}{7}$

**Solve.**

7. Andrew's dad brought home a group of 25 parts to build boxcars. 4 of the parts are steering wheels. What fraction of the parts are steering wheels? $\frac{4}{25}$
8. Andrew's dad also had 16 small tires. What fraction of the group of 25 parts are tires? $\frac{16}{25}$



Grade 4 21 Chapter 13

**Analyze the Strategy** Use Exercises 1–4 to analyze and discuss the problem-solving strategy.

### BL Alternate Teaching Strategy

**If** students have trouble drawing a picture to solve problems…

**Then** use one of these reteach options:

1 CRM **Daily Reteach Worksheets** (pp. 18–19)

2 Provide students with counters or other manipulatives to help them solve the problems. The use of manipulatives may also help them think of pictures they could use.

## 3 Practice

### Using the Exercises

**Exercise 9** Explain to students that $\frac{1}{3}$ of an hour means one hour divided into three equal parts.

**Exercise 11** Students may need help finding one-fourth of 16. Remind them that $\frac{1}{4}$ means one out of four, so they can group the books by fours.

## 4 Assess

### Formative Assessment

Present students with the following problem:

*Benita made a model of the Pentagon. If the perimeter of the model was 40 inches, how long was each side?*

- **Describe the steps you would take to solve this problem.** Sample answer: I know a pentagon has 5 sides, so I divided 40 by 5 to get 8 inches for each side of the model.
- **Find the solution.** Each side is 8 inches long.

**Quick Check** **Are students continuing to struggle with drawing a picture to solve problems?**

**If Yes** → CRM Reteach Worksheets (pp. 18–19)

**If No** → Independent Work Options (p. 544B)
CRM Skills Practice Worksheet (p. 20)
CRM Enrich Worksheet (p. 22)

# Lesson Planner

## Objective

Identify equivalent fractions.

## Vocabulary

**equivalent fractions**

## Resources

**Materials:** grid paper, rulers

**Manipulatives:** fraction models

## 1 Introduce

### Introduce the Concept

- Write out four equivalent fractions on slips of paper, such as $\frac{1}{3}$, $\frac{2}{6}$, $\frac{3}{9}$, and $\frac{4}{12}$. Divide the class into four groups and have each one make a large rectangle of the same size on a piece of grid paper. Hand each group a slip and ask them to shade that fraction of the rectangle.
- Compare the models. **What do you notice about the four models?** Each represents the same fractional amount.
- Point out that the four fractions are equivalent.

## 2 Teach

**Activity 1** After students use two $\frac{1}{6}$ fraction models to equal $\frac{1}{3}$, ask them to think about the relationship of the fractions' numerators and denominators.



Explore

Math Activity for 13-4

# Equivalent Fractions

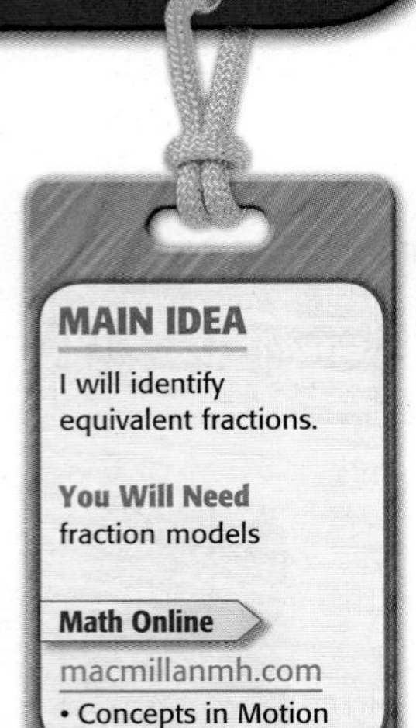


Fractions that represent the same amount are **equivalent fractions.**

**ACTIVITY** **Model Equivalent Fractions**

**1 Identify two fractions that are equivalent to $\frac{1}{3}$.**

**Step 1** **Model $\frac{1}{3}$.**

Start with 1 whole. Then, use the $\frac{1}{3}$ fraction model to show $\frac{1}{3}$.

**Step 2** **Find a fraction equivalent to $\frac{1}{3}$.**

Using $\frac{1}{6}$ fraction models, place them below the $\frac{1}{3}$ fraction model. How many $\frac{1}{6}$ fraction models are used?

**Step 3** **Find another fraction equivalent to $\frac{1}{3}$.**

Use $\frac{1}{12}$ fraction models to equal the length of the $\frac{1}{3}$ fraction model. Count the number of $\frac{1}{12}$ fraction models.

So, $\frac{1}{3}$, $\frac{2}{6}$, and $\frac{4}{12}$ are equivalent fractions.

## ACTIVITY Model Equivalent Fractions

**2 Identify three equivalent fractions.**

**Step 1** Draw three identical number lines that show zero and one.

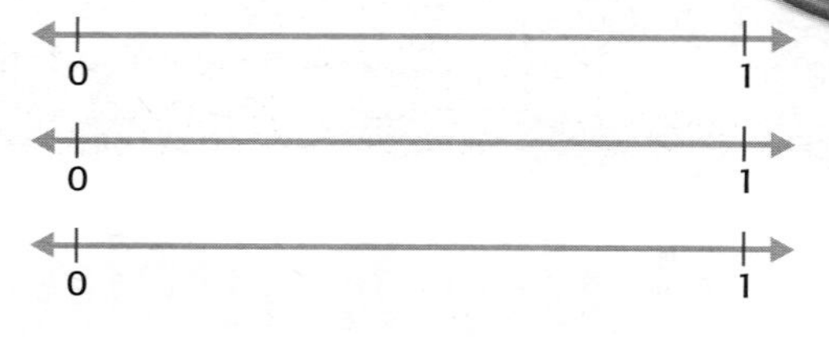


**Step 2** Divide the first number line into fourths. Divide the second number line into eighths. Divide the third number line into sixteenths.

Notice that $\frac{1}{4} = \frac{2}{8} = \frac{4}{16}$.

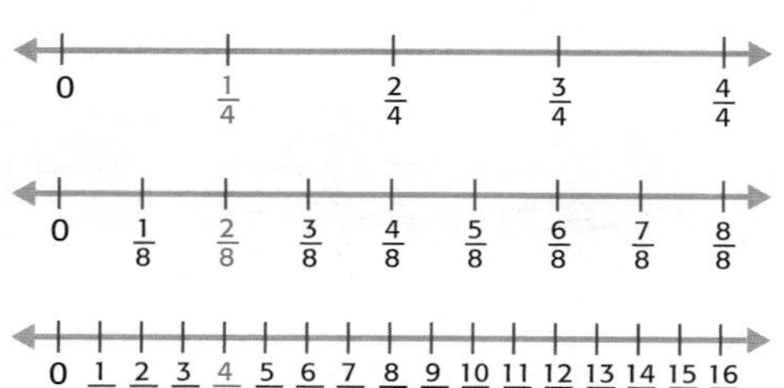


### Think About It

1. **Algebra** Copy and complete $\frac{1}{3} = \frac{\blacksquare}{9} = \frac{\blacksquare}{15}$. 3; 5
2. Refer to Activity 2. Find two fractions equivalent to $\frac{3}{4}$. Sample answer: $\frac{6}{8}$ and $\frac{12}{16}$

### CHECK What You Know

**Determine whether each pair of fractions is equivalent. Use fraction models or number lines.**

3. $\frac{2}{4}$ and $\frac{6}{12}$ yes
4. $\frac{6}{8}$ and $\frac{5}{10}$ no
5. $\frac{2}{3}$ and $\frac{3}{5}$ no
6. $\frac{9}{12}$ and $\frac{3}{4}$ yes

**Find two equivalent fractions for each fraction. Use fraction models or number lines.** 7–10. Sample answers are given.

7. $\frac{1}{5}$ $\frac{2}{10}$ and $\frac{3}{15}$
8. $\frac{2}{6}$ $\frac{1}{3}$ and $\frac{4}{12}$
9. $\frac{4}{8}$ $\frac{2}{4}$ and $\frac{8}{16}$
10. $\frac{2}{12}$ $\frac{1}{6}$ and $\frac{4}{24}$
11. **WRITING IN MATH** Explain what it means for two fractions to be equivalent. Sample answer: They represent the same amount.

**Activity 2** Provide grid paper and rulers for students to create their number lines. Have them make the number lines so that the points 0 and 1 will be 16 boxes apart. That way, all the number line labels will fall on the lines. This will make comparisons easier for the students.

**Step 2** To divide a line into fourths, divide it into four sections of equal length. Repeat this process for each fraction. The denominator of each fraction equals the number of equal sections the number line is to be divided into. $\frac{1}{4} = \frac{2}{8} = \frac{4}{16}$ because these fractions are located the same distance from 0 and 1 on the number lines.

### Think About It

Assign Exercises 1–2 in the Think About It section to assess student comprehension of the concept presented in the Activity.

## 3 Assess

### Formative Assessment

Use the **Check What You Know** Exercises 3–11 to assess whether students understand how to find equivalent fractions.

**From Concrete to Abstract** Exercise 9 will help bridge the gap between using manipulatives to find equivalent fractions and finding equivalent fractions using paper and pencil. Students may recognize $\frac{4}{8}$ as being equivalent to $\frac{1}{2}$. Ask them how they knew this without using manipulatives.

**Extending the Concept** Students should see the connection to dividing (or multiplying) the numerator and denominator by the same number to find equivalent fractions. As in Exercise 9, they could divide both 4 and 8 by 2 or by 4 to produce an equivalent fraction. Provide additional examples for students to try without the manipulatives if time allows.

LESSON 13-4

# Equivalent Fractions

## Lesson Planner

### Objective

Find equivalent fractions.

### Vocabulary

**equivalent fractions**

### Resources

**Materials:** colored paper, grid paper

**Literature Connection:** *Fraction Fun* by David A. Adler

**Alternate Lesson:** Use *IMPACT Mathematics:* Unit D to provide practice with equivalent fractions.

**Teacher Technology**

TeacherWorks • Interactive Classroom

### Focus on Math Background

Students should understand that fractions that have different numerators and denominators can name the same number. Finding an equivalent fraction can be thought of as "renaming" a number, with the value remaining the same. Open-ended exercises allow students to see that there are many fractions that are equivalent to a given fraction.

Since finding equivalent fractions underlies all operations with fractions, it is essential that students easily find equivalent fractions that have larger numerators and denominators and also ones with smaller numerators and denominators. Practice with a variety of concrete models, such as fractions strips and fraction circles, is often helpful, and measuring with a ruler marked in inches can be a particularly effective experience.

## Daily Routine

Use these suggestions before beginning the lesson on p. 548.

### 5-Minute Check

(Reviews Lesson 13-3)

**Solve. Use the draw a picture strategy.**

A pizza is cut into 12 equal slices. Half of the pizza has sausage and peppers on it, two slices have eggplant, and the rest of the pizza is plain cheese. What fraction of the pizza is plain? $\frac{4}{12}$ or $\frac{1}{3}$

### Problem of the Day

The combined ages of Akila's three cousins is 12. They are all two years apart, and one of them is exactly half of the total ages. Find their ages. 2, 4, and 6

### Building Math Vocabulary

Write the lesson vocabulary word and its definition on the board.

Have students use the word *equivalent* in a sentence. Then ask each student to write down and illustrate an example of equivalent fractions. You may wish to collect and display these on a large poster board.

# Differentiated Instruction

## Small Group Options

LOGICAL

### Option 1 Below Level BL

**Materials:** chart paper

- Review the meaning of the term *equivalent fractions*.
- Write the fraction $\frac{1}{2}$ on the chart paper.
- **Can you think of any fractions that are equivalent to $\frac{1}{2}$?**
- Write any correct answers in such a way that they are written in order as follows:

Fractions equivalent to ___:
$\frac{1}{2}, \frac{2}{4}, \frac{3}{6}, \frac{4}{8}, \frac{5}{10}$, etc.

- **Do you see a pattern here?** Accept any reasonable answer, but you are looking for the students to notice that the numerator is half of the denominator.
- Tell students if they know that, they can find the missing numerator or denominator for any fraction equivalent to $\frac{1}{2}$.
- Write a few examples on the chart paper with missing numerators or denominators.

VISUAL, LOGICAL

### Option 2 English Language Learners ELL

**Materials:** overhead money
**Core Vocabulary:** equivalent, half a dollar, 50 cents
**Common Use Verb:** is the same as
**See Math** This strategy helps students better understand the concept of equivalent fractions through pictures and native language.

- Show $\frac{1}{2}$ of a circle and ask for the word *half* in students' native languages.
- Show a dollar folded in half and say, "This is **half a dollar**."
- Show 50¢ in quarters and ask if this is also half a dollar. Write and show $\frac{1}{4} + \frac{1}{4} = \frac{2}{4} = \frac{1}{2}$.
- Have students demonstrate other ways to show half of a whole as time permits.

## Independent Work Options

SPATIAL

### Option 1 Early Finishers OL AL

**Materials:** sets of 30 index cards showing equivalent fractions, made ahead of time

- In groups of four, students will play "memory" to make pairs of equivalent fractions.
- Place all the cards facedown on a table. Players will take turns flipping over two cards until they find a pair of equivalent fractions. If a player finds a pair, he or she gets to keep the pair and continues turning over pairs of cards until he or she no longer turns over an equivalent pair. The winner is the player with the most pairs at the end of the game.

### Option 2 Student Technology

**Math Online** macmillanmh.com

Personal Tutor • Extra Examples

Math Adventures

### Option 3 Learning Station: Science (p. 534H)

Direct students to the Science Learning Station for opportunities to explore and extend the lesson concept.

### Option 4 Problem-Solving Practice

Reinforce problem-solving skills and strategies with the Problem-Solving Practice worksheet.

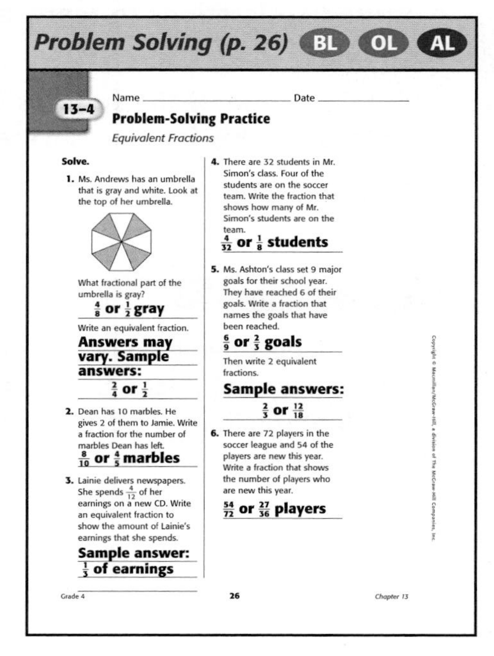

**Problem Solving (p. 26)** BL OL AL

13–4 Name ______ Date ______

**Problem-Solving Practice**
*Equivalent Fractions*

**Solve.**

1. Ms. Andrews has an umbrella that is gray and white. Look at the top of her umbrella.
   What fractional part of the umbrella is gray?
   **$\frac{4}{8}$ or $\frac{1}{2}$ gray**
   Write an equivalent fraction.
   **Answers may vary. Sample answers: $\frac{2}{4}$ or $\frac{1}{2}$**
2. Dean has 10 marbles. He gives 2 of them to Jamie. Write a fraction for the number of marbles Dean has left.
   **$\frac{8}{10}$ or $\frac{4}{5}$ marbles**
3. Lainie delivers newspapers. She spends $\frac{4}{12}$ of her earnings on a new CD. Write an equivalent fraction to show the amount of Lainie's earnings that she spends.
   **Sample answer: $\frac{1}{3}$ of earnings**
4. There are 32 students in Mr. Simon's class. Four of the students are on the soccer team. Write the fraction that shows how many of Mr. Simon's students are on the team.
   **$\frac{4}{32}$ or $\frac{1}{8}$ students**
5. Ms. Ashton's class set 9 major goals for their school year. They have reached 6 of their goals. Write a fraction that names the goals that have been reached.
   **$\frac{6}{9}$ or $\frac{2}{3}$ goals**
   Then write 2 equivalent fractions.
   **Sample answers: $\frac{2}{3}$ or $\frac{12}{18}$**
6. There are 72 players in the soccer league and 54 of the players are new this year. Write a fraction that shows the number of players who are new this year.
   **$\frac{54}{72}$ or $\frac{27}{36}$ players**

Grade 4 26 Chapter 13

# 13-4 Equivalent Fractions

## 1 Introduce

### Activity Choice 1 • Hands-On

- Hand out 6 blue cards, 4 red cards, and 2 yellow cards, 1 to each of 12 students.
- **What fraction of the students have blue cards?** $\frac{6}{12}$
- Pair the 12 students up so that every blue card is with either a yellow or red card. Show students that 1 out of every 2 cards is blue.
- **What fraction is this?** $\frac{1}{2}$
- Explain that this is an example of equivalent fractions.
- Depending on ability and time, this activity can be extended by adding cards or colors to create other fractions.

### Activity Choice 2 • Literature

Introduce the lesson with *Fraction Fun* by David A. Adler. For a related math activity, see p. TR63.

## 2 Teach

### Scaffolding Questions

Draw and color 12 squares on the board to represent the 12 cards used in Activity Choice 1.

- **What fraction of the squares is red?** $\frac{4}{12}$
- **What is another way to write this fraction?** $\frac{1}{3}$
- **Write two fractions to represent the yellow squares.** $\frac{2}{12}, \frac{1}{6}$
- **What fraction of the squares is yellow or red? Write this fraction several ways.** $\frac{6}{12}, \frac{1}{2}, \frac{2}{4}, \frac{3}{6}$

### GET READY to Learn

Have students open their books and read the information in **Get Ready to Learn**. Introduce **equivalent fractions**. As a class, work through **Examples 1–4**.



# 13-4 Equivalent Fractions

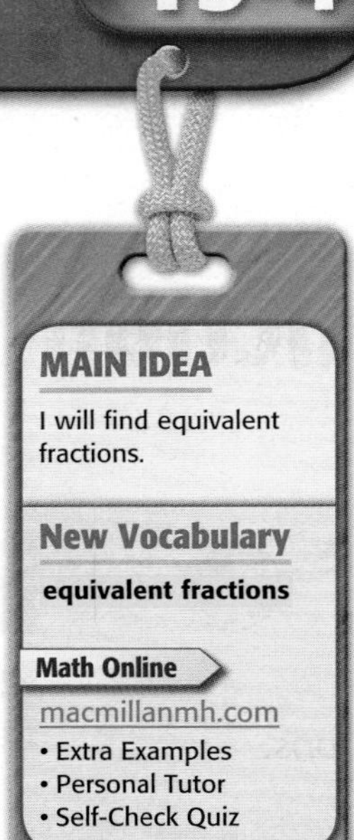


### GET READY to Learn

Megan has 8 fish in an aquarium. Four fish are green. So, Megan says that $\frac{4}{8}$ of the fish are green. Megan could use another fraction to represent $\frac{4}{8}$.

The fraction models below show that $\frac{4}{8}$ is the same as $\frac{1}{2}$. Fractions that represent the same amount are **equivalent fractions**.

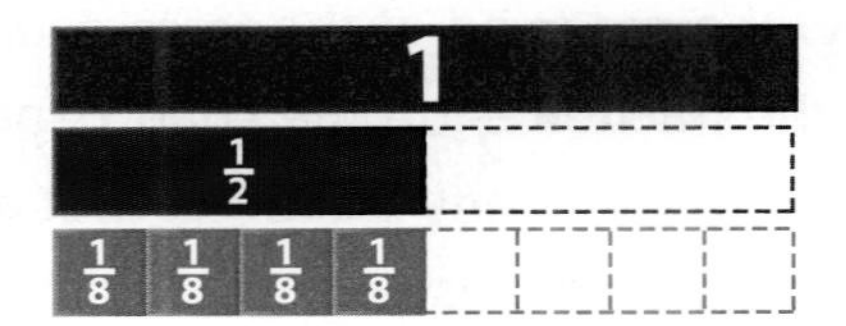


**EXAMPLE** Find Equivalent Fractions

**1 Find three fractions that are equivalent to $\frac{4}{8}$.**

To find equivalent fractions, you can use multiplication or division.

| One Way: Multiply | | Another Way: Divide | |
|---|---|---|---|
| $\frac{4 \times 2}{8 \times 2} = \frac{8}{16}$ | Multiply the numerator and the denominator by the same number, 2. | $\frac{4 \div 2}{8 \div 2} = \frac{2}{4}$ <br> $\frac{2 \div 2}{4 \div 2} = \frac{1}{2}$ | Divide the numerator and the denominator by the same number, 2. |

So, $\frac{8}{16}, \frac{2}{4}$, or $\frac{1}{2}$ are equivalent to $\frac{4}{8}$.



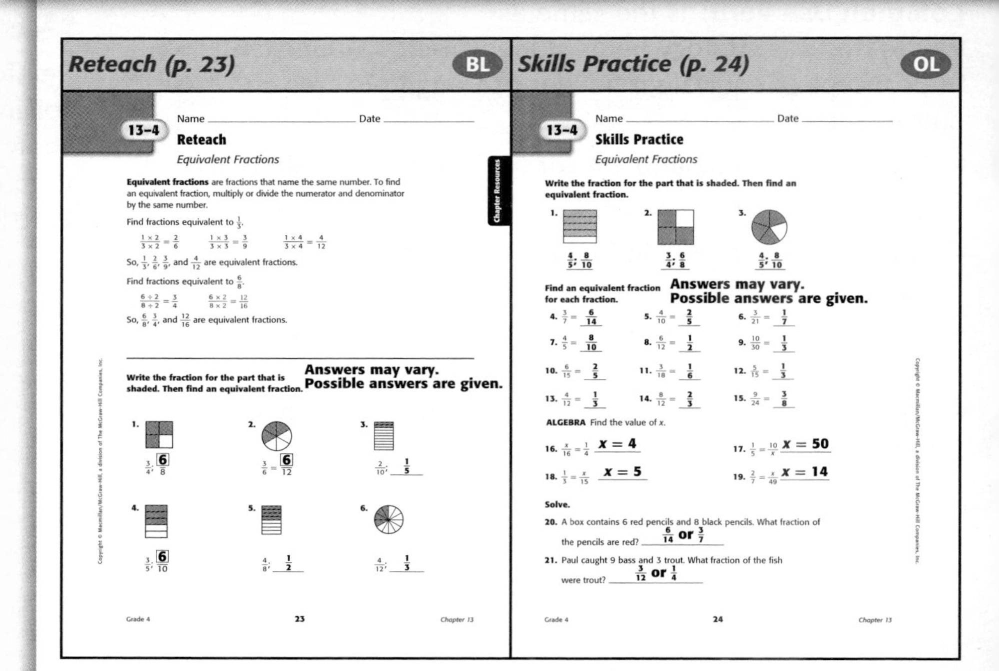

**Reteach (p. 23)** BL

13-4 Name ______ Date ______

**Reteach**

*Equivalent Fractions*

**Equivalent fractions** are fractions that name the same number. To find an equivalent fraction, multiply or divide the numerator and denominator by the same number.

Find fractions equivalent to $\frac{1}{3}$.

$\frac{1 \times 2}{3 \times 2} = \frac{2}{6}$ $\frac{1 \times 3}{3 \times 3} = \frac{3}{9}$ $\frac{1 \times 4}{3 \times 4} = \frac{4}{12}$

So, $\frac{1}{3}, \frac{2}{6}, \frac{3}{9}$, and $\frac{4}{12}$ are equivalent fractions.

Find fractions equivalent to $\frac{6}{8}$.

$\frac{6 \div 2}{8 \div 2} = \frac{3}{4}$ $\frac{6 \times 2}{8 \times 2} = \frac{12}{16}$

So, $\frac{6}{8}, \frac{3}{4}$, and $\frac{12}{16}$ are equivalent fractions.

**Write the fraction for the part that is shaded. Then find an equivalent fraction.** **Answers may vary. Possible answers are given.**

1. $\frac{3}{4}$; $\frac{6}{8}$
2. $\frac{3}{6} = \frac{6}{12}$
3. $\frac{2}{10}$; $\frac{1}{5}$
4. $\frac{3}{5}$; $\frac{6}{10}$
5. $\frac{4}{8}$; $\frac{1}{2}$
6. $\frac{4}{12}$; $\frac{1}{3}$

Grade 4 23 *Chapter 13*



Chapter Resources

**Skills Practice (p. 24)** OL

13-4 Name ______ Date ______

**Skills Practice**

*Equivalent Fractions*

**Write the fraction for the part that is shaded. Then find an equivalent fraction.**

1. $\frac{4}{5}$; $\frac{8}{10}$
2. $\frac{3}{4}$; $\frac{6}{8}$
3. $\frac{4}{5}$; $\frac{8}{10}$

**Find an equivalent fraction for each fraction.** **Answers may vary. Possible answers are given.**

4. $\frac{3}{7} = \frac{6}{14}$
5. $\frac{4}{10} = \frac{2}{5}$
6. $\frac{3}{21} = \frac{1}{7}$
7. $\frac{4}{5} = \frac{8}{10}$
8. $\frac{6}{12} = \frac{1}{2}$
9. $\frac{10}{30} = \frac{1}{3}$
10. $\frac{6}{15} = \frac{2}{5}$
11. $\frac{3}{18} = \frac{1}{6}$
12. $\frac{5}{15} = \frac{1}{3}$
13. $\frac{4}{12} = \frac{1}{3}$
14. $\frac{8}{12} = \frac{2}{3}$
15. $\frac{9}{24} = \frac{3}{8}$

**ALGEBRA** Find the value of $x$.

16. $\frac{x}{16} = \frac{1}{4}$ $x = 4$
17. $\frac{1}{5} = \frac{10}{x}$ $x = 50$
18. $\frac{1}{3} = \frac{x}{15}$ $x = 5$
19. $\frac{2}{7} = \frac{x}{49}$ $x = 14$

**Solve.**

20. A box contains 6 red pencils and 8 black pencils. What fraction of the pencils are red? $\frac{6}{14}$ or $\frac{3}{7}$
21. Paul caught 9 bass and 3 trout. What fraction of the fish were trout? $\frac{3}{12}$ or $\frac{1}{4}$

Grade 4 24 *Chapter 13*

You can also use manipulatives, pictures, or a number line to find equivalent fractions.

**Remember**
You can find many equivalent fractions for any fraction.

**EXAMPLE** Use Concrete Models

**2** **Dale has $\frac{3}{4}$ of his book completed. Use fraction models to find an equivalent fraction.**

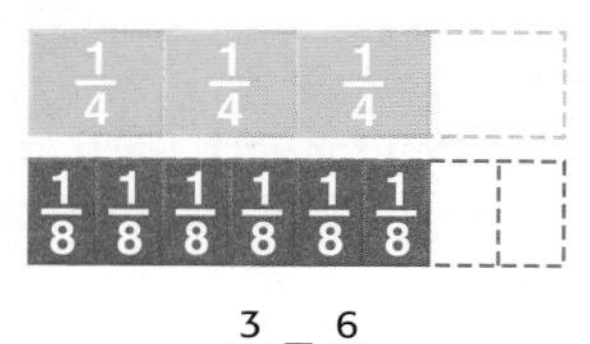


$\frac{3}{4} = \frac{6}{8}$

So, $\frac{6}{8}$ is an equivalent fraction to $\frac{3}{4}$.

**EXAMPLE** Draw a Picture to Model Equivalent Fractions

**3** **Find an equivalent fraction to $\frac{8}{24}$.**
Draw a model.

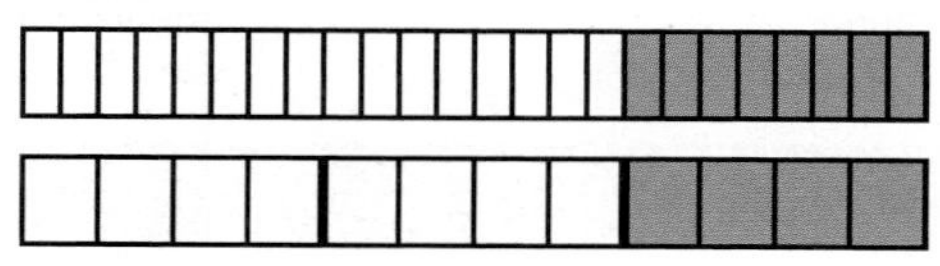

So, $\frac{4}{12}$ is an equivalent fraction.

**EXAMPLE** Fractions on a Number Line

**4** **Write the letter on the number line that best represents $\frac{2}{8}$. Find an equivalent fraction.**

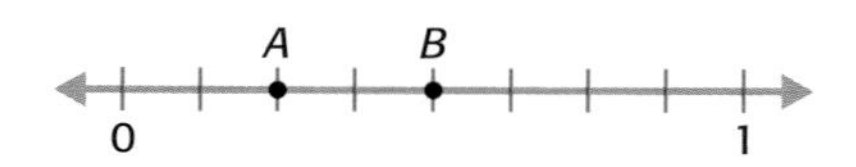


The number line is divided into eighths.

So, $A = \frac{2}{8}$. An equivalent fraction is $\frac{1}{4}$.



Enrich (p. 27) AL

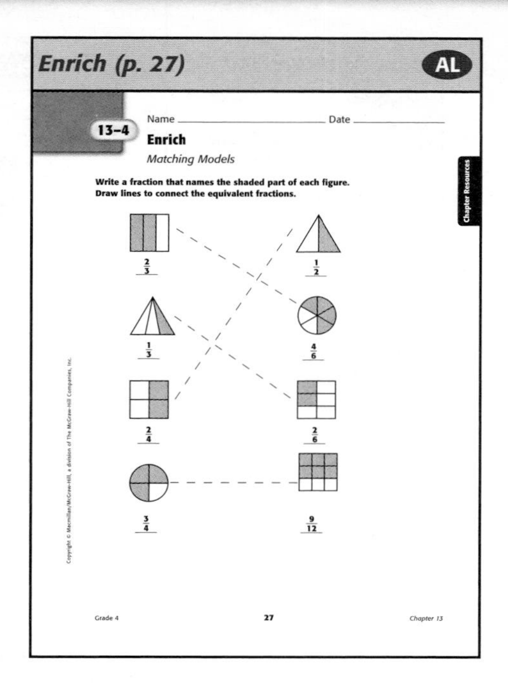
13-4 Name ______ Date ______
Enrich
*Matching Models*

Write a fraction that names the shaded part of each figure. Draw lines to connect the equivalent fractions.

$\frac{2}{3}$ $\frac{1}{2}$
$\frac{1}{3}$ $\frac{4}{6}$
$\frac{2}{4}$ $\frac{2}{6}$
$\frac{3}{4}$ $\frac{9}{12}$

Grade 4 27 Chapter 13

## Find Equivalent Fractions

**Example 1** It may be helpful for students to draw a pictorial model to see that these fractions represent the same amount.

### ADDITIONAL EXAMPLES

1. Find three fractions that are equivalent to $\frac{4}{6}$.
   Sample answer: $\frac{2}{3}$, $\frac{8}{12}$, $\frac{12}{18}$
2. Sam has finished $\frac{2}{3}$ of her dinner. Sol has finished the same amount of his dinner. Use fraction models to find an equivalent fraction.
   Sample answer: $\frac{4}{6}$
3. Find an equivalent fraction to $\frac{10}{15}$.
   Sample answer: $\frac{2}{3}$
4. Write the letter on the number line that best represents $\frac{4}{6}$. *B*

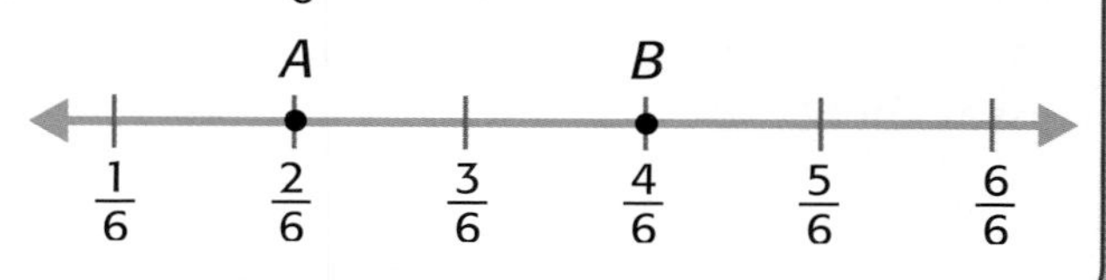


**CHECK What You Know**

As a class, have students complete Exercises 1–11 in **Check What You Know** as you observe their work.

**Exercise 11** Assess student comprehension before assigning practice exercises.

## BL Alternate Teaching Strategy

**If** students have trouble finding equivalent fractions...

**Then** use one of these reteach options:

1. CRM **Daily Reteach Worksheet** (p. 23)
2. Provide grid paper. Have students cut one piece in half and write the fraction each piece represents. $\frac{1}{2}$ Then have them cut each piece in half again or use another sheet of paper.
   - **How many fourths equals one half?** 2
   - Repeat by cutting each fourth to create eighths. Show that four of these equals one half.
   - Help students make the connection from the physical cutting of paper to multiplying or dividing to find equivalent fractions.

# 3 Practice

Differentiate practice using these leveled assignments for Exercises 12–31.

| Level | Assignment |
|---|---|
| BL Below/Approaching Level | 12–14, 18–20, 23, 25, 27 |
| OL On Level | 13–17, 19–22, 23, 25–28, 30 |
| AL Above/Beyond Level | 12–28 even, 29–31 |

Have students discuss and complete the Higher Order Thinking. Suggest that students draw pictorial models to check their answers.

**WRITING IN ▶MATH** Have students complete Exercise 31 in their Math Journals. You may choose to use this exercise as an optional formative assessment.

**Write the fraction for the part that is shaded. Then find an equivalent fraction.** See Examples 1–3 (pp. 548–549)

**1.**  $\frac{2}{4} = \frac{1}{2}$

**2.** 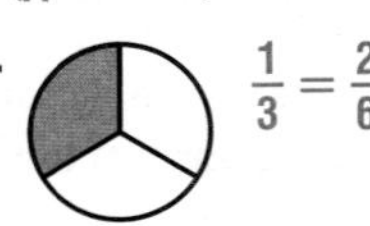 $\frac{1}{3} = \frac{2}{6}$

**3.** 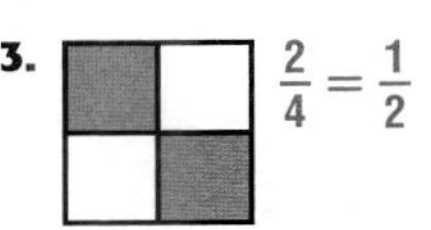 $\frac{2}{4} = \frac{1}{2}$

1–3. Sample equivalent fractions are given.

**Find an equivalent fraction for each fraction.**
See Examples 1–3 (pp. 548–549) 4–8. Sample answers are given.

**4.** $\frac{1}{4}$ $\frac{2}{8}$ **5.** $\frac{4}{6}$ $\frac{2}{3}$ **6.** $\frac{1}{5}$ $\frac{2}{10}$ **7.** $\frac{8}{10}$ $\frac{4}{5}$ **8.** $\frac{1}{3}$ $\frac{2}{6}$

**9.** Tell which letter on the number line below best represents $\frac{6}{10}$. Then find an equivalent fraction. See Example 4 (p. 549) *B*; $\frac{3}{5}$

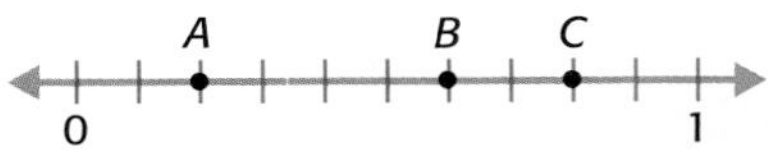


**10.** Dexter has 4 juice boxes. Three are grape flavored. Write two fractions that describe the part of the juice boxes that is grape. $\frac{3}{4}$ and $\frac{6}{8}$

**11.** Talk About It Tell why $\frac{3}{4}$, $\frac{6}{8}$, and $\frac{9}{12}$ are equivalent fractions. Give an example of another set of three equivalent fractions. See Ch. 13 Answer Appendix.

EXTRA PRACTICE See page R35.

**Write the fraction for the part that is shaded. Then find an equivalent fraction.** See Examples 1–3 (pp. 548–549)

**12.** 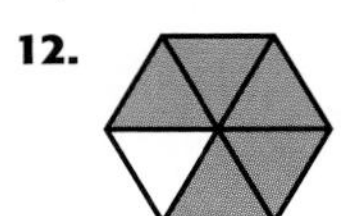 $\frac{5}{6} = \frac{10}{12}$

**13.** $\frac{3}{5} = \frac{6}{10}$

**14.** 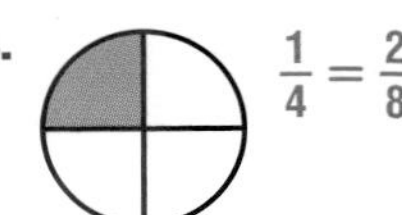 $\frac{1}{4} = \frac{2}{8}$

**15.** $\frac{5}{8} = \frac{10}{16}$

**16.**  $\frac{1}{5} = \frac{2}{10}$

**17.** 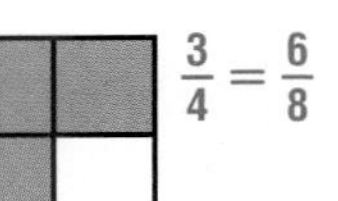 $\frac{3}{4} = \frac{6}{8}$

12–17. Sample equivalent fractions are given.

**Find an equivalent fraction for each fraction.**
See Examples 1–3 (pp. 548–549)

**18.** $\frac{2}{7}$ $\frac{4}{14}$ **19.** $\frac{2}{5}$ $\frac{4}{10}$ **20.** $\frac{6}{10}$ $\frac{3}{5}$ **21.** $\frac{2}{12}$ $\frac{1}{6}$ **22.** $\frac{2}{3}$ $\frac{8}{12}$

18–22. Sample answers given.



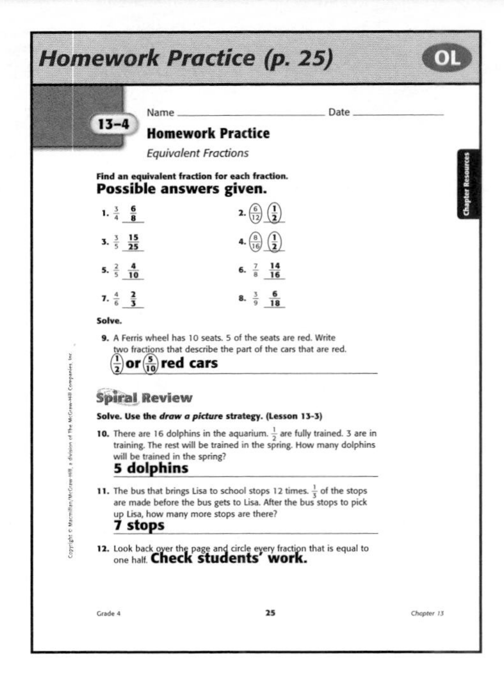
Homework Practice (p. 25) OL

13–4 Name ______ Date ______

**Homework Practice**

*Equivalent Fractions*

Find an equivalent fraction for each fraction.
**Possible answers given.**

1. $\frac{3}{4}$ $\frac{6}{8}$ 2. $\frac{6}{12}$ $\frac{1}{2}$
3. $\frac{3}{5}$ $\frac{15}{25}$ 4. $\frac{8}{16}$ $\frac{1}{2}$
5. $\frac{2}{5}$ $\frac{4}{10}$ 6. $\frac{7}{8}$ $\frac{14}{16}$
7. $\frac{4}{6}$ $\frac{2}{3}$ 8. $\frac{3}{9}$ $\frac{6}{18}$

Solve.

9. A Ferris wheel has 10 seats. 5 of the seats are red. Write two fractions that describe the part of the cars that are red.
$\frac{1}{2}$ or $\frac{5}{10}$ red cars

**Spiral Review**

Solve. Use the *draw a picture* strategy. (Lesson 13-3)

10. There are 16 dolphins in the aquarium. $\frac{1}{2}$ are fully trained. 3 are in training. The rest will be trained in the spring. How many dolphins will be trained in the spring?
**5 dolphins**

11. The bus that brings Lisa to school stops 12 times. $\frac{1}{3}$ of the stops are made before the bus gets to Lisa. After the bus stops to pick up Lisa, how many more stops are there?
**7 stops**

12. Look back over the page and circle every fraction that is equal to one half. **Check students' work.**

Grade 4 25 Chapter 13

Tell which letter on the number line best represents the given fraction. Then find an equivalent fraction. See Example 4 (p. 549)

23. $\frac{3}{4}$ 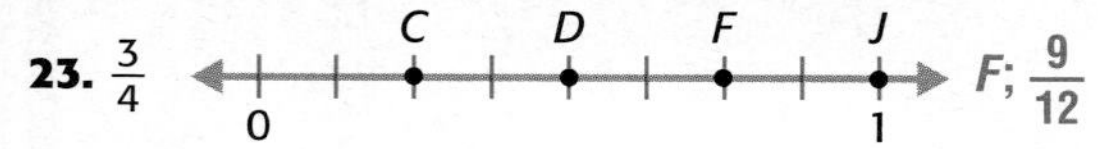

$F$; $\frac{9}{12}$

24. $\frac{4}{14}$ 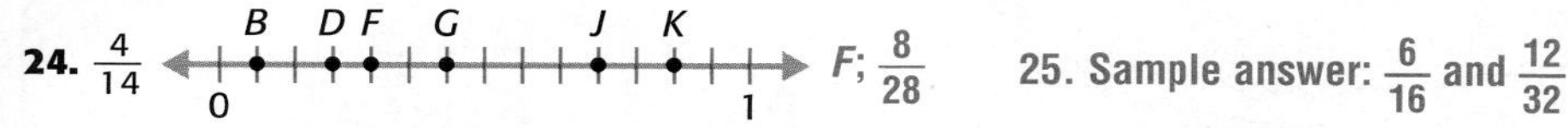

$F$; $\frac{8}{28}$

25. Sample answer: $\frac{6}{16}$ and $\frac{12}{32}$

25. A roller coaster has 16 cars. Six of the cars are green. Write two fractions for the part of the cars that is green.

26. **Measurement** Lucas ran $\frac{1}{2}$ mile. Candace ran $\frac{4}{6}$ mile. Did they run the same distance? Explain. See margin.

## Real-World PROBLEM SOLVING

*Science* Giraffes grow to a height of about 20 feet. Their neck is about $\frac{2}{5}$ their total height. Giraffes spend about $\frac{5}{6}$ of a day eating.

27. What fraction of a day does a giraffe spend eating? Write another fraction that represents this amount. $\frac{5}{6}$; $\frac{10}{12}$

28. What fraction of the total height is the length of a giraffe's neck? Write a fraction equivalent to this fraction. $\frac{2}{5}$; $\frac{4}{10}$

## H.O.T. Problems

29–31. See Ch. 13 Answer Appendix.

29. **OPEN ENDED** Write a fraction equivalent to $\frac{2}{5}$. Write a fraction equivalent to $\frac{3}{6}$. Which fraction represents a greater amount? Explain.

30. **FIND THE ERROR** Rachel and Miguel are finding a fraction equivalent to $\frac{6}{18}$. Who is correct? Explain.

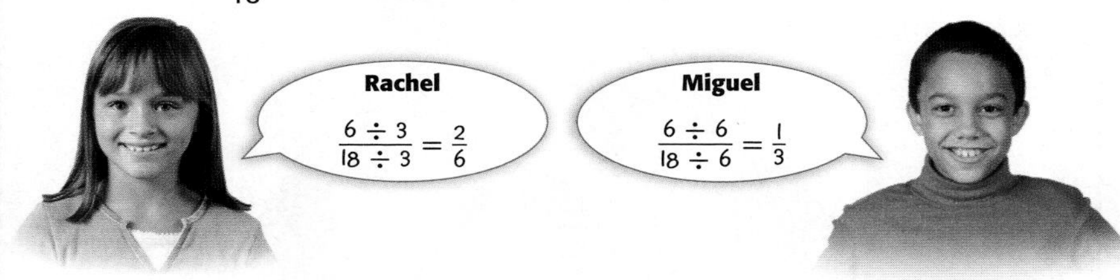


31. **WRITING IN MATH** Can you always find an equivalent fraction for a fraction? Explain.



# 4 Assess

##  Formative Assessment

Students should understand how to find equivalent fractions for any fraction.

- **Explain the steps you would take to find an equivalent fraction for the fraction $\frac{4}{12}$ without using a model.** Sample answer: Multiply (or divide) the numerator and denominator by the same number.
- **Now show how to use a pictorial model to find an equivalent fraction.** Check students' work.

**Quick Check** **Are students continuing to struggle with finding equivalent fractions?**

**If Yes** → Small Group Options (p. 548B)
Strategic Intervention Guide (p. 24)

**If No** → Independent Work Options (p. 548B)
CRM Skills Practice Worksheet (p. 24)
CRM Enrich Worksheet (p. 27)

**Name the Math** Ask students to write the steps they would take to find two equivalent fractions for $\frac{12}{20}$.

### Additional Answer

**26.** no; $\frac{1}{2}$ and $\frac{4}{6}$ do not name the same distance.

# Fractions Made Equal

### Math Concept:
### Make Equivalent Fractions

**Materials:** 10 index cards

Introduce the game on p. 552 to your students to play as a class, in small groups, or at a learning workstation to review concepts introduced in this chapter.

## Instructions

- Students cut each index card in half and label each card with one fraction, as shown on p. 552.
- Students shuffle the cards and spread them out, facedown, on the table.
- Students play in pairs. Player 1 turns over one card and writes an equivalent fraction. If Player 1 is correct, Player 1 keeps the card. If Player 1 is incorrect, the card is placed back on the table, facedown.
- Player 2 takes a turn and follows the same procedure. Play continues until all of the cards have been taken. The player with the most cards wins.

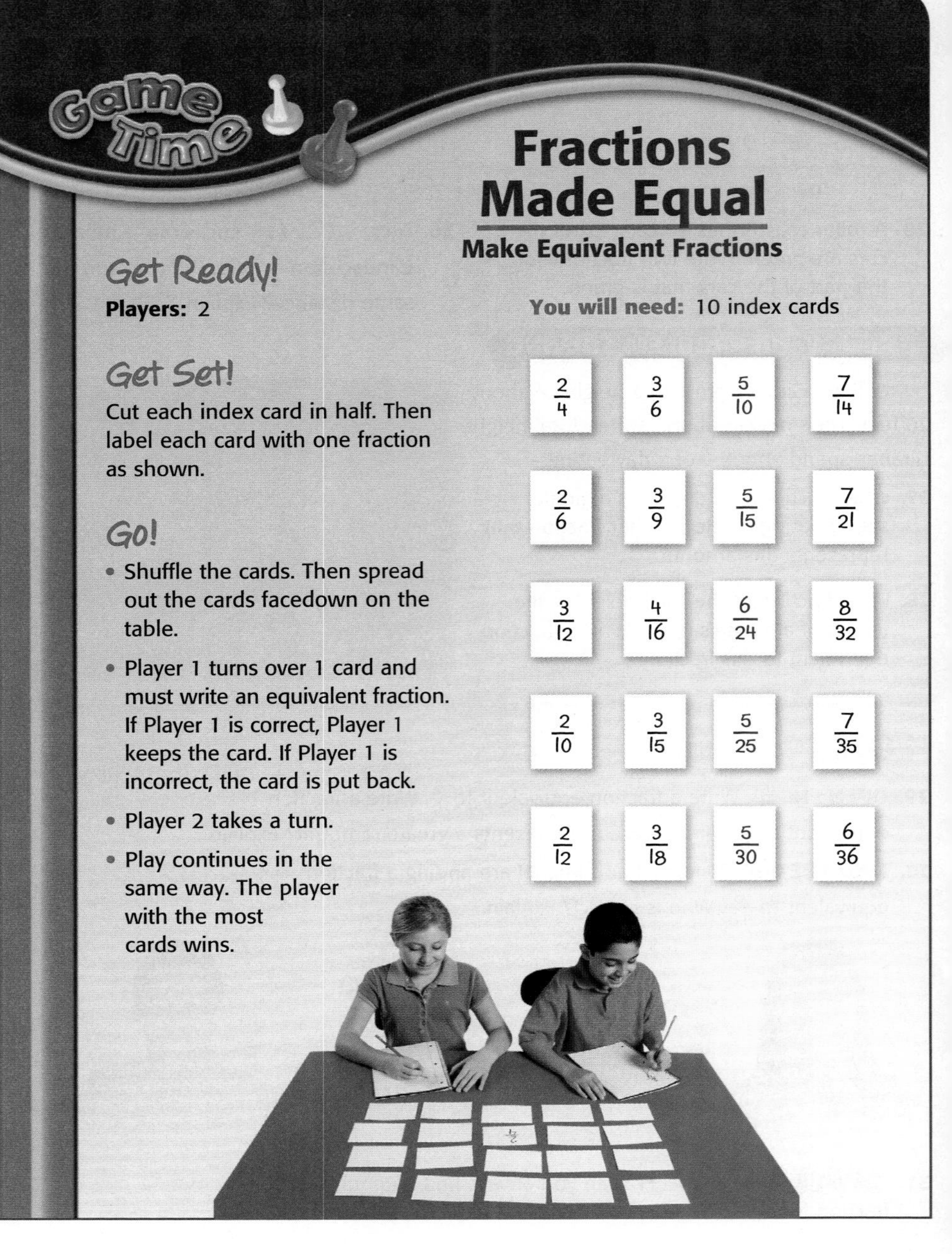

Game Time

**Fractions Made Equal**

**Make Equivalent Fractions**

*Get Ready!*

**Players:** 2

**You will need:** 10 index cards

*Get Set!*

Cut each index card in half. Then label each card with one fraction as shown.

*Go!*

- Shuffle the cards. Then spread out the cards facedown on the table.
- Player 1 turns over 1 card and must write an equivalent fraction. If Player 1 is correct, Player 1 keeps the card. If Player 1 is incorrect, the card is put back.
- Player 2 takes a turn.
- Play continues in the same way. The player with the most cards wins.



552 **Chapter 13** Describe and Compare Fractions

## Extend the Game

Have students make the game using fractions they come up with themselves.

## Differentiated Practice

Use these leveled suggestions to differentiate the game for all learners.

| Level | Assignment |
|---|---|
| BL Below/Approaching Level | Students use fraction models and blocks to model the fractions shown. |
| OL On Level | Have students play the game with the rules as written. |
| AL Above/Beyond Level | Students write two equivalent fractions for each fraction. |

# CHAPTER 13 Mid-Chapter Check

Lessons 13-1 through 13-4

**Write the fraction that names the shaded part of the whole.** (Lesson 13-1)

1. 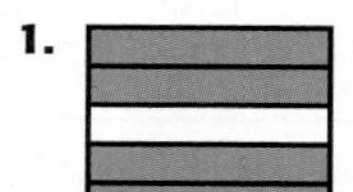 $\frac{4}{5}$

2. $\frac{5}{12}$

3–4. See Ch. 13 Answer Appendix.

**Draw a picture and shade part of it to show the fraction.** (Lesson 13-1)

3. $\frac{1}{8}$

4. $\frac{3}{7}$

5. The flag of Italy is shown. What fraction of the flag is green? (Lesson 13-1) $\frac{1}{3}$

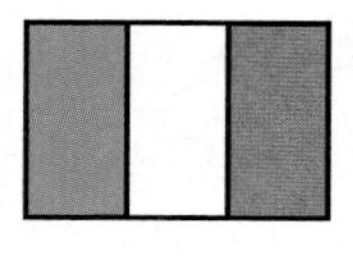

6. **MULTIPLE CHOICE** What fraction of the hearts is shaded? (Lesson 13-2) D

A $\frac{4}{10}$

C $\frac{5}{9}$

B $\frac{1}{2}$

D $\frac{6}{10}$

7. Draw a picture that represents the statement below. (Lesson 13-2)

*Three of the five leaves are shaded.*

See Ch. 13 Answer Appendix.

8. There are 3 red apples, 6 green apples, and 1 yellow apple on a table. Of the apples, what fraction is green? (Lesson 13-2) $\frac{6}{10}$

**Write the fraction that names the part of the set of smile faces.** (Lesson 13-2)

9. red $\frac{3}{7}$

10. green $\frac{1}{7}$

11. Janey is planting 12 trees in her yard. There are 5 maple trees and the rest are oak. What fraction of the trees is oak? (Lesson 13-3) $\frac{7}{12}$

12. Galeno spent $\frac{1}{2}$ of his money on a movie ticket and $\frac{1}{4}$ of his money on a snack. He had \$8 before the movie. How much money does he have now? (Lesson 13-3) \$2

13–16. Sample answers are given.

**Find an equivalent fraction for each fraction.** (Lesson 13-4)

13. $\frac{1}{3}$ $\frac{3}{9}$

14. $\frac{4}{5}$ $\frac{8}{10}$

15. $\frac{1}{2}$ $\frac{3}{6}$

16. $\frac{2}{6}$ $\frac{4}{12}$

17. Jin's mom used 12 of the 20 stamps she had bought. Jin said that she used $\frac{3}{5}$ of the stamps. Is Jin correct? Explain. (Lesson 13-4)

17, 18. See Ch. 13 Answer Appendix.

18. **WRITING IN MATH** Is $\frac{1}{4}$ of the rectangle green? Explain why or why not. (Lesson 13-1)

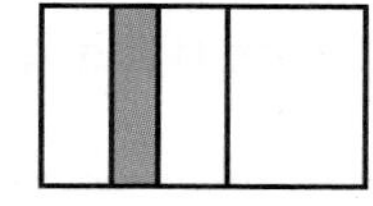



# CHAPTER 13 Mid-Chapter Check

## Lessons 13-1 through 13-4

### Formative Assessment

Use the Mid-Chapter Check to assess students' progress in the first half of the chapter.

**ExamView** Assessment Suite Customize and create multiple versions of your Mid-Chapter Check and the test answer keys.

### FOLDABLES Dinah Zike's Foldables

Use these lesson suggestions to incorporate the Foldables during the chapter.

**Lessons 13-1 and 13-2** Students read, write, and identify fractions that are part of a whole and parts of a set beneath the top left tab. Vocabulary, physical examples, and student work can be stored in the center pocket.

**Lesson 13-4** Students read, write, and identify equivalent fractions beneath the middle left tab. Vocabulary and student work can be stored in the center pocket.

# Data-Driven Decision Making

Based on the results of the Mid-Chapter Check, use the following to review concepts that continue to present students with problems.

| Exercises | State/Local Standards | What's the Mathematics? | Error Analysis | Resources for Review |
|---|---|---|---|---|
| **1–10, 18** Lessons 13-1, 13-2 | | Identify, write, and read fractions for parts of a whole and a set. | Does not know improper fractions. Does not know difference between numerator and denominator. | Strategic Intervention Guide (pp. 22, 24, 26)<br>CRM Chapter 13 Resource Masters (Reteach)<br>Math Adventures<br>My Math Zone Chapter 13<br>Math Online Extra Examples • Concepts in Motion |
| **11–12** Lesson 13-3 | | Solve fraction problems. | Cannot read and interpret how to write fractions for a real-life situation. | |
| **13–17** Lesson 13-4 | | Find equivalent fractions. | Does not know how to get simplest form. Does not know difference between numerator and denominator. | |

LESSON 13-5

# Compare and Order Fractions

## Lesson Planner

### Objective

Compare and order simple fractions.

### Review Vocabulary

**number line**

### Resources

**Manipulatives:** fraction models

**Literature Connection:** *Inchworm and a Half* by Elinor J. Pinczes

**Alternate Lesson:** Use *IMPACT Mathematics:* Unit D to provide practice with comparing and ordering fractions.

**Teacher Technology**

TeacherWorks • Interactive Classroom

## Daily Routine

Use these suggestions before beginning the lesson on p. 554.

### 5-Minute Check

(Reviews Lesson 3-4)

**Use models to find an equivalent fraction for each fraction.** Sample answers are given.

1. $\frac{2}{4}$ $\frac{1}{2}, \frac{3}{6}, \frac{4}{8}$, etc.
2. $\frac{5}{15}$ $\frac{1}{3}, \frac{2}{6}, \frac{10}{30}$, etc.
3. $\frac{8}{10}$ $\frac{4}{5}, \frac{16}{20}, \frac{12}{15}$, etc.
4. $\frac{12}{16}$ $\frac{3}{4}, \frac{6}{8}, \frac{9}{12}$, etc.

### Problem of the Day

A group of friends swam a relay race. Margie swam $\frac{1}{3}$ of the laps, and Charles swam $\frac{1}{6}$ of the laps. If the race was less than 10 laps, how many laps did it have? 6

### Focus on Math Background

Students can compare two fractions in several ways: using models, using number lines, or using equivalent fractions. When using equivalent fractions to compare and order fractions, the fractions must have the same denominator. Once this is achieved, the fraction with the greater numerator is the greater fraction. There is no need to emphasize *least* common denominators here.

One technique that can be used to find a common denominator is to write successive multiples of the different denominators until a common multiple is found. In this case, 15 is a common multiple and therefore a common denominator.

### Review Math Vocabulary

Write the review vocabulary term and its definition on the board.

Have each student draw a number line, labeling it 0–3. Have students use different colored pencils to mark the number lines in the following scales: halves, thirds, fourths, fifths, and sixths.

# Differentiated Instruction

## Small Group Options

### Option 1 Below Level BL

SPATIAL, KINESTHETIC

**Materials:** 1-inch grid paper, markers or colored pencils

- Provide 1-inch grid paper for students. Have students draw two 2-by-5 inch rectangles.
- Allow them to color in squares and then compare which areas are larger.
- Have them name the fraction.
- Repeat with areas of different sizes.

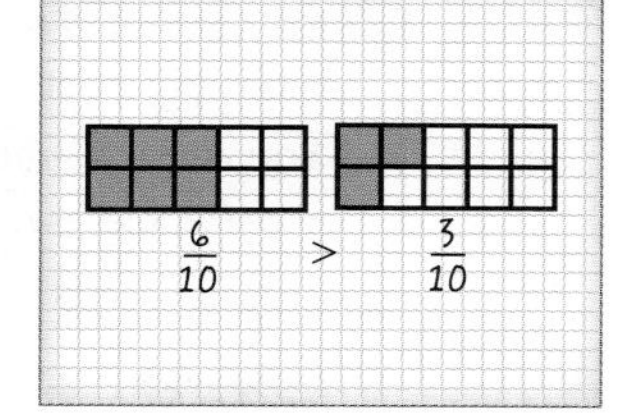


### Option 2 English Language Learners ELL

LOGICAL, SOCIAL

**Materials:** fraction strips
**Core Vocabulary:** fifth, sixth, seventh
**Common Use Verb:** listen for

**Do Math** This strategy helps students recognize, compare, and practice saying fractional quantities.

- Pass out fraction strips.
- Say: "Put them in order."
- On the overhead, place the fractions in order, reading the fractions.
- Have students repeat individually.
- When students read their fractions, have other students listen for incorrect order. Answers may be challenged and re-worked with the first student.
- Repeat as time permits.

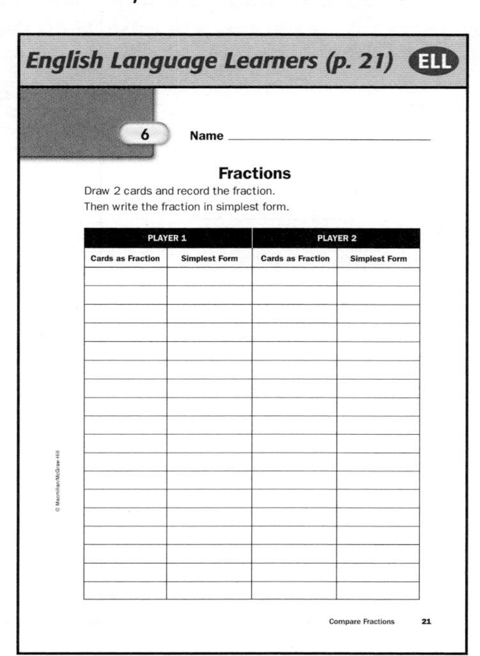

*English Language Learners (p. 21)* ELL

6 Name ____________

**Fractions**

Draw 2 cards and record the fraction.
Then write the fraction in simplest form.

| PLAYER 1 | | PLAYER 2 | |
|---|---|---|---|
| Cards as Fraction | Simplest Form | Cards as Fraction | Simplest Form |
| | | | |

Compare Fractions 21

*Use this worksheet to provide additional support for English Language Learners.*

## Independent Work Options

### Option 1 Early Finishers OL AL

SOCIAL

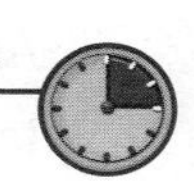

**Materials:** sets of cards with all fractions through fifths printed on them: $\frac{1}{2}, \frac{2}{2}, \frac{1}{3}, \frac{2}{3}, \frac{3}{3}, \frac{1}{4}, \frac{3}{4}, \frac{3}{5}, \frac{4}{5}, \frac{5}{5}$

- Students play the game like the card game "War."
- The game is started by shuffling the cards. Deal each card, facedown, until the entire deck has been dealt.
- Players both flip one card. The player with the greatest value keeps both cards. In a tie, each player buries the card in his or her own deck.
- Play until one player has all the cards.

### Option 2 Student Technology

**Math Online** macmillanmh.com

Personal Tutor • Extra Examples

Math Adventures

### Option 3 Learning Station: Writing (p. 534G)

Direct students to the Writing Learning Station for opportunities to explore and extend the lesson concept.

### Option 4 Problem-Solving Practice

Reinforce problem-solving skills and strategies with the Problem-Solving Practice worksheet.

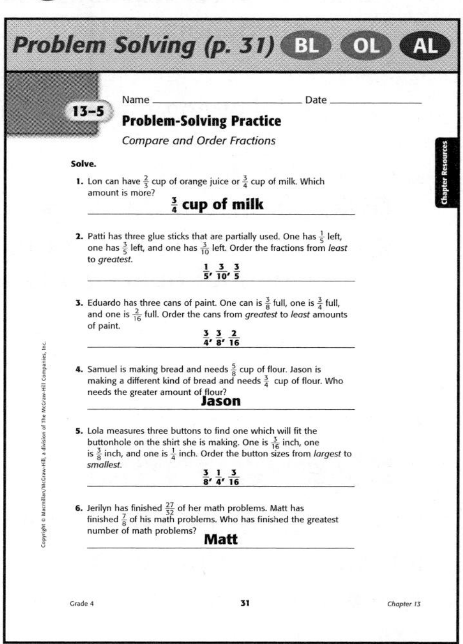

*Problem Solving (p. 31)* BL OL AL

13–5 Name ____________ Date ____________

**Problem-Solving Practice**

*Compare and Order Fractions*

Chapter Resources

**Solve.**

1. Lon can have $\frac{2}{3}$ cup of orange juice or $\frac{3}{4}$ cup of milk. Which amount is more?
   **$\frac{3}{4}$ cup of milk**
2. Patti has three glue sticks that are partially used. One has $\frac{1}{5}$ left, one has $\frac{3}{5}$ left, and one has $\frac{3}{10}$ left. Order the fractions from *least* to *greatest*.
   **$\frac{1}{5}, \frac{3}{10}, \frac{3}{5}$**
3. Eduardo has three cans of paint. One can is $\frac{3}{8}$ full, one is $\frac{3}{4}$ full, and one is $\frac{2}{16}$ full. Order the cans from *greatest* to *least* amounts of paint.
   **$\frac{3}{4}, \frac{3}{8}, \frac{2}{16}$**
4. Samuel is making bread and needs $\frac{5}{8}$ cup of flour. Jason is making a different kind of bread and needs $\frac{3}{4}$ cup of flour. Who needs the greater amount of flour?
   **Jason**
5. Lola measures three buttons to find one which will fit the buttonhole on the shirt she is making. One is $\frac{3}{16}$ inch, one is $\frac{3}{8}$ inch, and one is $\frac{1}{4}$ inch. Order the button sizes from *largest* to *smallest*.
   **$\frac{3}{8}, \frac{1}{4}, \frac{3}{16}$**
6. Jerilyn has finished $\frac{27}{32}$ of her math problems. Matt has finished $\frac{7}{8}$ of his math problems. Who has finished the greatest number of math problems?
   **Matt**



Grade 4 31 Chapter 13

# Compare and Order Fractions

## 1 Introduce

### Activity Choice 1 • Hands-On

- Hand out sets of fraction models to students.
- **Which is larger, $\frac{1}{5}$ or $\frac{1}{4}$?** $\frac{1}{4}$
- Ask students to identify three fractions that are larger than $\frac{3}{5}$. $\frac{2}{3}, \frac{3}{4}, \frac{4}{5}$
- Ask students to arrange the following fractions in order from least to greatest: $\frac{3}{5}, \frac{1}{5}, \frac{4}{5}, \frac{5}{5}, \frac{2}{5}$. $\frac{1}{5}, \frac{2}{5}, \frac{3}{5}, \frac{4}{5}, \frac{5}{5}$
- Repeat with tenths. Ask students to describe the rule that can help order fractions when the denominators are the same. (When denominators are the same, arrange by numerators.)

### Activity Choice 2 • Literature

Introduce the lesson with *Inchworm and a Half* by Elinor J. Pinczes. For a related math activity, see p. TR64.

## 2 Teach

### Scaffolding Questions

Present students with the following list of fractions: $\frac{1}{2}, \frac{3}{4}, \frac{5}{6}, \frac{1}{3}, \frac{3}{4}, \frac{1}{6}$.

- **Use fraction models to help order them from least to greatest.** $\frac{1}{6}, \frac{1}{4}, \frac{1}{3}, \frac{1}{2}, \frac{3}{4}, \frac{5}{6}$
- **Without using fraction models, why is it harder to order fractions that do not have the same denominator?** harder to compare values
- List the following fractions on the board: $\frac{1}{7}, \frac{1}{4}, \frac{1}{5}, \frac{1}{3}, \frac{1}{6}, \frac{1}{2}, \frac{1}{8}$.
- **Order the listed fractions from least to greatest and describe a rule that can be used when all numerators are the same.** $\frac{1}{8}, \frac{1}{7}, \frac{1}{6}, \frac{1}{5}, \frac{1}{4}, \frac{1}{3}, \frac{1}{2}$; When numerators are the same, the fraction values increase as the denominators get smaller.

### GET READY to Learn

Have students open their books and read the information in **Get Ready to Learn**. Review **number line**. As a class, work through **Examples 1–3**.



# 13-5 Compare and Order Fractions

**MAIN IDEA**

I will compare and order simple fractions.

**Math Online**

macmillanmh.com
- Extra Examples
- Personal Tutor
- Self-Check Quiz

### GET READY to Learn

Ramon has an insect collection. The table shows the lengths of four insects in his collection. Which is longer, a field cricket or a whirligig beetle?

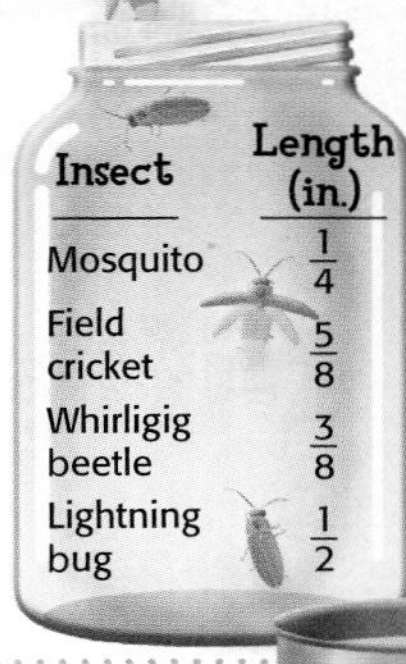

| Insect | Length (in.) |
|---|---|
| Mosquito | $\frac{1}{4}$ |
| Field cricket | $\frac{5}{8}$ |
| Whirligig beetle | $\frac{3}{8}$ |
| Lightning bug | $\frac{1}{2}$ |

To compare fractions, you can use models, number lines, and equivalent fractions.

### Real-World EXAMPLES Compare Fractions

**1 MEASUREMENT Which insect is longer, a field cricket or a whirligig beetle?**

You can use fraction models to compare $\frac{5}{8}$ and $\frac{3}{8}$.

The models show that $\frac{5}{8} > \frac{3}{8}$.

So, the field cricket is longer than the whirligig beetle.

**2 Which is longer, a mosquito or lightning bug?**

You need to compare $\frac{1}{4}$ and $\frac{1}{2}$.

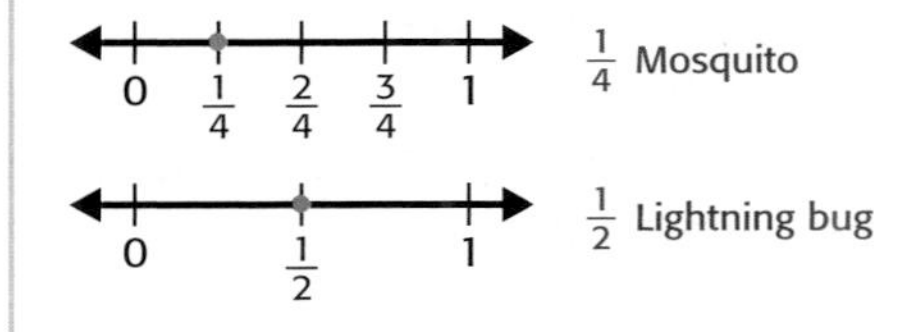


So, the lightning bug is longer than the mosquito.



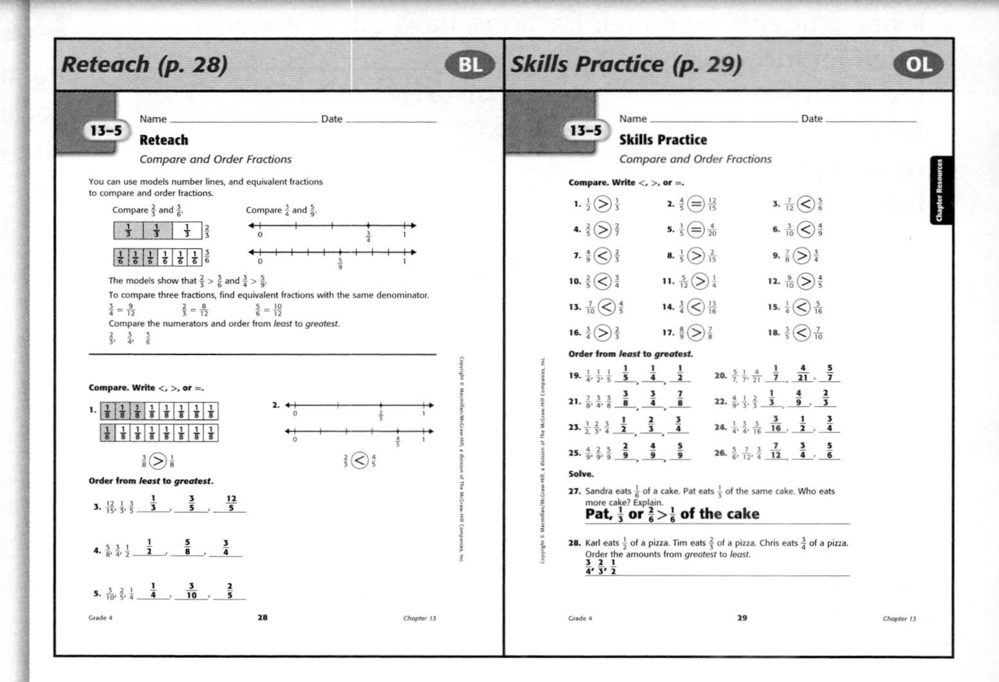

**Reteach (p. 28)** BL

13-5 Name ________ Date ________

**Reteach**

*Compare and Order Fractions*

You can use models number lines, and equivalent fractions to compare and order fractions.

Compare $\frac{2}{3}$ and $\frac{3}{6}$. Compare $\frac{3}{4}$ and $\frac{5}{9}$.

The models show that $\frac{2}{3} > \frac{3}{6}$ and $\frac{3}{4} > \frac{5}{9}$.

To compare three fractions, find equivalent fractions with the same denominator.

$\frac{3}{4} = \frac{9}{12}$ $\frac{2}{3} = \frac{8}{12}$ $\frac{5}{6} = \frac{10}{12}$

Compare the numerators and order from *least* to *greatest*.

$\frac{2}{3}, \frac{3}{4}, \frac{5}{6}$

**Compare. Write $<$, $>$, or $=$.**

1. $\frac{3}{8}$ (>) $\frac{1}{8}$
2. $\frac{2}{3}$ (<) $\frac{4}{5}$

**Order from *least* to *greatest*.**

3. $\frac{12}{15}, \frac{1}{3}, \frac{3}{5}$ **$\frac{1}{3}$, $\frac{3}{5}$, $\frac{12}{5}$**
4. $\frac{5}{8}, \frac{3}{4}, \frac{1}{2}$ **$\frac{1}{2}$, $\frac{5}{8}$, $\frac{3}{4}$**
5. $\frac{3}{10}, \frac{2}{5}, \frac{1}{4}$ **$\frac{1}{4}$, $\frac{3}{10}$, $\frac{2}{5}$**

Grade 4 28 Chapter 13



**Skills Practice (p. 29)** OL

13-5 Name ________ Date ________

**Skills Practice**

*Compare and Order Fractions*

**Compare. Write $<$, $>$, or $=$.**

1. $\frac{1}{2}$ (>) $\frac{1}{3}$
2. $\frac{4}{5}$ (=) $\frac{12}{15}$
3. $\frac{7}{12}$ (<) $\frac{5}{6}$
4. $\frac{2}{5}$ (>) $\frac{2}{7}$
5. $\frac{1}{5}$ (=) $\frac{4}{20}$
6. $\frac{3}{10}$ (<) $\frac{4}{9}$
7. $\frac{4}{9}$ (<) $\frac{2}{3}$
8. $\frac{1}{5}$ (>) $\frac{2}{15}$
9. $\frac{7}{8}$ (>) $\frac{3}{4}$
10. $\frac{2}{5}$ (<) $\frac{3}{4}$
11. $\frac{5}{12}$ (>) $\frac{1}{4}$
12. $\frac{9}{10}$ (>) $\frac{4}{5}$
13. $\frac{7}{10}$ (<) $\frac{4}{5}$
14. $\frac{3}{4}$ (<) $\frac{13}{16}$
15. $\frac{1}{4}$ (<) $\frac{5}{16}$
16. $\frac{3}{4}$ (>) $\frac{2}{3}$
17. $\frac{8}{9}$ (>) $\frac{7}{8}$
18. $\frac{3}{5}$ (<) $\frac{7}{10}$

**Order from *least* to *greatest*.**

19. $\frac{1}{4}, \frac{1}{2}, \frac{1}{5}$ **$\frac{1}{5}$, $\frac{1}{4}$, $\frac{1}{2}$**
20. $\frac{5}{7}, \frac{1}{7}, \frac{4}{21}$ **$\frac{1}{7}$, $\frac{4}{21}$, $\frac{5}{7}$**
21. $\frac{7}{8}, \frac{3}{4}, \frac{3}{8}$ **$\frac{3}{8}$, $\frac{3}{4}$, $\frac{7}{8}$**
22. $\frac{4}{9}, \frac{1}{3}, \frac{2}{3}$ **$\frac{1}{3}$, $\frac{4}{9}$, $\frac{2}{3}$**
23. $\frac{1}{2}, \frac{2}{3}, \frac{3}{4}$ **$\frac{1}{2}$, $\frac{2}{3}$, $\frac{3}{4}$**
24. $\frac{1}{4}, \frac{3}{4}, \frac{3}{16}$ **$\frac{3}{16}$, $\frac{1}{2}$, $\frac{3}{4}$**
25. $\frac{4}{9}, \frac{2}{9}, \frac{5}{9}$ **$\frac{2}{9}$, $\frac{4}{9}$, $\frac{5}{9}$**
26. $\frac{5}{6}, \frac{7}{12}, \frac{3}{4}$ **$\frac{7}{12}$, $\frac{3}{4}$, $\frac{5}{6}$**

**Solve.**

27. Sandra eats $\frac{1}{6}$ of a cake. Pat eats $\frac{1}{3}$ of the same cake. Who eats more cake? Explain.
**Pat, $\frac{1}{3}$ or $\frac{2}{6} > \frac{1}{6}$ of the cake**

28. Karl eats $\frac{1}{2}$ of a pizza. Tim eats $\frac{2}{3}$ of a pizza. Chris eats $\frac{3}{4}$ of a pizza. Order the amounts from *greatest* to *least*.
**$\frac{3}{4}, \frac{2}{3}, \frac{1}{2}$**

Grade 4 29 Chapter 13

Chapter Resources

**EXAMPLE** Order Fractions

3 Order $\frac{2}{3}$, $\frac{1}{2}$, and $\frac{7}{12}$ from least to greatest.

| One Way: Number Lines | Another Way: Equivalent Fractions |
|---|---|
| Use a number line. | Find equivalent fractions with the same denominator. $\frac{2 \times 4}{3 \times 4} = \frac{8}{12}$ $\frac{1 \times 6}{2 \times 6} = \frac{6}{12}$ Compare the numerators. Order from least to greatest. $\frac{6}{12}, \frac{7}{12}, \frac{8}{12}$ → $\frac{1}{2}, \frac{7}{12}, \frac{2}{3}$ |
| $\frac{1}{2} < \frac{7}{12} < \frac{2}{3}$ | |

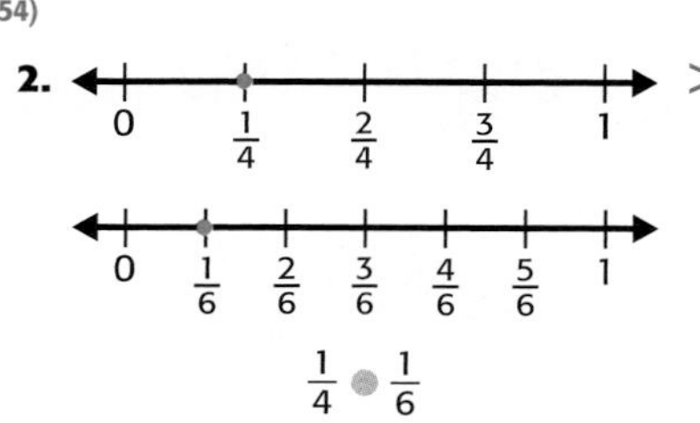


So, the order from least to greatest is $\frac{1}{2}, \frac{7}{12}, \frac{2}{3}$.

8. Sample answer. Write the fractions with a common denominator. Then compare the numerators.

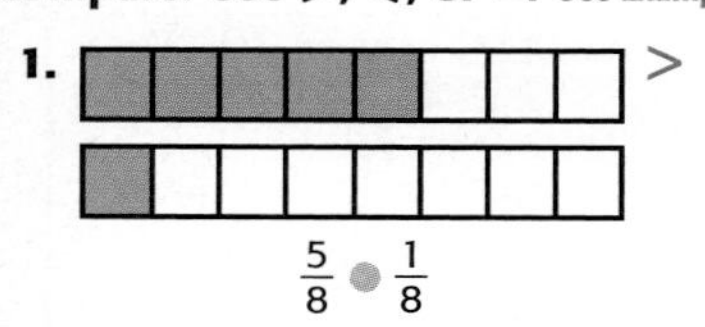

★ indicates multi-step problem

## CHECK What You Know

**Compare. Use >, <, or =.** See Examples 1 and 2 (p. 554)

1. $\frac{5}{8} \bullet \frac{1}{8}$ >

2. $\frac{1}{4} \bullet \frac{1}{6}$ >

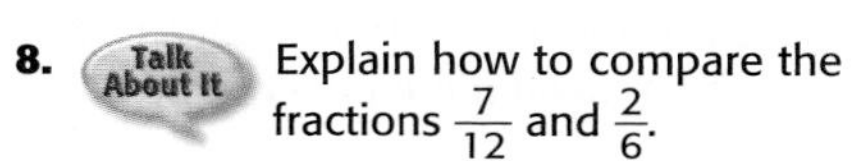


3. $\frac{3}{4} \bullet \frac{1}{2}$ >

4. $\frac{3}{6} \bullet \frac{3}{4}$ <

**Order from least to greatest.** See Example 3 (p. 555)

5. $\frac{3}{8}, \frac{2}{6}, \frac{4}{8}$ $\frac{2}{6}, \frac{3}{8}, \frac{4}{8}$

6. $\frac{1}{16}, \frac{7}{8}, \frac{3}{4}$ $\frac{1}{16}, \frac{3}{4}, \frac{7}{8}$

★7. **Measurement** Griff worked for $\frac{1}{3}$ of an hour. Sasha worked for $\frac{3}{12}$ of an hour. Who worked for a longer time? Griff

8. **Talk About It** Explain how to compare the fractions $\frac{7}{12}$ and $\frac{2}{6}$.



**Enrich (p. 32)** AL

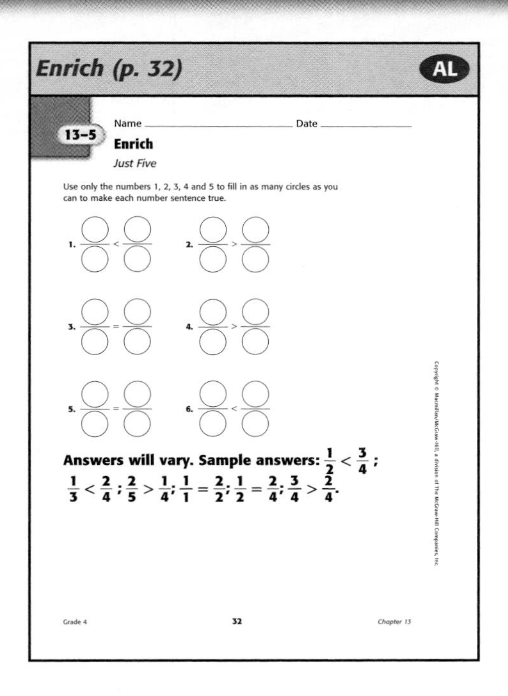
13-5 Enrich

Just Five

Use only the numbers 1, 2, 3, 4 and 5 to fill in as many circles as you can to make each number sentence true.

Answers will vary. Sample answers: $\frac{1}{2} < \frac{3}{4}$; $\frac{1}{3} < \frac{2}{4}$; $\frac{2}{5} > \frac{1}{4}$; $\frac{1}{1} = \frac{2}{2}$; $\frac{1}{2} = \frac{2}{4}$; $\frac{3}{4} > \frac{2}{4}$.

Grade 4 32 Chapter 13

### Order Fractions

**Example 3** Remind students that they need to find equivalent fractions in which each fraction has the same denominator. Tell them to list multiples of each denominator until they reach a multiple that all three have in common. This should be the new denominator.

**ADDITIONAL EXAMPLES**

1. Use the data table from the Get Ready to Learn example. Which insect is longer, a mosquito or a whirligig beetle? whirligig beetle
2. Use the data table from the Get Ready to Learn example. Which insect is longer, a field cricket or a lightning bug? field cricket
3. Order $\frac{1}{2}, \frac{5}{6}, \frac{1}{3}$ from least to greatest. $\frac{1}{3}, \frac{1}{2}, \frac{5}{6}$

**CHECK What You Know**

As a class, have students complete Exercises 1–8 in **Check What You Know** as you observe their work.

**Exercise 8** Assess student comprehension before assigning practice exercises.

## BL Alternate Teaching Strategy

**If** students have trouble comparing and ordering simple fractions…

**Then** use one of these reteach options:

1. CRM **Daily Reteach Worksheet** (p. 28)
2. Provide fraction models to help students compare and order fractions as they complete the exercises. The fraction models will also help students to check their answers.

# 3 Practice

Differentiate practice using these leveled assignments for Exercises 9–30.

| Level | Assignment |
|---|---|
| BL Below/Approaching Level | 9, 11, 13–15, 19–20, 22–23, 26 |
| OL On Level | 9–17, 20–25, 27–28, 29–30 |
| AL Above/Beyond Level | 10–26 even, 27–30 |

Have students discuss and complete the Higher Order Thinking problems. Remind students to use what they observed in Activity Choice 1 and the Scaffolding Questions to help them with the Higher Order Thinking problems.

**WRITING IN MATH** Have students complete Exercise 30 in their Math Journals. You may choose to use this exercise as an optional formative assessment.

## Practice and Problem Solving

EXTRA PRACTICE See page R35.

**Compare. Use >, <, or =.** See Examples 1 and 2 (p. 554)

**9.** 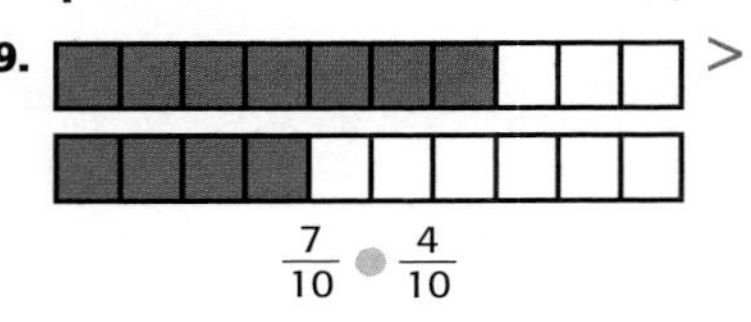 $\frac{7}{10}$ ● $\frac{4}{10}$ >

**10.** 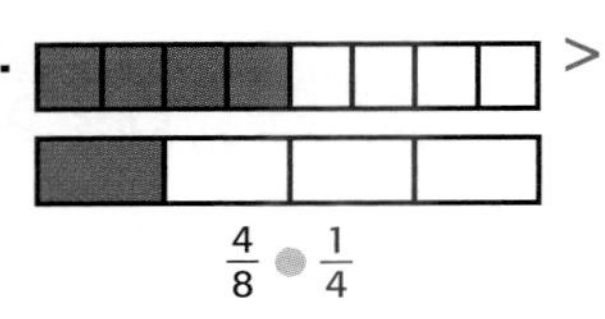 $\frac{4}{8}$ ● $\frac{1}{4}$ >

**11.** 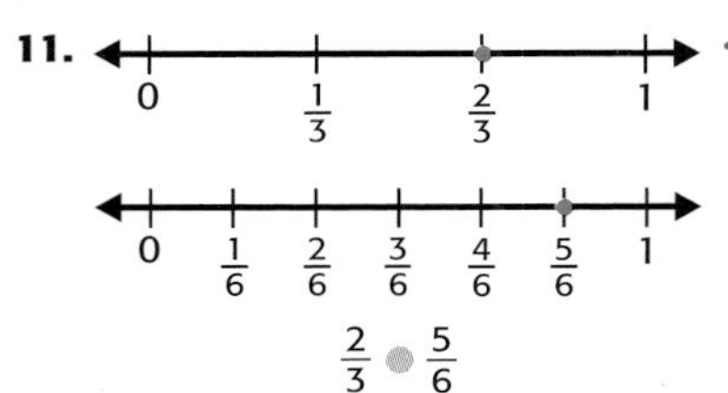 $\frac{2}{3}$ ● $\frac{5}{6}$ <

**12.** 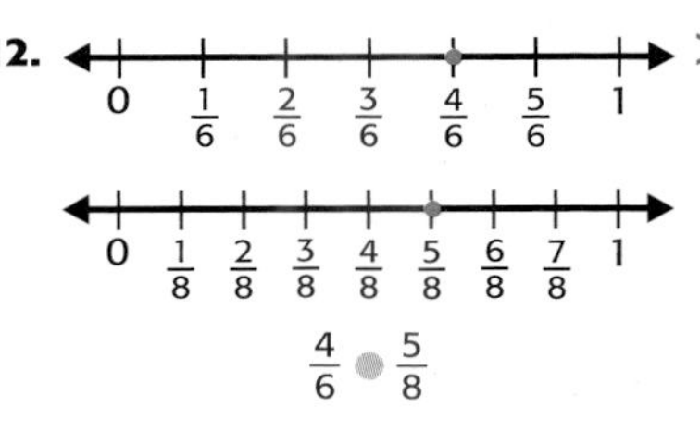 $\frac{4}{6}$ ● $\frac{5}{8}$ >

**13.** $\frac{2}{6}$ ● $\frac{1}{3}$ =

**14.** $\frac{3}{5}$ ● $\frac{5}{6}$ <

**15.** $\frac{4}{5}$ ● $\frac{8}{10}$ =

**16.** $\frac{2}{3}$ ● $\frac{5}{9}$ >

**17.** $\frac{4}{10}$ ● $\frac{1}{2}$ <

**18.** $\frac{5}{8}$ ● $\frac{2}{3}$ <

**Order from least to greatest.** See Example 3 (p. 555)

**19.** $\frac{4}{6}, \frac{1}{3}, \frac{3}{3}$ $\frac{1}{3}, \frac{4}{6}, \frac{3}{3}$

**20.** $\frac{3}{4}, \frac{2}{3}, \frac{7}{8}$ $\frac{2}{3}, \frac{3}{4}, \frac{7}{8}$

**21.** $\frac{3}{10}, \frac{3}{4}, \frac{3}{5}$ $\frac{3}{10}, \frac{3}{5}, \frac{3}{4}$

**22.** Which meat makes up most of Mr. Collin's sandwich? ham

**23.** Allison took a survey. Find the favorite weekend activity.

Favorite Weekend Activities

| Activity | Fraction of Friends |
|---|---|
| Movie | $\frac{2}{6}$ |
| Mall | $\frac{1}{4}$ |
| Basketball | $\frac{5}{12}$ |

playing basketball

**24.** ★ Aisha ate $\frac{1}{4}$ of the carrots in the bag. Enrique ate $\frac{3}{12}$ of the carrots in the bag. Who ate more carrots? They ate the same amount of carrots.

**25.** ★ Suzanne practiced volleyball for $\frac{2}{3}$ hour on Saturday and $\frac{1}{6}$ hour on Sunday. Which day did she practice longer? Saturday

**26.** ★ **Measurement** The table shows how much time each student needs to finish an art project. Does Simón need more or less time than Phil? Explain. Simón needs less time than Phil. Since $\frac{4}{12} < \frac{3}{4}$.

| Student | Time |
|---|---|
| Simón | $\frac{4}{12}$ hour |
| Phil | $\frac{3}{4}$ hour |



**COMMON ERROR!**

**Exercise 26** Some students may assume $\frac{4}{12}$ is the greater fraction because it has the greater numerator (and denominator). Remind students to compare the numerators once the denominators are the same.

## H.O.T. Problems

**27. OPEN ENDED** Write three fractions that are *not* greater than $\frac{1}{2}$. **Sample answer: $\frac{1}{3}$, $\frac{1}{4}$, and $\frac{1}{8}$**

**28. WHICH ONE DOESN'T BELONG?** Identify the set of fractions that does not belong with the other three sets. Explain.

$\frac{1}{4}, \frac{5}{8}, \frac{15}{16}$ | $\frac{2}{9}, \frac{1}{3}, \frac{1}{2}$ | $\frac{2}{5}, \frac{1}{2}, \frac{7}{10}$ | $\frac{3}{4}, \frac{1}{2}, \frac{2}{12}$

**See Ch. 13 Answer Appendix.**

**29. CHALLENGE** Identify a fraction that is greater than $\frac{150}{300}$. **Sample answer: $\frac{400}{500}$**

**30. WRITING IN MATH** Explain how to decide if $\frac{3}{4}$ is greater than or less than $\frac{3}{5}$. **Sample answer: Find an equivalent fraction with a common denominator for each of the fractions. Then compare the numerators.**

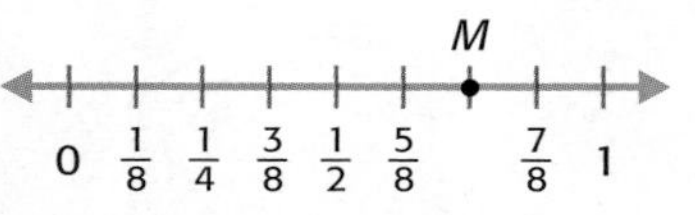

## TEST Practice

**31.** What fraction is equivalent to the fraction represented by point *M* on the number line? (Lesson 13-4) **D**

(Number line with point *M*: 0, $\frac{1}{8}$, $\frac{1}{4}$, $\frac{3}{8}$, $\frac{1}{2}$, $\frac{5}{8}$, M, $\frac{7}{8}$, 1)

**A** $\frac{1}{4}$ **C** $\frac{1}{2}$

**B** $\frac{3}{8}$ **D** $\frac{3}{4}$

**32.** Which set of fractions is ordered from greatest to least? (Lesson 13-5) **F**

**F** $\frac{3}{5}, \frac{6}{15}, \frac{2}{10}$

**G** $\frac{2}{10}, \frac{3}{5}, \frac{6}{15}$

**H** $\frac{2}{10}, \frac{6}{15}, \frac{3}{5}$

**J** $\frac{6}{15}, \frac{3}{5}, \frac{2}{10}$

## Spiral Review

**Find an equivalent fraction for each fraction.** (Lesson 13-4)

**33.** $\frac{1}{2}$ **$\frac{2}{4}$** **34.** $\frac{2}{3}$ **$\frac{4}{6}$** **35.** $\frac{3}{5}$ **$\frac{6}{10}$**

**36.** ★ Toya has 8 coins in her piggy bank. One fourth of the coins are quarters. Three of the coins are dimes. The rest of the coins are pennies. How many pennies does Toya have? (Lesson 13-3) **3**

**Find each product.** (Lesson 6-4)

**37.** $37 \times 4$ **148** **38.** $51 \times 7$ **357** **39.** $85 \times 9$ **765**



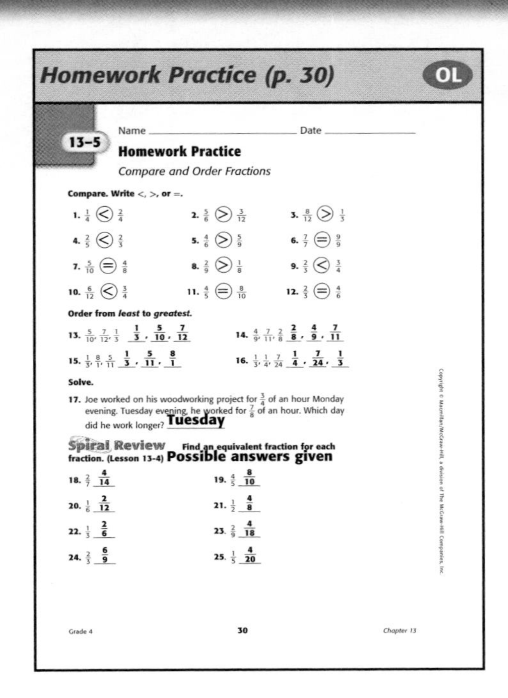

**Homework Practice (p. 30)** OL

Name ______ Date ______

13–5 **Homework Practice**

*Compare and Order Fractions*

**Compare. Write <, >, or =.**

1. $\frac{1}{4}$ (<) $\frac{2}{4}$ 2. $\frac{5}{6}$ (>) $\frac{3}{12}$ 3. $\frac{8}{12}$ (>) $\frac{1}{3}$

4. $\frac{2}{5}$ (<) $\frac{2}{3}$ 5. $\frac{4}{6}$ (>) $\frac{5}{9}$ 6. $\frac{7}{7}$ (=) $\frac{9}{9}$

7. $\frac{5}{10}$ (=) $\frac{4}{8}$ 8. $\frac{2}{9}$ (>) $\frac{1}{8}$ 9. $\frac{2}{3}$ (<) $\frac{3}{4}$

10. $\frac{6}{12}$ (<) $\frac{3}{4}$ 11. $\frac{4}{5}$ (=) $\frac{8}{10}$ 12. $\frac{2}{3}$ (=) $\frac{4}{6}$

**Order from *least* to *greatest*.**

13. $\frac{5}{10}, \frac{7}{12}, \frac{1}{3}$ **$\frac{1}{3}, \frac{5}{10}, \frac{7}{12}$** 14. $\frac{4}{9}, \frac{7}{11}, \frac{2}{8}$ **$\frac{2}{8}, \frac{4}{9}, \frac{7}{11}$**

15. $\frac{1}{3}, \frac{8}{1}, \frac{5}{11}$ **$\frac{1}{3}, \frac{5}{11}, \frac{8}{1}$** 16. $\frac{1}{3}, \frac{1}{4}, \frac{7}{24}$ **$\frac{1}{4}, \frac{7}{24}, \frac{1}{3}$**

**Solve.**

17. Joe worked on his woodworking project for $\frac{3}{4}$ of an hour Monday evening. Tuesday evening, he worked for $\frac{7}{8}$ of an hour. Which day did he work longer? **Tuesday**

**Spiral Review** Find an equivalent fraction for each fraction. (Lesson 13-4) **Possible answers given**

18. $\frac{2}{7}$ **$\frac{4}{14}$** 19. $\frac{4}{5}$ **$\frac{8}{10}$**

20. $\frac{1}{6}$ **$\frac{2}{12}$** 21. $\frac{1}{2}$ **$\frac{4}{8}$**

22. $\frac{1}{3}$ **$\frac{2}{6}$** 23. $\frac{2}{9}$ **$\frac{4}{18}$**

24. $\frac{2}{3}$ **$\frac{6}{9}$** 25. $\frac{1}{5}$ **$\frac{4}{20}$**



Grade 4 30 Chapter 13

# 4 Assess

## Formative Assessment

Provide students with the following lists of fractions.

List 1: $\frac{1}{4}, \frac{2}{3}, \frac{3}{4}, \frac{1}{2}, \frac{1}{3}, \frac{3}{5}$

List 2: $\frac{5}{6}, \frac{1}{6}, \frac{3}{6}, \frac{4}{6}, \frac{2}{6}, \frac{6}{6}$

- **Write each list in order from least to greatest.**
  List 1: $\frac{1}{4}, \frac{1}{3}, \frac{1}{2}, \frac{3}{5}, \frac{2}{3}, \frac{3}{4}$ List 2: $\frac{1}{6}, \frac{2}{6}, \frac{3}{6}, \frac{4}{6}, \frac{5}{6}, \frac{6}{6}$
- **Why is List 2 easier to order?**
  The denominators are already the same.

**Quick Check** **Are students continuing to struggle with comparing and ordering simple fractions?**

**If Yes** → Small Group Options (p. 510B)

**If No** → Independent Work Options (p. 510B)
CRM Skills Practice Worksheet (p. 29)
CRM Enrich Worksheet (p. 32)

**Ticket Out The Door** Ask students to order the fractions $\frac{2}{3}, \frac{1}{2}, \frac{1}{4}$, and $\frac{6}{8}$ from least to greatest. Have them write the answer on a piece of paper to hand to you as they leave the class. $\frac{1}{4}, \frac{1}{2}, \frac{2}{3}, \frac{6}{8}$

## TEST Practice

**Reviews Lessons 13-4 and 13-5**

Assign the Test Practice problems to provide daily reinforcement of test-taking skills.

## Spiral Review

**Reviews Lessons 6-4, 13-3, and 13-4**

Review and assess mastery of skills and concepts from previous chapters.

# Lesson Planner

## Objective

Interpret information and data from science to solve problems.

### National Standards 

Students should develop an understanding of the characteristics of organisms.

## Activate Prior Knowledge

Before you turn students' attention to the pages, ask them to discuss the human skeleton.

- **What purpose does the human skeleton serve?** holds the body up, lets it move
- **Where is the smallest bone located?** in the ear

## Using the Student Page

Ask students to read the information on p. 559 and answer these questions:

- **What fraction of the bones in an adult human is located in the vertebral column?** $\frac{25}{200}$ or $\frac{1}{8}$
- **Would it be correct to say that the hands make up $\frac{2}{8}$ of the bones in an adult human skeleton? Explain.** Yes, because $\frac{50}{200}$ is equal to $\frac{2}{8}$.





# No BONES about it . . .

Every human has a skeleton made up of bones. Your skeletal system is very important. Not only does it protect your internal organs, but it also allows you to stand up and walk. Without a skeleton you would be nothing but skin and guts!

Humans are born with 350 bones in their body. But, by the time you are 25, you will have only about 200 bones. This is because some of the bones join together to make a single bone.

The shortest bone is in the ear. It can be as short as $\frac{1}{10}$ of an inch. The longest bone, the femur, is located in the thigh. It is about $\frac{1}{4}$ of your height.

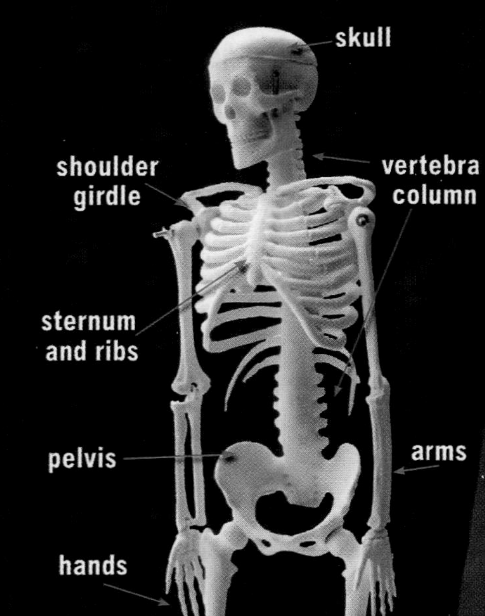


**Did You Know?**
Of the bones in your skeleton, about $\frac{3}{20}$ are found in your spine.

ADULT HUMAN SKELETON

| Body Part | Number of Bones |
|---|---|
| Skull | 22 |
| Middle ears | 6 |
| Throat | 1 |
| Shoulder girdle | 4 |
| Sternum and ribs | 25 |
| Vertebral column | 24 |
| Arms | 6 |
| Hands | 54 |
| Pelvis | 4 |
| Legs | 8 |
| Feet | 52 |

Source: BBC Education

## Real-World Math

**Use the information on pages 558 and 559 to solve each problem.**

1. What fraction of the bones in an adult human is located in the skull?
2. Which two body parts contain $\frac{1}{2}$ of the bones in an adult human? Explain your reasoning.
3. Which body part contains $\frac{8}{206}$ of the bones in an adult human?
4. About what fraction of the bones at birth does a human have when an adult?
5. Are more bones in an adult human located in the skull or in the spine?
6. The backbone is approximately 28 inches. What fraction of a foot is 28 inches?
7. Use your height to determine the length of your femur bone in inches.

**1–7. See margin.**



### Additional Answers

1. $\frac{22}{206}$ or $\frac{11}{103}$
2. hands and feet; $54 + 52 \approx 50 + 50$ or 100, 100 is about half of 206
3. legs
4. about $\frac{200}{300}$ or $\frac{2}{3}$
5. spine
6. $\frac{28}{12}$
7. Check students' work.

## Real-World Math

Assign the exercises on p. 559. Encourage students to choose a problem-solving strategy before beginning each exercise. If necessary, review the strategies suggested in Lesson 12-9, p. 518.

**Exercise 1** Remind students that the adult human skeleton contains about 200 bones.

**Exercise 4** Remind students that they need to write the fraction in its simplest equivalent form to answer this question.

**Exercise 6** Remind students that the bone count for feet in the chart is for both feet, and this question asks about only one foot.

## Extend the Activity

Have students form pairs and calculate the length of their partners' femurs in inches using their heights.

LESSON

# 13-6 Mixed Numbers

## Lesson Planner

### Objective

Write mixed numbers and improper fractions.

### Vocabulary

**mixed number**, **improper fraction**

### Resources

**Materials:** the paper plate fraction pieces made in Activity Choice 1 from Lesson 13-1.

**Literature Connection:** *Fraction Action* by Loreen Leedy

**Alternate Lesson:** Use *IMPACT Mathematics:* Unit D to provide practice with mixed numbers.

**Teacher Technology**

TeacherWorks • Interactive Classroom

## Daily Routine

Use these suggestions before beginning the lesson on p. 560.

### 5-Minute Check

(Reviews Lesson 12-5)

**Use models to compare. Write >, <, or =.**

1. $\frac{2}{5}$ ● $\frac{1}{3}$ >
2. $\frac{3}{4}$ ● $\frac{1}{4}$ >
3. $\frac{4}{6}$ ● $\frac{2}{3}$ =
4. $\frac{3}{10}$ ● $\frac{1}{2}$ <
5. $\frac{4}{9}$ ● $\frac{1}{3}$ >
6. $\frac{3}{4}$ ● $\frac{7}{8}$ <

### Problem of the Day

I have 8 coins in my pocket that total 77 cents. What coins are in my pocket? 2 quarters, 1 dime, 3 nickels, 2 pennies

### Focus on Math Background

The term "improper fraction" can give the impression that it is incorrect to write a fraction in which the numerator is greater than the denominator. The phrase "fraction that is greater than one" may be more meaningful to students at this stage.

- To understand the concept of changing a mixed number to an improper fraction, students must recognize a mixed number as an implied sum:

$$1\frac{3}{7} = 1 + \frac{3}{7} = \frac{7}{7} + \frac{3}{7} = \frac{10}{7}$$

- To change an improper fraction to a mixed number, students must use the skills of division with remainders that were introduced in Chapter 7.

### Building Math Vocabulary

Write the lesson vocabulary words and their definitions on the board.

Write several mixed numbers and improper fractions on separate pieces of paper. Show one piece of paper to the class at a time. Ask the students, as a class, to identify each number as an "improper fraction" or "mixed number."

#### Visual Vocabulary Cards

Use Visual Vocabulary Cards 20 and 25 to reinforce the vocabulary introduced in this lesson. (The Define/Example/Ask routine is printed on the back of each card.)

mixed number

# Differentiated Instruction

## Small Group Options

SOCIAL, LOGICAL

### Option 1 Gifted and Talented AL

**Materials:** recipes, paper, pencils

Ask students to bring in traditional family recipes. Have students write the recipes doubled and halved.

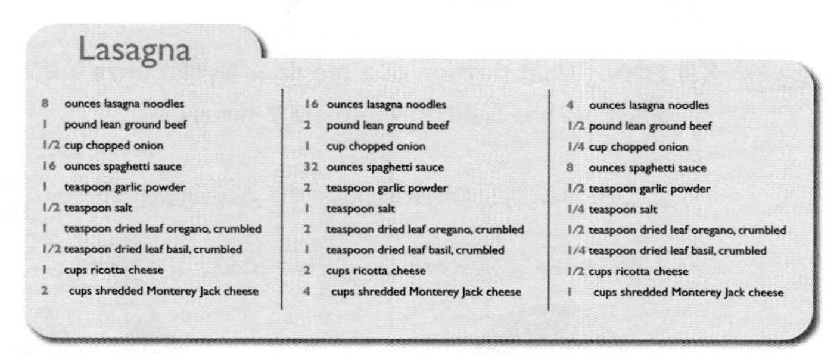

Lasagna

| | | |
|---|---|---|
| 8 ounces lasagna noodles | 16 ounces lasagna noodles | 4 ounces lasagna noodles |
| 1 pound lean ground beef | 2 pound lean ground beef | 1/2 pound lean ground beef |
| 1/2 cup chopped onion | 1 cup chopped onion | 1/4 cup chopped onion |
| 16 ounces spaghetti sauce | 32 ounces spaghetti sauce | 8 ounces spaghetti sauce |
| 1 teaspoon garlic powder | 2 teaspoon garlic powder | 1/2 teaspoon garlic powder |
| 1/2 teaspoon salt | 1 teaspoon salt | 1/4 teaspoon salt |
| 1 teaspoon dried leaf oregano, crumbled | 2 teaspoon dried leaf oregano, crumbled | 1/2 teaspoon dried leaf oregano, crumbled |
| 1/2 teaspoon dried leaf basil, crumbled | 1 teaspoon dried leaf basil, crumbled | 1/4 teaspoon dried leaf basil, crumbled |
| 1 cups ricotta cheese | 2 cups ricotta cheese | 1/2 cups ricotta cheese |
| 2 cups shredded Monterey Jack cheese | 4 cups shredded Monterey Jack cheese | 1 cups shredded Monterey Jack cheese |

INTERPERSONAL, LINGUISTIC

### Option 2 English Language Learners ELL

**Materials:** chalkboard, journals
**Core Vocabulary:** whole, parts, together
**Common Use Verb:** mix

**Write Math** This strategy uses scaffolded writing to allow students to expand on the concept and vocabulary of mixed fractions.

- Draw a picture of a whole pizza and another pizza with eight total pieces and three missing.
- Prompt students to write a sentence describing the picture. "I see …"
- Tell students to write a fraction describing the picture. Allow students to form small groups to discuss how to do this. Have groups present answers and discuss their reasoning.
- Demonstrate to students how a traditional mixed number should look: $1\frac{3}{8}$.
- Tell students it is called mixed because it has a fraction and a whole number: 1 is for the whole pizza, the $\frac{3}{8}$ is for the second pizza.
- Repeat as time permits with different fractions.

## Independent Work Options

SOCIAL, LOGICAL

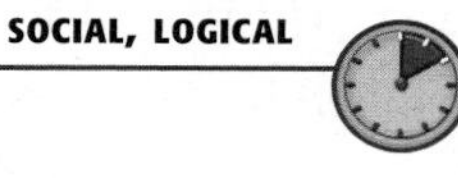

### Option 1 Early Finishers OL AL

**Materials:** paper and pencil

- Have students work in small groups. Have them list the numbers 1–12 on scraps of paper.
- Students take turns choosing two numbers. They should use these numbers to create an improper fraction.
- Whoever converts the improper fraction to a mixed number first gets to go next.

### Option 2 Student Technology

**Math Online** macmillanmh.com

Personal Tutor • Extra Examples

Math Adventures

### Option 3 Learning Station: Health (p. 534H)

Direct students to the Health Learning Station for opportunities to explore and extend the lesson concept.

### Option 4 Problem-Solving Practice

Reinforce problem-solving skills and strategies with the Problem-Solving Practice worksheet.

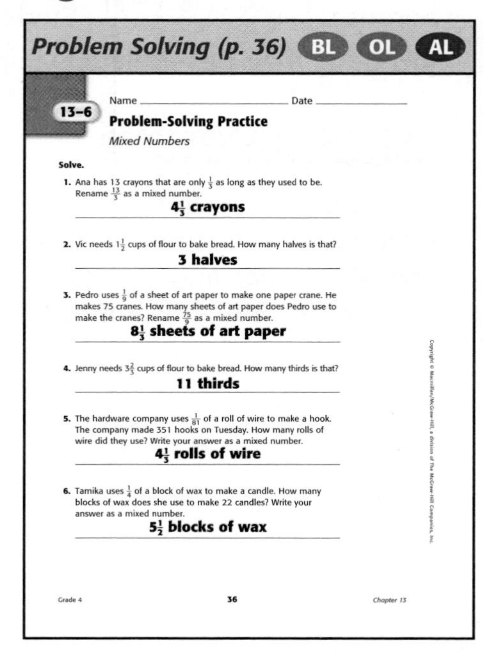

*Problem Solving (p. 36)* BL OL AL

13–6 Name ____________ Date ____________

**Problem-Solving Practice**

*Mixed Numbers*

**Solve.**

1. Ana has 13 crayons that are only $\frac{1}{3}$ as long as they used to be. Rename $\frac{13}{3}$ as a mixed number.
   **$4\frac{1}{3}$ crayons**
2. Vic needs $1\frac{1}{2}$ cups of flour to bake bread. How many halves is that?
   **3 halves**
3. Pedro uses $\frac{1}{9}$ of a sheet of art paper to make one paper crane. He makes 75 cranes. How many sheets of art paper does Pedro use to make the cranes? Rename $\frac{75}{9}$ as a mixed number.
   **$8\frac{1}{3}$ sheets of art paper**
4. Jenny needs $3\frac{2}{3}$ cups of flour to bake bread. How many thirds is that?
   **11 thirds**
5. The hardware company uses $\frac{1}{81}$ of a roll of wire to make a hook. The company made 351 hooks on Tuesday. How many rolls of wire did they use? Write your answer as a mixed number.
   **$4\frac{1}{3}$ rolls of wire**
6. Tamika uses $\frac{1}{4}$ of a block of wax to make a candle. How many blocks of wax does she use to make 22 candles? Write your answer as a mixed number.
   **$5\frac{1}{2}$ blocks of wax**



Grade 4 36 Chapter 13

# 13-6 Mixed Numbers

## 1 Introduce

**Activity Choice 1 • Hands-On** 

- Ask students to get out their pie pieces from Activity Choice 1 from Lesson 12-1.
- Demonstrate how to arrange 5 quarter pieces into $1\frac{1}{4}$ pies. Have students work in groups of 3.
- **How many fourths pieces are needed to make $1\frac{3}{4}$ pies?** 7 fourths
- Explain that 7 fourths is written $\frac{7}{4}$.
- Tell students these are called improper fractions since the numerator is greater than or equal to the denominator.

**Activity Choice 2 • Literature**

Introduce the lesson with *Fraction Action* by Loreen Leedy. For a related math activity, see p. TR64.

## 2 Teach

### Scaffolding Questions

With or without the use of the paper plate manipulatives, ask students the following questions.

- **How many fourths is $2\frac{3}{4}$?** $\frac{11}{4}$
- **How many pies is $\frac{12}{4}$?** 3
- **How many pies is $\frac{5}{3}$?** $1\frac{2}{3}$

Write the following on the board: $2\frac{3}{4} = \frac{11}{4}$ because $\frac{4}{4} + \frac{4}{4} + \frac{3}{4} = \frac{11}{4}$. Students can verify this using their paper plate manipulatives.

**GET READY to Learn**

Have students open their books and read the information in **Get Ready to Learn**. Introduce **mixed number** and **improper fraction**. As a class, work through **Examples 1–4**.



# 13-6 Mixed Numbers

**MAIN IDEA**

I will write mixed numbers and improper fractions.

**New Vocabulary**

mixed number
improper fraction

**Math Online**

macmillanmh.com
- Extra Examples
- Personal Tutor
- Self-Check Quiz

**GET READY to Learn**

Nyoko is selling pies at a bake sale. Each pie has 5 slices. Each slice of pie is sold separately. There are 7 slices left. What fraction of the pies is left?

A **mixed number** has a whole number part and a fraction part. An **improper fraction** has a numerator that is greater than or equal to its denominator.

| Mixed Numbers | Improper Fractions |
|---|---|
| $1\frac{1}{2}$ $2\frac{3}{4}$ $3\frac{5}{6}$ | $\frac{3}{2}$ $\frac{11}{4}$ $\frac{23}{6}$ |

**Real-World EXAMPLE**

**1 FOOD What fraction of a pie does Nyoko have left?**

Each pie has 5 slices. There are 7 slices left.

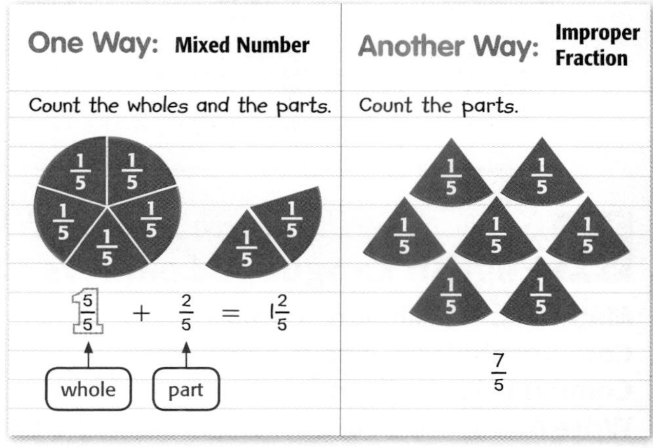


So, $1\frac{2}{5}$ or $\frac{7}{5}$ of a pie is left.

560 **Chapter 13** Describe and Compare Fractions

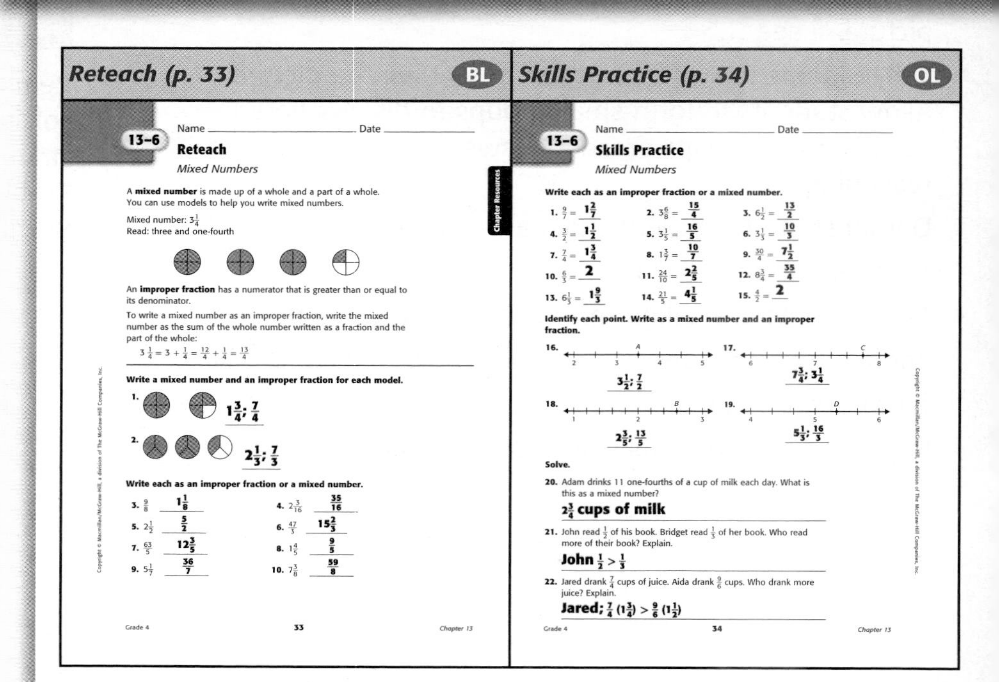

**Reteach (p. 33)** BL

13-6 Name ______ Date ______

**Reteach**

*Mixed Numbers*

A **mixed number** is made up of a whole and a part of a whole. You can use models to help you write mixed numbers.

Mixed number: $3\frac{1}{4}$
Read: three and one-fourth

An **improper fraction** has a numerator that is greater than or equal to its denominator.

To write a mixed number as an improper fraction, write the mixed number as the sum of the whole number written as a fraction and the part of the whole:

$3\frac{1}{4} = 3 + \frac{1}{4} = \frac{12}{4} + \frac{1}{4} = \frac{13}{4}$

**Write a mixed number and an improper fraction for each model.**

1. $1\frac{3}{4}; \frac{7}{4}$
2. $2\frac{1}{3}; \frac{7}{3}$

**Write each as an improper fraction or a mixed number.**

3. $\frac{9}{8}$ $1\frac{1}{8}$
4. $2\frac{3}{16}$ $\frac{35}{16}$
5. $2\frac{1}{2}$ $\frac{5}{2}$
6. $\frac{47}{3}$ $15\frac{2}{3}$
7. $\frac{63}{5}$ $12\frac{3}{5}$
8. $1\frac{4}{5}$ $\frac{9}{5}$
9. $5\frac{1}{7}$ $\frac{36}{7}$
10. $7\frac{3}{8}$ $\frac{59}{8}$

Grade 4 33 Chapter 13



**Skills Practice (p. 34)** OL

13-6 Name ______ Date ______

**Skills Practice**

*Mixed Numbers*

**Write each as an improper fraction or a mixed number.**

1. $\frac{9}{7} = 1\frac{2}{7}$
2. $3\frac{6}{8} = \frac{15}{4}$
3. $6\frac{1}{2} = \frac{13}{2}$
4. $\frac{3}{2} = 1\frac{1}{2}$
5. $3\frac{1}{5} = \frac{16}{5}$
6. $3\frac{1}{3} = \frac{10}{3}$
7. $\frac{7}{4} = 1\frac{3}{4}$
8. $1\frac{3}{7} = \frac{10}{7}$
9. $\frac{30}{4} = 7\frac{1}{2}$
10. $\frac{6}{3} = 2$
11. $\frac{24}{10} = 2\frac{2}{5}$
12. $8\frac{3}{4} = \frac{35}{4}$
13. $6\frac{1}{3} = 1\frac{9}{3}$
14. $\frac{21}{5} = 4\frac{1}{5}$
15. $\frac{4}{2} = 2$

**Identify each point. Write as a mixed number and an improper fraction.**

16. $3\frac{1}{2}; \frac{7}{2}$
17. $7\frac{3}{4}; 3\frac{1}{4}$
18. $2\frac{3}{5}; \frac{13}{5}$
19. $5\frac{1}{3}; \frac{16}{3}$

**Solve.**

20. Adam drinks 11 one-fourths of a cup of milk each day. What is this as a mixed number?
**$2\frac{3}{4}$ cups of milk**

21. John read $\frac{1}{2}$ of his book. Bridget read $\frac{1}{3}$ of her book. Who read more of their book? Explain.
**John $\frac{1}{2} > \frac{1}{3}$**

22. Jared drank $\frac{7}{4}$ cups of juice. Aida drank $\frac{9}{6}$ cups. Who drank more juice? Explain.
**Jared; $\frac{7}{4}\ (1\frac{3}{4}) > \frac{9}{6}\ (1\frac{1}{2})$**

Grade 4 34 Chapter 13

You can change from a mixed number to an improper fraction. You can also change from an improper fraction to a mixed number.

**EXAMPLES** Mixed Number to Improper Fraction

**2 Write $1\frac{3}{8}$ as an improper fraction.**

$1\frac{3}{8} = 1 + \frac{3}{8}$ Write the mixed number as the sum of a whole and part.

$= \frac{8}{8} + \frac{3}{8}$ Write the whole number as a fraction.

$= \frac{8 + 3}{8}$ Add.

$= \frac{11}{8}$

**Remember**

The fraction bar stands for *divided by*. So, $\frac{11}{8}$ means *11 divided by 8*.

**3 Write $\frac{11}{8}$ as a mixed number.**

Divide the numerator by the denominator.

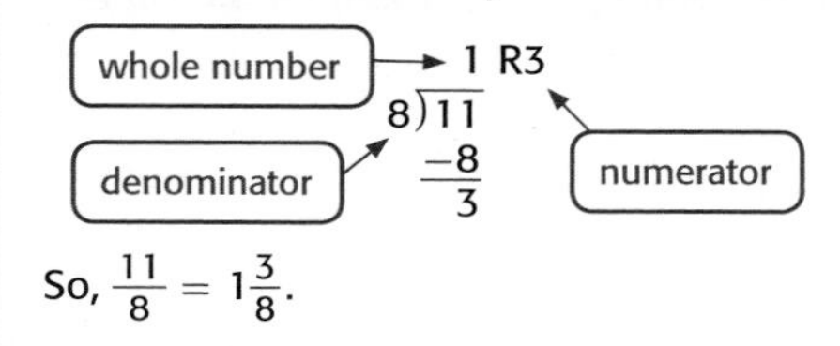


So, $\frac{11}{8} = 1\frac{3}{8}$.

You can show improper fractions and mixed numbers on a number line.

**EXAMPLE** Use a Number Line

**4 Identify point *A* as a mixed number and improper fraction.**

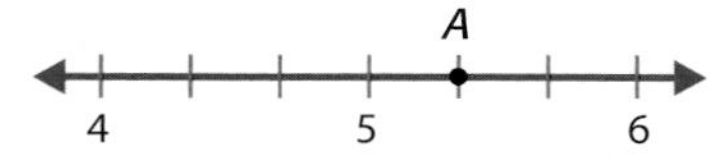


Each interval on the number line is one third. So, point *A* is $5\frac{1}{3}$.

A

4 5 $5\frac{1}{3}$ 6

$5\frac{1}{3} = \frac{3}{3} + \frac{3}{3} + \frac{3}{3} + \frac{3}{3} + \frac{3}{3} + \frac{1}{3}$

$= \frac{3 + 3 + 3 + 3 + 3 + 1}{3} = \frac{16}{3}$

So, Point *A* is $5\frac{1}{3}$ or $\frac{16}{3}$.



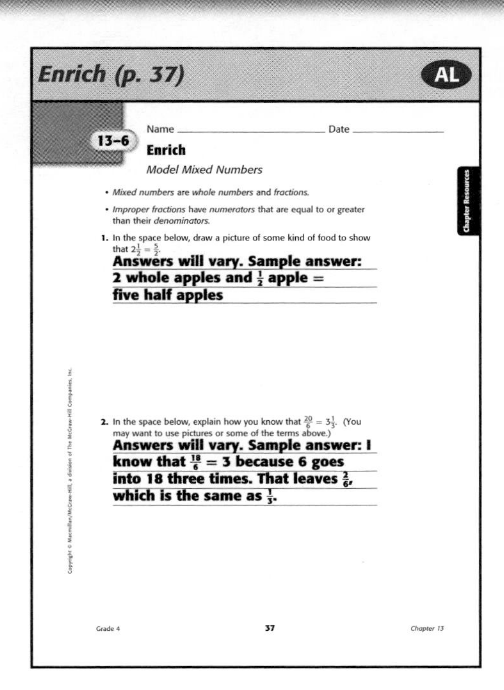

**Enrich (p. 37)** AL

13–6

Name ________ Date ________

**Enrich**

*Model Mixed Numbers*

- *Mixed numbers are whole numbers and fractions.*
- *Improper fractions have numerators that are equal to or greater than their denominators.*

1. In the space below, draw a picture of some kind of food to show that $2\frac{1}{2} = \frac{5}{2}$.
**Answers will vary. Sample answer: 2 whole apples and $\frac{1}{2}$ apple = five half apples**

2. In the space below, explain how you know that $\frac{20}{6} = 3\frac{1}{3}$. (You may want to use pictures or some of the terms above.)
**Answers will vary. Sample answer: I know that $\frac{18}{6} = 3$ because 6 goes into 18 three times. That leaves $\frac{2}{6}$, which is the same as $\frac{1}{3}$.**

Chapter Resources



Grade 4 37 Chapter 13

## Use a Number Line

**Example 4** Remind students that they need to first determine the scale of the number line. In this example, the interval between 5 and 6 has been divided into 3 equal parts, so the scale is in thirds. Draw this number line on the board with all the thirds labeled to illustrate.

**ADDITIONAL EXAMPLES**

1. What fraction of the lasagna is left?
$1\frac{3}{10}$ or $\frac{13}{10}$

2. Write $2\frac{3}{5}$ as an improper fraction. $\frac{13}{5}$

3. Write $\frac{10}{3}$ as a mixed number. $3\frac{1}{3}$

4. Identify point *A* on the number line. Write it as a mixed number and an improper fraction.
$8\frac{2}{5}$, $\frac{42}{5}$

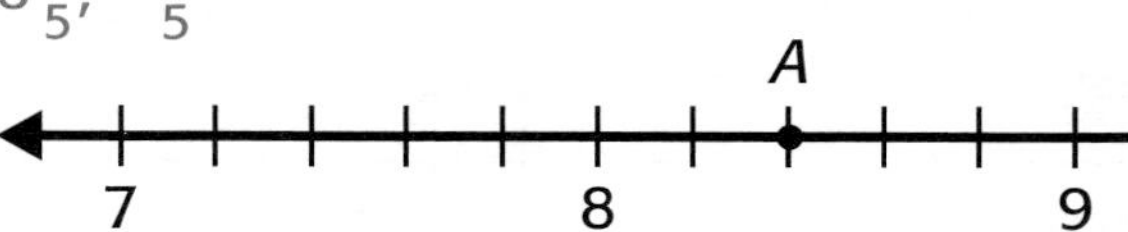

## CHECK What You Know

As a class, have students complete Exercises 1–11 in **Check What You Know** as you observe their work.

**Exercise 11** Assess student comprehension before assigning practice exercises.

## BL Alternate Teaching Strategy

**If** students have trouble writing mixed numbers and improper fractions…

**Then** use one of these reteach options:

1. CRM **Daily Reteach Worksheet** (p. 33)
2. Have student make models or pictures to represent the mixed numbers and then count up the pieces to find the numerator of the improper fraction.

# 3 Practice

Differentiate practice using these leveled assignments for Exercises 12–31.

| Level | Assignment |
|---|---|
| BL Below/Approaching Level | 12–13, 15–18, 23, 25, 27–28 |
| OL On Level | 12–20, 24, 25–28, 30 |
| AL Above/Beyond Level | 12–28 even, 29–31 |

Have students discuss and complete the Higher Order Thinking problems. For Exercise 30, encourage students to work the problem before trying to find the error.

**WRITING IN MATH** Have students complete Exercise 31 in their Math Journals. You may choose to use this exercise as an optional formative assessment.

### COMMON ERROR!

**Exercises 23–24** Students may have difficulty determining the fraction indicated on the number lines. Help students determine the scale on each number line.



★ indicates multi-step problem

## CHECK What You Know

**Write a mixed number and an improper fraction for each model.** See Example 1 (p. 560)

**1.**

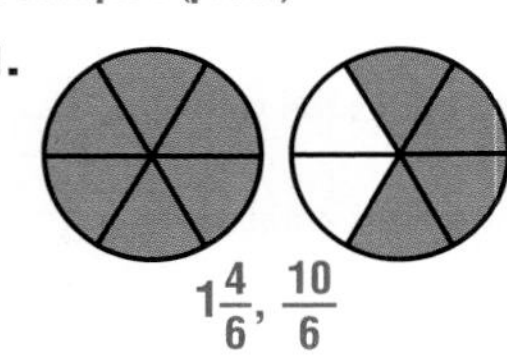

$1\frac{4}{6}, \frac{10}{6}$

**2.**

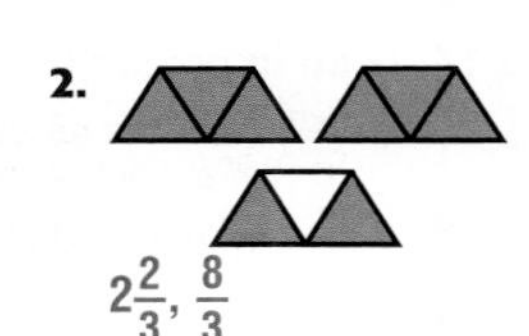

$2\frac{2}{3}, \frac{8}{3}$

**3.**

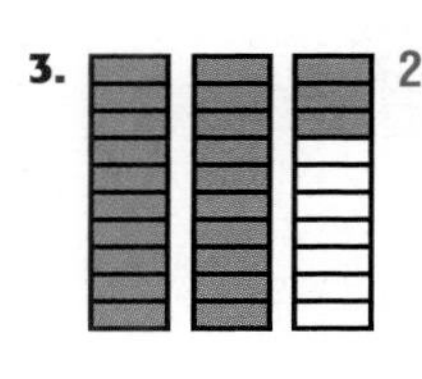

$2\frac{3}{10}, \frac{23}{10}$

**Write each as an improper fraction or a mixed number. Use models if needed.** See Examples 2 and 3 (p. 561)

**4.** $1\frac{2}{5}$ $\frac{7}{5}$ **5.** $2\frac{3}{4}$ $\frac{11}{4}$ **6.** $\frac{9}{4}$ $2\frac{1}{4}$ **7.** $\frac{13}{3}$ $4\frac{1}{3}$

**Identify each point as a mixed number and an improper fraction.** See Example 4 (p. 561)

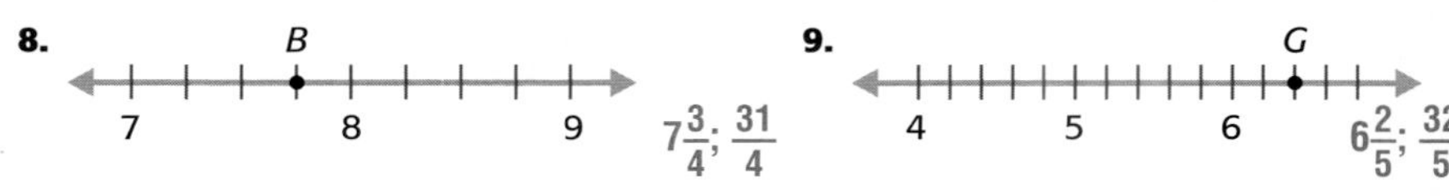


**8.** $7\frac{3}{4}, \frac{31}{4}$ **9.** $6\frac{2}{5}, \frac{32}{5}$

**10.** Andrew's family ate $1\frac{3}{8}$ pizzas and Sheri's family ate $1\frac{4}{16}$ pizzas. Who ate more pizzas? Andrew's family

**11.** Talk About It Explain how to compare $2\frac{3}{5}$ and $\frac{17}{5}$. Sample answer: Convert $2\frac{3}{5}$ into an improper fraction, then compare the numerator.

## Practice and Problem Solving

EXTRA PRACTICE See page R35.

**Write a mixed number and an improper fraction for each model.** See Example 1 (p. 560)

**12.**

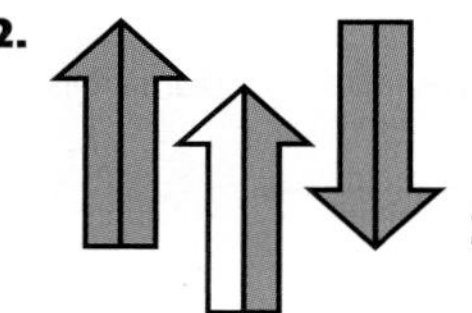

$2\frac{1}{2}, \frac{5}{2}$

**13.**

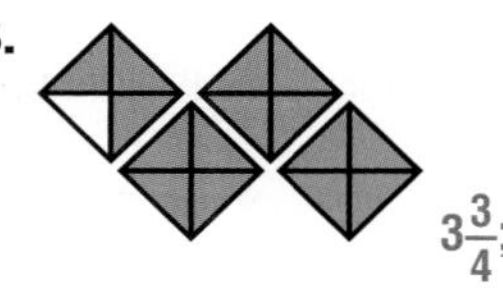

$3\frac{3}{4}, \frac{15}{4}$

**14.**

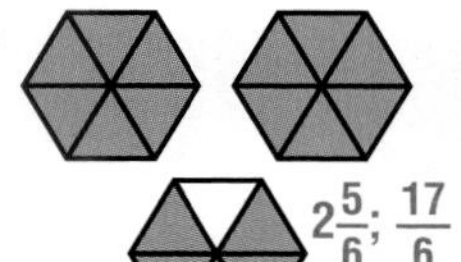

$2\frac{5}{6}, \frac{17}{6}$

**Write each as an improper fraction or a mixed number. Use models if needed.** See Examples 2 and 3 (p. 561)

**15.** $1\frac{3}{4}$ $\frac{7}{4}$ **16.** $2\frac{7}{10}$ $\frac{27}{10}$ **17.** $6\frac{7}{8}$ $\frac{55}{8}$ **18.** $8\frac{5}{8}$ $\frac{69}{8}$

**19.** $\frac{7}{3}$ $2\frac{1}{3}$ **20.** $\frac{17}{5}$ $3\frac{2}{5}$ **21.** $\frac{45}{8}$ $5\frac{5}{8}$ **22.** $\frac{50}{6}$ $8\frac{1}{3}$

**Identify each point as a mixed number and an improper fraction.**
See Example 4 (p. 561) 23, 24. See margin.

**23.** 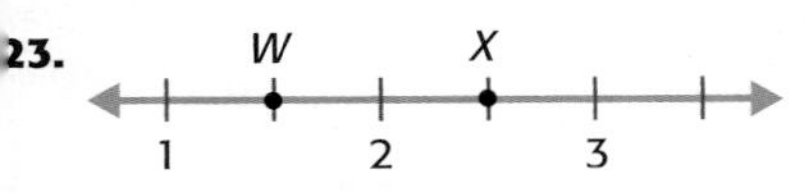


**24.** 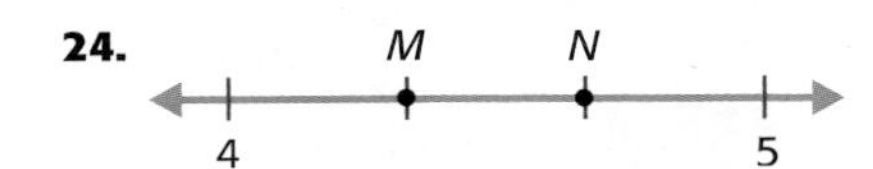


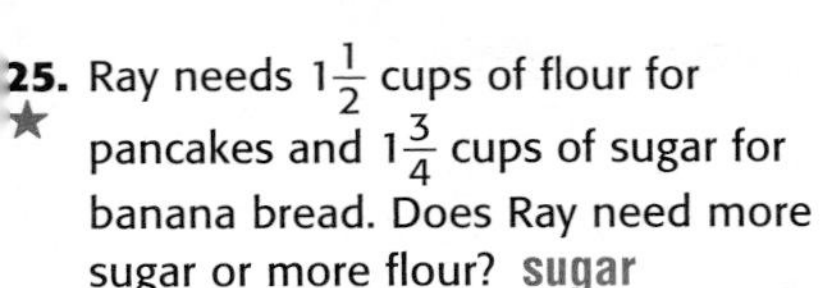

**25.** ★ Ray needs $1\frac{1}{2}$ cups of flour for pancakes and $1\frac{3}{4}$ cups of sugar for banana bread. Does Ray need more sugar or more flour? sugar

**26.** ★ Percy drank $2\frac{3}{5}$ cups of water after the first half of the soccer match and $2\frac{4}{6}$ cups of water after the second half. When did he drink more water? after the second half

## Real-World PROBLEM SOLVING

**Travel** A diagram of a horseback riding tour is shown. There are resting stops along the trail.

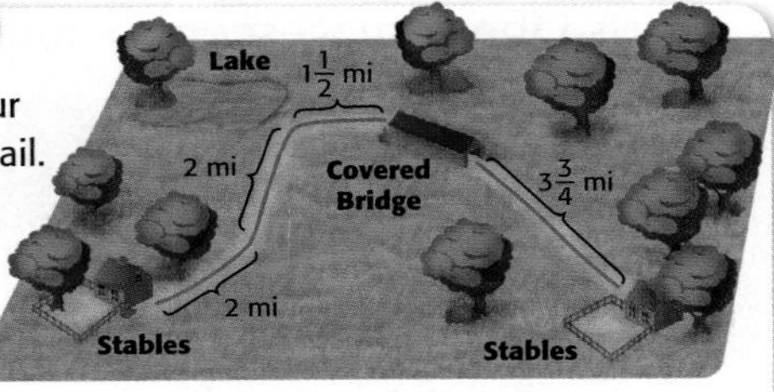


**27.** ★ Joaquin and his family started at the stables on the left. They are at the covered bridge. How many miles of the trail have they traveled? $5\frac{1}{2}$

**28.** Joaquin reached the end of the trail in 2 hours and 15 minutes. Write the amount of time he spent on the trail as an improper fraction. $\frac{135}{60}$

## H.O.T. Problems

**29. OPEN ENDED** Name an improper fraction that can be written as a whole number. Sample answer: $\frac{24}{6}$

**30. FIND THE ERROR** Heather and Wesley are writing $4\frac{3}{5}$ as an improper fraction. Who is correct? Explain.

30. Sample answer: Heather; Wesley forgot to add the numerator to the product of 4 and 5.

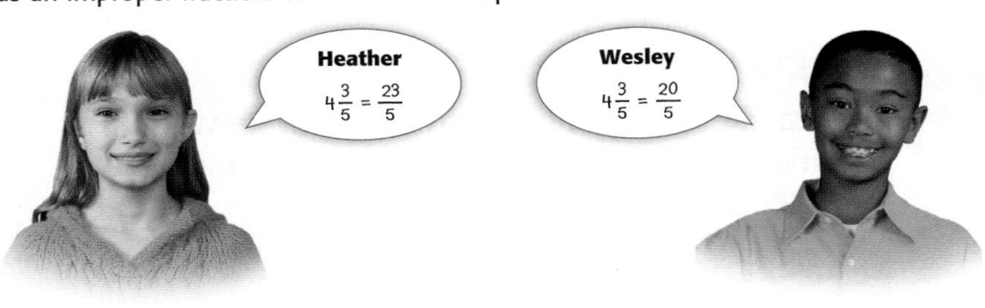


**31. WRITING IN MATH** Compare fractions, mixed numbers, and improper fractions. See margin.



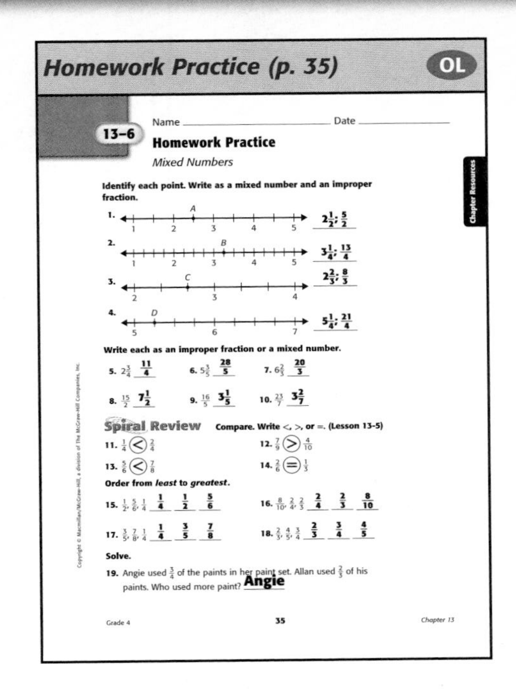

**Homework Practice (p. 35)** OL

13-6 **Homework Practice**
*Mixed Numbers*

Name ______ Date ______

**Identify each point. Write as a mixed number and an improper fraction.**

1. A — $2\frac{1}{2}; \frac{5}{2}$
2. B — $3\frac{1}{4}; \frac{13}{4}$
3. C — $2\frac{2}{3}; \frac{8}{3}$
4. D — $5\frac{1}{4}; \frac{21}{4}$

**Write each as an improper fraction or a mixed number.**

5. $2\frac{3}{4}$ $\frac{11}{4}$ 6. $5\frac{3}{5}$ $\frac{28}{5}$ 7. $6\frac{2}{3}$ $\frac{20}{3}$

8. $\frac{15}{2}$ $7\frac{1}{2}$ 9. $\frac{16}{5}$ $3\frac{1}{5}$ 10. $\frac{23}{7}$ $3\frac{2}{7}$

**Spiral Review** Compare. Write <, >, or =. (Lesson 13-5)

11. $\frac{1}{4}$ (<) $\frac{2}{4}$ 12. $\frac{5}{6}$ (>) $\frac{4}{10}$
13. $\frac{5}{6}$ (<) $\frac{7}{8}$ 14. $\frac{2}{6}$ (=) $\frac{1}{3}$

**Order from *least* to *greatest*.**

15. $\frac{1}{4}, \frac{1}{2}, \frac{5}{6}$ 16. $\frac{2}{4}, \frac{2}{3}, \frac{8}{10}$
17. $\frac{1}{4}, \frac{3}{5}, \frac{7}{8}$ 18. $\frac{2}{3}, \frac{3}{4}, \frac{4}{5}$

**Solve.**

19. Angie used $\frac{3}{4}$ of the paints in her paint set. Allan used $\frac{2}{3}$ of his paints. Who used more paint? Angie

Grade 4 35 Chapter 13

# 4 Assess

## Formative Assessment

Draw a picture of $2\frac{3}{8}$ pizzas on the board.

- **How much pizza is there? Write the answer two ways.** $2\frac{3}{8}; \frac{19}{8}$
- **What does the numerator of the improper fraction represent?** the number of slices left
- **What does the whole number of the mixed number represent?** the number of whole pizzas left
- **Are the denominators of improper fractions and their equivalent mixed number always the same?** yes

**Quick Check** **Are students continuing to struggle with writing mixed numbers and improper fractions?**

**If Yes** → Strategic Intervention Guide (p. 94)

**If No** → Independent Work Options (p. 560B)
CRM Skills Practice Worksheet (p. 34)
CRM Enrich Worksheet (p. 37)

**Name the Math** Ask students to write the steps they would take to convert a mixed number to an improper fraction. Ask them to include an example with their explanation.

### Additional Answers

**23.** $W = 1\frac{1}{2}; \frac{3}{2}; x = 2\frac{1}{2}; \frac{5}{2}$

**24.** $M = 4\frac{1}{3}; \frac{13}{3}; N = 4\frac{2}{3}; \frac{14}{3}$

**31.** Sample answer: A fraction is a number with a numerator and denominator. A mixed number is a number that contains a whole number and a fraction. An improper fraction is a fraction with a numerator that is greater than or equal to the denominator.

# 13-7 Problem-Solving Investigation
## Choose a Strategy

## Lesson Planner

### Objective

Choose the best strategy to solve a problem.

### Resources

**Manipulatives:** counters

**Teacher Technology**
TeacherWorks • Interactive Classroom

**Real-World Problem Solving Library**
**Math and Social Studies: *Life in the United States***
Use these leveled books to reinforce and extend problem-solving skills and strategies.

Leveled for:
- OL On Level
- ELL Sheltered English
- SP Spanish

For additional support, see the Real-World Problem Solving Teacher Guide.

## Daily Routine

Use these suggestions before beginning the lesson on p. 564.

### 5-Minute Check

(Reviews Lesson 12-6)

**Write each as an improper fraction or a mixed number. Use models if needed.**

1. $1\frac{2}{3}$ $\frac{5}{3}$
2. $\frac{7}{6}$ $1\frac{1}{6}$
3. $\frac{9}{2}$ $4\frac{1}{2}$
4. $2\frac{2}{5}$ $\frac{12}{5}$
5. $4\frac{1}{8}$ $\frac{33}{8}$
6. $\frac{13}{10}$ $1\frac{3}{10}$

### Problem of the Day

Suzanne baked a blackberry pie to share with 5 friends. What is the least number of straight cuts she could make to divide it evenly for 6? 3

# Differentiated Instruction

## Small Group Options

### Option 1 Below Level BL

**Materials:** 3 index cards per student; 24 centimeter cubes per student

- Students are given the following problem: *There are 24 fish in an aquarium. Of the 24, $\frac{1}{2}$ are clownfish. There are 8 fewer stingrays than clownfish. There are 4 more eels than stingrays. Find the total amount of each kind of fish.*
- Ask: **"What would be the best problem solving strategy to solve this problem?"** guess and check
- To solve the problem, have partners work together to label 3 index cards as clownfish, eels, and stingrays.
- Students will then use centimeter cubes and the guess and check strategy to find how many of each fish there are in the aquarium. 12 clownfish; 4 stingrays; 8 eels

### Option 2 English Language Learners ELL

LINGUISTIC

**Materials:** index cards with fractions in simplest form or that can be simplified
**Core Vocabulary:** reduce, pass it, your neighbor
**Common Use Verb:** recognize
**Talk Math** This strategy helps students choose the most effective strategy to recognize simplest forms of fractions.

- Put students in a circle and give each a few fraction cards.
- Say: "Take a card. Identify the type of fraction and say 'simplest form' or '**reduce**' and **pass it** to **your neighbor**."
- Have students speak at the same time and pass cards quickly. Periodically stop play and ask each student to reduce their card if it is not in the simplest form.
- Repeat as time permits.

## Independent Work Options

### Option 1 Early Finishers OL AL

SOCIAL, LOGICAL

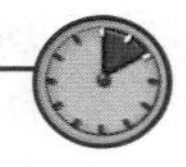

**Materials:** paper, pencils

- Ask students to pretend they are teaching a small group of students problem-solving skills. They need to come up with a few examples to show students how to use different strategies to solve various problems.
- Ask students to write the problems, their solutions, and give detailed explanations of each problem.

### Option 2 Student Technology

macmillanmh.com

Personal Tutor • Extra Examples

### Option 3 Learning Stations: Social Studies (p. 534G)

Direct students to the Social Studies Learning Station for opportunities to explore and extend the lesson concept.

# 1 Introduce

**Activity • Review**

- Ask students to think about the strategy they would use to solve the following problem:

  *Jenna and Ahmed were helping clean up a beach. Each hour they worked, they filled four bags of garbage. If they filled 12 bags, how long did they work?* make a table; 3 hours
- **How long did it take for them to fill 8 bags?** 2 hours
- If Miguel works with Jenna and Ahmed, they can pick up 6 bags of garbage each hour. **How long would it take this team to pick up 24 bags of garbage?** 4 hours

# 2 Teach

Have students read the problem on reptiles at the zoo. Guide them through the problem-solving steps.

**Understand** Using the questions, review what students know and need to find.

**Plan** Have them discuss their strategy.

**Solve** Guide students to use the solve a simpler problem strategy to solve the problem.

- **Explain why it would be easier to find one-sixth of 42 than one-sixth of 420.** You can model 42 easier than 420.
- **What is one-sixth of 42?** 7
  **What is one-sixth of 420?** 70

**Check** Have students look back at the problem to make sure that the answer fits the facts given.

- **Using your knowledge of fractions, explain why 70 is a reasonable answer.** Sample answer: $\frac{70}{420} = \frac{1}{6}$

## COMMON ERROR!

**Exercise 3** Students may incorrectly find the total cost because they divided by 3 rather than 4. Encourage students to reread the problem.



# 13-7 Problem-Solving Investigation

**MAIN IDEA** I will choose the best strategy to solve a problem.

**P.S.I. TEAM +**

ANICA: My class visited the zoo. I learned that one sixth of the animals at the zoo are reptiles. There are 420 animals at the zoo. How many animals are reptiles?

YOUR MISSION: Find how many animals are reptiles.

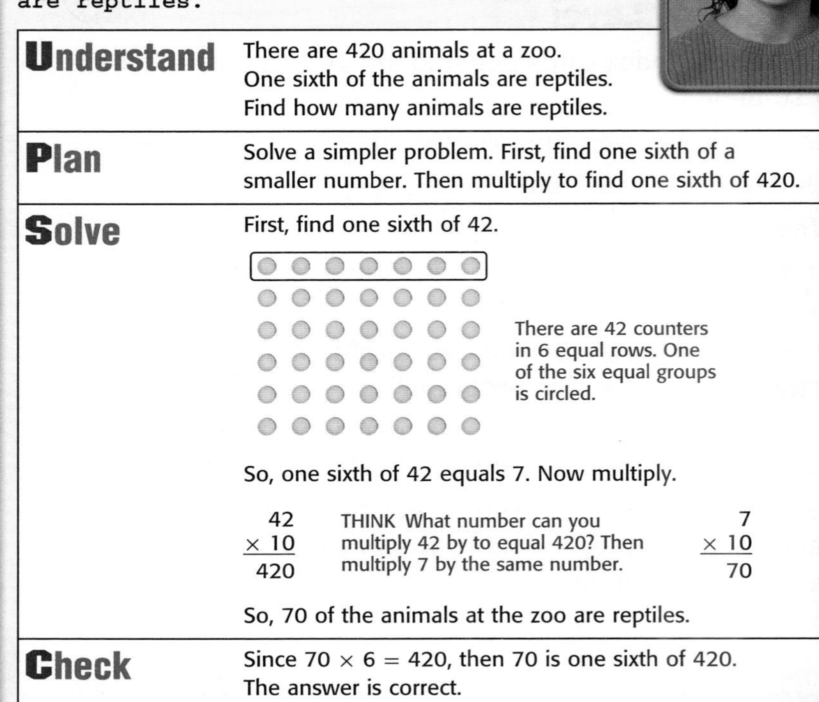

| | |
|---|---|
| **Understand** | There are 420 animals at a zoo.<br>One sixth of the animals are reptiles.<br>Find how many animals are reptiles. |
| **Plan** | Solve a simpler problem. First, find one sixth of a smaller number. Then multiply to find one sixth of 420. |
| **Solve** | First, find one sixth of 42.<br>There are 42 counters in 6 equal rows. One of the six equal groups is circled.<br>So, one sixth of 42 equals 7. Now multiply.<br>$42 \times 10 = 420$ THINK What number can you multiply 42 by to equal 420? Then multiply 7 by the same number. $7 \times 10 = 70$<br>So, 70 of the animals at the zoo are reptiles. |
| **Check** | Since $70 \times 6 = 420$, then 70 is one sixth of 420.<br>The answer is correct. |



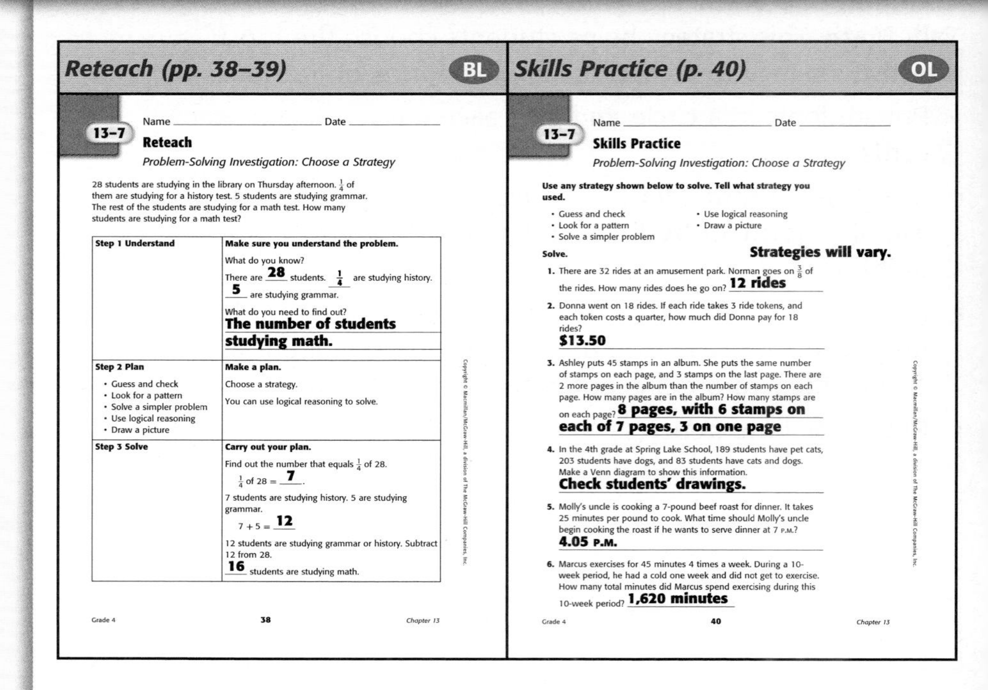

**Reteach (pp. 38–39)** BL

13-7 Name ______ Date ______

**Reteach**

*Problem-Solving Investigation: Choose a Strategy*

28 students are studying in the library on Thursday afternoon. $\frac{1}{4}$ of them are studying for a history test. 5 students are studying grammar. The rest of the students are studying for a math test. How many students are studying for a math test?

| | |
|---|---|
| **Step 1 Understand** | **Make sure you understand the problem.**<br>What do you know?<br>There are **28** students. **$\frac{1}{4}$** are studying history. **5** are studying grammar.<br>What do you need to find out?<br>**The number of students studying math.** |
| **Step 2 Plan**<br>• Guess and check<br>• Look for a pattern<br>• Solve a simpler problem<br>• Use logical reasoning<br>• Draw a picture | **Make a plan.**<br>Choose a strategy.<br>You can use logical reasoning to solve. |
| **Step 3 Solve** | **Carry out your plan.**<br>Find out the number that equals $\frac{1}{4}$ of 28.<br>$\frac{1}{4}$ of 28 = **7**.<br>7 students are studying history. 5 are studying grammar.<br>7 + 5 = **12**<br>12 students are studying grammar or history. Subtract 12 from 28.<br>**16** students are studying math. |

Grade 4 38 Chapter 13



**Skills Practice (p. 40)** OL

13-7 Name ______ Date ______

**Skills Practice**

*Problem-Solving Investigation: Choose a Strategy*

**Use any strategy shown below to solve. Tell what strategy you used.**

- Guess and check
- Look for a pattern
- Solve a simpler problem
- Use logical reasoning
- Draw a picture

**Solve.** **Strategies will vary.**

1. There are 32 rides at an amusement park. Norman goes on $\frac{3}{8}$ of the rides. How many rides does he go on? **12 rides**
2. Donna went on 18 rides. If each ride takes 3 ride tokens, and each token costs a quarter, how much did Donna pay for 18 rides? **$13.50**
3. Ashley puts 45 stamps in an album. She puts the same number of stamps on each page, and 3 stamps on the last page. There are 2 more pages in the album than the number of stamps on each page. How many pages are in the album? How many stamps are on each page? **8 pages, with 6 stamps on each of 7 pages, 3 on one page**
4. In the 4th grade at Spring Lake School, 189 students have pet cats, 203 students have dogs, and 83 students have cats and dogs. Make a Venn diagram to show this information. **Check students' drawings.**
5. Molly's uncle is cooking a 7-pound beef roast for dinner. It takes 25 minutes per pound to cook. What time should Molly's uncle begin cooking the roast if he wants to serve dinner at 7 P.M.? **4.05 P.M.**
6. Marcus exercises for 45 minutes 4 times a week. During a 10-week period, he had a cold one week and did not get to exercise. How many total minutes did Marcus spend exercising during this 10-week period? **1,620 minutes**

Grade 4 40 Chapter 13

★ indicates multi-step problem

## Mixed Problem Solving

EXTRA PRACTICE See page R36.

**Use any strategy shown below to solve. Tell what strategy you used.**

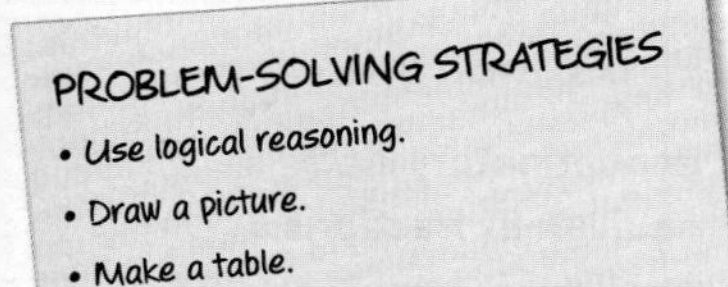


★1. **Measurement** A chef wants to cook an 8-pound turkey. It takes 20 minutes per pound to fully cook. What time should the chef start cooking the turkey for it to be done at 5:00 P.M? **2:20 P.M.**

2. After Malcolm buys three packages of stickers like the one shown, the number of stickers in his collection will double. How many stickers will he have? **54 stickers**

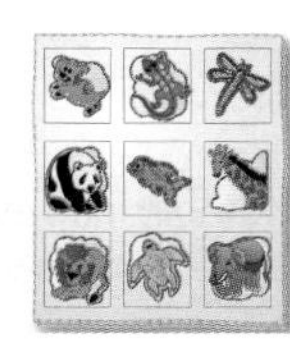

★3. Dario and three of his friends shared the cost of renting a rowboat. It cost $12 an hour, and they used the boat for 3 hours. How much did each friend pay? **$9**

4. **Algebra** A geometric pattern is shown. What is the next figure in the pattern?

**See Ch. 13 Answer Appendix.**

★5. Mei has some coins. She has 3 more quarters than nickels and 2 more dimes than quarters. If Mei has 4 nickels, how much money does she have? **$2.85**

★6. A customer buys small, medium, and large sweatshirts. The total cost is $68. How many of each size were bought?

**1 small, 1 medium, and 2 large**

★7. **Measurement** Daisy exercises for 30 minutes 2 times a day. If she keeps up this schedule for 30 days, how many minutes will she exercise in all? **1,800 min**

★8. **Measurement** Randall's goal is to run one mile the first week and double the number of miles each week for the next 6 weeks. How many miles will he run the sixth week? **32 miles**

9. **Algebra** Find the area of the fifth figure in the pattern shown. **25 square units**

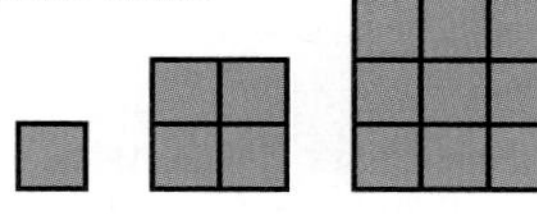

10. **WRITING IN MATH** Write a few sentences to explain what it means to solve a problem by solving a simpler problem. **See Ch. 13 Answer Appendix.**



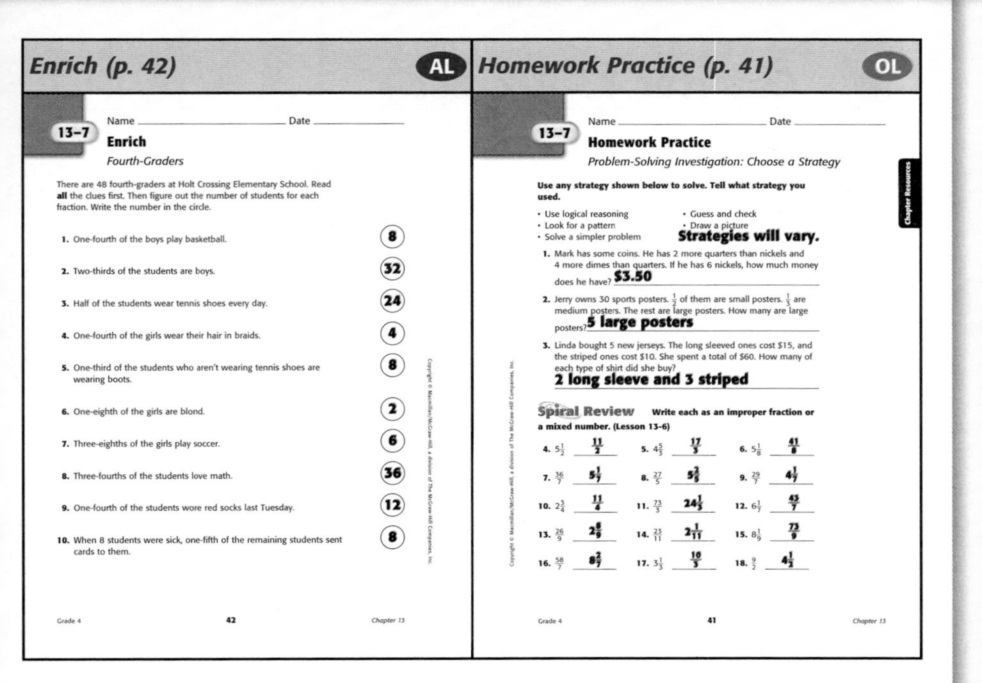

### Enrich (p. 42) AL

13–7 Name ________ Date ________

**Enrich**

*Fourth-Graders*

There are 48 fourth-graders at Holt Crossing Elementary School. Read **all** the clues first. Then figure out the number of students for each fraction. Write the number in the circle.

1. One-fourth of the boys play basketball. **8**
2. Two-thirds of the students are boys. **32**
3. Half of the students wear tennis shoes every day. **24**
4. One-fourth of the girls wear their hair in braids. **4**
5. One-third of the students who aren't wearing tennis shoes are wearing boots. **8**
6. One-eighth of the girls are blond. **2**
7. Three-eighths of the girls play soccer. **6**
8. Three-fourths of the students love math. **36**
9. One-fourth of the students wore red socks last Tuesday. **12**
10. When 8 students were sick, one-fifth of the remaining students sent cards to them. **8**



Grade 4 42 Chapter 13

### Homework Practice (p. 41) OL

13–7 Name ________ Date ________

**Homework Practice**

*Problem-Solving Investigation: Choose a Strategy*

**Use any strategy shown below to solve. Tell what strategy you used.**

- Use logical reasoning
- Look for a pattern
- Solve a simpler problem
- Guess and check
- Draw a picture

**Strategies will vary.**

1. Mark has some coins. He has 2 more quarters than nickels and 4 more dimes than quarters. If he has 6 nickels, how much money does he have? **$3.50**
2. Jerry owns 30 sports posters. $\frac{1}{2}$ of them are small posters. $\frac{1}{3}$ are medium posters. The rest are large posters. How many are large posters? **5 large posters**
3. Linda bought 5 new jerseys. The long sleeved ones cost $15, and the striped ones cost $10. She spent a total of $60. How many of each type of shirt did she buy? **2 long sleeve and 3 striped**

**Spiral Review** **Write each as an improper fraction or a mixed number. (Lesson 13-6)**

| | | |
|---|---|---|
| 4. $5\frac{1}{2}$ **$\frac{11}{2}$** | 5. $4\frac{5}{3}$ **$\frac{17}{3}$** | 6. $5\frac{1}{8}$ **$\frac{41}{8}$** |
| 7. $\frac{36}{7}$ **$5\frac{1}{7}$** | 8. $\frac{27}{5}$ **$5\frac{2}{5}$** | 9. $\frac{29}{7}$ **$4\frac{1}{7}$** |
| 10. $2\frac{3}{4}$ **$\frac{11}{4}$** | 11. $\frac{73}{3}$ **$24\frac{1}{3}$** | 12. $6\frac{1}{7}$ **$\frac{43}{7}$** |
| 13. $\frac{26}{9}$ **$2\frac{8}{9}$** | 14. $\frac{23}{11}$ **$2\frac{1}{11}$** | 15. $8\frac{1}{9}$ **$\frac{73}{9}$** |
| 16. $\frac{58}{7}$ **$8\frac{2}{7}$** | 17. $3\frac{1}{3}$ **$\frac{10}{3}$** | 18. $\frac{9}{2}$ **$4\frac{1}{2}$** |

Chapter Resources



Grade 4 41 Chapter 13

## BL Alternate Teaching Strategy

**If** students have trouble using the solve a simpler problem strategy…

**Then** use one of these reteach options:

1 CRM **Daily Reteach Worksheets** (pp. 38–39)

2 Suggest that students make a table and look for a pattern. Lead them to see that the seventh number in the pattern is 42. They should now be able to multiply both 42 and 7 by 10 to find the number of animals that are reptiles.

# 3 Practice

### Using the Exercises

**Exercise 1** Suggest that students first find the total cooking time.

**Exercise 4** Students may want to make a model and then turn it to find the next figure in the pattern.

# 4 Assess

### Formative Assessment

Present the following problem to the class:

*A survey shows that $\frac{1}{2}$ of students in a class of 24 have a pet. Of these students with pets, $\frac{1}{4}$ have dogs. How many students have pet dogs?*

- **Tell what problem-solving strategy you used to solve this problem.** Sample answer: draw a picture
- **Explain your answer.** Sample answer: The class has 24 students in it. Half of 24 is 12, so 12 students have pets. One-fourth of 12 is three, so three students have dogs.

**Quick Check** **Are students continuing to struggle with choosing the best strategy to solve a problem?**

**If Yes** → Small Group Options (p. 564B)
Strategic Intervention Guide (p. 98)

**If No** → Independent Work Options (p. 564B)
CRM Skills Practice Worksheet (p. 40)
CRM Enrich Worksheet (p. 42)

# Chapter 13 Study Guide and Review

## FOLDABLES Dinah Zike's Foldables

Use these lesson suggestions for incorporating the Foldables during the chapter. Students can then use their Foldables to review for the test.

**Lesson 13-5** Beneath the top right tab, students demonstrate their abilities to compare and order simple fractions on a number line. Vocabulary and student work can be stored in the center pocket.

**Lesson 13-6** Students read, write, and identify mixed numbers beneath the middle right tab. Vocabulary and student work can be stored in the center pocket.

## Key Vocabulary

The page references after each word denote where that term was first introduced. If students have difficulty answering Exercises 1–6, remind them that they can use these page references to refresh their memories about the vocabulary.

## Vocabulary Review

Review chapter vocabulary using one of the following options.

- **Visual Vocabulary Cards** (10, 19, 20, 25, 30)
- **eGlossary** at macmillanmh.com



# Chapter 13 Study Guide and Review

### FOLDABLES Study Organizer GET READY to Study

**Be sure the following Key Vocabulary words and Key Concepts are written in your Foldable.**

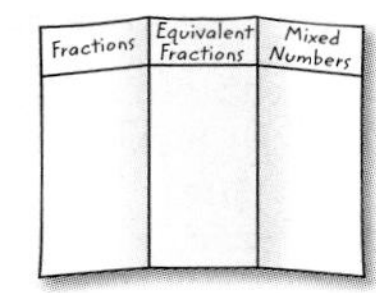


### Key Concepts

- A **fraction** names part of a whole or part of a set. (p. 537)

$\frac{4}{5}$ ← numerator ← denominator

- **Equivalent fractions** represent the same amount. (p. 548)

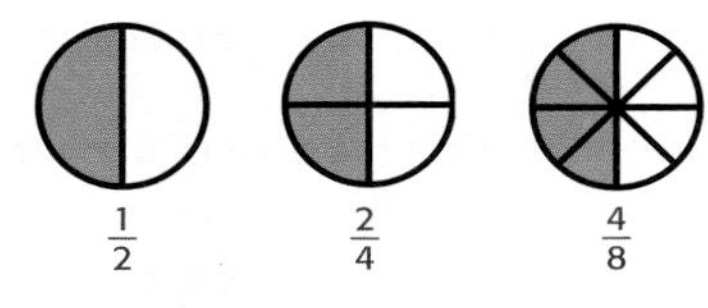


- **Mixed numbers** have a whole number and a fractional part. (p. 560)

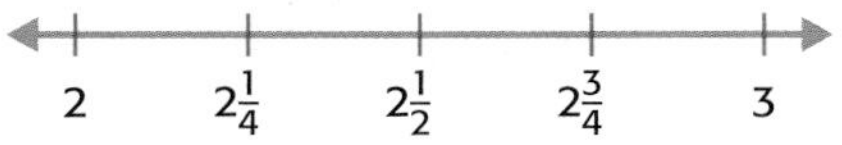

Number line: 2, $2\frac{1}{4}$, $2\frac{1}{2}$, $2\frac{3}{4}$, 3

### Key Vocabulary

**denominator** (p. 537)
**equivalent fractions** (p. 548)
**fraction** (p. 537)
**mixed number** (p. 560)
**numerator** (p. 537)

### Vocabulary Check

**Complete each sentence with the correct vocabulary word.**

1. In the fraction $\frac{3}{4}$, the 4 is the __?__. denominator
2. A number that names part of a whole or part of a set is a(n) __?__. fraction
3. A(n) __?__ has a whole number part and a fraction part. mixed number
4. In the fraction $\frac{3}{4}$, the 3 is the __?__. numerator
5. Fractions that represent the same amount are __?__. equivalent fractions
6. In a fraction, the __?__ is the top number and the __?__ is the bottom number. numerator; denominator

## Chapter 13 Project

### Fraction Party

Alone, in pairs, or in small groups, have students discuss the results of their completed chapter project with the class. Assess their work using the Chapter Project rubric found in Chapter 13 Resource Masters, p. 53.

## Lesson-by-Lesson Review

### 13-1 Parts of a Whole (pp. 537–539)

**Example 1**
**What fraction of the figure is shaded?**

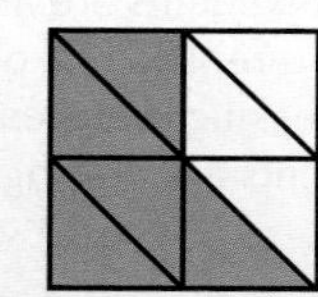

**Write** parts shaded → $5$; total parts in all → $8$

**Read** *five eighths* or *five divided by eight*

So, $\frac{5}{8}$ of the figure is shaded.

**Write the fraction that names part of the whole that is shaded.**

7.  $\frac{3}{4}$

8.  $\frac{7}{8}$

**Draw a picture and shade part of it to show the fraction.** 9, 10. See margin.

9. $\frac{2}{3}$

10. $\frac{5}{6}$

11. What fraction of the waffle is missing? $\frac{1}{4}$

### 13-2 Parts of a Set (pp. 540–543)

**Example 2**
**What fraction of the crayons shown is *not* red?**

**Write** crayons not red → $3$; total crayons → $5$

**Read** *three fifths* or *three divided by five*

So, $\frac{3}{5}$ of the crayons are *not* red.

**Write the fraction that names the part of the set of shapes.**

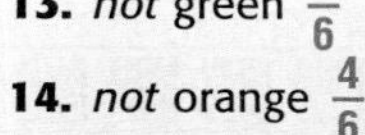

12. *not* purple $\frac{4}{6}$

13. *not* green $\frac{5}{6}$

14. *not* orange $\frac{4}{6}$

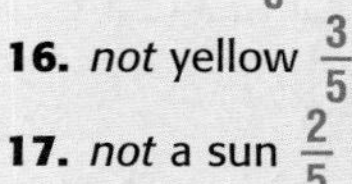

15. *not* red $\frac{2}{5}$

16. *not* yellow $\frac{3}{5}$

17. *not* a sun $\frac{2}{5}$

18. There are five cars. Two fifths of the cars are blue. Draw a picture to show the set. See students' work.



# Lesson-by-Lesson Review

Have students complete the Lesson-by-Lesson Review on pp. 567–570. Then you can use ExamView® Assessment Suite to customize another review worksheet that practices all the objectives of this chapter or only the objectives on which your students need more help.

**Intervention** If the given examples are not sufficient to review the topics covered by the questions, use the page references next to the exercises to review that topic in the Student Edition.

### Additional Answers

9. 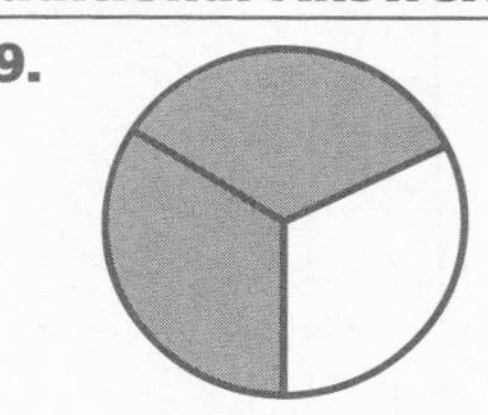

10. 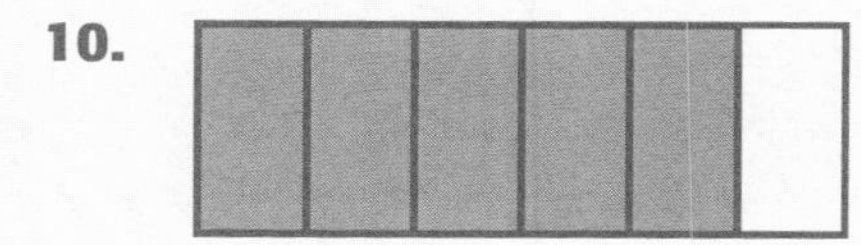

## 13-3 Problem-Solving Strategy: Draw a Picture (pp. 544–545)

**Example 3**
**Marcela has 24 crayons. Of them, $\frac{1}{3}$ are blue. Four are yellow, and the rest are green. How many crayons are green?**

**Understand**

**What facts do you know?**

- There are 24 crayons.
- $\frac{1}{3}$ are blue.
- 4 are yellow.
- The rest are green.

**What do you need to find?**

Find how many crayons are green.

**Plan** Draw a picture.

**Solve** Divide 24 equal parts. Shade $\frac{1}{3}$ to show the blue crayons. Shade 4 to show the yellow crayons.

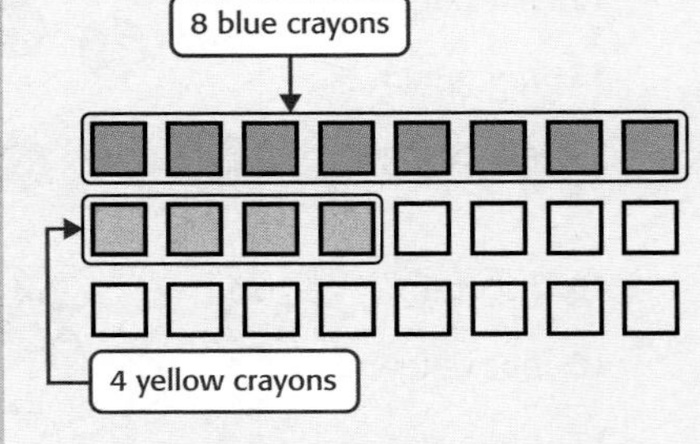


There are 12 parts left. So, 12 of the crayons are green.

**Check** Since 8 + 4 + 12 = 24 crayons, the answer makes sense.

**19.** The 24 students in Ms. Cameron's class are working on art projects. One half of them are painting. Eight students are making a clay sculpture. The rest of the students are making sketches. How many students are making sketches? 4

**20.** **Measurement** Serefina took part in the activities listed. How long did she eat a snack?

| Serefina's Activities | |
|---|---|
| **Activity** | **Time Spent** |
| Read a book | $\frac{1}{2}$ of an hour |
| Watch TV | 20 minutes |
| Eat a snack | rest of the hour |

10 min

**21.** Of 15 cars, 7 are blue and $\frac{1}{5}$ are red. The rest of the cars are black. How many cars are black? 5

**22.** Jeff had 28 grapes. He ate $\frac{1}{2}$ of them for lunch. Then he ate 10 more as a snack. How many are left? 4

**23.** Marisa has a marble collection. One-fourth of her 16 marbles are blue. Her red marbles are shown below. The rest of the marbles are green. How many are green? 7

568 Chapter 13 Describe and Compare Fractions

## 13-4 Equivalent Fractions (pp. 548–551)

**Example 4**

Find two fractions equivalent to $\frac{4}{6}$.

**One Way: Multiply**

$\frac{4 \times 2}{6 \times 2} = \frac{8}{12}$ Multiply the numerator and the denominator by the same number, 2.

**Another Way: Divide**

$\frac{4 \div 2}{6 \div 2} = \frac{2}{3}$ Divide the numerator and the denominator by the same number, 2.

So, $\frac{8}{12}$ and $\frac{2}{3}$ are equivalent to $\frac{4}{6}$.

**Find an equivalent fraction for each fraction.** 24–29. See margin.

**24.** $\frac{1}{5}$ **25.** $\frac{1}{3}$ **26.** $\frac{1}{4}$

**27.** $\frac{6}{8}$ **28.** $\frac{7}{14}$ **29.** $\frac{9}{12}$

**Write an equivalent fraction for each amount.** 30–32. See margin.

**30.** Dave hit 4 out of 8 baseballs.

**31.** Teresa's team won 9 out of 12 tennis matches.

**32.** Lara ate 4 out of 8 celery sticks.

## 13-5 Compare and Order Fractions (pp. 554–557)

**Example 5**

**Dakota has a red and a blue pencil. The red pencil is $\frac{1}{2}$ of a foot long. The blue pencil is $\frac{3}{8}$ of a foot long. Which pencil is longer?**

You can use number lines to compare the length of the pencils.

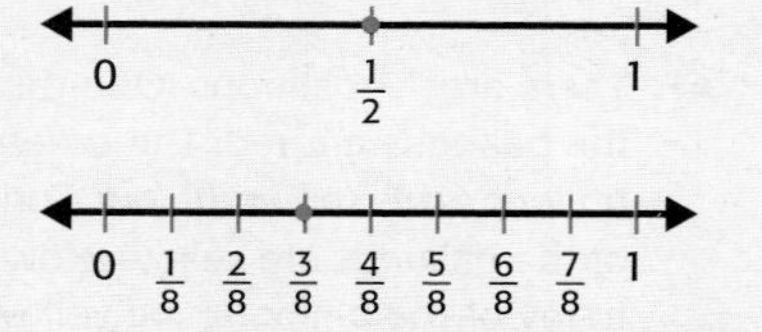


So, the red pencil is longer than the blue pencil.

36, 37. See margin.

**Compare. Use >, <, or =.**

**33.**

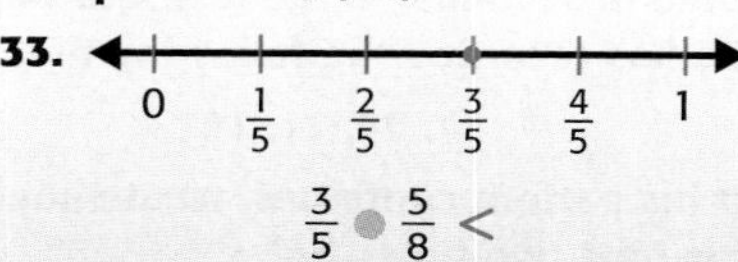


$\frac{3}{5} \bullet \frac{5}{8}$ <

**34.** $\frac{4}{5} \bullet \frac{8}{10}$ = **35.** $\frac{6}{6} \bullet \frac{5}{6}$ >

**Order from least to greatest.**

**36.** $\frac{2}{3}, \frac{3}{7}, \frac{4}{35}$ **37.** $\frac{1}{4}, \frac{3}{16}, \frac{7}{8}$

**38. Measurement** Patrick took $\frac{3}{4}$ of an hour to finish a test. José took $\frac{3}{8}$ of an hour to finish. Who took more time to finish the test? Patrick



## Additional Answers

**24.** Sample answer: $\frac{2}{10}$

**25.** Sample answer: $\frac{2}{6}$

**26.** Sample answer: $\frac{2}{8}$

**27.** Sample answer: $\frac{3}{4}$

**28.** Sample answer: $\frac{1}{2}$

**29.** Sample answer: $\frac{3}{4}$

**30.** Sample answer: $\frac{1}{2}$

**31.** Sample answer: $\frac{3}{4}$

**32.** Sample answer: $\frac{1}{2}$

**36.** $\frac{4}{35}, \frac{3}{7}, \frac{2}{3}$

**37.** $\frac{3}{16}, \frac{1}{4}, \frac{7}{8}$

# CHAPTER 13 Study Guide and Review

## Additional Answers

**45.**

| Day | Amount Earned ($) |
|---|---|
| 1 | 35 |
| 2 | 70 |
| 3 | 105 |
| 4 | 140 |
| 5 | 175 |
| 6 | 210 |
| 7 | 245 |

7 days

**46.** 

## 13-6 Mixed Numbers (pp. 560–563)

**Example 6**
**A fourth grade class had a pizza party. The amount of pizza eaten can be represented as $3\frac{1}{5}$. Write the amout of the pizza eaten as an improper fraction.**

$3\frac{1}{5} = \frac{5}{5} + \frac{5}{5} + \frac{5}{5} + \frac{1}{5}$

$= \frac{5 + 5 + 5 + 1}{5}$

$= \frac{16}{5}$

So, $3\frac{1}{5} = \frac{16}{5}$.

**Write a mixed number and an improper fraction for each model.**

**39.** $1\frac{2}{5}; \frac{7}{5}$

**40.** $2\frac{5}{6}; \frac{17}{6}$

**Write each as an improper fraction or a mixed number. Use models if needed.**

**41.** $\frac{18}{4}$ $4\frac{1}{2}$

**42.** $\frac{32}{8}$ 4

**43.** $2\frac{3}{4}$ $\frac{11}{4}$

**44.** $3\frac{7}{8}$ $\frac{31}{8}$

## 13-7 Problem-Solving Investigation: Choose a Strategy (pp. 564–565)

**Example 7**
**Charlie runs track daily and records his time in seconds. In the last four days he has recorded the following times:**

**27, 24, 21, 18**

**If his pattern continues, what should his next two times be?**

Look for a pattern in the times. Then extend to solve the problem.

Notice that each of Charlie's times goes down by three. So, the pattern is subtract 3.

27, 24, 21, 18, 15, 12
(−3 −3 −3 −3 −3)

So, Charlie's next two times will be 15 and 12 seconds.

**Use any strategy to solve.**

**45.** Kellie earned $35 a day for chopping wood. If she earned a total of $245, how many days did she chop wood?
45, 46. See margin.

**46.** Draw the next figure in the pattern.

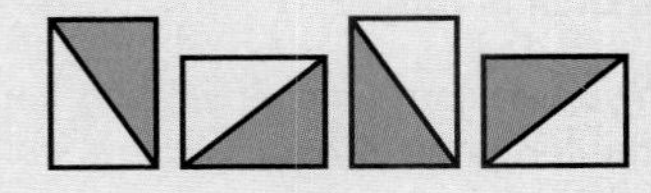

**47.** There are 12 balloons. One-third of the balloons are red. The *green balloons are shown below.* The rest of the balloons are yellow. How many of the balloons are yellow? 3

# Chapter Test

Math Online macmillanmh.com
• Chapter Test

For Exercises 1 and 2, tell whether each statement is *true* or *false*.

1. An improper fraction has a numerator that is less than its denominator. false
2. To find an equivalent fraction, multiply or divide the numerator and denominator by the same number. true

3–6. Sample answers are given.

**Find an equivalent fraction for each fraction.**

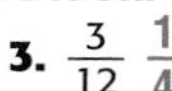

3. $\frac{3}{12}$ $\frac{1}{4}$
4. $\frac{24}{40}$ $\frac{3}{5}$
5. $\frac{1}{5}$ $\frac{2}{10}$
6. $\frac{1}{3}$ $\frac{2}{6}$

7. Madison and Alan each ate the amount of apple pie shown. How much of one whole apple pie is left if the shaded parts represent pieces of pie?

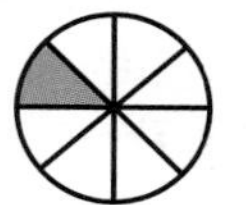
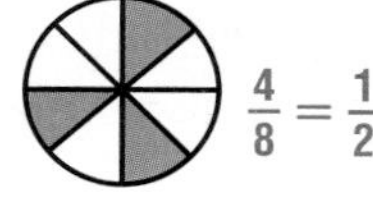

$\frac{4}{8} = \frac{1}{2}$

8. **MULTIPLE CHOICE** Which fraction is NOT equivalent to the shaded area of the circle? D

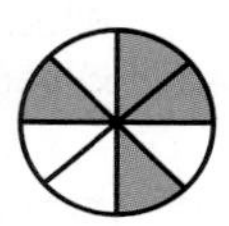

A $\frac{1}{2}$  C $\frac{4}{8}$

B $\frac{2}{4}$  D $\frac{7}{12}$

**Compare. Use >, <, or =.**

9. $\frac{2}{4}$ ● $\frac{3}{4}$ <
10. $\frac{4}{10}$ ● $\frac{1}{2}$ <

**Write each mixed number as an improper fraction.**

11. $2\frac{3}{4}$ $\frac{11}{4}$
12. $4\frac{5}{12}$ $\frac{53}{12}$
13. There are 12 fish in Nicolas's aquarium. One-half of the fish are goldfish. Four of the fish are tetras. The rest of the fish are rainbow fish. How many of the fish are rainbow fish? 2

**Identify each point as a mixed number and an improper fraction.**

14.

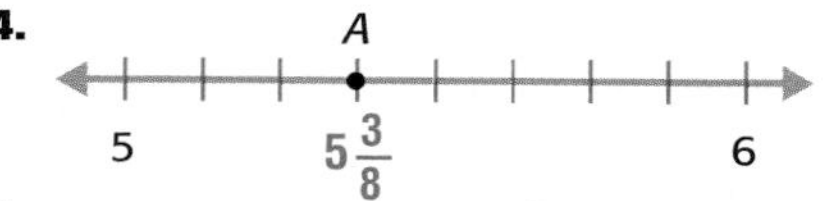


$5\frac{3}{8}$

15.

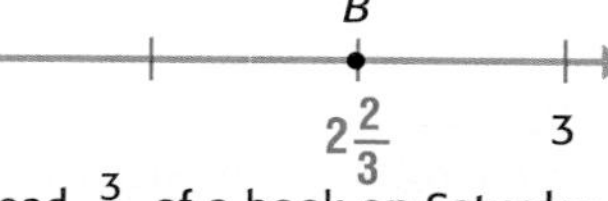


$2\frac{2}{3}$

16. Abby read $\frac{3}{10}$ of a book on Saturday. Then she read $\frac{4}{10}$ of the book on Sunday. What fraction of the book does Abby still have to read? $\frac{3}{10}$
17. **MULTIPLE CHOICE** Identify the improper fraction below that is NOT equivalent to $2\frac{4}{5}$. H

F $\frac{28}{10}$  H $\frac{15}{5}$

G $\frac{42}{15}$  J $\frac{56}{20}$

18. **WRITING IN MATH** Explain how $\frac{2}{7}$ and $\frac{6}{21}$ are equivalent fractions.

See Ch. 13 Answer Appendix.

Summative Assessment 571

# Chapter Test

## Summative Assessment

Use these alternate leveled chapter tests to differentiate assessment for the specific needs of your students.

| Leveled Chapter 13 Tests | | | |
|---|---|---|---|
| **Form** | **Type** | **Level** | **CRM Pages** |
| 1 | Multiple Choice | BL | 55–56 |
| 2A | Multiple Choice | OL | 57–58 |
| 2B | Multiple Choice | OL | 59–60 |
| 2C | Free Response | OL | 61–62 |
| 2D | Free Response | OL | 63–64 |
| 3 | Free Response | AL | 65–66 |

BL = below/approaching grade level

OL = on grade level

AL = above/beyond grade level

## Vocabulary Test

CRM **Chapter 13 Resource Masters** (p. 50)

**ExamView** Assessment Suite Customize and create multiple versions of your Chapter Test and the test answer keys.

# Data-Driven Decision Making

Based on the results of the Chapter Test, use the following to review concepts that continue to present students with problems.

| Exercises | State/Local Standards | What's the Mathematics? | Error Analysis | Resources for Review |
|---|---|---|---|---|
| 2–6, 8 | | Find equivalent fractions. | Does not know equivalent fractions. Does not know difference between numerator and denominator. | Strategic Intervention Guide (pp. 22, 24, 26, 94, 98)<br>CRM Chapter 13 Resource Masters (Reteach)<br>Math Adventures My Math Zone Chapter 13<br>Math Online Extra Examples • Concepts in Motion |
| 9–10 | | Compare and order fractions. | Does not know which fraction is smaller. | |
| 11–13 | | Improper fractions. | Does not know how to write an improper fraction. | |

CHAPTER 13

# Test Practice

## Formative Assessment

- Use Student Edition pp. 572–573 as practice and cumulative review. The questions are written in the same style as many state tests.
- You can also use these two pages to benchmark student progress, or as an alternate homework assignment.

Additional practice pages can be found in the Chapter 13 Resource Masters.

CRM **Chapter 13 Resource Masters**
Cumulative Test Practice

- Multiple Choice format (pp. 55–60)
- Free Response format (pp. 61–66)

Create practice worksheets or tests that align to your state standards.

**Math Online** Have students visit macmillanmh.com for additional practice to reinforce your state standards.

---

**Math Online** macmillanmh.com
• Test Practice

CHAPTER 13

# Test Practice

Cumulative, Chapters 1–13

**PART I** **Multiple Choice**

**Read each question. Then fill in the correct answer on the answer sheet provided by your teacher or on a sheet of paper.**

**1.** Danielle ate $\frac{1}{3}$ of an orange. Which fraction is equivalent to $\frac{1}{3}$? **C**

**A** $\frac{2}{4}$ **C** $\frac{3}{9}$

**B** $\frac{5}{12}$ **D** $\frac{2}{8}$

**2.** Which number is 100,000 more than 32,769,201? **H**

**F** 32,769,201 **H** 32,869,201

**G** 32,779,201 **J** 42,769,201

**3.** Kathryn walked $\frac{2}{5}$ of a mile in the morning. Which model shows the fraction of a mile Kathryn walked? **B**

**A** 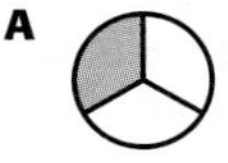

**C** 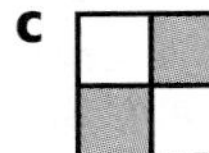

**B** 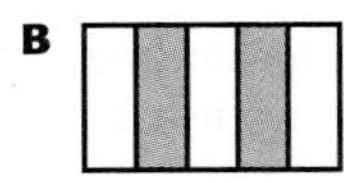

**D** 

**4.** Which set of fractions is in order from least to greatest? **J**

**F** $\frac{6}{10}, \frac{4}{5}, \frac{1}{2}$ **H** $\frac{1}{2}, \frac{4}{5}, \frac{6}{10}$

**G** $\frac{4}{5}, \frac{1}{2}, \frac{6}{10}$ **J** $\frac{1}{2}, \frac{6}{10}, \frac{4}{5}$

**5.** Tionna jogged $2\frac{3}{5}$ miles. Write $2\frac{3}{5}$ as an improper fraction. **D**

**A** $\frac{13}{10}$ **C** $\frac{12}{5}$

**B** $\frac{10}{5}$ **D** $\frac{13}{5}$

**6.** Megan's dog is $3\frac{1}{2}$ years old. Which point best represents $3\frac{1}{2}$ on the number line? **J**

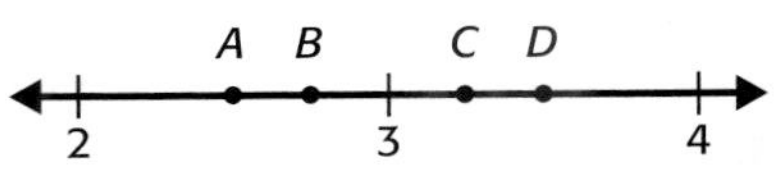


**F** point *A* **H** point *C*

**G** point *B* **J** point *D*

**7.** What is the value of the expression below if $c = 4$? **B**

$$21 - (c + 7)$$

**A** 7 **C** 11

**B** 10 **D** 32

**8.** Look at the figures. Which fraction is shown by the shaded part of the figures? **H**

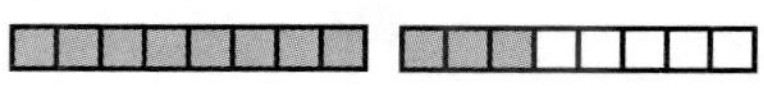

**F** $1\frac{1}{4}$ **H** $1\frac{3}{8}$

**G** $1\frac{1}{2}$ **J** $1\frac{5}{8}$



## Test-Taking Tip

Tell students that if they are having difficulty working a problem, they can go on to the next one and come back to it later if time permits.

**Preparing for Standardized Tests**
For test-taking strategies and practice, see pages R42–R55.

9. Which expression is shown below? A

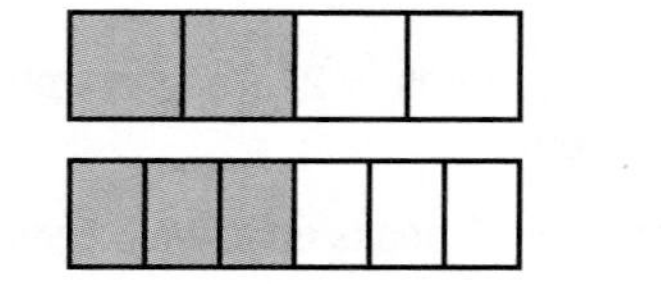

A $\frac{2}{4} = \frac{3}{6}$ C $\frac{2}{4} < \frac{3}{6}$

B $\frac{2}{4} > \frac{3}{6}$ D $\frac{2}{4} + \frac{3}{6}$

10. Which fraction is equivalent to $\frac{8}{12}$? G

F $\frac{1}{4}$ H $\frac{3}{4}$

G $\frac{2}{3}$ J $\frac{3}{5}$

11. What fraction does *N* represent? B

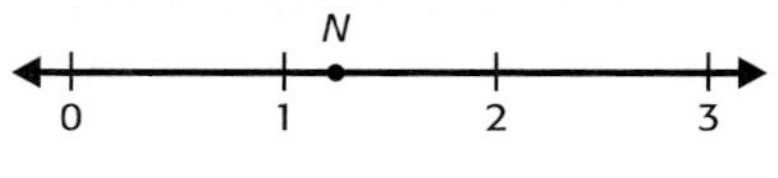


A $\frac{3}{4}$ C $1\frac{3}{4}$

B $1\frac{1}{4}$ D $2\frac{1}{4}$

12. Santos read a 280-page book in 7 days. He read the same number of pages each day. How many pages did he read each day? H

F 30 H 40

G 36 J 42

## PART 2 Short Response

**Record your answers on the answer sheet provided by your teacher or on a sheet of paper.**

13. Malia answered 8 out of 10 questions on a quiz correctly. Write a fraction that is equivalent to $\frac{8}{10}$.
Sample answer: $\frac{4}{5}$

14. What fraction does the model represent? $2\frac{3}{4}$

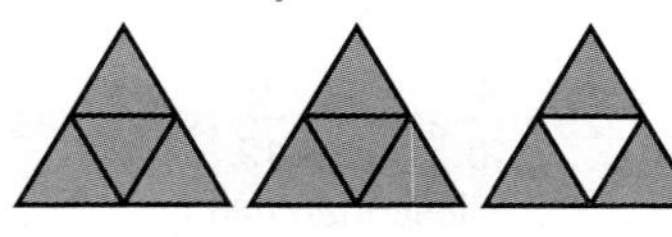

15. Amanda swam $3\frac{2}{3}$ laps in a pool. Write $3\frac{2}{3}$ as an improper fraction. $\frac{11}{3}$

## PART 3 Extended Response

**Record your answers on the answer sheet provided by your teacher or on a sheet of paper.**

16. Draw a model to show $\frac{5}{6}$. Explain how the model shows $\frac{5}{6}$.
16, 17. See margin.

17. Write a fraction equivalent to $\frac{5}{6}$. Draw a model to explain your reasoning.

| NEED EXTRA HELP? | | | | | | | | | | | | | | | | | |
|---|---|---|---|---|---|---|---|---|---|---|---|---|---|---|---|---|---|
| If You Missed Question... | 1 | 2 | 3 | 4 | 5 | 6 | 7 | 8 | 9 | 10 | 11 | 12 | 13 | 14 | 15 | 16 | 17 |
| Go to Lesson... | 13-4 | 1-2 | 13-1 | 13-5 | 13-6 | 13-6 | 5-1 | 13-6 | 13-5 | 13-4 | 13-6 | 8-2 | 13-4 | 13-6 | 13-6 | 13-1 | 13-4 |



# Answer Sheet Practice

Have students simulate taking a state test by recording their answers on a practice recording sheet.

CRM **Chapter 13 Resource Masters**
Student Recording Sheet (p. 71)

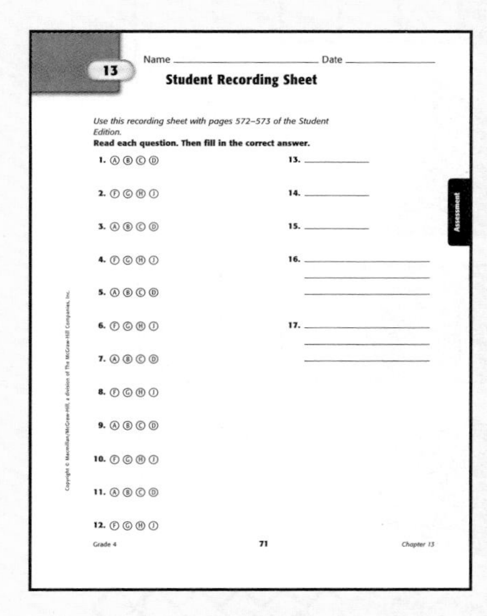
Name ______ Date ______
13
Student Recording Sheet
Use this recording sheet with pages 572–573 of the Student Edition.
Read each question. Then fill in the correct answer.
1. Ⓐ Ⓑ Ⓒ Ⓓ 13. ______
2. Ⓕ Ⓖ Ⓗ Ⓙ 14. ______
3. Ⓐ Ⓑ Ⓒ Ⓓ 15. ______
4. Ⓕ Ⓖ Ⓗ Ⓙ 16. ______
5. Ⓐ Ⓑ Ⓒ Ⓓ
6. Ⓕ Ⓖ Ⓗ Ⓙ 17. ______
7. Ⓐ Ⓑ Ⓒ Ⓓ
8. Ⓕ Ⓖ Ⓗ Ⓙ
9. Ⓐ Ⓑ Ⓒ Ⓓ
10. Ⓕ Ⓖ Ⓗ Ⓙ
11. Ⓐ Ⓑ Ⓒ Ⓓ
12. Ⓕ Ⓖ Ⓗ Ⓙ
Grade 4 71 Chapter 13

## Additional Answers

16. Sample answer: 5 parts out of 6 parts are shaded;

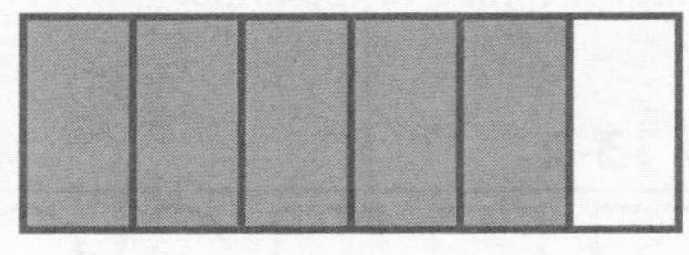

17. Sample answer: $\frac{10}{12}$

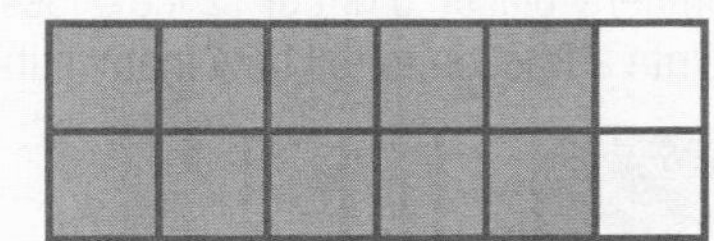

## Page 538, Lesson 13-1

4. 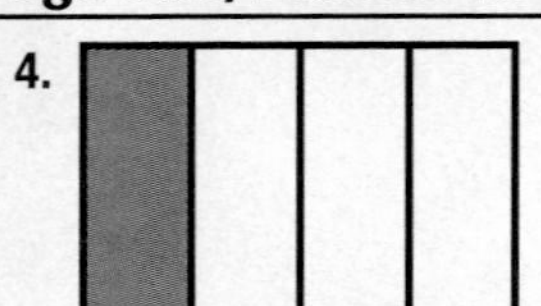

5. 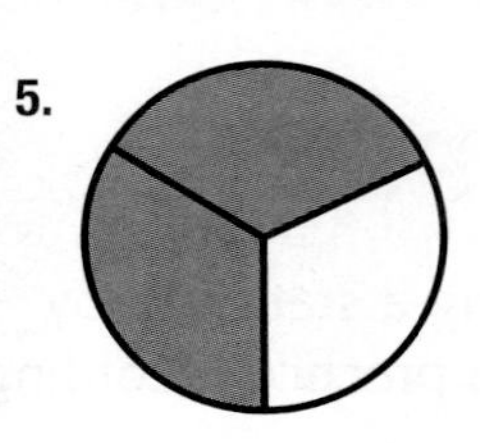

6. 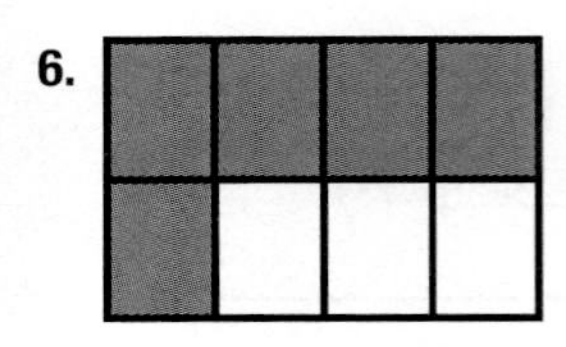

15. 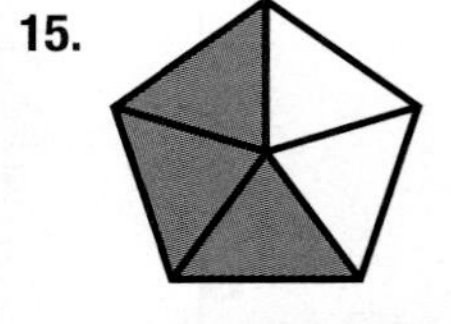

16. 

17. 

18. 

27. Sample answer: The new fraction would be $\frac{2}{10}$. This is less than $\frac{2}{5}$ because the whole is divided up into more pieces. Each piece is smaller. Therefore, 2 of the tenths are smaller than 2 of the fifths.

## Page 543, Lesson 13-2

22. Sample answer:

24. Sample answer: Kimberly placed 5 out of 12 ice cubes from an ice cube tray in her water. Write a fraction to tell how many cubes are left in the tray.

27. Sample answer: 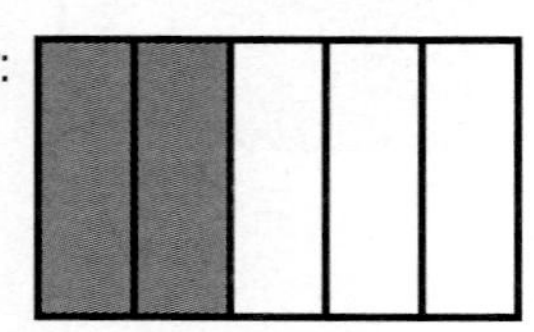

28. Sample answer: 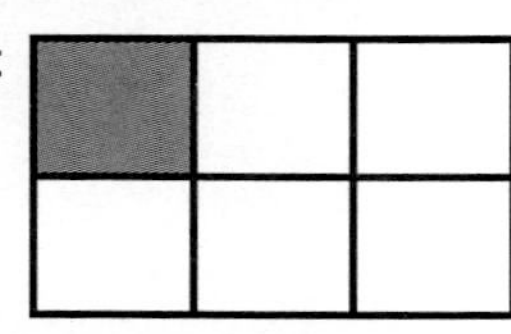

29. Sample answer: 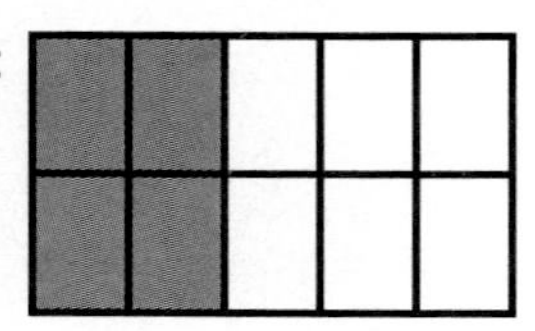

## Page 545, Lesson 13-3

2. Sample answer: There are three rows of circles, so 1 of the three rows should be shaded. Since there are 5 circles per row, 5 circles will be shaded.

4. Sample answer: 8 turtles + 2 snakes + 14 lizards = 24. The pet store has 24 reptiles. So, you know the answer is correct.

11. Sample answer: Draw a picture to represent 16 books on a shelf. Then label the books using the information given.

## Page 550, Lesson 13-4

11. Sample answer: When you multiply the numerators and denominators of all three fractions by 6, 3, and 2 respectively, the result is $\frac{18}{24}, \frac{1}{3}, \frac{2}{6}$, and $\frac{3}{9}$.

29. $\frac{4}{10}$ and $\frac{6}{12}$; $\frac{6}{12}$ is the greater amount because it is greater than half and $\frac{4}{10}$ is less than half.

30. Sample answer: Both are correct; they each found an equivalent fraction.

31. yes; You can always multiply the numerator and denominator by the same number to create an equivalent fraction.

## Page 553, Mid-Chapter Check

3.
4.
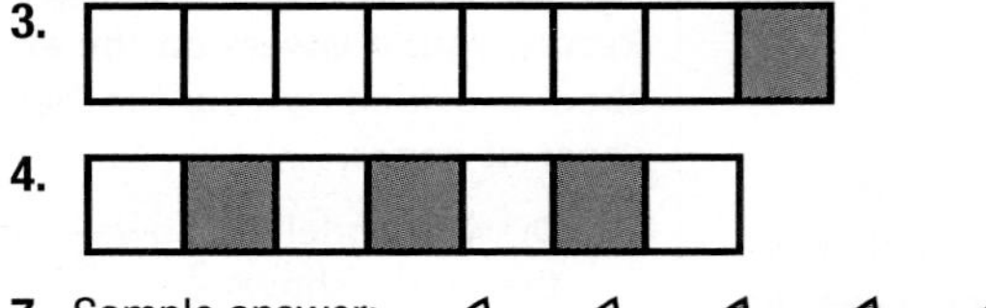

7. Sample answer: 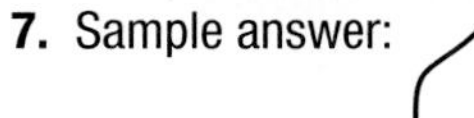 

17. Sample answer: yes; When the numerator and denominator of $\frac{12}{20}$ are divided by 4, the result is $\frac{3}{5}$.

18. Sample answer: no; The parts of the shaded figure are not equal.

## Page 557, Lesson 13-5

28. Sample answer: $\frac{3}{4}, \frac{1}{2}, \frac{2}{12}$; It is not ordered from least to greatest.

## Page 565, Lesson 13-7

4. 

10. Sample answer: A problem that contains large numbers can be solved by solving a problem that has smaller numbers first. Then a connection needs to be made between the smaller and larger numbers.

## Page 571, Chapter Test

18. Sample answer: The numerator and denominator of $\frac{2}{7}$ can both be multiplied by the same number; 3, to get $\frac{6}{21}$.

## NOTES

# Chapter Overview

## Chapter-at-a-Glance

In Chapter 14, the emphasis is on the relationship between fractions, mixed numbers and decimals and on decimal place value.

| Lesson | Math Objective | State/Local Standards |
|---|---|---|
| EXPLORE 14-1 **Fractions and Decimals** (pp. 577–578) | Use models to show tenths and hundredths. | |
| 14-1 **Tenths and Hundredths** (pp. 579–581) | Identify, read, and write tenths and hundredths as decimals and fractions. | |
| 14-2 **Relate Mixed Numbers and Decimals** (pp. 582–585) | Identify, read, and write decimals greater than 1. | |
| 14-3 **Problem-Solving Strategy: Make a Model** (pp. 586–587) | Solve problems by making a model. | |
| 14-4 **Locate Fractions and Decimals On a Number Line** (pp. 588–589) | Locate fractions and decimals on a number line. | |
| 14-5 **Compare and Order Decimals** (pp. 590–592) | Compare and order decimals. | |
| 14-6 **Problem-Solving Investigation: Choose a Strategy** (pp. 594–595) | Choose the best strategy to solve a problem. | |
| 14-7 **Fraction and Decimal Equivalents** (pp. 596–599) | Find fraction and decimal equivalents. | |
| 14-8 **Decimals, Fractions, and Mixed Numbers** (pp. 602–604) | Compare and order decimals, fractions, and mixed numbers. | |

## Use Place Value to Represent Decimals

**BIG Idea** Once students have an understanding of fractions, they are ready to relate decimals to fractions. They should know how to model decimals, fractions, and mixed numbers using grids and number lines. Students will require a basic understanding of decimals to solve problems with money and measurements, especially those involving length, time, and weight. They will need to learn fraction and decimal equivalents. Ideally, students should develop the ability to compare and order quantities without referring to models.

**Algebra** Students compare and order decimals, fractions, and mixed numbers and learn about equivalents. These ideas prepare them for algebra concepts, such as writing inequalities and equations. (Lesson 14-8)

**G4-FP2** *Number and Operations:* **Developing an understanding of decimals, including the connections between fractions and decimals**

Students understand decimal notation as an extension of the base-ten system of writing whole numbers that is useful for representing more numbers, including numbers between 0 and 1, between 1 and 2, and so on. Students relate their understanding of fractions to reading and writing decimals that are greater than or less than 1, identifying equivalent decimals, comparing and ordering decimals, and estimating decimal or fractional amounts in problem solving. They connect equivalent fractions and decimals by comparing models to symbols and locating equivalent symbols on the number line.

**G4-FP8C** *Number and Operations:* Building on their work in grade 3, students extend their understanding of place value and ways of representing numbers to 100,000 in various contexts. They use estimation in determining the relative sizes of amounts or distances. Students develop understandings of strategies for multidigit division by using models that represent division as the inverse of multiplication, as partitioning, or as successive subtraction. By working with decimals, students extend their ability to recognize equivalent fractions. Students' earlier work in grade 3 with models of fractions and multiplication and division facts supports their understanding of techniques for generating equivalent fractions and simplifying fractions.

## Skills Trace

### Vertical Alignment

#### Third Grade

**In third grade, students learned to:**

- Describe fractional parts of whole objects.
- Model equivalent fractions.
- Compare fractional parts of whole objects.

#### Fourth Grade

**During this chapter, students learn to:**

- Identify, read, and write tenths and hundredths as decimals and fractions.
- Compare and order decimals.
- Identify fractions that have decimal equivalents.

**After this chapter, students learn to:**

- Add and subtract decimals.

#### Fifth Grade

**In fifth grade, students learn to:**

- Round whole numbers and decimal numbers.
- Write decimals as fractions and visa versa.
- Represent decimals on a number line.
- Add and subtract decimals.

**Backmapping and Vertical Alignment** **McGraw-Hill's *Math Connects*** program was conceived and developed with the final results in mind: student success in Algebra 1 and beyond. The authors, using the **NCTM Focal Points and Focal Connections** as their guide, developed this brand-new series by backmapping from Algebra 1 concepts, and vertically aligning the topics so that they build upon prior skills and concepts and serve as a foundation for future topics.

## Math Vocabulary

The following math vocabulary words for Chapter 14 are listed in the glossary of the ***Student Edition***. You can find interactive definitions in 13 languages in the ***eGlossary*** at macmillanmh.com.

**decimal** A number that uses place value, numbers, and a decimal point to show parts of a whole. (p. 579A)

**decimal point** A period separating the ones and the tenths in a number. (p. 579A)

**hundredth** A place value position. One of one hundred equal parts. (p. 579A)

**tenth** One of ten equal parts or $\frac{1}{10}$. (p. 579A)

**Visual Vocabulary Cards**

Use Visual Vocabulary Card 9 to reinforce the vocabulary in this lesson. (The Define/Example/Ask routine is printed on the back of each card.)

decimal

# Chapter Planner

| Suggested Pacing | | |
|---|---|---|
| Instruction | Review & Assessment | TOTAL |
| 9 days | 1 day | **10 days** |

**Diagnostic Assessment**
Quick Check (p. 576)

| | Explore 14-1 (Pacing: 1 day) | Lesson 14-1 (Pacing: 1 day) | Lesson 14-2 (Pacing: 1 day) |
|---|---|---|---|
| **Lesson/ Objective** | **Fractions and Decimals** (pp. 577–578) **Objective:** Use models to show tenths and hundredths. | **Tenths and Hundredths** (pp. 579–581) **Objective:** Identify, read, and write tenths and hundredths as decimals and fractions. | **Relate Mixed Numbers and Decimals** (pp. 582–585) **Objective:** Identify, read, and write decimals greater than 1. |
| **State/Local Standards** | | | |
| **Math Vocabulary** | | **decimal**, **decimal point**, **tenth**, **hundredth** | |
| **Lesson Resources** | **Materials** tenths grids, hundredths grids, WorkMat 6: Place-Value Chart | **Materials** tenths and hundredths grids, colored pencils or markers, WorkMat 6: Place-Value Chart **Manipulatives** play money: dimes and pennies **Other Resources** CRM Leveled Worksheets (pp. 8–12) Daily Reteach • 5-Minute Check • Problem of the Day | **Materials** WorkMat 6: Place-Value Chart, hundredths grid **Other Resources** CRM Leveled Worksheets (pp. 13–17) Daily Reteach • 5-Minute Check • Problem of the Day |
| **Technology** | | Math Adventures | |
| **Math Online** | Concepts in Motion | Personal Tutor | |
| **Reaching All Learners** | | English Learners, p. 579B ELL Below Level, p. 579B BL Early Finishers, p. 579B OL AL | English Learners, p. 582B ELL Below Level, p. 582B BL Early Finishers, p. 582B OL AL |
| **Alternate Lesson** | | *IMPACT Mathematics:* Unit E | *IMPACT Mathematics:* Unit E |

**KEY**

BL Below/Approaching Level — OL On Level — AL Above/Beyond Level — ELL English Learners

SE Student Edition — TE Teacher Edition — CRM Chapter 14 Resource Masters — CD-Rom

Transparency — Real-World Problem Solving Library

# Use Place Value to Represent Decimals

| | Lesson 14-3 (Pacing: 1 day) | Lesson 14-4 (Pacing: 1 day) | Lesson 14-5 (Pacing: 1 day) |
|---|---|---|---|
| **Lesson/ Objective** | **Problem-Solving Strategy Make a Model** (pp. 586–587)<br>**Objective:** Solve problems by making a model. | **Locate Fractions and Decimals On a Number Line** (pp. 588–589)<br>**Objective:** Locate fractions and decimals on a number line. | **Compare and Order Decimals** (pp. 590–592)<br>**Objective:** Compare and order decimals. |
| **State/Local Standards** | | | |
| **Math Vocabulary** | | | |
| **Lesson Resources** | **Manipulatives**<br>counters<br>**Other Resources**<br>CRM Leveled Worksheets (pp. 18–22)<br>Daily Reteach • 5-Minute Check • Problem of the Day<br>*Growing Goods in a Growing Country* | **Materials**<br>number lines<br>**Other Resources**<br>CRM Leveled Worksheets (pp. 23–27)<br>Daily Reteach • 5-Minute Check • Problem of the Day | **Materials**<br>hundredths grids, number lines<br>**Manipulatives**<br>money<br>**Other Resources**<br>CRM Leveled Worksheets (pp. 28–32)<br>Daily Reteach • 5-Minute Check • Problem of the Day |
| **Technology** | | Math Adventures | Interactive Classroom |
| **Math Online** | Personal Tutor | Personal Tutor | |
| **Reaching All Learners** | English Learners, p. 586B ELL<br>Gifted and Talented, p. 586B AL<br>Early Finishers, p. 586B OL AL | English Learners, p. 588B ELL<br>Gifted and Talented, p. 588B AL<br>Early Finishers, p. 588B OL AL | English Learners, p. 590B ELL<br>Gifted and Talented, p. 590B AL<br>Early Finishers, p. 590B OL AL |
| **Alternate Lesson** | | *IMPACT Mathematics:* Unit E | *IMPACT Mathematics:* Unit E |

**Formative Assessment**
Mid-Chapter Check (p. 593)

# Chapter Planner

| | Lesson 14-6 (Pacing: 1 day) | Lesson 14-7 (Pacing: 1 day) | Lesson 14-8 (Pacing: 1 day) |
|---|---|---|---|
| **Lesson/ Objective** | **Problem-Solving Investigation**<br>**Choose a Strategy**<br>(pp. 594–595)<br>**Objective:** Choose the best strategy to solve a problem. | **Fraction and Decimal Equivalents**<br>(pp. 596–599)<br>**Objective:** Find fraction and decimal equivalents. | **Decimals, Fractions, and Mixed Numbers**<br>(pp. 602–604)<br>**Objective:** Compare and order decimals, fractions, and mixed numbers. |
| **State/Local Standards** | | | |
| **Math Vocabulary** | | | |
| **Lesson Resources** | **Materials**<br>index cards<br>**Manipulatives**<br>counters<br>**Other Resources**<br>CRM Leveled Worksheets (pp. 33–37)<br>Daily Reteach • 5-Minute Check • Problem of the Day<br>*Growing Goods in a Growing Country* | **Materials**<br>hundredths grids, number lines<br>**Other Resources**<br>CRM Leveled Worksheets (pp. 38–42)<br>Daily Reteach • 5-Minute Check • Problem of the Day | **Materials**<br>hundredths grids, colored pencils or markers, number lines<br>**Other Resources**<br>CRM Leveled Worksheets (pp. 43–47)<br>Daily Reteach • 5-Minute Check • Problem of the Day |
| **Technology** | Math Adventures | | |
| **Math Online** | Personal Tutor | Personal Tutor | |
| **Reaching All Learners** | English Learners, p. 594B ELL<br>Gifted and Talented, p. 594B AL<br>Early Finishers, p. 594B OL AL | English Learners, p. 596B ELL<br>Below Level, p. 596B BL<br>Early Finishers, p. 596B OL AL | English Learners, p. 602B ELL<br>Below Level, p. 602B BL<br>Early Finishers, p. 602B OL AL |
| **Alternate Lesson** | | | *IMPACT Mathematics:* Unit E |

**Problem Solving in Music** (p. 600)

**Game Time** (p. 605)

**Summative Assessment**
- Study Guide/Review (p. 606)
- Chapter Test (p. 611)
- Test Practice (p. 612)

## Assessment Options

### Diagnostic Assessment

- SE *Option 1:* Quick Check (p. 576)
- *Option 2:* Online Quiz macmillanmh.com
- CRM *Option 3:* Diagnostic Test (p. 49)
- CRM *Option 4:* Chapter Pretest (p. 50)

### Formative Assessment

- TE Alternate Teaching Strategies (in every lesson)
- SE Talk About It (in every lesson)
- SE Writing in Math (in every lesson)
- SE Check What You Know (in every lesson)
- TE Ticket Out the Door (p. 581)
- TE Into the Future (p. 599)
- TE Yesterday's News (pp. 595, 604)
- SE Mid-Chapter Check (p. 593)
- CRM Lesson Quizzes (pp. 51–53)
- CRM Mid-Chapter Test (p. 54)

### Summative Assessment

- SE Chapter Test (p. 611)
- SE Test Practice (p. 612)
- CRM Vocabulary Test (p. 55)
- CRM Leveled Chapter Tests (pp. 60–71)
- CRM Cumulative Test Practice (pp. 74–76)
- CRM Oral Assessment (pp. 56–57)
- ExamView® Assessment Suite
- Advance Tracker

## Mc Graw Hill Professional Development

Targeted professional development has been articulated throughout **McGraw-Hill's *Math Connects*** program. The **McGraw-Hill Professional Development Video Library** provides short videos that support the **NCTM Focal Points and Focal Connections.** For more information visit **macmillanmh.com**.

Model Lessons

Instructional Strategies

## Assessment Tips

As students work on the relationship of fractions and decimals, take time to observe their understanding of this concept.

- Record individual student observations on an address label.
- Make sure address labels are dated.
- Paste the label on the inside cover of a student's file folder.
- You will be able to chart progress over time.

## Teacher Notes

# Learning Stations

## Cross-Curricular Links

### Writing

individual | LOGICAL

**Money Fractions**

- Explain which fractions are used in our system of money.
- What fraction of a dollar are each of the coins we use?
- How are they expressed in decimals?
- Compare the coin values to each other, and place their decimal values in order from smallest to largest. Explain how you have placed them in order.

**Materials:**
- paper
- pencil

### Art

pair | VISUAL

**Decimal Pictures**

Using a hundredths grid, challenge your partner to figure out how much of each color you used to make a picture.

- Each partner makes a picture on a hundredths grid by coloring in squares. Color in each square on the grid with one of eight colors: red, yellow, orange, blue, green, violet, brown, and black.
- Challenge your partner to make a color key for your picture, showing in decimals how many hundredths of each color there are.

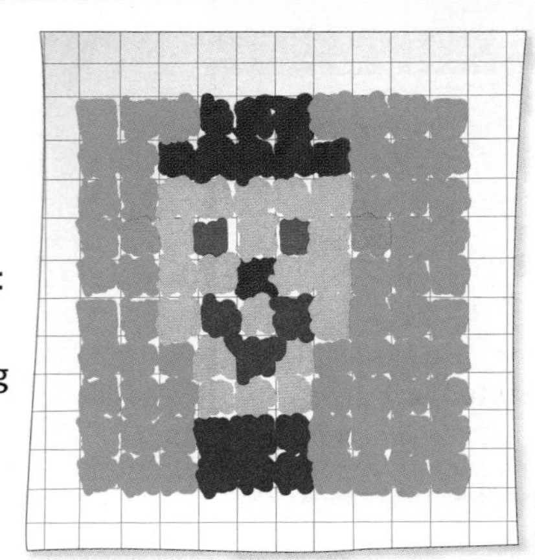

**Materials:**
- hundredths grids on paper
- markers in red, yellow, orange, blue, green, violet, brown, and black
- plain paper
- pencils

### Reading

group | SPATIAL

**Where Do You Sit?**

- Read *Sir Cumference And The First Round Table* by Cindy Neuschwander by yourself or with the class.
- Model a round table by putting your desks into a circle. If you look at this circle as a pie and divide it into wedges, what fraction expresses how much each of you gets of the table pie? Can you express the fraction in decimal form?
- Model a rectangular table by putting your desks together facing each other in a long rectangle, two desks wide. Now what fraction expresses how much each of you gets of the table? How is this model similar or different from the previous model?

**Materials:**
- *Sir Cumference And The First Round Table* by Cindy Neuschwander
- desks

# Use Place Value to Represent Decimals

## Science

individual | LOGICAL

### Plant Care

Plant fertilizer usually contains nitrogen, phosphorus, and potassium.

- The numbers 20-20-20 mean that there is 20 percent of each of the three main ingredients. Follow the instructions to mix the fertilizer.
- Write a fraction label for your plant before you fertilize it. Express the amounts of each main ingredient in fraction and in decimal form.
- What percent of the fertilizer is none of those three ingredients? 40% Express this other category in fraction and decimal form.
- What if you were using 5-1-1 fish fertilizer? How would you write the ingredient amounts in decimals?

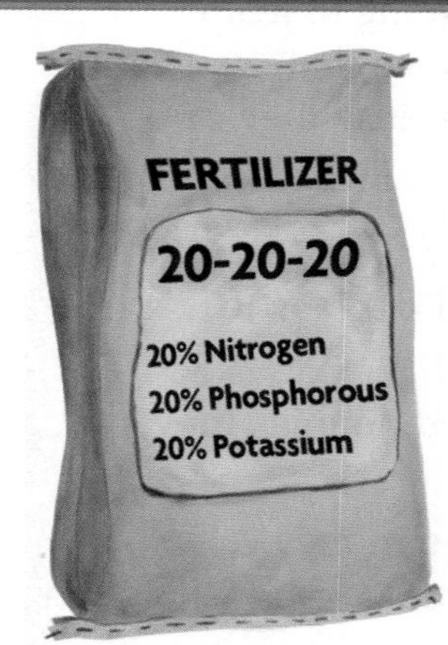


**Materials:**
- 20-20-20 plant fertilizer
- gallon watering can
- access to water
- foliage plant
- paper
- pencil

## Health

individual | VISUAL

### Healthy Shopping

Make your own healthy store circular, where the prices are all in fractions.

- Clip out examples of healthy foods from grocery store sale circulars. Be sure to include the prices.
- Make your own shopping circular. Glue the examples of the foods you chose onto paper.
- Underneath each food, write the price but write the cents in fraction form.

**Materials:**
- grocery store sale circulars
- scissors
- glue
- markers
- paper

## Social Studies

pair | LOGICAL

### Olympic Race

In the Olympics, an athlete's performance is valued using decimals. Make a set of Olympic score cards, then race to place them in order.

- Make a set of 24 score cards.
- To score each performance card, place a 1 in the hundreds place. Then roll a number cube to find the tens place, the ones place, the tenths place, and the hundredths place of your score.
- Shuffle the cards, then evenly divide them.
- Each person races to place the scores in order from highest to lowest. The person who places the scores in order first wins.

Jana Riley's
skating score: 156.54

**Materials:**
- index cards
- number cubes
- pencils

CHAPTER 14

# Introduce the Chapter

## Real World: Dimes and Pennies

**Materials:** 10 dimes and 10 pennies, writing paper

Share with students that they are going to learn about decimals in this chapter. Explain that decimals are similar to fractions because they can be used to name parts of a whole.

Have students:

- Choose a number of dimes and pennies to place on their table.
- Write the value of the dimes and pennies they chose using the dollar sign.
- Choose just dimes and write the money value.
- Choose just pennies and write the money value.

Ask students to choose one of their numbers to read aloud. Have them read it both as a money amount and as symbols from left to right ("32 cents; dollar sign, zero point three two").

Direct students to Student Edition p. 574. Have students read the paragraph at the top of the page.

- **How are dimes a model of tenths?** A dollar has the value of 10 dimes, so each dime is one tenth of a dollar.
- **How are pennies a model of hundredths?** A dollar has the same value as 100 pennies, so each penny is one hundredth of a dollar.

## WRITING IN ►MATH

**Starting the Chapter**
Have students make a list in their Math Journals of situations where they have seen decimals used. The list might include such things as money, sports records, length, time, or weight. Suggest that they give specific examples.

**Key Vocabulary** Introduce the key vocabulary in the chapter using the routine below.

<u>Define:</u> A decimal is a number with one or more digits to the right of the decimal point.
<u>Example:</u> The amount $2.05 represents a number with a decimal.
<u>Ask:</u> Can you name a dollar amount that uses a decimal?

**Read-Aloud Anthology** For an optional reading activity to introduce this chapter's math concepts, see the Read-Aloud Anthology on p. TR39.

CHAPTER 14

# Use Place Value to Represent Decimals

**BIG Idea** What are decimals?

**Decimals** are numbers that use place value and a decimal point to show part of a whole.

**Example** There are 10 dimes in a dollar. One dime is $\frac{1}{10}$ of a dollar. There are 100 pennies in a dollar. One penny is $\frac{1}{100}$ of a dollar.

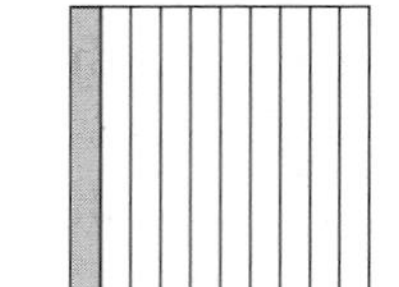

One dime is $\frac{1}{10}$ of a dollar.

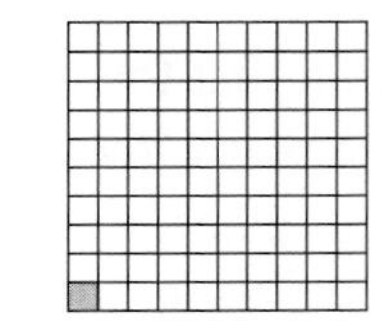

One penny is $\frac{1}{100}$ of a dollar.

### What will I learn in this chapter?

- Identify, read, write, and model decimals.
- Relate decimals, fractions, and mixed numbers.
- Compare and order decimals.
- Solve problems by making a model.

### Key Vocabulary

**decimal**
**decimal point**
**tenth**
**hundredth**

Math Online **Student Study Tools at** macmillanmh.com



## Chapter 14 Project

### Bake Sale Equivalents

Students plan a bake sale and price their goods in fraction form.

- Students write a price list for the items they will sell, expressing the prices in fraction form.
- Students are given play money to buy one item each, and figure out how much in decimal form they need to buy the item.
- Challenge students to write the price fractions in simplest form.

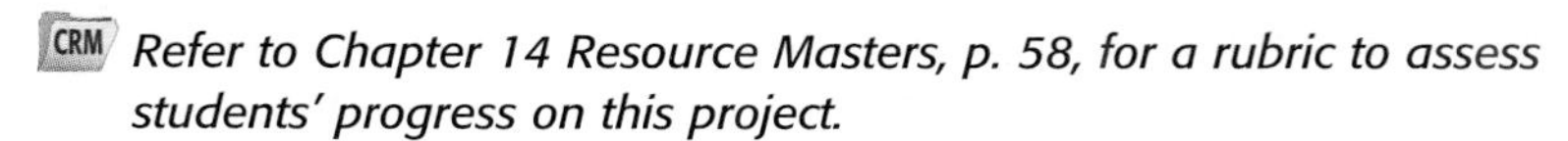

CRM *Refer to Chapter 14 Resource Masters, p. 58, for a rubric to assess students' progress on this project.*

**FOLDABLES Study Organizer**

Make this Foldable to help you organize information about decmials. Begin with one sheet of 11″ × 17″ paper.

1. **Fold** the short sides so they meet in the middle.
2. **Fold** again so the top meets the bottom.

3. **Unfold** and cut as shown to make four tabs.

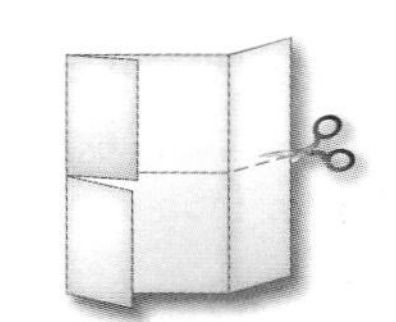

4. **Label** the outside of each tab as shown.

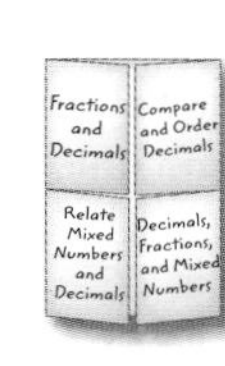




## ELL National ESL Standards Alignment for Chapter 14

| Lesson, Page | ESL Standard | Modality | Level |
|---|---|---|---|
| 14-1, p. 579B | Goal 1, Standard 3, k | Auditory, Linguistic | Beginning |
| 14-2, p. 582B | Goal 2, Standard 2, a | Auditory, Visual | Intermediate |
| 14-3, p. 586B | Goal 2, Standard 2, i | Intrapersonal, Social | Advanced |
| 14-4, p. 588B | Goal 2, Standard 2, d | Spatial, Kinesthetic | Intermediate |
| 14-5, p. 590B | Goal 2, Standard 1, g | Social, Logical | Beginning |
| 14-6, p. 594B | Goal 2, Standard 1, c | Linguistic, Interpersonal | Intermediate |
| 14-7, p. 596B | Goal 1, Standard 3, c | Linguistic, Auditory | Intermediate |
| 14-8, p 602B | Goal 2, Standard 3, d | Intrapersonal, Linguistic | Advanced |

The National ESL Standards can be found in the Teacher Reference Handbook.

## FOLDABLES Dinah Zike's Foldables

Guide students through the directions on p. 575 to create their own Foldables graphic organizers for decimals. Students may also use their Foldables to study and review for chapter assessments.

**When to Use It** Lessons 14-2, 14-4, 14-5, and 14-8. (Additional instructions for using the Foldables with these lessons are found on pp. 593 and 606.)

## Chapter 14 Literature List

| Lesson | Book Title |
|---|---|
| 14-1 | **Follow the Money**<br>Loreen Leedy |
| 14-2 | **Follow the Money**<br>Loreen Leedy |
| 14-3 | **Gator Pie**<br>Louise Mathews |
| 14-4 | **Twizzlers Percentages Book**<br>Jerry Pallotta |
| 14-5 | **The Toothpaste Millionaire**<br>Jean Merrill |
| 14-7 | **Henry Hikes to Fitchburg**<br>D.B. Johnson |
| 14-8 | **Eating Fractions**<br>Bruce McMillan |
| Any | **Sir Cumference and the First Round Table: A Math Adventure**<br>Cindy Neuschwander |

- Read the Math at Home letter found in the Chapter 14 Resource Masters, p. 4, with the class and have each student sign it. (A Spanish version is found on p. 5.)
- Send home copies of the Math at Home letter with each student.

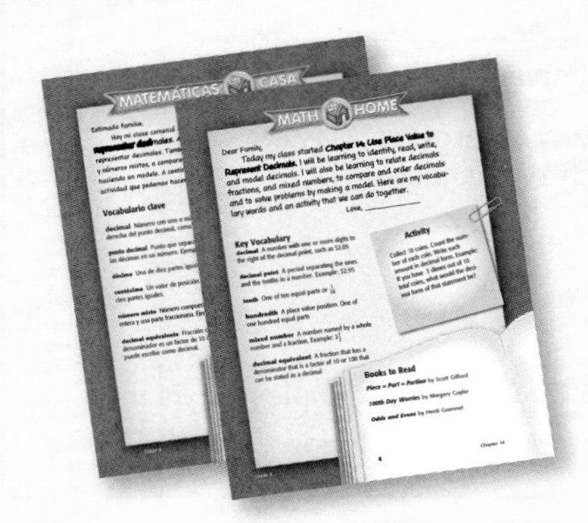

# Diagnostic Assessment

Check for students' prerequisite skills before beginning the chapter.

- **Option 1:** ***Quick Check***
  SE Student Edition, p. 576
- **Option 2:** ***Online Assessment***
  Math Online macmillanmh.com
- **Option 3:** ***Diagnostic Tests***
  CRM Chapter 14 Resource Masters, p. 49–50

# RTI (Response to Intervention)

**Apply the Results** Based on the results of the diagnostic assessment on Student Edition p. 576, use the chart below to address individual needs before beginning the chapter.

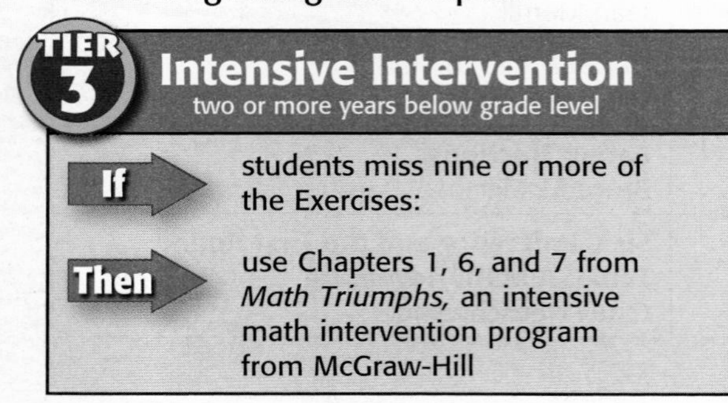

**TIER 3 Intensive Intervention**
two or more years below grade level

**If** students miss nine or more of the Exercises:

**Then** use Chapters 1, 6, and 7 from *Math Triumphs,* an intensive math intervention program from McGraw-Hill

# ARE YOU READY for Chapter 14?

You have two ways to check prerequisite skills for this chapter.

**Option 2**

Math Online Take the Chapter Readiness Quiz at macmillanmh.com.

**Option 1**

Complete the Quick Check below.

## QUICK Check

(Used in Lessons 14-1, 14-2, and 14-6)

**Write a fraction to describe the part that is green.** (Lesson 13-1)

1. 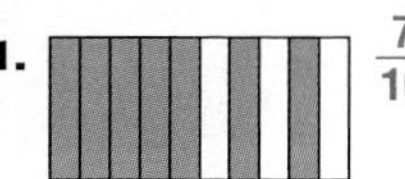 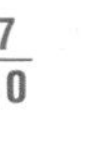 $\frac{7}{10}$
2. 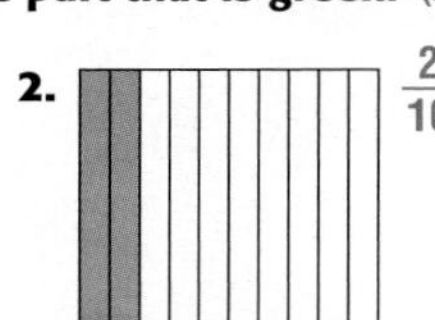  $\frac{2}{10}$
3. 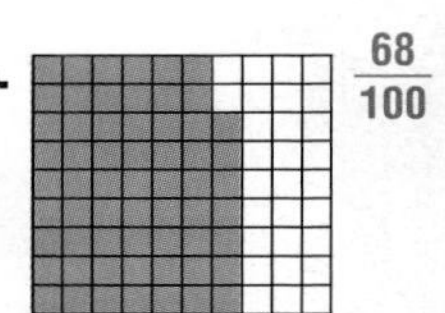 $\frac{68}{100}$

**Write each as a fraction.** (Lessons 13-1 and 13-2) (Used in Lessons 14-1 and 14-2)

4. four tenths $\frac{4}{10}$
5. eight tenths $\frac{8}{10}$
6. twenty hundredths $\frac{20}{100}$
7. **Measurement** On Tuesday, seven-tenths of an inch of rain fell. Write the amount of rain that fell as a fraction. $\frac{7}{10}$

**Algebra Copy and complete.** (Lesson 13-4) (Used in Lesson 14-6)

8. $\frac{1}{5} = \frac{■}{10}$ 2
9. $\frac{4}{5} = \frac{■}{10}$ 8
10. $\frac{1}{2} = \frac{■}{10}$ 5
11. $\frac{1}{4} = \frac{■}{100}$ 25
12. $\frac{2}{5} = \frac{■}{100}$ 40
13. $\frac{1}{2} = \frac{■}{100}$ 50
14. In Salvador's aquarium, $\frac{4}{10}$ of the fish are yellow and $\frac{6}{10}$ are blue. Are there more blue or yellow fish in Salvador's aquarium? Explain how you know. blue fish; $\frac{6}{10} > \frac{4}{10}$



| TIER 2 Strategic Intervention<br>below/approaching grade level | TIER 1 On-Level | Above/Beyond Level |
|---|---|---|
| **If** students miss five to eight in: **Exercises 1–14** | **If** students miss three or four in: **Exercises 1–14** | **If** students miss two or less in: **Exercises 1–14** |
| **Then** choose a resource: | **Then** choose a resource: | **Then** choose a resource: |
| Strategic Intervention Guide (p. 110)<br>CRM Chapter 12 Resource Masters Reteach Worksheets<br>Math Online Extra Examples • Personal Tutor • Concepts in Motion | TE Learning Stations (pp. 574G–574H)<br>TE Chapter Project (p. 530)<br>CRM Game: Make it Low!<br>Math Adventures<br>My Math Zone Chapter 13<br>Math Online Fact Dash | TE Learning Stations (pp. 574G–574H)<br>TE Chapter Project (p. 574)<br>Real-World Problem Solving: *Growing Goods in a Growing Country*<br>My Math Zone Chapters 13 and 14<br>Math Online Games |

Math Activity for 14-1

# Fractions and Decimals

**MAIN IDEA**

I will use models to show tenths and hundredths.

**You Will Need**
tenths grid
hundredths grid

**Math Online** macmillanmh.com
- Concepts in Motion

A fraction shows part of a whole. A decimal also shows a part of a whole. A **decimal** is a number that uses place value, numbers, and a decimal point to show part of a whole.

one whole

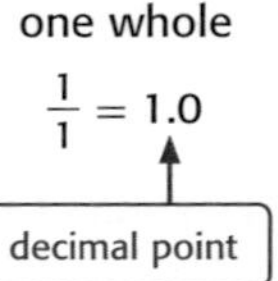

$\frac{1}{1} = 1.0$

decimal point

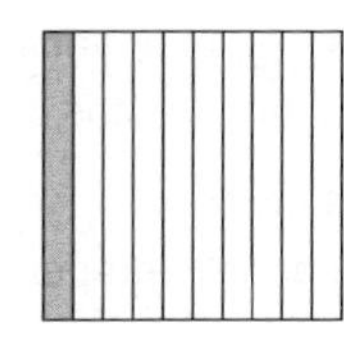

one **tenth**

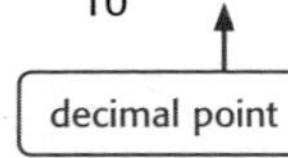

$\frac{1}{10} = 0.1$

decimal point

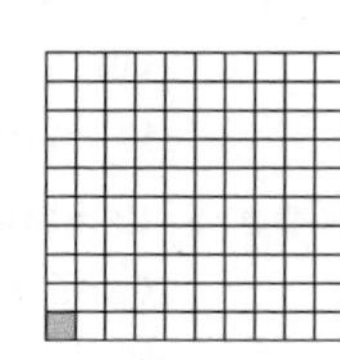

one **hundredth**

$\frac{1}{100} = 0.01$

decimal point

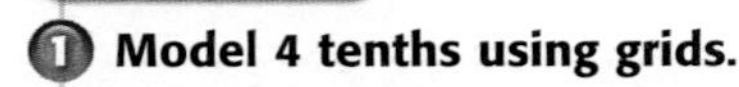

ACTIVITY

**1 Model 4 tenths using grids.**

**Step 1** **Use a tenths grid.**
Shade 4 of the 10 parts to show 4 tenths.

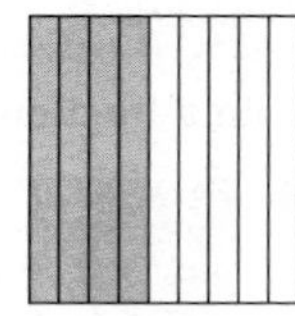

**Step 2** **Use a hundredths grid.**
Shade 40 of the 100 parts to show 40 hundredths.

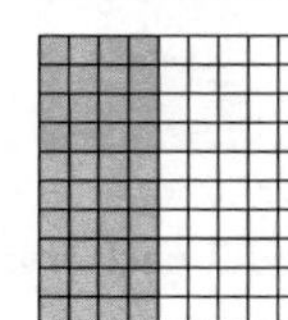

**Step 3** **Compare.**
Compare the grids. Write the fraction for each shaded part.

**Step 4** **Write decimals.**
How is 4 tenths written as a decimal?
How is 40 hundredths written as a decimal?

Math Activity for 14-1

# Lesson Planner

## Objective

Use models to show tenths and hundredths.

## Resources

**Materials:** tenths grids, hundredths grids, WorkMat 6 Place-Value Chart

**Teacher Technology**

**Math Online** macmillanmh.com

Concepts in Motion

## 1 Introduce

### Introduce the Concept

- Before beginning this lesson, assess the students' understanding of the concept of fractional parts of one whole.
- **Which is greater, $\frac{3}{10}$ or $\frac{3}{100}$? How do you know?** $\frac{3}{10}$; Sample answer: because it is 3 out of a whole that is divided into 10 parts and $\frac{3}{100}$ is 3 out of a whole that is divided into 100 parts.

## 2 Teach

**Activity 1** After reviewing the fraction name that each figure shows, introduce the decimal form, naming the ones place, and the tenths and hundredths places. Have students work with the different grids to shade the decimals shown. A place-value chart can help students identify where placeholder zeros belong.

**Activity 2** Distribute coins to students. Guide students to see equivalencies between dimes and pennies and tenths and hundredths.

## Think About It

Assign **Think About It** Exercises 1–3 to assess student comprehension of the concept presented in the Activity.

# 3 Assess

### Formative Assessment

Use **Check What You Know** Exercises 4–16 to assess whether students understand how to use models to show tenths and hundredths.

**From Concrete to Abstract** Use Exercise 16 to bridge the gap between writing a fraction with a denominator of 10 as a decimal.

### Extending the Concept

- **Which is greater, 0.59, 0.09, or 0.5? Explain.**
  Sample answer: 0.59 is greater because it would have 5 rows of 10 and 9 more squares of a hundredths grid shaded. 0.09 would have only 9 squares shaded and 0.05 would have only 5 rows shaded.

### Additional Answer

2. No; 2 hundredths is less than 2 tenths. See students' drawings.

ACTIVITY

2 **Model 77 hundredths using coins.**

**Step 1** **Use dimes.**
One dime is $\frac{1}{10}$ of a dollar. Count out 7 dimes to represent 7 tenths or $\frac{7}{10}$.

**Step 2** **Use pennies.**
One penny is $\frac{1}{100}$ of a dollar. Count out 7 pennies to represent 7 hundredths or $\frac{7}{100}$.

**Step 3** **Combine the coins.**
Combine the dimes and pennies to represent $\frac{77}{100}$ or 0.77.

## Think About It

1. Do $\frac{4}{10}$, $\frac{40}{100}$, 0.4, and 0.40 represent the same number? Explain. yes; When you model these numbers, the same area is shaded.
2. Is 0.02 greater than 0.2? Support your answer with models. See margin.
3. Is 0.3 greater than 0.30? Explain. no; They are equivalent.

## CHECK What You Know

**Write a fraction and a decimal for each shaded part.**

4. 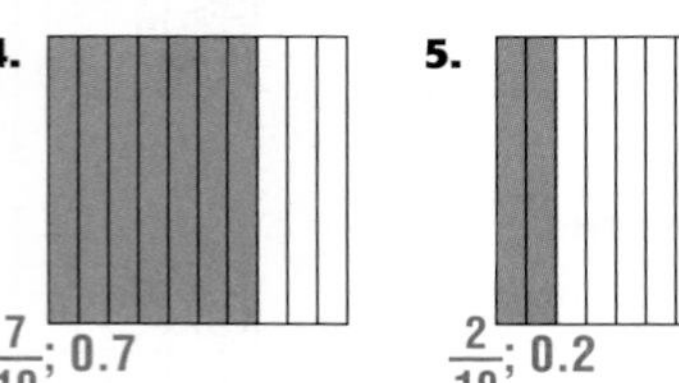 $\frac{7}{10}$; 0.7

5. $\frac{2}{10}$; 0.2

6.  $\frac{45}{100}$; 0.45

7. 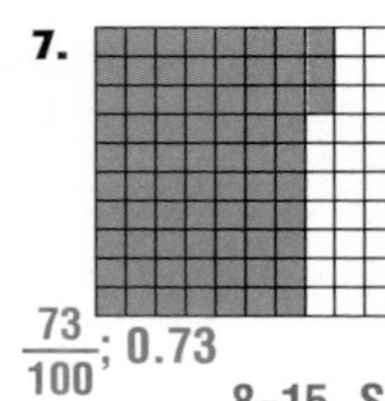 $\frac{73}{100}$; 0.73

**Model each fraction. Then write as a decimal.**

8. $\frac{1}{10}$ 0.1
9. $\frac{3}{10}$ 0.3
10. $\frac{60}{100}$ 0.60
11. $\frac{82}{100}$ 0.82

8–15. See Ch. 14 Answer Appendix for models.

**Model each decimal. Then write as a fraction.**

12. 0.5 $\frac{5}{10}$
13. 0.75 $\frac{75}{100}$
14. 0.3 $\frac{3}{10}$
15. 0.25 $\frac{25}{100}$

16. WRITING IN MATH Explain how to write a fraction with a denominator of 10 as a decimal. See Ch. 14 Answer Appendix.

LESSON 14-1

# Tenths and Hundredths

## Lesson Planner

### Objective

Identify, read, and write tenths and hundredths as decimals and fractions.

### Vocabulary

**decimal**, **decimal point**, **tenth**, **hundredth**

### Resources

**Materials:** tenths and hundredths grids, colored pencils or markers, WorkMat 6: Place-Value Chart

**Manipulatives:** play money: dimes and pennies

**Literature Connection:** *Follow the Money* by Loreen Leedy

**Alternate Lesson:** Use *IMPACT Mathematics:* Unit E to provide practice with decimals.

**Teacher Technology**
TeacherWorks • Interactive Classroom

### Focus on Math Background

In Chapter 13, students learned to express rational numbers as fractions, and in this lesson, they explore expressing them as decimals. Place value provides the foundation for the understanding of decimals. At this point, students should understand that a place value on the left is 10 times the place value on its right. As they explore decimals, they should begin to understand that it is also true that a place value on the right is one-tenth the place value on its left. For example, the value of the tenths place is ten times the value of the hundredths place, while the value of the hundredths place is one-tenth the value of the tenths place.

## Daily Routine

Use these suggestions before beginning the lesson on p. 579.

### 5-Minute Check

(Reviews Lesson 13-7)

**Use any strategy to solve.**

Kayla is 18 years old. She is twice as old as her brother Mike. Their sister Anna is 3 years younger than Mike. How old is Anna? 6

### Problem of the Day

Jenn and Marco each have 24 sports cards. One third of Jenn's cards are baseball cards. Three eighths of Marco's cards are baseball cards. Who has more baseball cards? Explain. Marco: $\frac{3}{8}$ of $24 = 9$; Jenn: $\frac{1}{3}$ of $24 = 8$

### Building Math Vocabulary

Write the lesson vocabulary words and their definitions on the board.

Have students record the new vocabulary words and their definitions in their Math Journals. Have students write 0.52 and label the decimal point, the tenths place, and the hundredths place.

#### Visual Vocabulary Cards

Use Visual Vocabulary Card 9 to reinforce the vocabulary introduced in this lesson. (The Define/Example/Ask routine is printed on the back of each card.)

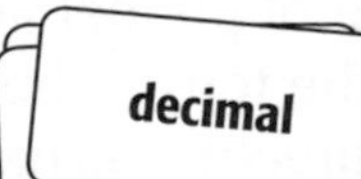

# Differentiated Instruction

## Small Group Options

**Option 1** VISUAL, SPATIAL, LOGICAL

### Below Level BL

**Materials:** pennies, dimes, chart paper

- Ask students the following questions:
- **How many dimes do you need to make a dollar?** 10
- Remind students that one dime is $\frac{1}{10}$ of a dollar.
- **How many pennies make a dollar?** 100
- Remind students that one penny is $\frac{1}{100}$ of a dollar.
- Write 25¢, 32¢, 76¢, and 98¢ on the chart paper.
- Ask students to arrange these amounts of money in dimes and pennies, using the most dimes possible for each amount.
- **How many dimes did you need to make 25¢?** 2
- **How many pennies did you need to make 25¢?** 5
- Written as a decimal, 25¢ looks like $0.25. The 2 is the tenths or dimes, and the 5 is the hundredths or pennies.
- Repeat this process with the other amounts.

**Option 2** AUDITORY, LINGUISTIC

### English Language Learners ELL

**Materials:** paper, pencil
**Core Vocabulary:** tenths, /th/, ending sound
**Common Use Verb:** stress

**Talk Math** This strategy uses speed to practice the "th" sound in a controlled situation.

- Post 0.5 and say: "5 tenths," emphasizing the /ths/ sound.
- Have students repeat chorally.
- Continue with other decimals as time permits. Students should not have their pronunciation corrected in this type of phonemic practice. Demonstrate the placement of the tongue between the teeth and then pulled back as breath is exhaled over it. The /th/ sound is uncommon and requires direct instruction and accuracy.

## Independent Work Options

**Option 1** SPATIAL

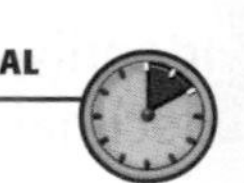

### Early Finishers OL AL

**Materials:** several 10-by-10 grids, colored pencils or markers, 0–5 number cube, 5–10 number cube

- Have students write 0.__ __ below their first grid.
- Then have them roll a 0–5 number cube and write the digit rolled in the tenths place.
- Have them roll a 5–10 number cube and write the digit rolled in the hundredths place. If a 10 is rolled, roll again.

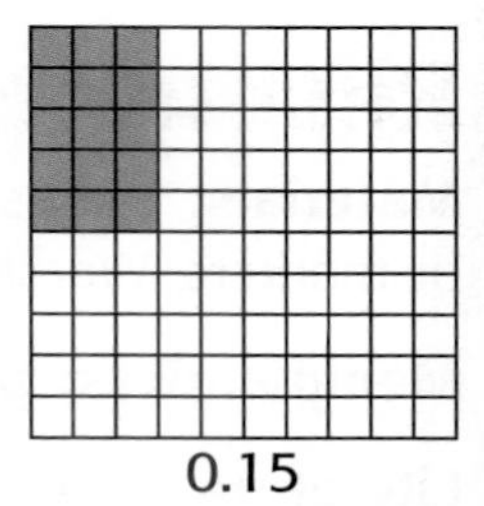
0.15

- Ask them to shade in the grid to show the number rolled.

### Student Technology

Math Online macmillanmh.com

Personal Tutor • Extra Examples

Math Adventures

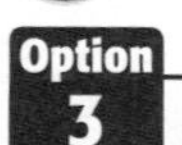

### Learning Station: Health (p. 574H)

Direct students to the Health Learning Station for opportunities to explore and extend the lesson concept.

**Option 4**

### Problem-Solving Practice

Reinforce problem-solving skills and strategies with the Problem-Solving Practice worksheet.

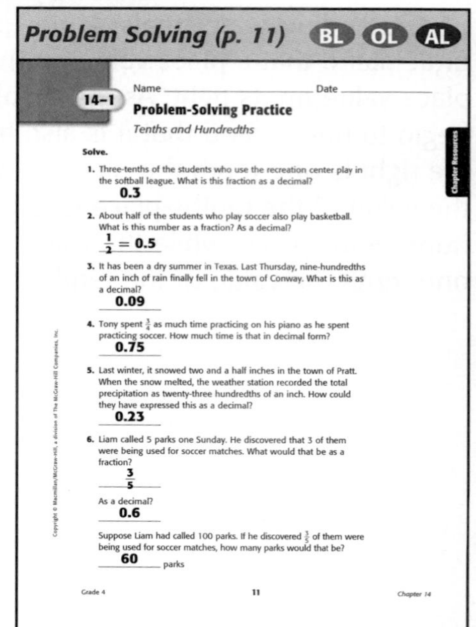
**Problem Solving (p. 11)** BL OL AL

14–1 Name ______ Date ______

**Problem-Solving Practice**

*Tenths and Hundredths*

Chapter Resources

**Solve.**

1. Three-tenths of the students who use the recreation center play in the softball league. What is this fraction as a decimal?
   **0.3**
2. About half of the students who play soccer also play basketball. What is this number as a fraction? As a decimal?
   $\frac{1}{2} = 0.5$
3. It has been a dry summer in Texas. Last Thursday, nine-hundredths of an inch of rain finally fell in the town of Conway. What is this as a decimal?
   **0.09**
4. Tony spent $\frac{3}{4}$ as much time practicing on his piano as he spent practicing soccer. How much time is that in decimal form?
   **0.75**
5. Last winter, it snowed two and a half inches in the town of Pratt. When the snow melted, the weather station recorded the total precipitation as twenty-three hundredths of an inch. How could they have expressed this as a decimal?
   **0.23**
6. Liam called 5 parks one Sunday. He discovered that 3 of them were being used for soccer matches. What would that be as a fraction?
   $\frac{3}{5}$
   As a decimal?
   **0.6**
   Suppose Liam had called 100 parks. If he discovered $\frac{3}{5}$ of them were being used for soccer matches, how many parks would that be?
   **60** parks



Grade 4 11 Chapter 14

# 14-1 Tenths and Hundredths

**GET READY to Learn**

It costs 85 cents for a child to ride the light rail system. Can you write this part of a dollar as a fraction and as a decimal?

**MAIN IDEA**

I will identify, read, and write tenths and hundredths as decimals and fractions.

**New Vocabulary**

decimal
decimal point
tenth
hundredth

**Math Online**

macmillanmh.com
- Extra Examples
- Personal Tutor
- Self-Check Quiz

A **decimal** is a number that uses place value and a **decimal point** to show part of a whole.

**EXAMPLE** Read and Write Decimals

1 **MONEY** **Write 85 cents as a fraction and as a decimal.**

The amount 85 cents means 85 pennies out of 1 dollar.

**One Way:** Use a Model

Draw a hundreds model. Shade 85 out of 100 parts to show 85 cents.

**Read** eighty-five hundredths

**Write** $\frac{85}{100}$ or 0.85

**Another Way:** Place Value

| Hundreds | Tens | Ones | Tenths | Hundredths |
|---|---|---|---|---|
| | | 0 | . 8 | 5 |

**Read** eighty-five hundredths

**Write** $\frac{85}{100}$ or 0.85

So, 85 cents is $\frac{85}{100}$ as a fraction and 0.85 as a decimal.

# 14-1 Tenths and Hundredths

## 1 Introduce

### Activity Choice 1 • Hands-On

- Give each student 3 tenths grids and 3 hundredths grids.
- Write 0.2, 0.7, and 0.5 on the board. Have students shade their tenths grids to show each number.
- **What fractional part of each grid is shaded?** $\frac{2}{10}$, $\frac{7}{10}$, $\frac{5}{10}$ or $\frac{1}{2}$
- Write 0.02, 0.07 and 0.05 on the board. Have students shade hundredths grids.
- **What fractional part of each grid is shaded?** $\frac{2}{100}$, $\frac{7}{100}$, $\frac{5}{100}$

### Activity Choice 2 • Literature

Introduce the lesson with *Follow the Money* by Loreen Leedy. For a related math activity, see p. TR64.

## 2 Teach

### Scaffolding Questions

Write the number 0.47 on the board.

- **Which grid, tenths or hundredths, would you choose to show this number? Why?** the hundredths grid because there are hundredths in the number
- **How many columns of 10 squares would you shade?** 4
- **How many more small squares should be shaded?** 7
- **How many squares out of 100 should be shaded to show this number?** 47
- **Which number is greater, 0.4 or 0.47? How do you know?** 0.47 is greater because it has 4 rows of 10 shaded and 7 more small squares shaded. 0.4 has just 4 rows of 10 shaded.

**GET READY to Learn**

Have students open their books and read the information in **Get Ready to Learn**. Introduce **decimal**, **decimal point**, **tenth**, and **hundredth**. As a class, work through **Examples 1 and 2**.

## Write Tenths and Hundredths

**Example 2** Help students to understand that when there is any digit, including zero, in the hundredths place, the number is read with the word "hundredths" following it. So, 0.50 is read as "50 hundredths."

### ADDITIONAL EXAMPLES

1. Write 39 cents as a fraction and as a decimal. $\frac{39}{100}$, 0.39
2. Write $\frac{4}{10}$ as two different decimals. 0.4, 0.40

### CHECK What You Know

As a class, have students complete Exercises 1–12 in **Check What You Know** as you observe their work.

**Exercise 12** Assess student comprehension before assigning practice exercises.

## BL Alternate Teaching Strategy

**If** students have trouble identifying and reading decimals with tenths and hundredths…

**Then** use one of these reteach options:

1. CRM **Daily Reteach Worksheet** (p. 8)
2. Have students use dimes and pennies to represent tenths and hundredths. Write 0.6, 0.21, and 0.08 on the board. Show each number with dimes and pennies.
   - **If the number has just dimes, what label is used to name the decimal?** tenths
   - **If the number has dimes and pennies or just pennies, what label is used?** hundredths
   - Repeat using several other numbers.

### ! COMMON ERROR!

**Exercises 26 and 33** Students may write the non-zero digit in the tenths place instead of the hundredths place. Have students refer to a grid model and place-value chart to determine where each digit should be written to correctly represent each number.



Some fractions can be written as **tenths** and **hundredths**.

**EXAMPLE** Write Tenths and Hundredths

2. **Write $\frac{5}{10}$ as two different decimals.**

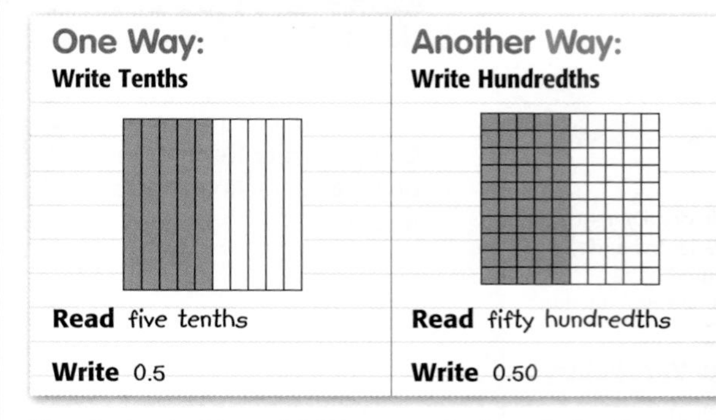


The decimals 0.5 and 0.50 are equivalent decimals.

### CHECK What You Know

**Write a fraction and a decimal for each shaded part.** See Example 1 (p. 579)

1. 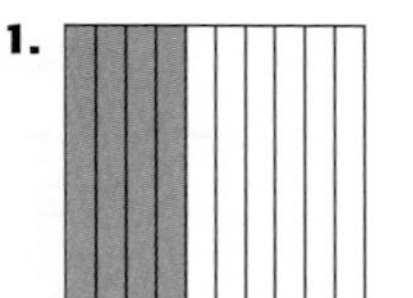 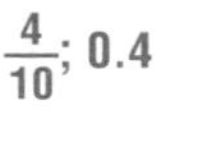 $\frac{4}{10}$; 0.4
2. 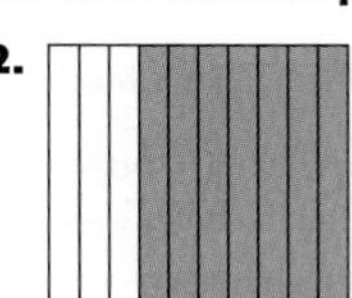 $\frac{7}{10}$; 0.7
3. 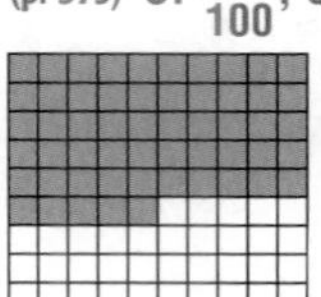 $\frac{55}{100}$; 0.55

**Write as a fraction and as a decimal.** See Example 1 (p. 579)

4. one tenth $\frac{1}{10}$; 0.1
5. twenty-five hundredths $\frac{25}{100}$; 0.25
6. seven hundredths $\frac{7}{100}$; 0.07

**Write each fraction as a decimal.** See Example 2 (p. 580)

7. $\frac{6}{10}$ 0.6
8. $\frac{9}{10}$ 0.9
9. $\frac{10}{100}$ 0.10
10. $\frac{69}{100}$ 0.69

11. **Measurement** A baby owl weighs about twenty-three hundredths of a kilogram. Write this amount as a fraction and decimal. $\frac{23}{100}$; 0.23
12. **Talk About It** Shade all of the boxes along the outer edge of a hundreds grid. Write a fraction and decimal for the shaded part. Why is it not 0.40? See Ch. 14 Answer Appendix.



**Reteach (p. 8)** BL | **Skills Practice (p. 9)** OL

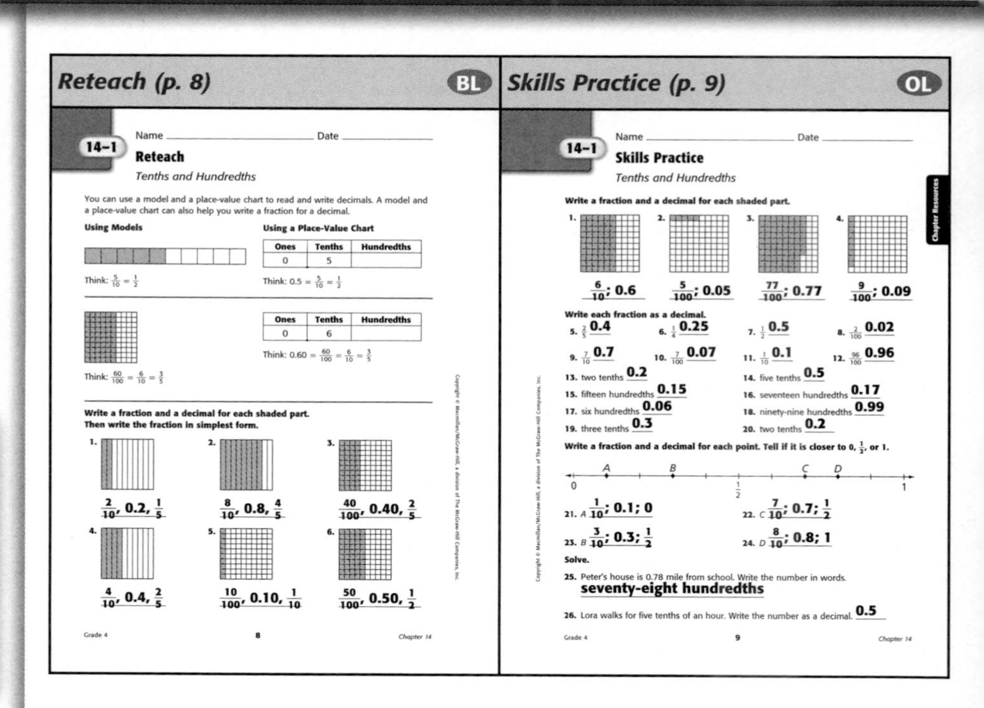
14–1 Reteach
*Tenths and Hundredths*

You can use a model and a place-value chart to read and write decimals. A model and a place-value chart can also help you write a fraction for a decimal.

Write a fraction and a decimal for each shaded part. Then write the fraction in simplest form.

1. $\frac{2}{10}$, 0.2, $\frac{1}{5}$
2. $\frac{8}{10}$, 0.8, $\frac{4}{5}$
3. $\frac{40}{100}$, 0.40, $\frac{2}{5}$
4. $\frac{4}{10}$, 0.4, $\frac{2}{5}$
5. $\frac{10}{100}$, 0.10, $\frac{1}{10}$
6. $\frac{50}{100}$, 0.50, $\frac{1}{2}$

14–1 Skills Practice
*Tenths and Hundredths*

Write a fraction and a decimal for each shaded part.

1. $\frac{6}{10}$; 0.6
2. $\frac{5}{100}$; 0.05
3. $\frac{77}{100}$; 0.77
4. $\frac{9}{100}$; 0.09

Write each fraction as a decimal.

5. 0.4
6. 0.25
7. 0.5
8. 0.02
9. 0.7
10. 0.07
11. 0.1
12. 0.96
13. two tenths 0.2
14. five tenths 0.5
15. fifteen hundredths 0.15
16. seventeen hundredths 0.17
17. six hundredths 0.06
18. ninety-nine hundredths 0.99
19. three tenths 0.3
20. two tenths 0.2

Write a fraction and a decimal for each point. Tell if it is closer to 0, $\frac{1}{2}$, or 1.

21. A $\frac{1}{10}$; 0.1; 0
22. C $\frac{7}{10}$; 0.7; $\frac{1}{2}$
23. B $\frac{3}{10}$; 0.3; $\frac{1}{2}$
24. D $\frac{8}{10}$; 0.8; 1

Solve.

25. Peter's house is 0.78 mile from school. Write the number in words. seventy-eight hundredths
26. Lora walks for five tenths of an hour. Write the number as a decimal. 0.5

## Practice and Problem Solving

EXTRA PRACTICE See page R36.

**Write a fraction and a decimal for each shaded part.** See Example 1 (p. 579) 15. $\frac{3}{10}$; 0.3

**13.** 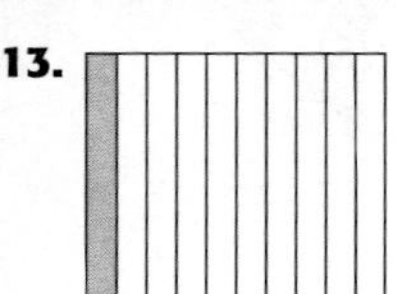 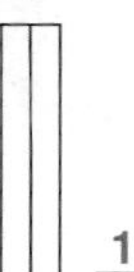 $\frac{1}{10}$; 0.1

**14.** 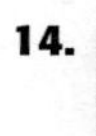 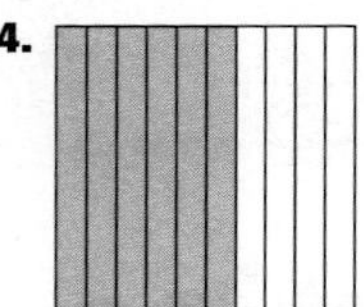 $\frac{6}{10}$; 0.6

**15.** 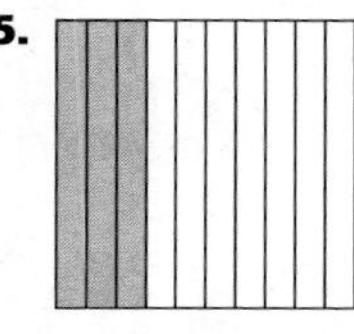

**16.** 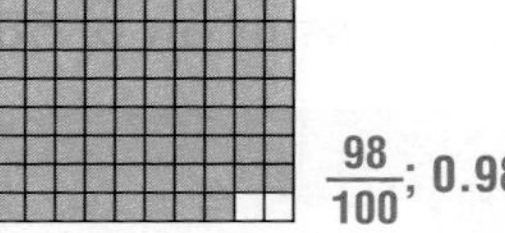 $\frac{98}{100}$; 0.98

**17.** 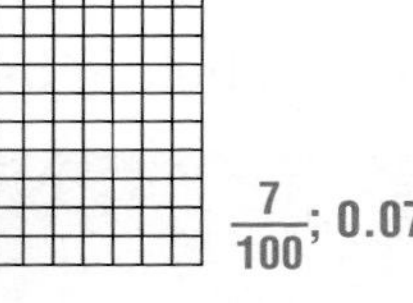 $\frac{7}{100}$; 0.07

**18.** 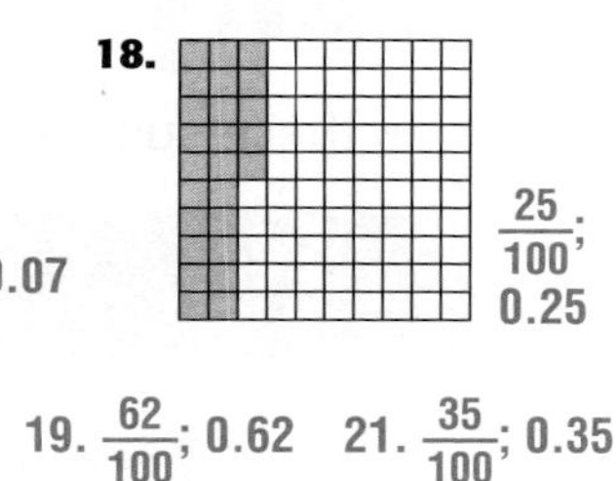 $\frac{25}{100}$; 0.25

**Write as a fraction and as a decimal.** See Example 1 (p. 579) 19. $\frac{62}{100}$; 0.62 21. $\frac{35}{100}$; 0.35

**19.** sixty-two hundredths
**20.** two tenths $\frac{2}{10}$; 0.2
**21.** thirty-five hundredths
**22.** eight tenths $\frac{8}{10}$; 0.8
**23.** fourteen hundredths $\frac{14}{100}$; 0.14
**24.** six tenths $\frac{6}{10}$; 0.6

**Write each fraction as a decimal.** See Example 2 (p. 580)

**25.** $\frac{22}{100}$ 0.22
**26.** $\frac{2}{100}$ 0.02
**27.** $\frac{2}{10}$ 0.2
**28.** $\frac{50}{100}$ 0.50
**29.** $\frac{75}{100}$ 0.75
**30.** $\frac{80}{100}$ 0.80

**31. Measurement** On Monday, it snowed $\frac{6}{10}$ of an inch. 0.6

**32. Measurement** A car traveled $\frac{3}{10}$ of a mile in 18 seconds. 0.3

**33.** Each state has a representation of $\frac{2}{100}$ in the U.S. Senate. 0.02

**34.** Cody learned that $\frac{4}{10}$ of the students in his class are left handed. 0.4

### H.O.T. Problems

**35. OPEN ENDED** Write a fraction whose decimal value is between $\frac{2}{10}$ and $\frac{25}{100}$. Write the fraction and its decimal equivalent. Sample answer: $\frac{22}{100} = 0.22$

**36. CHALLENGE** Decide whether the following sentence is true or false. Explain. *The fraction $\frac{6}{1,000}$ equals 0.006.* 36, 37. See Ch.14 Answer Appendix.

**37. WRITING IN ▶MATH** Write a summary statement about decimals equivalent to fractions that have denominators of 10 and 100.



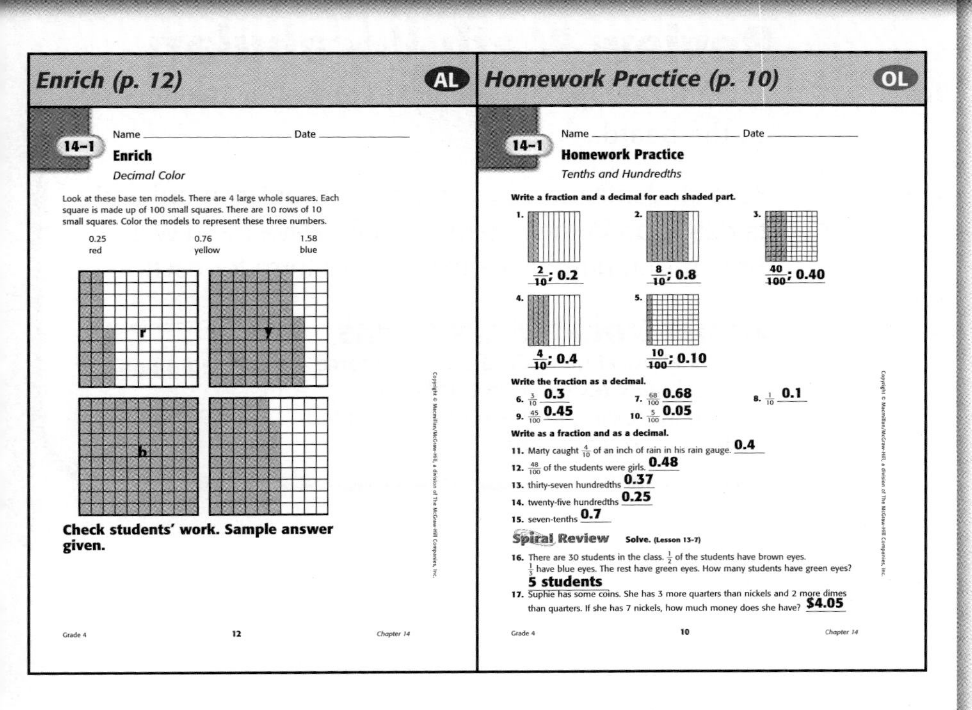
**Enrich (p. 12)** AL

14-1 Name ________ Date ________
**Enrich**
*Decimal Color*

Look at these base ten models. There are 4 large whole squares. Each square is made up of 100 small squares. There are 10 rows of 10 small squares. Color the models to represent these three numbers.

0.25 red 0.76 yellow 1.58 blue

**Check students' work. Sample answer given.**

Grade 4 12 Chapter 14

**Homework Practice (p. 10)** OL

14-1 Name ________ Date ________
**Homework Practice**
*Tenths and Hundredths*

**Write a fraction and a decimal for each shaded part.**

1. $\frac{2}{10}$; 0.2
2. $\frac{8}{10}$; 0.8
3. $\frac{40}{100}$; 0.40
4. $\frac{4}{10}$; 0.4
5. $\frac{10}{100}$; 0.10

**Write the fraction as a decimal.**

6. $\frac{3}{10}$ 0.3
7. $\frac{68}{100}$ 0.68
8. $\frac{1}{10}$ 0.1
9. $\frac{45}{100}$ 0.45
10. $\frac{5}{100}$ 0.05

**Write as a fraction and as a decimal.**

11. Marty caught $\frac{4}{10}$ of an inch of rain in his rain gauge. 0.4
12. $\frac{48}{100}$ of the students were girls. 0.48
13. thirty-seven hundredths 0.37
14. twenty-five hundredths 0.25
15. seven-tenths 0.7

**Spiral Review** Solve. (Lesson 13-7)

16. There are 30 students in the class. $\frac{1}{2}$ of the students have brown eyes. $\frac{1}{3}$ have blue eyes. The rest have green eyes. How many students have green eyes? 5 students
17. Sophie has some coins. She has 3 more quarters than nickels and 2 more dimes than quarters. If she has 7 nickels, how much money does she have? $4.05

Grade 4 10 Chapter 14

## 3 Practice

Differentiate practice using these leveled assignments for Exercises 13–37.

| Level | Assignment |
|---|---|
| BL Below/Approaching Level | 13–16, 19–21, 25–27, 31–32 |
| OL On Level | 14–18, 20–23, 25–29, 31–34, 35 |
| AL Above/Beyond Level | 14–34 even, 35–37 |

Have students discuss and complete the Higher Order Thinking problems. For Exercise 35, encourage them to use a hundredths grid to model $\frac{2}{10}$ and $\frac{25}{100}$.

**WRITING IN ▶MATH** Have students complete Exercise 37 in their Math Journals. You may choose to use this exercise as an optional formative assessment.

## 4 Assess

### Formative Assessment

Write 0.5, 0.50, and 0.05 on the board.

- **Read each decimal.** 5 tenths, 50 hundredths, 5 hundredths
- **How are fractions and decimals alike?** Sample answer: They can each be used to represent a part of a whole.

**Quick Check** **Are students continuing to struggle with tenths and hundredths as decimals?**

**If Yes** → Small Group Options (p. 579B)

**If No** → Independent Work Options (p. 579B)
CRM Skills Practice Worksheet (p. 9)
CRM Enrich Worksheet (p. 12)

**Ticket Out the Door** Write the fractions $\frac{7}{10}$ and $\frac{49}{100}$ on the board. Have students shade in hundredths grids to show each number and write the decimal below. Collect these as students exit the classroom.

LESSON 14-2

# Relate Mixed Numbers and Decimals

## Lesson Planner

### Objective

Identify, read, and write decimals greater than 1.

### Review Vocabulary

**mixed number**

### Resources

**Materials:** WorkMat 6: Place-Value Chart, hundredths grid

**Literature Connection:** *Follow the Money* by Loreen Leedy

**Alternate Lesson:** Use *IMPACT Mathematics:* Unit E to provide practice with mixed numbers and decimals.

**Teacher Technology**
TeacherWorks • Interactive Classroom

### Focus on Math Background

As students have related mixed numbers to improper fractions in Lesson 13-6, they should recognize the similarity with converting mixed numbers to mixed decimals. The use of correct wording should be emphasized, that is, the word "and" should be reserved for indicating the decimal point.

Help students avoid thinking of the decimal point as the "center" of the place-value system. The ones place is the true center, as the place names have a kind of symmetry about the ones:

hundreds tens ones . tenths hundreths

## Daily Routine

Use these suggestions before beginning the lesson on p. 582.

### 5-Minute Check

(Reviews Lesson 13-1)

**Write each as a fraction and as a decimal.**

1. six tenths $\frac{6}{10}$, 0.6
2. fifty-four hundredths $\frac{54}{100}$, 0.54
3. three hundredths $\frac{3}{100}$, 0.03
4. forty hundredths $\frac{40}{100}$, 0.40

### Problem of the Day

Todd finished the homework in $\frac{1}{3}$ of an hour. It took Lori $\frac{2}{5}$ of an hour, Miguel $\frac{2}{6}$ of an hour, and Ramira $\frac{1}{4}$ of an hour. In what order did they finish their homework? Ramira, Todd and Miguel (tie), Lori

### Review Math Vocabulary

Write the review vocabulary word and its definition on the board.

Have students record the review vocabulary word and its definition in their Math Journals. Have them write three mixed numbers and the word form for each.

**Visual Vocabulary Cards**

Use Visual Vocabulary Card 25 to reinforce the vocabulary reviewed in this lesson. (The Define/Example/Ask routine is printed on the back of each card.)

# Differentiated Instruction

## Small Group Options

**Option 1** LOGICAL, VISUAL, SPATIAL

### Below Level BL

**Materials:** dimes, pennies, bills, chart paper

- Review briefly the place-value chart including tens, ones, tenths, and hundredths.
- Give each student one \$5 bill, one \$1 bill, 3 dimes, and 4 pennies.
- **What is the total?** \$6.34
- Write this total on the chart paper.
- Remind students that the bills represent the whole numbers or whole dollars and the coins represent the decimal or fraction of the dollar. Review the fact that dimes are tenths and pennies are hundredths.
- Practice this by assigning the following sums of dollars and cents: \$10.48, \$8.51, \$3.76.

\$10.48

| Ones | | | Hundredths | |
|---|---|---|---|---|
| tens | ones | | tenths | hundredths |
| 1 | 0 | . | 4 | 8 |

\$8.51

| Ones | | | Hundredths | |
|---|---|---|---|---|
| tens | ones | | tenths | hundredths |
| 0 | 8 | . | 5 | 1 |

\$3.76

| Ones | | | Hundredths | |
|---|---|---|---|---|
| tens | ones | | tenths | hundredths |
| 0 | 3 | . | 7 | 6 |

**Option 2** AUDITORY, VISUAL

### English Language Learners ELL

**Materials:** chart paper/butcher paper divided into decimals, pictures, mixed numbers, and fractions.
**Core Vocabulary:** pick out, compare, indicate
**Common Use Verb:** select
**Hear Math** This strategy practices recognizing visual forms from auditory forms.

- Say, "There are many ways to write the same number."
- Say a number. Model different ways to write the number in each section.
- Draw several pictures and forms of different numbers, showing two versions of a least one number.
- Say a number and have students select which pictures or forms indicate that number.

## Independent Work Options

**Option 1** SOCIAL

### Early Finishers

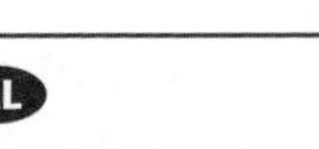

**Materials:** 10 pairs of index cards, with either a mixed number or its equivalent decimal

- Have students work in pairs.
- Have them place the cards facedown on a table.
- Students can play a matching game to find the pairs of numbers that are equivalent.

**Option 2**

### Student Technology

**Math Online** macmillanmh.com

Personal Tutor • Extra Examples

**Option 3**

### Learning Station: Art (p. 594G)

Direct students to the Art Learning Station for opportunities to explore and extend the lesson concept.

**Option 4**

### Problem-Solving Practice

Reinforce problem-solving skills and strategies with the Problem-Solving Practice worksheet.

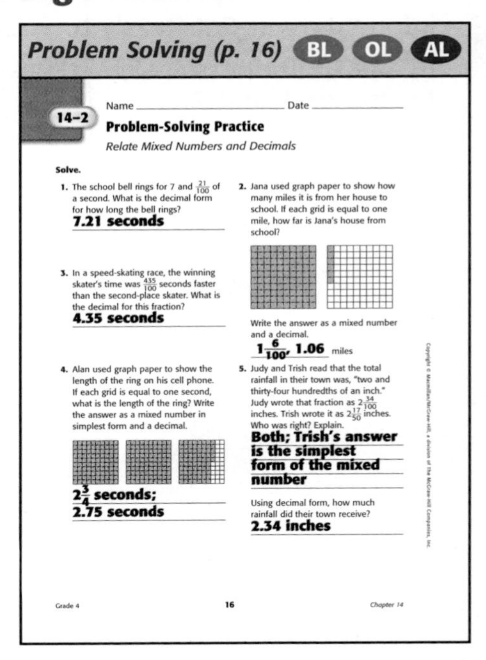

*Problem Solving (p. 16)* BL OL AL

14–2 Name ________ Date ________

**Problem-Solving Practice**

*Relate Mixed Numbers and Decimals*

**Solve.**

1. The school bell rings for 7 and $\frac{21}{100}$ of a second. What is the decimal form for how long the bell rings?
**7.21 seconds**

2. Jana used graph paper to show how many miles it is from her house to school. If each grid is equal to one mile, how far is Jana's house from school?
Write the answer as a mixed number and a decimal.
**$1\frac{6}{100}$, 1.06** miles

3. In a speed-skating race, the winning skater's time was $\frac{435}{100}$ seconds faster than the second-place skater. What is the decimal for this fraction?
**4.35 seconds**

4. Alan used graph paper to show the length of the ring on his cell phone. If each grid is equal to one second, what is the length of the ring? Write the answer as a mixed number in simplest form and a decimal.
**$2\frac{3}{4}$ seconds; 2.75 seconds**

5. Judy and Trish read that the total rainfall in their town was, "two and thirty-four hundredths of an inch." Judy wrote that fraction as $2\frac{34}{100}$ inches. Trish wrote it as $2\frac{17}{50}$ inches. Who was right? Explain.
**Both; Trish's answer is the simplest form of the mixed number**
Using decimal form, how much rainfall did their town receive?
**2.34 inches**



Grade 4 16 Chapter 14

# 14-2 Relate Mixed Numbers and Decimals

## 1 Introduce

### Activity Choice 1 • Hands-On

- Write the following on the board:
  $2\frac{3}{4}, 3\frac{1}{5}, 4\frac{6}{10}, 5\frac{1}{2}$
- Have volunteers come to the board and draw pictorial models of each mixed number.
- **What decimal does $\frac{6}{10}$ represent?** 0.6

### Activity Choice 2 • Literature

Introduce the lesson with *Follow the Money* by Loreen Leedy. For a related math activity, see p. TR64

## 2 Teach

### Scaffolding Questions

Write the number $5.83 on the board.

- **How many dollars are there?** 5
- **How many dimes and pennies are there?** 8 dimes and 3 pennies
- **Without the dollar sign, how is 5.83 read?** five and eighty-three hundredths
- **How would 5.83 be shown as a model?** Sample answer: Shade five whole hundredths grids and 8 rows and 3 squares of a sixth hundredths grid

### GET READY to Learn

Have students open their books and read the information in **Get Ready to Learn**. Review **mixed number**. As a class, work through **Examples 1 and 2**.



# 14-2 Relate Mixed Numbers and Decimals

**MAIN IDEA**

I will identify, read, and write decimals greater than 1.

**Math Online**

macmillanmh.com

- Extra Examples
- Personal Tutor
- Self-Check Quiz

### GET READY to Learn

Giant saguaro (*sah-WAH-ro*) cacti are found in Arizona and Mexico. A saguaro's growth is slow. It takes about 30 years for one to grow $2\frac{5}{10}$ feet tall and start flowering.

A mixed number like $2\frac{5}{10}$ is a fraction greater than one. You can write mixed numbers as decimals.

**EXAMPLE** Mixed Numbers as Decimals

1. **Write $2\frac{5}{10}$ as a decimal.**

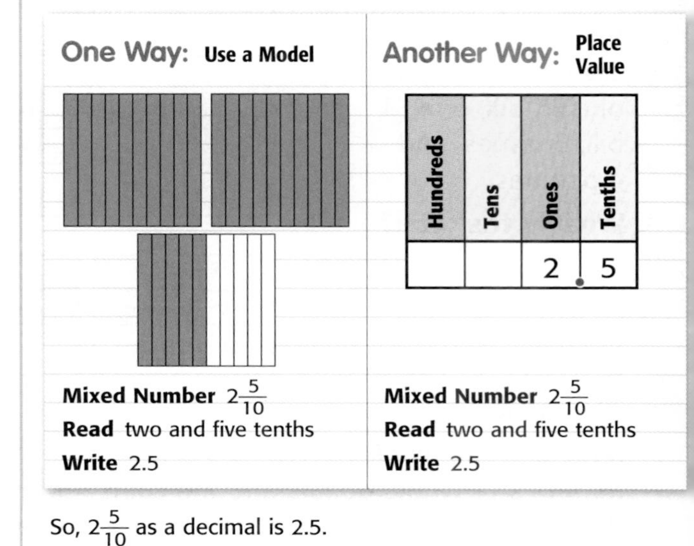


**One Way:** Use a Model

**Mixed Number** $2\frac{5}{10}$
**Read** two and five tenths
**Write** 2.5

**Another Way:** Place Value

**Mixed Number** $2\frac{5}{10}$
**Read** two and five tenths
**Write** 2.5

So, $2\frac{5}{10}$ as a decimal is 2.5.



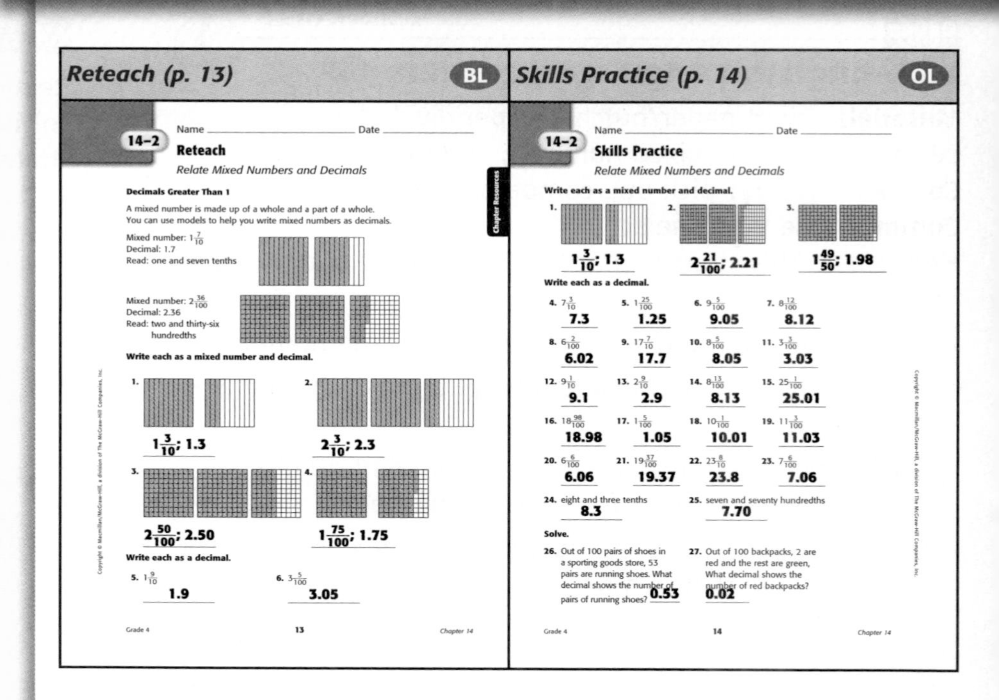

**Reteach (p. 13)** BL

14–2 Name ______ Date ______

**Reteach**

*Relate Mixed Numbers and Decimals*

**Decimals Greater Than 1**

A mixed number is made up of a whole and a part of a whole. You can use models to help you write mixed numbers as decimals.

Mixed number: $1\frac{7}{10}$
Decimal: 1.7
Read: one and seven tenths

Mixed number: $2\frac{36}{100}$
Decimal: 2.36
Read: two and thirty-six hundredths

**Write each as a mixed number and decimal.**

1. $1\frac{3}{10}$; 1.3
2. $2\frac{3}{10}$; 2.3
3. $2\frac{50}{100}$; 2.50
4. $1\frac{75}{100}$; 1.75

**Write each as a decimal.**

5. $1\frac{9}{10}$ 1.9
6. $3\frac{5}{100}$ 3.05

Grade 4 13 Chapter 14



**Skills Practice (p. 14)** OL

14–2 Name ______ Date ______

**Skills Practice**

*Relate Mixed Numbers and Decimals*

**Write each as a mixed number and decimal.**

1. $1\frac{3}{10}$; 1.3
2. $2\frac{21}{100}$; 2.21
3. $1\frac{49}{50}$; 1.98

**Write each as a decimal.**

4. $7\frac{3}{10}$ 7.3
5. $1\frac{25}{100}$ 1.25
6. $9\frac{5}{100}$ 9.05
7. $8\frac{12}{100}$ 8.12
8. $6\frac{2}{100}$ 6.02
9. $17\frac{7}{10}$ 17.7
10. $8\frac{5}{100}$ 8.05
11. $3\frac{3}{100}$ 3.03
12. $9\frac{1}{10}$ 9.1
13. $2\frac{9}{10}$ 2.9
14. $8\frac{13}{100}$ 8.13
15. $25\frac{1}{100}$ 25.01
16. $18\frac{98}{100}$ 18.98
17. $1\frac{5}{100}$ 1.05
18. $10\frac{1}{100}$ 10.01
19. $11\frac{3}{100}$ 11.03
20. $6\frac{6}{100}$ 6.06
21. $19\frac{37}{100}$ 19.37
22. $23\frac{8}{10}$ 23.8
23. $7\frac{6}{100}$ 7.06
24. eight and three tenths 8.3
25. seven and seventy hundredths 7.70

**Solve.**

26. Out of 100 pairs of shoes in a sporting goods store, 53 pairs are running shoes. What decimal shows the number of pairs of running shoes? 0.53
27. Out of 100 backpacks, 2 are red and the rest are green, What decimal shows the number of red backpacks? 0.02

Grade 4 14 Chapter 14

**2 MEASUREMENT The length of an iguana is $1\frac{9}{100}$ yards. Write $1\frac{9}{100}$ as a decimal.**

You can use a model or a place-value chart.

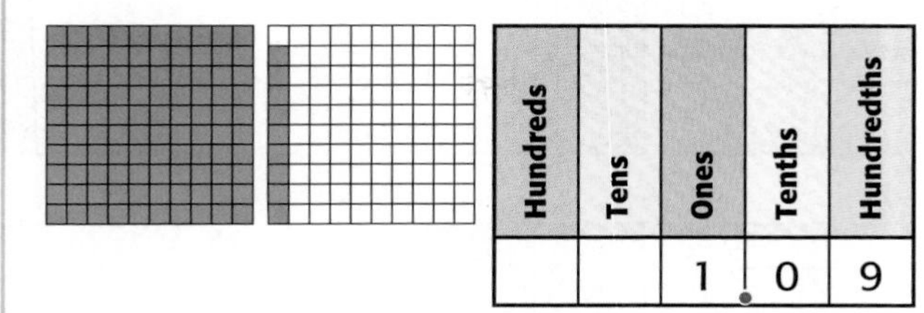

| Hundreds | Tens | Ones | Tenths | Hundredths |
|---|---|---|---|---|
| | | 1 . | 0 | 9 |

**Mixed Number** $1\frac{9}{100}$

**Read** one and nine hundredths

**Write** 1.09

## Remember

When reading a decimal, the word *and* represents the decimal.

12. Sample answer: yes; If each number is modeled on a tenths or hundredths grid, they show the same amount.

## CHECK What You Know

**Write each as a mixed number and decimal.** See Examples 1 and 2 (pp. 582–583)

1. 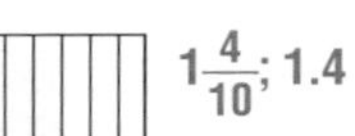 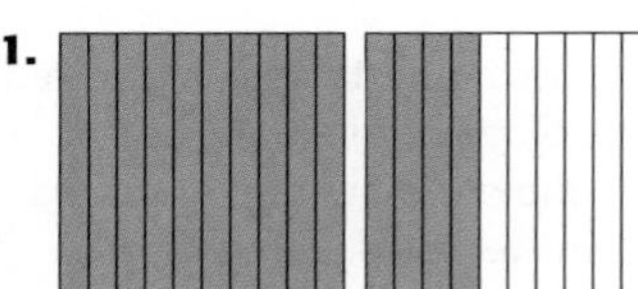 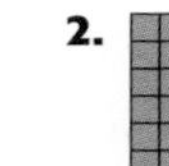 $1\frac{4}{10}$; 1.4
2. 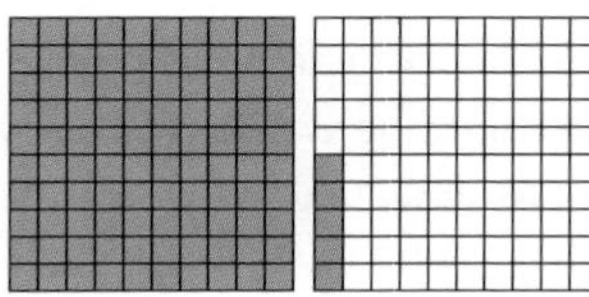 $1\frac{5}{100}$; 1.05
3. twelve and three tenths $12\frac{3}{10}$; 12.3
4. twelve and three hundredths $12\frac{3}{100}$; 12.03
5. three and six tenths $3\frac{6}{10}$; 3.6
6. sixteen and thirty-two hundredths $16\frac{32}{100}$; 16.32

**Write each mixed number as a decimal.** See Examples 1 and 2 (pp. 582–583)

7. $5\frac{3}{10}$ 5.3
8. $12\frac{5}{10}$ 12.5
9. $6\frac{50}{100}$ 6.50
10. $24\frac{8}{100}$ 24.08
11. **Measurement** Jodi ran the 100-meter dash in 14.6 seconds. Tyra ran the 100-meter dash in 14.64 seconds. Write each girl's time as a mixed number. $14\frac{6}{10}$; $14\frac{64}{100}$
12. **Talk About It** Do the numbers $8\frac{5}{10}$, $8\frac{1}{2}$, and 8.5 name the same amount? Explain your reasoning.



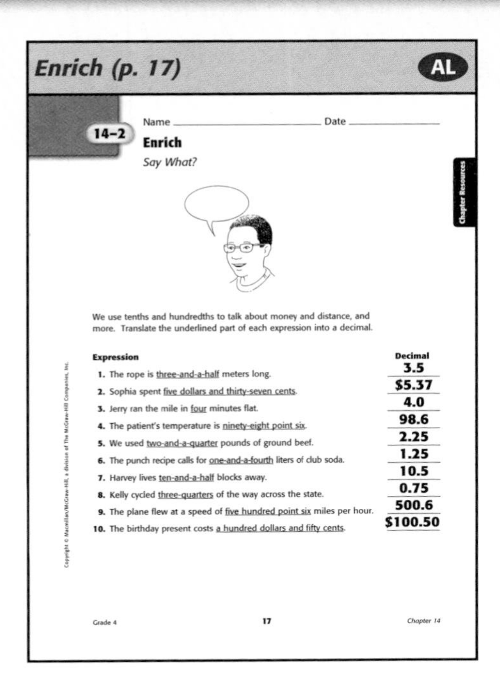

*Enrich (p. 17)* **AL**

**14–2** Name ______________ Date ______________

**Enrich**

*Say What?*

Chapter Resources

We use tenths and hundredths to talk about money and distance, and more. Translate the underlined part of each expression into a decimal.

| Expression | Decimal |
|---|---|
| 1. The rope is three-and-a-half meters long. | 3.5 |
| 2. Sophia spent five dollars and thirty-seven cents. | $5.37 |
| 3. Jerry ran the mile in four minutes flat. | 4.0 |
| 4. The patient's temperature is ninety-eight point six. | 98.6 |
| 5. We used two-and-a-quarter pounds of ground beef. | 2.25 |
| 6. The punch recipe calls for one-and-a-fourth liters of club soda. | 1.25 |
| 7. Harvey lives ten-and-a-half blocks away. | 10.5 |
| 8. Kelly cycled three-quarters of the way across the state. | 0.75 |
| 9. The plane flew at a speed of five hundred point six miles per hour. | 500.6 |
| 10. The birthday present costs a hundred dollars and fifty cents. | $100.50 |



Grade 4 17 Chapter 14

## Mixed Numbers as Decimals

**Example 1** Tell students that in a decimal, the digits to the left of a decimal point are whole numbers and the digits to the right of the decimal point are parts of a whole number.

## ADDITIONAL EXAMPLES

1. Write $3\frac{4}{10}$ as a decimal. 3.4
2. The length of a chameleon is $6\frac{78}{100}$ inches. Write $6\frac{78}{100}$ as a decimal. 6.78

## CHECK What You Know

As a class, have students complete Exercises 1–12 in **Check What You Know** as you observe their work.

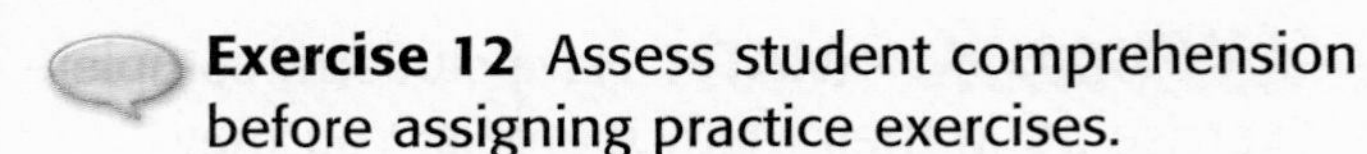

**Exercise 12** Assess student comprehension before assigning practice exercises.

## BL Alternate Teaching Strategy

**If** students have trouble reading and writing decimals with tenths and hundredths correctly…

**Then** use one of these reteach options:

1. CRM **Daily Reteach Worksheet** (p. 13)
2. Have students use place-value charts until they can identify and write the numbers correctly. Write the mixed number $5\frac{8}{100}$ on the board.
   - **What digit is in the ones place?** 5
   - **Are there any tenths?** no
   - **What digit will be in the tenths place?** 0
   - **What digit is in the hundredths place?** 8
   - Repeat using fractions with tenths, tenths and hundredths, and just hundredths.

# 3 Practice

Differentiate practice using these leveled assignments for Exercises 13–36.

| Level | Assignment |
|---|---|
| BL Below/Approaching Level | 15–16, 19–22, 24–25, 27–31 |
| OL On Level | 13–17, 20–26, 28–33, 34 |
| AL Above/Beyond Level | 13–33 odd, 34–36 |

Have students discuss and complete the Higher Order Thinking problems. Encourage them to use hundredths grids to demonstrate their answers.

**WRITING IN MATH** Have students complete Exercise 36 in their Math Journals. You may choose to use this exercise as an optional formative assessment.

### Additional Answers

**19.** $19\frac{100}{100}$; 20

**20.** $56\frac{1}{100}$; 56.01

### COMMON ERROR!

**Exercise 26** Students may fail to notice the denominator of the fraction and write the decimal as 60.2 rather than 60.02. Point out the denominator of 100, and if necessary, have students use a hundredths grid to model the decimal part of the number.

## Practice and Problem Solving

See page R36.

**Write each as a mixed number and decimal.** See Examples 1 and 2 (pp. 582–583)

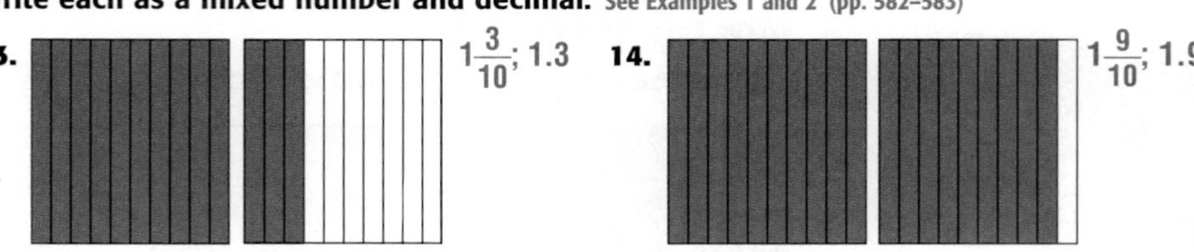

**13.** $1\frac{3}{10}$; 1.3 **14.** $1\frac{9}{10}$; 1.9

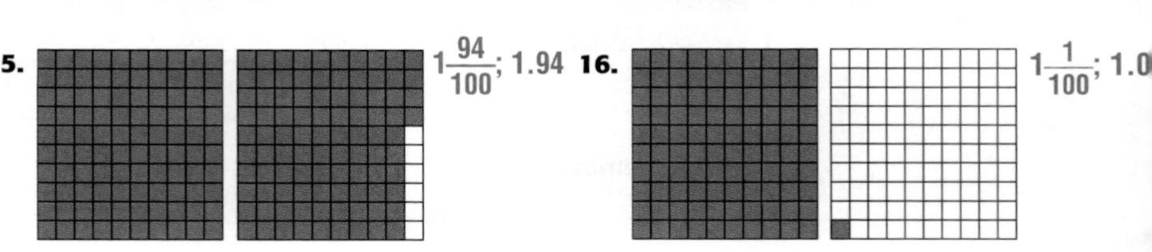

**15.** $1\frac{94}{100}$; 1.94 **16.** $1\frac{1}{100}$; 1.01

**17.** one and five tenths $1\frac{5}{10}$; 1.5

**18.** sixteen and seven tenths $16\frac{7}{10}$; 16.7

**19.** nineteen and one hundred hundredths

**20.** fifty-six and one hundredth

19, 20. See margin.

**Write each mixed number as a decimal.** See Examples 1 and 2 (pp. 582–583)

**21.** $2\frac{5}{10}$ 2.5 **22.** $6\frac{6}{10}$ 6.6 **23.** $50\frac{1}{10}$ 50.1 **24.** $78\frac{8}{10}$ 78.8

**25.** $10\frac{16}{100}$ 10.16 **26.** $60\frac{2}{100}$ 60.02 **27.** $5\frac{25}{100}$ 5.25 **28.** $22\frac{75}{100}$ 22.75

**29. Measurement** Aaron has grown $3\frac{4}{10}$ feet since he was born. Write a decimal to show how many feet Aaron has grown. 3.4 ft

**30. Measurement** Coastal Plains received 5.52 inches of rain. Write a mixed number to show the number of inches Coastal Plains received. $5\frac{52}{100}$ in.

### Data File

The Freedom Trail is a 2.5-mile walking trail in Boston, Massachusetts, that leads to 16 historical sites.

**31.** Guided tours of the Freedom Trail usually last $2\frac{5}{10}$ hours. Write $2\frac{5}{10}$ as a decimal. 2.5

**32.** The Bunker Hill Monument is open from 9 A.M. to 4:30 P.M. Write the number of hours the monument is open as a decimal and a fraction. $7\frac{5}{10}$ and 7.5

Bunker Hill Monument, Boston

## H.O.T. Problems

**33. OPEN ENDED** Write a mixed number and decimal that are less than five and eight tenths. Sample answer: $5\frac{50}{100}$; 5.5

**34. FIND THE ERROR** Brianna and Nick are writing $2\frac{3}{4}$ as a decimal. Who is correct? Explain your reasoning. See margin.

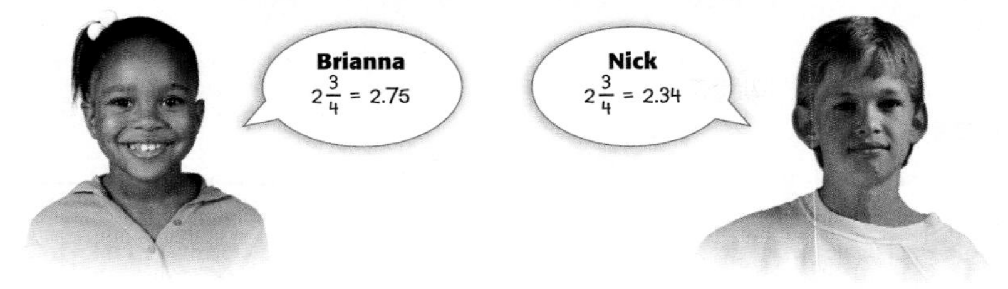


**35. WRITING IN MATH** Are $2\frac{4}{8}$ and 2.5 equivalent? Explain.
Sample answer: 2.5 and $2\frac{4}{8}$ are equal because $2\frac{4}{8} = 2\frac{5}{10}$.

## TEST Practice

**36.** Which number represents the shaded parts of the figure? (Lesson 14-1) B

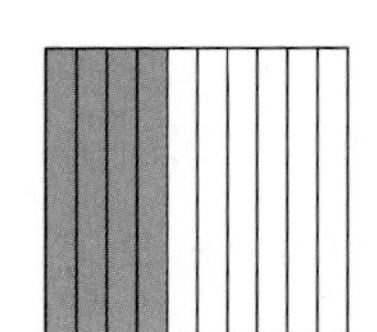

**A** 0.04

**B** 0.4

**C** 4.0

**D** 4.4

**37.** Which of the following is seven and seven hundredths? (Lesson 14-2) G

**F** 0.77

**G** 7.07

**H** 7.7

**J** $7\frac{7}{10}$

## Spiral Review

**Write as a fraction and as a decimal.** (Lesson 14-1)

**38.** five tenths $\frac{5}{10}$; 0.5

**39.** fifty-six hundredths $\frac{56}{100}$; 0.56

**40.** Justino read $\frac{16}{10}$ books this week. How many books did he read written as a mixed number? (Lesson 13-6) $1\frac{6}{10}$

**41. Measurement** Select two containers. Estimate and then measure whether each container has a capacity that is greater than, less than, or equal to 2 liters. (Lesson 12-3) See students' work.



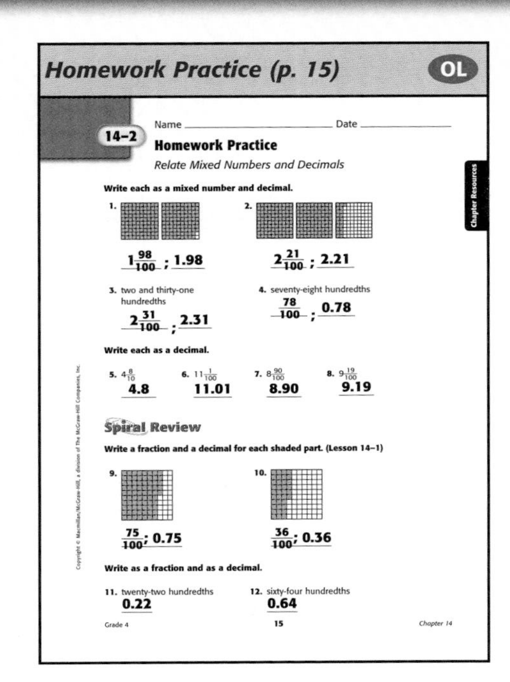

*Homework Practice (p. 15)* OL

14-2 Name ______ Date ______

**Homework Practice**

*Relate Mixed Numbers and Decimals*

**Write each as a mixed number and decimal.**

1. $1\frac{98}{100}$; 1.98

2. $2\frac{21}{100}$; 2.21

3. two and thirty-one hundredths $2\frac{31}{100}$; 2.31

4. seventy-eight hundredths $\frac{78}{100}$; 0.78

**Write each as a decimal.**

5. $4\frac{8}{10}$ 4.8

6. $11\frac{1}{100}$ 11.01

7. $8\frac{90}{100}$ 8.90

8. $9\frac{19}{100}$ 9.19

**Spiral Review**

**Write a fraction and a decimal for each shaded part.** (Lesson 14–1)

9. $\frac{75}{100}$; 0.75

10. $\frac{36}{100}$; 0.36

**Write as a fraction and as a decimal.**

11. twenty-two hundredths 0.22

12. sixty-four hundredths 0.64

Grade 4 15 Chapter 14

# 4 Assess

### Formative Assessment

Write $6\frac{4}{10}$ on the board.

- **Explain how you would write this as a decimal.** Sample answer: Using a place-value chart, put the 6 in the ones place and the 4 in the tenths place.
- **Write $6\frac{4}{10}$ as a decimal.** 6.4

**Quick Check** **Are students continuing to struggle with reading and writing mixed numbers and decimals?**

**If Yes** → Small Group Options (p. 582B)

**If No** → Independent Work Options (p. 582B)
CRM Skills Practice Worksheet (p. 14)
CRM Enrich Worksheet (p. 17)

**Yesterday's News** Ask students how they used yesterday's lesson on tenths and hundredths to help them understand today's lesson on mixed numbers and decimals.

### Reviews Lessons 14-1 and 14-2

Assign the Test Practice problems to provide daily reinforcement of test-taking skills.

## Spiral Review

### Reviews Lessons 12-3, 13-6, and 14-1

Review and assess mastery of skills and concepts from previous chapters.

### Additional Answer

**34.** Sample answer: Brianna; Nick is incorrect because he used the numerator and denominator as the decimal instead of multiplying the numerator and denominator by 25, then changing $\frac{75}{100}$ into .75

# 14-3 Problem-Solving Strategy
## Make a Model

# Lesson Planner

## Objective

Solve problems by making a model.

## Resources

**Manipulatives:** counters

**Literature Connection:** *Gator Pie* by Louise Mathews

**Teacher Technology**

TeacherWorks • Interactive Classroom

**Real-World Problem Solving Library**
**Math and Social Studies:**
***Growing Goods in a Growing Country***

Use these leveled books to reinforce and extend problem-solving skills and strategies.

Leveled for:

- OL On Level
- ELL Sheltered English
- SP Spanish

For additional support, see the Real-World Problem Solving Teacher Guide.

# Daily Routine

Use these suggestions before beginning the lesson on p. 586.

## 5-Minute Check

(Reviews Lesson 14-2)

**Write each as a mixed number and decimal.**

1. sixteen and three tenths $16\frac{3}{10}$; 16.3
2. four and seventy-five hundredths $4\frac{75}{100}$; 4.75
3. thirty-three and seven hundredths $33\frac{7}{100}$; 33.07
4. nine and five tenths $9\frac{5}{10}$ or $9\frac{1}{2}$; 9.5 or 9.50

## Problem of the Day

Maria, Zach, and Jill share a pizza. Maria eats $\frac{1}{6}$, Zach eats $\frac{1}{3}$, and Jill eats $\frac{1}{2}$ of the pizza. Who eats the most? Explain. Jill; $\frac{1}{2} = \frac{3}{6}$, $\frac{1}{3} = \frac{2}{6}$, $\frac{3}{6} > \frac{2}{6} > \frac{1}{6}$

# Differentiated Instruction

## Small Group Options

Option 1 VISUAL, SPATIAL, LOGICAL, SOCIAL 

### Gifted and Talented AL

**Materials:** quarters, dimes, nickels, pennies, chart paper, markers

- Copy the following problem on chart paper:

  *Erica has 7 pennies and 2 dimes. Binta has 2 nickels, 1 dime, and 5 pennies. Caleb has 1 quarter, 2 dimes, and 1 nickel. How can they share these coins so that everyone has the same amount of money?* Erica gives 3 pennies to Caleb. Binta gives 1 penny to Caleb. Caleb gives 1 dime to Erica. Caleb gives 1 dime to Binta. All three now have 34¢.
- Encourage students to use the coins to model the problem. Have them work independently and share their answers with a partner upon completion.

Option 2 INTRAPERSONAL 

### English Language Learners ELL

**Materials:** paper, markers
**Core Vocabulary:** model, locate, prove
**Common Use Verb:** go along with
**Do Math** This strategy practices problem-solving with models and incorporates it with spoken explanation.

- Explain to students that sometimes making a model can help them to solve a problem.
- Give the students paper and markers.
- Have students complete one problem in the practice section and make a model to go along with it. Have students work out their solution on paper. Display and have the students explain their work.

## Independent Work Options

Option 1 LOGICAL 

### Early Finishers OL AL

**Materials:** pencil and paper

- Have students write a word problem about a birthday or other kind of party in which a model can be used to find the solution. Ask them to write their solution and model on a separate piece of paper.

Option 2 

### Student Technology

**Math Online** macmillanmh.com

Personal Tutor • Extra Examples

Option 3

### Learning Station: Art (p. 574G)

Direct students to the Art Learning Station for opportunities to explore and extend the lesson concept.

## 1 Introduce

**Activity Choice 1 • Review**

- Write the following problem on the board:
  *The zoo is 6 miles south of the park. Derick lives 3 miles north of the park. Ravi lives 8 miles south of the park. Jill lives 2 miles south of Derick. How far does each person live from the zoo?* Derick: 9 miles, Ravi: 2 miles, Jill: 7 miles
- **Which strategy would you use to solve this problem?** draw a picture

**Activity Choice 2 • Literature**

Introduce the lesson with *Gator Pie* by Louise Mathews. For a related math activity, see p. R112.

## 2 Teach

Have students read the problem on the birthday party seating chart. Guide them through the problem-solving steps.

**Understand** Using the questions, review what students know and need to find.

**Plan** Have students discuss their strategy.

**Solve** Guide students to use the make a model strategy to solve the problem.

- **If one square table is used, how many people can be seated? if two are used? if three are used?** 16, 20, 24
- **How does crossing off groups of 4 help you to find the solution?** The number of card tables needed is when there are no people left to be seated after crossing off groups of 4.

**Check** Have students look back at the problem to make sure that the answer fits the facts given.

**COMMON ERROR!**

**Exercise 9** Students may forget to add all or part of the original 5 miles plus the 5 miles back to get her brother. Drawing a model can show the total distance she rode.



# 14-3 Problem-Solving Strategy

**MAIN IDEA** I will solve problems by making a model.

Luisa needs to seat 22 guests for her birthday party. They have an oval table that can seat 10 people. They also have square tables that each seat 4 people. How many square tables are needed to seat the guests?

**Understand**

**What facts do you know?**

- An oval table seats 10 people.
- There will be 22 guests altogether.
- Each square table seats 4 people.

**What do you need to find?**

- The number of square tables needed to seat the guests.

**Plan**

You can make a model to see how many tables are needed.

**Solve**

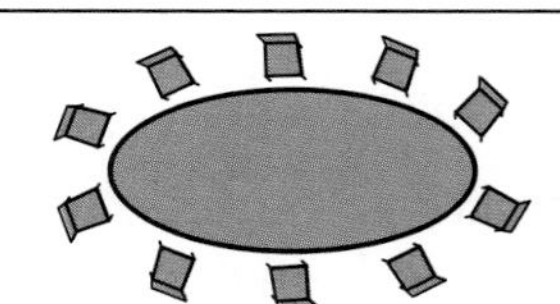

The oval table can seat 10 people.
$22 - 10 = 12$

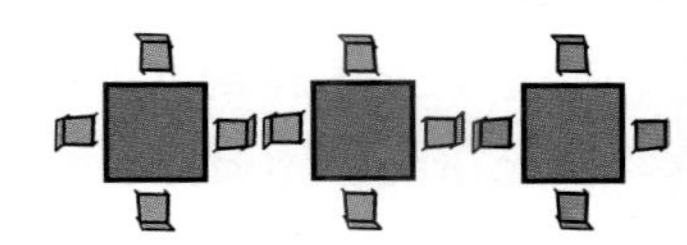

12 people will sit at square tables.
$12 - 12 = 0$

So, three is the fewest number of square tables needed to seat the guests.

**Check**

Look back. The fewest number of square tables needed is 3. This makes sense because $22 - 10 - (3 \times 4) = 0$. So, the answer is correct. ✓



### *Reteach (pp. 18–19)* BL

14-3 Name ________ Date ________

**Reteach**

*Problem-Solving Strategy: Make a Model*

Alicia baked 24 muffins for her class bake sale. They sell for $1 for 4. How much money will she make for her class?

| | |
|---|---|
| **Step 1 Understand** | **Be sure you understand the problem.**<br>What do you know?<br>• Alicia baked **24** muffins.<br>• Muffins sell for **$1** for **4**.<br>• You need to find how much her **muffins will make for the class.** |
| **Step 2 Plan** | **Make a plan.**<br>Make a model by drawing the muffins in groups of 4 with a $1 tag on each group. |
| **Step 3 Solve** | **Carry out your plan.**<br>Add up the $1 tags for all 6 groups.<br>So, 24 muffins will make $6 for the class. |
| **Step 4 Check** | **Is the solution reasonable?**<br>Reread the problem.<br>How can you check your answer? **6 × $1 = $6** |

**Solve using the *make a model* strategy.**

1. Isabel makes and sells pairs of earrings. She uses 5 beads for each earring and charges $0.25 per bead. How much will 10 pairs of earrings sell for? **$25.00**
2. There are 2 elephants in a circus act. In their routines, each act uses 2 other animals. How many animals perform altogether? **6 animals**
3. Mrs. Lee decides to make apple pies. If there are 5 apples in each pie and she makes 4 pies, how many apples will she use altogether? **20 apples**

Grade 4 18 *Chapter 14*



### *Skills Practice (p. 20)* OL

14-3 Name ________ Date ________

**Skills Practice**

*Problem-Solving Strategy: Make a Model*

**Solve. Use the *make a model strategy***

1. There are 4 jars of fingerpaint in a box. Each child will get 2 jars to use to paint. If there is a class of 16 children, how many boxes of paint will they need? **8 boxes**
2. Ron walked to the store which was 8 blocks away. Then he walked 6 blocks to the park. He had to stop back at the store because he forgot to get something, and then he went home. How many blocks did he walk? **28 blocks**
3. There were 3 cats at the pet shop. The first cat had 6 kittens. The other two cats each had 8 kittens. What was the total number of cats in the pet shop after the kittens were born? **25 cats**
4. Elena needs to make three dresses. If one dress requires $2\frac{1}{4}$ yards of fabric, how many yards will Elena need for three dresses? **$6\frac{3}{4}$ yards**
5. If you have a box of 96 crayons that you want to share with 11 classmates, how many crayons will each classmate receive? Hint: Don't forget to keep crayons for yourself. **8 crayons**
6. Write a problem that can be solved by making a model. Then, ask a classmate to solve the problem. **Check students' answers.**

Grade 4 20 *Chapter 14*

## ANALYZE the Strategy

**Refer to the problem on the previous page.**

1. Explain how a model was used to find the fewest number of tables.
2. Explain another strategy you could use to solve Luisa's problem.

**1, 2. See Ch. 14 Answer Appendix.**

3. Suppose there were 30 guests. How many square tables would be needed? **5 square tables**
4. Look back at Exercise 3. Check your answer. How do you know that it is correct? Show your work. **Sample answer: 30 – 10 = 20, 20 ÷ 4 = 5**

★ indicates multi-step problem

## PRACTICE the Strategy

**Solve. Use the make a model strategy.**

★5. Eileen opened 8 boxes of clay for her project. Each box had 4 sticks of gray clay and half as many sticks of red clay. How many sticks of clay were there in all? **48 sticks**

6. Cesar is making a model of the longest bridge in the table for a school project. The scale he is using is one inch equals 200 feet. How many inches long will the model be? **21 in.**

| Bridges | |
|---|---|
| **Bridge** | **Length (ft)** |
| Drawbridge | 4,200 |
| Suspension Bridge | 3,478 |
| Cable-Stayed Bridge | 2,310 |

★7. **Measurement** Katia is painting her living room. The room has 3 walls that are 16 feet long and 9 feet tall. A gallon of paint covers 150 square feet. How many gallons should she buy to cover all 3 walls? **3 gallons**

8. **Measurement** Every day Marvin runs 3,200 meters around the school track. How many times does he run around the track? **8**

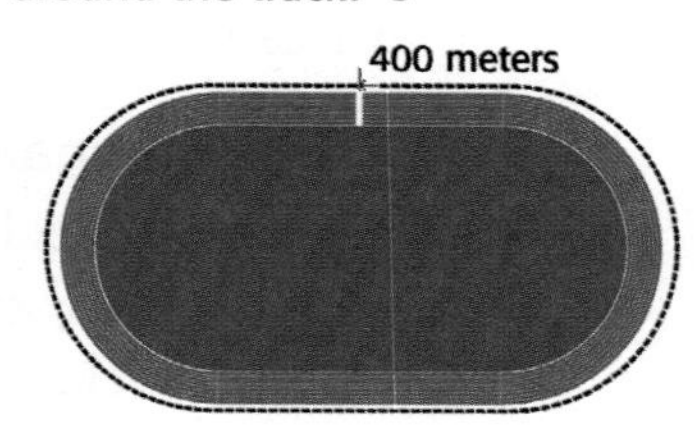


9. Mariana rode her bike 5 miles. Then she went back to get her brother. They rode together for 17 miles. How far did Mariana go altogether? **27 miles**

10. ★ A volleyball court measures 18 meters by 9 meters. A basketball court measures 29 meters by 15 meters. How many volleyball courts could be placed in a basketball court? **1**

11. **WRITING IN MATH** The bottom layer of a pyramid-shaped display has four boxes. There is one less box in each layer. There are four layers. The answer is 10. What is the question? **See Ch. 14 Answer Appendix.**



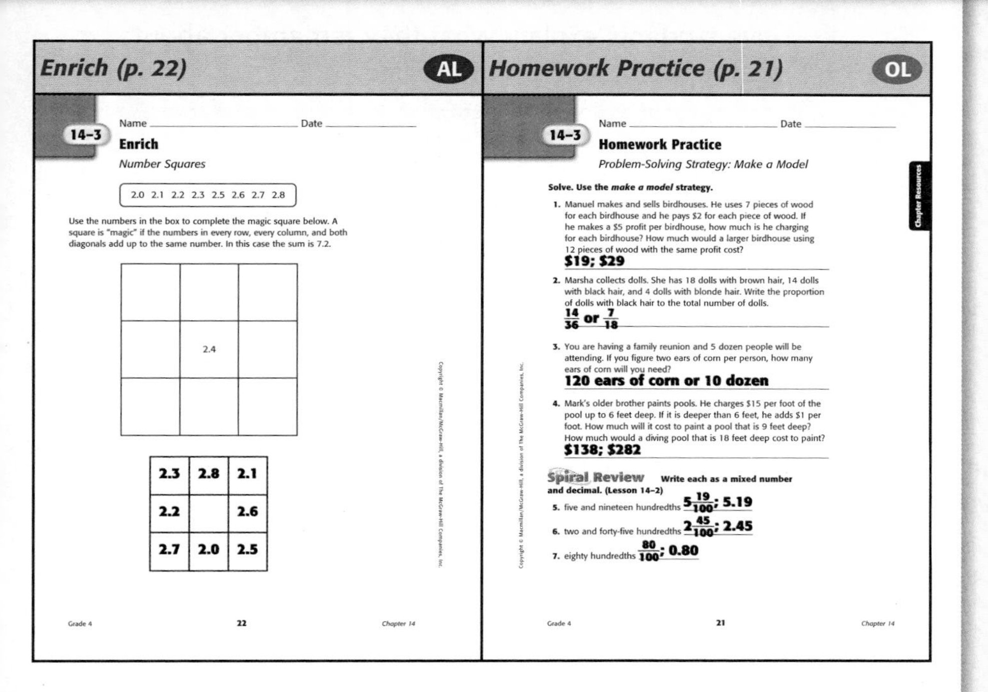

### Enrich (p. 22) AL

14-3 Name ______________ Date ______________

**Enrich**

*Number Squares*

2.0 2.1 2.2 2.3 2.5 2.6 2.7 2.8

Use the numbers in the box to complete the magic square below. A square is "magic" if the numbers in every row, every column, and both diagonals add up to the same number. In this case the sum is 7.2.

| | | |
|---|---|---|
| | | |
| | 2.4 | |
| | | |

| | | |
|---|---|---|
| **2.3** | **2.8** | **2.1** |
| **2.2** | | **2.6** |
| **2.7** | **2.0** | **2.5** |





### Homework Practice (p. 21) OL

14-3 Name ______________ Date ______________

**Homework Practice**

*Problem-Solving Strategy: Make a Model*

**Solve. Use the *make a model* strategy.**

1. Manuel makes and sells birdhouses. He uses 7 pieces of wood for each birdhouse and he pays $2 for each piece of wood. If he makes a $5 profit per birdhouse, how much is he charging for each birdhouse? How much would a larger birdhouse using 12 pieces of wood with the same profit cost?
**$19; $29**
2. Marsha collects dolls. She has 18 dolls with brown hair, 14 dolls with black hair, and 4 dolls with blonde hair. Write the proportion of dolls with black hair to the total number of dolls.
$\frac{14}{36}$ **or** $\frac{7}{18}$
3. You are having a family reunion and 5 dozen people will be attending. If you figure two ears of corn per person, how many ears of corn will you need?
**120 ears of corn or 10 dozen**
4. Mark's older brother paints pools. He charges $15 per foot of the pool up to 6 feet deep. If it is deeper than 6 feet, he adds $1 per foot. How much will it cost to paint a pool that is 9 feet deep? How much would a diving pool that is 18 feet deep cost to paint?
**$138; $282**

**Spiral Review** **Write each as a mixed number and decimal. (Lesson 14-2)**

5. five and nineteen hundredths $5\frac{19}{100}$; **5.19**
6. two and forty-five hundredths $2\frac{45}{100}$; **2.45**
7. eighty hundredths $\frac{80}{100}$; **0.80**

Chapter Resources





**Analyze the Strategy** Use Exercises 1–4 to analyze and discuss the problem-solving strategy.

### BL Alternate Teaching Strategy

**If** students have trouble with making a model…

**Then** use one of these reteach options:

1. CRM **Daily Reteach Worksheet** (pp. 18–19)
2. Have them use manipulatives to make their model. For example, have students use colored counters to show each problem. They can move the counters appropriately as each fact in the problem is read.

## 3 Practice

### Using the Exercises

**Exercise 7** requires students to first find the area of one wall, and then multiply by 3 to find the total area to be painted before dividing or estimating to find the number of gallons of paint required.

**Exercise 10** assumes that students understand that the dimensions of the volleyball and basketball courts must remain unchanged as the solution to the problem is found.

## 4 Assess

### Formative Assessment

Have students make a model to solve the following problem:

*Julia went on a hike with her family. They started their hike at 2,000 ft above sea level and climbed to 4,000 ft. They then descended to 3,000 ft and climbed back up to 6,500 ft. How many feet did they hike uphill?* 5,500 ft

**Quick Check** **Are students continuing to struggle with making a model to solve problems?**

**If Yes** → CRM Reteach Worksheet (pp. 18–19)

**If No** → Independent Work Options (p. 586B)
CRM Skills Practice Worksheet (p. 20)
CRM Enrich Worksheet (p. 22)

LESSON 14-4

# Locate Fractions and Decimals on a Number Line

## Lesson Planner

### Objective

Locate fractions and decimals on a number line.

### Review Vocabulary

**number line**

### Resources

**Materials:** number lines

**Literature Connection:** *Twizzlers Percentages Book* by Jerry Pallotta

**Alternate Lesson:** Use *IMPACT Mathematics:* Unit E to provide practice with decimals.

**Teacher Technology**

TeacherWorks • Interactive Classroom • Concepts in Motion

## Daily Routine

Use these suggestions before beginning the lesson on p. 588.

### 5-Minute Check

(Reviews Lessons 14-3)

**Solve. Use the make a model strategy.**

Adriana jogged six blocks north, three blocks west, two blocks south, and then seven blocks north. How many blocks north did she jog? 13 blocks north; See students' models.

### Problem of the Day

Maria is making 3 necklaces each of which uses 89 beads, and 3 bracelets each of which uses 75 beads. How many beads will she need in all? 492 beads

### Focus on Math Background

In Grade 3, students named missing fractions in a set of labeled points on a number line. In this lesson, they must name points representing fractions and mixed numbers when no labels are provided other than whole numbers.

Students should understand that the denominator of a fraction identifies the number of equal parts in a whole. Thus, the number line pictured here is subdivided into sixths, because there are 6 subdivisions or equal-size spaces between 2 and 3.

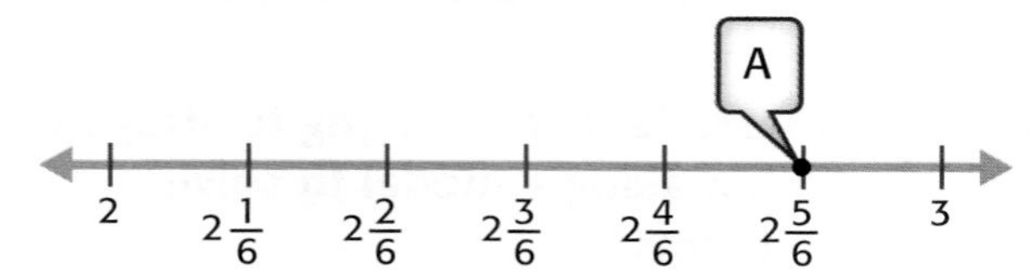


The numerator of a fraction counts the number of equal parts, so point A is located at a point that is $\frac{5}{6}$ of the way from 2 to 3. Point A represents $2\frac{5}{6}$.

### Building Math Vocabulary

Write the lesson review vocabulary term and its definition on the board.

Have students explain what they remember about locating points on a number line.

# Differentiated Instruction

## Small Group Options

LOGICAL

### Option 1 Gifted and Talented AL

**Materials:** chart paper, markers, paper, pencils

- Draw a large number line on the chart paper, but do not label any numbers on it. Draw a rectangle under and away from the number line. Write the following numbers in the number bank you created with the rectangle: $1\frac{3}{4}$, 3.5, $2\frac{1}{2}$, 1.25, $3\frac{1}{4}$
- Tell the students that their task is to place whole numbers on this number line and then put these numbers on it as well. The whole numbers that should appear are 1, 2, 3, possibly 4. Each of the decimals or mixed numbers should be in the proper place.

SPATIAL, KINESTHETIC

### Option 2 English Language Learners ELL

**Materials:** lined paper, pencils, scissors, tape
**Core Vocabulary:** central line, left/right side, vertical/horizontal
**Common Use Verb:** determine
**Do Math** This strategy helps students determine fraction and decimal placements on a number line.

- Have pairs cut and tape vertical strips together so there are 100 or more horizontal lines running from top to bottom like a thermometer. Label zero and 100 and cut on the zero and 100 lines so all strips are exactly 100 lines long.
- Draw a central line. On the left, write the appropriate two-digit decimal (.01, .02, etc.).
- Write: "$\frac{1}{2}$." Have students write "$\frac{1}{2}$" across the line from the decimal 0.50.
- Model folding the strip to determine where the fraction would go for fractions that are not in base ten. Discuss equivalents and other ways to figure out where they would be placed.
- Repeat as time permits.

## Independent Work Options

VISUAL, SPATIAL

### Option 1 Early Finishers AL

**Materials:** paper and pencil

- Have students draw their own number lines using halves, fourths, fifths, or tenths.
- Tell them to label a point on the number line with a letter and then exchange papers with another student in class. That student is to name the labeled point as a fraction and as a decimal.
- Students should agree on answers.

### Option 2 Student Technology

Math Online macmillanmh.com

Personal Tutor • Extra Examples

Math Adventures

### Option 3 Learning Station: Writing (p. 574G)

Direct students to the Writing Learning Station for opportunities to explore and extend the lesson concept.

### Option 4 Problem-Solving Practice

Reinforce problem-solving skills and strategies with the Problem-Solving Practice worksheet.

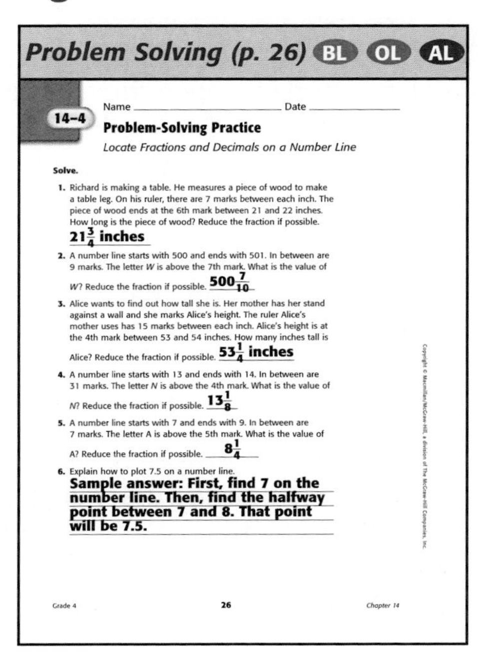

Problem Solving (p. 26) BL OL AL

14–4 Name ______ Date ______

**Problem-Solving Practice**

*Locate Fractions and Decimals on a Number Line*

**Solve.**

1. Richard is making a table. He measures a piece of wood to make a table leg. On his ruler, there are 7 marks between each inch. The piece of wood ends at the 6th mark between 21 and 22 inches. How long is the piece of wood? Reduce the fraction if possible. **$21\frac{3}{4}$ inches**
2. A number line starts with 500 and ends with 501. In between are 9 marks. The letter *W* is above the 7th mark. What is the value of *W*? Reduce the fraction if possible. **$500\frac{7}{10}$**
3. Alice wants to find out how tall she is. Her mother has her stand against a wall and she marks Alice's height. The ruler Alice's mother uses has 15 marks between each inch. Alice's height is at the 4th mark between 53 and 54 inches. How many inches tall is Alice? Reduce the fraction if possible. **$53\frac{1}{4}$ inches**
4. A number line starts with 13 and ends with 14. In between are 31 marks. The letter *N* is above the 4th mark. What is the value of *N*? Reduce the fraction if possible. **$13\frac{1}{8}$**
5. A number line starts with 7 and ends with 9. In between are 7 marks. The letter A is above the 5th mark. What is the value of A? Reduce the fraction if possible. **$8\frac{1}{4}$**
6. Explain how to plot 7.5 on a number line. **Sample answer: First, find 7 on the number line. Then, find the halfway point between 7 and 8. That point will be 7.5.**



Grade 4 26 Chapter 14

# 14-4 Locate Fractions and Decimals on a Number Line

## 1 Introduce

### Activity Choice 1 • Hands-On

- Write the following numbers on the board: 240, 265, 300, 320.
- Have students work in groups to draw and locate points on a number line.
- What did you count by to locate the points? Answers can vary.
- Have one student from each group draw that group's number line on the board.

### Activity Choice 2 • Literature

Introduce the lesson with *Twizzlers Percentages Book* by Jerry Pallotta. For additional support, see p. TR65.

## 2 Teach

### Scaffolding Questions

Write the mixed number $4\frac{5}{10}$ on the board.

- **Between what two whole numbers would you find $4\frac{5}{10}$?** 4 and 5
- Show students how to draw a number line by dividing the space between 4 and 5 into tenths.
- **How would you locate $4\frac{5}{10}$ on the number line?** Count over 5 marks from the 4.
- **What decimal does this represent?** 4.5

### GET READY to Learn

Have students open their books and read the information in Get Ready to Learn. Review **number line**. As a class, work through **Examples 1 and 2**.

*You may want to use coins and remind students that one quarter is equal to $0.25, therefore $\frac{1}{4} = 0.25$.

### COMMON ERROR!

**Exercises 6 and 8** Students may have trouble identifying the markings as fifths. Remind them to count the number of equal-sized spaces between the whole numbers to help determine the denominator.

---

# 14-4 Locate Fractions and Decimals on a Number Line

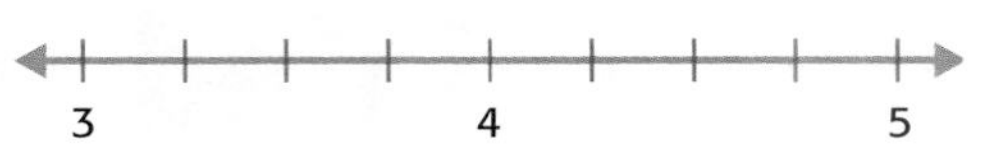

**MAIN IDEA**

I will locate fractions and decimals on a number line.

**Math Online**
macmillanmh.com
- Extra Examples
- Personal Tutor
- Self-Check Quiz

Curtis is trying to find $4\frac{1}{4}$ on the number line. He knows that the point is between 4 and 5.

3 4 5

You can locate fractions and decimals on a number line. Use the markings between the whole numbers to determine the fraction or decimal value of a certain point on a number line.

**EXAMPLE** Locate Points on a Number Line

**1 Locate $4\frac{1}{4}$ on the number line.**

First find 4. Then, find the $\frac{1}{2}$ mark between 4 and 5.
Finally, find the $\frac{1}{4}$ mark halfway between 4 and $4\frac{1}{2}$.

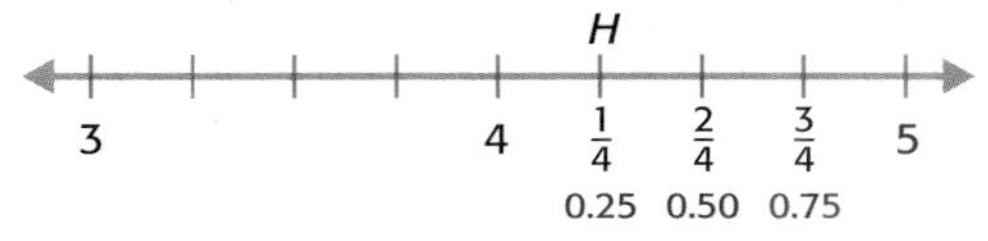


Points on a number line can be represented by a letter. So, $H = 4\frac{1}{4}$ or 4.25.

**EXAMPLE** Name Points on a Number Line

**2 What number does point $N$ represent on the number line?**

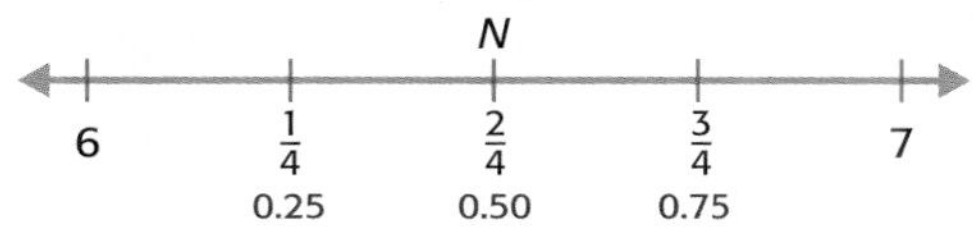


Since $N$ is between 6 and 7, you know $N$ represents a fraction or decimal. The three marks between 6 and 7 let you know the denominator will be 4. Make equivalent fractions to determine the decimal. So, $N$ is $6\frac{2}{4}$ or 6.5

588 Chapter 14 Use Place Value to Represent Decimals

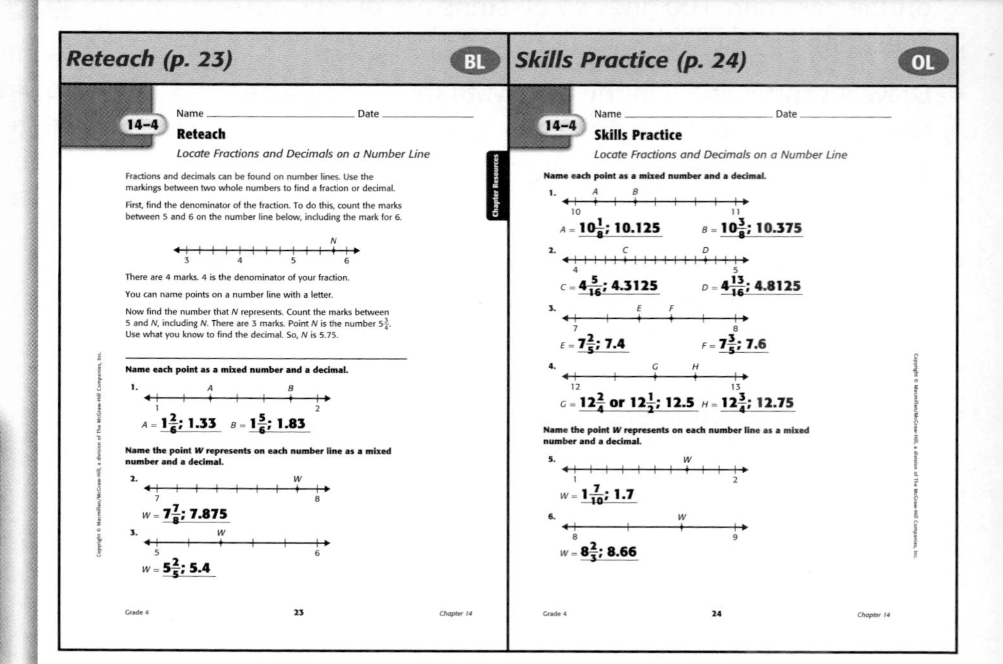

**Reteach (p. 23)** BL

14-4 Name ________ Date ________

**Reteach**

*Locate Fractions and Decimals on a Number Line*

Fractions and decimals can be found on number lines. Use the markings between two whole numbers to find a fraction or decimal.

First, find the denominator of the fraction. To do this, count the marks between 5 and 6 on the number line below, including the mark for 6.

There are 4 marks. 4 is the denominator of your fraction.

You can name points on a number line with a letter.

Now find the number that $N$ represents. Count the marks between 5 and $N$, including $N$. There are 3 marks. Point $N$ is the number $5\frac{3}{4}$. Use what you know to find the decimal. So, $N$ is 5.75.

**Name each point as a mixed number and a decimal.**

1. $A = 1\frac{2}{6}$; 1.33  $B = 1\frac{5}{6}$; 1.83

**Name the point $W$ represents on each number line as a mixed number and a decimal.**

2. $W = 7\frac{7}{8}$; 7.875
3. $W = 5\frac{2}{5}$; 5.4

Grade 4 23 Chapter 14

Chapter Resources



**Skills Practice (p. 24)** OL

14-4 Name ________ Date ________

**Skills Practice**

*Locate Fractions and Decimals on a Number Line*

**Name each point as a mixed number and a decimal.**

1. $A = 10\frac{1}{8}$; 10.125  $B = 10\frac{3}{8}$; 10.375
2. $C = 4\frac{5}{16}$; 4.3125  $D = 4\frac{13}{16}$; 4.8125
3. $E = 7\frac{2}{5}$; 7.4  $F = 7\frac{3}{5}$; 7.6
4. $G = 12\frac{2}{4}$ or $12\frac{1}{2}$; 12.5  $H = 12\frac{3}{4}$; 12.75

**Name the point $W$ represents on each number line as a mixed number and a decimal.**

5. $W = 1\frac{7}{10}$; 1.7
6. $W = 8\frac{2}{3}$; 8.66

Grade 4 24 Chapter 14

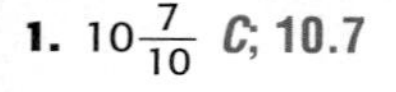

## CHECK What You Know

**Tell which letter represents each mixed number on the number line. Write as a decimal.** See Example 1 (p. 588)

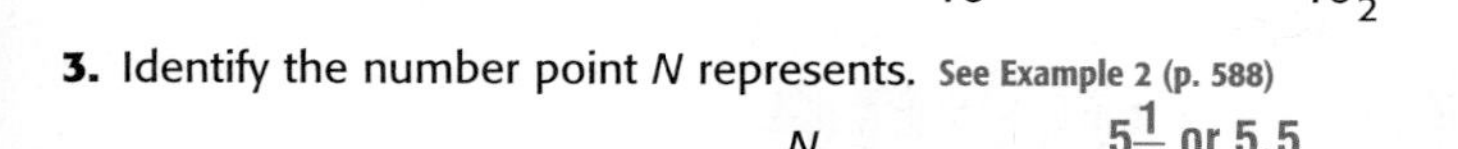

**1.** $10\frac{7}{10}$ *C*; **10.7** **2.** $10\frac{2}{10}$ *A*; **10.2**



**3.** Identify the number point *N* represents. See Example 2 (p. 588)

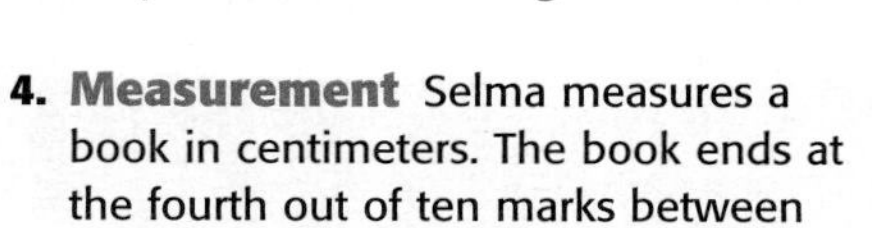
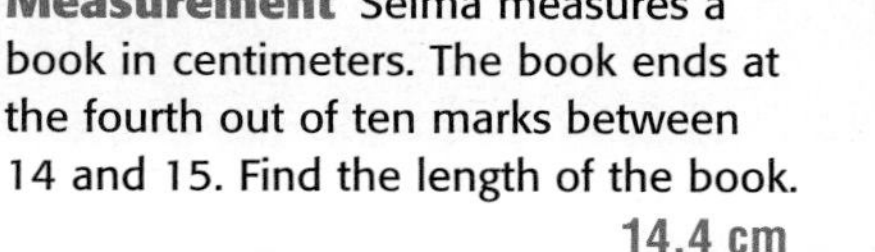


**$5\frac{1}{2}$ or 5.5**

**4. Measurement** Selma measures a book in centimeters. The book ends at the fourth out of ten marks between 14 and 15. Find the length of the book. **14.4 cm**

**5.** 

Explain the difference between finding $\frac{1}{2}$ on a number line and finding the halfway point on a number line. **See Ch. 14 Answer Appendix.**

## Practice and Problem Solving

EXTRA PRACTICE See page R37.

**Tell which letter represents each mixed number on the number line. Write as a decimal.** See Example 1 (p. 588)

**6.** $12\frac{1}{2}$ *F*; **12.5** **7.** $12\frac{3}{4}$ *G*; **12.75**

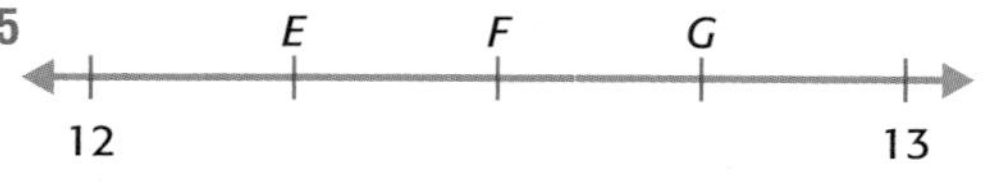


**8.** $2\frac{3}{5}$ *Y*; **2.6** **9.** $2\frac{1}{5}$ *X*; **2.2**

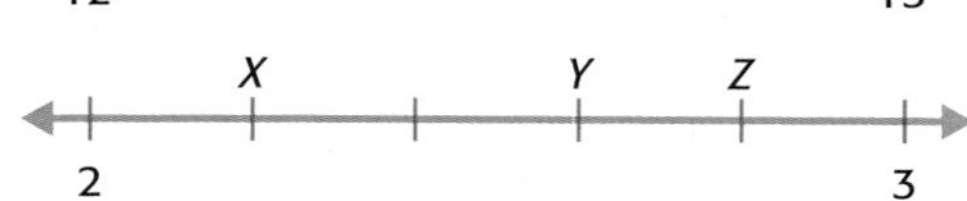


**Identify the number point *N* represents.** See Example 2 (p. 588)

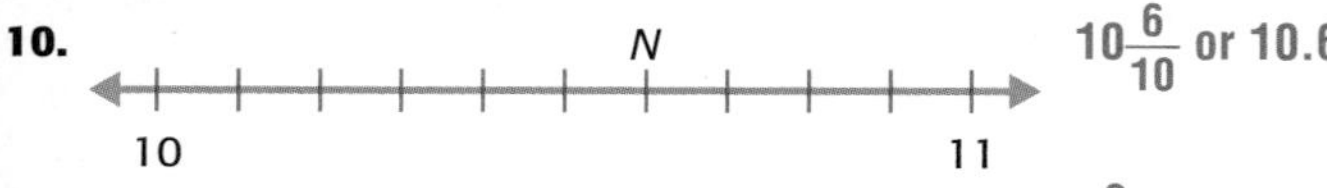

**10.** **$10\frac{6}{10}$ or 10.6**



**11.** **$8\frac{2}{5}$ or 8.4**



### H.O.T. Problems

**12. OPEN ENDED** Create a number line that shows four points. One point must be $12\frac{3}{4}$. **12, 13. See Ch. 14 Answer Appendix.**

**13. WRITING IN MATH** Explain how to show 2.5 on a number line.



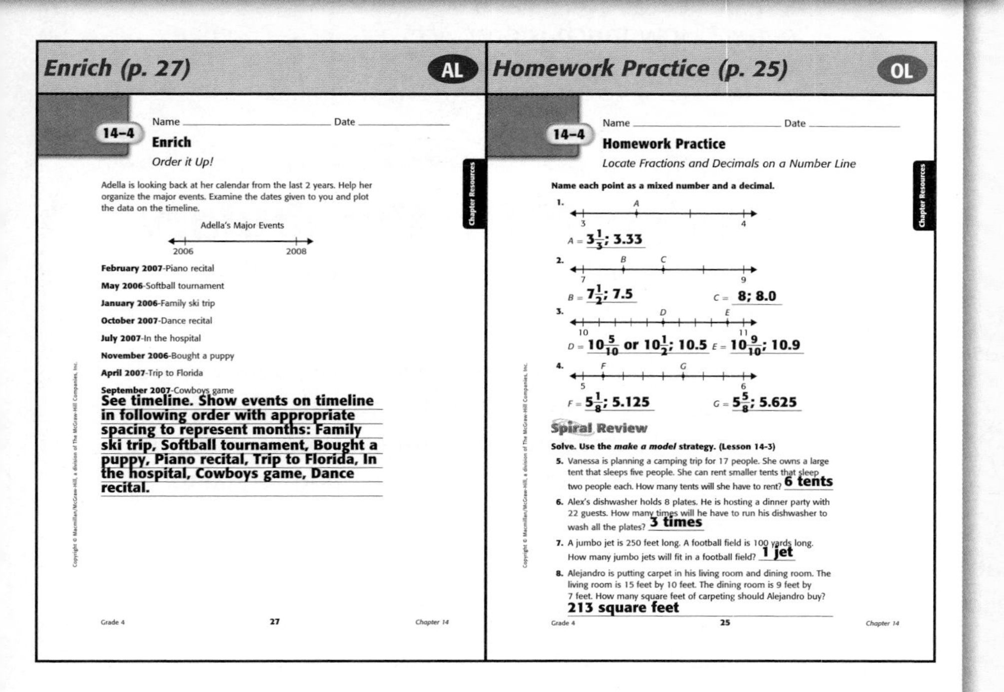

**Enrich (p. 27)** AL

14–4 Name ______ Date ______

**Enrich**

*Order it Up!*

Adella is looking back at her calendar from the last 2 years. Help her organize the major events. Examine the dates given to you and plot the data on the timeline.

Adella's Major Events

2006 2008

**February 2007**-Piano recital

**May 2006**-Softball tournament

**January 2006**-Family ski trip

**October 2007**-Dance recital

**July 2007**-In the hospital

**November 2006**-Bought a puppy

**April 2007**-Trip to Florida

**September 2007**-Cowboys game

**See timeline. Show events on timeline in following order with appropriate spacing to represent months: Family ski trip, Softball tournament, Bought a puppy, Piano recital, Trip to Florida, In the hospital, Cowboys game, Dance recital.**

Grade 4 27 Chapter 14

**Homework Practice (p. 25)** OL

14–4 Name ______ Date ______

**Homework Practice**

*Locate Fractions and Decimals on a Number Line*

**Name each point as a mixed number and a decimal.**

1. A = **$3\frac{1}{3}$; 3.33**

2. B = **$7\frac{1}{2}$; 7.5** C = **8; 8.0**

3. D = **$10\frac{5}{10}$ or $10\frac{1}{2}$; 10.5** E = **$10\frac{9}{10}$; 10.9**

4. F = **$5\frac{1}{8}$; 5.125** G = **$5\frac{5}{8}$; 5.625**

**Spiral Review**

**Solve. Use the *make a model* strategy. (Lesson 14-3)**

5. Vanessa is planning a camping trip for 17 people. She owns a large tent that sleeps five people. She can rent smaller tents that sleep two people each. How many tents will she have to rent? **6 tents**

6. Alex's dishwasher holds 8 plates. He is hosting a dinner party with 22 guests. How many times will he have to run his dishwasher to wash all the plates? **3 times**

7. A jumbo jet is 250 feet long. A football field is 100 yards long. How many jumbo jets will fit in a football field? **1 jet**

8. Alejandro is putting carpet in his living room and dining room. The living room is 15 feet by 10 feet. The dining room is 9 feet by 7 feet. How many square feet of carpeting should Alejandro buy? **213 square feet**

Grade 4 25 Chapter 14

### CHECK What You Know

As a class, have students complete Exercises 1–5 in **Check What You Know** as you observe their work.

**Exercise 5** Assess student comprehension before assigning practice exercises.

BL

### Alternate Teaching Strategy

**If** students have trouble finding points on a number line…

**Then** use one of these reteach options:

1 CRM **Daily Reteach Worksheet** (p. 23)

2 Have students draw number lines showing halves, fourths, fifths, and tenths along with their decimal equivalents. Have students refer to these cards when doing problems.

## 3 Practice

Differentiate practice using these leveled assignments for Exercises 6–13.

| Level | Assignment |
|---|---|
| BL Below/Approaching Level | 6–7, 10 |
| OL On Level | 7–9, 11, 12 |
| AL Above/Beyond Level | 6–10 even, 12–13 |

## 4 Assess

### Formative Assessment

- **How would you locate the point $2\frac{3}{4}$ on a number line? Explain.** Sample answer: Between 2 and 3, divide the space into 4 equal spaces. The mark closest to 3 represents $2\frac{3}{4}$.
- **What decimal does this represent?** 2.75

**Quick Check** **Are students continuing to struggle with naming fractions and decimals on a number line?**

**If Yes** → Small Group Options (p. 588B)
Strategic Intervention Guide (p. 110)

**If No** → Independent Work Options (p. 588B)
CRM Skills Practice Worksheet (p. 24)
CRM Enrich Worksheet (p. 27)

LESSON 14-5

# Compare and Order Decimals

## Lesson Planner

### Objective

Compare and order decimals.

### Review Vocabulary

**compare, order**

### Resources

**Materials:** hundredths grids, number lines

**Manipulatives:** money

**Literature Connection:** *The Toothpaste Millionaire* by Jean Merrill

**Alternate Lesson:** Use *IMPACT Mathematics:* Unit E to provide practice with decimals.

**Teacher Technology**
TeacherWorks • Interactive Classroom

### Focus on Math Background

Students should see a large variety of models for representing decimals. Number lines, place-value charts, tenths, or hundredths grids and physical models like base-ten blocks, can all help in the comparison process. Again, building on similar experiences comparing and ordering whole numbers (Chapter 1) and fractions (Chapter 13) is helpful. Students know from Grade 3 that whole dollar amounts can be written with 0 cents (e.g., \$3 = \$3.00), so writing extra 0s to provide the same number of decimal places for comparison of different decimals should make sense. Caution is advised here, though, as trailing 0s in applied contexts usually indicate extra precision.

## Daily Routine

Use these suggestions before beginning the lesson on p. 590.

### 5-Minute Check

(Reviews Lesson 14-4)

**Tell which letter represents each mixed number on the number line. Write as a decimal.**

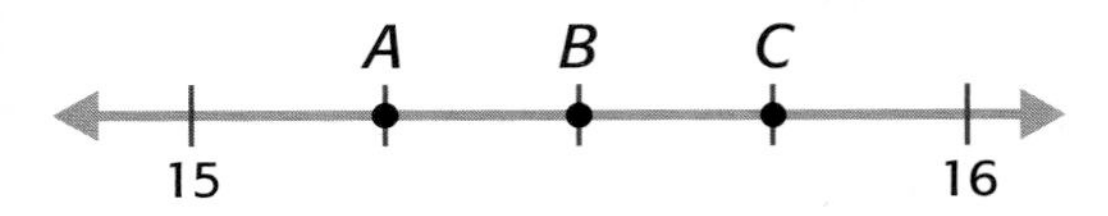


1. $15\frac{1}{4}$ A; 15.25
2. $15\frac{1}{2}$ B; 15.5
3. $15\frac{3}{4}$ C; 15.75
4. Identify the number point $N$ represents. $20\frac{2}{10}$, 20.2

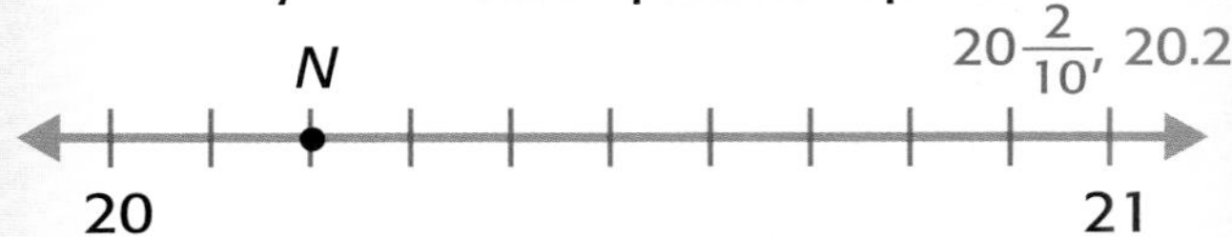


### Problem of the Day

Mrs. Brady's class uses 68 sheets of paper each day for 4 days. Mr. Clay's class uses 83 sheets of paper each day for 3 days. Which class uses more paper? How much more? Mrs. Brady's; 23 sheets

### Review Math Vocabulary

Write the review vocabulary words and their definitions on the board.

Have students write the Review Vocabulary words and definitions in their Math Journals. Then have them write three comparison sentences using the phrases "greater than," "less than," and "equal to."

# Differentiated Instruction

## Small Group Options

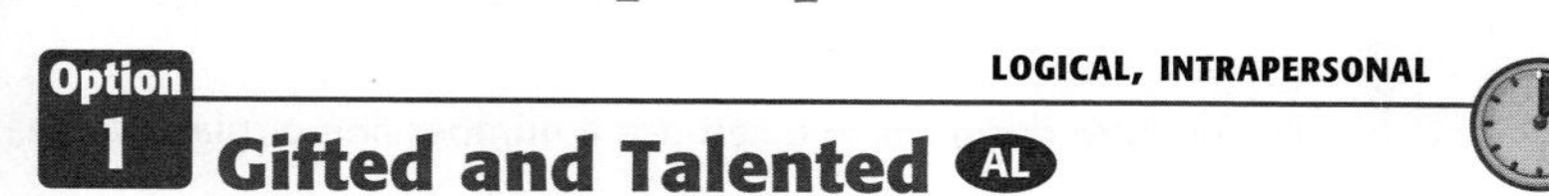

### Option 1 Gifted and Talented AL

LOGICAL, INTRAPERSONAL

**Materials:** index cards

- Tell students to use index cards to make three sets of number cards with the digits 0–9 on them, one digit per card.
- Next, have them shuffle the cards and place them facedown in a pile.
- Ask students to draw two cards and place them faceup.
- Challenge students to write the least and greatest numbers using these digits.

### Option 2 English Language Learners ELL

SOCIAL, LOGICAL

**Materials:** play money
**Core Vocabulary:** important, bills, change
**Common Use Verb:** discuss why

**Do Math** This strategy uses money to link the concept of comparing and ordering decimals.

- Pass out the same amount of bills, but vary the amount of change to each student.
- Ask each student to count the money and write down the amount.
- Call students up in pairs to discuss with the class who has more money.
- Demonstrate to students that they must look at the amount of change or the numbers to the right of the decimal to find which amounts are greater.
- Expand the activity by varying the dollar bills. Ask the whole group to rank their amounts.

*Use this worksheet to provide additional support for English Language Learners.*

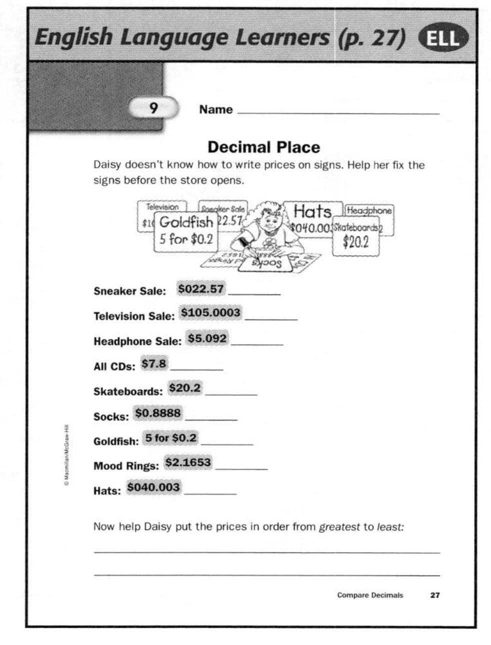

*English Language Learners (p. 27)* ELL

9 Name ____________

**Decimal Place**

Daisy doesn't know how to write prices on signs. Help her fix the signs before the store opens.



**Sneaker Sale:** $022.57 ________
**Television Sale:** $105.0003 ________
**Headphone Sale:** $5.092 ________
**All CDs:** $7.8 ________
**Skateboards:** $20.2 ________
**Socks:** $0.8888 ________
**Goldfish:** 5 for $0.2 ________
**Mood Rings:** $2.1653 ________
**Hats:** $040.003 ________

Now help Daisy put the prices in order from *greatest* to *least:*

________________________________

________________________________



Compare Decimals 27

## Independent Work Options

### Option 1 Early Finishers OL AL

SOCIAL

**Materials:** place-value charts, spinners numbered 0–9

- Provide pairs of students with place-value charts and a spinner.
- Have one student spin 4 times as the second student records each number on the place-value chart, with the first spin recorded as tens, the second spin as ones, the third spin as tenths, and the fourth spin as hundredths.
- Repeat to make four numbers in all. Have students order their four place-value charts from least to greatest and then greatest to least. Repeat with four more numbers.

### Option 2 Student Technology

Tech Link

**Math Online** macmillanmh.com

Personal Tutor • Extra Examples

Math Adventures

### Option 3 Learning Station: Social Studies (p. 574H)

Direct students to the Social Studies Learning Station for opportunities to explore and extend the lesson concept.

### Option 4 Problem-Solving Practice

Reinforce problem-solving skills and strategies with the Problem-Solving Practice worksheet.

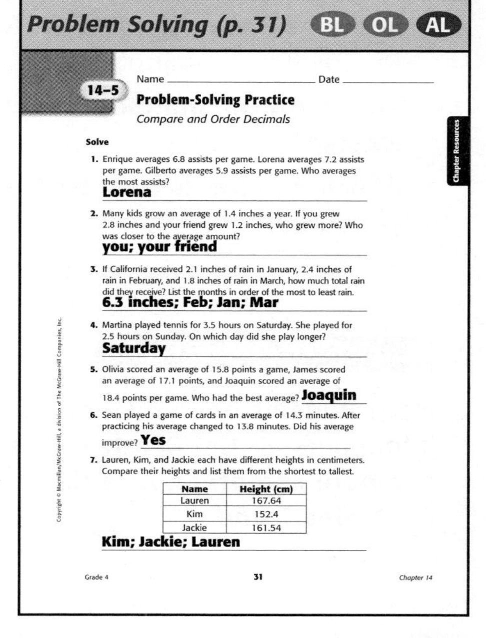

*Problem Solving (p. 31)* BL OL AL

14–5 Name ____________ Date ____________

**Problem-Solving Practice**

*Compare and Order Decimals*

**Solve**

1. Enrique averages 6.8 assists per game. Lorena averages 7.2 assists per game. Gilberto averages 5.9 assists per game. Who averages the most assists?
   **Lorena**
2. Many kids grow an average of 1.4 inches a year. If you grew 2.8 inches and your friend grew 1.2 inches, who grew more? Who was closer to the average amount?
   **you; your friend**
3. If California received 2.1 inches of rain in January, 2.4 inches of rain in February, and 1.8 inches of rain in March, how much total rain did they receive? List the months in order of the most to least rain.
   **6.3 inches; Feb; Jan; Mar**
4. Martina played tennis for 3.5 hours on Saturday. She played for 2.5 hours on Sunday. On which day did she play longer?
   **Saturday**
5. Olivia scored an average of 15.8 points a game, James scored an average of 17.1 points, and Joaquin scored an average of 18.4 points per game. Who had the best average? **Joaquin**
6. Sean played a game of cards in an average of 14.3 minutes. After practicing his average changed to 13.8 minutes. Did his average improve? **Yes**
7. Lauren, Kim, and Jackie each have different heights in centimeters. Compare their heights and list them from the shortest to tallest.

| Name | Height (cm) |
|---|---|
| Lauren | 167.64 |
| Kim | 152.4 |
| Jackie | 161.54 |

**Kim; Jackie; Lauren**

Chapter Resources



Grade 4 31 Chapter 14

# 14-5 Compare and Order Decimals

## 1 Introduce

### Activity Choice 1 • Hands-On

- Write the following money amounts on the board: \$1.62, \$1.25, \$1.50, \$1.05.
- Have students use dollars, dimes, and pennies to show each amount of money.
- **How would each number be read without the dollar sign?** one and 62 hundredths, one and 25 hundredths, one and 50 hundredths, and one and 5 hundredths.
- **Which number shows the greatest amount of money? How do you know?** \$1.62; Sample answer: 62 cents is greater than 25 cents, 50 cents, and 5 cents.

### Activity Choice 2 • Literature

Introduce the lesson with *The Toothpaste Millionaire* by Jean Merrill. For a related math activity, see p. TR65.

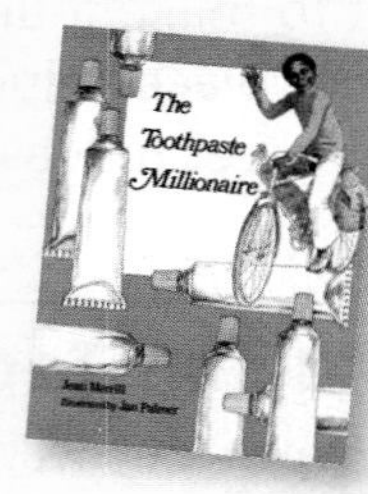


## 2 Teach

### Scaffolding Questions

Draw a number line from 5 to 7 on the board. Make tick marks to show tenths between the whole numbers. Write 6.8 and 6.3 on the board.

- **Where is 6.8 located on the number line?** 8 marks to the right of 6
- **Where is 6.3 located?** 3 marks to the right of 6
- **Which is greater, 6.8 or 6.3? How do you know?** 6.8; Sample answer: 6.8 is farther to the right on the number line.
- **Where on the number line would 6.89 be located?** between 6.8 and 6.9, very close to 6.9
- **Which number is less, 5.53 or 5.52? How do you know?** 5.52; It is located closer to 5.5 than 5.53 is.

### GET READY to Learn

Have students open their books and read the information in **Get Ready to Learn**. Review **compare** and **order**. As a class, work through **Examples 1 and 2**.



# 14-5 Compare and Order Decimals

**MAIN IDEA**

I will compare and order decimals.

**Math Online**
macmillanmh.com
- Extra Examples
- Personal Tutor
- Self-Check Quiz

The table shows the results from a skateboarding competition. Who has the higher score, Doria or Elise?

**Skateboarding Results**

| Name | Score |
|---|---|
| Doria | 79.7 |
| Lina | 79.2 |
| Holly | 78.9 |
| Elise | 79.5 |
| Jane | 78.8 |

To compare decimals, you can use a number line or place value.

**Real-World EXAMPLE** Compare Decimals

**1 SCORES Who has the higher score, Doria or Elise?**

Doria has a score of 79.7, while Elise has a score of 79.5.

**One Way: Number Line**

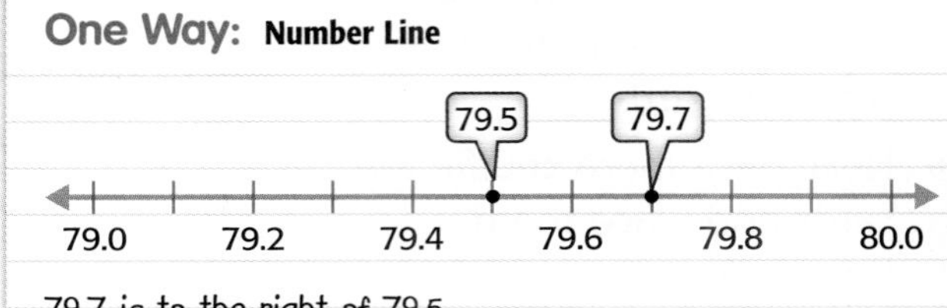


79.7 is to the right of 79.5.
So, $79.7 > 79.5$.

**Another Way: Place Value**

Line up the decimal points.
Then compare the digits in each place-value position.
In the tenths place, $7 > 5$.
So, 79.7 is greater than 79.5.

| Tens | Ones | Tenths |
|---|---|---|
| 7 | 9 | 7 |
| 7 | 9 | 5 |

So, Doria has the higher score.



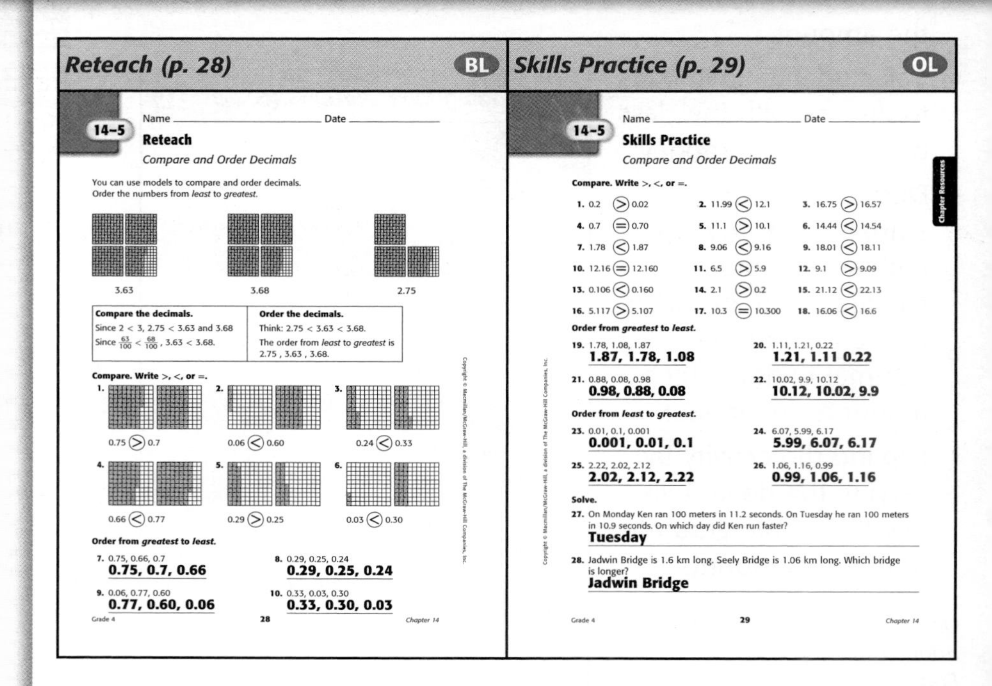

**Reteach (p. 28)** BL

14-5 Name ________ Date ________

**Reteach**

*Compare and Order Decimals*

You can use models to compare and order decimals.
Order the numbers from *least* to *greatest*.

3.63 3.68 2.75

| Compare the decimals. | Order the decimals. |
|---|---|
| Since $2 < 3$, $2.75 < 3.63$ and 3.68<br>Since $\frac{63}{100} < \frac{68}{100}$, $3.63 < 3.68$. | Think: $2.75 < 3.63 < 3.68$.<br>The order from *least* to *greatest* is 2.75, 3.63, 3.68. |

**Compare. Write $>$, $<$, or $=$.**

1. $0.75 > 0.7$
2. $0.06 < 0.60$
3. $0.24 < 0.33$
4. $0.66 < 0.77$
5. $0.29 > 0.25$
6. $0.03 < 0.30$

**Order from *greatest* to *least*.**

7. 0.75, 0.66, 0.7 **0.75, 0.7, 0.66**
8. 0.29, 0.25, 0.24 **0.29, 0.25, 0.24**
9. 0.06, 0.77, 0.60 **0.77, 0.60, 0.06**
10. 0.33, 0.03, 0.30 **0.33, 0.30, 0.03**

Grade 4 28 Chapter 14



**Skills Practice (p. 29)** OL

14-5 Name ________ Date ________

**Skills Practice**

*Compare and Order Decimals*

**Compare. Write $>$, $<$, or $=$.**

1. $0.2 > 0.02$
2. $11.99 < 12.1$
3. $16.75 > 16.57$
4. $0.7 = 0.70$
5. $11.1 > 10.1$
6. $14.44 < 14.54$
7. $1.78 < 1.87$
8. $9.06 < 9.16$
9. $18.01 < 18.11$
10. $12.16 = 12.160$
11. $6.5 > 5.9$
12. $9.1 > 9.09$
13. $0.106 < 0.160$
14. $2.1 > 0.2$
15. $21.12 < 22.13$
16. $5.117 > 5.107$
17. $10.3 = 10.300$
18. $16.06 < 16.6$

**Order from *greatest* to *least*.**

19. 1.78, 1.08, 1.87 **1.87, 1.78, 1.08**
20. 1.11, 1.21, 0.22 **1.21, 1.11 0.22**
21. 0.88, 0.08, 0.98 **0.98, 0.88, 0.08**
22. 10.02, 9.9, 10.12 **10.12, 10.02, 9.9**

**Order from *least* to *greatest*.**

23. 0.01, 0.1, 0.001 **0.001, 0.01, 0.1**
24. 6.07, 5.99, 6.17 **5.99, 6.07, 6.17**
25. 2.22, 2.02, 2.12 **2.02, 2.12, 2.22**
26. 1.06, 1.16, 0.99 **0.99, 1.06, 1.16**

**Solve.**

27. On Monday Ken ran 100 meters in 11.2 seconds. On Tuesday he ran 100 meters in 10.9 seconds. On which day did Ken run faster? **Tuesday**
28. Jadwin Bridge is 1.6 km long. Seely Bridge is 1.06 km long. Which bridge is longer? **Jadwin Bridge**

Grade 4 29 Chapter 14

Chapter Resources

You can also order decimals.

**EXAMPLE** Order Decimals

**Vocabulary Link**
order

**Everyday Use** select desired items

**Math Use** to arrange in a logical pattern

**2** **Order 9.86, 9.8, 9.92, and 9.09 from greatest to least.**

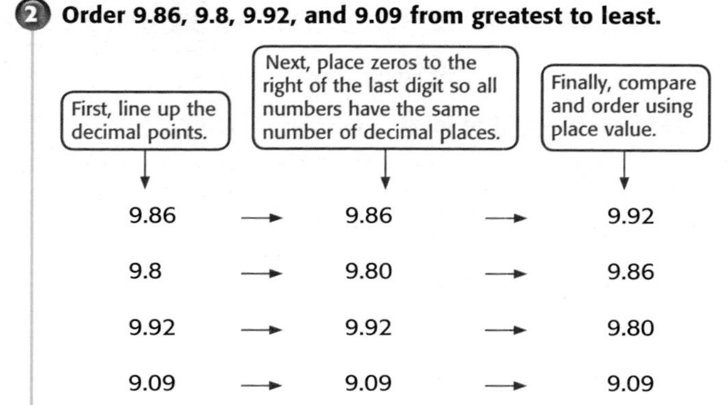


The order from greatest to least is 9.92, 9.86, 9.8, and 9.09.

**10. Sample answer: Graph each number on the number line and compare their locations to determine the order.**

## CHECK What You Know

**Compare. Use >, <, or =.** See Example 1 (p. 590)

**1.** 0.2 ● 0.6 <  **2.** 12.07 ● 1.207 >  **3.** 5.60 ● 5.6 =

**Order from greatest to least.** See Example 2 (p. 591)

**4.** 3.2, 4.5, 3.9, 4.1 **4.5, 4.1, 3.9, 3.2**

**5.** 0.12, 1.2, 1.21, 12.0 **12.0, 1.21, 1.2, 0.12**

**6.** $6.52, $5.62, $6.50, $5.60 **$6.52, $6.50, $5.62, $5.60**

**For Exercises 7 and 8, use the number line to compare and order each set of decimals from least to greatest.**

**7.** 5.7, 5.2, 4.7, 4.2 **4.2, 4.7, 5.2, 5.7**

**8.** 4.2, 4.8, 6.2, 5.8 **4.2, 4.8, 5.8, 6.2**

**9. Measurement** Four friends are going to different summer camps. The table shows the distance between each camp and their hometown. Order the distances from least to greatest. **42.35, 42.5, 64.25, 64.87**

**Traveling to Camp**

| Name | Distance (mi) |
|---|---|
| Bill | 64.25 |
| Sami | 42.5 |
| Latesha | 64.87 |
| Irena | 42.35 |

**10.** Talk About It Tell how to order 5.5, 5.3, 5.4, and 5.0 from greatest to least.



**Enrich (p. 32)** AL

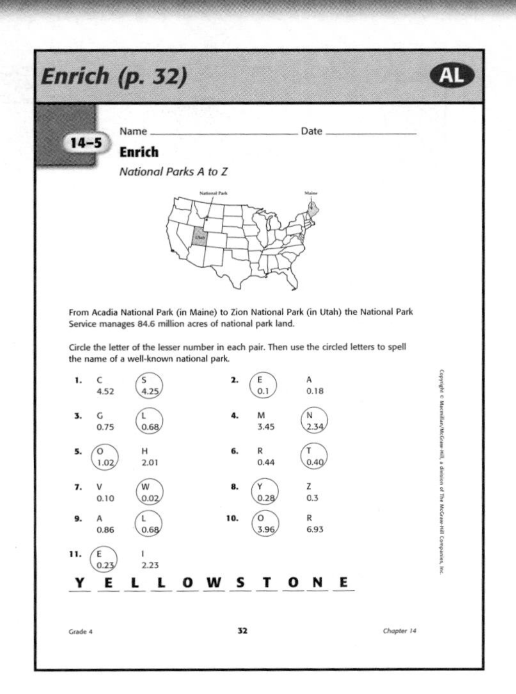

14-5 Name ________ Date ________

**Enrich**

*National Parks A to Z*



From Acadia National Park (in Maine) to Zion National Park (in Utah) the National Park Service manages 84.6 million acres of national park land.

Circle the letter of the lesser number in each pair. Then use the circled letters to spell the name of a well-known national park.

1. C 4.52 (S) 4.25
2. (E) 0.1 A 0.18
3. G 0.75 (L) 0.68
4. M 3.45 (N) 2.34
5. (O) 1.02 H 2.01
6. R 0.44 (T) 0.40
7. V 0.10 (W) 0.02
8. (Y) 0.28 Z 0.3
9. A 0.86 (L) 0.68
10. (O) 3.96 R 6.93
11. (E) 0.23 I 2.23

Y E L L O W S T O N E

Grade 4 32 Chapter 14

## Order Decimals

**Example 2** Tell students that lining up the decimal points first when comparing decimals will help them to compare the place values in each number.

### ADDITIONAL EXAMPLES

**1** Jun's time in the 100-meter dash was 13.6 seconds, and Manuel's was 13.3 seconds. Who ran the race in the least time? Manuel

**2** Order 4.56, 4.32, and 5.23 from least to greatest. 4.32, 4.56, 5.23

### CHECK What You Know

As a class, have students complete Exercises 1–10 in **Check What You Know** as you observe their work.

**Exercise 10** Assess student comprehension before assigning practice exercises.

### BL Alternate Teaching Strategy

**If** students have trouble comparing and ordering decimals…

**Then** use one of these reteach options:

1 CRM **Daily Reteach Worksheet** (p. 28)

2 Have students shade hundredth grids for 2.57 and 2.37. Have them compare the grids to find which number is the least.

- Then write 4.31, 4.52, and 4.36 on the board. Have students shade grids for each number and then order their grids from least to greatest.
- **Which place do you look at first to order these decimals?** ones
- **Which place do you look at second?** tenths **third?** hundredths

### COMMON ERROR!

**Exercises 19–24** Students may order numbers from least to greatest because they misread directions. Remind students to read carefully and identify whether they will order the numbers from greatest to least or least to greatest.

# 3 Practice

Differentiate practice using these leveled assignments for Exercises 11–32.

| Level | Assignment |
|---|---|
| BL Below/Approaching Level | 11–14, 19–21, 25, 27–28 |
| OL On Level | 12–18, 20–24, 28, 31 |
| AL Above/Beyond Level | 11–29 odd, 30–32 |

Have students discuss and complete the Higher Order Thinking problems. In order to use number lines effectively, encourage students to show only what the problems describe.

**WRITING IN MATH** Have students complete Exercise 34 in their Math Journals. You may choose to use this exercise as an optional formative assessment.

# 4 Assess

### Formative Assessment

Write 14.67, 13.97, 14.62, and 14.09 on the board.

- **How do you know that 13.97 has the least value?** 13 is less than 14.
- **What is the order, from least to greatest, of the other 3 decimals?** 14.09, 14.62, 14.67

**Quick Check** **Are students continuing to struggle with comparing and ordering decimals?**

**If Yes** → CRM Reteach Worksheet (p. 28)

**If No** → Independent Work Options (p. 590B)
CRM Skills Practice Worksheet (p. 29)
CRM Enrich Worksheet (p. 32)

**Name the Math** Order 9.56, 9.58, 9.37, and 9.92 from greatest to least. Students should show their work and explain the steps they took.



## Practice and Problem Solving

See page R37.

**Compare. Use >, <, or =.** See Example 1 (p. 590)

**11.** 0.74 ● 7.4 <
**12.** 16.33 ● 16.3 >
**13.** 0.56 ● 0.58 <
**14.** 0.8 ● 0.80 =
**15.** 1 ● 0.09 >
**16.** 0.90 ● 0.9 =
**17.** 82.6 ● 82.60 =
**18.** 1.06 ● 1.05 >

**Order from greatest to least.** See Example 2 (p. 591)

**19.** 0.4, 0.42, 0.54 **0.54, 0.42, 0.4**
**20.** 0.08, 0.80, 0.82 **0.82, 0.80, 0.08**
**21.** $12.50, $1.25, $12.05 **$12.50, $12.05, $1.25**
**22.** $19.62, $19.56, $19.60 **$19.62, $19.60, $19.56**
**23.** 0.5, 0.55, 0.6 **0.6, 0.55, 0.5**
**24.** 68.16, 81.6, 68.1 **81.6, 68.16, 68.1**

**For Exercises 25–28, use the number line to compare and order each set of decimals from least to greatest.**

**25.** 6.3, 8.1, 7.5, 7.7 **6.3, 7.5, 7.7, 8.1**
**26.** 7.5, 6.2, 7.75, 6.25 **6.2, 6.25, 7.5, 7.75**
**27.** 6.45, 7.52, 8.01, 6.25 **6.25, 6.45, 7.52, 8.01**
**28.** 8.05, 7.75, 6.8, 7.57 **6.8, 7.57, 7.75, 8.05**

**29.** Marlon averages 5.6 rebounds per game. Tina averages 5.9 rebounds per game. Bret averages 4.3 rebounds per game. Who averages the most rebounds? Explain. **Tina; 5.9 is greater than the other numbers.**

**30. Measurement** Rita ran the 100-meter dash four times, which is timed in seconds. Her times were 16.25, 15.36, 16.55, and 15.23. What was her slowest time? **16.55 sec**

**31. Measurement** The table at the right shows the distances Seth biked. Did he bike more the first weekend or the last weekend? **last weekend**

**Distance Biked in July**

| Weekend | Distance (mi) |
|---|---|
| 1 | 3.25 |
| 2 | 3.5 |
| 3 | 3 |
| 4 | 3.6 |

## H.O.T. Problems

**32. OPEN ENDED** Draw a number line that contains two whole numbers. Divide the number line in tenths. Identify the location of three decimals on the number line. **32, 34. See Ch. 14 Answer Appendix.**

**33. NUMBER SENSE** What number is halfway between 4.36 and 4.48 on a number line? **4.42**

**34. WRITING IN MATH** Write a real-world problem about comparing and ordering decimals.



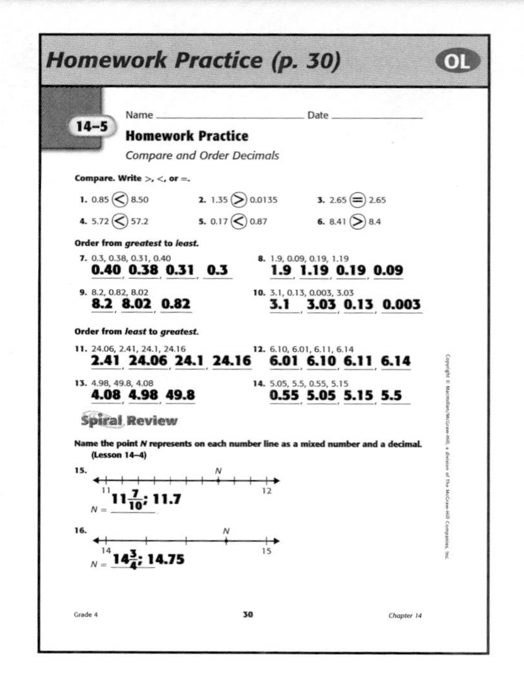

**Homework Practice (p. 30)** OL

14–5 Name ______ Date ______

**Homework Practice**

*Compare and Order Decimals*

**Compare. Write >, <, or =.**

1. 0.85 (<) 8.50
2. 1.35 (>) 0.0135
3. 2.65 (=) 2.65
4. 5.72 (<) 57.2
5. 0.17 (<) 0.87
6. 8.41 (>) 8.4

**Order from *greatest* to *least*.**

7. 0.3, 0.38, 0.31, 0.40 **0.40, 0.38, 0.31, 0.3**
8. 1.9, 0.09, 0.19, 1.19 **1.9, 1.19, 0.19, 0.09**
9. 8.2, 0.82, 8.02 **8.2, 8.02, 0.82**
10. 3.1, 0.13, 0.003, 3.03 **3.1, 3.03, 0.13, 0.003**

**Order from *least* to *greatest*.**

11. 24.06, 2.41, 24.1, 24.16 **2.41, 24.06, 24.1, 24.16**
12. 6.10, 6.01, 6.11, 6.14 **6.01, 6.10, 6.11, 6.14**
13. 4.98, 49.8, 4.08 **4.08, 4.98, 49.8**
14. 5.05, 5.5, 0.55, 5.15 **0.55, 5.05, 5.15, 5.5**

**Spiral Review**

**Name the point *N* represents on each number line as a mixed number and a decimal. (Lesson 14–4)**

15. 11 N 12 $N =$ **$11\frac{7}{10}$; 11.7**

16. 14 N 15 $N =$ **$14\frac{3}{4}$; 14.75**

Grade 4 30 Chapter 14

# Chapter 14 Mid-Chapter Check

Lessons 14-1 through 14-5

**Write a fraction and a decimal for each shaded part.** (Lesson 14-1)

1. 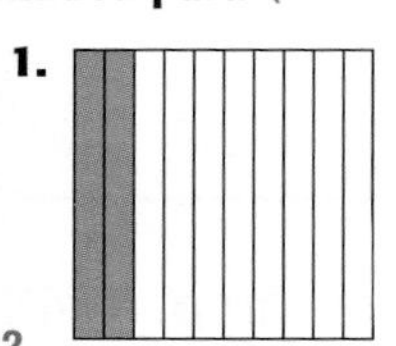
$\frac{2}{10}$; 0.2

2. 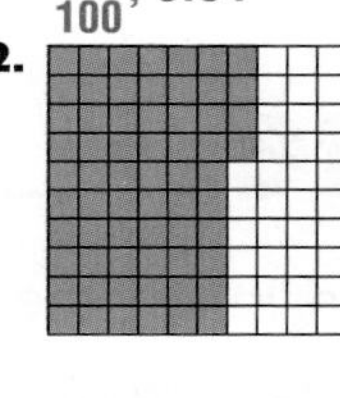
$\frac{64}{100}$; 0.64

**Write each fraction as a decimal.** (Lesson 14-1)

3. $\frac{7}{10}$ 0.7
4. $\frac{34}{100}$ 0.34

**Write as a fraction and as a decimal.** (Lesson 14-1) 5. $\frac{3}{4}$; 0.75 6. $\frac{1}{5}$; 0.2

5. three fourths
6. one fifth

7. **MULTIPLE CHOICE** Which of the following numbers is *six and six hundredths*? B (Lesson 14-1)

   **A** 0.66 **C** 6.6

   **B** 6.06 **D** $6\frac{6}{10}$

**Write each mixed number as a decimal.** (Lesson 14-2)

8. $9\frac{1}{10}$ 9.1
9. $10\frac{3}{100}$ 10.03
10. $7\frac{1}{100}$ 7.01
11. $2\frac{3}{10}$ 2.3

**Write each as a mixed number and decimal.** (Lesson 14-2)

12. seven and three fourths $7\frac{3}{4}$; 7.75
13. two and six tenths $2\frac{6}{10}$; 2.6

14. **MULTIPLE CHOICE** Which number represents the shaded parts of the figure? (Lesson 14-2) G

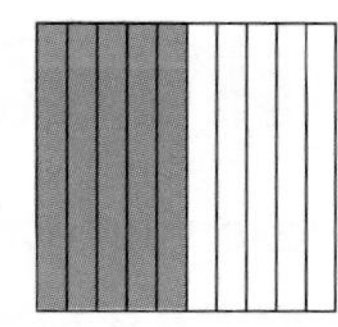

   **F** 0.05 **H** 5.0

   **G** 0.5 **J** 5.5

15. Trey has 18 coins. One half are nickels. One third are dimes. The rest are quarters. How much are Trey's coins worth? Use the make a model strategy. (Lesson 14-3) $1.80

**Identify the numbers points *N* and *P* represent.** (Lesson 14-4)

16. 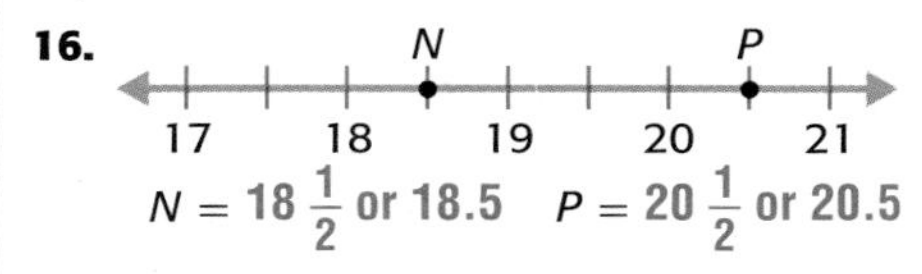

$N = 18\frac{1}{2}$ or 18.5 $P = 20\frac{1}{2}$ or 20.5

**Compare. Use >, <, or =.** (Lesson 14-5)

17. 6.4 ● 6.4 =
18. 13.09 ● 1.309 >

**Order from greatest to least.** (Lesson 14-5)

19. 1.2, 2.5, 1.9, 2.1 2.5; 2.1; 1.9; 1.2
20. 0.32, 3.2, 1.31, 13.0 13.0; 3.2, 1.31; 0.32

21. WRITING IN MATH Explain why $\frac{3}{10}$ and $\frac{30}{100}$ are equal. See margin.



# Chapter 14 Mid-Chapter Check

## Lessons 14-1 through 14-5

### Formative Assessment

Use the Mid-Chapter Check to assess students' progress in the first half of the chapter.

**ExamView** Assessment Suite Customize and create multiple versions of your Mid-Chapter Check and the test answer keys.

### FOLDABLES Dinah Zike's Foldables

Use these lesson suggestions to incorporate the Foldable during the chapter.

**Lesson 14-2** Under the bottom left flap, relate mixed numbers and decimals.

**Lesson 14-4** Under the top left flap, students draw or glue a number line and relate a fraction to a decimal.

**Lesson 14-5** Under the top right flap, compare and order decimals to two places on a number line.

### Additional Answer

21. Sample answer: $\frac{30}{100}$ is an equivalent fraction for $\frac{3}{10}$. If the numerator and denominator for $\frac{3}{10}$ are both multiplied by 10, the outcome is $\frac{30}{100}$.

# Data-Driven Decision Making

Based on the results of the Mid-Chapter Check, use the following resources to review concepts that continue to give students problems.

| Exercises | State/Local Standards | What's the Math? | Error Analysis | Resources for Review |
|---|---|---|---|---|
| **1–7** Lesson 14-1 | | Identify, read, and write tenths and hundredths as decimals and fractions. | Figures wrong number for coins. Does not add amount of denominations, just number of coins. | Strategic Intervention Guide (p. 110)<br>CRM Chapter 14 Resource Masters (Reteach)<br>Math Adventures<br>My Math Zone Chapter 14<br>Math Online Extra Examples • Concepts in Motion |
| **8–14** Lesson 14-2 | | Use models to show tenths and hundredths. Identify, read, and write decimals greater than 1. | Confuses hundredths and tenths. Does not know how to convert a fraction to a decimal. Does not know where to put decimal point. | |
| **17–20** Lesson 14-5 | | Compare and order decimals. | Confuses <, >, and = signs. Orders from least to greatest. Does not understand place value with decimals. | |

# 14-6 Problem-Solving Investigation
## Choose a Strategy

# Lesson Planner

## Objective
Choose the best strategy to solve a problem.

## Resources
**Materials:** index cards

**Manipulatives:** counters

**Teacher Technology**
TeacherWorks • Interactive Classroom

**Real-World Problem Solving Library**
**Math and Social Studies:**
***Growing Goods in a Growing Country***
Use these leveled books to reinforce and extend problem-solving skills and strategies.

Leveled for:
- OL On Level
- ELL Sheltered English
- SP Spanish

For additional support, see the Real-World Problem Solving Teacher Guide.

# Daily Routine

Use these suggestions before beginning the lesson on p. 594.

## 5-Minute Check

(Reviews Lesson 14-5)

**Order from greatest to least.**

1. 9.65, 9.68, 9.52, 9.59 9.68, 9.65, 9.59, 9.52
2. 17.05, 17.50, 17.55, 17.45 17.55, 17.50, 17.45, 17.05
3. 22.62, 22.17, 22.06, 22.68 22.68, 22.62, 22.17, 22.06
4. 51.21, 53.45, 53.54, 51.54 53.54, 53.45, 51.54, 51.21

## Problem of the Day

A spinner has 4 equal sections. One of the sections is red. If you were to spin the spinner 100 times, how many times would you predict that the spinner would land on red? Explain. 25 times; The spinner is divided into fourths and one fourth of 100 is 25 spins landing on red.

# Differentiated Instruction

## Small Group Options

LOGICAL, LINGUISTIC

### Gifted and Talented AL

**Materials:** chart paper, markers, paper, pencils

- Write the following problem on the board:

  *Nancy's class wants to sit together for lunch. The cafeteria has square tables that will seat one person on each side. How many of those tables do they need to push together so that all 24 students can sit together at a rectangular table?* 11 square tables

- Encourage the students to draw a picture to show their answer. Ask them to exchange ideas with a partner.

2 3 4 5 6 7 8 9 10 11 12

1 [ ][ ][ ][ ][ ][ ][ ][ ][ ][ ][ ] 13

24 23 22 21 20 19 18 17 16 15 14

Option 2 LINGUISTIC, INTERPERSONAL

### English Language Learners ELL

**Materials:** graph paper, manipulatives
**Core Vocabulary:** showed this with, used, reviewed
**Common Use Verb:** make

**Talk Math** This strategy provides the student with more practice choosing a strategy to solve a problem.

- Show a problem and solution with manipulatives.
- Ask the students to write the problem that the model illustrates.
- As a group, solve the problem and review students' problems.
- Discuss whether the problems correctly show the model and whether there are multiple problems.
- Repeat for other methods to show the problem (draw a picture, make an organized list, etc.) as time permits.

## Independent Work Options

Option 1 LINGUISTIC

### Early Finishers OL AL

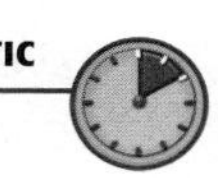

**Materials:** index cards, pencils

- Ask students to write a word problem on an index card.
- The problem should include one piece of information on which 2–3 other pieces of information in the problem are based. Students can be encouraged to use phrases, such as *half as many, twice as many, more than,* or *less than.*
- Have students exchange problems and use one of the problem-solving strategies to find the answers.

### Student Technology

**Math Online** macmillanmh.com

Personal Tutor • Extra Examples

Option 3

### Learning Station: Writing (p. 574G)

Direct students to the Writing Learning Station for opportunities to explore and extend the lesson concept.

# 14-6 Problem-Solving Investigation

## 1 Introduce

**Activity • Review**

- Write the following problem on the board. Have students work with partners.

  *Five flavors of frozen yogurt are offered at a picnic: vanilla, chocolate, strawberry, mint chip, and banana. How many flavor combinations are there for two-scoop cones?*
- **What strategies can be used to make sure to include every combination?** make a model, draw a picture
- **Solve.** 15 combinations; vv, vc, vs, vm, vb, cc, cs, cm, cb, ss, sm, sb, mm, mb, bb

## 2 Teach

Have students read the problem on sharing a pizza. Guide them through the problem-solving steps.

**Understand** Using the questions, review what students know and need to find.

**Plan** Have them discuss their strategy.

**Solve** Guide students to use the logical reasoning strategy to solve the problem.

- **Why is it important to know that Sandeep's mother ate 2 slices?** Sandeep's brother ate twice as many slices as his mother, so we can reason that Sandeep's brother ate 4 slices because his mother ate 2.
- **What information can be found based on the number of pieces that Sandeep's brother ate?** the number of pieces Sandeep and his father ate, which is 1 fewer than the number Sandeep's brother ate

**Check** Have students look back at the problem to make sure that the answer fits the facts given.

### ! COMMON ERROR!

**Exercise 9** requires students to divide a number into two unequal parts. Encourage them to use 24 counters as a model and move the counters into groups until the groups match the description in the problem.



# 14-6 Problem-Solving Investigation

**MAIN IDEA** I will choose the best strategy to solve a problem.

**P.S.I. TEAM +**

SANDEEP: My father and I each ate $\frac{1}{4}$ of a pizza. My brother ate 1 more slice than I did and twice as many as my mother. She ate 2 slices.

YOUR MISSION: Find the number of slices of pizza Sandeep's family ate.

**Understand** You know how much pizza each person ate. Find the total number of slices of pizza the family ate.

**Plan** Use logical reasoning to determine the answer.

**Solve** Start with what is known.

- Mother: 2 slices
- Brother: twice as much as his mother or $2 \times 2 = 4$ slices
- Sandeep: 1 less slice than his brother or 3 slices
- Father: 3 slices

So, Sandeep's family ate $2 + 4 + 3 + 3 = 12$ slices of pizza.

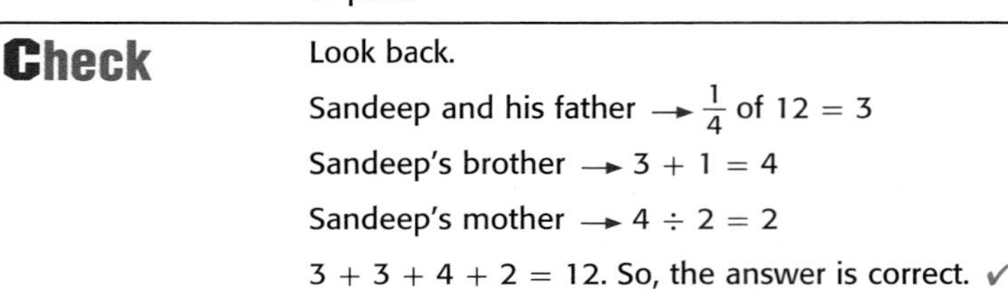

**Check** Look back.

Sandeep and his father → $\frac{1}{4}$ of $12 = 3$

Sandeep's brother → $3 + 1 = 4$

Sandeep's mother → $4 \div 2 = 2$

$3 + 3 + 4 + 2 = 12$. So, the answer is correct. ✓



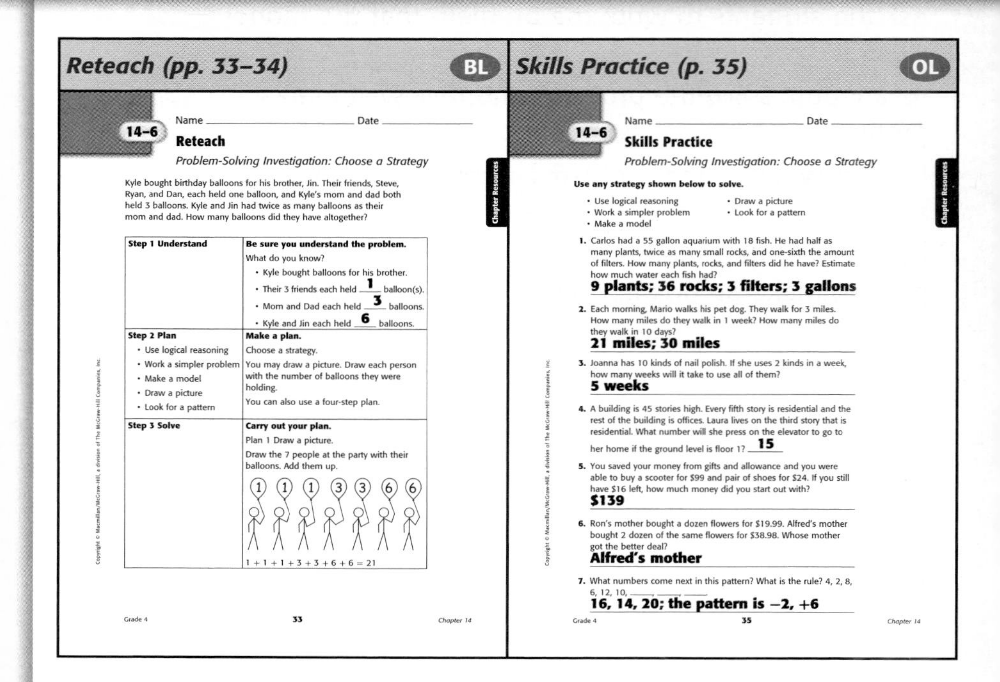

**Reteach (pp. 33–34)** BL

14–6 Name ______ Date ______

**Reteach**

*Problem-Solving Investigation: Choose a Strategy*

Kyle bought birthday balloons for his brother, Jin. Their friends, Steve, Ryan, and Dan, each held one balloon, and Kyle's mom and dad both held 3 balloons. Kyle and Jin had twice as many balloons as their mom and dad. How many balloons did they have altogether?

| | |
|---|---|
| **Step 1 Understand** | **Be sure you understand the problem.** What do you know? • Kyle bought balloons for his brother. • Their 3 friends each held **1** balloon(s). • Mom and Dad each held **3** balloons. • Kyle and Jin each held **6** balloons. |
| **Step 2 Plan** • Use logical reasoning • Work a simpler problem • Make a model • Draw a picture • Look for a pattern | **Make a plan.** Choose a strategy. You may draw a picture. Draw each person with the number of balloons they were holding. You can also use a four-step plan. |
| **Step 3 Solve** | **Carry out your plan.** Plan 1 Draw a picture. Draw the 7 people at the party with their balloons. Add them up. 1 1 1 3 3 6 6 $1 + 1 + 1 + 3 + 3 + 6 + 6 = 21$ |

Chapter Resources



Grade 4 33 Chapter 14

**Skills Practice (p. 35)** OL

14–6 Name ______ Date ______

**Skills Practice**

*Problem-Solving Investigation: Choose a Strategy*

**Use any strategy shown below to solve.**

- Use logical reasoning
- Work a simpler problem
- Make a model
- Draw a picture
- Look for a pattern

1. Carlos had a 55 gallon aquarium with 18 fish. He had half as many plants, twice as many small rocks, and one-sixth the amount of filters. How many plants, rocks, and filters did he have? Estimate how much water each fish had?
   **9 plants; 36 rocks; 3 filters; 3 gallons**
2. Each morning, Mario walks his pet dog. They walk for 3 miles. How many miles do they walk in 1 week? How many miles do they walk in 10 days?
   **21 miles; 30 miles**
3. Joanna has 10 kinds of nail polish. If she uses 2 kinds in a week, how many weeks will it take to use all of them?
   **5 weeks**
4. A building is 45 stories high. Every fifth story is residential and the rest of the building is offices. Laura lives on the third story that is residential. What number will she press on the elevator to go to her home if the ground level is floor 1? **15**
5. You saved your money from gifts and allowance and you were able to buy a scooter for $99 and pair of shoes for $24. If you still have $16 left, how much money did you start out with?
   **$139**
6. Ron's mother bought a dozen flowers for $19.99. Alfred's mother bought 2 dozen of the same flowers for $38.98. Whose mother got the better deal?
   **Alfred's mother**
7. What numbers come next in this pattern? What is the rule? 4, 2, 8, 6, 12, 10, ___, ___, ___
   **16, 14, 20; the pattern is −2, +6**

Chapter Resources



Grade 4 35 Chapter 14

★ indicates multi-step problem

## Mixed Problem Solving

See page R38.

**Use any strategy shown below to solve. Tell what strategy you used.**

PROBLEM-SOLVING STRATEGIES
- Look for a pattern.
- Work a simpler problem.
- Use logical reasoning.
- Draw a picture.
- Make a model.

1. Gina cut an apple into 8 slices and ate 3 of them. Rudy cut an apple into 4 slices and ate 2 of them. If the apples were the same size, who ate more? $\frac{2}{4} > \frac{3}{8}$; Rudy ate more.

2. Sarah's dad gave her the money shown. He gave $7 to each of her two brothers. He had $16 left. How much money did Sarah's dad start with? $39

★3. Craig paid $75 for a snowboard that he used 32 times. Owen paid twice as much as Craig but used his board 82 times. Who got a better deal per use? Explain.
See Ch. 14 Answer Appendix.

4. **Measurement** Felicia is building a garden. The garden will have an area of 48 square feet. Give three pairs of possible side lengths.
Sample answer: $6 \times 8$, $12 \times 4$, or $16 \times 3$

5. **Algebra** What is the rule for the pattern shown? What number comes next?

5, 13, 10, 18, 15, . . .

Add 8 and subtract 3; 23

6. **Measurement** Adriano's driveway is rectangular in shape. The area of the driveway is 345 square feet. The length is shown. What is the width of the driveway? 15 ft

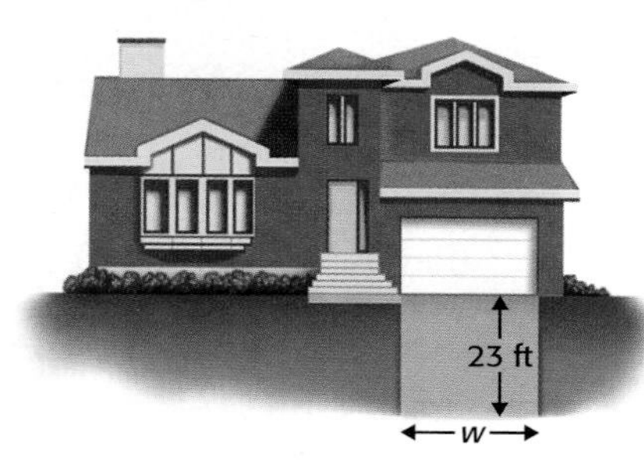


7. Paige and Mustafa were in a snow skiing competition. Paige earned a score of 88.6, while Mustafa earned a score of 88.59. Who won? Explain.
Paige; $88.6 > 88.59$

8. **Measurement** Alani started her homework at 4:25 P.M. She stopped at 5:15 P.M. to eat dinner. She started her work again at 5:50 P.M. She then worked another 15 minutes and finished. How many minutes did she do her homework? 65 min

9. **WRITING IN MATH** The sum of Roman and his younger sister's age together equals 24. Roman's age is twice the amount of his sister's. How old is Roman and his sister? Explain.
See Ch. 14 Answer Appendix.



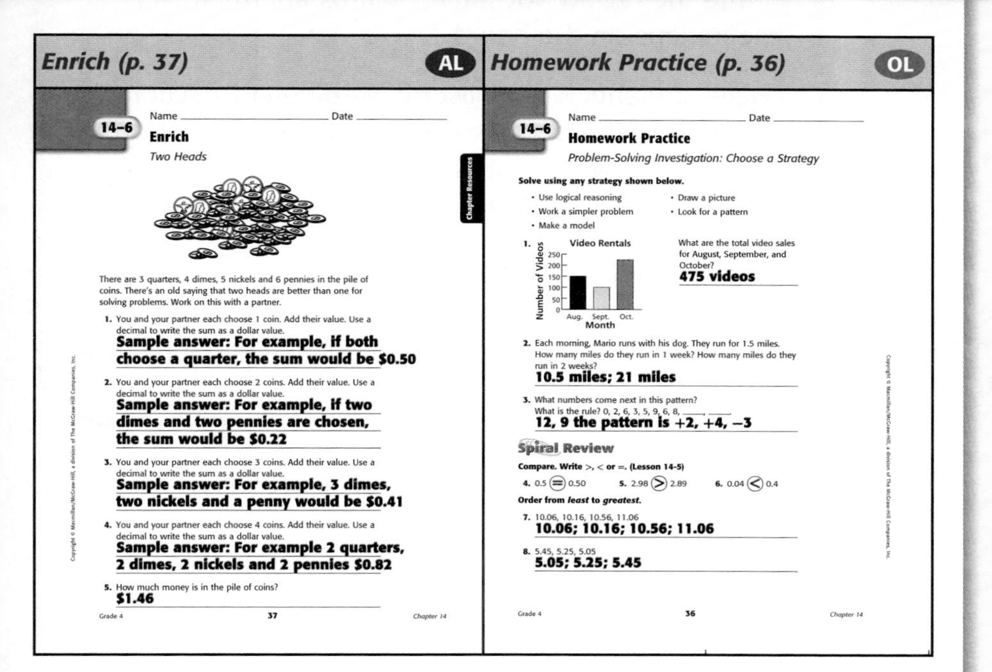

### Enrich (p. 37) AL

14–6 Name ________________ Date ________

**Enrich**

*Two Heads*

There are 3 quarters, 4 dimes, 5 nickels and 6 pennies in the pile of coins. There's an old saying that two heads are better than one for solving problems. Work on this with a partner.

1. You and your partner each choose 1 coin. Add their value. Use a decimal to write the sum as a dollar value.
**Sample answer: For example, if both choose a quarter, the sum would be $0.50**
2. You and your partner each choose 2 coins. Add their value. Use a decimal to write the sum as a dollar value.
**Sample answer: For example, if two dimes and two pennies are chosen, the sum would be $0.22**
3. You and your partner each choose 3 coins. Add their value. Use a decimal to write the sum as a dollar value.
**Sample answer: For example, 3 dimes, two nickels and a penny would be $0.41**
4. You and your partner each choose 4 coins. Add their value. Use a decimal to write the sum as a dollar value.
**Sample answer: For example 2 quarters, 2 dimes, 2 nickels and 2 pennies $0.82**
5. How much money is in the pile of coins?
**$1.46**



Grade 4 37 Chapter 14

### Homework Practice (p. 36) OL

14–6 Name ________________ Date ________

**Homework Practice**

*Problem-Solving Investigation: Choose a Strategy*

**Solve using any strategy shown below.**
- Use logical reasoning
- Draw a picture
- Work a simpler problem
- Look for a pattern
- Make a model

1. Video Rentals (Number of Videos 0–250; Month: Aug., Sept., Oct.)
What are the total video sales for August, September, and October?
**475 videos**
2. Each morning, Mario runs with his dog. They run for 1.5 miles. How many miles do they run in 1 week? How many miles do they run in 2 weeks?
**10.5 miles; 21 miles**
3. What numbers come next in this pattern? What is the rule? 0, 2, 6, 3, 5, 9, 6, 8, ____, ____.
**12, 9 the pattern is +2, +4, −3**

**Spiral Review**

**Compare. Write >, < or =. (Lesson 14-5)**

4. 0.5 (=) 0.50
5. 2.98 (>) 2.89
6. 0.04 (<) 0.4

**Order from *least* to *greatest*.**

7. 10.06, 10.16, 10.56, 11.06
**10.06; 10.16; 10.56; 11.06**
8. 5.45, 5.25, 5.05
**5.05; 5.25; 5.45**



Grade 4 36 Chapter 14

## BL Alternate Teaching Strategy

**If** students have trouble choosing the best strategy to solve a problem...

**Then** use one of these reteach options:

1. CRM **Daily Reteach Worksheet** (pp. 33–34)
2. Have students write a list of questions on an index card to ask themselves after reading a problem. Questions might include: Is there a pattern? Can I draw a picture or model of the problem? Is there information in the problem that leads to other information?

# 3 Practice

### Using the Exercises

**Exercise 4** has many correct answers. Above-level students could be encouraged to find a solution with fractional dimensions such as 4.8 feet × 10 feet.

**Exercise 8** has extra information. Have students read the problem carefully to identify what is needed to solve the problem.

# 4 Assess

### Formative Assessment

Pose the following problem to students. Have them use any strategy to solve and tell which strategy they used.

*Four towns are located along the highway. Summerville is 5 miles west of Centerville, Browning is 27 miles east of Centerville, and Stamish is 3 miles west of Browning. How far apart are Centerville and Stamish?* 24 miles; sample method: draw a picture

**Quick Check** **Are students continuing to struggle with choosing the best strategy to solve a problem?**

**If Yes** → CRM Reteach Worksheet (pp. 33–34)

**If No** → Independent Work Options (p. 590B)
CRM Skills Practice Worksheet (p. 35)
CRM Enrich Worksheet (p. 37)

# Fraction and Decimal Equivalents

## Lesson Planner

### Objective

Find fraction and decimal equivalents.

### Review Vocabulary

**fraction, decimal**

### Resources

**Materials:** number line, hundredths grids

**Literature Connection:** *Henry Hikes to Fitchburg* by D.B. Johnson

**Teacher Technology**

TeacherWorks • Interactive Classroom

## Daily Routine

Use these suggestions before beginning the lesson on p. 596.

### 5-Minute Check

(Reviews Lesson 14-6)

**Use any strategy to solve.**

Five students sold tickets for the school play. Paige and Selena each sold 6 more than Lexi. Lexi sold one half as many as Alonzo. Alonzo sold 11 more than John, who sold 17 tickets. How many tickets did the 5 students sell in all? 99 tickets

### Problem of the Day

How many quarts of water would be needed to give every student in the class one cup of water? Answer will vary with class size. 4 cups = 1 qt

### Focus on Math Background

*All* fractions have decimal equivalents.

- Some fractions can be represented by terminating decimals. For example, $\frac{1}{2}$ is equivaqlent to 0.5.
- Other fractions are represented by repeating decimals. These decimals do not terminate, but instead, repeat one or more digits endlessly. For example, $\frac{2}{3}$ is equivalent to 0.666....

In this lesson, students will consider only those fractions that can be expressed as tenths or hundredths. In other words, this lesson is limited to fractions whose denominators are factors of 10 or 100, for example, halves, fourths, tens, twentieths, and twenty-fifths.

### Review Math Vocabulary

Write the review vocabulary words and their definitions on the board.

Have students write a list of five different fractions with 10 as the denominator and five fractions with 100 as the denominator. Then have them write the decimal equivalent for each.

#### Visual Vocabulary Cards

Use Visual Vocabulary Cards 8 and 18 to reinforce the vocabulary reviewed in this lesson. (The Define/Example/Ask routine is printed on the back of each card.)

# Differentiated Instruction

## Small Group Options

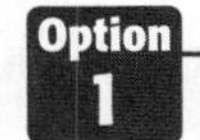

VISUAL, LOGICAL

### Option 1 Below Level BL

**Materials:** dimes and pennies

- Ask students to identify the value of the dime and the penny. Their answers should include 10¢ and 1¢.
- Ask students to identify the fraction of a dollar for each. The dime is $\frac{1}{10}$ and the penny is $\frac{1}{100}$.
- **If you have 2 dimes, what fraction of a dollar do you have?** $\frac{2}{10}$
- **How do you write this fraction as a decimal?** 0.2
- **How much money is that?** 20¢
- **Then how can you compare 20¢ and 0.2 of a dollar?** They are equal. 20¢ = 0.2 of a dollar
- **How do you write 20¢ as a decimal?** 0.20
- **How can you compare 0.20 and 0.2?** They are equal.
- Try this with other amounts of dimes. Add pennies if time allows. Students should use coins to help them.

LINGUISTIC, AUDITORY

### Option 2 English Language Learners ELL

**Materials:** index cards, pocket chart
**Core Vocabulary:** and, before, after
**Common Use Verb:** splits

**Talk Math** This strategy clarifies the written use of the decimal point and the verbal use of "and" in numbers and decimals and helps students read numbers correctly.

- Pass out cards and have students write "and" while you display these numbers on large index cards: $3\frac{1}{2}$, 1.35, $45\frac{5}{8}$, $12\frac{1}{3}$, $26\frac{2}{3}$, 34.136, 2.13.
- Say the number. Cut or tear apart on the decimal point or the fraction. Re-read while separating the torn card and inserting an "and" card. Practice reading "and" between whole numbers, fractions, and decimals.

## Independent Work Options

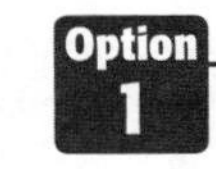

LOGICAL

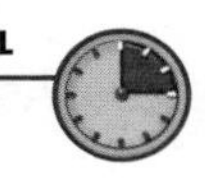

### Option 1 Early Finishers

**Materials:** index cards, pencils

- Write *fourths, fifths*, and *tenths* on the board.
- Have students label an index card with the title *Fourths*. Have them write $\frac{1}{4}$, $\frac{2}{4}$, and $\frac{3}{4}$ down the left edge of the card. Then have them write the decimal equivalents for each fraction.
- Have the students repeat the procedure with all of the fifths and tenths.

Fourths

| | |
|---|---|
| $\frac{1}{4}$ | 0.25 |
| $\frac{2}{4}$ | 0.5 |
| $\frac{3}{4}$ | 0.75 |

### Option 2 Student Technology

Tech Link

Math Online macmillanmh.com

Personal Tutor • Extra Examples

Math Adventures

### Option 3 Learning Station: Reading (p. 574G)

Direct students to the Reading Learning Station for opportunities to explore and extend the lesson concept.

### Option 4 Problem-Solving Practice

Reinforce problem-solving skills and strategies with the Problem-Solving Practice worksheet.

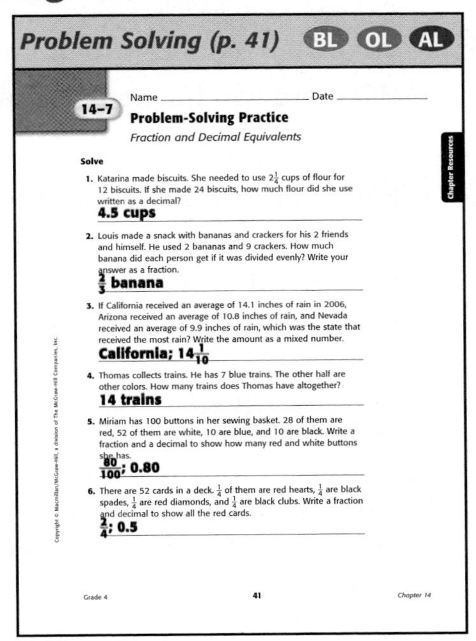

**Problem Solving (p. 41)** BL OL AL

14–7 Name ________ Date ________

**Problem-Solving Practice**

*Fraction and Decimal Equivalents*

Chapter Resources

**Solve**

1. Katarina made biscuits. She needed to use $2\frac{1}{4}$ cups of flour for 12 biscuits. If she made 24 biscuits, how much flour did she use written as a decimal?
   **4.5 cups**
2. Louis made a snack with bananas and crackers for his 2 friends and himself. He used 2 bananas and 9 crackers. How much banana did each person get if it was divided evenly? Write your answer as a fraction.
   **$\frac{2}{3}$ banana**
3. If California received an average of 14.1 inches of rain in 2006, Arizona received an average of 10.8 inches of rain, and Nevada received an average of 9.9 inches of rain, which was the state that received the most rain? Write the amount as a mixed number.
   **California; $14\frac{1}{10}$**
4. Thomas collects trains. He has 7 blue trains. The other half are other colors. How many trains does Thomas have altogether?
   **14 trains**
5. Miriam has 100 buttons in her sewing basket. 28 of them are red, 52 of them are white, 10 are blue, and 10 are black. Write a fraction and a decimal to show how many red and white buttons she has.
   **$\frac{80}{100}$; 0.80**
6. There are 52 cards in a deck. $\frac{1}{4}$ of them are red hearts, $\frac{1}{4}$ are black spades, $\frac{1}{4}$ are red diamonds, and $\frac{1}{4}$ are black clubs. Write a fraction and decimal to show all the red cards.
   **$\frac{2}{4}$; 0.5**



Grade 4 41 Chapter 14

# Fraction and Decimal Equivalents

## 1 Introduce

### Activity Choice 1 • Hands-On

- Have students draw a number line showing only the whole numbers 20, 21, and 22 on the width of a piece of notebook paper.
- Ask students to mark $20\frac{1}{2}$. Then have them mark tenths between 20 and 21.
- **How many tenths are equal to $\frac{1}{2}$?** 5 tenths
- Have students mark the line between 21 and 22 to show tenths. Label the marked points.
- **Where would the mark for 21.25 be?** halfway between 21.2 and 21.3
- **Where would the mark for 21.75 be?** halfway between 21.7 and 21.8
- Ask students to mark $21\frac{1}{4}$, $21\frac{2}{4}$ and $21\frac{3}{4}$.
- **What decimal is the same as $21\frac{1}{4}$?** 21.25
- **What decimal is the same as $21\frac{3}{4}$?** 21.75

### Activity Choice 2 • Literature

Introduce the lesson with *Henry Hikes to Fitchburg* by D.B. Johnson. For a related math activity, see p. TR66

## 2 Teach

### Scaffolding Questions

Write the fraction $\frac{3}{5}$ on the board.

- **What could be a first step in finding a decimal that is equivalent to $\frac{3}{5}$?** Sample answer: Find an equivalent fraction with 10 or 100 as the denominator.
- **What are two fractions that are equivalent to $\frac{3}{5}$?** $\frac{6}{10}$, $\frac{60}{100}$
- **What decimals are equivalent to $\frac{3}{5}$?** 0.6, 0.60
- Tell students that some fractions will not be equivalent to fractions with denominators of 10. **What decimal is equivalent to $\frac{1}{4}$?** 0.25

### GET READY to Learn

Have students open their books and read the information in **Get Ready to Learn**. Review **fraction** and **decimal**. As a class, work through **Examples 1 and 2.**



# 14-7 Fraction and Decimal Equivalents

**MAIN IDEA**

I will find fraction and decimal equivalents.

**Math Online**

macmillanmh.com

- Extra Examples
- Personal Tutor
- Self-Check Quiz

### GET READY to Learn

Nicole and Austin's family is taking a trip. Nicole says that the odometer (mileage tracker) shows they have driven 0.5 mile. Austin says $\frac{1}{2}$ mile. Can they both be correct?

When a fraction and a decimal name the same amount, they are fraction and decimal equivalents.

**EXAMPLE** Fraction and Decimal Equivalents

**1 Determine whether 0.5 and $\frac{1}{2}$ are equivalent.**

Use tenths and hundredths grids to model that 0.5 and $\frac{1}{2}$ name the same amount.

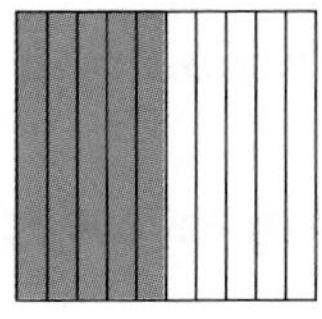

$0.5 = \frac{5}{10} = \frac{1}{2}$

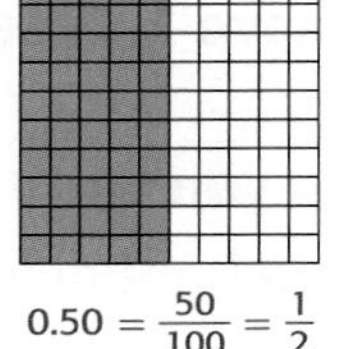

$0.50 = \frac{50}{100} = \frac{1}{2}$

The number lines also show that they name the same amount.

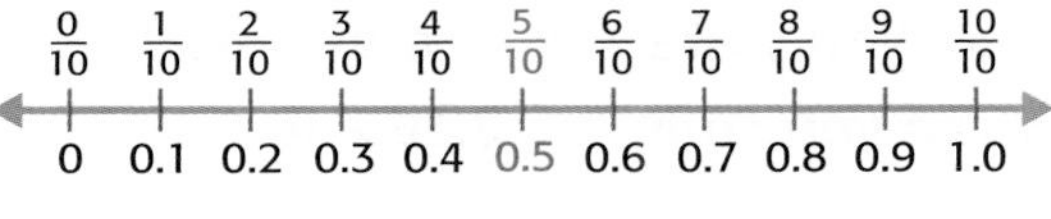


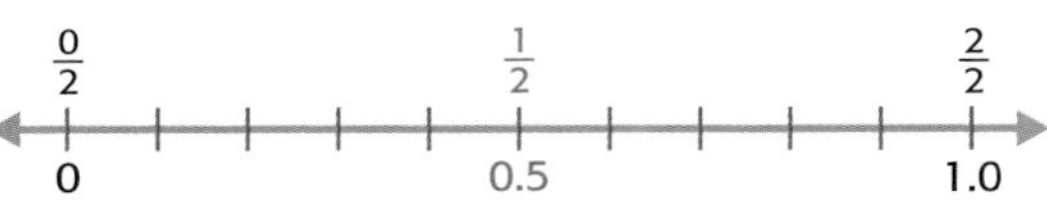


So, 0.5 and $\frac{1}{2}$ are equivalent.



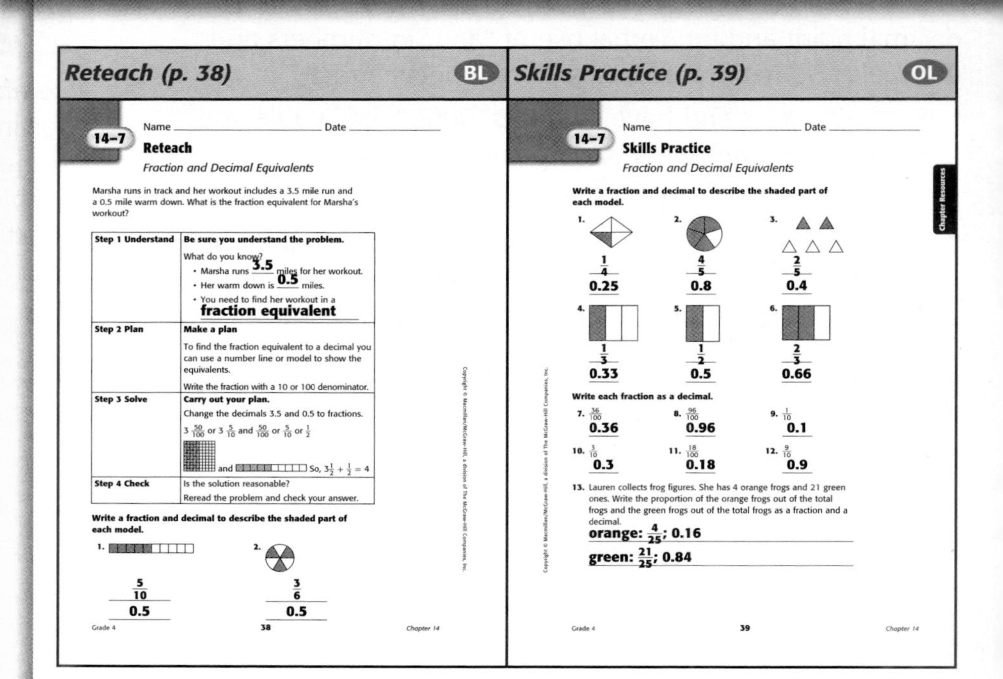

**Reteach (p. 38)** BL

14-7 Name ______ Date ______

**Reteach**

*Fraction and Decimal Equivalents*

Marsha runs in track and her workout includes a 3.5 mile run and a 0.5 mile warm down. What is the fraction equivalent for Marsha's workout?

| Step 1 Understand | Be sure you understand the problem.<br>What do you know?<br>• Marsha runs **3.5** miles for her workout.<br>• Her warm down is **0.5** miles.<br>• You need to find her workout in a **fraction equivalent** |
|---|---|
| Step 2 Plan | Make a plan<br>To find the fraction equivalent to a decimal you can use a number line or model to show the equivalents.<br>Write the fraction with a 10 or 100 denominator. |
| Step 3 Solve | Carry out your plan.<br>Change the decimals 3.5 and 0.5 to fractions.<br>$3\frac{50}{100}$ or $3\frac{5}{10}$ and $\frac{50}{100}$ or $\frac{5}{10}$ or $\frac{1}{2}$<br>and So, $3\frac{1}{2} + \frac{1}{2} = 4$ |
| Step 4 Check | Is the solution reasonable?<br>Reread the problem and check your answer. |

**Write a fraction and decimal to describe the shaded part of each model.**

1. $\frac{5}{10}$ 0.5
2. $\frac{3}{6}$ 0.5

Grade 4 38 Chapter 14



**Skills Practice (p. 39)** OL

14-7 Name ______ Date ______

**Skills Practice**

*Fraction and Decimal Equivalents*

**Write a fraction and decimal to describe the shaded part of each model.**

1. $\frac{1}{4}$ 0.25
2. $\frac{4}{5}$ 0.8
3. $\frac{2}{5}$ 0.4
4. $\frac{1}{3}$ 0.33
5. $\frac{1}{2}$ 0.5
6. $\frac{2}{3}$ 0.66

**Write each fraction as a decimal.**

7. $\frac{36}{100}$ 0.36
8. $\frac{96}{100}$ 0.96
9. $\frac{1}{10}$ 0.1
10. $\frac{3}{10}$ 0.3
11. $\frac{18}{100}$ 0.18
12. $\frac{9}{10}$ 0.9
13. Lauren collects frog figures. She has 4 orange frogs and 21 green ones. Write the proportion of the orange frogs out of the total frogs and the green frogs out of the total frogs as a fraction and a decimal.
**orange: $\frac{4}{25}$; 0.16**
**green: $\frac{21}{25}$; 0.84**

Grade 4 39 Chapter 14

Chapter Resources

To find a decimal that is equivalent to a fraction, it helps to write the fraction with a denominator of 10 or 100.

**EXAMPLE** **Find Fraction and Decimal Equivalents**

**2** **Write a fraction and decimal to describe the shaded part of the model.**

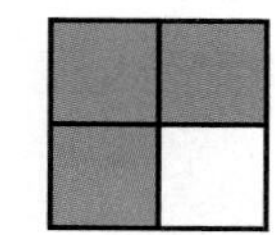

$\frac{3 \times 25}{4 \times 25} = \frac{75}{100}$ ← THINK What number can you multiply the denominator by to get 100?

$\frac{75}{100} = 0.75$ Write $\frac{75}{100}$ as a decimal.

So, $\frac{3}{4}$ and 0.75 describe the shaded part of the model.

Here are some common fraction and decimal equivalents.

**Fraction-Decimal Equivalents** *Key Concept*

| | | | |
|---|---|---|---|
| $\frac{1}{2} = 0.5$ | $\frac{1}{4} = 0.25$ | $\frac{2}{4} = 0.5$ | $\frac{3}{4} = 0.75$ |
| $\frac{1}{5} = 0.2$ | $\frac{2}{5} = 0.4$ | $\frac{3}{5} = 0.6$ | $\frac{4}{5} = 0.8$ |

1. $\frac{3}{10}$; 0.3
2. $\frac{50}{100}$, $\frac{5}{10}$, or $\frac{1}{2}$; 0.5
3. $\frac{60}{100}$, $\frac{6}{10}$, or $\frac{3}{5}$; 0.6
4. $\frac{25}{100}$ or $\frac{1}{4}$; 0.25

## CHECK What You Know

**Write a fraction and decimal to describe the shaded part of each model.** See Examples 1 and 2 (pp. 596–597)

1. 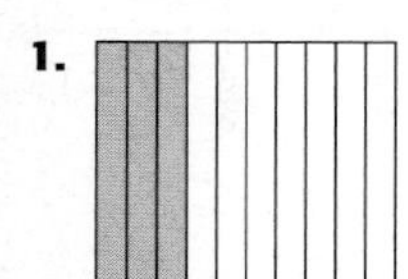
2.  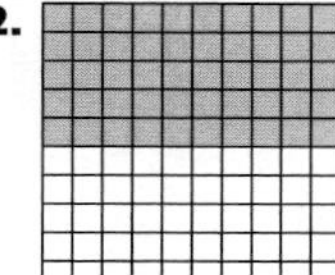
3. 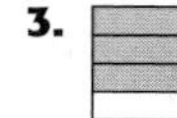 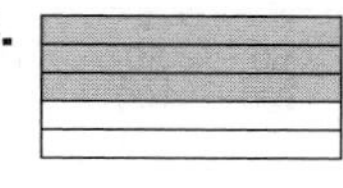
4. 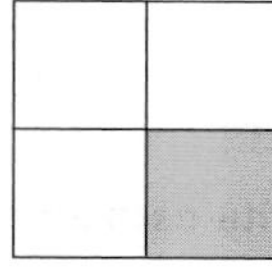

**Write each fraction as a decimal.** See Example 2 (p. 597)

5. $\frac{6}{10}$ 0.6
6. $\frac{6}{100}$ 0.06
7. $\frac{2}{4}$ 0.5
8. $\frac{4}{5}$ 0.8
9. Lupe got 20 out of 25 questions correct on a quiz. Write her score as a decimal and a fraction. $\frac{20}{25}$, 0.8
10. 

What do you notice about $\frac{3}{4}$, $\frac{6}{8}$, and $\frac{12}{16}$? See Ch. 14 Answer Appendix.



*Enrich (p. 42)* **AL**

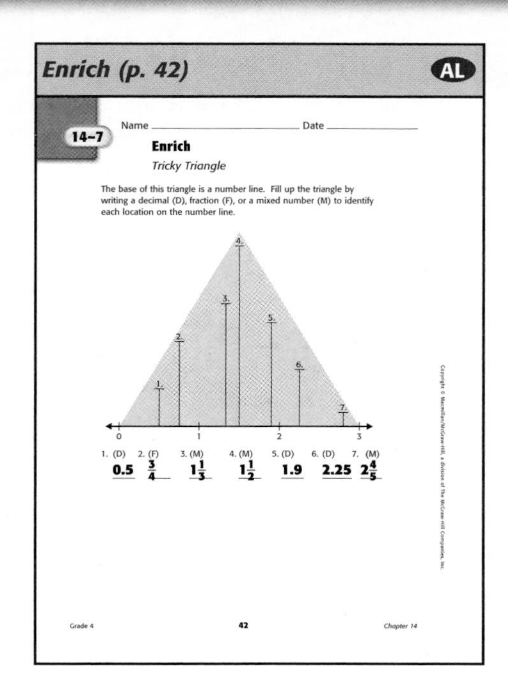

14-7 Name ________ Date ________

**Enrich**

*Tricky Triangle*

The base of this triangle is a number line. Fill up the triangle by writing a decimal (D), fraction (F), or a mixed number (M) to identify each location on the number line.

1. (D) 0.5 2. (F) $\frac{3}{4}$ 3. (M) $1\frac{1}{3}$ 4. (M) $1\frac{1}{2}$ 5. (D) 1.9 6. (D) 2.25 7. (M) $2\frac{4}{5}$

Grade 4 42 Chapter 14

## Find Fraction and Decimal Equivalents

**Example 2** Be sure students understand that finding an equivalent fraction with tenths or hundredths as the denominator must come before writing the equivalent decimal.

### ADDITIONAL EXAMPLES

**1** Determine whether 0.7 and $\frac{4}{5}$ are equivalent. no; $\frac{4}{5} = 0.8$

**2** Write a fraction and a decimal to describe the shaded part of the model. $\frac{3}{5}$, 0.6

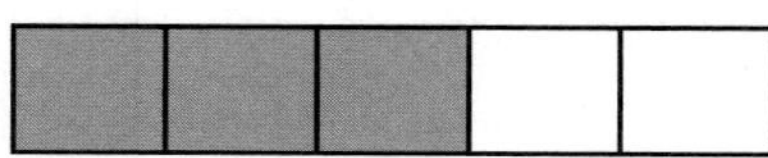

### CHECK What You Know

As a class, have students complete Exercises 1–10 in **Check What You Know** as you observe their work.

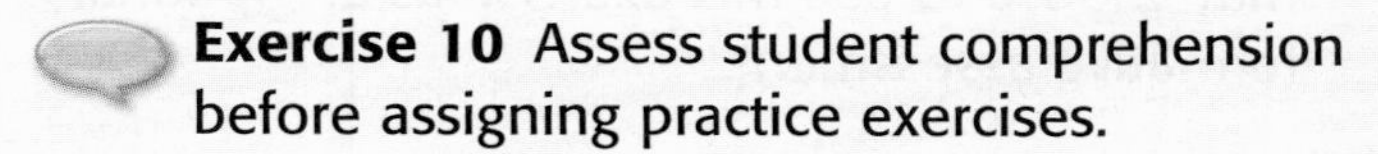

**Exercise 10** Assess student comprehension before assigning practice exercises.

## BL Alternate Teaching Strategy

**If** students have trouble finding decimal equivalents…

**Then** use one of these reteach options:

1. CRM **Daily Reteach Worksheet** (p. 38)
2. Review Lesson 12-4 on finding equivalent fractions. Remind them that they can multiply to find equivalent fractions. Show the following:

$$\frac{3}{4} = \frac{\blacksquare}{10} \text{ or } \frac{\blacksquare}{100}$$

- **Is there any number that you can multiply by 4 to get 10?** no
- **To get 100?** yes, 25
- **How would you change $\frac{3}{4}$ to hundredths?** Multiply the numerator and denominator of $\frac{3}{4}$ by 25 to get $\frac{75}{100}$.

## COMMON ERROR!

**Exercise 10** Students may think that $\frac{6}{8}$ and $\frac{12}{16}$ do not have equivalent decimals with tenths and hundredths because 8 and 16 are not factors of 10 or 100. Help students to discover that those two fractions are equivalent to $\frac{3}{4}$ and are therefore equivalent to 0.75.

# 3 Practice

Differentiate practice using these leveled assignments for Exercises 11–39.

| Level | Assignment |
|---|---|
| BL Below/Approaching Level | 11–14, 19–22, 27–28, 31–33 |
| OL On Level | 12–18, 21–26, 28–30, 32–35, 37 |
| AL Above/Beyond Level | 12–36 even, 37–39 |

Have students discuss and complete the Higher Order Thinking problems. Encourage them to show their work clearly as they work with equivalent fractions and decimals.

**WRITING IN MATH** Have students complete Exercise 39 in their Math Journals. You may choose to use this exercise as an optional formative assessment.

## Additional Answers

**11.** $\frac{8}{10}$; 0.8

**12.** $\frac{75}{100}$; 0.75

**13.** $\frac{2}{4}$; 0.5

**14.** $\frac{2}{5}$; 0.4

**15.** $\frac{40}{100}$; 0.4

**16.** $\frac{3}{6}$; 0.5

**17.** $\frac{3}{5}$; 0.6

**18.** $\frac{5}{10}$; 0.5



## Practice and Problem Solving

See page R38.

**Write a fraction and decimal to describe the shaded part of each model.** See Examples 1 and 2 (pp. 596–597) **11–18. See margin.**

**11.** 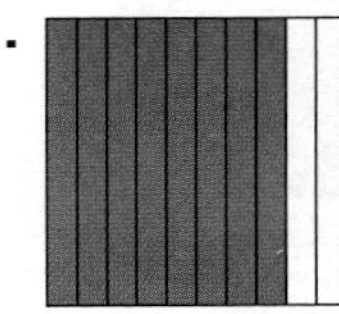 **12.** 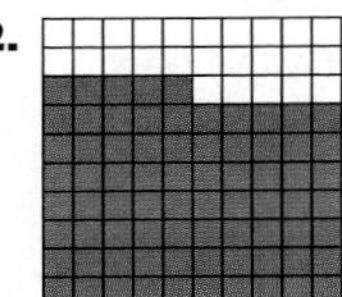 **13.** 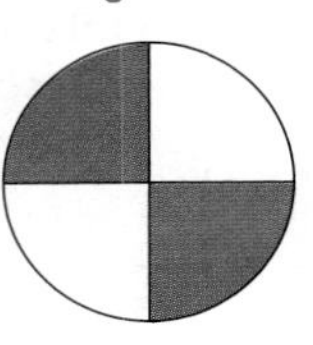 **14.** 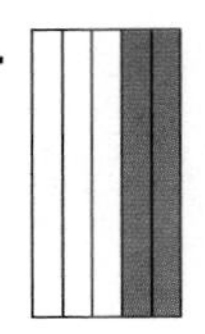

**15.** 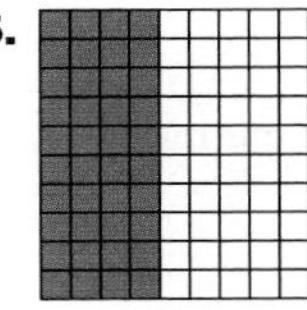 **16.** 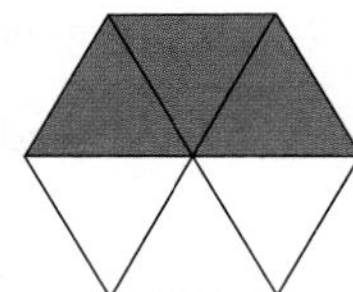 **17.** 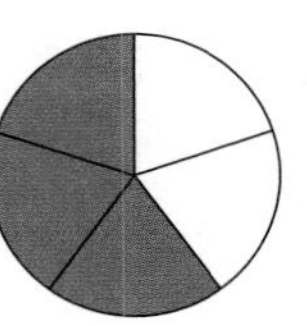 **18.** 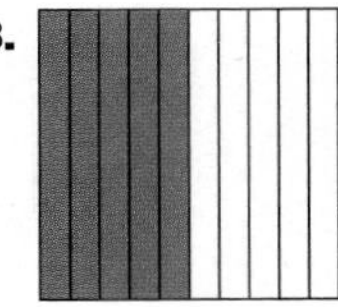

**Write each fraction as a decimal.** See Example 2 (p. 597)

**19.** $\frac{78}{100}$ 0.78 **20.** $\frac{4}{10}$ 0.4 **21.** $\frac{3}{5}$ 0.6 **22.** $\frac{35}{100}$ 0.35

**23.** $\frac{1}{4}$ 0.25 **24.** $\frac{4}{5}$ 0.8 **25.** $\frac{7}{25}$ 0.28 **26.** $\frac{1}{10}$ 0.1

**Recreate the number line using decimal equivalents.** See Example 1 (p. 596)

**27.** 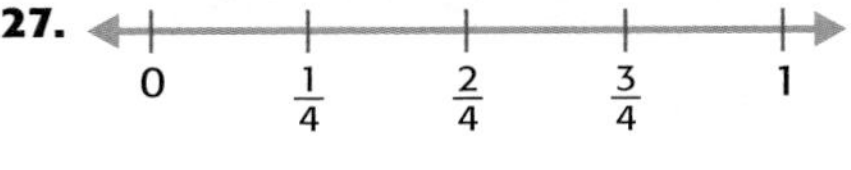


**28.** 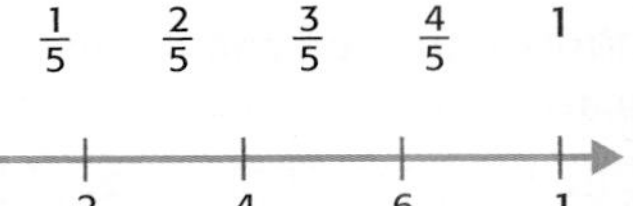


**29.** 0, $\frac{20}{100}$, $\frac{40}{100}$, $\frac{60}{100}$, $\frac{80}{100}$, 1

**30.** 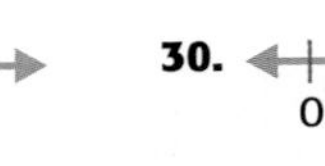 0, $\frac{2}{8}$, $\frac{4}{8}$, $\frac{6}{8}$, 1

**27–30. See Ch. 14 Answer Appendix.**

**Write each amount as a fraction and a decimal.**

**31. Measurement** Diana swam 3 out of 4 laps. 0.75; $\frac{3}{4}$

**32.** Vince read 6 out of 10 pages in a chapter of a book. 0.6; $\frac{6}{10}$

**33.** Robin ate 8 out of her 10 orange slices. 0.8; $\frac{8}{10}$

**34.** Cathy has completed 18 out of 20 math problems. 0.9; $\frac{18}{20}$

**35.** Maya has painted 1 out of 4 walls of her bedroom. 0.25; $\frac{1}{4}$

**36.** Jack has opened 3 out of 5 of his birthday presents. 0.6; $\frac{6}{10}$

## H.O.T. Problems

**37. OPEN ENDED** Create a model and shade in a fraction of it. Write two fractions and a decimal to describe the shaded area of the model.

**37–39. See Ch. 14 Answer Appendix.**

**38. CHALLENGE** Talia collects stuffed frogs. She has 25 frogs, and $\frac{2}{25}$ of them are multicolored. The rest are green. How many green frogs are in her collection? Explain how you found your answer.

**39. WRITING IN MATH** Demetri is completing 0.■ = $\frac{5}{50}$. Explain how he can find the correct answer.

## TEST Practice

**40.** Look at the number line and detemine which order of numbers correctly shows the location of the points. (Lesson 14-5) **B**

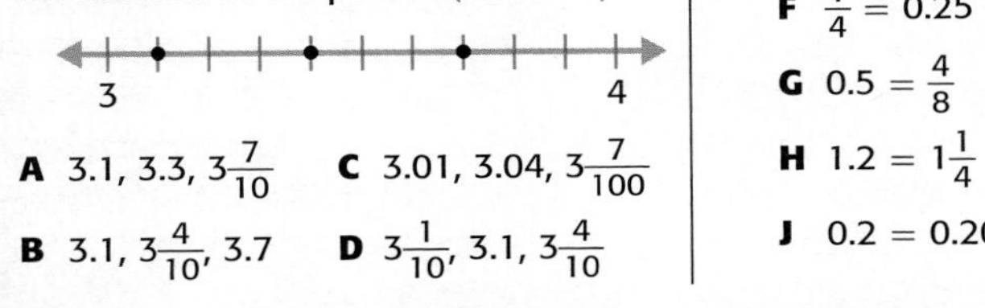

**A** 3.1, 3.3, $3\frac{7}{10}$ **C** 3.01, 3.04, $3\frac{7}{100}$

**B** 3.1, $3\frac{4}{10}$, 3.7 **D** $3\frac{1}{10}$, 3.1, $3\frac{4}{10}$

**41.** Which of the number sentences is false? (Lesson 14-7) **H**

**F** $\frac{1}{4} = 0.25$

**G** $0.5 = \frac{4}{8}$

**H** $1.2 = 1\frac{1}{4}$

**J** $0.2 = 0.20$

## Spiral Review

**42.** Elliott's age and his brother's age have a sum of 15. Elliott's age is twice as much as his brother's. How old are the boys? (Lesson 14-6) **10, 5**

**Compare. Use >, <, or =.** (Lesson 14-5)

**43.** 0.70 ● 0.07 **>** **44.** 8.75 ● 8.7 **>** **45.** 19.70 ● 19.7 **=**

**Identify these quadrilaterals as *square, rhombus, rectangle, parallelogram,* or *trapezoid.*** (Lesson 9-6)

**46.**  **parallelogram**

**47.** 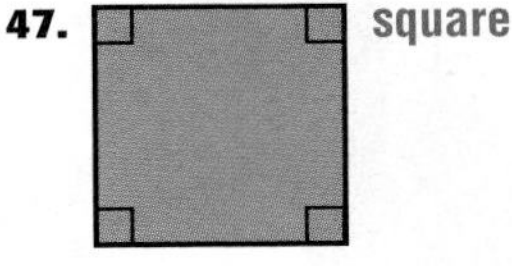 **square**

**Estimate. Check your estimate.** (Lesson 8-4)

**48.** 153 ÷ 3 **150 ÷ 3 = 50**

**49.** 347 ÷ 5 **350 ÷ 5 = 70**

**50.** 638 ÷ 8 **640 ÷ 8 = 80**



### Homework Practice (p. 40) OL

14–7 Name ________ Date ________

**Homework Practice**

*Fraction and Decimal Equivalents*

**Write a fraction and decimal to describe the shaded part of each model.**

1. $\frac{1}{5}$ 0.2
2. $\frac{1}{10}$ 0.1
3. $\frac{6}{10}$ 0.6
4. $\frac{9}{100}$ 0.09

**Write each fraction as a decimal.**

5. $\frac{77}{100}$ **0.77** 6. $\frac{12}{100}$ **0.12** 7. $\frac{5}{10}$ **0.5**

8. $\frac{8}{10}$ **0.8** 9. $\frac{55}{100}$ **0.55**

**Spiral Review**

**Use any strategy shown below to solve. (Lesson 14-6)**

- Look for a pattern
- Work a simpler problem
- Use logical reasoning
- Draw a picture
- Make a model

**10.** Nadia's mom gave her $5 for lunch. Her two younger sisters each received $4 for lunch. Nadia's mom had $19 left over. How much money did she start with? **$32**

**11.** What is the rule for the pattern shown? What number comes next? 12, 16, 15, 19, **add 4 then subtract 1; 18**

Grade 4 40 Chapter 14

# 4 Assess

## Formative Assessment

Write the fraction $\frac{1}{5}$ on the board.

- **How would you find the decimal equivalent of $\frac{1}{5}$?** Sample answer: Change $\frac{1}{5}$ to $\frac{2}{10}$ and then change $\frac{2}{10}$ to the decimal 0.2.
- **What is another decimal that is equivalent to 0.2?** 0.20

**Quick Check** **Are students continuing to struggle with fraction and decimal equivalents?**

**If Yes** → Small Group Options (p. 596B)

**If No** → Independent Work Options (p. 596B)
CRM Skills Practice Worksheet (p. 39)
CRM Enrich Worksheet (p. 42)

**Into the Future** Have students write a few sentences about how they think today's lesson on fraction and decimal equivalents will help them with tomorrow's lesson on decimals, fractions, and mixed numbers.

## TEST Practice

### Reviews Lessons 14-5 and 14-7

Assign the Test Practice problems to provide daily reinforcement of test-taking skills.

## Spiral Review

### Reviews Lessons 8-4, 9-6, 14-5, and 14-6

Review and assess mastery of skills and concepts from previous chapters.

# Lesson Planner

## Objective

Interpret information and data from music to solve problems.

### National Standard 

Students read whole, half, dotted half, quarter, and eighth notes and rests in $\frac{2}{4}$, $\frac{3}{4}$ and $\frac{4}{4}$ meter signatures.

## Activate Prior Knowledge

Before you turn students' attention to the pages, ask them to discuss musical notes.

- **What are musical notes based on?** fractions
- **Which musical note is equivalent to 1?** a whole note

## Using the Student Page

Ask students to read the information on p. 600 and answer these questions:

- **If you have seven quarter notes in a row, what mixed number does that represent?** $1\frac{3}{4}$
- **How many half notes are equivalent to 10 whole notes?** 20





# Decimal Note-ation

**Musical notes are a universal language. Musical notes are based on fractions. The most common musical notes include whole, half, quarter, eighth, and sixteenth notes. These values represent the duration of the notes. The durations of the notes are not specific; they are relative to the other notes. For example, a one-eighth note is twice as long as a one-sixteenth note, a one-fourth note is twice as long as a one-eighth note, and so on.**

**Did You Know?** Beethoven was the first musician to use the one-hundred twenty-eighth note.

## Musical Notes and Equivalent Fractions

| Note | Notation | Fractional Equivalent |
|---|---|---|
| Whole | 𝅝 | $\frac{1}{1}$ |
| Half | 𝅗𝅥 | $\frac{1}{2}$ |
| Quarter | ♩ | $\frac{1}{4}$ |

## Real-World Math

**Use the table above to solve each problem.**

**Write the value of each musical note as a decimal.**

1. 𝅝 1.0
2. 𝅗𝅥 0.5
3. ♩ 0.25
4. Refer to Exercises 1–3. Draw a number line that shows these values. See margin.

**Write the value of each musical note as a mixed number. Then write each mixed number as a decimal.**

5. 𝅝 𝅗𝅥 $1\frac{1}{2}$, 1.5
6. 𝅝 ♩ ♩ ♩ $1\frac{3}{4}$, 1.75
7. 𝅝 𝅝 𝅝 𝅝 ♩ $4\frac{1}{4}$, 4.25
8. Draw three musical notes that represent a value of 2.5. See margin.
9. Draw four musical notes that represent a value of $2\frac{1}{4}$. See margin.

### Additional Answers

4. 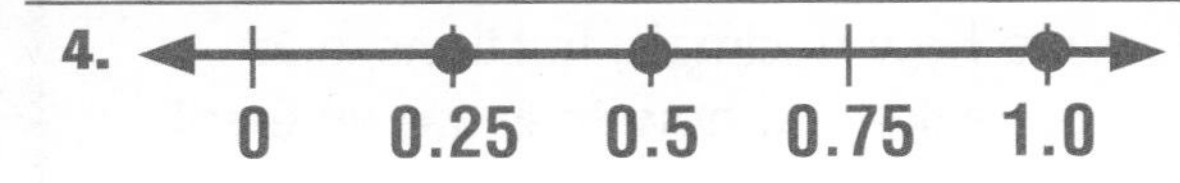


8. 

9. 

## Real-World Math

Assign the exercises on p. 601. Encourage students to choose a problem-solving strategy before beginning each exercise. If necessary, review the strategies suggested in Lesson 14-6, p. 595.

**Exercise 1** Remind students that a whole note may have a different number of beats depending on the time signature, but it always equals one measure.

**Exercise 5** Remind students to use the fraction part of the mixed number to get the decimal.

**Exercise 7** Remind students to use the fraction part of the mixed number to get the decimal.

**WRITING IN MATH** Have students create a word problem that uses the information found in the text and in the chart on pp. 600–601.

## Extend the Activity

Explain the eighth-note to students in relation to the other notes, and have them express fractions and decimals in musical phrases using the new note they have learned.

LESSON 14-8

# Decimals, Fractions, and Mixed Numbers

## Lesson Planner

### Objective

Compare and order decimals, fractions, and mixed numbers.

### Review Vocabulary

**decimal, fraction, mixed number**

### Resources

**Materials:** hundredths grids, colored pencils or markers, number lines

**Literature Connection:** *Eating Fractions* by Bruce McMillan

**Alternate Lesson:** Use *IMPACT Mathematics:* Unit E to provide practice with decimals.

**Teacher Technology**

TeacherWorks • Interactive Classroom

## Daily Routine

Use these suggestions before beginning the lesson on p. 602.

### 5-Minute Check

(Reviews Lesson 14-7)

**Write as a decimal.**

1. $\frac{34}{100}$ 0.34
2. $\frac{7}{10}$ 0.7
3. $\frac{2}{5}$ 0.4
4. $\frac{4}{25}$ 0.16
5. $\frac{2}{4}$ 0.5
6. $\frac{4}{5}$ 0.8

### Problem of the Day

Amy's family hiked for 1 hour and 25 minutes before they took a 10-minute rest. Then they hiked for 1 hour and 15 minutes until they reached the lake. If they arrived at the lake at 1:05 P.M., what time did they begin? 10:15 A.M.

### Focus on Math Background

An advantage of a number line for comparisons is that a common denominator is not needed. Students should also be able to use conversion to decimal form with place-value charts to compare halves, fourths, fifths, tenths, and hundredths. They should be able to provide several representations (e.g., number lines, place-value charts, common denominators, concrete models) to demonstrate such comparisons. But after much practice with such representations, they should also be able to order simple fractions mentally as well.

### Review Math Vocabulary

Write the review vocabulary words and their definitions on the board.

Have students write how decimals, fractions, and mixed numbers are alike and how they are different.

#### Visual Vocabulary Cards

Use Visual Vocabulary Cards 8, 18 and 25 to reinforce the vocabulary reviewed in this lesson. (The Define/Example/Ask routine is printed on the back of each card.)

# Differentiated Instruction

## Small Group Options

SOCIAL, LOGICAL

### Below Level BL

**Materials:** index cards with decimals, mixed numbers, and fractions written on them, string, paper clips, tape

- Divide the class into small groups and give each group a stack of cards.
- Have students use tape to hang a piece of string from a chosen location in the classroom.
- Each student chooses a card. They should then work together to order the numbers from least to greatest on the string with paper clips.
- Have students peer-check answers and assist any member having difficulty.

Option 2

INTRAPERSONAL, LINGUISTIC

### English Language Learners ELL

**Materials:** journals
**Core Vocabulary:** point, I know, complete
**Common Use Verb:** traded

**Write Math** This strategy uses a scripted sentence to help students write about ordering decimals, fractions, and mixed numbers.

- Write 3.65 and $3\frac{1}{4}$ on the board. Ask: "Which number is greater?"
- Demonstrate to students how to change the fraction to a decimal by saying "I traded $3\frac{1}{4}$ to 3.25, and **I know** 2 is less than six."
- Repeat for another set of numbers.
- Ask students to complete the following sentence in their journal: I traded ____ to ____, and I know ____ is greater than ____.

*Use this worksheet to provide additional support for English Language Learners.*

**English Language Learners (p. 25) ELL**

8 Name ____________

**Decimals**

You're a baseball team manager. Name your baseball team and each player. Decide how many times each player was at bat. How many hits were made? Calculate each player's batting average. Round to the thousandths, the hundredths, and the tenths place.

Team name: ____________

| PLAYER AND POSITION | AT BAT | HITS | .000 | .00 | .0 | FRACTION |
|---|---|---|---|---|---|---|
| 1. | | | | | | |
| 2. | | | | | | |
| 3. | | | | | | |
| 4. | | | | | | |
| 5. | | | | | | |
| 6. | | | | | | |
| 7. | | | | | | |
| 8. | | | | | | |
| 9. | | | | | | |

Decimals to the Thousandths 25

## Independent Work Options

Option 1

SPATIAL

### Early Finishers OL AL

**Materials:** set of 20 index cards marked with mixed numbers and decimals

- Have students play the game in pairs. They will shuffle the index cards and place them facedown in a pile.
- Tell students to take turns drawing cards until they have each drawn four. They will then order their cards from least to greatest on the table.
- Have students check each other's work.

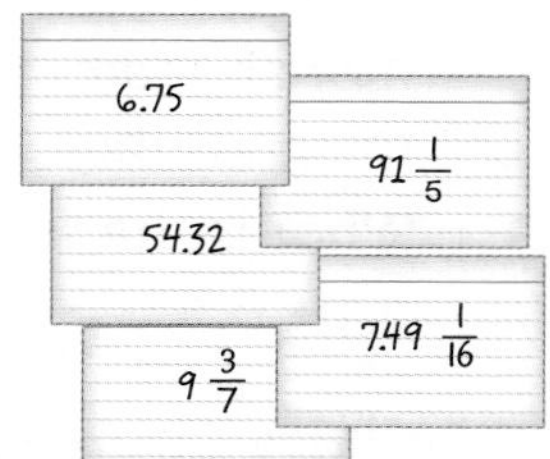


Option 2

### Student Technology

Tech Link

macmillanmh.com

Personal Tutor • Extra Examples

### Learning Station: Science (p. 574H)

Direct students to the Science Learning Station for opportunities to explore and extend the lesson concept.

Option 4

### Problem-Solving Practice

Reinforce problem-solving skills and strategies with the Problem-Solving Practice worksheet.

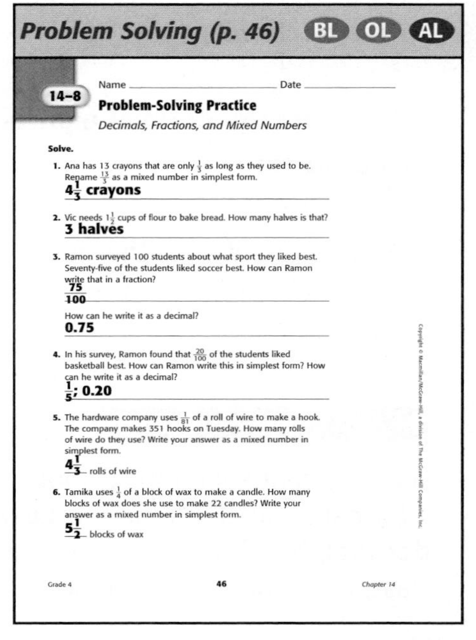

**Problem Solving (p. 46) BL OL AL**

14–8 Name ____________ Date ____________

**Problem-Solving Practice**

*Decimals, Fractions, and Mixed Numbers*

**Solve.**

1. Ana has 13 crayons that are only $\frac{1}{3}$ as long as they used to be. Rename $\frac{13}{3}$ as a mixed number in simplest form.
**$4\frac{1}{3}$ crayons**
2. Vic needs $1\frac{1}{2}$ cups of flour to bake bread. How many halves is that?
**3 halves**
3. Ramon surveyed 100 students about what sport they liked best. Seventy-five of the students liked soccer best. How can Ramon write that in a fraction?
**$\frac{75}{100}$**
How can he write it as a decimal?
**0.75**
4. In his survey, Ramon found that $\frac{20}{100}$ of the students liked basketball best. How can Ramon write this in simplest form? How can he write it as a decimal?
**$\frac{1}{5}$; 0.20**
5. The hardware company uses $\frac{1}{81}$ of a roll of wire to make a hook. The company makes 351 hooks on Tuesday. How many rolls of wire do they use? Write your answer as a mixed number in simplest form.
**$4\frac{1}{3}$** rolls of wire
6. Tamika uses $\frac{1}{4}$ of a block of wax to make a candle. How many blocks of wax does she use to make 22 candles? Write your answer as a mixed number in simplest form.
**$5\frac{1}{2}$** blocks of wax



Grade 4 46 Chapter 14

# 14-8 Decimals, Fractions, and Mixed Numbers

## 1 Introduce

### Activity Choice 1 • Hands-On

- Write the following decimals on the board: 0.56, 0.48, 0.72, 0.07.
- Have students shade hundredths grids to show each number. Then have them order their grids from least to greatest.
- **How do you know which decimal is the least and which is the greatest?** 0.07 has the fewest squares shaded, and 0.72 has the most shaded.
- Have students shade $\frac{1}{4}$, $\frac{1}{2}$, and $\frac{3}{4}$ of three more hundredths grids. Have them order all of the grids they shaded from least to greatest.
- **What is the final order?** 0.07, $\frac{1}{4}$, 0.48, $\frac{1}{2}$, 0.56, 0.72, $\frac{3}{4}$

### Activity Choice 2 • Literature

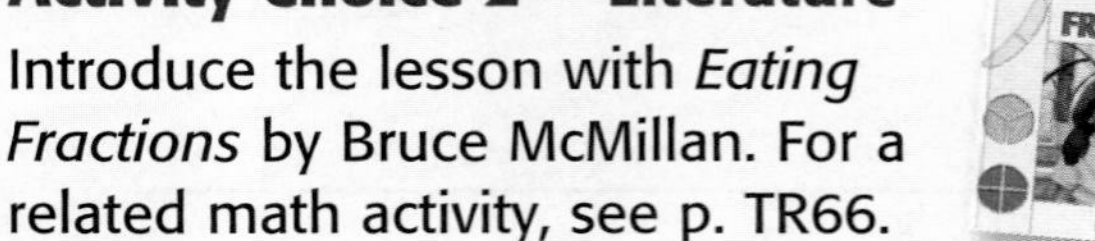

Introduce the lesson with *Eating Fractions* by Bruce McMillan. For a related math activity, see p. TR66.

## 2 Teach

### Scaffolding Questions

Write the following on the board: $\frac{2}{8}$, $\frac{3}{5}$, $\frac{3}{6}$, $\frac{4}{20}$.

- **How do you change these fractions to decimals?** Write each fraction with a denominator of 10 or 100, then write them as decimals.
- **In the fraction $\frac{2}{8}$, 8 is not a factor of 10 or 100. What is another way to think about this fraction?** $\frac{2}{8} = \frac{1}{4}$ and 4 is a factor of 100. So $\frac{2}{8} = \frac{1}{4} = 0.25$.
- **What are the decimal equivalents for each of the fractions?** $\frac{2}{8} = 0.25$, $\frac{3}{5} = 0.6$, $\frac{3}{6} = 0.5$, $\frac{4}{20} = 0.20$
- Have students use the decimal equivalents of the fractions to order the fractions from least to greatest. $\frac{4}{20}$, $\frac{2}{8}$, $\frac{3}{6}$, $\frac{3}{5}$

### GET READY to Learn

Have students open their books and read the information in **Get Ready to Learn**. Review **decimal**, **fraction**, and **mixed number**. As a class, work through **Example 1**.



# 14-8 Decimals, Fractions, and Mixed Numbers

**MAIN IDEA**

I will compare and order decimals, fractions, and mixed numbers.

**Math Online**

macmillanmh.com
- Extra Examples
- Personal Tutor
- Self-Check Quiz

### GET READY to Learn

The table shows the number of inches Walter grew each year for four years. At what age did Walter grow the most inches? the fewest inches?

**Walter's Change in Growth**

| Age | Growth (in.) |
|---|---|
| 7 | 2.5 |
| 8 | $2\frac{1}{4}$ |
| 9 | 2.0 |
| 10 | $2\frac{3}{4}$ |

To compare fractions and decimals, you can write the fractions as decimals and then compare.

### Real-World EXAMPLE

**1 MEASUREMENT At what age did Walter grow the most inches? the fewest inches?**

**Step 1** Write $2\frac{1}{4}$ and $2\frac{3}{4}$ as decimals.

$2\frac{1}{4} = 2.25$ $\quad$ $2\frac{3}{4} = 2.75$

**Step 2** Compare 2.5, $2\frac{1}{4}$, 2.0, and $2\frac{3}{4}$.

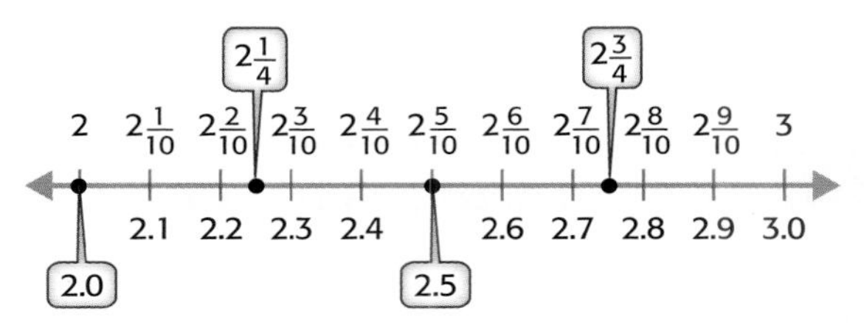


The order from greatest to least is $2\frac{3}{4}$, 2.5, $2\frac{1}{4}$, and 2.0. So, Walter grew the most when he was 10 and the least when he was 9.



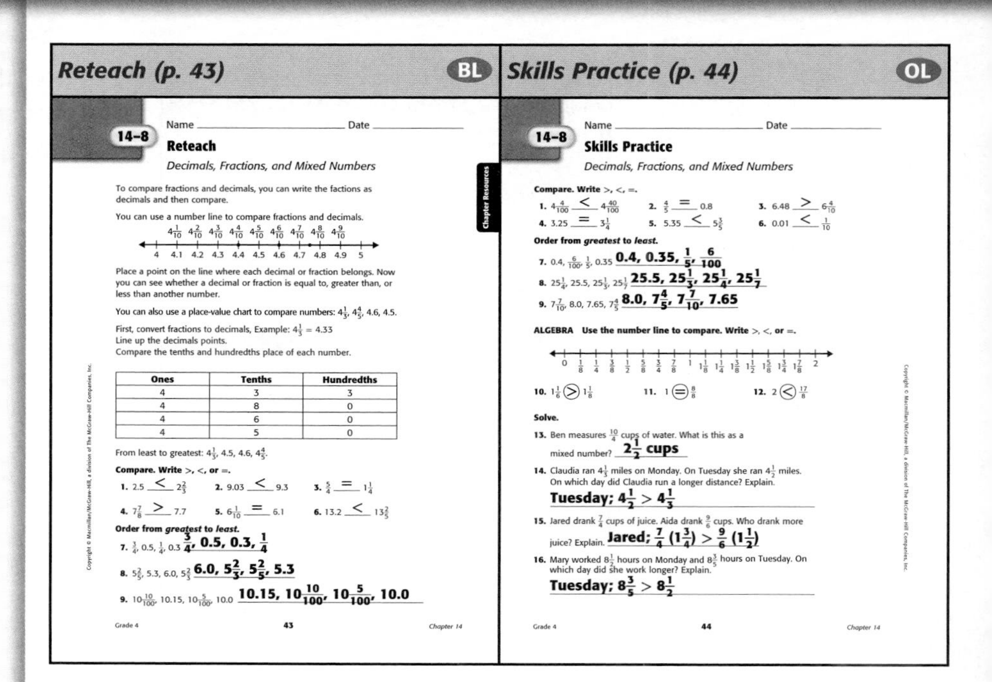

**Reteach (p. 43)** BL

14-8 Name ______ Date ______

**Reteach**

*Decimals, Fractions, and Mixed Numbers*

To compare fractions and decimals, you can write the factions as decimals and then compare.

You can use a number line to compare fractions and decimals.

$4\frac{1}{10}$ $4\frac{2}{10}$ $4\frac{3}{10}$ $4\frac{4}{10}$ $4\frac{5}{10}$ $4\frac{6}{10}$ $4\frac{7}{10}$ $4\frac{8}{10}$ $4\frac{9}{10}$

4 4.1 4.2 4.3 4.4 4.5 4.6 4.7 4.8 4.9 5

Place a point on the line where each decimal or fraction belongs. Now you can see whether a decimal or fraction is equal to, greater than, or less than another number.

You can also use a place-value chart to compare numbers: $4\frac{1}{3}$, $4\frac{4}{5}$, 4.6, 4.5.

First, convert fractions to decimals, Example: $4\frac{1}{3} = 4.33$
Line up the decimals points.
Compare the tenths and hundredths place of each number.

| Ones | Tenths | Hundredths |
|---|---|---|
| 4 | 3 | 3 |
| 4 | 8 | 0 |
| 4 | 6 | 0 |
| 4 | 5 | 0 |

From least to greatest: $4\frac{1}{3}$, 4.5, 4.6, $4\frac{4}{5}$.

**Compare. Write >, <, or =.**

1. 2.5 __<__ $2\frac{2}{3}$ 2. 9.03 __<__ 9.3 3. $\frac{5}{4}$ __=__ $1\frac{1}{4}$
4. $7\frac{7}{8}$ __>__ 7.7 5. $6\frac{1}{10}$ __=__ 6.1 6. 13.2 __<__ $13\frac{2}{5}$

**Order from *greatest* to *least*.**

7. $\frac{3}{4}$, 0.5, $\frac{1}{4}$, 0.3 **$\frac{3}{4}$, 0.5, 0.3, $\frac{1}{4}$**
8. $5\frac{2}{5}$, 5.3, 6.0, $5\frac{2}{3}$ **6.0, $5\frac{2}{3}$, $5\frac{2}{5}$, 5.3**
9. $10\frac{10}{100}$, 10.15, $10\frac{5}{100}$, 10.0 **10.15, $10\frac{10}{100}$, $10\frac{5}{100}$, 10.0**

Grade 4 43 Chapter 14



Chapter Resources

**Skills Practice (p. 44)** OL

14-8 Name ______ Date ______

**Skills Practice**

*Decimals, Fractions, and Mixed Numbers*

**Compare. Write >, <, =.**

1. $4\frac{4}{100}$ __<__ $4\frac{40}{100}$ 2. $\frac{4}{5}$ __=__ 0.8 3. 6.48 __>__ $6\frac{4}{10}$
4. 3.25 __=__ $3\frac{1}{4}$ 5. 5.35 __<__ $5\frac{3}{5}$ 6. 0.01 __<__ $\frac{1}{10}$

**Order from *greatest* to *least*.**

7. 0.4, $\frac{6}{100}$, $\frac{1}{5}$, 0.35 **0.4, 0.35, $\frac{1}{5}$, $\frac{6}{100}$**
8. $25\frac{1}{4}$, 25.5, $25\frac{1}{3}$, $25\frac{1}{7}$ **25.5, $25\frac{1}{3}$, $25\frac{1}{4}$, $25\frac{1}{7}$**
9. $7\frac{7}{10}$, 8.0, 7.65, $7\frac{4}{5}$ **8.0, $7\frac{4}{5}$, $7\frac{7}{10}$, 7.65**

**ALGEBRA Use the number line to compare. Write >, <, or =.**

0 $\frac{1}{8}$ $\frac{1}{4}$ $\frac{3}{8}$ $\frac{1}{2}$ $\frac{5}{8}$ $\frac{3}{4}$ $\frac{7}{8}$ 1 $1\frac{1}{8}$ $1\frac{1}{4}$ $1\frac{3}{8}$ $1\frac{1}{2}$ $1\frac{5}{8}$ $1\frac{3}{4}$ $1\frac{7}{8}$ 2

10. $1\frac{1}{6}$ (>) $1\frac{1}{8}$ 11. 1 (=) $\frac{8}{8}$ 12. 2 (<) $\frac{17}{8}$

**Solve.**

13. Ben measures $\frac{10}{4}$ cups of water. What is this as a mixed number? **$2\frac{1}{2}$ cups**
14. Claudia ran $4\frac{1}{3}$ miles on Monday. On Tuesday she ran $4\frac{1}{2}$ miles. On which day did Claudia run a longer distance? Explain. **Tuesday; $4\frac{1}{2} > 4\frac{1}{3}$**
15. Jared drank $\frac{7}{4}$ cups of juice. Aida drank $\frac{9}{6}$ cups. Who drank more juice? Explain. **Jared; $\frac{7}{4}$ $(1\frac{3}{4}) > \frac{9}{6}$ $(1\frac{1}{2})$**
16. Mary worked $8\frac{1}{2}$ hours on Monday and $8\frac{3}{5}$ hours on Tuesday. On which day did she work longer? Explain. **Tuesday; $8\frac{3}{5} > 8\frac{1}{2}$**

Grade 4 44 Chapter 14

## CHECK What You Know

**Use a number line to compare. Use >, <, or =.** See Example 1 (p. 602)

**1.** 1.25 ● $1\frac{1}{4}$ =  **2.** 9.2 ● $9\frac{2}{10}$ =  **3.** $3\frac{3}{100}$ ● 3.3 <  **4.** 6.6 ● $6\frac{5}{10}$ >

**Use a number line to order from greatest to least.** See Example 1 (p. 602)

**5.** 6.34, $6\frac{1}{4}$, 6.5, and $6\frac{21}{100}$ **5.** 6.5, 6.34, $6\frac{1}{4}$, $6\frac{21}{100}$

**6.** $6\frac{1}{5}$, 6.48, $6\frac{4}{10}$, and 6.12 6.48, $6\frac{4}{10}$, $6\frac{1}{5}$, 6.12

**7.** Which plant food produced a plant with highest growth? Explain. See margin.

| Plant Food | Feed Me! | Magic Touch | Feed Booster | Garden Growth |
|---|---|---|---|---|
| Plant Growth (in.) | $3\frac{7}{10}$ | 3.1 | $3\frac{1}{2}$ | 3.36 |

**8.** Talk About It Is the number sentence $5.5 = 5\frac{3}{6} = \frac{44}{8}$ true? Explain.
yes; All of those numbers are equal to 5.5.

## Practice and Problem Solving

EXTRA PRACTICE
See page R38.

**Use a number line to compare. Use >, <, or =.** See Example 1 (p. 602)

**9.** 7 ● $6\frac{9}{10}$ >  **10.** 3.03 ● $3\frac{3}{100}$ =  **11.** $\frac{16}{4}$ ● 4 =  **12.** 8.2 ● 8 >

**13.** 5.3 ● 5.03 >  **14.** $4\frac{1}{10}$ ● 4.1 =  **15.** 12.5 ● $12\frac{2}{5}$ >  **16.** 15.36 ● 15.4 <

**Use a number line to order from greatest to least.** See Example 1 (p. 602) 17–20. See margin.

**17.** $10\frac{1}{2}$, 10.9, $10\frac{36}{100}$, 10.75  **18.** 5.71, $5\frac{67}{100}$, $4\frac{5}{10}$, 4.75

**19.** $\frac{5}{10}$, $\frac{3}{4}$, 0.38, $\frac{25}{100}$, $\frac{1}{1}$  **20.** $\frac{4}{5}$, 2.25, $2\frac{3}{4}$, 2.77

**Write the letter that represents each mixed number or decimal.**

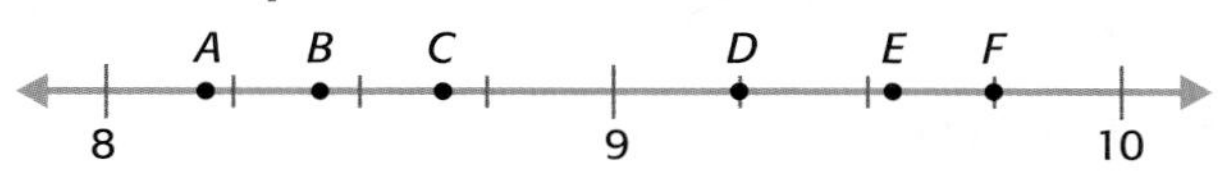


**21.** $9\frac{6}{10}$ *E*  **22.** 8.2 *A*  **23.** $8\frac{3}{5}$ *C*  **24.** $9\frac{1}{4}$ *D*

**25. Measurement** The table at the right shows the amount of rainfall Capitol City received during three months. Order the amounts of rain received from greatest to least.
3.25; $3\frac{2}{10}$, $2\frac{89}{100}$

| Month | Rainfall (in.) |
|---|---|
| March | $2\frac{89}{100}$ |
| April | 3.25 |
| May | $3\frac{2}{10}$ |



### Additional Answers

**7.** Sample answer: Feed Me!; Find the fractional equivalent for each decimal, then compare.

**17.** 10.9; 10.75; $10\frac{1}{2}$; $10\frac{36}{100}$

**18.** 5.71, $5\frac{67}{100}$, 4.75, $4\frac{5}{10}$

**19.** $\frac{1}{1}$, $\frac{3}{4}$, $\frac{5}{10}$, 0.38; $\frac{25}{100}$

**20.** 2.77; $2\frac{3}{4}$, 2.25, $\frac{4}{5}$

### Real-World Example

**Example 1** Be sure students understand that they can first convert fractions to decimals before comparing and ordering them.

### ADDITIONAL EXAMPLE

**1** Mr. Chi cut four boards of lengths 17.35 cm, $17\frac{1}{2}$ cm, 17.2 cm, and $17\frac{6}{8}$ cm. Order the lengths from least to greatest.
17.2 cm, 17.35 cm, $17\frac{1}{2}$ cm, $17\frac{6}{8}$ cm

### CHECK What You Know

As a class, have students complete Exercises 1–8 in **Check What You Know** as you observe their work.

**Exercise 8** Assess student comprehension before assigning practice exercises.

### BL Alternate Teaching Strategy

**If** students have trouble comparing and ordering decimals, fractions, and mixed numbers…

**Then** use one of these reteach options:

1 CRM **Daily Reteach Worksheet** (p. 43)

2 Have them use hundredths grids to model each number and then order the grids from most shaded to least shaded.

- **If you shade $\frac{1}{4}$ of a hundredths grid, how many squares are shaded?** 25
- **If $\frac{3}{4}$ of the grid is shaded, how many squares are shaded?** 75

## 3 Practice

Differentiate practice using these leveled assignments for Exercises 9–27.

| Level | Assignment |
|---|---|
| BL Below/Approaching Level | 9–12, 17–18, 21, 23, 25 |
| OL On Level | 10–15, 18–20, 22–25, 27 |
| AL Above/Beyond Level | 9–25 odd, 26–27 |

Have students discuss and complete the Higher Order Thinking problems. Encourage them to record the decimal equivalents for all of the mixed numbers in the problems before deciding on the correct answer.

# Assess

## Formative Assessment

Write the following numbers on the board: $32\frac{3}{5}$, 32.77, $32\frac{1}{20}$, 32.08.

- **What are the steps in ordering these numbers from greatest to least?** First, convert $32\frac{3}{5}$ and $32\frac{1}{20}$ to the decimals 32.6 and 32.05. Then use a number line to write the decimals from greatest to least.
- **What is the correct order?** 32.77, $32\frac{3}{5}$, 32.08, $32\frac{1}{20}$

**Quick Check** **Are students continuing to struggle with comparing and ordering decimals, fractions, and mixed numbers?**

**If Yes** → Small Group Options (p. 602B)

**If No** → Independent Work Options (p. 602B)
CRM Skills Practice Worksheet (p. 44)
CRM Enrich Worksheet (p. 47)

**Yesterday's News** Have students explain how yesterday's lesson on fraction and decimal equivalents helped them with today's lesson on comparing and ordering decimals, fractions, and mixed numbers.

## TEST Practice

### Reviews Lessons 14-7 and 14-8

Assign the Test Practice problems to provide daily reinforcement of test-taking skills.

## Spiral Review

### Reviews Lessons 14-5, 14-6, and 14-7

Review and assess mastery of skills and concepts from previous chapters.

### COMMON ERROR!

**Exercises 17–20** Students may try to order the numbers before converting the mixed numbers to decimals. Encourage them to write the list of numbers on a number line after converting the mixed numbers to decimals and then write them in order from greatest to least.



## H.O.T. Problems

**26. FIND THE ERROR** Alicia and Chris are identifying the number point *C* represents. Who is correct? Explain. **See Ch. 14 Answer Appendix.**

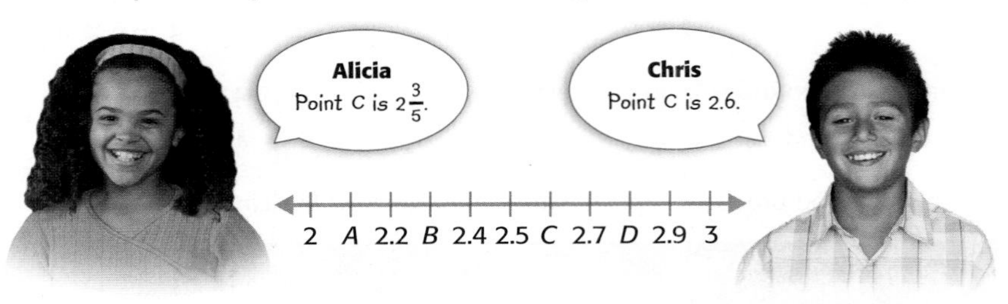


**27. WHICH ONE DOESN'T BELONG?** Identify the number that does not belong with the others. Explain. **3.05 does not belong because it does not equal 3.5**

| three and five tenths | 3 + 0.5 | $3\frac{1}{2}$ | 3.05 |
|---|---|---|---|

**28.** Which fraction means the same as 0.25? (Lesson 14-7) **B**

**A** $\frac{2}{10}$ **C** $\frac{2}{5}$
**B** $\frac{1}{4}$ **D** $\frac{5}{10}$

**29.** Which letter represents the number closest to 3.6? (Lesson 14-8) **J**

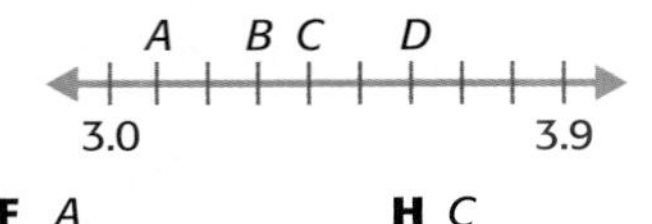


**F** *A* **H** *C*
**G** *B* **J** *D*

## Spiral Review

**Write each fraction as a decimal.** (Lesson 14-7)

**30.** $\frac{4}{10}$ **0.4** **31.** $\frac{35}{100}$ **0.35** **32.** $\frac{4}{5}$ **0.8**

**33. Measurement** Trent went to a movie. It started at 3:25 P.M. and lasted 135 minutes. What time was the movie over? (Lesson 14-6) **5:40 P.M.**

**Order from greatest to least.** (Lesson 14-5)

**34.** 1.5, 1.8, 1.2, 2.1 **2.1, 1.8, 1.5, 1.2**
**35.** 3.2, 2.3, 3.23, 2.32 **3.23, 3.2, 2.32, 2.3**
**36.** 7.8, 8.78, 7.88, 8.7 **8.78, 8.7, 7.88, 7.8**



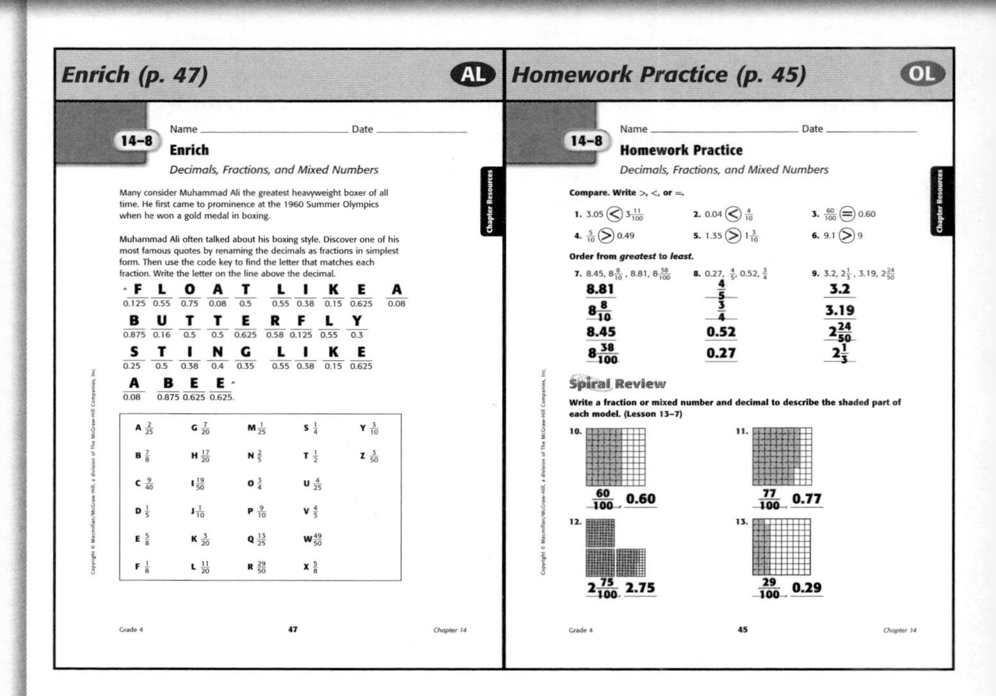

**Enrich (p. 47)** AL

14–8 Name ______ Date ______
**Enrich**
*Decimals, Fractions, and Mixed Numbers*

Many consider Muhammad Ali the greatest heavyweight boxer of all time. He first came to prominence at the 1960 Summer Olympics when he won a gold medal in boxing.

Muhammad Ali often talked about his boxing style. Discover one of his most famous quotes by renaming the decimals as fractions in simplest form. Then use the code key to find the letter that matches each fraction. Write the letter on the line above the decimal.

"F L O A T L I K E A
0.125 0.55 0.75 0.08 0.5 0.55 0.38 0.15 0.625 0.08
B U T T E R F L Y
0.875 0.16 0.5 0.5 0.625 0.58 0.125 0.55 0.3
S T I N G L I K E
0.25 0.5 0.38 0.4 0.35 0.55 0.38 0.15 0.625
A B E E."
0.08 0.875 0.625 0.625.

| | | | | |
|---|---|---|---|---|
| A $\frac{2}{25}$ | G $\frac{7}{20}$ | M $\frac{1}{25}$ | S $\frac{1}{4}$ | Y $\frac{3}{10}$ |
| B $\frac{7}{8}$ | H $\frac{17}{20}$ | N $\frac{2}{5}$ | T $\frac{1}{2}$ | Z $\frac{3}{50}$ |
| C $\frac{9}{40}$ | I $\frac{19}{50}$ | O $\frac{3}{4}$ | U $\frac{4}{25}$ | |
| D $\frac{1}{5}$ | J $\frac{1}{10}$ | P $\frac{9}{10}$ | V $\frac{4}{5}$ | |
| E $\frac{5}{8}$ | K $\frac{3}{20}$ | Q $\frac{13}{25}$ | W $\frac{49}{50}$ | |
| F $\frac{1}{8}$ | L $\frac{11}{20}$ | R $\frac{29}{50}$ | X $\frac{5}{8}$ | |

Grade 4 47 Chapter 14

**Homework Practice (p. 45)** OL

14–8 Name ______ Date ______
**Homework Practice**
*Decimals, Fractions, and Mixed Numbers*

**Compare. Write >, <, or =.**

**1.** 3.05 (<) $3\frac{11}{100}$ **2.** 0.04 (<) $\frac{4}{10}$ **3.** $\frac{60}{100}$ (=) 0.60
**4.** $\frac{5}{10}$ (>) 0.49 **5.** 1.35 (>) $1\frac{3}{10}$ **6.** 9.1 (>) 9

**Order from *greatest* to *least*.**

**7.** 8.45, $8\frac{8}{10}$, 8.81, $8\frac{38}{100}$ — **8.81, $8\frac{8}{10}$, 8.45, $8\frac{38}{100}$**
**8.** 0.27, $\frac{4}{5}$, 0.52, $\frac{3}{4}$ — **$\frac{4}{5}$, $\frac{3}{4}$, 0.52, 0.27**
**9.** 3.2, $2\frac{1}{3}$, 3.19, $2\frac{24}{50}$ — **3.2, 3.19, $2\frac{24}{50}$, $2\frac{1}{3}$**

**Spiral Review**

**Write a fraction or mixed number and decimal to describe the shaded part of each model. (Lesson 13–7)**

**10.** $\frac{60}{100}$, 0.60 **11.** $\frac{77}{100}$, 0.77
**12.** $2\frac{75}{100}$, 2.75 **13.** $\frac{29}{100}$, 0.29

Grade 4 45 Chapter 14

# Fraction and Decimal Game

**Compare Decimals to Fractions**

*Get Ready!*

**Players:** 2

**You Will Need:** 10 index cards

*Get Set!*

On each index card, write a statement using >, <, or =. Write 5 true statements and 5 false statements. A few examples are shown at the right.

$0.25 < \frac{1}{3}$ $0.5 > \frac{10}{20}$

$0.75 = \frac{3}{4}$ $0.8 < \frac{75}{100}$

*Go!*

- Shuffle the cards.
- Spread out the cards facedown on a desk.
- Player 1 turns over an index card and must say whether the statement is true or false.
- Player 1 keeps the card if the answer is correct, and draws again. If Player 1 is wrong, the index card is put back. Player 2 takes a turn.
- The player who collects the most cards, wins.

**Game Time** Fraction and Decimal Game **605**

## Differentiated Practice

Use these leveled suggestions to differentiate the game for all learners.

| Level | Assignment |
|---|---|
| BL Below/Approaching Level | Students use hundredths grids to model decimals and fractions. |
| OL On Level | Have students play the game with the rules as written. |
| AL Above/Beyond Level | Students rewrite false statements to make them true, and write fractions in their simplest forms for true statements. |

# Fraction and Decimal Game

**Math Concept:**
**Compare Decimals to Fractions**

**Materials:** 10 index cards per student, paper, pencils

Introduce the game on p. 605 to your students to play as a class, in small groups, or at a learning workstation to review concepts introduced in this chapter.

## Instructions

- Students each create a deck of 10 index cards with a >, <, or = statement that may or may not be true on each card, using fractions and decimals, as shown in the example on p. 605.
- Students play in pairs and shuffle their groups of 10 cards together to form a deck of 20 cards.
- Students place the deck, facedown, on the table. They roll a number cube to see who goes first (the highest roller goes first).
- Player 1 turns over a card and must say "true" if the statement is true or "false" if the statement is false. If Player 1 is correct, Player 1 keeps the card and draws again. If not, Player 1 puts the card back into the middle of the deck and Player 2 takes a turn to draw a card. The player who collects the most cards is the winner.
- Student pairs can trade decks with each other to continue playing.

## Extend the Game

Have students play the game using more than 20 cards, and teams of 3 or more players.

# Chapter 14 Study Guide and Review

## FOLDABLES Dinah Zike's Foldables

Use these lesson suggestions to incorporate the Foldables during the chapter. Students can then use their Foldables to review for the test.

**Lesson 14-8** Under the bottom right flap of the Foldable, have students compare and order simple fractions, mixed numbers, and decimals using a number line.

## Key Vocabulary

The page references after each word denote where that term was first introduced. If students have difficulty answering Exercises 1–6, remind them they can use the page references to review the vocabulary.

## Vocabulary Review

Review chapter vocabulary using one of the following options.

- **Visual Vocabulary Cards** (8, 18, 25)
- **eGlossary** at macmillanmh.com

Math Online macmillanmh.com
- STUDY TO GO
- Vocabulary Review

### FOLDABLES Study Organizer GET READY to Study

**Be sure the following Key Vocabulary words and Key Concepts are written in your Foldable.**

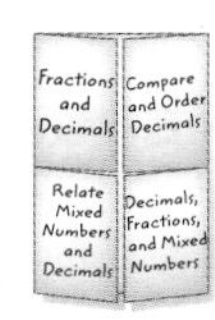


### Key Concepts

**Read, Write, and Model Decimals** (p. 579)

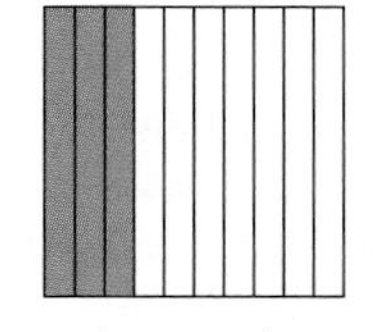

three tenths

$\frac{3}{10}$ or 0.3

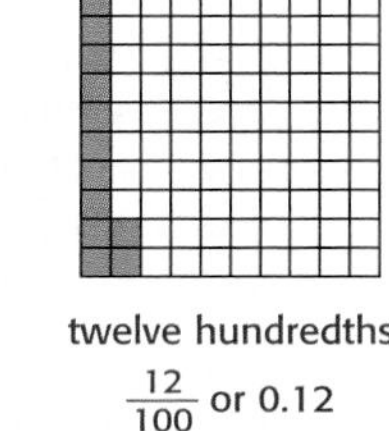

twelve hundredths

$\frac{12}{100}$ or 0.12

**Compare and Order Decimals** (p. 590)

- You can compare and order decimals, fractions, and mixed numbers using a number line.

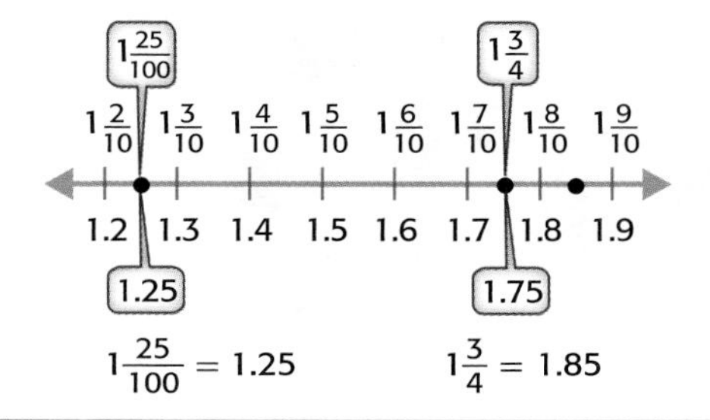


$1\frac{25}{100} = 1.25$ $1\frac{3}{4} = 1.85$

### Key Vocabulary

**decimal** (p. 579)
**decimal point** (p. 579)
**hundredth** (p. 580)
**tenth** (p. 580)

### Vocabulary Check

**Complete each sentence with the correct vocabulary word.**

1. In 0.56, the ___?___ is between the 0 and 5. **decimal point**
2. A(n) ___?___ is a number that uses place value, numbers, and a decimal point to show part of a whole. **decimal**
3. The underlined digit in 1.36 is in the ___?___ place. **tenths**
4. Since the number 0.36 has a 6 in the ___?___ place, the fraction is written as $\frac{36}{100}$. **hundredths**
5. The underlined digit in 0.42 is in the ___?___ place. **hundredths**
6. The ___?___ is always directly to the right of the ones place. **decimal point**

## Chapter 14 Project

### Bake Sale Equivalents

Alone, in pairs, or in small groups, have students discuss the results of their completed chapter project with the class. Assess their work using the Chapter Project rubric found in Chapter 14 Resource Masters, p. 58.

## Lesson-by-Lesson Review

### 14-1 Tenths and Hundredths (pp. 579–581)

**Example 1**

**Write eight tenths as two different decimals.**

Write tenths. Write hundredths.

eight tenths 0.8 — eighty hundredths 0.80

The decimals 0.8 and 0.80 are equivalent decimals.

**7.** Write a fraction and a decimal for the shaded part.

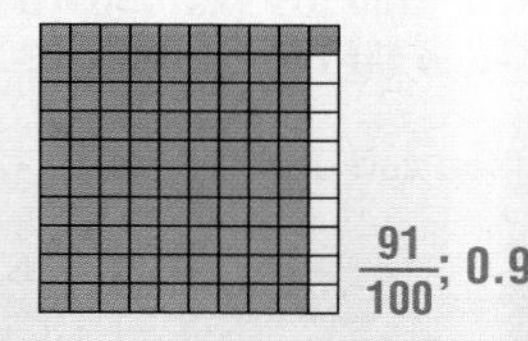

$\frac{91}{100}$; 0.91

**Write as a fraction and as a decimal.**

**8.** three tenths $\frac{3}{10}$; 0.3

**9.** twenty-two hundredths $\frac{22}{100}$; 0.22

**Write each fraction as a decimal.**

**10.** $\frac{1}{10}$ 0.1 **11.** $\frac{60}{100}$ 0.60

### 14-2 Relate Mixed Numbers and Decimals (pp. 582–585)

**Example 2**

**Write $7\frac{52}{100}$ as a decimal.**

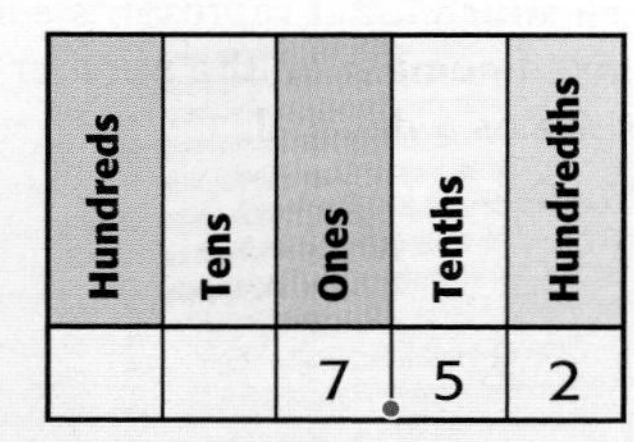


**Mixed Number** $7\frac{52}{100}$

**Read** seven and fifty-two hundredths

**Write** 7.52

**Write each as a mixed number and decimal.**

**12.** forty-six and seven tenths 12. $46\frac{7}{10}$; 46.7

**13.** fifty-one and three hundredths 13. $51\frac{3}{100}$; 51.03

**Write each mixed number as a decimal.**

**14.** $30\frac{3}{100}$ 30.03 **15.** $7\frac{8}{10}$ 7.8

**16. Measurement** A Burmese python is eight and twenty-three hundredths of a meter long. Write its length as a mixed number. $8\frac{23}{100}$



# Lesson-by-Lesson Review

Have students complete the Lesson-by-Lesson Review on pp. 607–610. Then you can use Exam*View*® Assessment Suite to customize another review worksheet that practices all the objectives of this chapter or only the objectives on which your students need more help.

**Intervention** If the given examples are not sufficient to review the topics covered by the questions, use the page references next to the exercises to review that topic in the Student Edition.

# Chapter 14 Study Guide and Review

## 14-3 Problem-Solving Strategy: Make a Model (pp. 586–587)

**Example 3**
**Leo jogged 3 miles. Then he jogged back to his house to get his skateboard. He rode his skateboard for 2 miles. How far did Leo travel?**

You can draw a model.

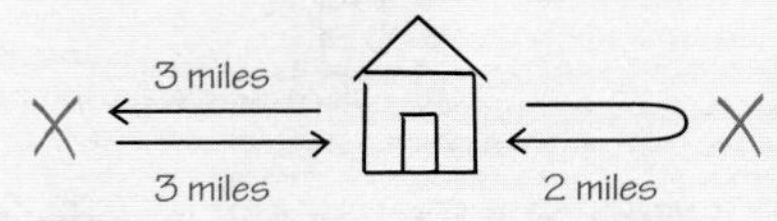


3 mi + 3 mi + 2 mi = 8 mi

So, Leo traveled 8 miles.

**Check** Work backward to check.
8 − 2 − 3 − 3 = 0 ✓

So, the answer is correct.

**17.** There are 12 coins in a piggy bank that equal \$2. What could be the coins in the piggy bank?
Sample answer: 7 quarters, 5 nickles

**18.** Raul paid \$12.50 for a shirt and socks. The socks cost \$1.75. How much was the shirt? \$10.75

**19.** One-fourth of 36 houses receive 1 newspaper each day. The rest of the houses receive 2 newspapers each day. How many newspapers are delivered each day to the 36 houses? 63

**20.** Chandra wants to arrange 18 square tables into one larger rectangular-shaped table with the least perimeter possible. How many tables will be in each row? 3 or 6

## 14-4 Locate Fractions and Decimals on a Number Line (pp. 588–589)

**Example 4**
**Locate $4\frac{1}{2}$ on the number line.**

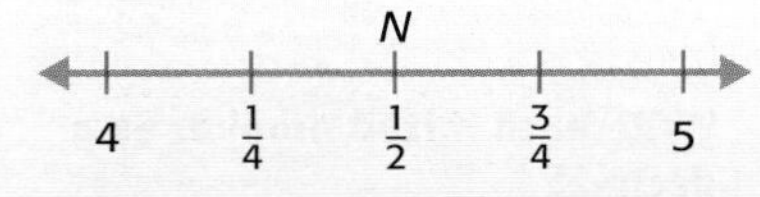


First find 4. Then, find the $\frac{1}{2}$ mark between 4 and 5.

Points on a number line can be represented by a letter.

So, $N = 4\frac{1}{2}$.

21. Y; 5.9
22. P; 16.5

**Tell which letter represents each mixed number on the number line. Write as a decimal.**

**21.** $5\frac{9}{10}$

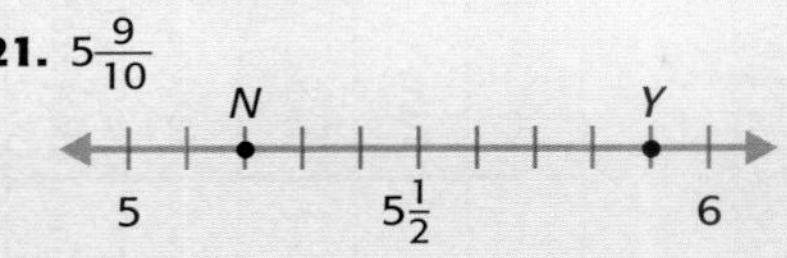


**22.** $16\frac{1}{2}$

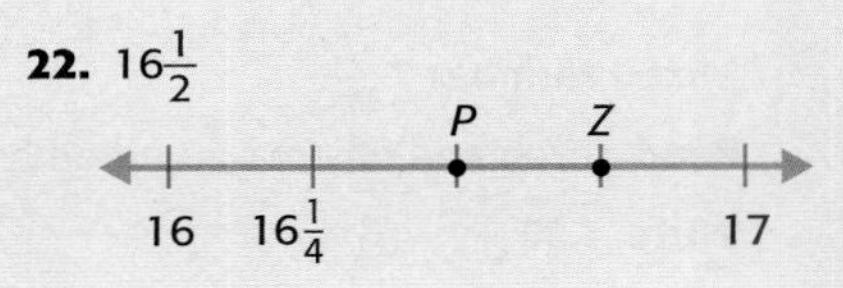

## 14-5 Compare and Order Decimals (pp. 590–592) 27–29. See margin.

**Example 5**
**Compare 7.26 and 7.62.**

| Hundreds | Tens | Ones | Tenths | Hundredths |
|---|---|---|---|---|
| | | 7. | 2 | 6 |
| | | 7. | 6 | 2 |

Since the ones column has the same digits, compare the tenths place.

6 > 2. So, 7.62 > 7.26.

**Compare. Use >, <, or =.**

**23.** 6.50 ● 6.5 = **24.** 2.06 ● 2.05 >

**25.** 0.58 ● 0.59 < **26.** 0.78 ● 0.87 <

**Order from greatest to least.**

**27.** 54.06, 54.6, 54.04, 54.4 27–29. See margin.

**28.** 80.17, 80.2, 80.3, 80.36

**29.** 4.3, 4.25, 4.4, 4.56

**30.** Marion Jones ran a 100-meter dash in 10.65 seconds. Florence Griffith Joyner ran the same distance in 10.49 seconds. Whose time is faster? Florence Griffith Joyner

## 14-6 Problem-Solving Investigation: Choose a Strategy (pp. 594–595)

**Example 6**
**Algebra What is the rule for the pattern 0, 3, 6, 9, 12, ■? What number comes next?**

Each number is 3 more than the number before it

0, 3, 6, 9, 12, ■
+3 +3 +3 +3

So, the rule is +3.

Use the rule, +3, to find the next number in the pattern. So, the next number in the pattern is 12 + 3 or 15.

**Use any strategy to solve.**

**31.** Steph is making a necklace with 15 beads. One third of the beads are red. The rest are black. How many are black? 10

**32.** Jonathan has a $20 bill. He buys a puzzle for $12.69. What will be his change? $7.31

**33.** Andrea pays the train fare of $2.75. What coins can Andrea use to pay for the fare using quarters, dimes, and nickels? See margin.

**34.** A scientist collected samples of bark from 258 trees. She took 4 samples from each tree. How many samples did she take in all? 1,032



### Additional Answers

**27.** Sample answer: 54.6, 54.4, 54.06, 54.04

**28.** Sample answer: 80.36, 80.3, 80.2, 80.17

**29.** Sample answer: 4.56, 4.4, 4.3, 4.25

**33.** Sample answer: 8 quarters, 6 dimes, 3 nickels

# CHAPTER 14 Study Guide and Review

## Additional Answers

**38.** 9.9; 9.75; $9\frac{1}{2}$; $9\frac{36}{100}$

**39.** 56.75; 54.71; $54\frac{67}{100}$; $5\frac{5}{10}$



### 14-7 Fraction and Decimal Equivalents (pp. 596–599)

**Write a fraction and decimal to describe the shaded area.**

**Example 7**

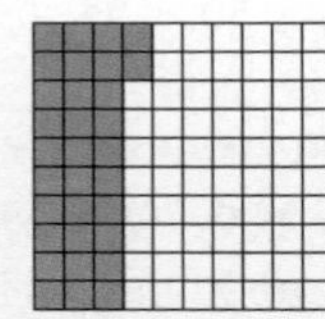

Thirty-two squares are shaded. So, that is $\frac{32}{100}$ or 0.32.

**Example 8**

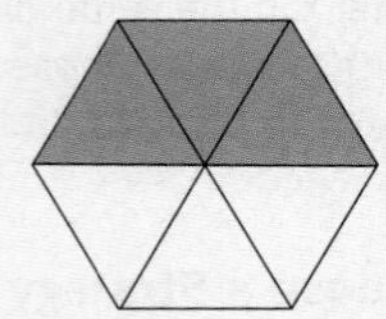

Three triangles are shaded. So, that is $\frac{3}{6}$ or 0.5.

**Write a fraction and decimal to describe the shaded part of each model.**

**35.** 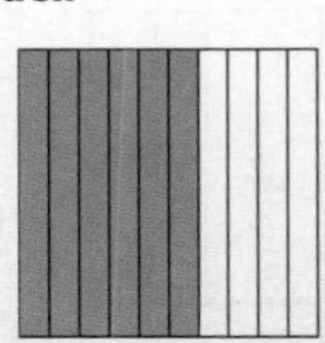 $\frac{6}{10}$; 0.6

**36.** 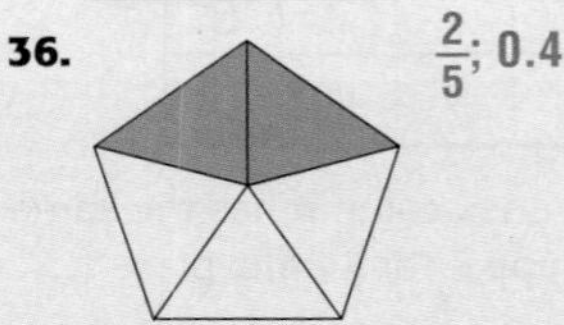 $\frac{2}{5}$; 0.4

**37.** Della gave her brother part of a sandwich and said, "Here is your $\frac{1}{2}$ of the sandwich." Her brother said, "Actually, you ate $\frac{2}{4}$ of it." Who is correct? Explain. **Both are correct because $\frac{2}{4} = \frac{1}{2}$.**

### 14-8 Decimals, Fractions, and Mixed Numbers (pp. 602–604)

**Example 9**
**Order 6.34, $6\frac{1}{4}$, 6.5, and $6\frac{21}{100}$ from greatest to least.**

Write the fractions as decimals. Then, compare.

$6\frac{1}{4} = 6.25$ $\quad$ $6\frac{21}{100} = 6.21$

The order is 6.5, 6.34, $6\frac{1}{4}$, $6\frac{21}{100}$.

**38, 39. See margin.**

**Use a number line to order from greatest to least.**

**38.** $9\frac{1}{2}$; 9.9; $9\frac{36}{100}$; 9.75

**39.** 54.71; $54\frac{67}{100}$; $5\frac{5}{10}$; 56.75

**40.** Some of the fastest Olympic 100-meter times in seconds are 9.85, $\frac{992}{100}$, 9.87, and $\frac{984}{100}$. Order these times from greatest to least. **$\frac{992}{100}$, 9.87, 9.85, $\frac{984}{100}$**



## Additional Answer

**18.** Sample answer: Since the denominator is 10, I know that the 7 should be in the tenths place. The number is 0.7.

# Chapter Test

Math Online macmillanmh.com
• Chapter Test

For Exercises 1 and 2, tell whether each statement is *true* or *false*.

1. To compare fractions and decimals, you can write the fractions as decimals and then compare. true
2. Some decimals can be represented as more than one equivalent fraction. true

Compare. Use >, <, or =.

3. $1.75 \bullet 1\frac{3}{4}$ =
4. $3\frac{2}{100} \bullet 3.2$ <

5. Write a fraction and a decimal for the shaded part. $\frac{5}{10}$, 0.5

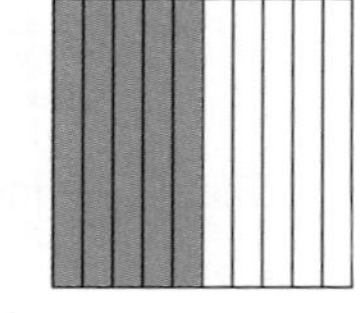

6. **MULTIPLE CHOICE** Which of the number sentences is false? C
   - A $\frac{1}{4} = 0.25$
   - C $1.2 = 1\frac{1}{4}$
   - B $0.75 = \frac{6}{8}$
   - D $0.2 = 0.20$

7. A teacher is arranging 24 desks in a classroom in even rows. How many desks should be placed in each row so that the teacher has the smallest perimeter to walk around? 4 or 6

Write as a fraction and as a decimal.

8. nine tenths $\frac{9}{10}$; 0.9
9. twenty hundredths $\frac{20}{100}$; 0.20

Write each mixed number as a decimal.

10. $4\frac{7}{10}$ 4.7
11. $18\frac{65}{100}$ 18.65

Write a fraction and a decimal to describe the shaded part of the model.

12. 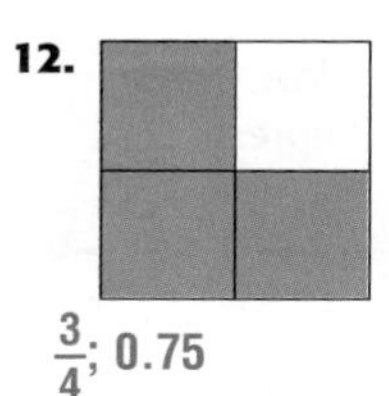
$\frac{3}{4}$; 0.75

13. 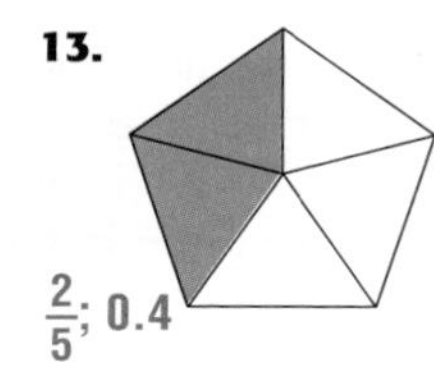
$\frac{2}{5}$; 0.4

Use a number line to order from greatest to least.

14. 7.8; 7.78; 8.78; 8.7 8.78; 8.7; 7.8; 7.78
15. $\frac{3}{4}$; 2.25; $2\frac{3}{4}$; 1.75 $2\frac{3}{4}$; 2.25; 1.75; $\frac{3}{4}$
16. 9.3; $9\frac{1}{4}$; $9\frac{3}{4}$; 9.5 $9\frac{3}{4}$; 9.5; 9.3; $9\frac{1}{4}$

17. **MULTIPLE CHOICE** Look at the number line. Which order of numbers correctly shows the location of the points? G

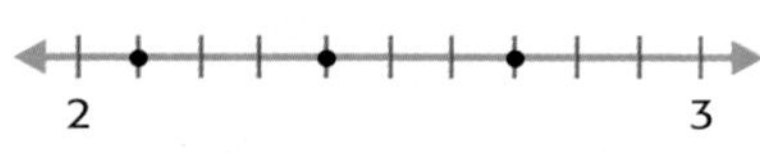


   - F 2.1, 2.2, $2\frac{7}{10}$
   - H 2.01, 2.04, $2\frac{7}{100}$
   - G 2.1, $2\frac{4}{10}$, 2.7
   - J $2\frac{1}{10}$, 2.1, $2\frac{4}{10}$

18. **WRITING IN MATH** Claire was given the following problem: $\frac{7}{10} = 0.\blacksquare$. Explain how you would find the correct answer. See margin.



# Chapter 14 Chapter Test

## Summative Assessment

Use these alternate leveled chapter tests to differentiate assessment for the specific needs of your students.

| Leveled Chapter 14 Tests | | | |
|---|---|---|---|
| Form | Type | Level | CRM Pages |
| 1 | Multiple Choice | BL | 60–61 |
| 2A | Multiple Choice | OL | 62–63 |
| 2B | Multiple Choice | OL | 64–65 |
| 2C | Free Response | OL | 66–67 |
| 2D | Free Response | OL | 68–69 |
| 3 | Free Response | AL | 70–71 |

BL = below/approaching grade level
OL = on grade level
AL = above/beyond grade level

## Vocabulary Test

CRM **Chapter 14 Resource Masters** (p. 55)

ExamView Assessment Suite Customize and create multiple versions of your Chapter Test and the test answer keys.

# Data-Driven Decision Making

Based on the results of the Chapter Test, use the following to review concepts that continue to present students with problems.

| Exercises | State/Local Standards | What's the Math? | Error Analysis | Resources for Review |
|---|---|---|---|---|
| 1–5, 12–17 | | Compare and order decimals, fractions, and mixed numbers.<br>Identify numbers on a number line. | Confuses <, >, and = signs.<br>Orders from least to greatest.<br>Does not understand place value with decimals. | Strategic Intervention Guide (p. 110)<br>CRM Chapter 14 Resource Masters (Reteach)<br>Math Adventures<br>My Math Zone Chapter 14<br>Math Online Extra Examples • Concepts in Motion |
| 6, 8–11, 15–16 | | Relate a fraction to a decimal. | Does not know how to convert fractions to decimals or decimals to fractions. | |

CHAPTER 14

# Test Practice

## Formative Assessment

- Use Student Edition pp. 612–613 as practice and cumulative review. The questions are written in the same style as many state tests.
- You can also use these two pages to benchmark student progress, or as an alternate homework assignment.

Additional practice pages can be found in the Chapter 14 Resource Masters.

CRM **Chapter 14 Resource Masters**
Cumulative Test Practice
- Multiple Choice format (pp. 60–65)
- Free Response format (pp. 66–71)

Create practice worksheets or tests that align to your state standards.

**Math Online** Have students visit macmillanmh.com for additional practice to reinforce your state standards.

## Test Practice
Cumulative, Chapters 1–14

**Math Online** macmillanmh.com
• Test Practice

**PART 1 Multiple Choice**

**Read each question. Then fill in the correct answer on the answer sheet provided by your teacher or on a sheet of paper.**

**1.** On the number line below, what number does point *K* represent? C

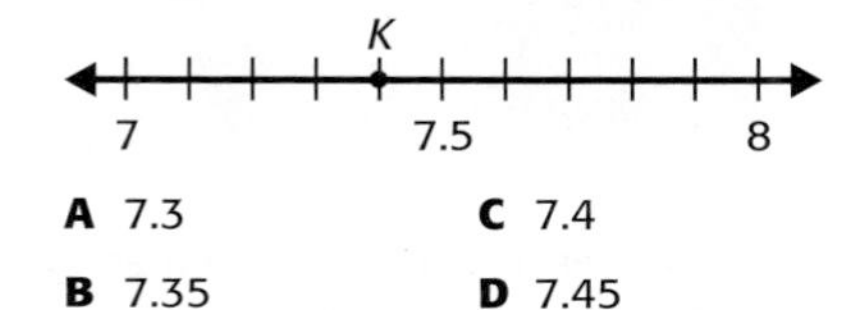


**A** 7.3
**B** 7.35
**C** 7.4
**D** 7.45

**2.** Which symbol makes the number sentence true? G

1.45 _____ 1.42

**F** <
**G** >
**H** =
**J** +

**3.** The clock below shows what time school ends. Volleyball practice begins 1 hour 15 minutes after school ends. At what time does volleyball practice begin? C

**A** 3:30
**B** 3:45
**C** 4:00
**D** 4:15

**4.** Which of the following has the greatest value? F

**F** 11.5
**G** 5.11
**H** 1.15
**J** 0.51

**5.** The function table shows some input and output values. D

| Input (x) | Output (y) |
|---|---|
| 1 | 1 |
| 2 | 4 |
| 3 | 7 |
| 4 | 10 |
| 5 | ■ |

What is the missing value?

**A** 8
**B** 10
**C** 11
**D** 13

**6.** Cindy grew $\frac{4}{5}$ of an inch in a year. Which decimal is equivalent to $\frac{4}{5}$? H

**F** 0.7
**G** 0.75
**H** 0.8
**J** 0.85

**7.** What solid figure has two circular faces? B

**A** cone
**B** cylinder
**C** prism
**D** sphere



## Test-Taking Tip

Tell students to be sure they read each answer choice carefully. They can then eliminate those answers that they know to be incorrect.

**8.** Which decimal does the model show? H

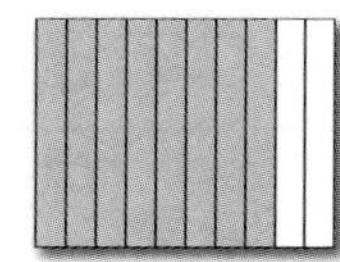

**F** 8 **H** 0.8
**G** 0.88 **J** 0.08

**9.** Kim has saved $59 to buy a bicycle helmet. She does not have enough money yet to buy the helmet. Let *h* represent the amount she still needs to buy the helmet. Which expression shows how much the helmet costs? A

**A** $59 + h$ **C** $h - 59$
**B** $59 - h$ **D** $h + (59 + h)$

**10.** On the number line below, what number does point *M* represent? H

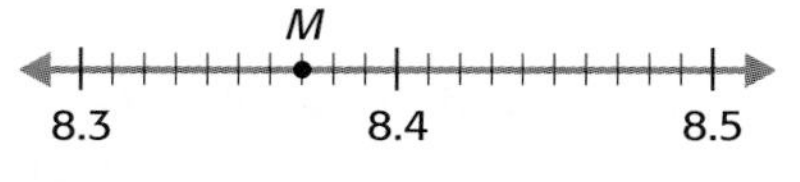


**F** 8.4 **H** 8.37
**G** 8.38 **J** 8.3

## PART 2 Short Response

**Record your answers on the answer sheet provided by your teacher or on a sheet of paper.**

**11.** Write 0.35 as a fraction. $\frac{35}{100}$

**12.** Order the decimals in the table from greatest to least. 1.5, 1.45, 1.31, 1.24

| Track Practice | |
|---|---|
| **Runner** | **Miles** |
| Darin | 1.24 |
| Kirk | 1.5 |
| Damon | 1.31 |
| Mauricio | 1.45 |

## PART 3 Extended Response

**Record your answers on the answer sheet provided by your teacher or on a sheet of paper.**

**13.** Use the number line below to answer each of the following questions.

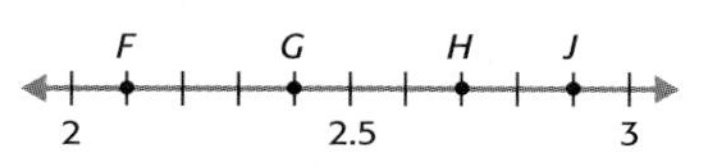


**a.** Which letter represents 2.7? Explain.

**b.** Which letter is closest to 2.3? Explain. 13a, 13b. See margin.

| NEED EXTRA HELP? | | | | | | | | | | | | | |
|---|---|---|---|---|---|---|---|---|---|---|---|---|---|
| If You Missed Question... | 1 | 2 | 3 | 4 | 5 | 6 | 7 | 8 | 9 | 10 | 11 | 12 | 13 |
| Go to Lesson... | 14-4 | 14-5 | 12-10 | 14-5 | 5-8 | 14-7 | 9-1 | 14-1 | 5-1 | 14-4 | 14-7 | 14-5 | 14-4 |



# Answer Sheet Practice

Have students simulate taking a state test by recording their answers on a practice recording sheet.

**CRM Chapter 14 Resource Masters**
Student Recording Sheet (p. 76)

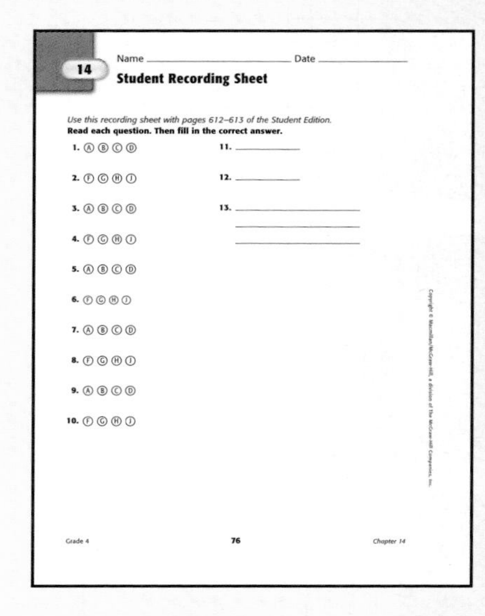

Name ______ Date ______

14 **Student Recording Sheet**

*Use this recording sheet with pages 612–613 of the Student Edition.*
**Read each question. Then fill in the correct answer.**

1. Ⓐ Ⓑ Ⓒ Ⓓ
2. Ⓕ Ⓖ Ⓗ Ⓙ
3. Ⓐ Ⓑ Ⓒ Ⓓ
4. Ⓕ Ⓖ Ⓗ Ⓙ
5. Ⓐ Ⓑ Ⓒ Ⓓ
6. Ⓕ Ⓖ Ⓗ Ⓙ
7. Ⓐ Ⓑ Ⓒ Ⓓ
8. Ⓕ Ⓖ Ⓗ Ⓙ
9. Ⓐ Ⓑ Ⓒ Ⓓ
10. Ⓕ Ⓖ Ⓗ Ⓙ

11. ______
12. ______
13. ______

Grade 4 76 Chapter 14

## Additional Answers

**13a.** Sample answer: H; There are 4 tick marks between 2.5 and 3.0. So, each tick mark represents 0.1. Since H is located on the second tick mark after 2.5, it represents 2.7.

**13b.** Sample answer: G; There are 4 tick marks between 2.0 and 2.5. So, each tick mark represents 0.1. The location of 2.3 is three tick marks after 2.0. *F* is located at 2.1, which is two tick marks before 2.3. *G* is located at 2.4, which is one tick mark after 2.3. So, *G* is closer.

## Page 578, Explore 14-1

8.
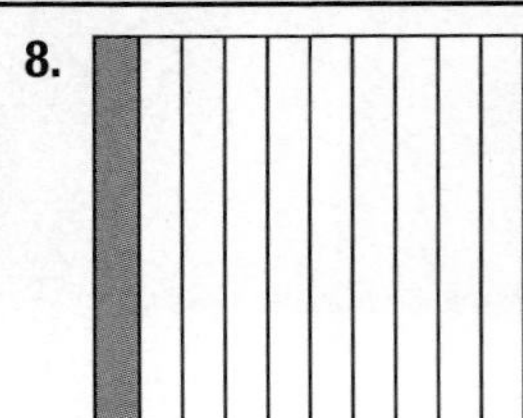

9.
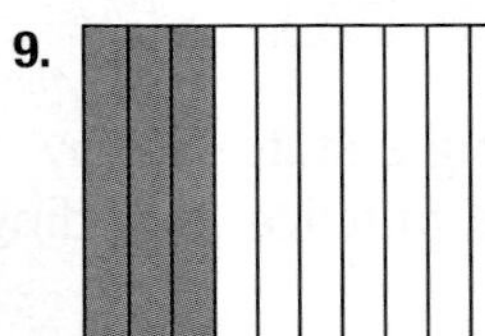

10.
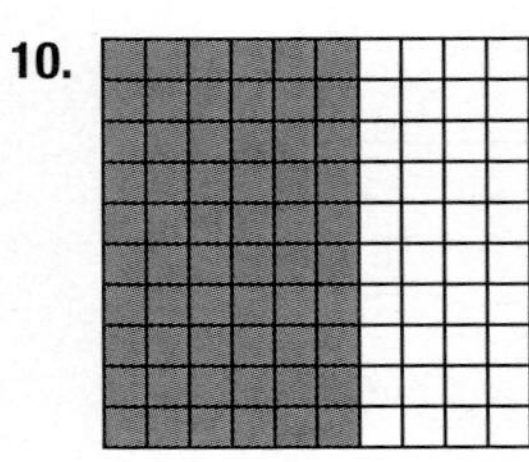

11.
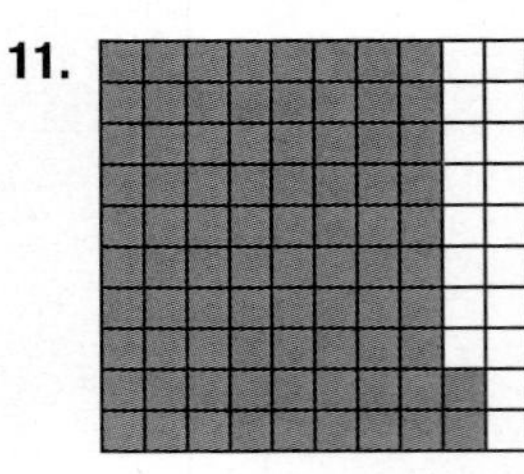

12.
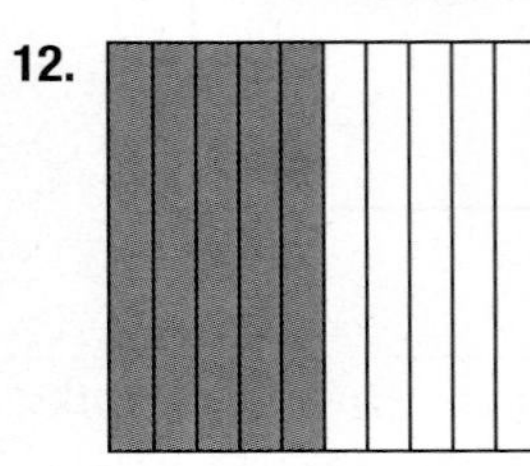

13.
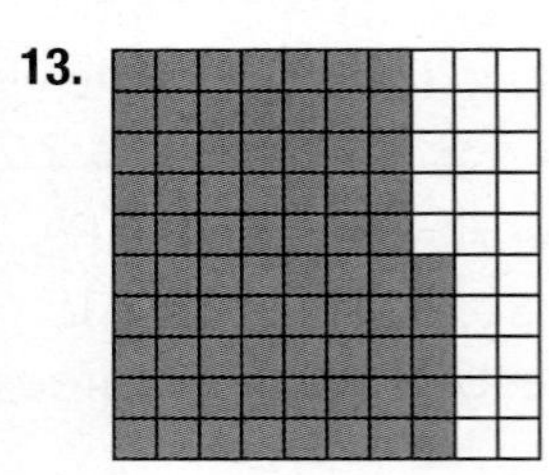

14.
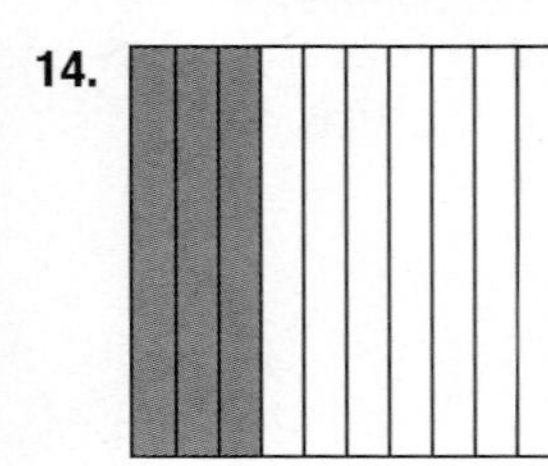

15.
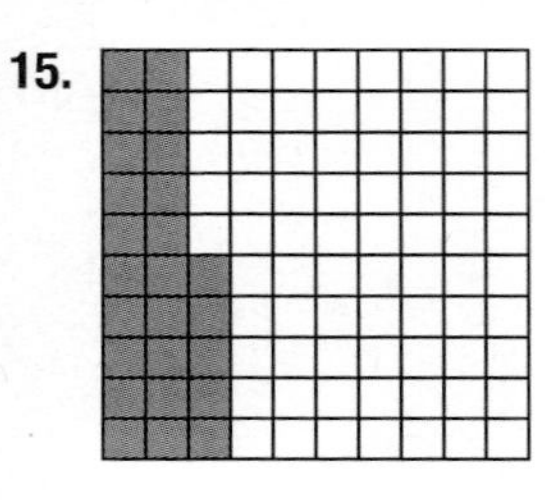

**16.** Sample answer: A fraction with a denominator of 10 is written as a decimal by writing the fraction's numerator in the tenths place.

Example: $\frac{6}{10} = 0.6$

## Pages 580–581, Lesson 14-1

**12.**

$\frac{36}{100}$, 0.36. It is not 0.40 because the boxes on the corner are shared with the other outer boxes.

**36.** Sample answer: true; the fraction's numerator is written in the place value that matches the fraction's denominator. So, $\frac{6}{10} = 0.6$, $\frac{6}{100} = 0.06$, and $\frac{6}{1000} = 0.006$.

**37.** Sample answer: Fractions that have 10 as a denominator are written as tenths as a decimal. Fractions that have a 100 as a denominator are written as hundredths as a decimal.

## Page 587, Lesson 14-3

**1.** Sample answer: The models show the card tables. The people could then be counted.

**2.** Sample answer: Luisa could have used a guess and check method by guessing the number of card tables and then checking to see if there were too many or too few seats.

**11.** Sample answer: How many boxes will be used to make the pyramid?

## Page 589, Lesson 14-4

**5.** Sample answer: $\frac{1}{2}$ is a specific point on a number line, whereas the halfway point on a number line can never be found because it goes on forever in both directions.

**12.** Sample answer:

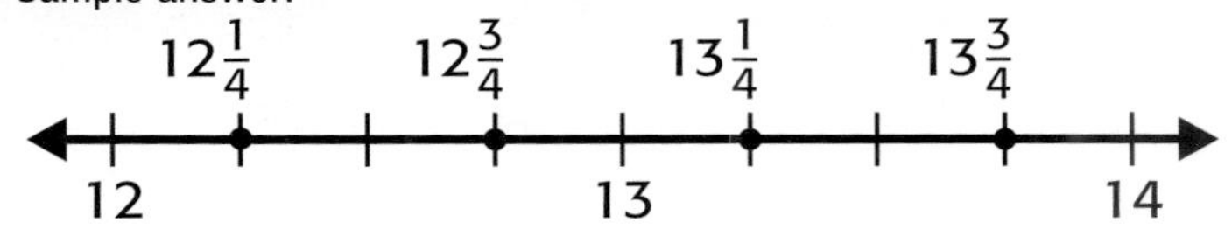


**13.** Sample answer: First find 2 on the number line. Then, determine the halfway point between 2 and 3. That point will be 2.5.

## Page 592, Lesson 14-5

**32.** Sample answer:

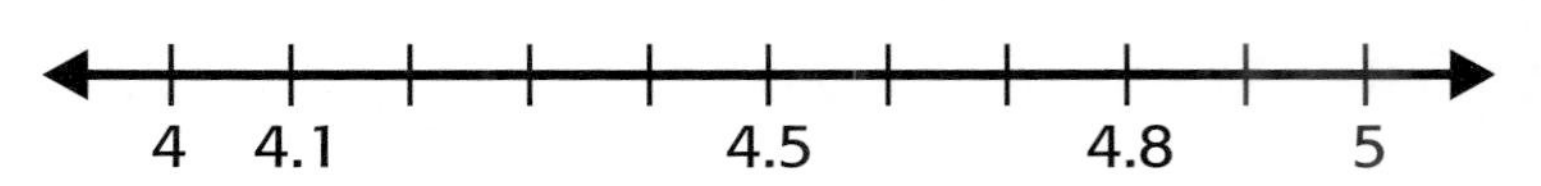


**34.** Sample answer: Three students said the alphabet as fast as they could. It took student A 8.65 seconds. It took student B 8.52 seconds. It took student C 8.7 seconds. Who said the alphabet the fastest?

## Page 595, Lesson 14-6

**3.** Sample answer: Owen; Craig paid $75 for a snowboard he used 32 times. So he paid $75 ÷ 32 or $2.34 per use. Owen paid 2 × $75 or $150 for a snowboard he used 82 times. So he paid $150 ÷ 82 or $1.83 per use. Owen got a better deal per use.

**9.** Sample answer: 16 and 8; Divide 24 by 3 to get 8. Multiply 8 by 2 to get 16.

## Pages 597, Lesson 14-7

**10.** Sample answer: Even though the fractions have different numerators and denominators, they all have the same value which is true because the decimal for each is 0.75.

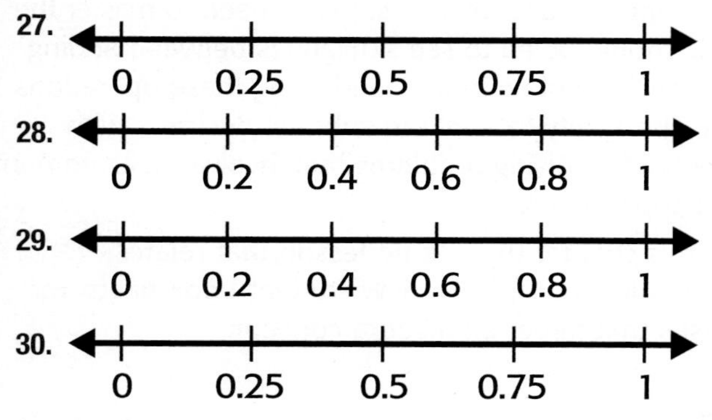


**37.** Sample answer:

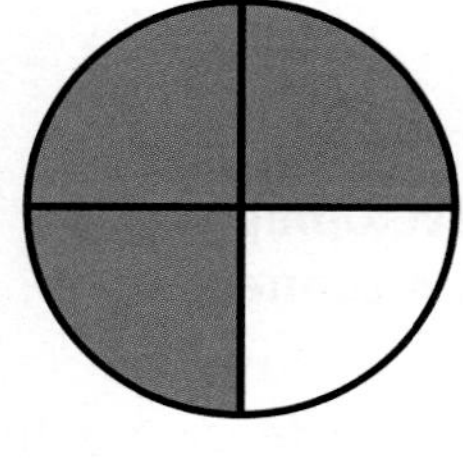

$\frac{6}{8}$, $\frac{3}{4}$, 0.75

**38.** 23; If there is a total of 25 frogs and 2 of those are multicolored that would mean the rest, or 23, are green.

**39.** Sample answer: I would multiply the denominator by 2 to have a denominator of 100. Then, multiply the numerator by 2 as well. This would mean the numerator would be 10 and the denominator would be 100. The decimal would then be 0.1.

## Page 604, Lesson 14-8

**26.** Sample answer: Both Alicia and Chris are correct. Point *C* is located at 2.6 or $2\frac{3}{5}$ on the number line.

# Chapter Overview

## Chapter-at-a-Glance

In Chapter 15, the emphasis is on adding and subtracting decimals.

| Lesson | Math Objective | State/Local Standards |
|---|---|---|
| **15-1 Round Decimals** (pp. 617–620) | Round decimals. | |
| **15-2 Estimate Decimal Sums and Differences** (pp. 622–625) | Estimate decimal sums and differences. | |
| **15-3 Problem-Solving Strategy: Work Backward** (pp. 626–627) | Solve problems by working backward. | |
| **EXPLORE 15-4 Addition of Decimals** (pp. 628–629) | Use models to add decimals. | |
| **15-4 Add Decimals** (pp. 630–632) | Add decimals. | |
| **15-5 Problem-Solving Investigation: Choose a Strategy** (pp. 634–635) | Choose the best strategy to solve a problem. | |
| **EXPLORE 15-6 Subtraction of Decimals** (pp. 636–637) | Use models to subtract decimals. | |
| **15-6 Subtract Decimals** (pp. 638–641) | Use models to subtract decimals. | |

## Add and Subtract Decimals

**BIG Idea** Students learn how to add and subtract decimals that are less than and greater than one. At first, using hundreds grids and colored pencils to explore the concept of adding and subtracting decimals will be helpful. It is important that students use rounding skills to estimate sums and differences.

Once these concepts are understood, students need to master the algorithm. They should begin to see similarities between adding and subtracting with whole numbers and using these operations with decimals. The ability to add and subtract decimals with fluency is essential for solving problems that involve measurement and real-world applications.

**Algebra** In this chapter there is no lesson that relates specifically to an algebra topic. Review student book pages for specific exercises that target an algebra concept.

**G4-FP2** *Number and Operations:* **Developing an understanding of decimals, including the connections between fractions and decimals**

Students understand decimal notation as an extension of the base-ten system of writing whole numbers that is useful for representing more numbers, including numbers between 0 and 1, between 1 and 2, and so on. Students relate their understanding of fractions to reading and writing decimals that are greater than or less than 1, identifying equivalent decimals, comparing and ordering decimals, and estimating decimal or fractional amounts in problem solving. They connect equivalent fractions and decimals by comparing models to symbols and locating equivalent symbols on the number line.

**G4-FP8C** *Number and Operations:* Building on their work in grade 3, students extend their understanding of place value and ways of representing numbers to 100,000 in various contexts. They use estimation in determining the relative sizes of amounts or distances. Students develop understandings of strategies for multidigit division by using models that represent division as the inverse of multiplication, as partitioning, or as successive subtraction. By working with decimals, students extend their ability to recognize equivalent fractions. Students' earlier work in grade 3 with models of fractions and multiplication and division facts supports their understanding of techniques for generating equivalent fractions and simplifying fractions.

# Skills Trace

## Vertical Alignment

### Third Grade

**In third grade, students learned to:**

- Add and subtract money amounts.
- Estimate sums and differences.

### Fourth Grade

**During this chapter, students learn to:**

- Round decimals.
- Use models to add and subtract decimals.

### Fifth Grade

**In fifth grade, students learn to:**

- Identify, compare, order, and represent the relationship of decimals and whole numbers.
- Add and subtract decimals and whole numbers, and estimate sums and differences.

**Backmapping and Vertical Alignment** **McGraw-Hill's *Math Connects*** program was conceived and developed with the final results in mind: student success in Algebra 1 and beyond. The authors, using the **NCTM Focal Points and Focal Connections** as their guide, developed this brand-new series by backmapping from Algebra 1 concepts, and vertically aligning the topics so that they build upon prior skills and concepts and serve as a foundation for future topics.

# Math Vocabulary

The following math vocabulary words for Chapter 15 are listed in the glossary of the ***Student Edition***. You can find interactive definitions in 13 languages in the ***eGlossary*** at macmillanmh.com.

**addend** Any numbers being added to together. (p. 630A)

**decimal** A number with one or more digits to the right of the decimal point, such as 8.37 or 0.05. (p. 617A)

**decimal point** A period separating the ones and the tenths in a number. (p. 617A)
**Example:** 0.8

**estimate** A number close to an exact value; an estimate indicates about how much. (p. 622A)
**Example:** 47 + 22 (estimate 50 + 20) about 70.

**sum** The answer to an addition problem. (p. 630A)

**Visual Vocabulary Cards**
Use Visual Vocabulary Cards 9 and 15 to reinforce the vocabulary in this lesson. (The Define/Example/Ask routine is printed on the back of each card.)

decimal

# Chapter Planner

| Suggested Pacing | | |
|---|---|---|
| Instruction | Review & Assessment | TOTAL |
| 8 days | 1 day | **9 days** |

**Diagnostic Assessment**
Quick Check (p. 616)

| | Lesson 15-1 (Pacing: 1 day) | Lesson 15-2 (Pacing: 1 day) | Lesson 15-3 (Pacing: 1 day) |
|---|---|---|---|
| **Lesson/ Objective** | **Round Decimals** (pp. 617–620)<br>**Objective:** Round decimals. | **Estimate Decimal Sums and Differences** (pp. 622–625)<br>**Objective:** Estimate decimal sums and differences. | **Problem-Solving Strategy Work Backward** (pp. 626–627)<br>**Objective:** Solve problems by working backward. |
| **State/Local Standards** | | | |
| **Math Vocabulary** | **decimal**, **decimal point** | | |
| **Lesson Resources** | **Materials**<br>WorkMat 1: Place-Value Chart, red and blue colored pencils, number lines<br>**Other Resources**<br>CRM Leveled Worksheets (pp. 8–12)<br>Daily Reteach • 5-Minute Check • Problem of the Day | **Materials**<br>Grid paper<br>**Manipulatives**<br>money<br>**Other Resources**<br>CRM Leveled Worksheets (pp. 13–17)<br>Daily Reteach • 5-Minute Check • Problem of the Day | **Manipulatives**<br>money<br>**Other Resources**<br>CRM Leveled Worksheets (pp. 18–22)<br>Daily Reteach • 5-Minute Check • Problem of the Day<br>*A Force to Reckon With* |
| **Technology** | Math Adventures | Math Adventures | |
| **Math Online** | Personal Tutor | Personal Tutor | Personal Tutor |
| **Reaching All Learners** | English Learners, p. 617B ELL<br>Below Level, p. 617B BL<br>Early Finishers, p. 617B OL | English Learners, p. 622B ELL<br>Below Level, p. 622B BL<br>Early Finishers, p. 622B OL AL | English Learners, p. 626B ELL<br>Gifted and Talented, p. 626B AL<br>Early Finishers, p. 626B OL AL |
| **Alternate Lesson** | | | |

**Game Time**
Match Up (p. 621)

| | Explore 15-4 (Pacing: 1 day) | Lesson 15-4 (Pacing: 1 day) | Lesson 15-5 (Pacing: 1 day) |
|---|---|---|---|
| **Lesson/ Objective** | **Addition of Decimals** (pp. 628–629)<br>**Objective:** Use models to add decimals. | **Add Decimals** (pp. 630–632)<br>**Objective:** Add decimals. | **Problem-Solving Investigation Choose a Strategy** (pp. 634–635)<br>**Objective:** Choose the best strategy to solve a problem. |
| **State/Local Standards** | | | |
| **Math Vocabulary** | | | |
| **Lesson Resources** | **Materials**<br>grid paper, colored pencils (two different colors per student) | **Materials**<br>WorkMat 1: Place-Value Chart, grid paper<br>**Manipulatives**<br>base-ten blocks<br>**Other Resources**<br>CRM Leveled Worksheets (pp. 23–27)<br>Daily Reteach • 5-Minute Check • Problem of the Day | **Other Resources**<br>CRM Leveled Worksheets (pp. 28–32)<br>Daily Reteach • 5-Minute Check • Problem of the Day<br>*A Force to Reckon With* |
| **Technology** | | Math Tool Chest<br>Math Adventures | |
| **Math Online** | Concepts in Motion | Personal Tutor | Personal Tutor |
| **Reaching All Learners** | | English Learners, p. 630B ELL<br>Below Level, p. 630B BL<br>Early Finishers, p. 630B OL | English Learners, p. 634B ELL<br>Below Level, p. 634B BL<br>Early Finishers, p. 634B OL AL |
| **Alternate Lesson** | | | |

**Formative Assessment**
Mid-Chapter Check (p. 633)

# Chapter Planner

| | Explore 15-6 (Pacing: 1 day) | Lesson 15-6 (Pacing: 1 day) |
|---|---|---|
| **Lesson/ Objective** | **Subtraction of Decimals** (pp. 636–637)<br>**Objective:** Use models to subtract decimals. | **Subtract Decimals** (pp. 638–641)<br>**Objective:** Use models to subtract decimals. |
| **State/Local Standards** | | |
| **Math Vocabulary** | | |
| **Lesson Resources** | **Materials**<br>grid paper, colored pencils (one color per student) | **Materials**<br>WorkMat 6: Place-Value Chart<br>**Manipulatives**<br>base-ten blocks<br>**Other Resources**<br>CRM Leveled Worksheets (pp. 33–37)<br>Daily Reteach • 5-Minute Check • Problem of the Day |
| **Technology** | | Math Adventures |
| **Math Online** | Concepts in Motion | Personal Tutor |
| **Reaching All Learners** | | English Learners, p. 638B ELL<br>Below Level, p. 638B BL<br>Early Finishers, p. 638B OL AL |
| **Alternate Lesson** | | |

**Problem Solving: History** (p. 642)

**Summative Assessment**
- Study Guide/Review (p. 644)
- Chapter Test (p. 649)
- Test Practice (p. 650)

## Assessment Options

### Diagnostic Assessment

- SE *Option 1:* Quick Check (p. 616)
- *Option 2:* Online Quiz macmillanmh.com
- CRM *Option 3:* Diagnostic Test (p. 39)
- CRM *Option 4:* Chapter Pretest (p. 40)

### Formative Assessment

- TE Alternate Teaching Strategies (in every lesson)
- SE Talk About It (in every lesson)
- SE Writing in Math (in every lesson)
- SE Check What You Know (in every lesson)
- TE Ticket Out the Door (p. 641)
- TE Into the Future (p. 632)
- TE Name the Math (p. 625)
- SE Mid-Chapter Check (p. 633)
- CRM Lesson Quizzes (pp. 41–43)
- CRM Mid-Chapter Test (p. 44)

### Summative Assessment

- SE Chapter Test (p. 649)
- SE Test Practice (p. 650)
- CRM Vocabulary Test (p. 45)
- CRM Leveled Chapter Tests (pp. 50–61)
- CRM Cumulative Test Practice (pp. 63–65)
- CRM Oral Assessment (pp. 46–47)
- ExamView® Assessment Suite
- Advance Tracker

## Teacher Notes

## Professional Development

Targeted professional development has been articulated throughout **McGraw-Hill's *Math Connects*** program. The **McGraw-Hill Professional Development Video Library** provides short videos that support the **NCTM Focal Points and Focal Connections.** For more information visit macmillanmh.com.

Model Lessons

Instructional Strategies

# Learning Stations

## Cross-Curricular Links

### Writing

individual | LOGICAL

**Saving Up**

- When you want to save money for something, do you save up the exact amount, or do you estimate what you will need to buy what you want? Explain.
- How do you keep track of how much you are saving?
- How might you use rounding to establish your goal for saving?
- Use an example from your own life, and describe how you saved your money for the item you wanted to buy.

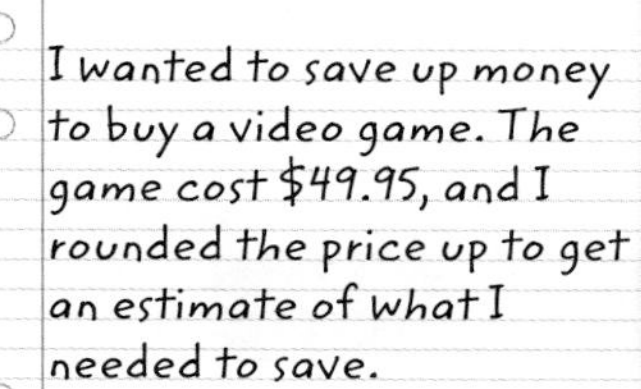


**Materials:**
- paper
- pencil

### Art

pair | VISUAL

**What is Missing?**

Make a picture on the back of a hundreds grid, take away some, and see if your partner can guess how much is missing.

- Each partner makes a picture on the blank side of a hundreds grid, by making a collage. Then, each partner cuts out a chunk of the picture, using the grid lines on the back as a guide.
- Challenge your partner to guess how much, in hundredths, of your picture is missing. Then, using the grid to get an exact count, each of you subtracts what is left from 100 to find out the exact missing amount.

**Materials:**
- paper hundreds grids
- magazines for collage
- scissors
- glue
- paper
- pencils

### Health

pair | SPATIAL

**Everyone Wins**

See how fast you can jump 10 jumping jacks.

- Each person takes a turn to jump 10 jumping jacks. While one person jumps, the other person keeps time using a digital stopwatch that measures in at least tenths of seconds.
- Record each person's time for the jumps. Then add up the times you recorded. How much time in total did both of you jump?

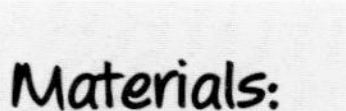

**Materials:**
- stopwatch
- paper
- pencils

## Science

pair | LOGICAL

### For the Birds

A bird that weighs 0.43 kilograms will eat up to 0.09 kilograms of food per day. Who is going to reach a kilogram of food first?

- Take turns rolling a number cube to find how many days you need to feed the bird. Add the amounts per day that you have to feed. Keep track of how much you have fed your bird on a separate hundredths grid for each person, filling in the squares for each amount you feed your bird.
- Continue rolling and adding. The first person to fill in the grid and reach 1.0 kilograms wins!

0.09 + 0.09 + 0.09 = 0.27

**Materials:**
- number cube
- hundredths grid
- pencils

## Music

group | LOGICAL

### How Much for Everyone?

- Make concert tickets out of index cards. Make 10 full-price tickets at $30.50, 5 half-price tickets at $15.25, and 3 super-saver tickets at $4.50.
- Place the tickets into a basket. Each person pulls out a ticket. Estimate, by rounding, how much money you will need to bring to pay for all of the tickets for your group.
- Now add together all of the ticket prices for the tickets you drew. Was your estimate reasonable? Put the tickets back in the basket and try again. See how low you can get your total price to be!

**Materials:**
- index cards
- markers
- basket
- paper
- pencils

## Social Studies

individual | LOGICAL

### Postage Stamps

The amount of stamps needed to mail a letter or a package depends on the weight of the item being mailed.

- Use decimal form to write stamp amounts of 1¢, 12¢, and 24¢ on the stickers.
- Roll one number cube. This number is the postage rate for mail of up to one ounce of weight. Add 2¢ for each additional ounce.
- Place an envelope or package onto the scale, how many stamps do you need?
- Place the exact or rounded up amount of stamps onto your mail.

0.01¢

**Materials:**
- envelopes, postcards, and packages of different weights
- $\frac{3}{4}$" round stickers
- number cube
- scale
- paper
- pencil

# Introduce the Chapter

## Real World: How Much Snow?

**Materials:** grid paper, colored pencils

Quickly review with students what they learned about decimals in the previous chapter. Tell students that they will learn how to add and subtract decimals in this chapter.

Pose the following problem: *On Saturday, 0.75 inches of snow fell in the city. It snowed another 0.24 inches on Sunday. How much snow fell on the two days combined?*

- **What operation will you use to solve?** addition
- **What numbers will you add?** 0.75 and 0.24

Have students make two 10-by-10 grids and shade squares to model each decimal addend on a separate grid. Remind them that each square stands for one hundredth.

- **How many squares are shaded in all on both grids?** 99
- **How do we write this as a decimal?** 0.99

Write 0.75 in. + 0.24 in. = 0.99 in. on the board.

Direct students to Student Edition p. 570. Have students read the paragraph at the top of the page.

- **When might we need to add or subtract decimals to solve problems in real life?** Sample answers: to find out how much change we should get when we buy things, to find the total length of two objects, etc.

## WRITING IN MATH

**Starting the Chapter**
Remind students that money amounts are often written as decimal numbers. Ask them to write about situations where they would need to add or subtract money amounts.

**Key Vocabulary** Introduce the key vocabulary in the chapter using the routine below.

Define: A decimal is a number with one or more digits to the right of the decimal point.
Example: 8.37 and 0.05 are examples of decimal numbers.
Ask: What are some decimal numbers that you use in daily life?

**Read-Aloud Anthology** For an optional reading activity to introduce this chapter's math concepts, see the Read-Aloud Anthology on p. TR40.

# Chapter 15 Add and Subtract Decimals

**BIG Idea** How do I subtract decimals?

You can use models to subtract decimals.

**Example** The Monarch butterfly is the state insect of Illinois. One Monarch butterfly has a wingspan of 0.41 feet, and another has a wingspan of 0.28 feet. The model shows that the wingspan of the first butterfly is 0.41 − 0.28 or 0.13 feet longer than the other.

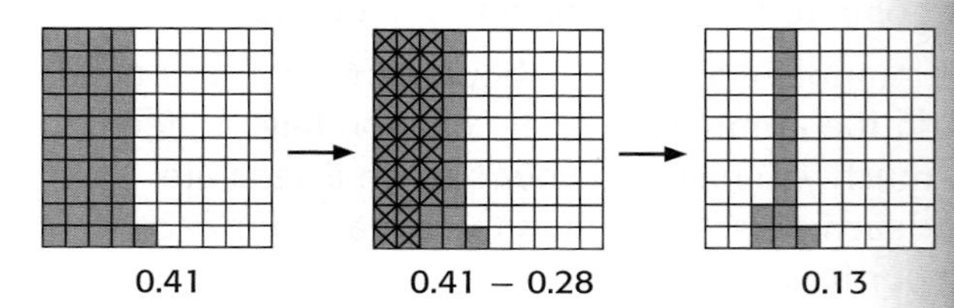


**What will I learn in this chapter?**

- Round decimals.
- Estimate decimal sums and differences.
- Add and subtract simple decimals.
- Solve problems by working backward.

**Key Vocabulary**

**decimal**
**decimal point**
**estimate**
**sum**
**difference**

**Math Online** Student Study Tools at macmillanmh.com

614 **Chapter 15** Add and Subtract Decimals

## Chapter 15 Project

### Shopping List

Students create a shopping list for a week's worth of groceries from a grocery store.

- Students use grocery store circulars to create a list of groceries they would buy for their families for one week. They may consult with their families to figure out what usually goes on the shopping list.
- Students write prices for the items on the list next to each item. They round the prices to the nearest dollar and add them up to estimate how much the weekly grocery bill will be.
- Challenge students to add up all of the prices without rounding to figure out an exact cost for the grocery bill.

CRM *Refer to Chapter 15 Resource Masters, p. 48, for a rubric to assess students' progress on this project.*

FOLDABLES® Study Organizer

Make this Foldable to help you organize information about decimals. Begin with one sheet of $8\frac{1}{2}$" × 11" paper.

1. **Fold** the paper lengthwise about 3 inches from the bottom.
2. **Fold** the paper in thirds.
3. **Open** and staple the edges to form 3 pockets.
4. **Label** as shown. Place two index cards in each pocket.

Round Decimals | Addition of Decimals | Subtraction of Decimals



| ELL National ESL Standards Alignment for Chapter 15 | | | |
|---|---|---|---|
| Lesson, Page | ESL Standard | Modality | Level |
| 15-1, p. 617B | Goal 2, Standard 3, h | Kinesthetic, Auditory | Beginning |
| 15-2, p. 622B | Goal 2, Standard 2, j | Auditory, Intrapersonal | Intermediate |
| 15-3, p. 626B | Goal 2, Standard 2, g | Logical | Advanced |
| 15-4, p. 630B | Goal 2, Standard 1, a | Visual, Logical | Intermediate |
| 15-5, p. 634B | Goal 1, Standard 3, e | Spatial | Advanced |
| 15-6, p. 638B | Goal 2, Standard 3, b | Linguistic, Social | Intermediate |

The National ESL Standards can be found in the Teacher Reference Handbook.

## FOLDABLES® Dinah Zike's Foldables

Guide students through the directions on p. 615 to create their own Foldables graphic organizers for adding and subtracting decimals. Students may also use their Foldables to study and review for chapter assessments.

**When to Use It** Lessons 15-1, 15-4, and 15-6. (Additional instructions for using the Foldables with these lessons are found on pp. 633 and 644.)

## Chapter 15 Literature List

| Lesson | Book Title |
|---|---|
| 15-1 | **If You Made a Million**<br>David M. Schwartz |
| 15-2 | **The Toothpaste Millionaire**<br>Jean Merrill |
| 15-3 | **A Chair for My Mother**<br>Vera B. Williams |
| 15-4 | **Henry Hikes to Fitchburg**<br>D.B. Johnson |
| 15-6 | **Henry Hikes to Fitchburg**<br>D.B. Johnson |
| Any | **The Hundred Penny Box**<br>Sharon Bell Mathis |
| Any | **Math Curse**<br>John Scieszka |

- Read the Math at Home letter found in the Chapter 15 Resource Masters, p. 4, with the class and have each student sign it. (A Spanish version is found on p. 5.)
- Send home copies of the Math at Home letter with each student.

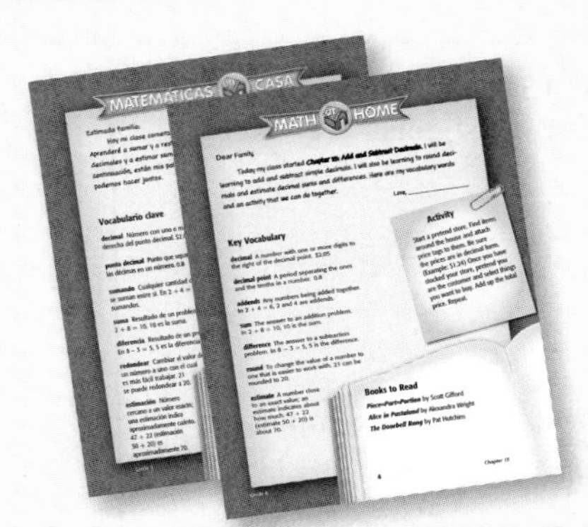

# Diagnostic Assessment

Check for students' prerequisite skills before beginning the chapter.

- **Option 1:** ***Quick Check***

  SE Student Edition, p. 616

- **Option 2:** ***Online Assessment***

  **Math Online** macmillanmh.com

- **Option 3:** ***Diagnostic Tests***

  CRM Chapter 15 Resource Masters, pp. 39–40

# RTI (Response to Intervention)

**Apply the Results** Based on the results of the diagnostic assessment on student p. 616, use the chart below to address individual needs before beginning the chapter.

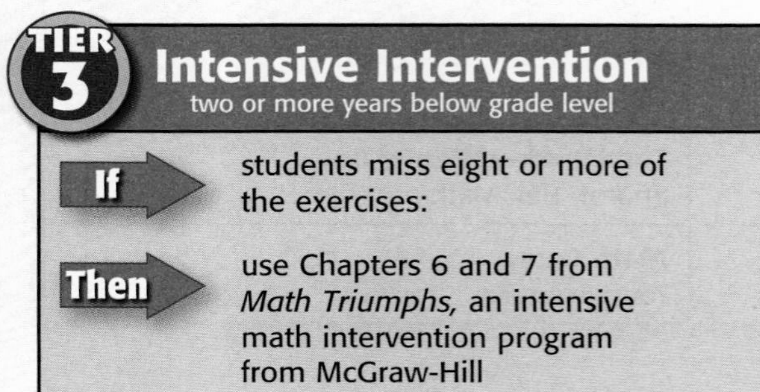

**TIER 3 Intensive Intervention**
two or more years below grade level

**If** students miss eight or more of the exercises:

**Then** use Chapters 6 and 7 from *Math Triumphs,* an intensive math intervention program from McGraw-Hill

## ARE YOU READY for Chapter 15?

You have two ways to check prerequisite skills for this chapter.

**Option 2**

**Math Online** Take the Chapter Readiness Quiz at macmillanmh.com.

**Option 1**

Complete the Quick Check below.

### QUICK Check

**Round each number to the indicated place value.** (Lesson 1-6) **(Used in Lessons 15-1 and 15-2)**

**1.** 852; hundreds **900**   **2.** 2,614; tens **2,610**   **3.** 26,703; ten thousands **30,000**

**4.** Alexis has $1,363 in her bank account. To the nearest thousand, how much money does she have in her account? **Sample answer: $1,000**

**Write a decimal for the shaded part of each figure.** (Lesson 14-1) **(Used in Lessons 15-4 and 15-6)**

**5.** **0.5**

**6.** **0.75**

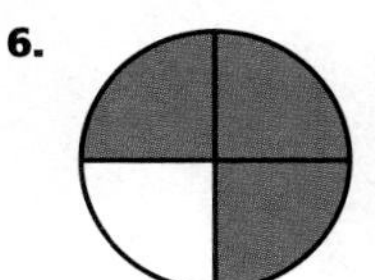

**7.** **0.2**

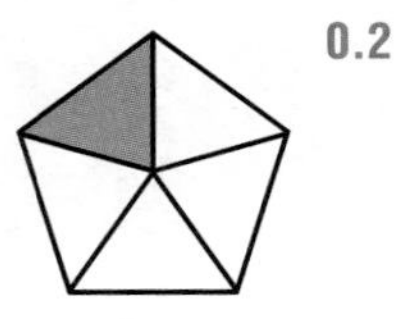

**8.** Tim ate part of the sandwich as shown. Write a decimal to represent the amount of the sandwich Tim ate. **0.75**

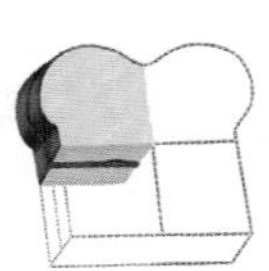

**Graph each decimal on a number line.** (Lesson 14-4) **(Used in Lesson 15-1)**

**9.** 0.15   **10.** 0.38   **11.** 1.75

**9–11. See Ch. 15 Answer Appendix.**

**12.** What decimal does the letter $D$ represent? **3.25**

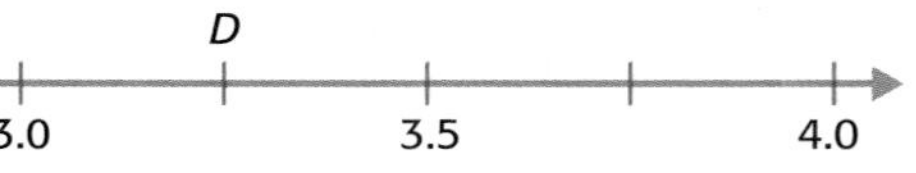




| TIER 2 Strategic Intervention<br>below/approaching grade level | TIER 1 On-Level | Above/Beyond Level |
|---|---|---|
| **If** students miss four to seven in: **Exercises 1–12** | **If** students miss two or three in: **Exercises 1–12** | **If** students miss one or less in: **Exercises 1–12** |
| **Then** choose a resource: | **Then** choose a resource: | **Then** choose a resource: |
| CRM Chapter 15 Resource Masters Reteach Worksheets<br>**Math Online** Extra Examples • Personal Tutor • Concepts in Motion | TE Learning Stations (pp. 614G–614H)<br>TE Chapter Project (p. 614)<br>CRM Game: Less is More<br>Math Adventures<br>My Math Zone Chapter 14<br>**Math Online** Fact Dash | TE Learning Stations (pp. 614G–614H)<br>TE Chapter Project (p. 614)<br>Real-World Problem Solving: *A Force to Reckon With*<br>My Math Zone Chapters 14 and 15<br>**Math Online** Games |

LESSON 15-1

# Round Decimals

## Lesson Planner

### Objective

Round decimals.

### Review Vocabulary

**decimal, decimal point**

### Resources

**Materials:** WorkMat 1: Place-Value Chart, red and blue colored pencils

**Manipulatives:** base-ten blocks

**Literature Connection:** *If You Made a Million* by David M. Schwartz

**Teacher Technology**
TeacherWorks • Interactive Classroom

## Daily Routine

Use these suggestions before beginning the lesson on p. 617.

### 5-Minute Check

(Reviews Lesson 14-8)

**Compare. Use >, <, or =.**

1. $6 \bullet 7\frac{3}{10}$ <
2. $5.6 \bullet 5$ >
3. $2\frac{1}{10} \bullet 2.1$ =
4. $4.7 \bullet 4.07$ >

**Order from greatest to least.**

5. $11\frac{1}{2}$, 11.9, $11\frac{38}{100}$, 11.25 11.9, $11\frac{1}{2}$, $11\frac{38}{100}$, 11.25
6. $3\frac{4}{5}$, 4.62, 3.2, $4\frac{5}{10}$ 4.62, $4\frac{5}{10}$, $3\frac{4}{5}$, 3.2

### Problem of the Day

There are three kinds of juice boxes for sale: orange, apple, and grape. If Steve wants two different kinds of juice boxes, how many combinations of juice boxes could he buy? 6

### Focus on Math Background

Having rounded whole numbers in Lesson 1-6, and compared decimals on a number line in Lesson 14-4, students are now ready to round decimals. Rounding to a given decimal place always involves consideration of the digit in the next place to the right.

Although students use rounding rules, they should not lose sight of the basic objective, which is to identify a closest neighbor in the place to which the number is being rounded. Numbers are usually rounded up when the digit to the right of the number to be rounded is a 5 or greater, because when additional digits exist, these digits cause the number to be closer to the higher choice.

### Review Math Vocabulary

Write the review vocabulary words and their definitions on the board.

Have students write the words and definitions in their Math Journals. Have them show several examples of decimals and label the decimal point in each log drawing an arrow to it.

#### Visual Vocabulary Cards

Use Visual Vocabulary Card 12 to reinforce the vocabulary reviewed in this lesson. (The Define/Example/Ask routine is printed on the back of each card.)

# Differentiated Instruction

## Small Group Options

AUDITORY, SOCIAL

### Option 1 Below Level BL

**Materials:** paper and pencil

- Have students work in pairs. One student says a decimal number out loud. The other student responds by saying the number rounded to its nearest whole number.
- Students take turns at each role.

KINESTHETIC, AUDITORY

### Option 2 English Language Learners ELL

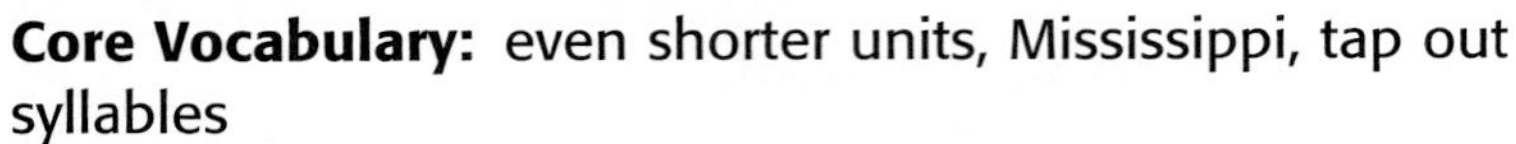

**Core Vocabulary:** even shorter units, Mississippi, tap out syllables
**Common Use Verb:** count Mississippi style
**Do Math** This strategy helps ELL students distinguish the proportions of 2-digit decimals to 1-digit decimals kinesthetically.

- Say: "Both a second and a decimal are small units, but there are even shorter units between them."
- Write a number line with "Mississippi" written underneath .1, .2, etc.
- Say: "Mississippi" takes about 1 second to say." Model counting Mississippi style, tapping your fingers on the syllables.
- Have students write their name on the board as you count and tap out the time. Mark it on the number line.
- Repeat with other words and estimates as time permits.

*Use this worksheet to provide additional support for English Language Learners.*

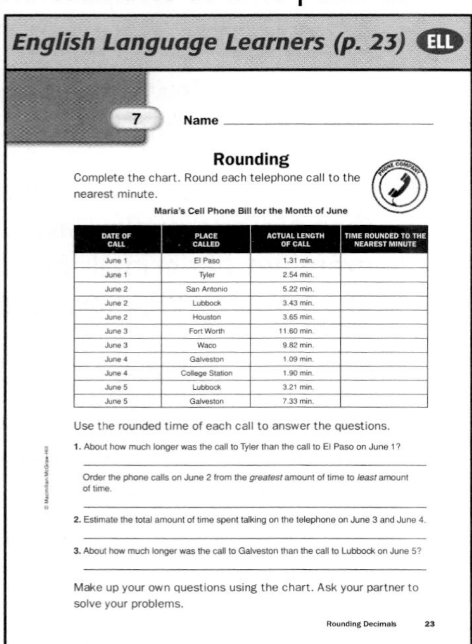

*English Language Learners (p. 23)* ELL

7 Name ____________

**Rounding**

Complete the chart. Round each telephone call to the nearest minute.

**Maria's Cell Phone Bill for the Month of June**

| DATE OF CALL | PLACE CALLED | ACTUAL LENGTH OF CALL | TIME ROUNDED TO THE NEAREST MINUTE |
|---|---|---|---|
| June 1 | El Paso | 1.31 min. | |
| June 1 | Tyler | 2.54 min. | |
| June 2 | San Antonio | 5.22 min. | |
| June 2 | Lubbock | 3.43 min. | |
| June 2 | Houston | 3.65 min. | |
| June 3 | Fort Worth | 11.60 min. | |
| June 3 | Waco | 9.82 min. | |
| June 4 | Galveston | 1.09 min. | |
| June 4 | College Station | 1.90 min. | |
| June 5 | Lubbock | 3.21 min. | |
| June 5 | Galveston | 7.33 min. | |

Use the rounded time of each call to answer the questions.

1. About how much longer was the call to Tyler than the call to El Paso on June 1?

   Order the phone calls on June 2 from the *greatest* amount of time to *least* amount of time.

2. Estimate the total amount of time spent talking on the telephone on June 3 and June 4.
3. About how much longer was the call to Galveston than the call to Lubbock on June 5?

Make up your own questions using the chart. Ask your partner to solve your problems.



Rounding Decimals 23

## Independent Work Options

INTRAPERSONAL, LOGICAL

### Option 1 Early Finishers OL

**Materials:** Student book pp. 618–619

- Have students look at Exercises 1–4 and 11–18 again and round each number to the nearest tenth instead of to the nearest whole number.
- If time allows, have students look at Exercises 5–8 and 19–26 and round each number to the nearest whole number instead of to the nearest tenth.

### Option 2 Student Technology

**Math Online** macmillanmh.com

Personal Tutor • Extra Examples

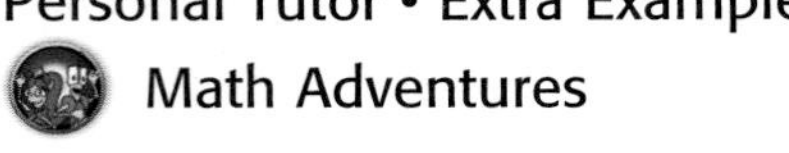

Math Adventures

### Option 3 Learning Station: Writing (p. 614G)

Direct students to the Writing Learning Station for opportunities to explore and extend the lesson concept.

### Option 4 Problem-Solving Practice

Reinforce problem-solving skills and strategies with the Problem-Solving Practice worksheet.

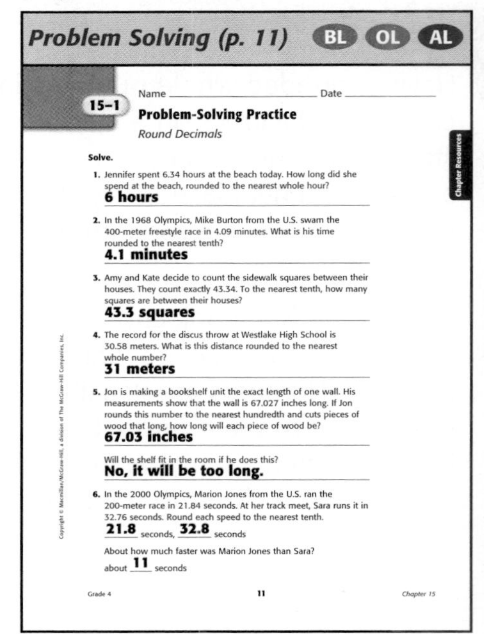

*Problem Solving (p. 11)* BL OL AL

15–1 Name ____________ Date ____________

**Problem-Solving Practice**

*Round Decimals*

Chapter Resources

**Solve.**

1. Jennifer spent 6.34 hours at the beach today. How long did she spend at the beach, rounded to the nearest whole hour?
   **6 hours**
2. In the 1968 Olympics, Mike Burton from the U.S. swam the 400-meter freestyle race in 4.09 minutes. What is his time rounded to the nearest tenth?
   **4.1 minutes**
3. Amy and Kate decide to count the sidewalk squares between their houses. They count exactly 43.34. To the nearest tenth, how many squares are between their houses?
   **43.3 squares**
4. The record for the discus throw at Westlake High School is 30.58 meters. What is this distance rounded to the nearest whole number?
   **31 meters**
5. Jon is making a bookshelf unit the exact length of one wall. His measurements show that the wall is 67.027 inches long. If Jon rounds this number to the nearest hundredth and cuts pieces of wood that long, how long will each piece of wood be?
   **67.03 inches**

   Will the shelf fit in the room if he does this?
   **No, it will be too long.**
6. In the 2000 Olympics, Marion Jones from the U.S. ran the 200-meter race in 21.84 seconds. At her track meet, Sara runs it in 32.76 seconds. Round each speed to the nearest tenth.
   **21.8** seconds, **32.8** seconds

   About how much faster was Marion Jones than Sara?
   about **11** seconds



Grade 4 11 *Chapter 15*

# 15-1 Round Decimals

**GET READY to Learn**

A bridge in Japan is about 1.22 miles long. What is 1.22 rounded to the nearest whole number?

**MAIN IDEA**

I will round decimals.

**Math Online**

macmillanmh.com
- Extra Examples
- Personal Tutor
- Self-Check Quiz

You can use a number line or rounding rules to round a two-place decimal like 1.22.

**Real-World EXAMPLE** Round Decimals

1. **BRIDGES A bridge in Japan is about 1.22 miles long. Round 1.22 to the nearest whole number.**

**One Way:** **Use a Number Line**

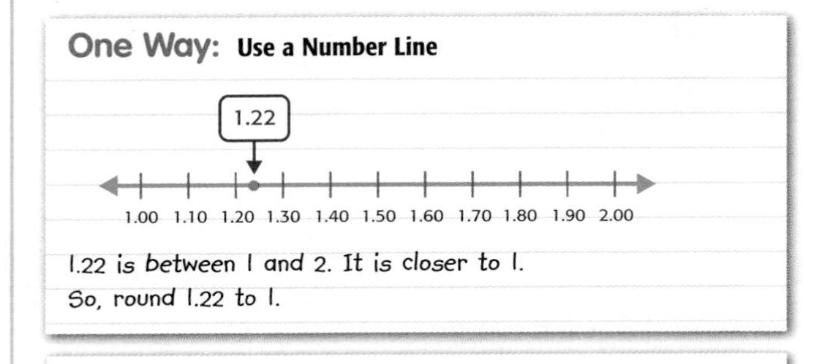


1.22 is between 1 and 2. It is closer to 1.
So, round 1.22 to 1.

**Another Way:** **Use Rounding Rules**

Use the same process that you use with rounding whole numbers.

Underline the digit to be rounded. In this case, the digit is in the ones place. → 1.22 ← Then look at the digit to the right. Since 2 is less than 5, the digit 1 remains the same.

To the nearest whole number, 1.22 rounds to 1.



# 15-1 Round Decimals

## 1 Introduce

**Activity Choice 1 • Hands-On**

- Review rounding rules with students. Remind them to first identify the digit in the place they are rounding to, then look at the digit directly to the right to help them decide how to round.
- **When the digit to the right is 5 or greater, do you round up or down?** round up
- **What do you do when that digit is less than 5?** round down
- Have students model the numbers 19, 25, 32, and 69 with base-ten blocks. Ask them to count the ones and use and the rounding rules to round each number to the nearest ten.
- Repeat by having groups of students combine their base-ten blocks and model and round 195, 249, 320, and 679 to the nearest hundred.
- Explain that the same rounding rules and procedures for rounding whole numbers are used for rounding decimals.

**Activity Choice 2 • Literature**

Introduce the lesson with *If You Made a Million* by David M. Schwartz. For a related math activity, see p. TR66.

## 2 Teach

**Scaffolding Questions**

Write 2.61 on the board. Have students identify the ones, tenths, and hundredths places.

- **What is the value of the digit in the ones place?** 2
- **How could you round 2.61 to the nearest whole number?** Sample answer: Look at the digit to the right of the 2. It is a 6, so I will round 2.61 up to 3.
- **Name the digit in the hundredths place.** 1 **How could you use this digit to help you round 2.61 to the nearest tenth?** Look at the 1 and round 2.61 down to 2.6.

**GET READY to Learn**

Have students open their books and read the information in **Get Ready to Learn**. Review **decimal** and **decimal point**. As a class, work through **Examples 1–3**.

## Real-World Example

**Example 1** Tell students that the number 1.22 million is being treated as a whole number in this example. Write 1,220,000 = 1.22 million on the board. Explain that larger numbers are often shortened in this way and provide additional examples, such as 48,520,000 = 48.52 million.

### ADDITIONAL EXAMPLES

1. About 2.25 million people live in Queens County, New York. How many people live in Queens County when rounded to the nearest whole number? 2 million
2. Round 46.45 to the nearest whole number. 46
3. A golfer had an average score of 72.84 in one season. Round this score to the nearest tenth. 72.8

### CHECK What You Know

As a class, have students complete Exercises 1–10 in **Check What You Know** as you observe their work.

**Exercise 10** Assess student comprehension before assigning practice exercises.

### BL Alternate Teaching Strategy

**If** students have trouble rounding to the nearest whole number or tenth...

**Then** use one of these reteach options:

1. CRM **Daily Reteach Worksheet** (p. 8)
2. Have students write 54.09, 35.14, and 44.67 in a place-value chart and identify the digit in each place. Ask them to round each number to the nearest whole number and then to the nearest tenth. Remind students to look at the tenths place and apply the rounding rules to round to the nearest whole number and to look at the hundredths place to round to the nearest tenth.

### ! COMMON ERROR!

Students may round to the incorrect place. Have students underline the digit in the place they are rounding to in red and circle the digit to the immediate right in blue.



**EXAMPLE** Round Decimals

**2** **Round 38.52 to the nearest whole number.**

Use the rounding rules.

Underline the digit to be rounded. In this case, the digit is in the ones place. → 33.52 ← Then look at the digit to the right. Since that digit is 5, add one to the underlined digit

To the nearest whole number, 38.52 rounds to 39.

**Real-World EXAMPLE** Round Decimals

**3** **SPORTS** **During one golf season, Tiger Woods had an average score of 68.41. Round this score to the nearest tenth.**

Use the rounding rules.

Underline the digit to be rounded. In this case, the digit is in the tenths place. → 68.41 ← Then look at the digit to the right. Since 1 is less than 5, the underlined digit remains the same.

To the nearest tenth, 68.41 rounds to 68.4.

### CHECK What You Know

**Round to the nearest whole number.** See Examples 1 and 2 (pp. 617–618)

1. 3.24 3
2. 9.87 10
3. 36.61 37
4. 83.14 83

**Round to the nearest tenth.** See Example 3 (p. 618)

5. 4.13 4.1
6. 8.45 8.5
7. 25.94 25.9
8. 67.28 67.3
9. **Measurement** Use the table to round the length of each bird to the nearest tenth of a foot.
   9, 10. See margin.
10. Talk About It How is rounding decimals similar to rounding whole numbers? How is it different?

**World's Smallest Birds**

| Bird | Length (feet) |
|---|---|
| Pygmy parrot | 0.29 |
| Bee hummingbird | 0.20 |
| Gouldian finch | 0.33 |
| New Zealand wren | 0.29 |

**Source:** *Scholastic Book of World Records*



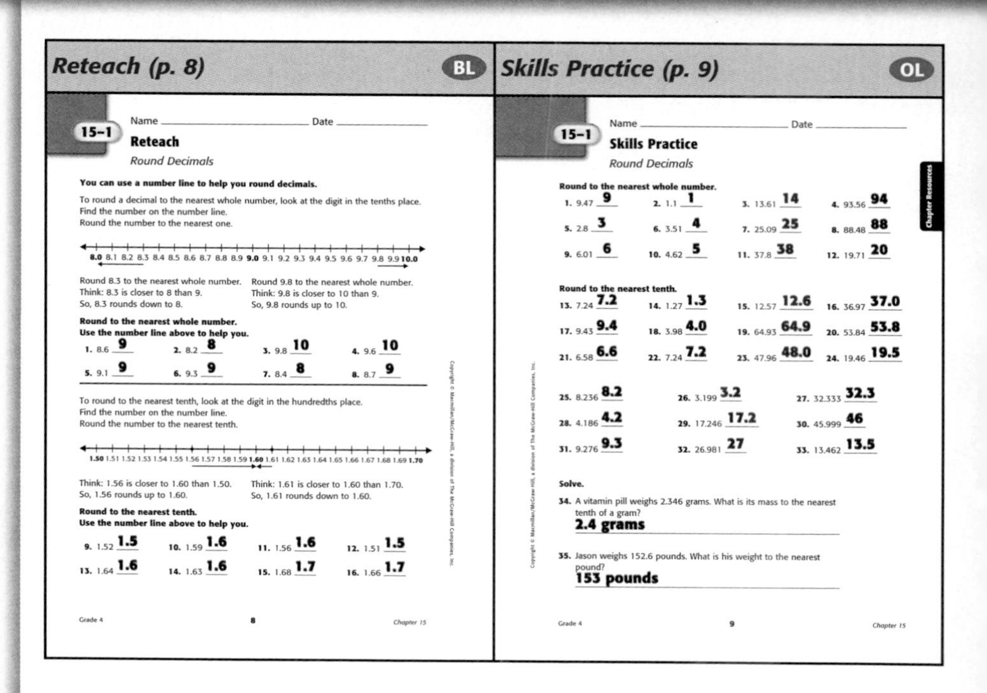

***Reteach (p. 8)*** BL

15–1 Name ________ Date ________

**Reteach**

*Round Decimals*

**You can use a number line to help you round decimals.**

To round a decimal to the nearest whole number, look at the digit in the tenths place.
Find the number on the number line.
Round the number to the nearest one.

8.0 8.1 8.2 8.3 8.4 8.5 8.6 8.7 8.8 8.9 9.0 9.1 9.2 9.3 9.4 9.5 9.6 9.7 9.8 9.9 10.0

Round 8.3 to the nearest whole number.
Think: 8.3 is closer to 8 than 9.
So, 8.3 rounds down to 8.

Round 9.8 to the nearest whole number.
Think: 9.8 is closer to 10 than 9.
So, 9.8 rounds up to 10.

**Round to the nearest whole number.**
**Use the number line above to help you.**

1. 8.6 **9**
2. 8.2 **8**
3. 9.8 **10**
4. 9.6 **10**
5. 9.1 **9**
6. 9.3 **9**
7. 8.4 **8**
8. 8.7 **9**

To round to the nearest tenth, look at the digit in the hundredths place.
Find the number on the number line.
Round the number to the nearest tenth.

1.50 1.51 1.52 1.53 1.54 1.55 1.56 1.57 1.58 1.59 1.60 1.61 1.62 1.63 1.64 1.65 1.66 1.67 1.68 1.69 1.70

Think: 1.56 is closer to 1.60 than 1.50.
So, 1.56 rounds up to 1.60.

Think: 1.61 is closer to 1.60 than 1.70.
So, 1.61 rounds down to 1.60.

**Round to the nearest tenth.**
**Use the number line above to help you.**

9. 1.52 **1.5**
10. 1.59 **1.6**
11. 1.56 **1.6**
12. 1.51 **1.5**
13. 1.64 **1.6**
14. 1.63 **1.6**
15. 1.68 **1.7**
16. 1.66 **1.7**





***Skills Practice (p. 9)*** OL

15–1 Name ________ Date ________

**Skills Practice**

*Round Decimals*

Chapter Resources

**Round to the nearest whole number.**

1. 9.47 **9**
2. 1.1 **1**
3. 13.61 **14**
4. 93.56 **94**
5. 2.8 **3**
6. 3.51 **4**
7. 25.09 **25**
8. 88.48 **88**
9. 6.01 **6**
10. 4.62 **5**
11. 37.8 **38**
12. 19.71 **20**

**Round to the nearest tenth.**

13. 7.24 **7.2**
14. 1.27 **1.3**
15. 12.57 **12.6**
16. 36.97 **37.0**
17. 9.43 **9.4**
18. 3.98 **4.0**
19. 64.93 **64.9**
20. 53.84 **53.8**
21. 6.58 **6.6**
22. 7.24 **7.2**
23. 47.96 **48.0**
24. 19.46 **19.5**
25. 8.236 **8.2**
26. 3.199 **3.2**
27. 32.333 **32.3**
28. 4.186 **4.2**
29. 17.246 **17.2**
30. 45.999 **46**
31. 9.276 **9.3**
32. 26.981 **27**
33. 13.462 **13.5**

**Solve.**

34. A vitamin pill weighs 2.346 grams. What is its mass to the nearest tenth of a gram?
    **2.4 grams**
35. Jason weighs 152.6 pounds. What is his weight to the nearest pound?
    **153 pounds**

## Practice and Problem Solving

See page R39.

**Round to the nearest whole number.** See Examples 1 and 2 (pp. 617–618)

**11.** 1.54 2 **12.** 6.38 6 **13.** 31.72 32 **14.** 49.63 50

**15.** 54.37 54 **16.** 59.72 60 **17.** 64.26 64 **18.** 81.48 81

**Round to the nearest tenth.** See Example 3 (p. 618)

**19.** 2.58 2.6 **20.** 7.31 7.3 **21.** 37.54 37.5 **22.** 42.07 42.1

**23.** 55.70 55.7 **24.** 63.05 63.1 **25.** 79.49 79.5 **26.** 97.33 97.3

**For Exercises 27 and 28, round to the nearest whole number.** 30, 31. See margin.

**27.** One of the world's largest insects is a stick insect. It is 1.83 feet long. About how long is this insect? 2 ft

**28.** Caley wants to buy a shirt for $22.53. About how much money will she need to buy the shirt? $23

**29.** One of the most valuable cars in the world is worth $2.29 million dollars. How much is this car worth to the nearest tenth? $2.3 million

**30.** **Measurement** Rebeca rounded the weights of various sports balls to the nearest whole number. Are her estimates reasonable? Explain.

| Ball | Actual Weight (oz) | Estimate (oz) |
|---|---|---|
| Soccer | 14.5 | 15 |
| Tennis | 2.1 | 2 |
| Lacrosse | 5.18 | 5 |

**31.** **Measurement** A city in Peru receives only 0.09 inches of rainfall each year. Is it reasonable to say that the city receives about 1 inch of rain each year? Explain.

### Real-World PROBLEM SOLVING

**School** Mr. Johnson is working on first quarter report cards. Use the table to the right to answer the questions.

**Mr. Johnson's Class**

| Student | Grade |
|---|---|
| Angelo | 92.52 |
| Nara | 88.27 |
| Jena | 85.46 |
| Doug | 76.81 |
| Jocelyn | 84.53 |
| Jodie | 88.59 |

**32.** For Angelo to earn an A, he must achieve a 93 or above. Mr. Johnson rounds his students' grades to the nearest whole number. Will Angelo get an A? Explain. See margin.

**33.** To the nearest whole number, who earned a higher score, Nara or Jodie? Jodie

**34.** To the nearest whole number, which two students earned the same grade? Jena and Jocelyn



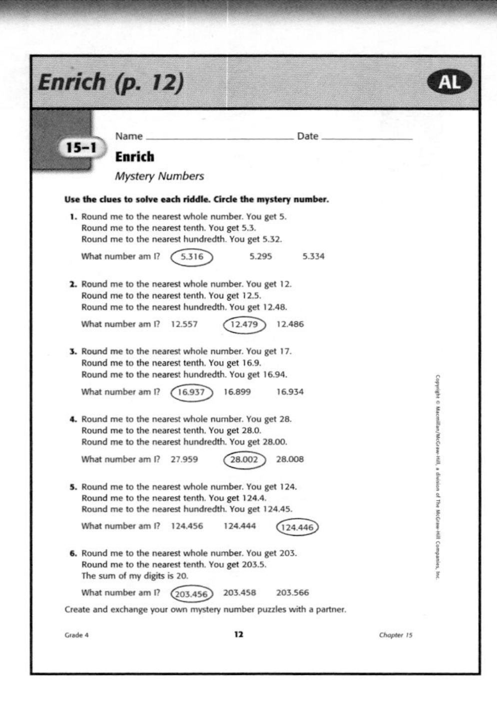
**Enrich (p. 12)** AL

15–1 Name ______ Date ______

**Enrich**

*Mystery Numbers*

**Use the clues to solve each riddle. Circle the mystery number.**

1. Round me to the nearest whole number. You get 5.
   Round me to the nearest tenth. You get 5.3.
   Round me to the nearest hundredth. You get 5.32.
   What number am I? (5.316) 5.295 5.334
2. Round me to the nearest whole number. You get 12.
   Round me to the nearest tenth. You get 12.5.
   Round me to the nearest hundredth. You get 12.48.
   What number am I? 12.557 (12.479) 12.486
3. Round me to the nearest whole number. You get 17.
   Round me to the nearest tenth. You get 16.9.
   Round me to the nearest hundredth. You get 16.94.
   What number am I? (16.937) 16.899 16.934
4. Round me to the nearest whole number. You get 28.
   Round me to the nearest tenth. You get 28.0.
   Round me to the nearest hundredth. You get 28.00.
   What number am I? 27.959 (28.002) 28.008
5. Round me to the nearest whole number. You get 124.
   Round me to the nearest tenth. You get 124.4.
   Round me to the nearest hundredth. You get 124.45.
   What number am I? 124.456 124.444 (124.446)
6. Round me to the nearest whole number. You get 203.
   Round me to the nearest tenth. You get 203.5.
   The sum of my digits is 20.
   What number am I? (203.456) 203.458 203.566

Create and exchange your own mystery number puzzles with a partner.

Grade 4 12 Chapter 15



# 3 Practice

Differentiate practice using these leveled assignments for Exercises 11–41.

| Level | Assignment |
|---|---|
| BL Below/Approaching Level | 11–14, 19–22, 27–29, 32 |
| OL On Level | 13–18, 20–26,27–30, 32–34, 36–37 |
| AL Above/Beyond Level | 11–33 odd, 35–41 |

Have students discuss and complete the Higher Order Thinking problems. For Exercises 38–40, have students first convert each mixed number to a decimal, then round.

**WRITING IN MATH** Have students complete Exercise 41 in their Math Journals. You may choose to use this exercise as an optional formative assessment.

### Additional Answers

**9.** pygmy parrot: 0.3; bee hummingbird: 0.2; gouldian finch: 0.3; New Zealand wren: 0.3

**10.** Sample answer: alike: the steps you take are the same; different: you are now looking at place value to the right of the decimal point.

**30.** Sample answer: yes; Rebeca correctly rounded each decimal to the nearest whole number.

**31.** Sample answer: no; 0.09 rounded to the nearest whole number equals 0.

**32.** Sample answer: yes; Angelo's grade before rounding was 92.52. His grade will be rounded up to 93, which results in an A for his quarter grade.

# 4 Assess

## Formative Assessment

- **How could you use a number line to round 42.17 to the nearest whole number? How could you use rounding rules?**
  Number line: Find 42.17 on a number line. It is closer to 42 than to 43, so round down to 42. Rounding rules: Look at the digit in the tenths place. It is 1, which is less than 5, so I round down to 42.

**Quick Check** **Are students continuing to struggle with rounding decimals?**

**If Yes** → Small Group Options (p. 617B)

**If No** → Independent Work Options (p. 617B)
CRM Skills Practice Worksheet (p. 9)
CRM Enrich Worksheet (p. 12)

**Yesterday's News** Have students write or talk about how rounding larger numbers to the nearest ten, hundred, thousand, ten thousand, and hundred thousand helped them learn how to round decimals to the nearest whole number and tenth.

## TEST Practice

### Reviews Lessons 14-8 and 15-1

Assign the Test Practice problems to provide daily reinforcement of test-taking skills.

## Spiral Review

### Reviews Lessons 12-5, 14-7, and 14-8

Review and assess mastery of skills and concepts from previous chapters.

### Additional Answer

**41.** Sample answer: Think of a decimal in the tenths that rounds down to 75. The answer is 75.4.

## H.O.T. Problems

**OPEN ENDED** Give a reasonable rounded estimate for each decimal.
35–37. Sample answers are given.

**35.** 23.81 pounds 24 lb **36.** 30.85 feet 30.9 ft **37.** 16.37 miles per gallon 16 mpg

**CHALLENGE** Round to the nearest tenth.

**38.** $1\frac{1}{4}$ 1.3 **39.** $2\frac{3}{4}$ 2.8 **40.** $4\frac{53}{100}$ 4.5

**41.** **WRITING IN MATH** Explain how to find the greatest decimal in tenths that rounds to 75. What is the decimal? See margin.

## TEST Practice

**42.** Order the numbers shown from greatest to least. (Lesson 14-8) C

**A** 2.46, $2\frac{1}{2}$, 2.64, $2\frac{1}{3}$

**B** 2.64, $2\frac{1}{2}$, $2\frac{1}{3}$, 2.46

**C** 2.64, $2\frac{1}{2}$, 2.46, $2\frac{1}{3}$

**D** $2\frac{1}{3}$, 2.46, $2\frac{1}{2}$, 2.64

**43.** The length of a vehicle is 205.83 inches. Find the total length to the nearest whole number. (Lesson 15-1) H

**F** 200 inches

**G** 205 inches

**H** 206 inches

**J** 210 inches

## Spiral Review

**Use a number line to compare. Use >, <, or =.** (Lesson 14-8)

**44.** 1.75 ● $1\frac{3}{4}$ = **45.** $7\frac{6}{100}$ ● 7.6 < **46.** 46.2 ● $46\frac{1}{4}$ <

**Write a fraction and decimal to describe the shaded part of each model.** (Lesson 14-7)

**47.** 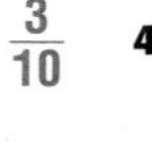 0.3; $\frac{3}{10}$

**48.** 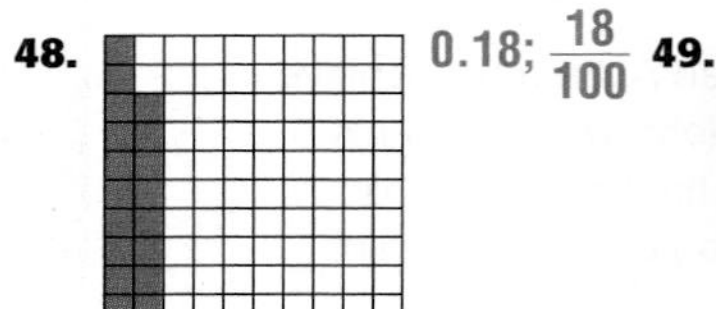 0.18; $\frac{18}{100}$

**49.** 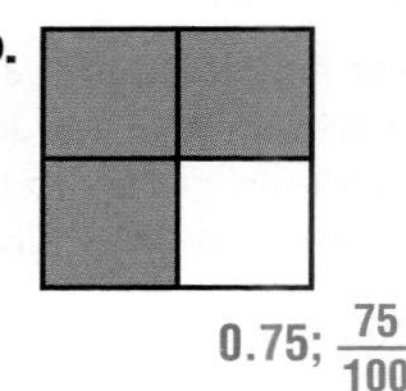 0.75; $\frac{75}{100}$

**50.** Alano, Sidney, and Tasha play instruments. Each student plays either the flute, the violin, or the cello. Sidney does not play the violin or the cello. Alano does not play the cello. What instruments do Alano, Sidney, and Tasha play? (Lesson 12-5) Alano: violin; Sidney: flute; Tasha: cello



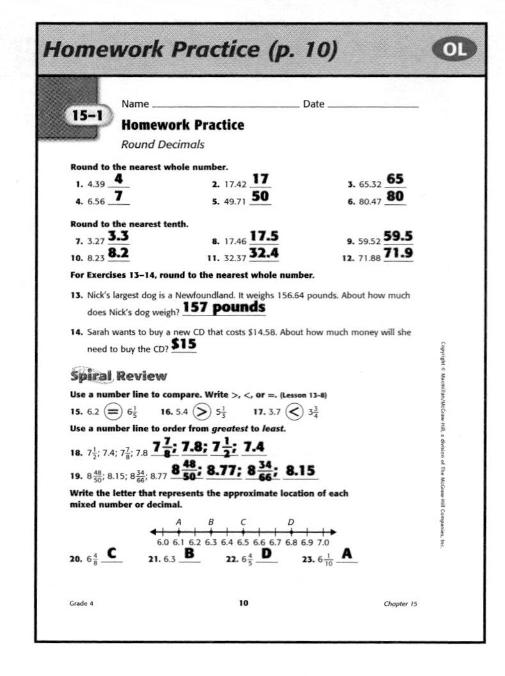

**Homework Practice (p. 10)** OL

15–1 Name ______ Date ______

**Homework Practice**

*Round Decimals*

**Round to the nearest whole number.**

1. 4.39 **4** 2. 17.42 **17** 3. 65.32 **65**
4. 6.56 **7** 5. 49.71 **50** 6. 80.47 **80**

**Round to the nearest tenth.**

7. 3.27 **3.3** 8. 17.46 **17.5** 9. 59.52 **59.5**
10. 8.23 **8.2** 11. 32.37 **32.4** 12. 71.88 **71.9**

**For Exercises 13–14, round to the nearest whole number.**

13. Nick's largest dog is a Newfoundland. It weighs 156.64 pounds. About how much does Nick's dog weigh? **157 pounds**

14. Sarah wants to buy a new CD that costs $14.58. About how much money will she need to buy the CD? **$15**

**Spiral Review**

**Use a number line to compare. Write >, <, or =.** (Lesson 13-8)

15. 6.2 (=) $6\frac{1}{5}$ 16. 5.4 (>) $5\frac{1}{3}$ 17. 3.7 (<) $3\frac{3}{4}$

**Use a number line to order from *greatest* to *least*.**

18. $7\frac{1}{2}$; 7.4; $7\frac{7}{8}$; 7.8 **$7\frac{7}{8}$; 7.8; $7\frac{1}{2}$; 7.4**

19. $8\frac{48}{50}$; 8.15; $8\frac{34}{66}$; 8.77 **$8\frac{48}{50}$; 8.77; $8\frac{34}{66}$; 8.15**

**Write the letter that represents the approximate location of each mixed number or decimal.**

A B C D
6.0 6.1 6.2 6.3 6.4 6.5 6.6 6.7 6.8 6.9 7.0

20. $6\frac{4}{8}$ **C** 21. 6.3 **B** 22. $6\frac{4}{5}$ **D** 23. $6\frac{1}{10}$ **A**

Grade 4 10 Chapter 15

## Match Up

**Round Decimals**

### Get Ready!

**Players:** 2 players

### Get Set!

Cut each index card in half. Then label each card with one decimal as shown.

**You will need:** 10 index cards

| 0.13 | 0.1 | 38.54 | 38.5 |
|---|---|---|---|
| 0.15 | 0.2 | 38.56 | 38.6 |
| 2.14 | 2.1 | 2.46 | 2.5 |
| 8.73 | 8.7 | 8.77 | 8.8 |
| 12.31 | 12.3 | 12.35 | 12.4 |

### Go!

- Shuffle the cards. Then spread the cards out facedown.
- Player 1 turns over two cards.
- If one decimal equals the other decimal after being rounded to the tenths place, Player 1 keeps the cards. Player 1 continues by choosing two more cards.
- If one decimal does not equal the other decimal after being rounded to the tenths place, the cards are turned over and Player 2 takes a turn.
- Continue playing until all matches are made. The player with the most cards wins.

**Game Time** Match Up 621

# Differentiated Practice

Use these leveled suggestions to differentiate the game for all learners.

| Level | Assignment |
|---|---|
| BL Below/Approaching Level | Students play with cards that round to the nearest whole number. |
| OL On Level | Have students play the game with the rules as written. |
| AL Above/Beyond Level | Students play with cards that round to the nearest hundredth. |

# Match Up

**Math Concept:**
**Round Decimals**

**Materials:** 10 index cards, scissors, paper, pencils

Introduce the game on p. 621 to your students to play as a class, in small groups, or at a learning workstation to review concepts introduced in this chapter.

## Instructions

- Students play in pairs. They cut the index cards in half and label each half with one decimal, as shown on p. 621.
- Students shuffle the cards and spread them out, facedown, on the table.
- Player 1 turns over two cards. If one decimal equals the other decimal after being rounded to the tenths place, Player 1 keeps the cards and continues by turning over two more cards. If the one decimal does not equal the other after being rounded to the tenths place, the cards are turned back over and Player 2 takes a turn.
- Play continues until all matches are made. The player with the most cards wins.

## Extend the Game

Have students make the game using their own card pairs. Have them make sure that the decimals in each card pair equal each other after being rounded to the tenths place.

LESSON 15-2

# Estimate Decimal Sums and Differences

## Lesson Planner

### Objective

Estimate decimal sums and differences.

### Review Vocabulary

**estimate**

### Resources

**Materials:** grid paper

**Manipulatives:** money

**Literature Connection:** *The Toothpaste Millionaire* by Jean Merrill

**Teacher Technology**
TeacherWorks • Interactive Classroom

## Daily Routine

Use these suggestions before beginning the lesson on p. 622.

### 5-Minute Check

(Reviews Lesson 15-1)

**Round to the nearest whole number. Use number lines and models.**

**1.** 1.43 1
**2.** 26.72 27
**3.** 53.54 54
**4.** 67.15 67
**5.** 3.16 3
**6.** 9.35 9
**7.** 48.51 49
**8.** 92.64 93

### Problem of the Day

Keri has 23 coins in her piggy bank. Only 4 of the coins are dimes. The rest are pennies. Keri picks a coin from the bank without looking. Is she more likely to pick a dime or penny? penny

### Focus on Math Background

Estimation is important for two reasons:

- In many real situations, an approximation is often all that is needed.
- Estimating provides a "reasonableness" check to an answer, and this can be used to help students spot errors in computation. Since estimates in this lesson are based on rounding, results may vary slightly depending on the place used for rounding.

When many numbers resulting from measurement are added, rounding up on 5s can produce a misleading overestimate. In such real-world situations, an alternate rounding rule is sometimes used—instead of rounding up on a 5, the measurements are rounded to the nearest even digit.

### Review Math Vocabulary

Write the review vocabulary word and its definition on the board.

Ask students to identify key words that tell them that an estimate, not an exact answer, is needed to solve a word problem. Then have them brainstorm real-world situations in which estimation is used.

**Visual Vocabulary Cards**
Use Visual Vocabulary Card 15 to reinforce the vocabulary reviewed in this lesson (The Define/Example/Ask routine is printed on the back of each card.)

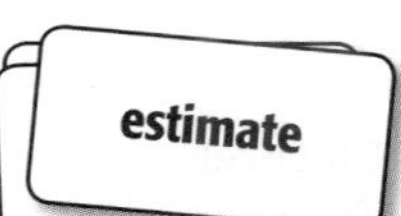

# Differentiated Instruction

## Small Group Options

**Option 1** SPATIAL

### Below Level BL

**Materials:** bills, coins, pencils, paper

- Tell students you are the "banker." Give each student an amount of coins and bills and ask him or her to count it.
- Tell students that if they have an amount of coins equal to or greater than 50¢, they may exchange it with you for another dollar. If they have coins that amount to 49¢ or less, they must turn it in to you.

- Do this several times with each student.
- Tell them this is how to round to the nearest dollar.
- Have students write an amount of money on the paper and round them to the nearest dollar.

**Option 2** AUDITORY, INTRAPERSONAL

### English Language Learners ELL

**Materials:** construction paper, number cubes
**Core Vocabulary:** speculation, deduce, suppose
**Common Use Verb:** speculate

**Hear Math** This strategy activates background knowledge and estimation skills to practice adding and subtracting decimals.

- Roll 2 number cubes and use them to make a 2-digit decimal, for example: 0.54.
- Say: "My roll rounds down to ______. [For example: 50 cents] Give me a decimal that might make 50 cents."
- As students speculate, discuss deductive reasoning using the core vocabulary (they can presume it is not less than $0.50, etc).
- Have students call out their speculations; the one that is closest to a dollar wins.
- Repeat as time permits. When a 10, 11, or 12 is rolled, students will have to estimate down.

## Independent Work Options

**Option 1** LOGICAL, LINGUISTIC

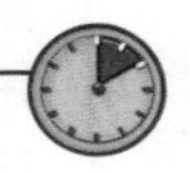

### Early Finishers OL AL

**Materials:** paper and pencil

- Write "8" on the board.
- Challenge students to write one decimal addition problem and one decimal subtraction problem where the estimated sum or difference is 8.
- Repeat with 13, 25, and 50.

**Option 2**

### Student Technology

**Math Online** macmillanmh.com

Personal Tutor • Extra Examples

 Math Adventures

**Option 3**

### Learning Station: Health (p. 614G)

Direct students to the Health Learning Station for opportunities to explore and extend the lesson concept.

**Option 4**

### Problem-Solving Practice

Reinforce problem-solving skills and strategies with the Problem-Solving Practice worksheet.

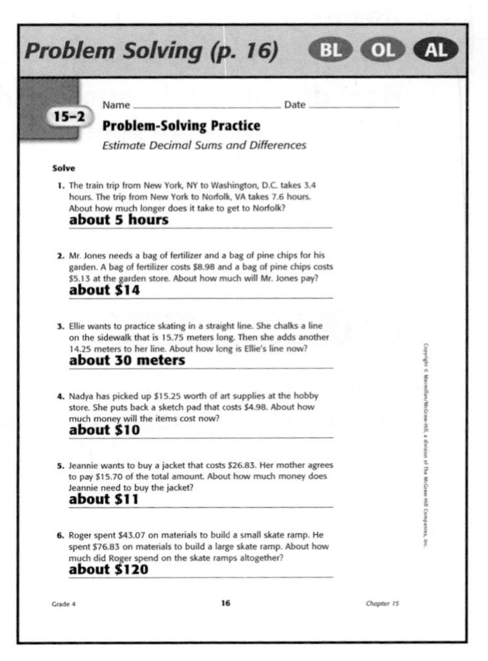

*Problem Solving (p. 16)* BL OL AL

15-2 Name ______ Date ______

**Problem-Solving Practice**

*Estimate Decimal Sums and Differences*

**Solve**

1. The train trip from New York, NY to Washington, D.C. takes 3.4 hours. The trip from New York to Norfolk, VA takes 7.6 hours. About how much longer does it take to get to Norfolk?
   **about 5 hours**
2. Mr. Jones needs a bag of fertilizer and a bag of pine chips for his garden. A bag of fertilizer costs $8.98 and a bag of pine chips costs $5.13 at the garden store. About how much will Mr. Jones pay?
   **about $14**
3. Ellie wants to practice skating in a straight line. She chalks a line on the sidewalk that is 15.75 meters long. Then she adds another 14.25 meters to her line. About how long is Ellie's line now?
   **about 30 meters**
4. Nadya has picked up $15.25 worth of art supplies at the hobby store. She puts back a sketch pad that costs $4.98. About how much money will the items cost now?
   **about $10**
5. Jeannie wants to buy a jacket that costs $26.83. Her mother agrees to pay $15.70 of the total amount. About how much money does Jeannie need to buy the jacket?
   **about $11**
6. Roger spent $43.07 on materials to build a small skate ramp. He spent $76.83 on materials to build a large skate ramp. About how much did Roger spend on the skate ramps altogether?
   **about $120**



Grade 4 16 Chapter 15

# 15-2 Estimate Decimal Sums and Differences

## 1 Introduce

### Activity Choice 1 • Hands-On

- Review rounding with students.
- Provide students with play money. Remind them that dollar amounts are written to the left of the decimal point and cents to the right. Point out that one cent is one hundredth of a dollar.
- Write the following money amounts on the board for students to model with bills and coins: $56.75, $32.42, $22.63, $18.35.
- Ask students to round each amount to the nearest dollar, or whole number. $57, $32, $23, $18
- Explain that rounding decimals can be used to estimate sums and differences.

### Activity Choice 2 • Literature

Introduce the lesson with *The Toothpaste Millionaire* by Jean Merrill. For a related math activity, see p. TR66.

## 2 Teach

### Scaffolding Questions

- **What do you look at when you round a decimal to the nearest ones place?** the tenths place
- **How do you know whether to round up or down?** Sample answer: Round to the number that is closer on the number line.
- **How do you think rounding decimals can help you estimate sums and differences?** I can round each decimal to the nearest whole number and add or subtract the rounded numbers to estimate the sum or difference.

### GET READY to Learn

Have students open their books and read the information in **Get Ready to Learn**. Review **estimate**. As a class, work through **Examples 1 and 2**.



# 15-2 Estimate Decimal Sums and Differences

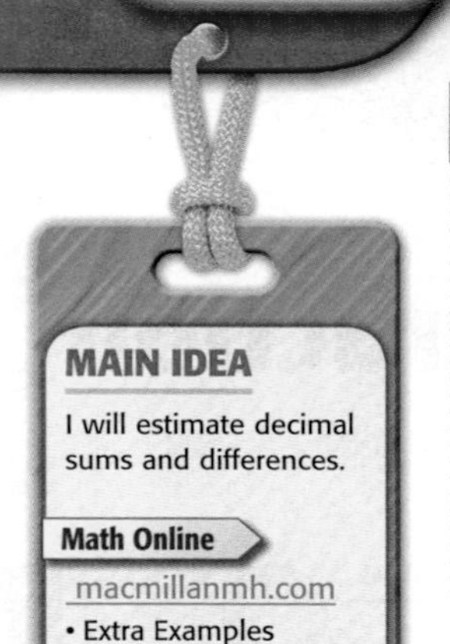


### GET READY to Learn

Martina is going white water rafting with her family. On the first day, they will travel 6.5 miles before lunch and 8.7 miles after lunch. *About* how far will they travel on the first day?

To estimate the sum of decimals, you can round each decimal to the nearest whole number and then add.

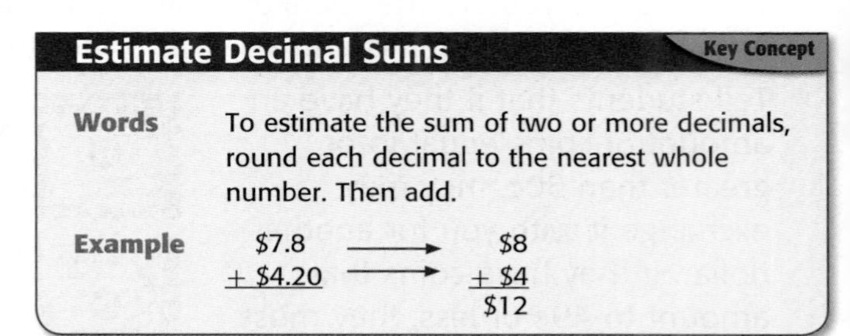

**Estimate Decimal Sums** — Key Concept

**Words** To estimate the sum of two or more decimals, round each decimal to the nearest whole number. Then add.

**Example**

| | | |
|---|---|---|
| $7.8 | → | $8 |
| + $4.20 | → | + $4 |
| | | $12 |

**Real-World EXAMPLE** Estimate Sums

**1 TRAVEL About how far will Martina and her family travel on the first day?**

You need to estimate 6.5 + 8.7. Round each addend to the nearest whole number. Then add.

| | | | |
|---|---|---|---|
| 6.50 | → | 7 | Round 6.5 to 7. |
| + 8.7 | → | + 9 | Round 8.7 to 9. |

So, Martina and her family will travel about 16 miles.

622 **Chapter 15** Add and Subtract Decimals

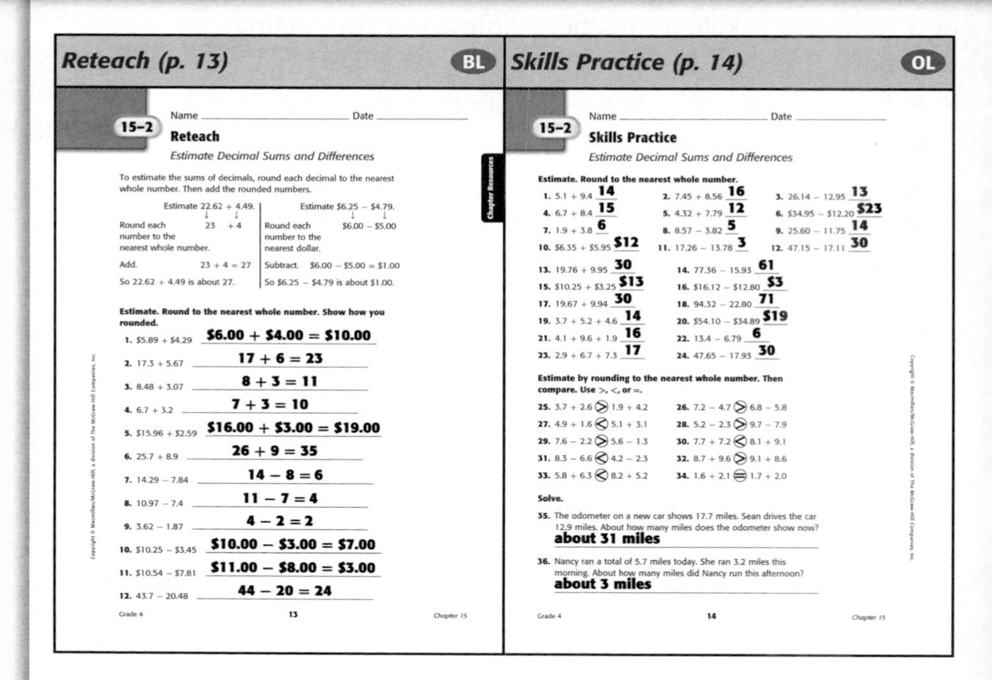

**Reteach (p. 13)** BL

15-2 Name ________ Date ________

**Reteach**

*Estimate Decimal Sums and Differences*

To estimate the sums of decimals, round each decimal to the nearest whole number. Then add the rounded numbers.

| | Estimate 22.62 + 4.49. | | Estimate $6.25 − $4.79. |
|---|---|---|---|
| Round each number to the nearest whole number. | 23 + 4 | Round each number to the nearest dollar. | $6.00 − $5.00 |
| Add. | 23 + 4 = 27 | Subtract. | $6.00 − $5.00 = $1.00 |
| So 22.62 + 4.49 is about 27. | | So $6.25 − $4.79 is about $1.00. | |

**Estimate. Round to the nearest whole number. Show how you rounded.**

1. $5.89 + $4.29 **$6.00 + $4.00 = $10.00**
2. 17.3 + 5.67 **17 + 6 = 23**
3. 8.48 + 3.07 **8 + 3 = 11**
4. 6.7 + 3.2 **7 + 3 = 10**
5. $15.96 + $2.59 **$16.00 + $3.00 = $19.00**
6. 25.7 + 8.9 **26 + 9 = 35**
7. 14.29 − 7.84 **14 − 8 = 6**
8. 10.97 − 7.4 **11 − 7 = 4**
9. 3.62 − 1.87 **4 − 2 = 2**
10. $10.25 − $3.45 **$10.00 − $3.00 = $7.00**
11. $10.54 − $7.81 **$11.00 − $8.00 = $3.00**
12. 43.7 − 20.48 **44 − 20 = 24**



Grade 4 13 Chapter 15

**Skills Practice (p. 14)** OL

15-2 Name ________ Date ________

**Skills Practice**

*Estimate Decimal Sums and Differences*

**Estimate. Round to the nearest whole number.**

1. 5.1 + 9.4 **14**
2. 7.45 + 8.56 **16**
3. 26.14 − 12.95 **13**
4. 6.7 + 8.4 **15**
5. 4.32 + 7.79 **12**
6. $34.95 − $12.20 **$23**
7. 1.9 + 3.8 **6**
8. 8.57 − 3.82 **5**
9. 25.60 − 11.75 **14**
10. $6.35 + $5.95 **$12**
11. 17.26 − 13.78 **3**
12. 47.15 − 17.11 **30**
13. 19.76 + 9.95 **30**
14. 77.36 − 15.93 **61**
15. $10.25 + $3.25 **$13**
16. $16.12 − $12.80 **$3**
17. 19.67 + 9.94 **30**
18. 94.32 − 22.80 **71**
19. 3.7 + 5.2 + 4.6 **14**
20. $54.10 − $34.89 **$19**
21. 4.1 + 9.6 + 1.9 **16**
22. 13.4 − 6.79 **6**
23. 2.9 + 6.7 + 7.3 **17**
24. 47.65 − 17.93 **30**

**Estimate by rounding to the nearest whole number. Then compare. Use >, <, or =.**

25. 3.7 + 2.6 **>** 1.9 + 4.2
26. 7.2 − 4.7 **>** 6.8 − 5.8
27. 4.9 + 1.6 **<** 5.1 + 3.1
28. 5.2 − 2.3 **>** 9.7 − 7.9
29. 7.6 − 2.2 **>** 5.6 − 1.3
30. 7.7 + 7.2 **<** 8.1 + 9.1
31. 8.3 − 6.6 **<** 4.2 − 2.3
32. 8.7 + 9.6 **>** 9.1 + 8.6
33. 5.8 + 6.3 **<** 8.2 + 5.2
34. 1.6 + 2.1 **=** 1.7 + 2.0

**Solve.**

35. The odometer on a new car shows 17.7 miles. Sean drives the car 12.9 miles. About how many miles does the odometer show now? **about 31 miles**
36. Nancy ran a total of 5.7 miles today. She ran 3.2 miles this morning. About how many miles did Nancy run this afternoon? **about 3 miles**



Grade 4 14 Chapter 15

**Remember**

When rounding to the nearest whole number, think about the whole number that comes before and after the number to be rounded.

## Estimate Decimal Differences

Key Concept

**Words** To estimate the difference of two decimals, round each decimal to the nearest whole number. Then subtract.

**Example**

$$\begin{array}{r} \$28.75 \\ -\ \$13.49 \end{array} \longrightarrow \begin{array}{r} \$29 \\ -\ \$13 \\ \hline \$16 \end{array}$$

### Real-World EXAMPLE — Estimate Differences

**2** **Mallory wants to buy a cell phone that costs $37.99. She has $45.25. About how much money will she have left to buy ring tones after she buys the phone?**

**Estimate** $45.25 – $37.99

Round each decimal to the nearest whole number. Then subtract.

$$\begin{array}{r} \$45.25 \\ -\ \$37.99 \end{array} \longrightarrow \begin{array}{r} \$45 \\ -\ \$38 \end{array}$$

Round $45.25 to $45. Round $37.99 to $38.

$$\begin{array}{r} \overset{3\ 15}{\$\cancel{4}\cancel{5}} \\ -\ \$38 \\ \hline \$\ 7 \end{array}$$

So, Mallory will have about $7 left to buy ring tones.

## CHECK What You Know

**Estimate. Round to the nearest whole number.** See Examples 1 and 2 (pp. 622–623)

1. 1.5 + 2.3 **2 + 2 = 4**
2. 5.4 – 3.61 **5 – 4 = 1**
3. 24.9 + 9.8 **25 + 10 = 35**
4. 62.8 – 9.5 **63 – 10 = 53**
5. $8.75 + $3.25 **$9 + $3 = $12**
6. 46.37 – 7.3 **46 – 7 = 39**
7. Reed is running in a charity run that is 3.12 miles long. Reed has run 1.2 miles so far. About how many miles does he have left to run? **3 – 1 = 2 miles**
8. Talk About It Explain how you could estimate to find the sum of 2.1 and 3.3. **See Ch.15 Answer Appendix.**



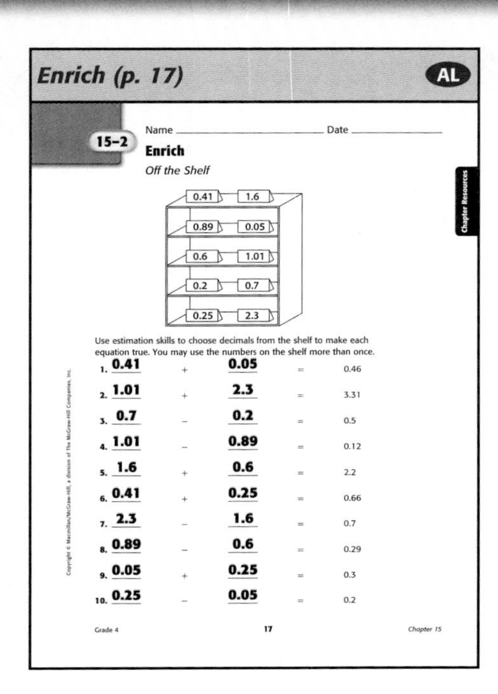

Enrich (p. 17) AL

15-2 Name ______ Date ______

**Enrich**

*Off the Shelf*

0.41, 1.6, 0.89, 0.05, 0.6, 1.01, 0.2, 0.7, 0.25, 2.3

Use estimation skills to choose decimals from the shelf to make each equation true. You may use the numbers on the shelf more than once.

1. **0.41** + **0.05** = 0.46
2. **1.01** + **2.3** = 3.31
3. **0.7** – **0.2** = 0.5
4. **1.01** – **0.89** = 0.12
5. **1.6** + **0.6** = 2.2
6. **0.41** + **0.25** = 0.66
7. **2.3** – **1.6** = 0.7
8. **0.89** – **0.6** = 0.29
9. **0.05** + **0.25** = 0.3
10. **0.25** – **0.05** = 0.2

Chapter Resources



Grade 4 17 Chapter 15

### Estimate Sums

**Example 1** Remind students that the word *about* tells them that an estimate, not an exact answer, is needed to solve the problem. Point out that 6.5 is written as 6.50. The zero is used as a placeholder in the hundredths place and is not necessary for solving the problem.

### ADDITIONAL EXAMPLES

1. Clara rides her bike 4.6 miles on Saturday and 6.25 miles on Sunday. About how many miles does she ride her bike altogether on both days? about 11 miles
2. Jairo has $38.55. If he buys a CD that costs $16.99, about how much money will he have left? about $22

### CHECK What You Know

As a class, have students complete Exercises 1–8 in **Check What You Know** as you observe their work.

**Exercise 8** Assess student comprehension before assigning practice exercises.

## BL Alternate Teaching Strategy

**If** students have trouble rounding each decimal to the nearest whole number to estimate…

**Then** use one of these reteach options:

1. CRM **Daily Reteach Worksheet** (p. 13)
2. Have students identify the two whole numbers that each decimal is between. Then have them draw a 10-by-10 grid on grid paper and shade the decimal portion of their number. They should recognize that if the grid is shaded less than half, they round to the number that comes before the number to be rounded, and if more than half is shaded, they round to the number that comes after.

# 3 Practice

Differentiate practice using these leveled assignments for Exercises 9–32.

| Level | Assignment |
|---|---|
| BL Below/Approaching Level | 9–10, 13–14, 17–18, 21–22, 25–26 |
| OL On Level | 9–13, 15, 17–19, 21–23, 25–29, 30 |
| AL Above/Beyond Level | 10–28 even, 30–32 |

Have students discuss and complete the Higher Order Thinking problems. Encourage students to work backward to solve Exercise 30.

**WRITING IN MATH** Have students complete Exercise 32 in their Math Journals. You may choose to use this exercise as an optional formative assessment.

**! COMMON ERROR!**

**Exercises 4–6 and 17–20** Students may round correctly, but make errors when they add or subtract numbers presented in horizontal form. Have students write the rounded numbers in vertical form before calculating the sum or difference.



★indicates a multi-step problem

## Practice and Problem Solving

**Estimate. Round to the nearest whole number.**

See Examples 1 and 2 (pp. 622–623) 11–14. See margin.

9. $2.5 + 4.8$ $3 + 5 = 8$
10. $9.8 + 8.2$ $10 + 8 = 18$
11. $8.5 + 11.7$
12. $19.6 + 2.4$
13. $\$17.50 + \$6.25$
14. $28.49 + 12.83$
15. $9.7 - 7.2$ $10 - 7 = 3$
16. $5.2 - 4.6$ $5 - 5 = 0$
17. $34.5 - 5.4$ $35 - 5 = 30$
18. $29.7 - 8.9$ $30 - 9 = 21$
19. $\$49.54 - \$25.15$ $\$50 - \$25 = \$25$
20. $78.29 - 39.85$ $\$78 - \$40 = \$38$

**Algebra Estimate by rounding to the nearest whole number. Then compare. Use $>$, $<$, or $=$.**

21. $18.34 + 3.67$ ● $12.29 + 7.95$ $>$
22. $14.58 - 6.91$ ● $21.62 - 12.19$ $<$
23. The hawk moth is the fastest flying insect. It can fly up to 33.3 miles per hour. A hornet can fly up to 13.3 miles per hour. About how much faster can the moth fly than the hornet? 20 mph
24. ★ Amit is buying some action figures for $12.29. He is also buying a pack of trading cards for $1.25. If he pays with a 20 dollar bill, about how much change will he get back? $7
25. Oscar is 4.3 feet tall. The giant ragwood plant is 8.9 feet tall. Is 8 – 4 a reasonable estimate of the difference in Oscar's and the plant's height to the nearest whole number? Explain. 25, 26. See margin.
26. Kyle ran one mile in 7.58 minutes. He ran a second mile in 8.23 minutes. Is 7.6 + 8.2 a reasonable estimate of the combined times to the nearest tenth? Explain.

### Real-World PROBLEM SOLVING

*Science* The table shows the speeds in which planets travel during their orbits, or trips around the Sun.

27. To the nearest whole number, what is the difference between the fastest and slowest orbital speeds of the planets listed? 22
28. About how much faster does Mercury travel than Earth? 11
29. Earth's orbital speed is faster than two other planets on the table. About how much faster does Earth travel than each of these planets? 4; 11

**Orbital Speeds of Planets**

| Planet | Speed (miles per second) |
|---|---|
| Mercury | 29.75 |
| Venus | 21.76 |
| Earth | 18.51 |
| Mars | 14.51 |
| Jupiter | 8.12 |

**Source:** *Scholastic Book of World Records*



## Additional Answers

**11.** $9 + 12 = 21$
**12.** $20 + 2 = 22$
**13.** $\$18 + \$6 = \$24$
**14.** $28 + 13 = 41$
**25.** no; The plant's height should round up, not down.
**26.** yes; Each number was rounded correctly.

## H.O.T. Problems

**30. OPEN ENDED** Write an addition and a subtraction problem that involves decimals and results in an estimated answer of $12. Sample answer: $36.25 – $23.99; $5.99 + $6.49

**31. CHALLENGE** Estimate 32.4 + 21.5 + 17.95 to the nearest whole number. 72

**32. WRITING IN ► MATH** Explain how you would estimate the difference of 9 and 5.52. Sample answer: Round 5.52 to 6, then subtract. 9 – 6 = 3.

## TEST Practice

**33.** The deepest plant root is 393.7 feet deep. What is the total depth of the root rounded to the nearest whole number? (Lesson 15-1) C

**A** 300 feet
**B** 390 feet
**C** 394 feet
**D** 400 feet

**34.** On Friday, Noah drove 166.5 miles. On Saturday, he drove 68.4 miles. On Sunday, he drove 72.75 miles. Approximately how many miles did Noah drive in three days? (Lesson 15-2) J

**F** 200 miles
**G** 210 miles
**H** 300 miles
**J** 310 miles

## Spiral Review

**Round to the nearest whole number.** (Lesson 15-1)

**35.** 28.5 29 **36.** 43.4 43 **37.** 84.2 84

**Use a number line to compare. Use >, <, or =.** (Lesson 14-8)

**38.** $3 \bullet 2\frac{7}{10}$ $>$ **39.** $7.03 \bullet 7\frac{3}{100}$ $=$ **40.** $\frac{25}{5} \bullet 5$ $=$

**41.** Identify the pattern in the shapes at the right. Continue the pattern by drawing the next four shapes. (Lesson 9-3) See Ch.15 Answer Appendix.

**42. Algebra** The table shows a pattern. Identify the rule. Then find the missing numbers. (Lesson 5-8) Multiply by 2. Then add 1; 6 and 11.

| Rule: ■ | | | | | |
|---|---|---|---|---|---|
| Input | 2 | 3 | 4 | 5 | ■ |
| Output | 5 | 7 | 9 | ■ | 13 |



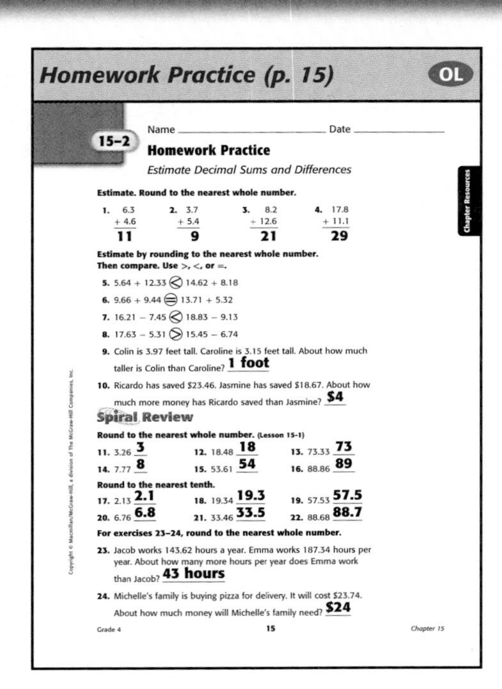

Homework Practice (p. 15) OL

15-2 Name ______ Date ______

**Homework Practice**

*Estimate Decimal Sums and Differences*

**Estimate. Round to the nearest whole number.**

1. 6.3 + 4.6 = **11**
2. 3.7 + 5.4 = **9**
3. 8.2 + 12.6 = **21**
4. 17.8 + 11.1 = **29**

**Estimate by rounding to the nearest whole number. Then compare. Use >, <, or =.**

5. 5.64 + 12.33 $<$ 14.62 + 8.18
6. 9.66 + 9.44 $=$ 13.71 + 5.32
7. 16.21 – 7.45 $<$ 18.83 – 9.13
8. 17.63 – 5.31 $>$ 15.45 – 6.74
9. Colin is 3.97 feet tall. Caroline is 3.15 feet tall. About how much taller is Colin than Caroline? **1 foot**
10. Ricardo has saved $23.46. Jasmine has saved $18.67. About how much more money has Ricardo saved than Jasmine? **$4**

**Spiral Review**

**Round to the nearest whole number.** (Lesson 15-1)

11. 3.26 **3** 12. 18.48 **18** 13. 73.33 **73**
14. 7.77 **8** 15. 53.61 **54** 16. 88.86 **89**

**Round to the nearest tenth.**

17. 2.13 **2.1** 18. 19.34 **19.3** 19. 57.53 **57.5**
20. 6.76 **6.8** 21. 33.46 **33.5** 22. 88.68 **88.7**

**For exercises 23–24, round to the nearest whole number.**

23. Jacob works 143.62 hours a year. Emma works 187.34 hours per year. About how many more hours per year does Emma work than Jacob? **43 hours**
24. Michelle's family is buying pizza for delivery. It will cost $23.74. About how much money will Michelle's family need? **$24**

Chapter Resources



Grade 4 15 Chapter 15

# 4 Assess

## Formative Assessment

- **How would you estimate the difference between 64.38 and 35.51?** Round 64.38 to 64. Round 35.51 to 36. 64 – 36 = 28.

**Quick Check** **Are students continuing to struggle with using rounding to estimate sums and differences?**

**If Yes** → Small Group Options (p. 622B)

**If No** → Independent Work Options (p. 622B)
CRM Skills Practice Worksheet (p. 14)
CRM Enrich Worksheet (p. 17)

**Name the Math** Write $10.55 + $15.29 on the board and ask students to explain how to estimate the sum.

## TEST Practice

### Reviews Lessons 15-1 and 15-2

Assign the Test Practice problems to provide daily reinforcement of test-taking skills.

## Spiral Review

### Reviews Lessons 5-8, 9-3, 14-8, and 15-1

Review and assess mastery of skills and concepts from previous chapters.

# Problem-Solving Strategy
# Work Backward

## Lesson Planner

### Objective
Solve problems by working backward.

### Resources
**Manipulatives:** money

**Literature Connection:** *A Chair for My Mother* by Vera B. Williams

**Teacher Technology**
TeacherWorks • Interactive Classroom

**Real-World Problem Solving Library**
**Math and Science: *A Force To Reckon With***
Use these leveled books to reinforce and extend problem-solving skills and strategies.

Leveled for:
- OL On Level
- ELL Sheltered English
- SP Spanish

For additional support, see the Real-World Problem Solving Teacher Guide.

## Daily Routine

Use these suggestions before beginning the lesson on p. 626.

### 5-Minute Check

(Reviews Lesson 15-2)

**Estimate. Round to the nearest whole number. Use models if needed.**

1. $1.5 + 3.4$ 5
2. $37.61 + 12.84$ 51
3. $28.9 - 8.27$ 21
4. $66.3 - 19.51$ 46
5. $2.18 + 17.4$ 19
6. $22.78 + 29.82$ 53
7. \$52.25 − \$44.77 \$7

### Problem of the Day

A baker has 42 muffins that she puts into seven containers. Each container holds the same number of muffins. How many muffins are there altogether in four containers? 24 muffins

# Differentiated Instruction

## Small Group Options

**Option 1** VISUAL, PAIR

### Gifted and Talented AL

**Materials:** index cards, chart paper, pencil

- Write the following problem on chart paper:
  ______ $-50 =$ ______ $\div 10 =$ ______ $+ 5 = 12$.
- **Demonstrate to students how the three blanks in this problem can be filled using the *work backward* strategy.**
  ______ $- \mathbf{50} =$ ______ $\div \mathbf{10} =$ ______ $+ \mathbf{5} = \mathbf{12}$.
  Start at the end.
  $12 = \mathbf{7} + 5$; $\mathbf{70} \div 10 = 7$; $\mathbf{120} - 50 = 70$
- Pass out an index card to each student and have each create a similar problem that requires the work backward strategy to solve.

**Option 2** LOGICAL

### English Language Learners ELL

**Materials:** clock, overhead fraction circles
**Core Vocabulary:** spread, break apart, rebuild
**Common Use Verb:** am finding
**Hear Math** This strategy gives students practice working backward and decoding key language.

- Put this problem on the overhead:
  *Maria has a math test on Friday. On Monday she studied for $\frac{3}{4}$ of an hour and on Wednesday she studied $1\frac{3}{4}$ hour. If she studied for a total of 4 hours, how much time did she spend studying on Thursday?*
- Read the problems. Say: "We are going to work backward to solve the problem."
- Separate the last sentence from the problem.
- Reread and discuss key words in context.
- Repeat, building the problem from sum to addends, having students write it out.

## Independent Work Options

**Option 1** LINGUISTIC, LOGICAL

### Early Finishers OL AL

**Materials:** paper and pencil

- Ask each student to write one word problem that can be solved using the work backward strategy.
- Have students exchange problems with a partner and solve.

**Option 2**

### Student Technology

**Math Online** macmillanmh.com

Personal Tutor • Extra Examples

**Option 3**

### Learning Stations: Art (p. 614G)

Direct students to the Art Learning Station for opportunities to explore and extend the lesson concept.

# 15-3 Problem-Solving Strategy

## 1 Introduce

**Activity Choice 1 • Review**

- Present students with the following problem: *Alex has 6 coins in his pocket with a total value of 72¢. What coins does he have?* 2 quarters, 2 dimes, 2 pennies
- **What problem-solving strategy could you use to solve the problem?** act it out
- Go over how to use the act it out strategy to solve the problem with play money.

**Activity Choice 2 • Literature**

Introduce the lesson with *A Chair for My Mother* by Vera B. Williams. For a related math activity, see p. TR67.

## 2 Teach

Have students read the problem on when Rey gets home from school. Guide them through the problem-solving steps.

**Understand** Using the questions, review what students know and need to find.

**Plan** Have them discuss their strategy.

**Solve** Guide students to use the work backward strategy to solve the problem.

- **What time will you work backward from?** 5:00 P.M.
- **What operation will you use?** subtraction
- **Why is important to work backward one step at a time?** Sample answer: because we use each step's answer to begin the next step

**Check** Have students look back at the problem to make sure that the answer fits the facts given.

**! COMMON ERROR!**

Students may use the wrong operation when working backward. Tell students that they should use inverse operations, or operations that "undo" the steps described in the problem, as they work backward. Have students make a list of the operations that undo addition, subtraction, multiplication, and division.



15-3 Problem-Solving Strategy

**MAIN IDEA** I will solve problems by working backward.

Rey has lacrosse practice in the evenings. He gets home from school and eats a snack for 15 minutes. Then he spends 1 hour doing his homework. It takes him 15 minutes to get to practice. Practice is at 5 P.M. What time does Rey get home from school?

**Understand**

**What facts do you know?**

- Rey eats for 15 minutes.
- He works on homework for 1 hour.
- It takes 15 minutes to get to practice at 5 P.M.

**What do you need to find?**

- What time Rey gets home from school.

**Plan**

Work backward to solve the problem.

**Solve**

Start with the end result. Then work backward one step at a time.

5 P.M. (practice starts) − 15 minutes (time to get to practice) = 4:45 P.M.

4:45 P.M. − 1 hour (homework) = 3:45 P.M.

3:45 P.M. − 15 minutes (time spent eating) = 3:30 P.M.

So, Rey gets home from school at 3:30 P.M.

**Check**

Look back. You can use addition to check.
15 minutes + 1 hour + 15 minutes = 1 hour and 30 minutes.
He gets home at 3:30 P.M. One hour and 30 minutes later is 5 P.M.
The answer is correct. ✓

626 Chapter 15 Add and Subtract Decimals

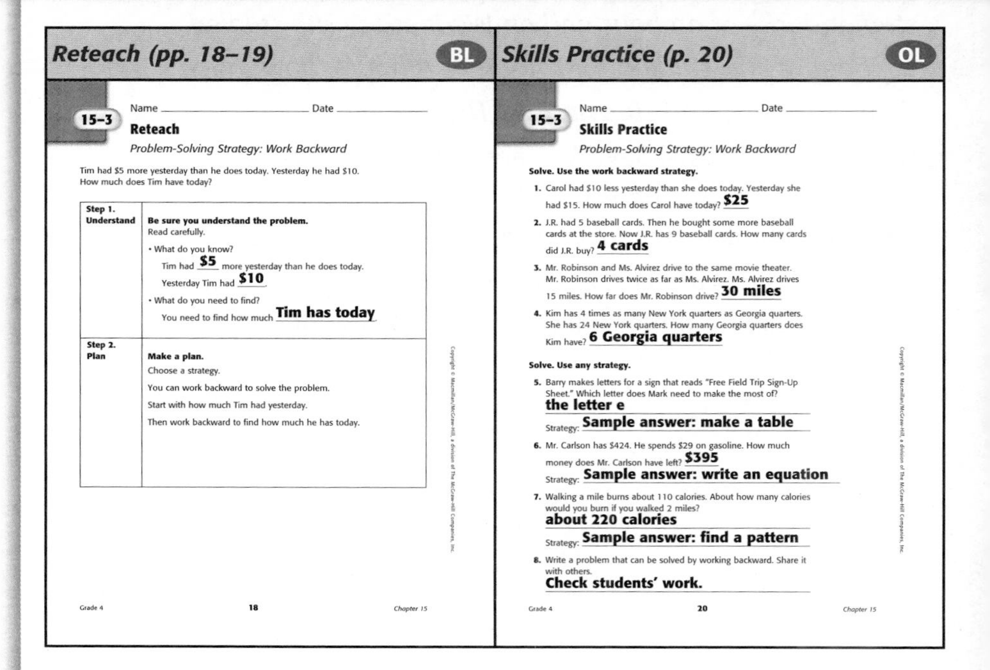

**Reteach (pp. 18–19)** BL

Name ______ Date ______

15-3 **Reteach**

*Problem-Solving Strategy: Work Backward*

Tim had $5 more yesterday than he does today. Yesterday he had $10. How much does Tim have today?

| | |
|---|---|
| **Step 1. Understand** | **Be sure you understand the problem.** Read carefully.<br>• What do you know?<br>Tim had **$5** more yesterday than he does today.<br>Yesterday Tim had **$10**.<br>• What do you need to find?<br>You need to find how much **Tim has today**. |
| **Step 2. Plan** | **Make a plan.**<br>Choose a strategy.<br>You can work backward to solve the problem.<br>Start with how much Tim had yesterday.<br>Then work backward to find how much he has today. |





**Skills Practice (p. 20)** OL

Name ______ Date ______

15-3 **Skills Practice**

*Problem-Solving Strategy: Work Backward*

**Solve. Use the work backward strategy.**

1. Carol had $10 less yesterday than she does today. Yesterday she had $15. How much does Carol have today? **$25**
2. J.R. had 5 baseball cards. Then he bought some more baseball cards at the store. Now J.R. has 9 baseball cards. How many cards did J.R. buy? **4 cards**
3. Mr. Robinson and Ms. Alvirez drive to the same movie theater. Mr. Robinson drives twice as far as Ms. Alvirez. Ms. Alvirez drives 15 miles. How far does Mr. Robinson drive? **30 miles**
4. Kim has 4 times as many New York quarters as Georgia quarters. She has 24 New York quarters. How many Georgia quarters does Kim have? **6 Georgia quarters**

**Solve. Use any strategy.**

5. Barry makes letters for a sign that reads "Free Field Trip Sign-Up Sheet." Which letter does Mark need to make the most of? **the letter e**
   Strategy: **Sample answer: make a table**
6. Mr. Carlson has $424. He spends $29 on gasoline. How much money does Mr. Carlson have left? **$395**
   Strategy: **Sample answer: write an equation**
7. Walking a mile burns about 110 calories. About how many calories would you burn if you walked 2 miles? **about 220 calories**
   Strategy: **Sample answer: find a pattern**
8. Write a problem that can be solved by working backward. Share it with others. **Check students' work.**

## ANALYZE the Strategy

**Refer to the problem on the previous page.** 1, 4. See Ch. 15 Answer Appendix.

1. Explain why 15 minutes was subtracted from 5 P.M. in the first step of solving the problem.
2. Suppose practice started at 4:30 P.M. What time would Rey get home from school? 3 P.M.
3. Suppose it takes Rey 45 minutes to complete his homework. What time would he get home from school? 3:45 P.M.
4. Look back to Exercise 3. Check your answer. How do you know it is correct? Explain.

★ indicates multi-step problem

## PRACTICE the Strategy

**Solve. Use the work backward strategy.**

5. Debbie bought a movie ticket. She then let her friend borrow $3. She now has $7. How much money did she have originally? $16

★6. Adrian volunteers at an animal shelter. It takes him 20 minutes to walk each dog shown. It takes him 15 minutes to give each dog a bath. He finished walking and bathing the dogs at 6 P.M. What time did he start? 4:50 P.M.

★7. A number is multiplied by 3. Next, 8 is subtracted from the product. Then, the difference is divided by 4. The result is 7. What is the number? 12

★8. Shantel jogs a mile in 8 minutes. She warms up for 10 minutes. She stretches for 5 minutes after she jogs. She jogs 2 miles, including warming up and stretching. She finishes at 8 A.M. What time does she start? 7:29 A.M.

★9. Nadina has two times as many pennies as dimes. The number of quarters she has is shown below. She has 4 more dimes than quarters. How much money does she have? $2.33

10. ★ A number is divided by 3. Next, 25 is added to the quotient. Then, the sum is multiplied by 4. The result is 116. What is the number? 12

11. **WRITING IN MATH** Explain how you used the work backward strategy in Exercise 10. See Ch. 15 Answer Appendix.



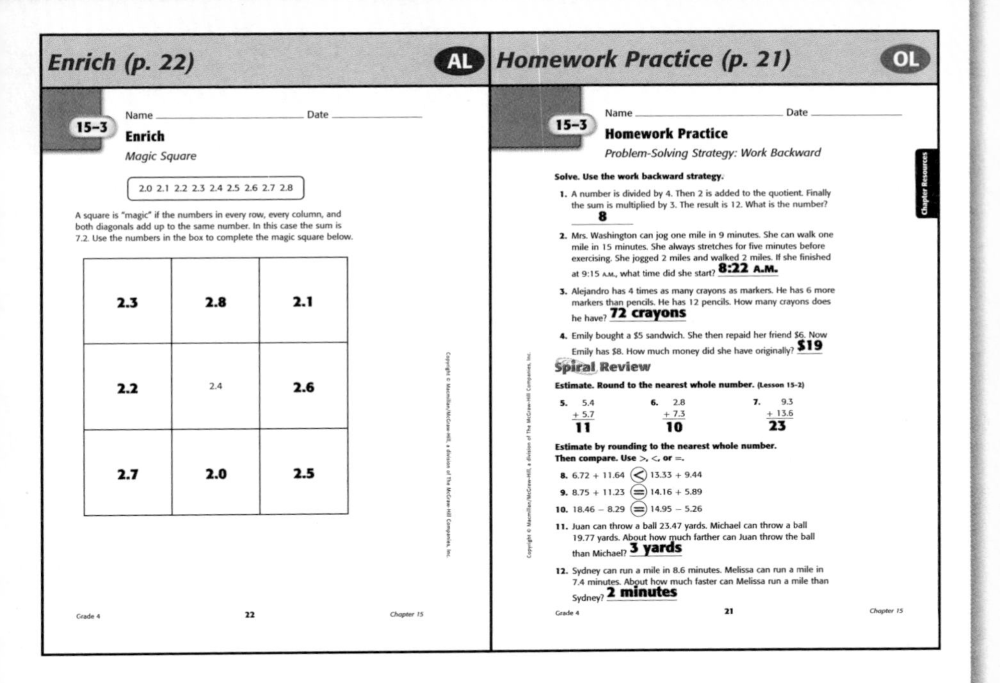

**Enrich (p. 22)** AL

15–3 Name ______ Date ______

**Enrich**

*Magic Square*

2.0 2.1 2.2 2.3 2.4 2.5 2.6 2.7 2.8

A square is "magic" if the numbers in every row, every column, and both diagonals add up to the same number. In this case the sum is 7.2. Use the numbers in the box to complete the magic square below.

| | | |
|---|---|---|
| **2.3** | **2.8** | **2.1** |
| **2.2** | 2.4 | **2.6** |
| **2.7** | **2.0** | **2.5** |



Grade 4 22 Chapter 15

**Homework Practice (p. 21)** OL

15–3 Name ______ Date ______

**Homework Practice**

*Problem-Solving Strategy: Work Backward*

Chapter Resources

**Solve. Use the work backward strategy.**

1. A number is divided by 4. Then 2 is added to the quotient. Finally the sum is multiplied by 3. The result is 12. What is the number? **8**
2. Mrs. Washington can jog one mile in 9 minutes. She can walk one mile in 15 minutes. She always stretches for five minutes before exercising. She jogged 2 miles and walked 2 miles. If she finished at 9:15 A.M., what time did she start? **8:22 A.M.**
3. Alejandro has 4 times as many crayons as markers. He has 6 more markers than pencils. He has 12 pencils. How many crayons does he have? **72 crayons**
4. Emily bought a $5 sandwich. She then repaid her friend $6. Now Emily has $8. How much money did she have originally? **$19**

**Spiral Review**

**Estimate. Round to the nearest whole number.** (Lesson 15-2)

5. 5.4 + 5.7 = **11**
6. 2.8 + 7.3 = **10**
7. 9.3 + 13.6 = **23**

**Estimate by rounding to the nearest whole number. Then compare. Use >, <, or =.**

8. 6.72 + 11.64 (<) 13.33 + 9.44
9. 8.75 + 11.23 (=) 14.16 + 5.89
10. 18.46 − 8.29 (=) 14.95 − 5.26
11. Juan can throw a ball 23.47 yards. Michael can throw a ball 19.77 yards. About how much farther can Juan throw the ball than Michael? **3 yards**
12. Sydney can run a mile in 8.6 minutes. Melissa can run a mile in 7.4 minutes. About how much faster can Melissa run a mile than Sydney? **2 minutes**



Grade 4 21 Chapter 15

**Analyze the Strategy** Use Exercises 1–4 to analyze and discuss the problem-solving strategy.

### BL Alternate Teaching Strategy

**If** students have trouble working backward to solve a time problem...

**Then** use one of these reteach options:

1. CRM **Daily Reteach Worksheet** (pp. 18–19)
2. Have students draw a timeline to help them solve the problem. Instruct students to draw a horizontal line and mark and label 5:00 P.M. on the far right. Then have them mark and label new times to the left of 5:00 P.M. as they work backward.

# 3 Practice

### Using the Exercises

**Exercise 7** Students use the inverse operation for each operation described, as they work backward from 7.

**Exercises 5 and 9** You may want to provide students with play money so they can act out the problems.

# 4 Assess

### Formative Assessment

- **How could you use the work backward strategy to help you decide when you must leave your house in the morning to get to school on time?** Sample answer: I can subtract the number of minutes for the bus ride and the minutes it takes to walk to the bus stop from the time that school starts to find out what time I must leave the house.

**Quick Check** **Are students continuing to struggle with solving problems by working backward?**

**If Yes** → Small Group Options (p. 626B)

**If No** → Independent Work Options (p. 626B)
CRM Skills Practice Worksheet (p. 20)
CRM Enrich Worksheet (p. 22)

# Lesson Planner

## Objective

Use models to add decimals.

## Resources

**Materials:** grid paper, colored pencils (two different colors per student)

**Teacher Technology**

Math Online macmillanmh.com

Concepts in Motion

## 1 Introduce

### Introduce the Concept

- Review modeling decimals with students. Distribute several sheets of grid paper and colored pencils to students and have them draw three 10-by-10 grids. Remind them that each grid represents one whole number, and that each square in the grid represents one hundredth.
- Write 1.45 and 0.3 on the board. Have students shade in their grids to first model 1.45, then 0.3.
- **What did you shade to show 1.45?** one whole 10-by-10 grid and 45 squares in another grid
- **How many hundredths is 0.3?** 30
- **How many squares did you shade to show 0.3?** 30
- Explain to students that they can use grid models to help them add decimals.

Math Activity for 15-4

# Addition of Decimals

You can use grid paper to explore adding decimals.

**MAIN IDEA**

I will use models to add decimals.

**You Will Need**

grid paper
colored pencil

Math Online
macmillanmh.com
• Concepts in Motion

**ACTIVITY**

**Use models to add decimals. Find 1.5 + 0.29.**

**Step 1** **Model 1.5.**

To show 1.5, shade one whole 10-by-10 grid and $\frac{50}{100}$ of a second grid.

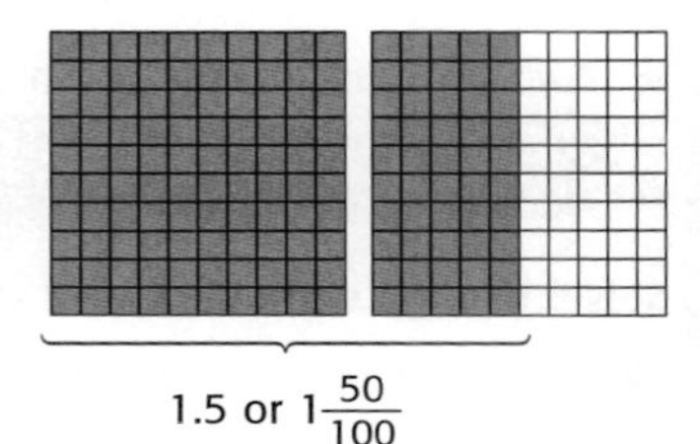

1.5 or $1\frac{50}{100}$

**Step 2** **Model 0.29.**

To show 0.29, shade $\frac{29}{100}$ of the second grid using a different color.

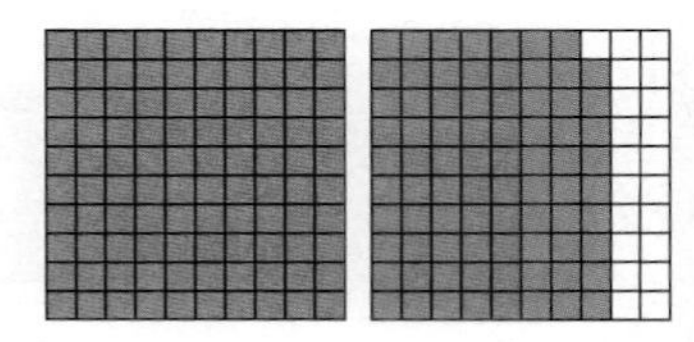

1.5 0.29 or $\frac{29}{100}$

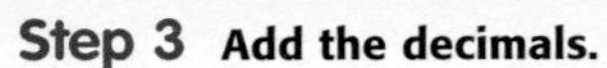

**Step 3** **Add the decimals.**

Count the total number of shaded squares. Write as a decimal.

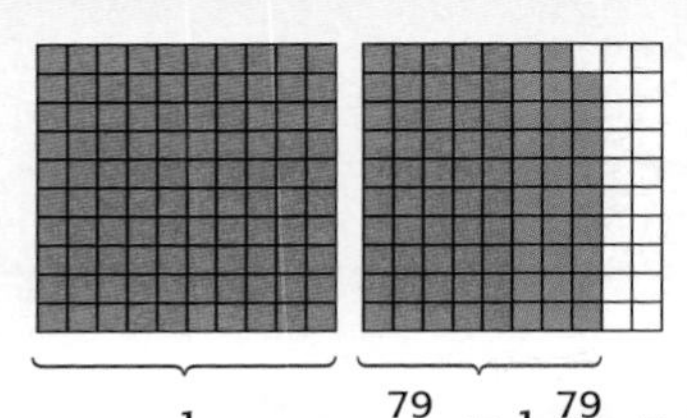

$1 \quad \frac{79}{100} = 1\frac{79}{100} = 1.79$

## Think About It 1–4. See margin.

1. Why did you draw two 10-by-10 grids to show 1.5?
2. Why did you shade 50 squares of the second grid?
3. Why did you shade 29 squares of the second grid?
4. How did you find the sum of the decimals?

## CHECK What You Know

**Add. Use the models.**

5. 1.15 + 0.57 **1.72**

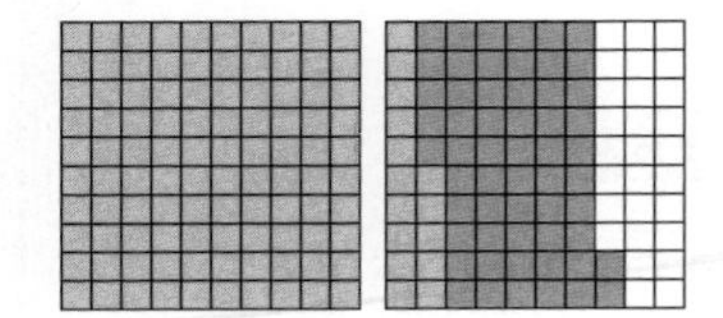

6. 0.25 + 0.46 **0.71**

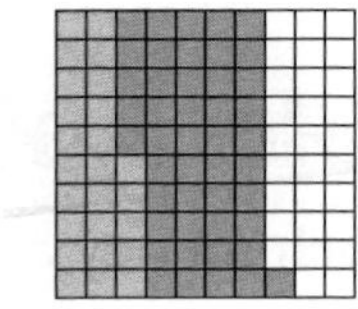

**Add. Use models if needed.**

7. $\begin{array}{r} 0.45 \\ +\ 0.30 \\ \hline 0.75 \end{array}$

8. $\begin{array}{r} 0.16 \\ +\ 0.58 \\ \hline 0.74 \end{array}$

9. $\begin{array}{r} 1.12 \\ +\ 1.50 \\ \hline 2.62 \end{array}$

10. $\begin{array}{r} 0.19 \\ +\ 1.62 \\ \hline 1.81 \end{array}$

11. $\begin{array}{r} 1.09 \\ +\ 1.58 \\ \hline 2.67 \end{array}$

12. $\begin{array}{r} 1.42 \\ +\ 0.26 \\ \hline 1.68 \end{array}$

13. 0.44 + 1.39 **1.83**

14. 1.28 + 2.10 **3.38**

15. 2.05 + 1.9 **3.95**

16. **WRITING IN MATH** Write the steps to use to find 2.34 + 1.76. See margin.



### Additional Answers

1. Sample answer: 1.5 is more than 1 and less than 2, so the first grid shows 1 and the second grid shows 0.5.
2. Sample answer: $0.5 = \frac{5}{10}$ or $\frac{50}{100}$, so 50 colored squares represents 0.5.
3. Sample answer: $0.29 = \frac{29}{100}$, so 29 colored squares represents 0.29; these colored squares are included in the same grid as 0.5 to show adding 0.29 to 1.5.
4. Sample answer: Count the number of colored grids and squares, all completely colored in grids = 1 whole number, and the partially colored in grids = digits to the right of the decimal.

16. Sample answer: Color in 2 whole grids and 34 squares of a third grid red. Then color 1 whole grid and 66 squares of the third grid blue. Then color 10 squares of a fourth grid green. Then count the shaded squares.

# 2 Teach

**Activity** Before beginning the Activity, have students draw two 10-by-10 grids on grid paper. Guide students through Steps 1 and 2.

- Have them choose a color and shade grids to model 1.5. Remind students that 5 tenths equals 50 hundredths.
- For Step 2, ask students to use a different color to shade 0.29 and to begin shading in squares directly after 1.5 in the second grid.
- Explain that Step 3 shows them how to use their models to find the sum. Have students count the shaded whole grids to find the number of ones and the shaded squares to find the hundredths.
- Point out to students that, in some cases, they may need to rename a grid with 100 hundredths as 1 one when counting squares to add. Provide the following example for students to model and discuss: 1.5 + 0.79.

## Think About It

Assign Exercises 1–4 to assess student comprehension of the concept presented in the Activity.

# 3 Assess

### Formative Assessment

Use **Check What You Know** Exercises 5–16 to assess whether students understand using models to add decimals.

**From Concrete to Abstract** Use Exercise 16 to bridge the gap between adding decimals with and without models.

**Extending the Concept** Have students use models to add 1.27 + 2.55 + 0.74.

LESSON 15-4

# Add Decimals

## Lesson Planner

### Objective

Add decimals.

### Review Vocabulary

**addend, sum**

### Resources

**Materials:** WorkMat 1: Place-Value Chart, grid paper

**Manipulatives:** base-ten blocks

**Literature Connection:** *Henry Hikes to Fitchburg* by D.B. Johnson

**Teacher Technology**
TeacherWorks • Interactive Classroom • Math Tool Chest

## Daily Routine

Use these suggestions before beginning the lesson on p. 630.

### 5-Minute Check

(Reviews Lesson 15-3)

**Solve. Use the work backward strategy.**

A number is added to 2. Next, the sum is divided by 3. Then, 1 is subtracted from the quotient. The result is 3. What is the number? 10

### Problem of the Day

Write each money amount as a decimal: $\frac{4}{5}$ of a quarter, $\frac{3}{5}$ of a nickel, $\frac{1}{5}$ of a dime, and $\frac{1}{10}$ of a half-dollar. Order the amounts from least to greatest. $0.20, $0.03, $0.02, $0.05; $0.02, $0.03, $0.05, $0.20

### Focus on Math Background

Decimal points are lined up when decimals are added vertically (which is not the case for multiplication). Expanded notation provides another way to see the similarity to fraction addition. Consider the following example:

$$\begin{array}{r} 2.34 \\ +1.52 \\ \hline \end{array}$$

This can be written horizontally as:

$2.34 + 1.52 = \left(2 + 3 \times \frac{1}{10} + 4 \times \frac{1}{100}\right) + \left(1 + 5 \times \frac{1}{10} + 2 \times \frac{1}{100}\right)$.

Commutative, associative, and distributive properties can then be used to obtain

$(2 + 1) + (3 + 5)\left(\frac{1}{10}\right) + (4 + 2)\left(\frac{1}{100}\right)$.

The 3 and 5 can be added because they both count tenths, and the 4 and 2 count hundredths. The result is $3 + \frac{8}{10} + \frac{6}{100}$ or 3.86.

### Review Math Vocabulary

Write the review vocabulary words and their definitions on the board.

Ask each student to write an addition sentence containing at least two addends and a sum. Have them exchange their work with a partner and underline the addends and circle the sum. Then write the following number sentences on the board for students to identify the addends and sums:

$16 = 11 + 2 + 3$

$$\begin{array}{r} 45 \\ +9 \\ \hline 54 \end{array}$$

# Differentiated Instruction

## Small Group Options

### Option 1 Below Level BL

SPATIAL, KINESTHETIC

**Materials:** red and yellow counters, 10 × 10 grids

- Have students place the counters on the grids to show 1.4 + 2.9 using a different color for each addend.
- Have students find the sum.

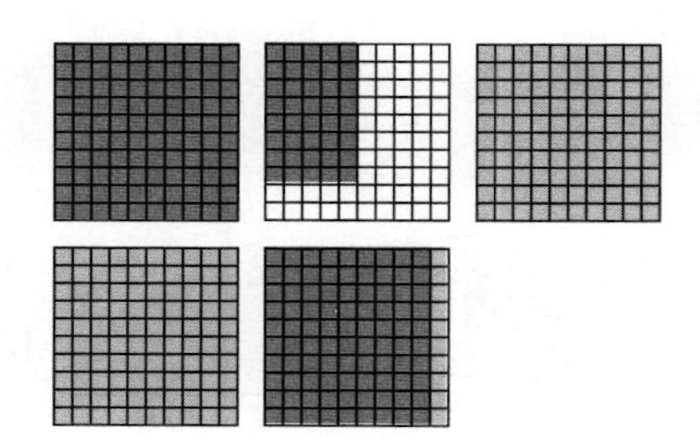

### Option 2 English Language Learners ELL

VISUAL, LOGICAL

**Materials:** rulers, rubber ball

**Core Vocabulary:** bring down, falling ball, straight down

**Common Use Verb:** fall

**Do Math** This strategy relates the decimal to a falling ball to help students remember to bring down the decimal.

- Write an addition problem on the board that has decimals.
- As you drop a ball, say: "What does the decimal look like?" like a falling ball
- Tell students that adding with decimals is the same as adding numbers, but the decimals fall straight down, like a falling ball.
- Write: "A falling ball goes straight down."
- Ask students to write problems that you read aloud.
- Check students' work to ensure they are lining up the decimals.

**English Language Learners (p. 109) ELL**

33 Name ______

**Adding Decimals**

Use the spinner. Record the distance traveled. Add it to the total. When you reach 50 miles or more, you've delivered the mail.

| SANTA FE TO ALBUQUERQUE | MILES TRAVELED |
|---|---|
| Day 1 | |
| Day 2 | |
| Total Day 1 + 2 | |
| Day 3 | |
| Total miles traveled | |
| Day 4 | |
| Total miles traveled | |
| Day 5 | |
| Total miles traveled | |
| Day 6 | |
| Total miles traveled | |
| Day 7 | |
| Total miles traveled | |
| Day 8 | |
| Total miles traveled | |
| Day 9 | |
| Total miles traveled | |
| Day 10 | |
| Total miles traveled | |
| Day 11 | |
| Total miles traveled | |
| Day 12 | |
| Total miles traveled | |

Add Decimals 109

*Use this worksheet to provide additional support for English Language Learners.*

## Independent Work Options

### Option 1 Early Finishers OL

VISUAL, SPATIAL

**Materials:** index cards, grid paper, colored pencils

- Ask students to write a different decimal on each of 4 index cards.
- Have students mix up their cards and place them facedown in a pile.
- Have them choose two cards and add the decimals using either grid models or pencil and paper.

### Option 2 Student Technology

**Math Online** macmillanmh.com

 Math Tool Chest Money

Personal Tutor • Extra Examples

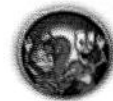 Math Adventures

### Option 3 Learning Station: Science (p. 614H)

Direct students to the Science Learning Station for opportunities to explore and extend the lesson concept.

### Option 4 Problem-Solving Practice

Reinforce problem-solving skills and strategies with the Problem-Solving Practice worksheet.

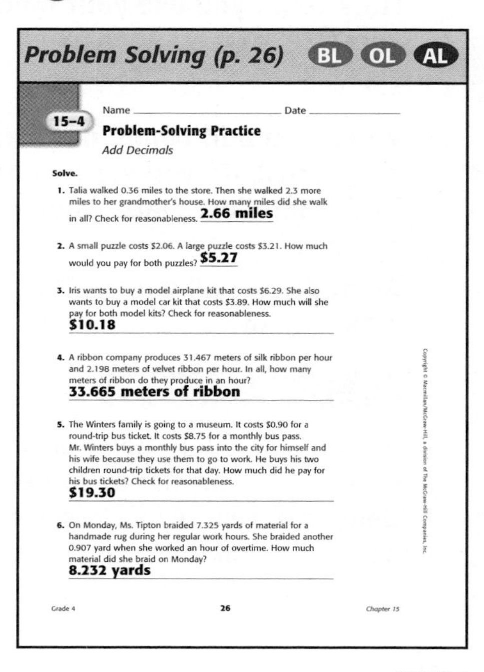

**Problem Solving (p. 26) BL OL AL**

Name ______ Date ______

15–4 **Problem-Solving Practice**

*Add Decimals*

**Solve.**

1. Talia walked 0.36 miles to the store. Then she walked 2.3 more miles to her grandmother's house. How many miles did she walk in all? Check for reasonableness. **2.66 miles**
2. A small puzzle costs $2.06. A large puzzle costs $3.21. How much would you pay for both puzzles? **$5.27**
3. Iris wants to buy a model airplane kit that costs $6.29. She also wants to buy a model car kit that costs $3.89. How much will she pay for both model kits? Check for reasonableness. **$10.18**
4. A ribbon company produces 31.467 meters of silk ribbon per hour and 2.198 meters of velvet ribbon per hour. In all, how many meters of ribbon do they produce in an hour? **33.665 meters of ribbon**
5. The Winters family is going to a museum. It costs $0.90 for a round-trip bus ticket. It costs $8.75 for a monthly bus pass. Mr. Winters buys a monthly bus pass into the city for himself and his wife because they use them to go to work. He buys his two children round-trip tickets for that day. How much did he pay for his bus tickets? Check for reasonableness. **$19.30**
6. On Monday, Ms. Tipton braided 7.325 yards of material for a handmade rug during her regular work hours. She braided another 0.907 yard when she worked an hour of overtime. How much material did she braid on Monday? **8.232 yards**

Grade 4 26 Chapter 15

# 15-4 Add Decimals

## 1 Introduce

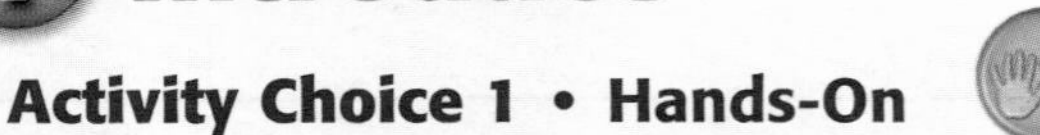

### Activity Choice 1 • Hands-On

- Write 567 + 424 in vertical form on the board. Provide small groups of students with base-ten blocks to model each addend.
- **What do you add first?** Add the ones, 7 and 4.
- **Do we need to regroup?** Yes, regroup 11 ones as 1 ten and 1 one.
- Have students combine ones and exchange 10 ones for 1 ten as you write this step of the algorithm on the board.
- Have students use models to add the tens and the hundreds, regrouping as necessary, as you complete the algorithm on the board.
- Tell students that the same rules and procedures used for adding whole numbers are also used for adding decimals.

### Activity Choice 2 • Literature

Introduce the lesson with *Henry Hikes to Fitchburg* by D.B. Johnson. For a related math activity, see p. TR67.

## 2 Teach

### Scaffolding Questions

Write 2.36 + 3.54 in vertical form on the board and guide students to model each decimal by shading 10-by-10 grids.

- **How could you use your models to find the sum?** There are 5 whole grids and 90 squares shaded; $5 + \frac{90}{100} = 5.90$.
- **When you add whole numbers with paper and pencil, do you start by adding the digits in the smallest place value or the largest place value?** smallest place value
- **What digits will you add first when you add 2.36 + 3.54?** digits in the hundredths places

### GET READY to Learn

Have students open their books and read the information in **Get Ready to Learn**. Review **addend** and **sum**. As a class, work through **Examples 1 and 2**.



# 15-4 Add Decimals

### GET READY to Learn

Darlene practiced the flute 1.5 hours on Saturday. On Sunday, she practiced 2.3 hours. How long did she practice during the two days?

In the previous Explore Activity, you used models to add decimals. You can also use paper and pencil to add decimals.

### Real-World EXAMPLE Add Decimals

**1 MEASUREMENT How many hours did Darlene practice the flute during the two days?**

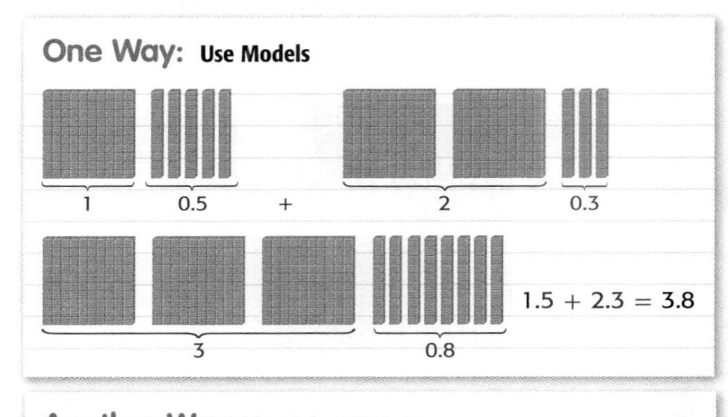


**Another Way: Paper and Pencil**

**Step 1** Line up the decimal points.

$$\begin{array}{r} 1.5 \\ +\ 2.3 \\ \hline \end{array}$$

**Step 2** Add.

$$\begin{array}{r} 1.5 \\ +\ 2.3 \\ \hline 3.8 \end{array}$$

Add the digits in each place value. Then bring down the decimal point.

So, Darlene practiced a total of 3.8 hours.



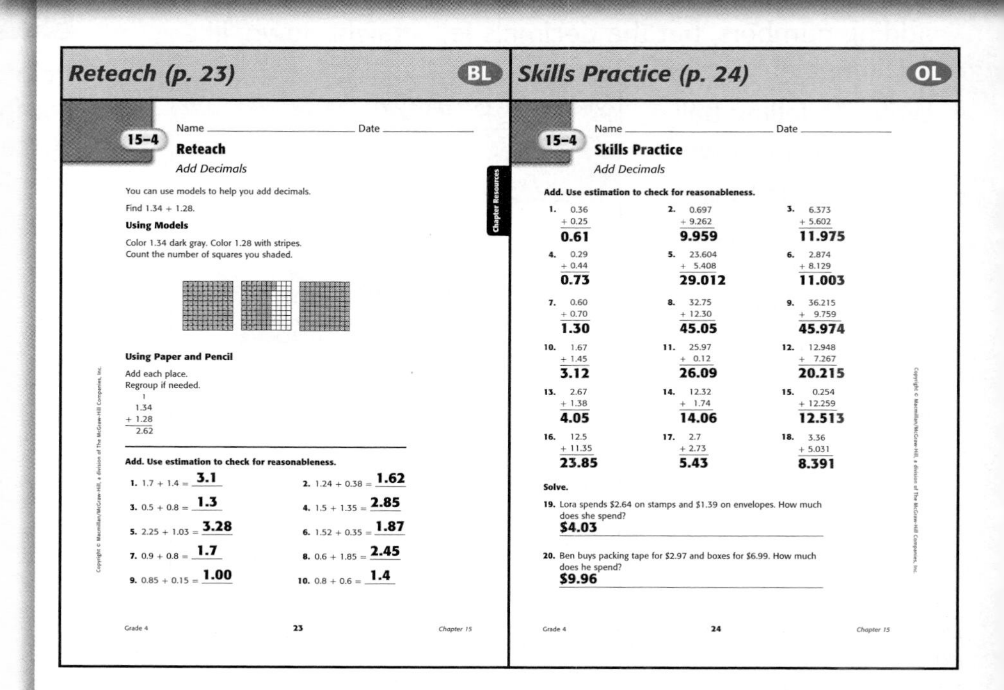

**Reteach (p. 23)** BL

15-4 Name ______ Date ______

**Reteach**

*Add Decimals*

You can use models to help you add decimals.

Find 1.34 + 1.28.

**Using Models**

Color 1.34 dark gray. Color 1.28 with stripes.
Count the number of squares you shaded.

**Using Paper and Pencil**

Add each place.
Regroup if needed.

$$\begin{array}{r} ^{1}\phantom{00} \\ 1.34 \\ +\ 1.28 \\ \hline 2.62 \end{array}$$

**Add. Use estimation to check for reasonableness.**

1. 1.7 + 1.4 = **3.1**
2. 1.24 + 0.38 = **1.62**
3. 0.5 + 0.8 = **1.3**
4. 1.5 + 1.35 = **2.85**
5. 2.25 + 1.03 = **3.28**
6. 1.52 + 0.35 = **1.87**
7. 0.9 + 0.8 = **1.7**
8. 0.6 + 1.85 = **2.45**
9. 0.85 + 0.15 = **1.00**
10. 0.8 + 0.6 = **1.4**

Chapter Resources



Grade 4 23 Chapter 15

**Skills Practice (p. 24)** OL

15-4 Name ______ Date ______

**Skills Practice**

*Add Decimals*

**Add. Use estimation to check for reasonableness.**

1. 0.36 + 0.25 = **0.61**
2. 0.697 + 9.262 = **9.959**
3. 6.373 + 5.602 = **11.975**
4. 0.29 + 0.44 = **0.73**
5. 23.604 + 5.408 = **29.012**
6. 2.874 + 8.129 = **11.003**
7. 0.60 + 0.70 = **1.30**
8. 32.75 + 12.30 = **45.05**
9. 36.215 + 9.759 = **45.974**
10. 1.67 + 1.45 = **3.12**
11. 25.97 + 0.12 = **26.09**
12. 12.948 + 7.267 = **20.215**
13. 2.67 + 1.38 = **4.05**
14. 12.32 + 1.74 = **14.06**
15. 0.254 + 12.259 = **12.513**
16. 12.5 + 11.35 = **23.85**
17. 2.7 + 2.73 = **5.43**
18. 3.36 + 5.031 = **8.391**

**Solve.**

19. Lora spends $2.64 on stamps and $1.39 on envelopes. How much does she spend? **$4.03**

20. Ben buys packing tape for $2.97 and boxes for $6.99. How much does he spend? **$9.96**



Grade 4 24 Chapter 15

## Real-World EXAMPLE Add Decimals

**2 FISH Australia has 17.22 percent of the world's coral reefs. Fiji has 3.52 percent of the world's coral reefs. What percentage of the world's coral reefs do these countries have in all?**

You need to find 17.22 + 3.52. **Estimate** 18 + 4 = 22

**Step 1** Line up the decimal points.

$$\begin{array}{r} 17.22 \\ +\ 3.52 \\ \hline \end{array}$$

**Step 2** Add.

$$\begin{array}{r} {}^{1}\phantom{.00} \\ 17.22 \\ +\ 3.52 \\ \hline 20.74 \end{array}$$

Add the digits in each place value. Regroup if necessary.

So, these two countries have 20.74 percent of the world's coral reefs.

**Check for Reasonableness**

The sum of 20.74 is close to the estimate of 22. So, the answer is reasonable. ✓

**Remember**

Line up the decimal points before you add to make sure you are adding the same place values together.

## CHECK What You Know

**Add. Use estimation to check for reasonableness.** **See Examples 1 and 2 (pp. 630–631)**

1. 1.4 + 0.7 **2.1; 1 + 1 = 2**
2. 4.72 + 3.9 **8.62; 5 + 4 = 9**
3. 9.8 + 7.33 **17.13; 10 + 7 = 17**
4. 4.82 + 6.27 **11.09; 5 + 6 = 11**
5. \$25.85 + \$8.49 **\$34.34; \$26 + \$8 = \$34**
6. 54.90 + 38.41 **93.31; 55 + 38 = 93**

**For Exercises 7 and 8, use the poster shown.**

7. Andre has his birthday dinner at Medieval Era, a dinner theatre with knights jousting. What is the total cost for Andre and his father? **\$82.90**
8. Suppose Andre's mother is also going to his birthday dinner. What is the total cost? **\$131.85**
9. **Talk About It** Why is it important to line up the decimal points before you add? **Sample answer: To make sure that you are adding the same place values together**



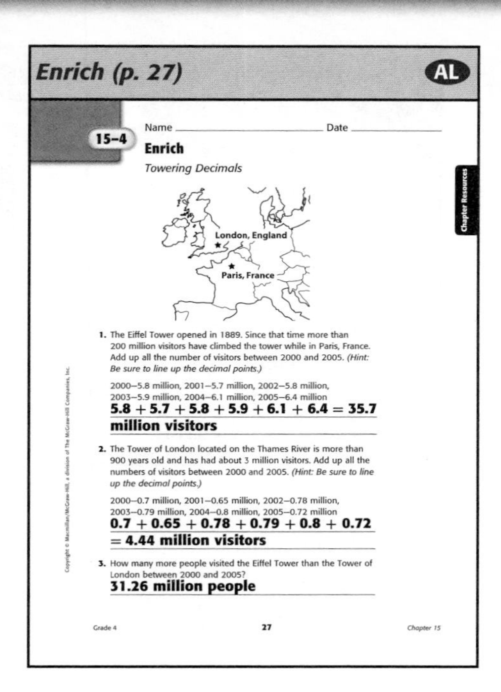

**Enrich (p. 27)** AL

Name ______________ Date ______________

15–4 **Enrich**

*Towering Decimals*

London, England

Paris, France

1. The Eiffel Tower opened in 1889. Since that time more than 200 million visitors have climbed the tower while in Paris, France. Add up all the number of visitors between 2000 and 2005. *(Hint: Be sure to line up the decimal points.)*

   2000–5.8 million, 2001–5.7 million, 2002–5.8 million, 2003–5.9 million, 2004–6.1 million, 2005–6.4 million

   **5.8 + 5.7 + 5.8 + 5.9 + 6.1 + 6.4 = 35.7 million visitors**

2. The Tower of London located on the Thames River is more than 900 years old and has had about 3 million visitors. Add up all the numbers of visitors between 2000 and 2005. *(Hint: Be sure to line up the decimal points.)*

   2000–0.7 million, 2001–0.65 million, 2002–0.78 million, 2003–0.79 million, 2004–0.8 million, 2005–0.72 million

   **0.7 + 0.65 + 0.78 + 0.79 + 0.8 + 0.72 = 4.44 million visitors**

3. How many more people visited the Eiffel Tower than the Tower of London between 2000 and 2005?

   **31.26 million people**

Chapter Resources



Grade 4 27 Chapter 15

## Add Decimals

**Example 1** When introducing the paper and pencil method of adding decimals for the first time, emphasize the importance of writing the problem in vertical form, lining up the decimal points, and writing 0 as a placeholder when necessary. Explain that these three steps help ensure that we add hundredths to hundredths, tenths to tenths, and ones to ones.

### ADDITIONAL EXAMPLES

1. Sandy slept 8.3 hours on Monday night and 7.6 hours on Tuesday night. How many hours did she sleep altogether? 15.9 hours
2. Kate spent \$1.25 for a juice box and \$1.79 for yogurt. How much did she spend in all? \$3.04

### CHECK What You Know

As a class, have students complete Exercises 1–9 in **Check What You Know** as you observe their work.

**Exercise 9** Assess student comprehension before assigning practice exercises

### BL Alternate Teaching Strategy

**If** students have trouble lining up decimal addends when using the pencil and paper method…

**Then** use one of these reteach options:

1. CRM **Daily Reteach Worksheet** (p. 23)
2. Have students find the sum of 1.7 and 8.85 by writing each decimal addend in the place-value chart. Tell them to write 0 as a placeholder in the hundredths place for 1.7. Then they can add hundredths to hundredths, tenths to tenths, and ones to ones and regroup when necessary. Have them write the sum in the chart as well.
3. Have students use Math Tool Chest to help complete the problem-solving exercises.

### COMMON ERROR!

Students may forget to write the decimal point in their final answer. Have students write the decimal point in the sum directly below the decimal points in the addends before they begin adding hundredths, tenths, and ones.

# 3 Practice

Differentiate practice using these leveled assignments for Exercises 10–26.

| Level | Assignment |
|---|---|
| BL Below/Approaching Level | 10–13, 18, 21, 23 |
| OL On Level | 10–16, 18–19, 22–24, 26 |
| AL Above/Beyond Level | 11–23 odd, 25–26 |

Have students discuss and complete the Higher Order Thinking problems. Students may use the guess and check strategy to complete Exercise 25.

**WRITING IN ►MATH** Have students complete Exercise 26 in their Math Journals. You may choose to use this exercise as an optional formative assessment.

# 4 Assess

## Formative Assessment

- **How is adding two decimal numbers with pencil and paper similar to adding two whole numbers? How is it different?**
  Similar: You add the numbers in each place value, one place value at a time, starting at the right, and regrouping if needed each time you add. Different: You need to line up the decimal points and write the decimal point in the sum.

**Quick Check** **Are students continuing to struggle with adding decimals?**

**If Yes** → Small Group Options (p. 630B)

**If No** → Independent Work Options (p. 630B)
CRM Skills Practice Worksheet (p. 24)
CRM Enrich Worksheet (p. 27)

**Into the Future** Have students predict what they will learn next about decimal numbers. Ask them to write a sample problem that they might have to solve.

## Practice and Problem Solving

See page R40.

**Add. Use estimation to check for reasonableness.** See Examples 1 and 2 (pp. 630–631)

10. 0.7 + 0.2 — 0.9; 1 + 0 = 1
11. 0.4 + 0.6 — 1; 0 + 1 = 1
12. 1.1 + 0.39 — 1.49; 1 + 0 = 1
13. 5.1 + 7.56 — 12.66; 5 + 8 = 13
14. 8.76 + 6.95 — 15.71; 9 + 7 = 16
15. 7.09 + 4.68 — 11.77; 7 + 5 = 12
16. \$9.82 + \$5.33 — \$15.15; \$10 + \$5 = \$15
17. \$12.33 + \$5.79 — 17. \$18.12; \$12 + \$6 = \$18
18. 47.28 + 36.05 — 83.33; 47 + 36 = 83
19. \$51.20 + \$29.75 — \$80.95; \$51 + \$30 = \$81
20. 3.21 + 14.7 + 9.35 — 27.26; 3 + 15 + 9 = 27
21. Two bones in a leg are the femur and tibia. The average adult male femur is 19.88 inches long. The tibia is 16.94 inches long. How long is the average adult male's leg? 36.82 in.
22. Maureen used 28.5 minutes of her cell phone plan on Saturday and 35.75 minutes on Sunday. How many minutes did Maureen use on these two days? 64.25 min

### Data File

Riverbanks Zoo and Garden in Columbia, South Carolina, is home to more than 2,000 animals and more than 4,200 species of plants.

23. Suppose an 11-year-old and his mom and dad want to camp overnight in the zoo. How much would it cost? \$47.75
24. Heath, Rodney, and Mia go to the zoo on a field trip with their fourth grade class. If they bring \$25, will they have enough money to enter the zoo? Explain. Sample answer: yes; \$7.25 + \$7.25 + \$7.25 = \$21.75

### H.O.T. Problems

25. **WHICH ONE DOESN'T BELONG?** Three of the decimals shown below have a sum equal to 14.04. Identify the number that does not belong with the other three. 1.15

26. **WRITING IN ►MATH** Explain how to find the sum of 136.28 and 264.57. See Ch. 15 Answer Appendix.



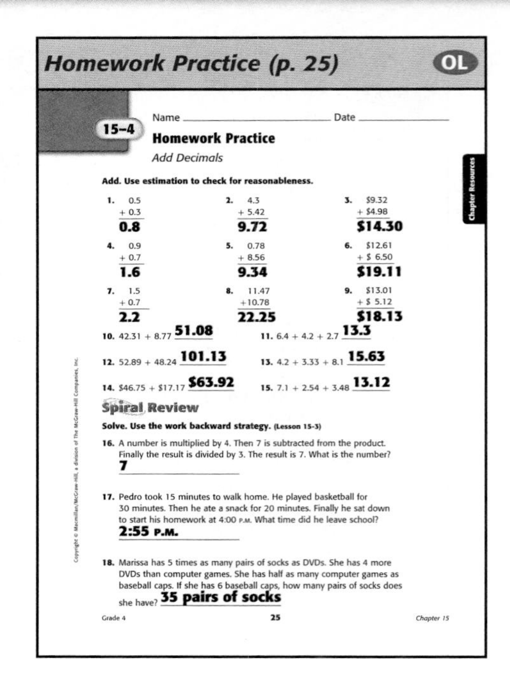

**Homework Practice (p. 25)** OL

Name ______________ Date ______________

15–4 **Homework Practice**
*Add Decimals*

**Add. Use estimation to check for reasonableness.**

1. 0.5 + 0.3 = **0.8**
2. 4.3 + 5.42 = **9.72**
3. \$9.32 + \$4.98 = **\$14.30**
4. 0.9 + 0.7 = **1.6**
5. 0.78 + 8.56 = **9.34**
6. \$12.61 + \$ 6.50 = **\$19.11**
7. 1.5 + 0.7 = **2.2**
8. 11.47 + 10.78 = **22.25**
9. \$13.01 + \$ 5.12 = **\$18.13**
10. 42.31 + 8.77 **51.08**
11. 6.4 + 4.2 + 2.7 **13.3**
12. 52.89 + 48.24 **101.13**
13. 4.2 + 3.33 + 8.1 **15.63**
14. \$46.75 + \$17.17 **\$63.92**
15. 7.1 + 2.54 + 3.48 **13.12**

**Spiral Review**

**Solve. Use the work backward strategy.** (Lesson 15-3)

16. A number is multiplied by 4. Then 7 is subtracted from the product. Finally the result is divided by 3. The result is 7. What is the number? **7**
17. Pedro took 15 minutes to walk home. He played basketball for 30 minutes. Then he ate a snack for 20 minutes. Finally he sat down to start his homework at 4:00 P.M. What time did he leave school? **2:55 P.M.**
18. Marissa has 5 times as many pairs of socks as DVDs. She has 4 more DVDs than computer games. She has half as many computer games as baseball caps. If she has 6 baseball caps, how many pairs of socks does she have? **35 pairs of socks**

Chapter Resources

Copyright © Macmillan/McGraw-Hill, a division of The McGraw-Hill Companies, Inc.

Grade 4 25 Chapter 15

# Mid-Chapter Check

Lessons 15-1 through 15-4

**Round to the nearest whole number.** (Lesson 15-1)

**1.** 4.55 5
**2.** 25.24 25
**3.** 8.58 9
**4.** 36.34 36

**5. Measurement** A bald eagle's nest is 2.4 meters wide. How wide is this to the nearest whole number? (Lesson 15-1) 2 m

**6. MULTIPLE CHOICE** The height of a monster truck is 15.4 feet. What is the height of the truck rounded to the nearest whole number? (Lesson 15-1) B

**A** 14
**C** 15.4
**B** 15
**D** 16

**Estimate. Round to the nearest whole number.** (Lesson 15-2)

**7.** 2.4 + 3.8 6
**8.** 9.4 − 5.82 3

**Algebra Estimate by rounding to the nearest whole number. Then compare. Use >, <, or =.** (Lesson 15-2)

**9.** 13.73 + 8.04 ● 9.8 + 12.52 <

**10.** 46.91 − 19.8 ● 53.4 − 20.26 <

**11.** Tamika Catchings, a professional basketball player, scores an average of 19.2 points per game. About how many points would Tamika score in two games? (Lesson 15-2) 38

**12.** A number is divided by 4. Next, 8 is added to the quotient. Then, the sum is multiplied by 2. The result is 28. What is the number? (Lesson 15-3) 24

**13. Measurement** Bruno is going on vacation and needs to leave for the airport at 1 P.M. What time does Bruno need to wake up? (Lesson 15-3) 7:30 A.M.

| Task | Time to Complete (hours) |
|---|---|
| Clean house | 3.25 |
| Eat lunch | 0.75 |
| Pack suitcase | 1.5 |

**Add. Use estimation to check for reasonableness.** (Lesson 15-4)

**14.** 14.5 + 7.8
**15.** 37.08 + 19.56

14, 15. See Ch.15 Answer Appendix.

**16. MULTIPLE CHOICE** Brad buys a movie ticket for $4.75, a pretzel for $1.50, and a soda for $2.25. How much money did Brad spend? (Lesson 15-4) F

**F** $8.50
**H** $9
**G** $8.75
**J** $9.25

17–19. See Ch. 15 Answer Appendix.

**Algebra Describe the pattern. Then identify the missing numbers.** (Lesson 15-4)

**17.** 0.8, 1.6, ■, 3.2, ■, ■

**18.** 1.23, 3.25, ■, ■, 9.31, ■

**19. WRITING IN MATH** Tell whether 40 is a reasonable estimate for the sum of 28.4 + 14.68. Explain. (Lesson 15-2)

Formative Assessment 633

# Mid-Chapter Check

## Lessons 15-1 through 15-4

### Formative Assessment

Use the Mid-Chapter Check to assess students' progress in the first half of the chapter.

**ExamView Assessment Suite** Customize and create multiple versions of your Mid-Chapter Check and the test answer keys.

### FOLDABLES Dinah Zike's Foldables

Use these lesson suggestions to incorporate the Foldable during the chapter.

**Lesson 15-1** Have students round decimals using a number line or rules. Store student work in the first pocket of the Foldable.

**Lesson 15-4** Ask students to demonstrate their ability to add decimals. Students store their notes and work in the second pocket of the Foldable.

# Data-Driven Decision Making

Based on the results of the Mid-Chapter Check, use the following resources to review concepts that continue to give students problems.

| Exercises | State/Local Standards | What's the Math? | Error Analysis | Resources for Review |
|---|---|---|---|---|
| **1–6** Lesson 15-1 | | Round two place decimals to one decimal or the nearest whole number. | Rounds only to the nearest tenth when asked for whole number rounding. Rounds to whole number when asked for tenth rounding. | CRM Chapter 15 Resource Masters (Reteach Worksheets) Math Adventures My Math Zone Chapter 15 Math Online Extra Examples • Concepts in Motion |
| **7–11, 19** Lesson 15-2 | | Estimate decimal sums and differences. | Works problem then rounds. Does not round to nearest whole number before estimation. | |
| **14–18** Lesson 15-4 | | Add simple decimals. Estimate to check for reasonableness of results. Find patterns in decimals. | Does not add correctly. Puts decimals for money in wrong places. Does not regroup for tenths to units place value. Does not find pattern to continue. | |

# 15-5 Problem-Solving Investigation
## Choose a Strategy

# Lesson Planner

## Objective
Choose the best strategy to solve a problem.

## Resources
**Manipulatives:** counters

**Teacher Technology**
TeacherWorks • Interactive Classroom

**Real-World Problem Solving Library**
***A Force to Reckon With***
Use these leveled books to reinforce and extend problem-solving skills and strategies.

Leveled for:
- OL On Level
- ELL Sheltered English
- SP Spanish

For additional support, see the Real-World Problem Solving Teacher Guide.

# Daily Routine

Use these suggestions before beginning the lesson on p. 634.

## 5-Minute Check

(Reviews Lesson 15-4)

**Add. Use estimation to check for reasonableness.**

1. 0.8 + 0.4 = 1.2
2. 8.2 + 1.46 = 9.66
3. 4.35 + 9.47 = 13.82
4. \$6.07 + \$6.89 = \$12.96
5. 24.38 + 33.92 = 58.30
6. 45.23 + 39.68 = 84.91
7. \$62.50 + \$19.52 \$82.02
8. 5.3 + 2.47 + 1.15 8.92

## Problem of the Day

Use each of the numbers 3, 5, 6, and 10 once. Write two fractions that are equivalent. $\frac{6}{10}$ and $\frac{3}{5}$

# Differentiated Instruction

## Small Group Options

LOGICAL

### Option 1 Below Level BL

**Materials:** chart paper, markers, paper, pencils

- Copy the following problem on the chart paper:

> A snail crawled 20 inches.
>
> A frog hopped $\frac{1}{2}$ yard.
>
> Which one traveled farther?

- Encourage students to decide what they need to know that is not in the problem. 1 yard = 36 inches
- Now students need to decide how many inches are in $\frac{1}{2}$ a yard. 18 inches
- **How much farther did the snail travel than the frog?** 2 inches

SPATIAL

### Option 2 English Language Learners ELL

**Materials:** magazines, tape, scissors
**Core Vocabulary:** favorite, findings, class's
**Common Use Verb:** survey

**See Math** This strategy generates understanding of choosing information through brainstorming and refining survey questions.

- Say: "The **class's favorite** color is pink."
- Ask students if they agree. If they disagree, ask how they could find out what the class's favorite color really is.
- Create a bar graph.
- Prompt survey questions and proceed with the survey.
- As students gather information, review the effectiveness of these questions.
- Have each group decide how to represent their findings.

## Independent Work Options

LINGUISTIC, AUDITORY

### Option 1 Early Finishers OL AL

**Materials:** paper and pencil

- Ask students to choose one strategy from the list of problem-solving strategies on p. 637.
- Challenge students to write a word problem that can be solved using the strategy they chose.
- Have students read their problems to classmates to solve.

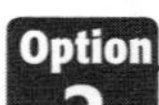

### Option 2 Student Technology

**Math Online** macmillanmh.com

Personal Tutor • Extra Examples

### Option 3 Learning Stations: Music (p. 614H)

Direct students to the Music Learning Station for opportunities to explore and extend the lesson concept.

# 15-5 Problem-Solving Investigation

## 1 Introduce

**Activity • Review**

- Present students with the following problem:
  *Mark decides to visit the museum. It takes him 10 minutes to walk from his house to the bus stop. He waits 5 minutes for the bus to arrive. The bus ride to the museum takes 35 minutes. He gets to the museum at 12:05 P.M. When did Mark leave his house?*
- **What problem-solving strategy will you use to solve the problem?** work backward
- Have volunteers describe each step to solve the problem. 11:15 A.M.

## 2 Teach

Have students read the problem on Jennifer and her friends' pets. Guide them through the problem-solving steps.

**Understand** Using the questions, review what students know and need to find.

**Plan** Have them discuss their strategy.

**Solve** Guide students to use logical reasoning to solve the problem.

- **How do you know that Jennifer owns a lizard?** Because the problem states she does not have a cat or a pet that starts with s (snake) or g (gerbil): the only pet left she could have is a lizard.
- **Why can you write nos in the rest of a column once you write a yes?** Each pet belongs to only one person.
- **Why will there be two yeses in Lorena's row?** Lorena owns two pets.

**Check** Have students look back at the problem to make sure that the answer fits the facts given.

### ! COMMON ERROR!

Students may make errors because they did not completely fill in their tables. Remind students to fill in all the cells in their tables. After they complete a column, have them double check that each yes and no in that column matches the facts in the problem.



# 15-5 Problem-Solving Investigation

**MAIN IDEA** I will choose the best strategy to solve a problem.

### P.S.I. TEAM +

JENNIFER: Two friends and I all have different kinds of pets. We have a lizard, a cat, a gerbil, and a snake. I do not have a cat. Rondell's pet is not a gerbil or a snake. Lorena's two pets are not lizards. My pet does not begin with the letters s or g.

YOUR MISSION: Find which person owns each pet.

**Understand** You know the clues for each person's pet. You need to find which person owns each pet.

**Plan** Make a table to show what you know. Then use logical reasoning to find which person owns each pet.

**Solve** Make a table. Write *yes* or *no* for each fact that you are given. Once you write yes in the table, you can write no in the rest of the boxes in that row and column.

| | Cat | Gerbil | Lizard | Snake |
|---|---|---|---|---|
| Jennifer | No | No | Yes | No |
| Lorena | No | Yes | No | Yes |
| Rondell | Yes | No | No | No |

So, Jennifer owns a lizard. Lorena owns a gerbil and a snake. Rondell owns a cat.

**Check** Look back. The solution matches the facts given in the problem. So, the answer is correct. ✓

634 Chapter 15 Add and Subtract Decimals

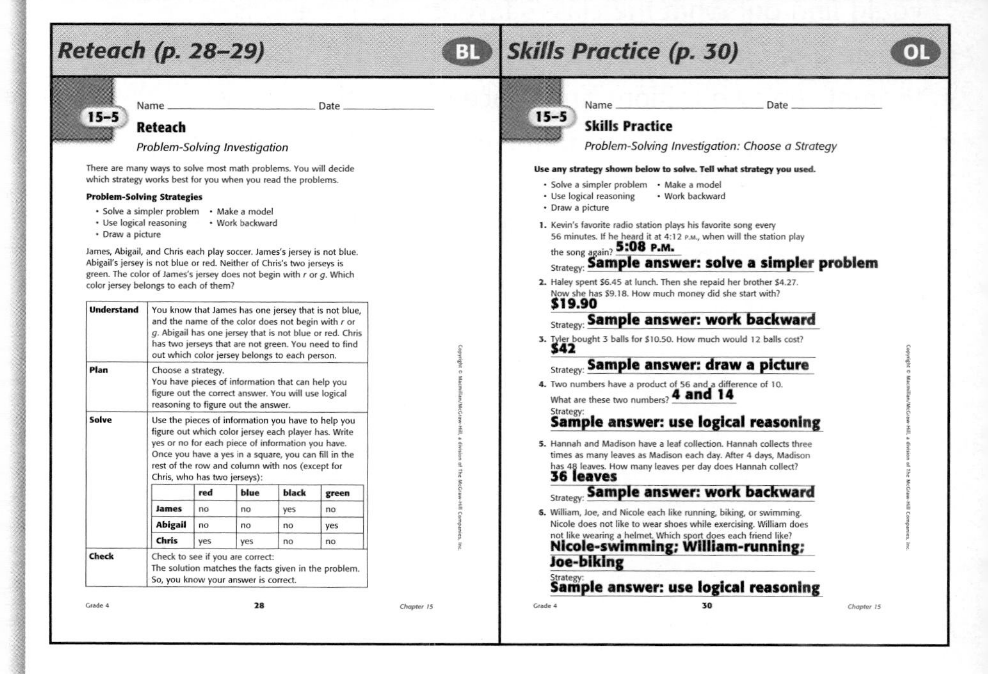

**Reteach (p. 28–29)** BL

15-5 Name ______ Date ______

**Reteach**

*Problem-Solving Investigation*

There are many ways to solve most math problems. You will decide which strategy works best for you when you read the problems.

**Problem-Solving Strategies**
- Solve a simpler problem
- Make a model
- Use logical reasoning
- Work backward
- Draw a picture

James, Abigail, and Chris each play soccer. James's jersey is not blue. Abigail's jersey is not blue or red. Neither of Chris's two jerseys is green. The color of James's jersey does not begin with *r* or *g*. Which color jersey belongs to each of them?

**Understand** You know that James has one jersey that is not blue, and the name of the color does not begin with *r* or *g*. Abigail has one jersey that is not blue or red. Chris has two jerseys that are not green. You need to find out which color jersey belongs to each person.

**Plan** Choose a strategy. You have pieces of information that can help you figure out the correct answer. You will use logical reasoning to figure out the answer.

**Solve** Use the pieces of information you have to help you figure out which color jersey each player has. Write yes or no for each piece of information you have. Once you have a yes in a square, you can fill in the rest of the row and column with nos (except for Chris, who has two jerseys):

| | red | blue | black | green |
|---|---|---|---|---|
| James | no | no | yes | no |
| Abigail | no | no | no | yes |
| Chris | yes | yes | no | no |

**Check** Check to see if you are correct: The solution matches the facts given in the problem. So, you know your answer is correct.

Grade 4 28 Chapter 15



**Skills Practice (p. 30)** OL

15-5 Name ______ Date ______

**Skills Practice**

*Problem-Solving Investigation: Choose a Strategy*

**Use any strategy shown below to solve. Tell what strategy you used.**
- Solve a simpler problem
- Make a model
- Use logical reasoning
- Work backward
- Draw a picture

1. Kevin's favorite radio station plays his favorite song every 56 minutes. If he heard it at 4:12 P.M., when will the station play the song again? **5:08 P.M.**
   Strategy: **Sample answer: solve a simpler problem**
2. Haley spent $6.45 at lunch. Then she repaid her brother $4.27. Now she has $9.18. How much money did she start with? **$19.90**
   Strategy: **Sample answer: work backward**
3. Tyler bought 3 balls for $10.50. How much would 12 balls cost? **$42**
   Strategy: **Sample answer: draw a picture**
4. Two numbers have a product of 56 and a difference of 10. What are these two numbers? **4 and 14**
   Strategy: **Sample answer: use logical reasoning**
5. Hannah and Madison have a leaf collection. Hannah collects three times as many leaves as Madison each day. After 4 days, Madison has 48 leaves. How many leaves per day does Hannah collect? **36 leaves**
   Strategy: **Sample answer: work backward**
6. William, Joe, and Nicole each like running, biking, or swimming. Nicole does not like to wear shoes while exercising. William does not like wearing a helmet. Which sport does each friend like? **Nicole-swimming; William-running; Joe-biking**
   Strategy: **Sample answer: use logical reasoning**

Grade 4 30 Chapter 15

★ indicates multi-step problem

## Mixed Problem Solving

**Use any strategy shown below to solve. Tell what strategy you used.**

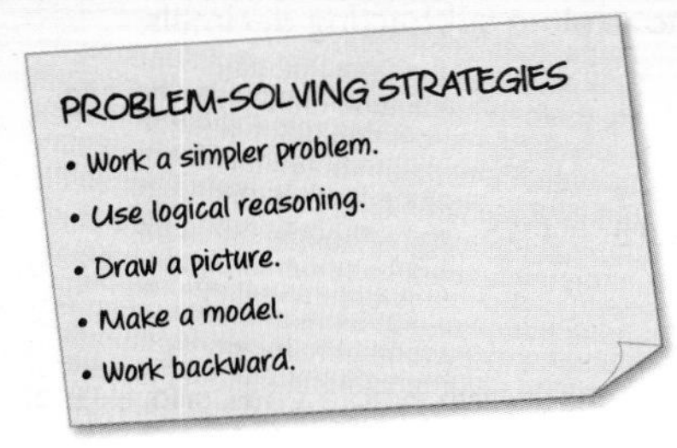


1. Reina is going bowling. Which route would be the shortest? Explain.

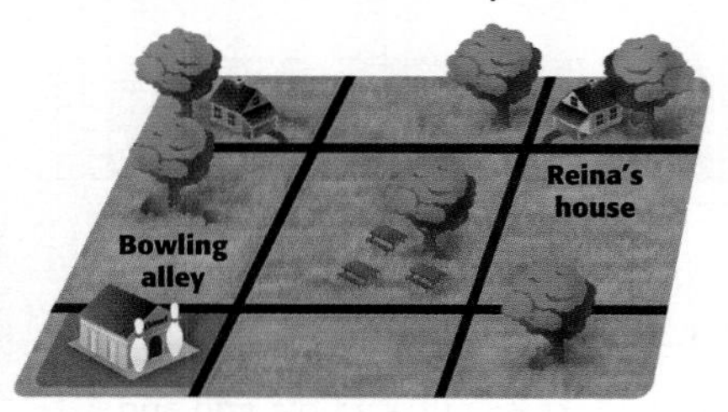


See Ch. 15 Answer Appendix.

2. Students voted for a new mascot. Six out of ten students voted for a tiger. There are 300 students. How many students voted for a tiger? **180 students**

★3. A number is divided by 3. Then the quotient is subtracted from 20. The result is 8. What is the number? **36**

4. Haley's comet can be seen from Earth about every 76 years. The next time it can be seen will be in 2062. When could the comet last be seen? **1986**

★5. Dean bought three comic books for $6. At the same price, how much would 10 comic books cost? **$20**

★6. Laurie spent 30 minutes on math homework. She spent half as much time doing her science homework. She spent 5 minutes longer on her reading homework than her science homework. How much time did Laurie spend on her homework? **65 min**

7. The toy car below cost $2.50. At the same price, how many toy cars can Domingo buy with $10? **4 cars**

★8. **Algebra** A type of bacteria doubles in number every 12 hours. After 2 days, there are 48 bacteria. How many bacteria were there at the beginning of the first day? **3 bacteria**

9. The product of two numbers is 24. Their difference is 5. What are these two numbers? **8 and 3**

10. Audrey biked the trail below. Find the value of $y$. $y = 3$

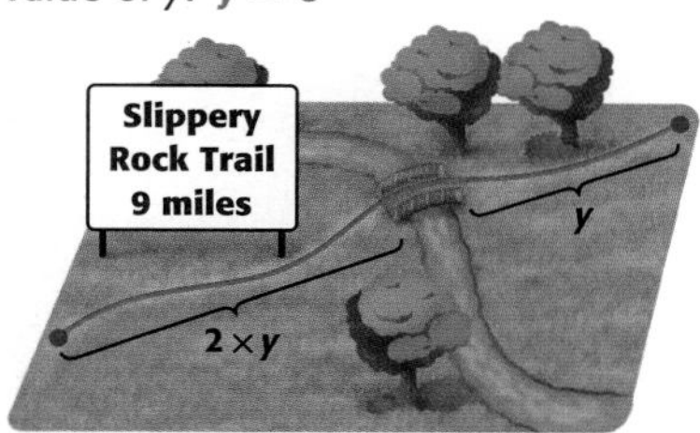


11. WRITING IN MATH The two busiest subway systems in the world have 3.1 and 2.84 billion passengers each year. The answer is 5.94 billion. What is the question? See Ch. 15 Answer Appendix.



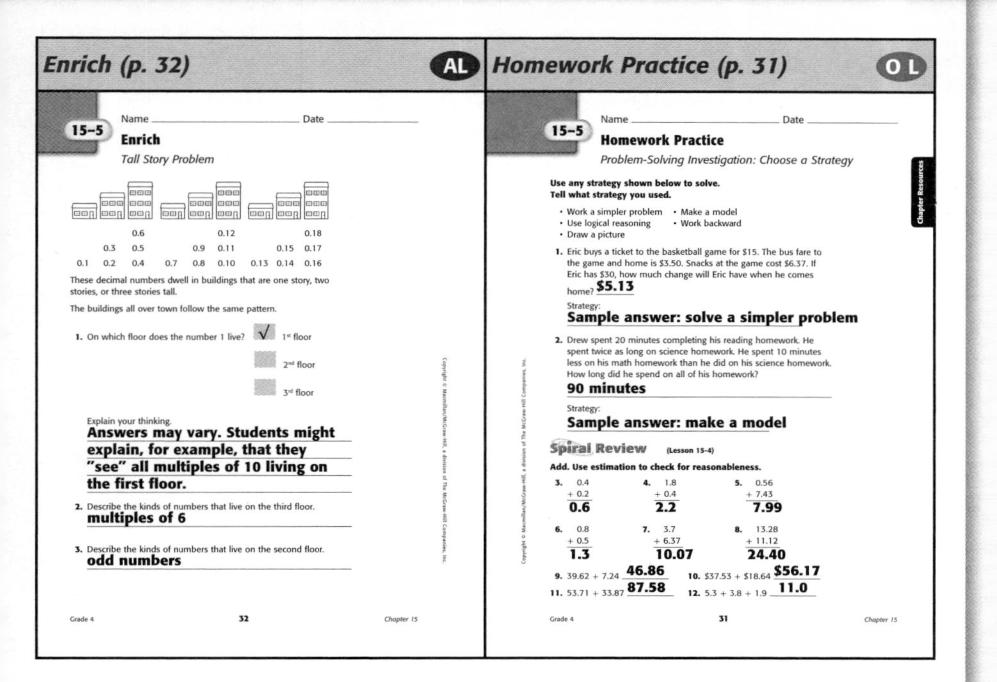

*Enrich (p. 32)* AL

15-5 Name ______ Date ______

**Enrich**

*Tall Story Problem*

| | | 0.6 | | | 0.12 | | | 0.18 |
|---|---|---|---|---|---|---|---|---|
| | 0.3 | 0.5 | | 0.9 | 0.11 | | 0.15 | 0.17 |
| 0.1 | 0.2 | 0.4 | 0.7 | 0.8 | 0.10 | 0.13 | 0.14 | 0.16 |

These decimal numbers dwell in buildings that are one story, two stories, or three stories tall.

The buildings all over town follow the same pattern.

1. On which floor does the number 1 live? √ 1st floor / 2nd floor / 3rd floor

Explain your thinking.
**Answers may vary. Students might explain, for example, that they "see" all multiples of 10 living on the first floor.**

2. Describe the kinds of numbers that live on the third floor. **multiples of 6**

3. Describe the kinds of numbers that live on the second floor. **odd numbers**



Grade 4 32 Chapter 15

*Homework Practice (p. 31)* OL

15-5 Name ______ Date ______

**Homework Practice**

*Problem-Solving Investigation: Choose a Strategy*

Chapter Resources

**Use any strategy shown below to solve.
Tell what strategy you used.**

- Work a simpler problem
- Use logical reasoning
- Draw a picture
- Make a model
- Work backward

1. Eric buys a ticket to the basketball game for $15. The bus fare to the game and home is $3.50. Snacks at the game cost $6.37. If Eric has $30, how much change will Eric have when he comes home? **$5.13**
Strategy: **Sample answer: solve a simpler problem**

2. Drew spent 20 minutes completing his reading homework. He spent twice as long on science homework. He spent 10 minutes less on his math homework than he did on his science homework. How long did he spend on all of his homework? **90 minutes**
Strategy: **Sample answer: make a model**

**Spiral Review** (Lesson 15-4)

**Add. Use estimation to check for reasonableness.**

3. 0.4 + 0.2 = **0.6**
4. 1.8 + 0.4 = **2.2**
5. 0.56 + 7.43 = **7.99**
6. 0.8 + 0.5 = **1.3**
7. 3.7 + 6.37 = **10.07**
8. 13.28 + 11.12 = **24.40**
9. 39.62 + 7.24 **46.86**
10. $37.53 + $18.64 **$56.17**
11. 53.71 + 33.87 **87.58**
12. 5.3 + 3.8 + 1.9 **11.0**



Grade 4 31 Chapter 15

## BL Alternate Teaching Strategy

**If** students have trouble setting up tables to solve logical reasoning problems…

**Then** use one of these reteach options:

1. CRM **Daily Reteach Worksheet** (pp. 28–29)
2. Have students begin by identifying the two types of data described in the problem (for example, names and pets). Have them decide which data they will write across the top for the columns and down the side for the rows. Once the table is constructed, have students use the information in the problem to fill in each cell of the table.

## 3 Practice

### Using the Exercises

**Exercises 3 and 4** Students may work backward to solve these problems. Encourage students to check their answers by substituting them into the problems and "working forward."

**Exercise 6** Point out that the problem asks for the amount of time Laurie spent on *all* of her homework.

**Exercise 11** Although the exact wording of students' questions will vary, they should all indicate addition.

## 4 Assess

### Formative Assessment

- **When might you use logical reasoning to solve a word problem?** Sample answer: when the problem has many clues that can help you figure out the answer

**Quick Check** **Are students continuing to struggle with choosing the best strategy to solve a problem?**

**If Yes** → Small Group Options (p. 636B)

**If No** → Independent Work Options (p. 636B)
CRM Skills Practice Worksheet (p. 30)
CRM Enrich Worksheet (p. 32)

# Lesson Planner

## Objective

Use models to subtract decimals.

## Resources

**Materials:** grid paper, colored pencils (one color per student)

**Teacher Technology**

Concepts in Motion

## 1 Introduce

### Introduce the Concept

- Review how to model decimals with students.
- Distribute grid paper and colored pencils to each student. Have them draw two 10-by-10 grids on the paper.
- **What does one whole grid stand for?** one whole number
- **What does one square in a grid represent?** one hundredth
- **If one column is shaded in a grid, what number does that show?** one tenth
- Have students shade their grids with colored pencils to model 1.34.
- **How do you know that your model shows 1.34?** One whole 10-by-10 grid is colored to show 1 and 34 squares are shaded to show 0.34.
- Explain to students that they can use grid models to help them subtract decimals.



Explore

Math Activity for 15-6

# Subtraction of Decimals

You can use grid paper to explore subtracting decimals.

**MAIN IDEA**

I will use models to subtract decimals.

**You Will Need**

grid paper
colored pencil

**Math Online**
macmillanmh.com
• Concepts in Motion

**ACTIVITY**

**Use models to find 2.75 − 1.15.**

**Step 1** **Model 2.75.**

To show 2.75, shade two whole grids and $\frac{75}{100}$ of a third grid.

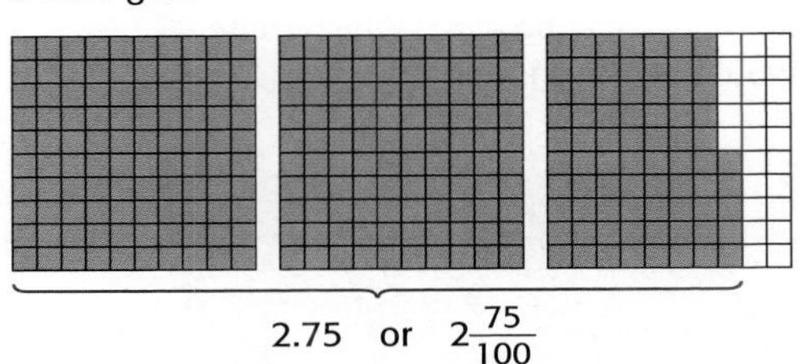

2.75 or $2\frac{75}{100}$

**Step 2** **Subtract 1.15.**

To subtract 1.15, cross out 1 whole grid and 15 squares of the third grid.

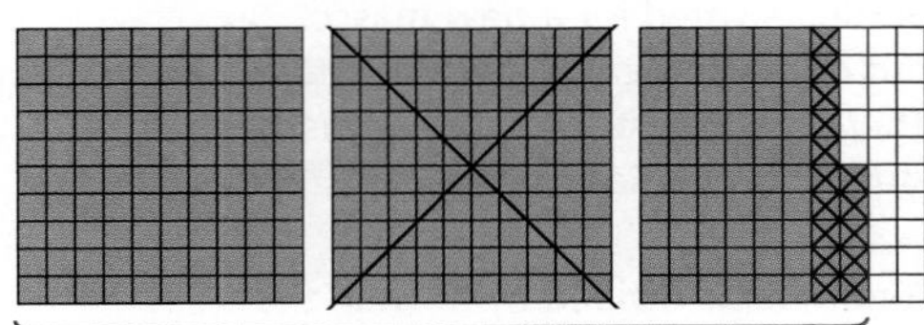

2.75 − 1.15 or $1\frac{15}{100}$

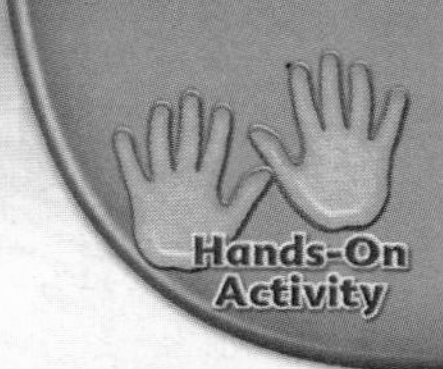


**Step 3** **Find the difference.**

Count the number of shaded squares left.

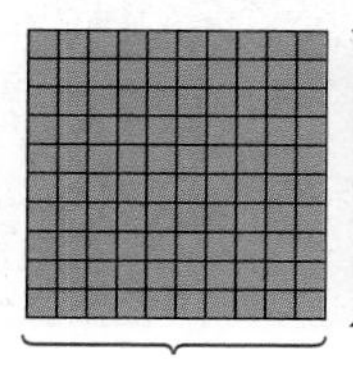
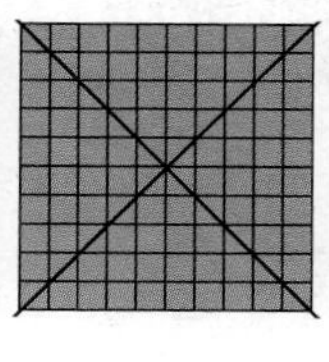
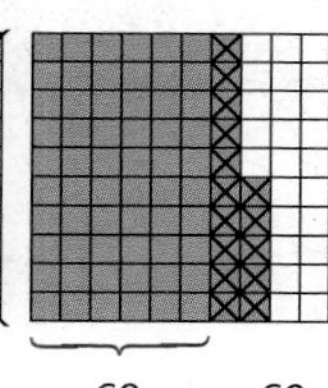

1

$\frac{60}{100} = 1\frac{60}{100} = 1.6$

## Think About It 1–3. See margin.

1. How did you model 2.75?
2. How did you model subtracting 1.15 from 2.75?
3. How did you find the difference?

## CHECK What You Know

**Subtract. Use the models.**

4. 1.46 − 0.34 **1.12**
5. 2.8 − 1.23 **1.57**

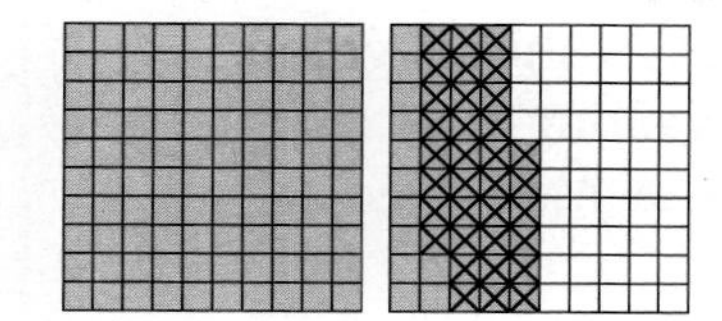
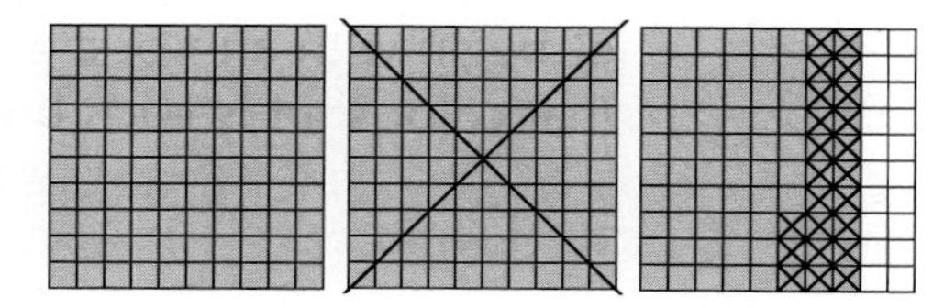

**Subtract. Use models if needed.**

6. $\begin{array}{r} 0.55 \\ -\ 0.29 \end{array}$ **0.26**
7. $\begin{array}{r} 0.99 \\ -\ 0.46 \end{array}$ **0.53**
8. $\begin{array}{r} 1.4 \\ -\ 1.11 \end{array}$ **0.29**
9. $\begin{array}{r} 2.6 \\ -\ 1.09 \end{array}$ **1.51**
10. $\begin{array}{r} 2.81 \\ -\ 1.29 \end{array}$ **1.52**
11. $\begin{array}{r} 3.77 \\ -\ 1.08 \end{array}$ **2.69**
12. 2.98 − 1.84 **1.14**
13. 3.45 − 2.73 **0.72**
14. 3.93 − 2.94 **0.99**
15. WRITING IN ➤MATH Explain how to find 3.46 − 2.62. See margin.



### Additional Answers

1. Sample answer: Since 2.75 is more than 2 and less than 3, the first two whole grids represent 2 and the third grid, represents 0.75.
2. Sample answer: To show the subtraction of 1.15, one whole grid was crossed off and 15 squares were crossed off of the third grid.
3. Sample answer: All shaded in grids equal a whole number, and the partially shaded grids equal digits to the right of the decimal. So, shade grids and squares to represent the minuend. Cross off grids and squares to represent subtracting the subtrahend. Then count the whole grids and partial grids left to find the difference of the decimals.
15. Sample answer: Shade in 3 whole grids and 46 squares of a fourth grid. Then cross off 2 whole grids and 46 squares from the fourth grid and 16 squares from the third grid. Next, count the remaining shaded squares. The result is 0.84.

## 2 Teach

**Activity** Before beginning the Activity, have students draw three 10-by-10 grids on grid paper. Have students complete Step 1 by shading grids to model 2.75.

Guide students to complete Steps 2 and 3. For Step 2, emphasize that students should first cross out the 15 squares to subtract hundredths, then cross out the 1 whole grid to subtract ones. Have students count the number of whole grids and squares remaining and write the difference as a decimal number. Remind them that 60 hundredths equals 6 tenths, and so 0.60 may be written as 0.6.

### Think About It

Assign Exercises 1–3 to assess student comprehension of the concept presented in the Activity.

## 3 Assess

### Formative Assessment

Use **Check What You Know** Exercises 4–15 to assess whether students understand using models to subtract decimals.

**From Concrete to Abstract** Use Exercise 15 to bridge the gap between crossing out and counting squares in decimal models and subtracting decimals.

LESSON 15-6

# Subtract Decimals

## Lesson Planner

### Objective

Use models to subtract decimals.

### Review Vocabulary

**decimal point**

### Resources

**Materials:** WorkMat: Place-Value Chart

**Manipulatives:** base-ten blocks

**Literature Connection:** *Henry Hikes to Fitchburg* by D.B. Johnson

**Teacher Technology**
TeacherWorks • Interactive Classroom

## Daily Routine

Use these suggestions before beginning the lesson on p. 638.

### 5-Minute Check

(Reviews Lesson 15-5)

**Use any strategy to solve. Tell what strategy you used.**

Finn, Malik, and Chris are all wearing different colored shirts. Their shirts are red, blue, or green. Malik's shirt is not blue. Finn's shirt color does not begin with an r or a g. Chris's shirt is green. What color shirt is each boy wearing? strategy: use logical reasoning; Finn: blue, Malik: red, Chris: green

### Problem of the Day

If you multiply 11 by itself, the product is 121. If you multiply my number by itself, the product is 1,225. What is my number? 35

### Focus on Math Background

For addition and subtraction of so-called "ragged decimals" that have unequal numbers of decimal places, extra 0s are included as placeholders. This is particularly important for subtraction when regrouping is needed. Thus

$$\begin{array}{r} 42.7 \\ -20.58 \\ \hline \end{array} \quad \text{becomes} \quad \begin{array}{r} 42.70 \\ -20.58 \\ \hline \end{array}$$

Note that the zero placeholder does not change the value of the minuend. To subtract, the 7 tenths must be renamed as "6 tenths plus 10 hundredths" so that the hundredths place subtraction can be carried out. Since students often make errors when subtracting across 0s in the minuend, estimation can be especially helpful here.

### Review Math Vocabulary

Write the review vocabulary word and its definition on the board.

Have students write several numbers that contain decimal points. Then ask them how they might explain the term *decimal point* if they could only use words, and not use the numbers they wrote.

# Differentiated Instruction

## Small Group Options

### Option 1 Below Level BL

SPATIAL, LOGICAL

**Materials:** dimes, 10 × 10 grid paper

- Place 4 dimes on the table.
- **How many dimes do you see?** 4
- **How much money is this?** 40¢
- **What fractional part of a dollar is one dime?** $\frac{1}{10}$
- **What fractional part of a dollar is 4 dimes?** $\frac{4}{10}$
- Remind the students that .4 is the same as .40.
- Shade $\frac{4}{10}$ of the grid paper to show that .4 = .40.
- **Does this work every time?** yes
- **Does adding a zero to the end of a decimal ever change its value?** no

### Option 2 English Language Learners ELL

LINGUISTIC, SOCIAL

**Materials:** index cards
**Core Vocabulary:** my actions, tell me, hold up
**Common Use Verb:** direct

**Talk Math** This strategy helps students to make predictions on how to solve a subtraction problem.

- Write on the board: decimal, subtract, move, and down.
- Have students write each on index cards (large enough for you to see).
- Write a subtraction problem on the board.
- As you work the problem, have students hold up the words to direct your actions.
- Watch for students who are having trouble.

*Use this worksheet to provide additional support for English Language Learners.*

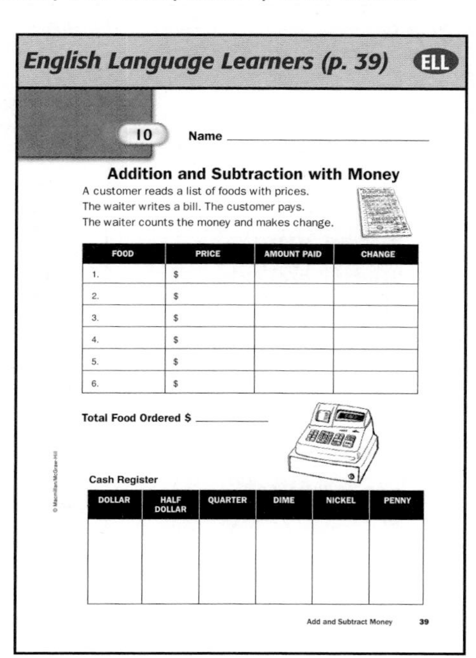

*English Language Learners (p. 39)* ELL

10 Name ______

**Addition and Subtraction with Money**

A customer reads a list of foods with prices.
The waiter writes a bill. The customer pays.
The waiter counts the money and makes change.

| FOOD | PRICE | AMOUNT PAID | CHANGE |
|---|---|---|---|
| 1. | $ | | |
| 2. | $ | | |
| 3. | $ | | |
| 4. | $ | | |
| 5. | $ | | |
| 6. | $ | | |

Total Food Ordered $ ______

Cash Register

| DOLLAR | HALF DOLLAR | QUARTER | DIME | NICKEL | PENNY |
|---|---|---|---|---|---|
| | | | | | |

Add and Subtract Money 39

## Independent Work Options

### Option 1 Early Finishers OL AL

LINGUISTIC

**Materials:** grid paper, colored pencils

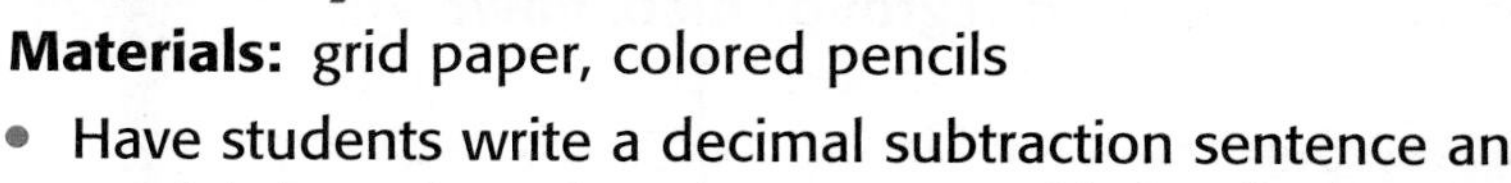

- Have students write a decimal subtraction sentence and model the subtraction on 10 × 10 grids by shading and crossing out grids and squares.
- Ask students to exchange grid models without revealing their subtraction sentences. Each student will examine a model and write the subtraction sentence that it shows.

### Option 2 Student Technology

Math Online macmillanmh.com

Personal Tutor • Extra Examples

Math Adventures

### Option 3 Learning Station: Social Studies (p. 614H)

Direct students to the Social Studies Learning Station for opportunities to explore and extend the lesson concept.

### Option 4 Problem-Solving Practice

Reinforce problem-solving skills and strategies with the Problem-Solving Practice worksheet.

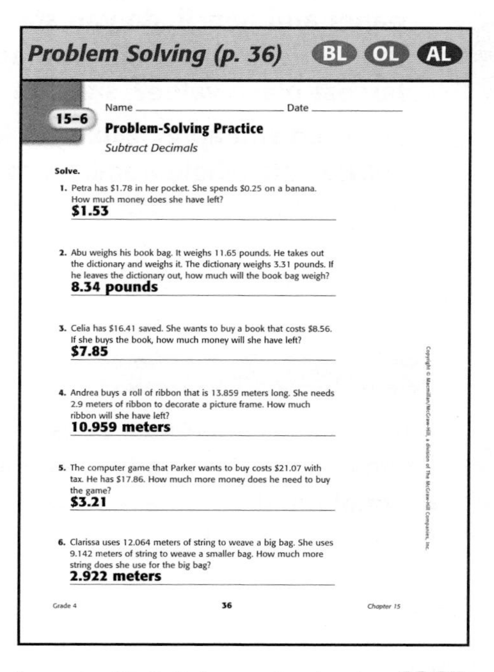

*Problem Solving (p. 36)* BL OL AL

Name ______ Date ______

15–6 **Problem-Solving Practice**
*Subtract Decimals*

**Solve.**

1. Petra has $1.78 in her pocket. She spends $0.25 on a banana. How much money does she have left?
**$1.53**
2. Abu weighs his book bag. It weighs 11.65 pounds. He takes out the dictionary and weighs it. The dictionary weighs 3.31 pounds. If he leaves the dictionary out, how much will the book bag weigh?
**8.34 pounds**
3. Celia has $16.41 saved. She wants to buy a book that costs $8.56. If she buys the book, how much money will she have left?
**$7.85**
4. Andrea buys a roll of ribbon that is 13.859 meters long. She needs 2.9 meters of ribbon to decorate a picture frame. How much ribbon will she have left?
**10.959 meters**
5. The computer game that Parker wants to buy costs $21.07 with tax. He has $17.86. How much more money does he need to buy the game?
**$3.21**
6. Clarissa uses 12.064 meters of string to weave a big bag. She uses 9.142 meters of string to weave a smaller bag. How much more string does she use for the big bag?
**2.922 meters**

Grade 4 36 Chapter 15

# 15-6 Subtract Decimals

## 1 Introduce

### Activity Choice 1 • Hands-On

- Write 485 − 326 in vertical form on the board. Have students model 485 with base-ten blocks.
- **What do you do first to subtract 326 from 485?** Subtract the ones.
- **Do you need to regroup? If so, how?** Yes. You cannot subtract 6 from 5. We need to regroup the 8 tens in 485 as 7 tens and 10 ones. Then you can subtract 15 ones − 6 ones = 9 ones.
- Have students subtract ones using base-ten blocks, while you write this first step of the algorithm (paper and pencil method) on the board.
- Have students subtract tens and hundreds as you complete the algorithm on the board. 159
- Tell students that they will use the same rules and procedures that they use for subtracting whole numbers for subtracting decimals.

### Activity Choice 2 • Literature

Introduce the lesson with *Henry Hikes to Fitchburg* by D.B. Johnson. For a related math activity, see p. TR67.

## 2 Teach

### Scaffolding Questions

- **When you subtract whole numbers with paper and pencil, do you start by subtracting the digits in the smallest place value or the largest place value?** smallest place value
- **How can you apply what you know about subtracting whole numbers to subtract 3.54 − 2.36?** First subtract the digits in the hundredths places; then the digits in the tenths place; and finally, the digits in the ones places.

### GET READY to Learn

Have students open their books and read the information in **Get Ready to Learn**. Review **decimal point**. As a class, work through **Examples 1 and 2**.

# 15-6 Subtract Decimals

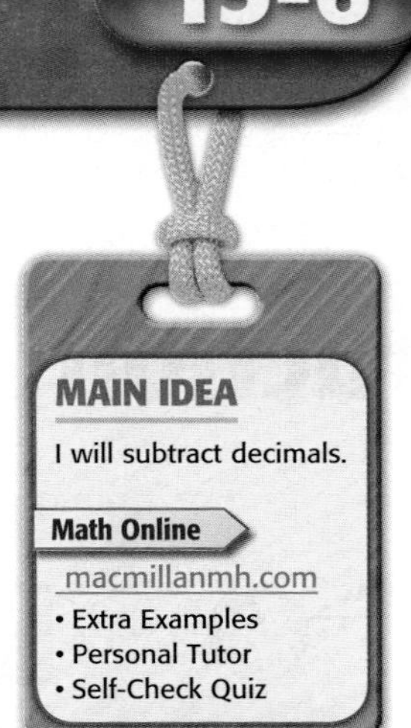


### GET READY to Learn

Albert Einstein was a very intelligent man who made many important scientific discoveries. His brain had a mass of 1.23 kilograms. This is less than the mass of an average adult male brain, which has a mass of about 1.4 kilograms. What is the difference in mass?

In the previous Explore Activity, you used models to subtract decimals.

### Real-World EXAMPLE — Subtract Decimals

**1 MEASUREMENT What is the difference in mass between Albert Einstein's brain and the mass of an average adult male brain?**

**Step 1** Draw a model of 1.4 on a hundredths grid.

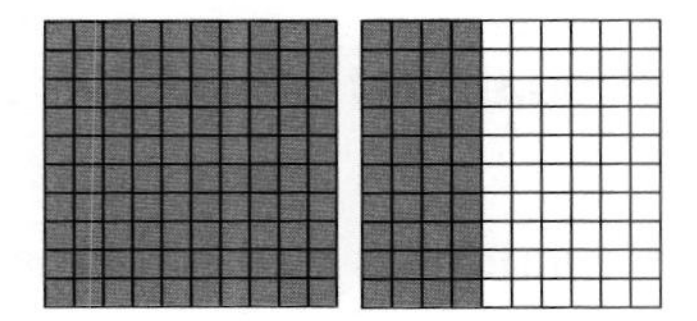

**Step 2** Subtract 1.23.

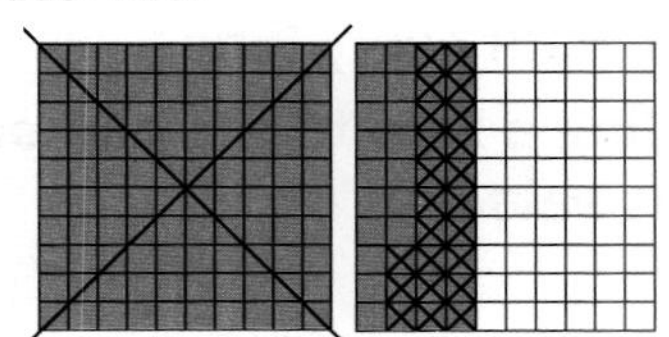

1.4 − 1.23 = 0.17

So, Einstein's brain had a mass of 0.17 kilogram less than the mass of an average adult male brain.

**638 Chapter 15** Add and Subtract Decimals

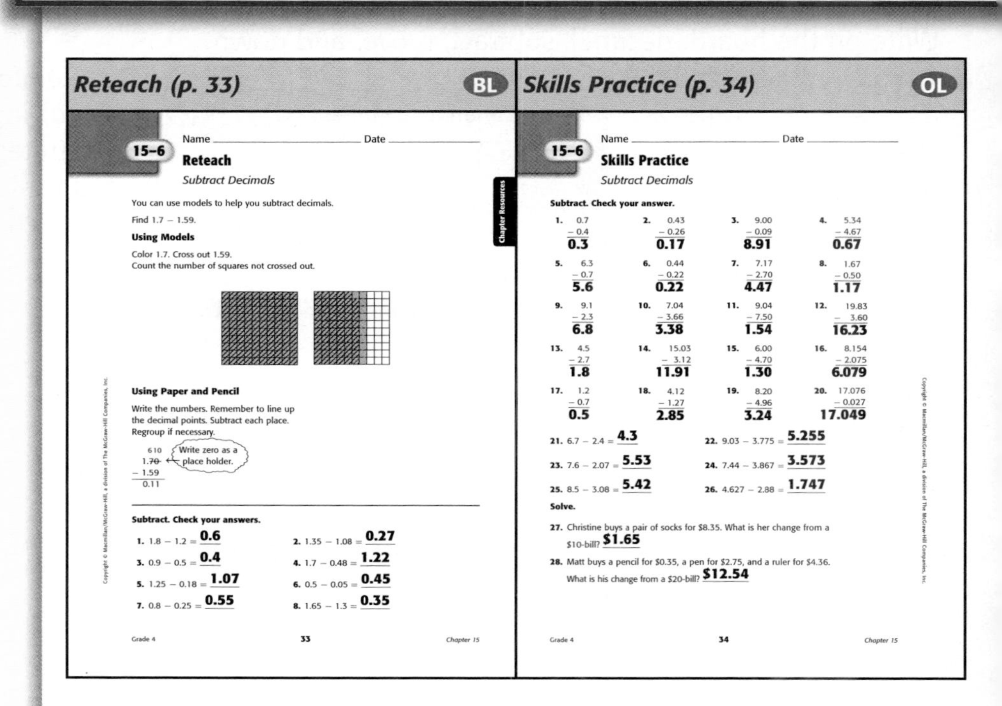

*Reteach (p. 33)* BL

15-6 Name ______ Date ______

**Reteach**

*Subtract Decimals*

You can use models to help you subtract decimals.

Find 1.7 − 1.59.

**Using Models**

Color 1.7. Cross out 1.59.
Count the number of squares not crossed out.

**Using Paper and Pencil**

Write the numbers. Remember to line up the decimal points. Subtract each place. Regroup if necessary.

```
   6 10
  1.7̶0̶  ← Write zero as a place holder.
− 1.59
  0.11
```

**Subtract. Check your answers.**

1. 1.8 − 1.2 = **0.6**
2. 1.35 − 1.08 = **0.27**
3. 0.9 − 0.5 = **0.4**
4. 1.7 − 0.48 = **1.22**
5. 1.25 − 0.18 = **1.07**
6. 0.5 − 0.05 = **0.45**
7. 0.8 − 0.25 = **0.55**
8. 1.65 − 1.3 = **0.35**

Chapter Resources



Grade 4 33 *Chapter 15*

*Skills Practice (p. 34)* OL

15-6 Name ______ Date ______

**Skills Practice**

*Subtract Decimals*

**Subtract. Check your answer.**

1. 0.7 − 0.4 = **0.3**
2. 0.43 − 0.26 = **0.17**
3. 9.00 − 0.09 = **8.91**
4. 5.34 − 4.67 = **0.67**
5. 6.3 − 0.7 = **5.6**
6. 0.44 − 0.22 = **0.22**
7. 7.17 − 2.70 = **4.47**
8. 1.67 − 0.50 = **1.17**
9. 9.1 − 2.3 = **6.8**
10. 7.04 − 3.66 = **3.38**
11. 9.04 − 7.50 = **1.54**
12. 19.83 − 3.60 = **16.23**
13. 4.5 − 2.7 = **1.8**
14. 15.03 − 3.12 = **11.91**
15. 6.00 − 4.70 = **1.30**
16. 8.154 − 2.075 = **6.079**
17. 1.2 − 0.7 = **0.5**
18. 4.12 − 1.27 = **2.85**
19. 8.20 − 4.96 = **3.24**
20. 17.076 − 0.027 = **17.049**
21. 6.7 − 2.4 = **4.3**
22. 9.03 − 3.775 = **5.255**
23. 7.6 − 2.07 = **5.53**
24. 7.44 − 3.867 = **3.573**
25. 8.5 − 3.08 = **5.42**
26. 4.627 − 2.88 = **1.747**

**Solve.**

27. Christine buys a pair of socks for $8.35. What is her change from a $10-bill? **$1.65**
28. Matt buys a pencil for $0.35, a pen for $2.75, and a ruler for $4.36. What is his change from a $20-bill? **$12.54**



Grade 4 34 *Chapter 15*

You can also use paper and pencil to solve.

**Real-World EXAMPLE** Subtract Decimals

**2 MEASUREMENT The average rock python is 24.6 feet long. The average king cobra is 17.7 feet long. How much longer is the rock python than the king cobra?**

Subtract 24.6 − 17.7 to find how much longer the rock python is than the king cobra.

**Estimate** 24.6 − 17.7 ⟶ 25 − 18 = 7

**Step 1** Line up the decimal points.

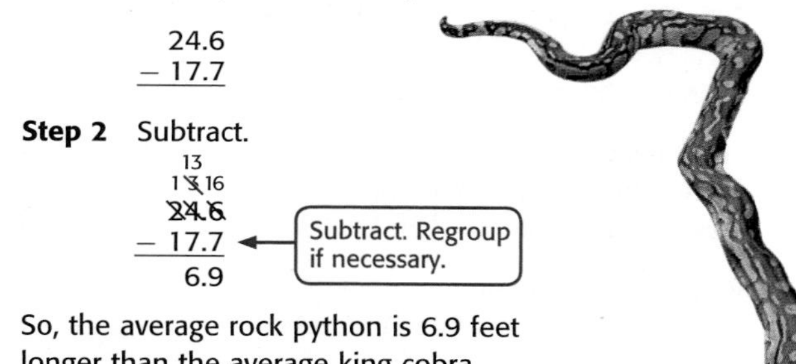

```
  24.6
− 17.7
```

**Step 2** Subtract.

```
   13
  1 3 16
  2 4.6
− 1 7.7   ← Subtract. Regroup if necessary.
    6.9
```

So, the average rock python is 6.9 feet longer than the average king cobra.

Rock Python

**Check for Reasonableness**
The answer, 6.9, is close to the estimate of 7. So, the answer is reasonable. ✓

Since 17.7 + 6.9 = 24.6, the answer is correct.

★ indicates multi-step problem

## CHECK What You Know

1–8. See margin.

**Subtract. Use estimation or addition to check.** See Examples 1 and 2 (pp. 638–639)

**1.** 1.4 − 1.0 **2.** 0.8 − 0.49 **3.** \$1.67 − \$0.58

**4.** 4.67 − 2.36 **5.** \$8.72 − \$2.95 **6.** 25.74 − 12.08

**7.** The height of the tallest woman in the world is 7.58 feet. The height of the tallest man in the world is 8.92 feet. How much taller is the tallest man than the tallest woman?

**8.** Talk About It Explain how subtracting decimals is similar to subtracting whole numbers. How is it different?



**Enrich (p. 37)** AL

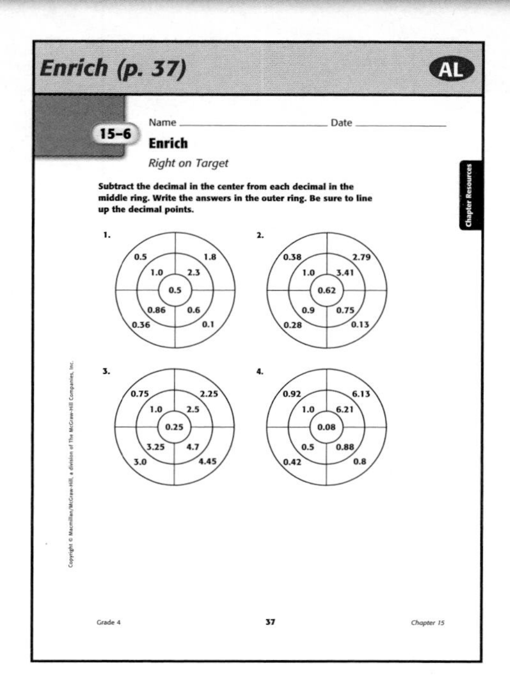

Name ____________ Date ____________

15-6 **Enrich**

*Right on Target*

**Subtract the decimal in the center from each decimal in the middle ring. Write the answers in the outer ring. Be sure to line up the decimal points.**

1. center 0.5; 0.5, 1.8, 1.0, 2.3, 0.86, 0.6, 0.36, 0.1

2. center 0.62; 0.38, 2.79, 1.0, 3.41, 0.9, 0.75, 0.28, 0.13

3. center 0.25; 0.75, 2.25, 1.0, 2.5, 3.25, 4.7, 3.0, 4.45

4. center 0.08; 0.92, 6.13, 1.0, 6.21, 0.5, 0.88, 0.42, 0.8

Grade 4 37 Chapter 15

## Subtract Decimals

**Example 2** Go over the regrouping that takes place in the paper and pencil method. For Step 2 of this method, suggest that students place the decimal point in the answer space before beginning to subtract.

### ADDITIONAL EXAMPLES

**1** A fruit stand sells a bag of grapes for \$1.70 and a bunch of bananas for \$1.19. What is the difference in price? \$0.51

**2** Lisa is 52.5 inches tall and her sister is 48.8 inches tall. How much taller is Lisa than her sister? 3.7 inches

### CHECK What You Know

As a class, have students complete Exercises 1–8 in **Check What You Know** as you observe their work.

**Exercise 8** Assess student comprehension before assigning practice exercises.

## BL Alternate Teaching Strategy

**If** students have trouble lining up decimal numbers correctly to subtract...

**Then** use one of these reteach options:

**1** CRM **Daily Reteach Worksheet** (p. 33)

**2** For any decimal subtraction problem, have students write each number one directly above the other in the place-value chart. Have them use 0 as a placeholder when necessary. Then have students subtract hundredths from hundredths, tenths from tenths, and ones from ones, regrouping when necessary.

### Additional Answers

**1.** 0.4; 0.4 + 1.0 = 1.4
**2.** 0.31; 0.31 + 0.49 = 0.8
**3.** \$1.09; \$1.09 + \$0.58 = \$1.67
**4.** 2.31; 2.31 + 2.36 = 4.67
**5.** \$5.77; \$5.77 + \$2.95 = \$8.72
**6.** 13.66; 13.66 + 12.08 = 25.74
**7.** 1.34 feet; 1.34 + 7.58 = 8.92
**8.** Sample answer: similar: you follow the same steps; different: you must write a decimal in the answer.

# 3 Practice

Differentiate practice using these leveled assignments for Exercises 9–29.

| Level | Assignment |
|---|---|
| BL Below/Approaching Level | 9–15, 21, 23, 25, 27 |
| OL On Level | 10–19, 23–28 |
| AL Above/Beyond Level | 10–26 even, 28–29 |

Have students discuss and complete the Higher Order Thinking problems. For Exercise 29, students may want to first choose a number between 9 and 10 and subtract that number from 24.84 to solve the problem.

### Additional Answers

**9.** 1.3; 1.3 + 1.4 = 2.7
**10.** 1.7; 1.7 + 3.8 = 5.5
**11.** 6.3; 6.3 + 0.9 = 7.2
**12.** 3.15; 3.15 + 1.45 = 4.6
**13.** 3.28; 3.28 + 3.56 = 6.84
**14.** $2.62; $2.62 + $7.05 = $9.67
**15.** 3.05; 3.05 + 8.87 = 11.92
**16.** $4.83; $4.83 + $14.55 = $19.38
**17.** 5.89; 5.89 + 15.91 = 21.80
**18.** $12.69; $12.69 + $12.40 = $25.09
**19.** 6.77; 6.77 + 28.17 = 34.94
**20.** 18.82; 18.82 + 38.05 = 56.87

### COMMON ERROR!

**Exercises 12 and 26** Students may make errors when they do not write in a 0 as a placeholder. Suggest that students write each number in the problem with the same number of digits to the right of the decimal point before they begin to subtract.



## Practice and Problem Solving

EXTRA PRACTICE See page R41.

9–20. See margin.

**Subtract. Use estimation or addition to check.** See Examples 1 and 2 (pp. 638–639)

**9.** 2.7 − 1.4
**10.** 5.5 − 3.8
**11.** 7.2 − 0.9
**12.** 4.6 − 1.45
**13.** 6.84 − 3.56
**14.** $9.67 − $7.05
**15.** 11.92 − 8.87
**16.** $19.38 − $14.55
**17.** 21.80 − 15.91
**18.** $25.09 − $12.40
**19.** 34.94 − 28.17
**20.** 56.87 − 38.05

**For Exercises 21 and 22, use the table.**

**Most Popular States for Tennis**

| State | Number of Players (millions) |
|---|---|
| California | 3.2 |
| Florida | 1.4 |
| Illinois | 1.0 |
| New York | 1.7 |
| Texas | 1.4 |

**Source:** *United States Tennis Association*

**21.** How many more people play tennis in the most popular state than in the least popular state? 2.2 million

**22.** What is the total number of people in Florida, Texas, and New York who play tennis? 4.5 million

**23.** ★ Julina is buying pet supplies. She has $25.50. She buys cat food for $8.99, a collar for $4.79, and cat toys for $3.25. How much money will Julina have left? $8.47

**24.** The average American eats 57.4 kilograms of fresh fruit and 67.2 kilograms of fresh vegetables each year. What is the difference in the yearly amount of fruit and vegetables an American eats? 9.8 kg

### Real-World PROBLEM SOLVING

*Science* The table at the right shows the heights of different dinosaurs.

**Dinosaur Heights**

| Dinosaur | Height (feet) |
|---|---|
| Abrictosaurus | 1.3 |
| Araucanoraptor | 2.75 |
| Bagaceratops | 1.5 |
| Microvenator | 2.5 |
| Supersaurus | 66.0 |
| Triceratops | 9.5 |
| Tyrannosaurus | 23.0 |

**Source:** *Arts & Letters Corporation*

**25.** What is the difference in height between the two shortest dinosaurs? 0.2 ft

**26.** How much taller is a Tyrannosaurus than a Araucanoraptor? 20.25 ft

**27.** Which two dinosaurs have a height difference of 1.45 feet? Araucanoraptor and Abrictosaurus

## H.O.T. Problems

**28. FIND THE ERROR** Morgan and Lloyd are finding 46.27 − 28.16. Who is correct? Explain. See margin.

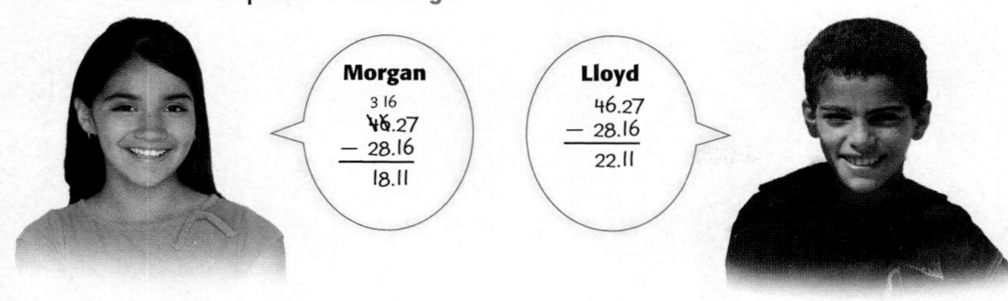


**29. OPEN ENDED** A number is subtracted from 24.84. The difference is greater than 9 and less than 10. What is the number?
Sample answer: 24.84 − 15 = 9.84

## TEST Practice

**30.** At the school store, Benito bought a package of pens for $1.34 and a set of map pencils for $2.78. What was the total cost? (Lesson 15-4) D

**A** $1.44

**B** $3.02

**C** $4.02

**D** $4.12

**31.** Sandy and her father have $100. They buy a fishing pole for $39.95 and cooking gear for $29.39. Which additional item could they buy? (Lesson 15-6) H

**F** Backpack

**G** Camp stove

**H** Lantern

**J** Sleeping bag

## Spiral Review

**32.** Mila volunteers at a food bank at 9 A.M. It takes 30 minutes to drive to the food bank, 20 minutes to eat breakfast, and 45 minutes to get ready in the morning. What is the latest time she can set her alarm to wake up? (Lesson 15-5) 7:25 A.M.

33, 35. See Ch.15 Answer Appendix.

**Add. Use estimation to check for reasonableness.** (Lesson 15-4)

**33.** 0.75 + 0.62

**34.** 4.49 + 0.76 5.25; 4 + 1 = 5

**35.** 8.40 + 6.87

**Estimate. Round to the nearest whole number.** (Lesson 15-2) 38. See Ch.15 Answer Appendix.

**36.** 2.5 + 4.3 3 + 4 = 7

**37.** 8.4 − 5.7 8 − 6 = 2

**38.** 22.9 + 5.4



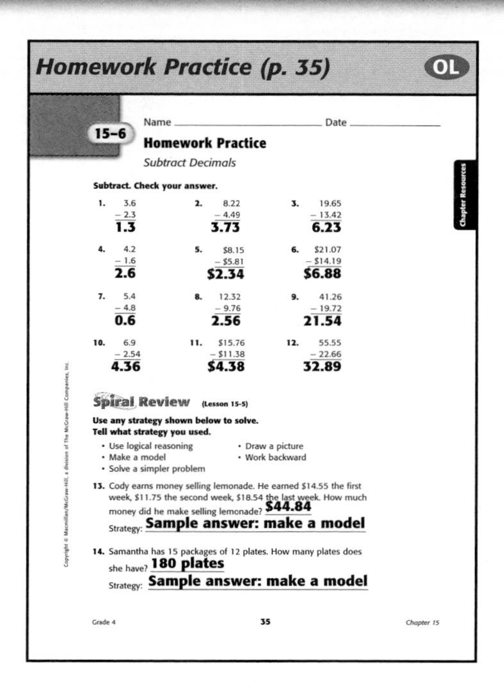

**Homework Practice (p. 35)** OL

15-6 Name ______ Date ______

**Homework Practice**

*Subtract Decimals*

**Subtract. Check your answer.**

1. 3.6 − 2.3 = **1.3**
2. 8.22 − 4.49 = **3.73**
3. 19.65 − 13.42 = **6.23**
4. 4.2 − 1.6 = **2.6**
5. $8.15 − $5.81 = **$2.34**
6. $21.07 − $14.19 = **$6.88**
7. 5.4 − 4.8 = **0.6**
8. 12.32 − 9.76 = **2.56**
9. 41.26 − 19.72 = **21.54**
10. 6.9 − 2.54 = **4.36**
11. $15.76 − $11.38 = **$4.38**
12. 55.55 − 22.66 = **32.89**

Chapter Resources

**Spiral Review** (Lesson 15-5)

**Use any strategy shown below to solve. Tell what strategy you used.**

- Use logical reasoning
- Make a model
- Solve a simpler problem
- Draw a picture
- Work backward

**13.** Cody earns money selling lemonade. He earned $14.55 the first week, $11.75 the second week, $18.54 the last week. How much money did he make selling lemonade? **$44.84**
Strategy: **Sample answer: make a model**

**14.** Samantha has 15 packages of 12 plates. How many plates does she have? **180 plates**
Strategy: **Sample answer: make a model**



Grade 4 35 Chapter 15

# 4 Assess

## Formative Assessment

- **Describe how to use models to subtract 1.75 − 1.38.** Color one whole grid and 75 squares in another grid. Cross out one whole grid and 38 squares and count the left over squares. 37 squares = 0.37
- **How would you use pencil and paper to subtract 1.75 − 1.38? Show your work.** Check students' work; 0.37

**Quick Check** **Are students continuing to struggle with subtracting decimals?**

**If Yes** → Small Group Options (p. 640B)

**If No** → Independent Work Options (p. 640B)
CRM Skills Practice Worksheet (p. 34)
CRM Enrich Worksheet (p. 37)

**Ticket Out the Door** Write 5.12 − 3.41 on the board. Have students write the answer to the problem on a piece of paper and give it to you as they leave at the end of class. 1.71

## TEST Practice

**Reviews Lessons 15-4 and 15-6**

Assign the Test Practice problems to provide daily reinforcement of test-taking skills.

## Spiral Review

**Reviews Lessons 15-2, 15-4, and 15-5**

Review and assess mastery of skills and concepts from previous chapters.

### Additional Answer

**28.** Sample answer: Morgan; Lloyd subtracted 6 from 8 in the ones place.

# Lesson Planner

## Objective

Interpret information and data from social studies to solve problems.

### National Standard 

Understands selected attributes and historical developments of societies in Africa, The Americas, Asia, and Europe.

## Activate Prior Knowledge

Before you turn students' attention to the pages, ask them to discuss the Olympic games.

- **During what two seasons are there Olympic games?** summer and winter
- **How often does each Olympic season occur?** every four years

## Using the Student Page

Ask students to read the information on p. 634 and answer these questions:

- **If the women's uneven bars scores were rounded to the nearest whole number, whose scores in that event would be tied?** Carly Patterson and Svetlana Khorkina
- **To which place would the men's total scores have to be rounded in order to have a three-way tie?** the tenths place





# Olympic Games

The Olympic games have been taking place since ancient times.

There are currently summer and winter games. Each season occurs every four years and includes different sports. There are over one hundred summer events including cycling, gymnastics, swimming and diving, and track and field, among others. A highlight of the summer games has always been the gymnastic events. These events mix strength, agility, style, and grace. Some of the events that take place in the gymnastic competition are floor exercise, horizontal bar, parallel bars, pommel horse, rings, and vault. Gymnasts are scored on a scale of one to ten, with ten being a perfect score and very difficult to earn.

**Recent Olympic Games Men's Individual Scores**

| Gymnast | Floor | Horse | Rings | Vault | Parallel Bars | High Bar | Total Score |
|---|---|---|---|---|---|---|---|
| Paul Hamm (U.S.) | 9.73 | 9.70 | 9.59 | 9.14 | 9.84 | 9.84 | 57.84 |
| Kim Dae-Eun (South Korea) | 9.65 | 9.54 | 9.71 | 9.41 | 9.78 | 9.73 | 57.82 |
| Yang Tae-Young (South Korea) | 9.51 | 9.65 | 9.73 | 9.70 | 9.71 | 9.48 | 57.78 |

**Recent Olympic Games Women's Individual Scores**

| Gymnast | Vault | Uneven Bars | Beam | Floor | Total Score |
|---|---|---|---|---|---|
| Carly Patterson (U.S.) | 9.38 | 9.58 | 9.73 | 9.71 | 38.34 |
| Svetlana Khorkina (Russia) | 9.46 | 9.73 | 9.46 | 9.56 | 38.21 |
| Zhang Nan (China) | 9.33 | 9.46 | 9.66 | 9.60 | 38.05 |

* All scores have been rounded to the nearest hundredth.

**Source:** International Olympic Committee

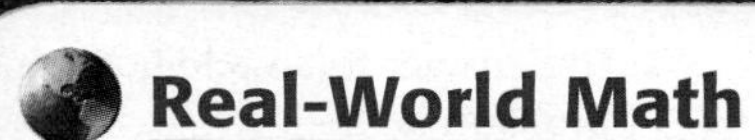

## Real-World Math

6. yes; When rounded to the nearest tenth the male athlete's scores are all 57.8, so all three men would get a gold medal.

**Use the information on page 642 to solve each problem.**

1. A summer Olympic games will be taking place in London, England, in the year 2012. What years will the four previous Olympic games have been held? 2008, 2004, 2000, 1996
2. What is the top female gymnast's total score rounded to the nearest whole number? 38
3. How much higher is Paul Hamm's score in the parallel bars than the vault when both scores are rounded to the nearest tenth? 0.7
4. What is the sum of Carly Patterson's two highest event scores when rounded to the nearest tenth? 19.4
5. Kim Dae-Eun's scores were higher than Paul Hamm's scores in two of the events. Identify the events. Find the difference in their scores for each event to the nearest tenth. rings 0.1; vault 0.3
6. The gymnasts that earn the top three total scores win gold, silver, and bronze medals. Suppose the scores were rounded to the tenths place. Would this scoring change the medals that were given out to the male athletes? Explain.
7. Which place value would the female gymnast's scores have to be rounded to in order to have a three-way tie for gold? Explain. to the nearest whole number



## Real-World Math

Assign the exercises on Student Edition p. 643. Encourage students to choose a problem-solving strategy before beginning each exercise. If necessary, review the strategies suggested in Lesson 15-5, p. 635.

**Exercise 1** Tell students that the summer and winter Olympics are held every four years, but the seasons alternate with each other every two years.

**Exercise 4** Tell students that they need to round before they subtract.

**Exercise 7** Remind students that a tie means the scores are exactly the same.

**WRITING IN MATH** Have students create a word problem that uses the information found in the text and in the chart on pp. 642–643.

# Extend the Activity

Have students round all individual event scores to the nearest tenth and then add them. They should then compare their results with the total scores on the charts rounded to the nearest tenth.

CHAPTER 15

# Study Guide and Review

## Dinah Zike's Foldables

**Lesson 15-6** Ask students to demonstrate their ability to subtract decimals. Students store their notes and work in the second pocket of the Foldable.

## Key Vocabulary

The page references after each word denote where that term was first introduced. If students have difficulty answering Exercises 1–6, remind them that they can use these page references to review the vocabulary terms.

## Vocabulary Review

Review chapter vocabulary using one of the following options.

- **Visual Vocabulary Card** (15)
- **eGlossary** at macmillanmh.com

CHAPTER 15

# Study Guide and Review

Math Online macmillanmh.com
- STUDY TO GO
- Vocabulary Review

FOLDABLES Study Organizer GET READY to Study

**Be sure the following Key Vocabulary words and Key Concepts are written in your Foldable.**

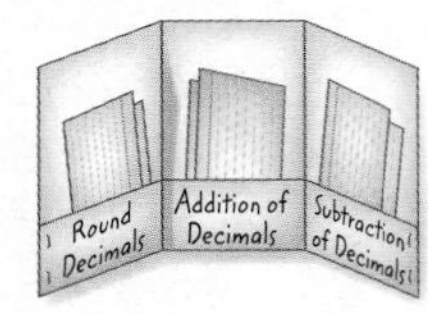


### Key Concepts

**Round Decimals** (p. 617)

- Round 4.36 to the nearest whole number.

4.36

Look at the digit to the right of the place you want to round to. Since it is less than 5, round down.

So, 4.36 rounds to 4.

**Estimate Sums and Differences** (p. 622)

- Round each addend to the nearest whole number. Then add.

$8.6 + 7.2 \longrightarrow 9 + 7 = 16$

**Add and Subtract Decimals** (pp. 630, 638)

Find 1.27 + 0.36.

$$\begin{array}{r} 1.27 \\ +\ 0.36 \\ \hline 1.63 \end{array}$$

Find 0.78 − 0.45.

$$\begin{array}{r} 1.78 \\ -\ 0.45 \\ \hline 1.33 \end{array}$$

### Key Vocabulary

**decimal** (pp. 579, 617)
**decimal point** (pp. 579, 617)
**difference** (pp. 71, 622)
**estimate** (pp. 58, 622)
**sum** (pp. 58, 622)

### Vocabulary Check

**Complete each sentence with the correct vocabulary word.**

1. The answer to an addition problem is the ___?___. **sum**
2. A(n) ___?___ is a period separating the ones and the tenths in a number. **decimal point**
3. A(n) ___?___ indicates about how much. **estimate**
4. The answer to a subtraction problem is the ___?___. **difference**
5. A(n) ___?___ is a number with one or more digits to the right of the decimal point. **decimal**
6. A(n) ___?___ is a number that is close to an exact amount. **estimate**

## Chapter 15 Project

### Shopping List

Alone, in pairs, or in small groups, have students discuss the results of their completed chapter projects with the class. Assess their work using the Chapter Project rubric found in Chapter 15 Resource Masters, p. 48.

## Lesson-by-Lesson Review

### 15-1 Round Decimals (pp. 617–620)

**Example 1**
**Round 12.16 to the nearest tenth.**

**One Way: Use a Number Line**

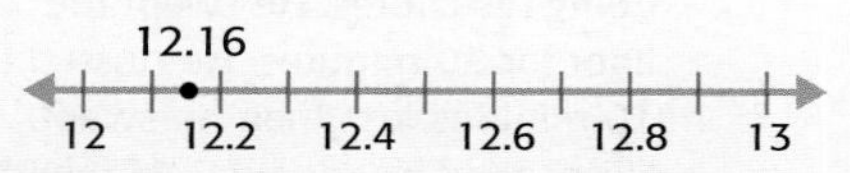


12.16 is closer to 12.2 than 12.1.

**Another Way: Use Place Value**

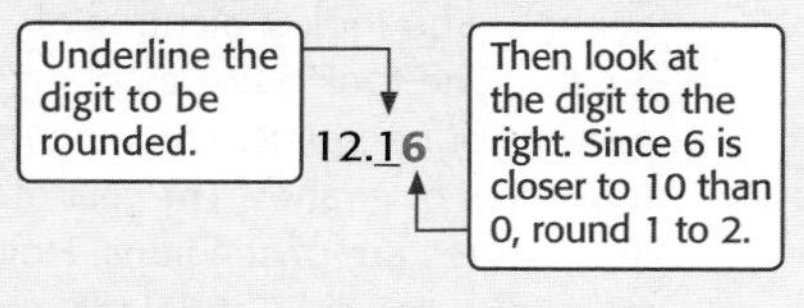


So, round 12.16 up to 12.2.

**Round to the nearest whole number.**

**7.** 4.12 4  **8.** 3.65 4

**9.** 12.40 12  **10.** 69.95 70

**11. Measurement** Marni hiked 3.65 miles on Saturday. About how many miles did she hike? 4

**12.** A baby panda weighs 4.36 ounces. About how many ounces does the baby panda weigh? 4

**13.** Travis spent $5.32 at lunch. About how much did he spend? $5

**Round to the nearest tenth.**

**14.** 7.45 7.5  **15.** 9.81 9.8

**16.** 32.78 32.8  **17.** 44.54 44.5

### 15-2 Estimate Decimal Sums and Differences (pp. 622–625)

**Example 2**
**Estimate 8.63 + 6.15.**

8.63 → 9
+ 6.15 → + 6
15

Round 8.63 to 9.
Round 6.15 to 6.

So, 8.63 + 6.15 is about 15.

**Example 3**
**Estimate 25.25 − 12.76.**

25.25 → 25
− 12.76 → − 13
12

Round 25.25 to 25.
Round 12.76 to 13.

So, 25.25 − 12.76 is about 12.

**Estimate. Round to the nearest whole number.** 18–22. See margin.

**18.** 4.88 + 14.56  **19.** 35.15 − 14.93

**20.** 9.51 + 7.43  **21.** 99.65 − 24.67

**22.** A basketball costs $17.95. It is on sale for $9.99. About how much less is the sale price than the original price?



# Lesson-by-Lesson Review

Have students complete the Lesson-by-Lesson Review on pp. 645–649. Then you can use Exam*View*® Assessment Suite to customize another review worksheet that practices all the objectives of this chapter or only the objectives on which your students need more help.

**Intervention** If the given examples are not sufficient to review the topics covered by the questions, use the page references next to the exercises to review that topic in the Student Edition.

### Additional Answers

**18.** 5 + 15 = 20
**19.** 35 − 15 = 20
**20.** 10 + 7 = 17
**21.** 100 − 25 = 75
**22.** $18 − $10 = $8

# CHAPTER 15 Study Guide and Review

## 15-3 Problem-Solving Strategy: Work Backward (pp. 626–627)

**Example 4**

**Felipe's basketball team is having a car wash. It takes 10 minutes to wash a car. Felipe's team finished washing 12 cars at 5 P.M. What time did the car wash start?**

**Understand**

**What facts do you know?**

- It takes 10 minutes to wash a car.
- Felipe's team finished washing 12 cars at 5 P.M.

**What do you need to find?**

- The time the car wash started.

**Plan** Work backward.

**Solve** Start with the end result. Then work backward.

| 12 | × | 10 | = | 120 |
|---|---|---|---|---|
| cars | | minutes to wash 1 car | | minutes to wash 10 cars |

5 P.M. − 120 minutes = 3 P.M.

120 min = 2 hr

The car wash started at 3 P.M.

**Check** It took 120 minutes or 2 hours to wash the cars. Two hours before 5 P.M. is 3 P.M. So, the answer is correct.

**23.** A number is added to 3. The sum is multiplied by 5. The result is 45. What is the number? **6**

**24.** **Measurement** Howard is doing his chores. He swept the floor for 20 minutes. He dusted for 10 minutes less than he swept. He cleaned his room for 45 minutes longer than he dusted. How long did it take Howard to clean his room? **55 min**

**25.** Gabriela took 18 pictures of animals. She took 2 pictures of gorillas. She took twice as many pictures of penguins. She took 6 pictures of giraffes. The rest of the pictures are of sea lions. How many pictures did Gabriela take of sea lions? **6 pictures**

**26.** Harrison, Colin, and Ruthie's favorite colors are red, blue, and green. Colin likes blue the best. Ruthie does not like green. What is Harrison's favorite color? **green**

**27.** A number is divided by 7. Nine is added to the quotient. Then 5 is subtracted from the sum. The result is 9. What is the number? **35**



646 Chapter 15 Add and Subtract Decimals

## 15-4 Add Decimals (pp. 630–632)

**Example 5**
**Find 2.7 + 12.38.**

**Step 1** Line up the decimal points.

$$\begin{array}{r} 2.70 \\ +\ 12.38 \\ \hline \end{array}$$

Place a zero in the hundredths place.

**Step 2** Add.

$$\begin{array}{r} {}^{1}\phantom{.00} \\ 2.70 \\ +\ 12.38 \\ \hline 15.08 \end{array}$$

Add the digits in each place value.

Regroup if necessary.

So, 2.7 + 12.38 = 15.08.

**Add. Use estimation to check for reasonableness.**

**28.** $\begin{array}{r} 3.6 \\ +\ 0.8 \\ \hline \end{array}$ 4.4; 4 + 1 = 5

**29.** $\begin{array}{r} 6.82 \\ +\ 4.7 \\ \hline \end{array}$ 11.52; 7 + 5 = 12

**30.** 5.03 + 18.9

**31.** 34.82 + 8.31

30, 31. See margin.

**32. Measurement** Lance Armstrong's fastest average speed during a Tour de France bicycle race was 25.45 miles per hour. At this rate, how far would Lance travel in two hours? 50.9 miles

## 15-5 Problem-Solving Investigation: Choose a Strategy (pp. 634–635)

**Example 6**
**There are 27 plants in a garden. There are twice as many tomato as cucumber plants and three more pepper than cucumber plants. There are 9 pepper plants. How many of each kind of plant is in the garden?**

Use logical reasoning to solve.

There are 9 pepper plants.

There are 3 more pepper than cucumber plants. So, the number of cucumber plants is 9 − 3 or 6.

There are twice as many tomato as cucumber plants. So, the number of tomato plants is 2 × 6 or 12.

**Check**
9 + 6 + 12 = 27
So, the answer is correct. ✓

**Use any strategy to solve.**

**33.** Monifa is putting up a tent for camping. The tent has four corners. Each corner needs three stakes. How many stakes does Monifa need? 12

**34.** Edwin is buying the books shown. How much will the books cost? $9.74

**35.** Use three of the following symbols +, −, ×, or ÷ to make the following math sentence true. Use each symbol only once. ×, +, ÷

3 ■ 4 ■ 6 ■ 1 = 18



### Additional Answers

**30.** 23.93; 5 + 19 = 24

**31.** 43.13; 35 + 8 = 43

# Chapter 15 Study Guide and Review

## Additional Answer

**44.** Gaboon Viper and Australian Taipan; 3.3 cm

## 15-6 Subtract Decimals (pp. 638–641)

**Example 7**

**A spider is one of the slowest moving animals. It travels at a speed of 1.2 miles per hour. A sloth is even slower. It travels at a speed of 0.07 miles per hour. How much faster is a spider than a sloth?**

To find out how much faster a spider is than a sloth, subtract 0.07 from 1.20.

**Step 1** Line up the decimal points.

$$\begin{array}{r} 1.20 \\ -\ 0.07 \\ \hline \end{array}$$

**Step 2** Subtract. Regroup if needed.

$$\begin{array}{r} \overset{1\,10}{1.\not{2}\not{0}} \\ -\ 0.07 \\ \hline 1.13 \end{array}$$

Subtract the digits in each place. Regroup.

The model shows 1.20 − 0.07 = 1.13.

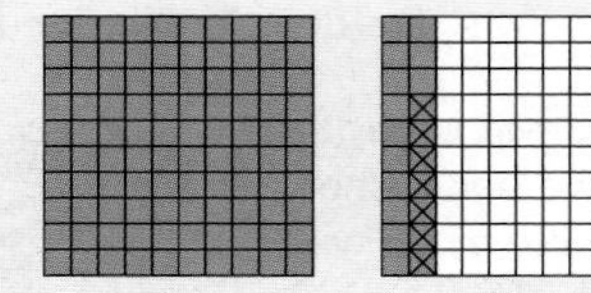

So, a spider is 1.13 miles per hour faster than a sloth.

### Check

You can use addition to check.

$$\begin{array}{r} 1.13 \\ +\ 0.07 \\ \hline 1.20 \end{array}$$

So, the answer is correct. ✓

**Subtract. Use estimation or addition to check.**

**36.** 2.6 − 0.7 **1.9**

**37.** 8.3 − 1.5 **6.8**

**38.** 6.9 − 3.81 **3.09**

**39.** 8.57 − 5.9 **2.67**

**40.** 26.08 − 16.4 **9.68**

**41.** 59.81 − 41.26 **18.55**

**42.** The longest space walk was 8.93 hours long. The second longest space walk was 8.48 hours long. How much longer was the longest space walk than the second longest space walk? **0.45 hrs**

**Measurement For Exercises 43 and 44, use the table. It shows the snakes that have the longest fangs.**

**Snakes' Fangs**

| Snake | Fang Length (cm) |
|---|---|
| Australian Taipan | 1.8 |
| Black Mamba | 2.5 |
| Bushmaster | 3.8 |
| Diamondback Rattlesnake | 2.5 |
| Gaboon Viper | 5.1 |

**Source:** *Scholastic Book of World Records*

**43.** What is the difference in length of the Gaboon Viper's and Black Mamba's fangs? **2.6 cm**

**44.** Which two snakes have the greatest difference in length of fangs? What is the difference? **See margin.**

# Chapter Test

Math Online macmillanmh.com
• Chapter Test

**Estimate. Round to the nearest whole number.**

1. 26.7 − 9.09 18
2. $31.56 + $5.01 $37
3. **Measurement** Boston, Massachusetts, receives an average of 3.6 inches of rain in April. It receives an average of 3.3 inches of rain in May. About how much rainfall does Boston receive during these two months? 7 in.
4. Eva has four coins. Two are the same and equal 50¢. One coin is a nickel. One coin is worth ten cents. What coins does Eva have?
2 quarters, 1 nickel, 1 dime

**Subtract. Use estimation or addition to check.**

5. 6.9 − 2.48
4.42; 7 − 2 = 5
6. 74.64 − 12.8
61.84; 75 − 13 = 62
7. Marie is 4.25 feet tall. Marie's brother is 3.5 feet tall. How much taller is Marie than her brother? 0.75 ft
8. **MULTIPLE CHOICE** What is 67.34 rounded to the nearest tenth? B

**A** 67 **C** 67.34
**B** 67.3 **D** 68

**Add. Use estimation to check for reasonableness.**

9. 4.97 + 8.4 13.37; 5 + 8 = 13
10. 6.26 + 29.4 35.66; 6 + 29 = 35

**Round to the nearest tenth.**

11. 3.05 3.1
12. 84.72 84.7
13. Hermán rode 16.72 kilometers on his bike. After he rested, he rode another 11.35 kilometers. How many kilometers did he ride altogether?
28.07 km
14. **MULTIPLE CHOICE** Raymond and his father are planning a camping trip. The advertisement for a campsite is shown below.

If Raymond and his father have $45 to spend on a campsite, how many nights will they be able to stay? G

**F** 2 **H** 4
**G** 3 **J** 5

**Algebra Find the missing number.**

15. $n + 1.2 = 3.6$ 2.4
16. $2.8 + n = 4.5$ 1.7
17. A number is subtracted from 15. The difference is multiplied by 4. Then the product is divided by 8. The result is 3. What is the number? 9
18. **WRITING IN MATH** Explain how to estimate 12.46 + 34.9 by rounding each number to the nearest whole number. See margin.



CHAPTER 15

# Chapter Test

## Summative Assessment

Use these alternate leveled chapter tests to differentiate assessment for the specific needs of your students.

| Leveled Chapter 15 Tests | | | |
|---|---|---|---|
| **Form** | **Type** | **Level** | **CRM Pages** |
| 1 | Multiple Choice | BL | 50–51 |
| 2A | Multiple Choice | OL | 52–53 |
| 2B | Multiple Choice | OL | 54–55 |
| 2C | Free Response | OL | 56–57 |
| 2D | Free Response | OL | 58–59 |
| 3 | Free Response | AL | 60–61 |

BL = below/approaching grade level
OL = on grade level
AL = above/beyond grade level

## Vocabulary Test

CRM **Chapter 15 Resource Masters** (p. 45)

ExamView Assessment Suite Customize and create multiple versions of your Chapter Test and the test answer keys.

**18.** Sample answer: 12.46 + 34.9 rounds to 12 + 35 = 47; Follow the rounding rules.

## Data-Driven Decision Making

Based on the results of the Chapter Test, use the following to review concepts that continue to present students with problems.

| Exercises | State/Local Standards | What's the Math? | Error Analysis | Resources for Review |
|---|---|---|---|---|
| 1–3, 8, 11–12 | | Round two place decimals to one decimal or the nearest whole number. | Cannot read and interpret problem to get answer.<br>Rounds to whole number, not tenth. | CRM Chapter 15 Resource Masters (Reteach)<br>Math Adventures<br>My Math Zone Chapter 15<br>Math Online Extra Examples • Concepts in Motion |
| 5–7 | | Subtract decimals. | Does not know to put a zero in a place value to subtract decimals. | |
| 9–10, 13, 18 | | Add decimals. | Does not line up decimals to add.<br>Does not carry tenths totals over to units position. | |

CHAPTER 15

# Test Practice

## Formative Assessment

- Use Student Edition pp. 650–651 as practice and cumulative review. The questions are written in the same style as many state tests.
- You can also use these two pages to benchmark student progress, or as an alternate homework assignment.

Additional practice pages can be found in the Chapter 15 Resource Masters.

CRM **Chapter 15 Resource Masters**
Cumulative Test Practice
- Multiple Choice format (pp. 50–55)
- Free Response format (pp. 56–61)

Create practice worksheets or tests that align to your state standards.

**Math Online** Have students visit macmillanmh.com for additional practice to reinforce your state standards.

## 15 Test Practice
Cumulative, Chapters 1–15

**Math Online** macmillanmh.com
- Test Practice

**PART I Multiple Choice**

**Read each question. Then fill in the correct answer on the answer sheet provided by your teacher or on a sheet of paper.**

**1.** Terrez drove 42.5 miles in one hour. He drove 51.3 miles in the next hour. How many miles did he drive? A

**A** 93.8 miles **C** 98.3 miles
**B** 93.9 miles **D** 938 miles

**2.** Carlita biked on Monday and on Wednesday. How many miles did she bike on the two days? H

| Distance Biked | |
|---|---|
| Day | Distance (mi) |
| Monday | 3.5 |
| Wednesday | 3.75 |

**F** 6.25 miles **H** 7.25 miles
**G** 6.75 miles **J** 7.75 miles

**3.** Pamela is 52.6 inches tall. Roberto is 54.2 inches tall. How much taller is Roberto than Pamela? C

**A** 2.6 inches **C** 1.6 inches
**B** 2.4 inches **D** 1.4 inches

**4.** Joy has $70. She buys these items.

If she rounds each amount to the nearest whole number, about how much change should she receive? F

**F** $10 **H** $18
**G** $15 **J** $20

**5.** What kind of triangle always has 3 acute angles and 3 sides the same length? D

**A** right **C** isoceles
**B** scalene **D** equilateral

**6.** During one week, Thurston ran 4.2 miles. The following week he ran 5.75 miles. About how much farther did Thurston run the following week? G

**F** 1 mile **H** 3 miles
**G** 2 miles **J** 10 miles

**7.** What is 35.18 rounded to the nearest tenth? B

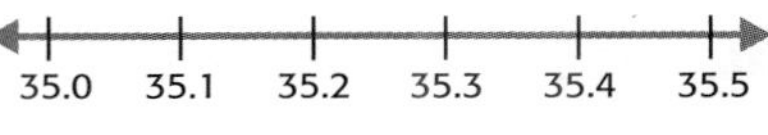


**A** 35.1 **C** 35.3
**B** 35.2 **D** 35.5



## Test-Taking Tip

Remind students to be sure that their answer choice answers the question being asked. They may wish to reread the question after choosing an answer to be sure it makes sense.

**Preparing for Standardized Tests**
For test-taking strategies and practice, see pages R42–R55.

**8.** Arturo bought a kite for \$19.95 and string for \$4.19. Which is the closest estimate of the total amount spent? H

**F** \$20 **H** \$24
**G** \$22 **J** \$25

**9.** Liseta earns \$34.75 each week walking dogs. About how much will she earn in 3 weeks? A

**A** \$105 **C** \$204
**B** \$180 **D** \$210

**10.** Which of the following is represented by the model? J

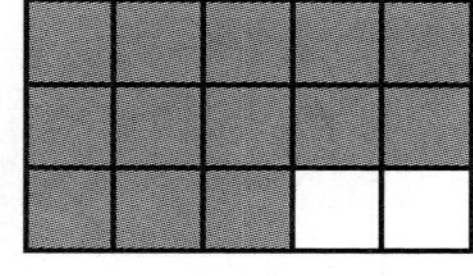

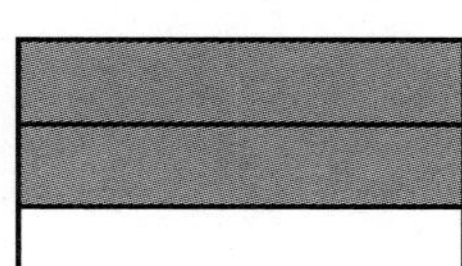

**F** $\frac{2}{13} > \frac{1}{3}$ **H** $\frac{1}{3} = \frac{2}{3}$
**G** $\frac{2}{3} > \frac{13}{15}$ **J** $\frac{13}{15} > \frac{2}{3}$

## PART 2 Short Response

**Record your answers on the answer sheet provided by your teacher or on a sheet of paper.**

**11.** One bag of apples weighs 7.23 pounds, and another bag weighs 6.45 pounds. How much do the two bags of apples weigh together? 13.68 lbs

**12.** Which point on the number line is greater than 6.5 and less than 7.0? L

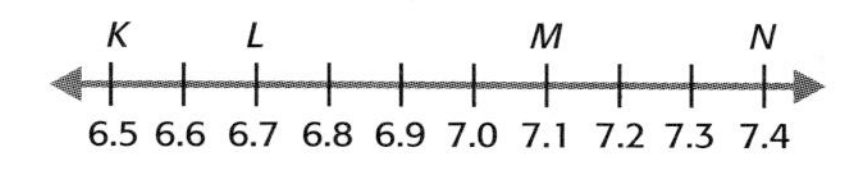


## PART 3 Extended Response

**Record your answers on the answer sheet provided by your teacher or on a sheet of paper.**

**13.** Mr. Perry sold the items shown below in a yard sale.

| Item | Original Price (\$) | Selling Price (\$) |
|---|---|---|
| CD | 16.99 | 1.50 |
| Stuffed animal | 12.50 | 0.75 |
| Table | 74.89 | 12 |
| Vase | 22.49 | 3.50 |

If Mr. Perry sold all four items, how much money would he make? Explain. See margin.

**NEED EXTRA HELP?**

| If You Missed Question... | 1 | 2 | 3 | 4 | 5 | 6 | 7 | 8 | 9 | 10 | 11 | 12 | 13 |
|---|---|---|---|---|---|---|---|---|---|---|---|---|---|
| Go to Lesson... | 15-4 | 15-4 | 15-6 | 15-2 | 9-5 | 15-2 | 15-1 | 15-2 | 15-2 | 13-5 | 15-4 | 14-5 | 15-4 |



# Answer Sheet Practice

Have students simulate taking a state test by recording their answers on a practice recording sheet.

CRM **Chapter 15 Resource Masters**
Student Recording Sheet (p. 70)

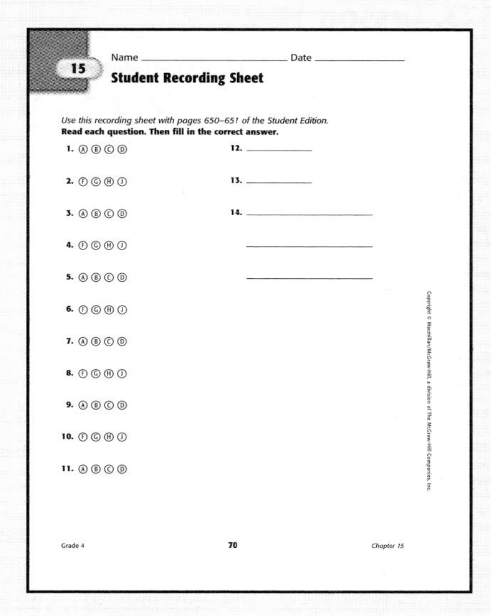
15
Name Date
**Student Recording Sheet**
*Use this recording sheet with pages 650–651 of the Student Edition.*
**Read each question. Then fill in the correct answer.**
1. 2. 3. 4. 5. 6. 7. 8. 9. 10. 11.
12. 13. 14.
Grade 4 70 Chapter 15

## Additional Answer

**13.** Sample answer: \$17.75;
\$1.50 + \$0.75 + \$12 + \$3.50 = \$17.75

## Page 616, Are You Ready

**9.**

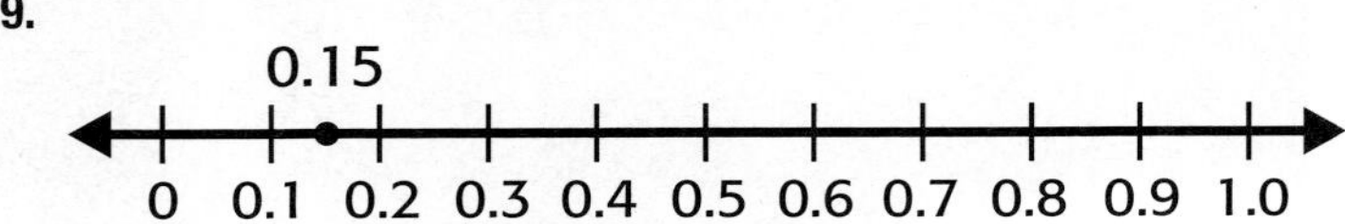


**10.**

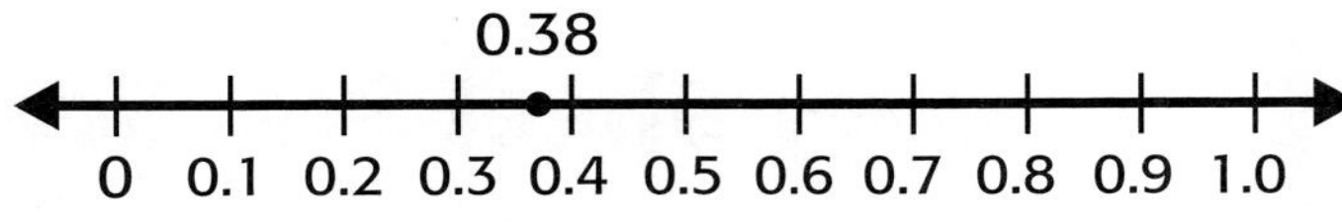


**11.**

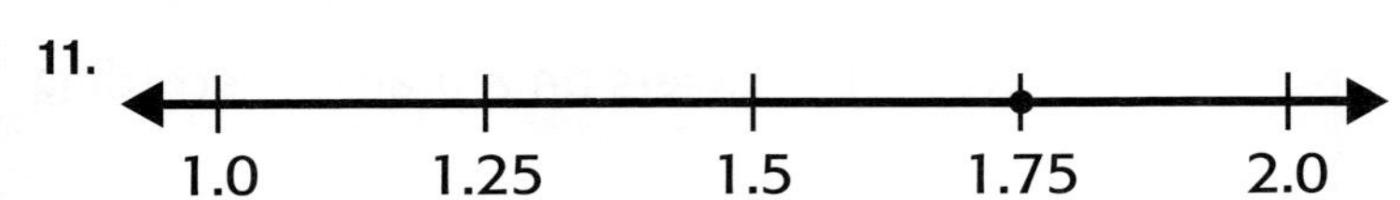


## Page 623, Lesson 15-2

**8.** Round each decimal to the nearest whole number. 2.1 rounds to 2 and 3.3 rounds to 3. Add the rounded values to find a reasonable answer.
$2 + 3 = 5$.

**41.** star, face, triangle, face; Then the pattern repeats.

## Page 627, Lesson 15-3

**1.** Sample answer: Working backward is the strategy used to solve the problem. So, subtract the last activity before practice from the time practice begins as a first step.

**4.** Sample answer: All of the activities that take place between school and practice take 15 minutes + 1 hour + 15 minutes or 1 hour 30 minutes. If practice starts at 5 P.M., one hour and 30 minutes earlier would be 3:30 P.M., which is the time Rey got home from school. The answer is correct.

**11.** Start with the end result and work backward one step at a time.
$116 \div 4 = 29$
$29 - 25 = 4$
$4 \times 3 = 12$

## Page 632, Lesson 15-4

**26.** Sample answer: Use the same process that is used with smaller numbers, just make sure the decimals are lined up and regroup where necessary.

## Page 633, Mid-Chapter Check

**14.** 22.3; $15 + 8 = 23$

**15.** 56.64; $37 + 20 = 57$

**17.** Sample answer: Add 0.8 to find the next number in the pattern; 2.4, 4.0, 4.8

**18.** Sample answer: Add 2.02 to find the next number in the pattern; 5.27, 7.29, 11.33

**19.** Sample answer: no; An estimated sum of 40 results from rounding the numbers to the nearest ten. A better estimate would result from rounding the numbers to a place value further to the right.

## Page 635, Lesson 15-5

**1.** Sample answer: Both routes are the same distance; one route heads a block west then a block south and the other route heads a block south then a block west.

**11.** Sample answer: How many passengers do both subway systems have each year?

## Page 641, Lesson 15-6

**33.** 1.37; $0.8 + 0.6 = 1.4$

**35.** 15.27; $8 + 7 = 15$

**38.** $23 + 5 = 28$

NOTES

# Looking Ahead

The lessons in **Looking Ahead** help students get ready for next year by introducing key standards from Grade 5. By presenting these important concepts and skills now, you can help students be better prepared for success in fifth grade.

These lessons are intended to be used at the end of the year after your state testing is completed. They can also be used to extend concepts and skills presented in Grade 4.

## End-of-Year Assessment

Use the **End-of-Year Test** to assess student comprehension of the skills and concepts presented in Grade 4.

CRM **Chapter 15 Resource Masters**
End-of-Year Test (pp. 66–69)

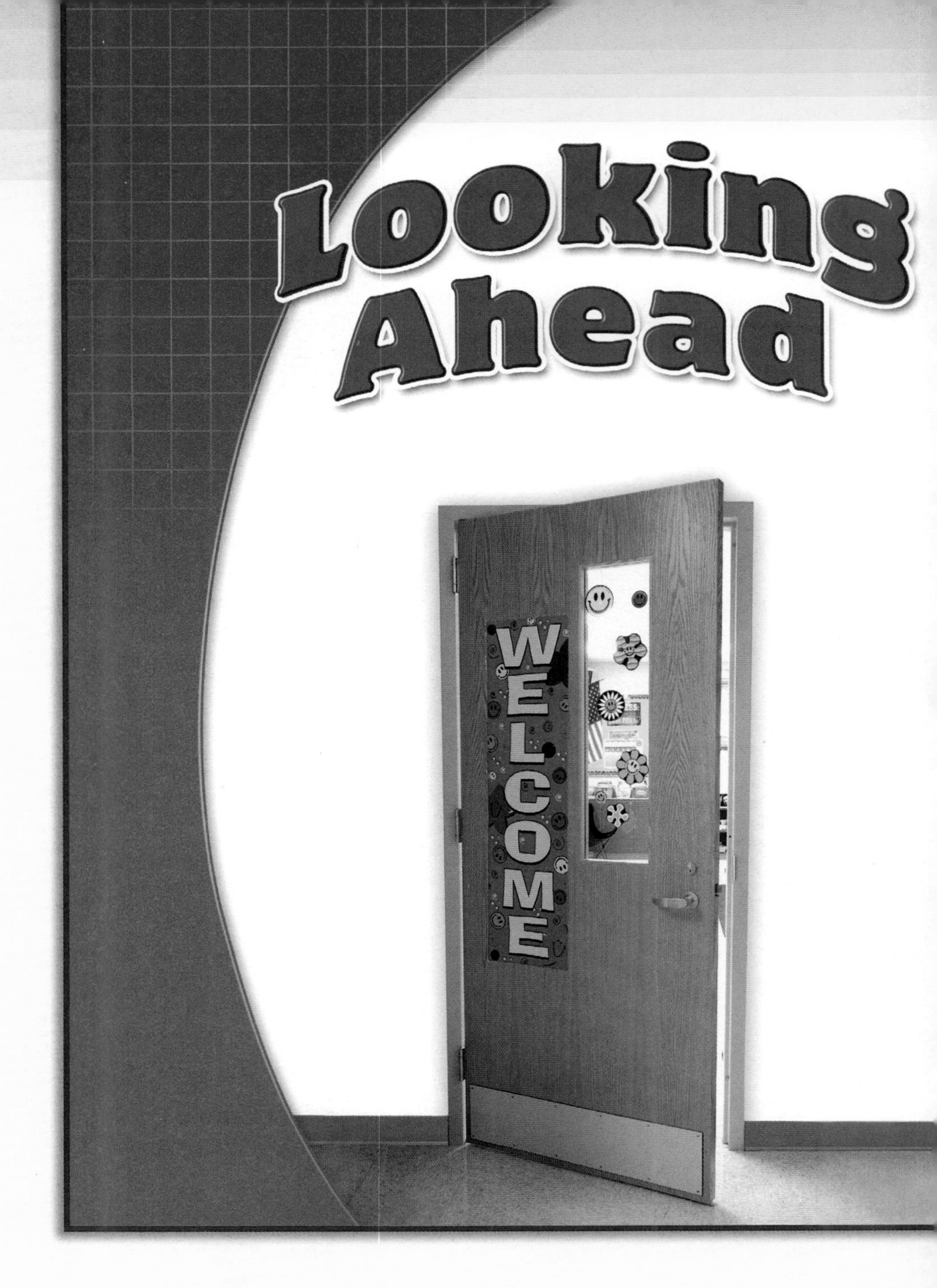

# Let's Look Ahead!

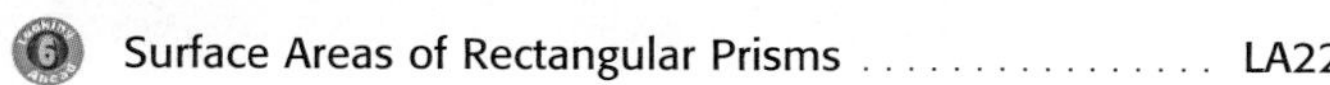

Looking Ahead

# Estimate Quotients Involving Two-Digit Divisors

Looking Ahead 1

## Lesson Planner

### Objective

Estimate quotients using rounding and compatible numbers.

### Review Vocabulary

**compatible numbers**

### Resources

**Teacher Technology**

TeacherWorks • Interactive Classroom

## Daily Routine

Use these suggestions before beginning the lesson on p. LA2.

### 5-Minute Check

(Reviews Lesson 15-6)

**Subtract. Use estimation or addition to check.**

**1.** $2.8 - 1.5 = 1.3$

**2.** $6.32 - 1.52 = 4.80$

**3.** $\$15.23 - \$12.35 = \$2.88$

**4.** $32.55 - 21.36 = 11.19$

### Problem of the Day

The daily newspaper costs $0.75 every day and the Sunday paper costs $2.50. A subscription costs $5.50 per week. How much money does having a subscription save in a 20-week period? $30

### Focus on Math Background

In Lesson 8-4 students learned to estimate quotients with a one-digit divisor. They worked with compatible numbers and discovered other ways of estimating. Here students will be asked to follow similar processes to estimate quotients with two-digit divisors. Remind students that estimation is used more often than finding exact quotients in real-life situations.

### Building Math Vocabulary

Write the lesson vocabulary word and its definition on the board.

Ask a volunteer to look up *compatible* in the dictionary and state its meaning. Have the class discuss how this definition relates to the term *compatible numbers* in math. Then have students write a sentence using *compatible numbers*.

# Differentiated Instruction

## Small Group Options

LOGICAL

### Option 1 Below Level BL

**Materials:** paper and pencil

- Hand students this problem on paper:

  *Jim's class is raising money for a class pet. There are 18 students present. A local store donates 95 snacks to eat while working. How many snacks will each student receive?* 5

- Ask students to create another question where estimation will work to find the answer.

LINGUISTIC, LOGICAL

### Option 2 English Language Learners ELL

**Materials:** pictures to represent nouns and verbs, mirror and flashlight

**Core Vocabulary:** nouns, verbs, divisor

**Common Use Verb:** divide

**See Math** This strategy helps students understand noun/verb patterns in language and division and apply it to dividing.

- Write column headers: *Verbs* (on the left) and *Nouns* (on the right). Say: "**Verbs** are action. **Nouns** are the people or things that do the action."

  Verbs Nouns
  acts actor

- Underneath, write: "act" and "actor." Draw an arrow from actor to act, and add an "s" to act while you show a picture of a recognizable actor, then pantomime acting as you move the picture to the verb.
- Repeat for: sail/sailor (sailor to a sail boat), inspect/inspector (detective using a magnifying glass), conduct/conductor (a wire to a glowing light bulb), protect/protector (a fireman's suit to a fireman coming out of a burning building), reflect/reflector (a mirror, then shining a flashlight on it).
- Repeat the process for divide/divisor. As the example, write:

  **45 ÷ 5 = 9**

- Write the scaffold "An actor acts" and review the list, to "A divisor divides." Allow students to chorally repeat the scaffolds.
- Repeat with other division problems as time permits. If students do not understand divisor, model it using manipulatives and paper arrows to divide the dividend into groups.

## Independent Work Options

LOGICAL

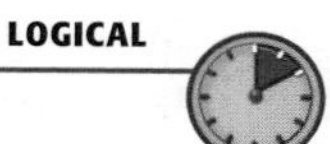

### Option 1 Early Finishers OL

**Materials:** paper and pencil

- Have each partner write any five basic division facts on a piece of paper.
- Have partners exchange papers and write division problems where the basic facts can be used to estimate the quotients. For example, a student could write $501 \div 70$ for the basic fact $49 \div 7 = 7$.
- Ask partners to exchange papers again and estimate the quotients for the new problems.

### Option 2 Student Technology

**Math Online** macmillanmh.com

Personal Tutor • Extra Examples

# Estimate Quotients Involving Two-Digit Divisors

## 1 Introduce

### Activity Choice 1 • Hands-On

- Review basic division facts.
- Have students write a basic division fact sentence on the board one at a time, with no facts repeated.
- Write one problem based on each fact that contains multiples of 10, 100, or 1,000. For example, for $42 \div 7 = 6$, you may write $420 \div 70 = \blacksquare$, $42{,}000 \div 7 = \blacksquare$, $4{,}200 \div 70 = \blacksquare$, etc.
- Ask students to solve the new problem that matches their basic fact.
- Tell students that they will use their knowledge of basic division facts to help them estimate quotients.

## 2 Teach

### Scaffolding Questions

- **How does knowing the fact $42 \div 7 = 6$ help you find the quotient for $42{,}000 \div 7$?** I can write the 6 in the quotient and then write three zeros after it.
- **What basic fact is close to $33 \div 9$?** $36 \div 9 = 4$
- **How could you use $36 \div 9$ to help you estimate $33 \div 9$?** Since 36 is close to 33, replace 33 with 36 in the problem and divide to estimate. $36 \div 9 = 4$, so $33 \div 9$ is about 4.
- **How do you think basic facts and patterns could help you estimate $3{,}300 \div 900$?** Replace 3,300 with 3,600 and then divide $3{,}600 \div 900$ to estimate.

### GET READY to Learn

Have students open their books and read the information in **Get Ready to Learn**. Review **compatible numbers**. As a class, work through **Examples 1–3**.



# Estimate Quotients Involving Two-Digit Divisors

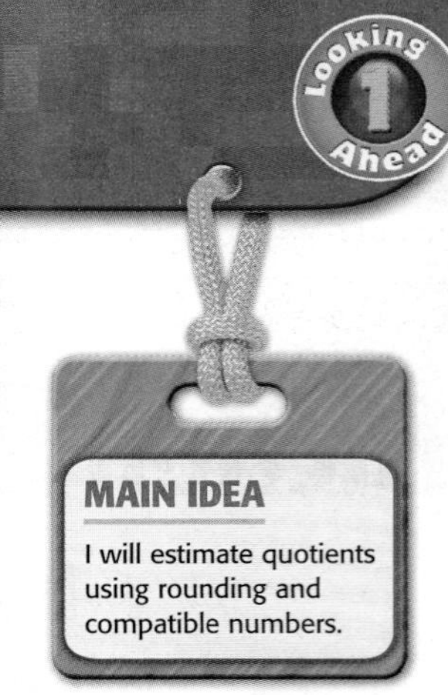

**MAIN IDEA**

I will estimate quotients using rounding and compatible numbers.

### GET READY to Learn

Two hundred forty-two people are going white water rafting on a river in one day. If each raft holds eight people, about how many groups of people are going white water rafting?

In Lesson 8-4, you learned how to estimate quotients when there is a one-digit divisor. You can use the same strategies to estimate quotients involving two-digit divisors.

**Real-World EXAMPLE** Estimate Quotients

**1** **SPORTS** **Estimate the quotient of 242 and 8 to find about how many groups of people are going white water rafting.**

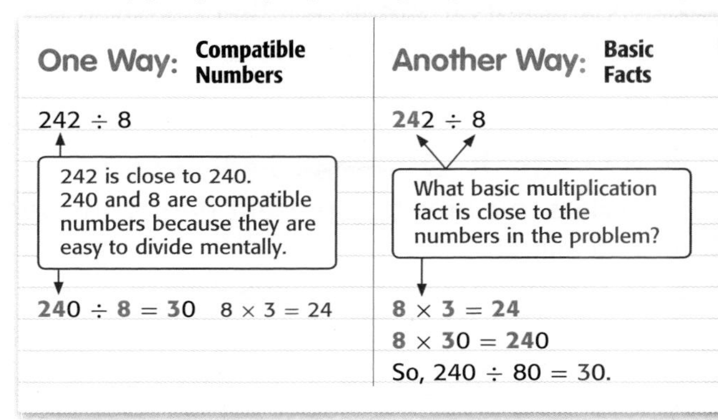

| One Way: Compatible Numbers | Another Way: Basic Facts |
|---|---|
| $242 \div 8$ | $242 \div 8$ |
| 242 is close to 240. 240 and 8 are compatible numbers because they are easy to divide mentally. | What basic multiplication fact is close to the numbers in the problem? |
| $240 \div 8 = 30$ $8 \times 3 = 24$ | $8 \times 3 = 24$ |
| | $8 \times 30 = 240$ |
| | So, $240 \div 80 = 30$. |

So, about 30 groups of people are going white water rafting.

**Check**

You know that $240 \div 8 = 30$ because $8 \times 30 = 240$. ✓

**Real-World EXAMPLE** Estimate Quotients

2 **GAMES** **Brenda is playing an arcade game. She wants a prize that is worth 825 points. She has enough money to play two games, which allows her to roll 18 balls. About how many points must each ball earn for Brenda to win the prize?**

You need to estimate 825 ÷ 18.

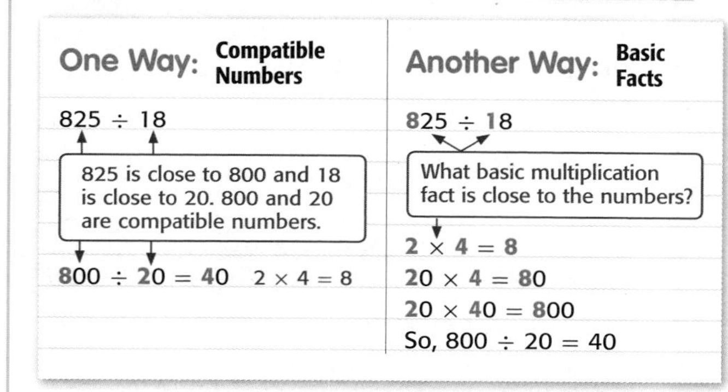

| One Way: **Compatible Numbers** | Another Way: **Basic Facts** |
|---|---|
| 825 ÷ 18 | 825 ÷ 18 |
| 825 is close to 800 and 18 is close to 20. 800 and 20 are compatible numbers. | What basic multiplication fact is close to the numbers? |
| 800 ÷ 20 = 40   2 × 4 = 8 | 2 × 4 = 8 |
| | 20 × 4 = 80 |
| | 20 × 40 = 800 |
| | So, 800 ÷ 20 = 40 |

So, each ball must earn about 40 points.

**Check** You know that 800 ÷ 20 = 40 because 20 × 40 = 800. ✓

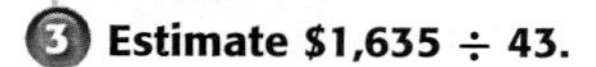

**EXAMPLE** Estimate Quotients

3 **Estimate $1,635 ÷ 43.**

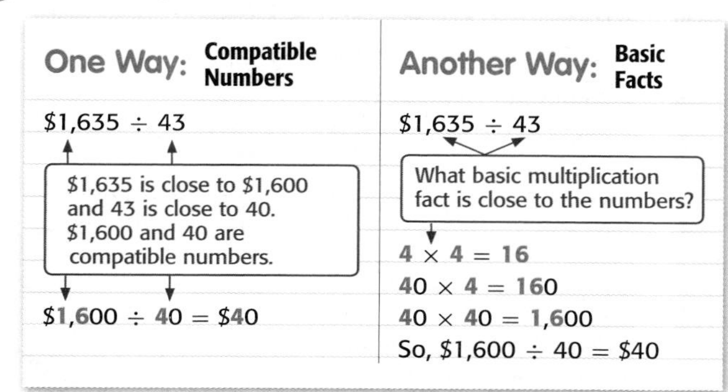

| One Way: **Compatible Numbers** | Another Way: **Basic Facts** |
|---|---|
| $1,635 ÷ 43 | $1,635 ÷ 43 |
| $1,635 is close to $1,600 and 43 is close to 40. $1,600 and 40 are compatible numbers. | What basic multiplication fact is close to the numbers? |
| $1,600 ÷ 40 = $40 | 4 × 4 = 16 |
| | 40 × 4 = 160 |
| | 40 × 40 = 1,600 |
| | So, $1,600 ÷ 40 = $40 |

**Check** How do you know the answer is correct?

**Remember**

Use the fact that multiplication and division are inverse operations to check your work.



## Estimate Quotients

**Example 3** Point out that the first way of estimating changes the divisor to create a basic division fact while the second way changes the dividend.

### ADDITIONAL EXAMPLES

1. Estimate 147 ÷ 2. about 70
2. Estimate 4,800 ÷ 80. about 60
3. Estimate 339 ÷ 52. about 7
4. Five students share 23 small pieces of pizza equally. About how many pieces does each student get? Sample answers: about 4 or about 5

### CHECK What You Know

As a class, have students complete Exercises 1–8 in **Check What You Know** as you observe their work.

**Exercise 8** Assess student comprehension before assigning practice exercises.

## BL Alternate Teaching Strategy

**If** students have trouble choosing compatible numbers to estimate…

**Then** use this reteach option:

1. Have students write 34,421 ÷ 72 on a piece of paper. Tell them to underline the first two digits in the dividend, 34, and the first digit in the divisor, 7.
   - Then have students write the first ten multiples of the underlined digit of the divisor: 1 × 7 = 7 through 10 × 7 = 70.
   - Ask students to examine the multiples and choose the one that is closest to 34 (35). Guide students to use the basic fact 35 ÷ 7 = 5 to help them estimate the quotient.

# 3 Practice

Differentiate practice using these leveled assignments for Exercises 9–34.

| Level | Assignment |
|---|---|
| BL Below/Approaching Level | 9–19, 27, 28 |
| OL On Level | 9–24, 27–29, 31 |
| AL Above/Beyond Level | 9–31 odd, 32–34 |

Have students discuss and complete the Higher Order Thinking problems. For Exercise 32, suggest that students use rounding and compatible numbers and mentally cross out zeros to make their predictions.

**WRITING IN MATH** Have students complete Exercise 34 in their Math Journals. You may choose to use this as an optional formative assessment.

### Additional Answer

8. Sample answer: Think of compatible numbers when estimating $447 \div 51$. So, $447 \div 51 \rightarrow 500 \div 50 = 10$.

**COMMON ERROR!**

Students may make place-value errors and write an incorrect number of zeros in the quotient. Have students multiply the quotient by the divisor to check their work for each exercise.

## CHECK What You Know

**Estimate. Check your estimate.** See Examples 1–3 (pp. LA2–LA3)

1. $158 \div 2$
   $160 \div 2 = 80$
2. $197 \div 4$
   $200 \div 4 = 50$
3. $\$273 \div 32$
   $\$270 \div 30 = \$9$
4. $315 \div 47$
   $300 \div 50 = 6$
5. $\$4,219 \div 63$
   $\$4,200 \div 60 = \$70$
6. $8,066 \div 87$
   $8,100 \div 90 = 90$
7. There are 158 girl scouts at a week-long nature camp. Twelve campers can stay in each cabin. About how many cabins are needed? $160 \div 10 = 16$
8. 

   Explain how to estimate $447 \div 51$. See margin.

## Practice and Problem Solving

**Estimate. Check your estimate.** See Examples 1–3 (pp. LA2–LA3)

9. $118 \div 3$
   $120 \div 3 = 40$
10. $\$144 \div 2$
    $\$140 \div 2 = \$70$
11. $356 \div 4$
    $360 \div 4 = 90$
12. $\$561 \div 8$
    $\$560 \div 8 = \$70$
13. $275 \div 38$
    $280 \div 40 = 7$
14. $351 \div 52$
    $350 \div 50 = 7$
15. $537 \div 56$
    $540 \div 60 = 9$
16. $\$642 \div 83$
    $\$640 \div 80 = \$8$
17. $1,492 \div 51$
    $1,500 \div 50 = 30$
18. $5,378 \div 56$
    $5,400 \div 60 = 90$
19. $4,930 \div 68$
    $4,900 \div 70 = 70$
20. $\$7,150 \div 93$
    $\$7,200 \div 90 = \$80$

**Algebra Find the value of *x*.**

21. $180 \div x = 90$
    2
22. $210 \div x = 70$
    3
23. $240 \div x = 6$
    40
24. $400 \div x = 5$
    80
25. $6,300 \div x = 70$
    90
26. $6,400 \div x = 80$
    80
27. Dexter is saving money to buy the bicycle and helmet at the right. If he saves the same amount of money each month for one year, about how much money should he save each month?
    $20

28. **Measurement** There are eight songs on a CD. The songs last a total of 2,372 seconds. If each song is the same length, about how long is each song? $2{,}400 \div 8 = 300$

29. **Measurement** Latoya rented three movies during the weekend. The movies lasted a total of 362 minutes. If each movie was the same length, about how long was each movie? $360 \div 3 = 120$

**For Exercises 30 and 31, use the table at the right. It shows the pets in a pet store.**

| Pet Store Animals | |
|---|---|
| **Type of Animal** | **Number in Store** |
| Bird | 117 |
| Fish | 453 |
| Hamster | 58 |
| Lizard | 32 |
| Snake | 16 |
| Turtle | 124 |

30. The birds in the pet store are divided equally into 6 cages. About how many birds are in each cage? $120 \div 6 = 20$

31. The fish in the pet store are divided equally into 9 tanks. About how many fish are in each tank? $450 \div 9 = 60$

35. Sample answer: Carrie's cell phone plan allows her to talk 175 minutes each month. About how many minutes does she get each week during a 4-week month?

## H.O.T. Problems

32. **OPEN ENDED** Connor's family is traveling by car to their vacation destination. They drive 298 miles in 5 hours. The answer is 60 miles per hour. What is the question? Sample answer: About how many miles did Connor drive each hour?

33. **CHALLENGE** Estimate 36,473 ÷ 900. 40

34. **FIND THE ERROR** Ella and Anthony are estimating 1,825 ÷ 25. Who is correct? Explain. Sample answer: Ella; Anthony rounded the divisor to 20 when he should have rounded it to 30.

Ella
$1{,}800 \div 30 = 60$

Anthony
$1{,}800 \div 20 = 90$

35. **WRITING IN MATH** Write a real-world problem in which you would estimate to find the answer to a division problem and the quotient is equal to 50.

# 4 Assess

### Formative Assessment

- **What are two different ways you could estimate 375 ÷ 5? Explain.** Sample answer: One way: Round the dividend to 400 and divide 400 ÷ 5 = 80. Another way: Change the dividend to 350 and use compatible numbers 350 ÷ 5 = 70.

**Quick Check** **Are students continuing to struggle with estimating quotients using rounding and compatible numbers?**

**If Yes** → Small Group Options (p. LA2B)

**If No** → Independent Work Options (p. LA2B)

**Name the Math** Write 560 ÷ 48 on the board. Have students describe each step they will use to estimate the quotient.

Looking Ahead 2

# Divide by Two-Digit Numbers

## Lesson Planner

### Objective

Divide up to a three-digit number by a two-digit number.

### Review Vocabulary

**dividend, divisor, quotient**

### Resources

**Manipulatives:** base-ten blocks
**Teacher Technology**
TeacherWorks • Interactive Classroom

## Daily Routine

Use these suggestions before beginning the lesson on p. LA6.

### 5-Minute Check

(Reviews Looking Ahead 1)

**Estimate. Check your estimate.**

**1.** $2\overline{)58}$ $60 \div 2 = 30$ **2.** $5\overline{)525}$ $500 \div 5 = 100$

**3.** $9\overline{)639}$ $630 \div 9 = 70$ **4.** $3\overline{)194}$ $180 \div 3 = 60$

### Problem of the Day

There are 156 students at the public library. Thirty students can take part in a special activity at a time. About how many times will the activity be done? about 5 times.

### Focus on Math Background

As in Chapter 8, students use the standard division algorithm to find a quotient. Estimation of the quotient *before* dividing is particularly important when dividing by two-digit numbers, as errors are often made in the placement of the first digit in the quotient. Continue to stress the importance of basic facts and place value.

Dividing a three-digit number by a two-digit number is essentially an extension of dividing a three-digit number by a one-digit number. However, this does not guarantee that students will not experience problems. When dividing three-digit numbers by two-digit numbers, as when dividing any size numbers, one thing does remain constant—you can always check the quotient by calculating the product of the quotient and the divisor and then adding the remainder.

### Review Math Vocabulary

Write the review vocabulary words and their definitions on the board.

Write several division sentences in various forms on the board. For example:

$12 \div 6 = 2$ $\quad 8\overline{)48}$ (6) $\quad 88 \div 7 = 12R4$ $\quad 4\overline{)205}$ (51 R1)

Have students identify the *dividend, divisor,* and *quotient* for each example.

# Differentiated Instruction

## Small Group Options

LOGICAL

### Option 1 Below Level BL

**Materials:** paper and pencil

- Student write 4 problems on their paper.
- Trade papers with their partner.
- Solve.
- Check by using estimation.

VISUAL/SPATIAL, SOCIAL

### Option 2 English Language Learners ELL

**Materials:** number cubes, manila paper
**Core Vocabulary:** fact family, similar, are related
**Common Use Verb:** can see
**Write Math** This strategy helps students integrate knowledge by writing.

- Write 9 × 4 = 36. Say: "Here are 3 number sentences that make the *fact family* for 4, 9, 36." Write 4 × 9 = 36; 36 ÷ 4 = 9; 36 ÷ 9 = 4.
- Ask: "***Can*** you ***see*** how these numbers ***are related?***"
- Write 90 × 4 = 360. Ask: "How is this number sentence the same as the one before? How is it different? What other sentences make the *fact family* of these numbers?"
- Students work with partners to write sentences.
- Repeat with 90 × 40 = 3,600.

## Independent Work Options

LINGUISTIC/AUDITORY

### Option 1 Early Finishers OL

**Materials:** paper and pencil

- Ask students to write a word problem that involves division of a three-digit number by a two-digit number.
- Have students read their problems aloud for their classmates to solve.

### Option 2 Student Technology

**Math Online** macmillanmh.com

Personal Tutor • Extra Examples

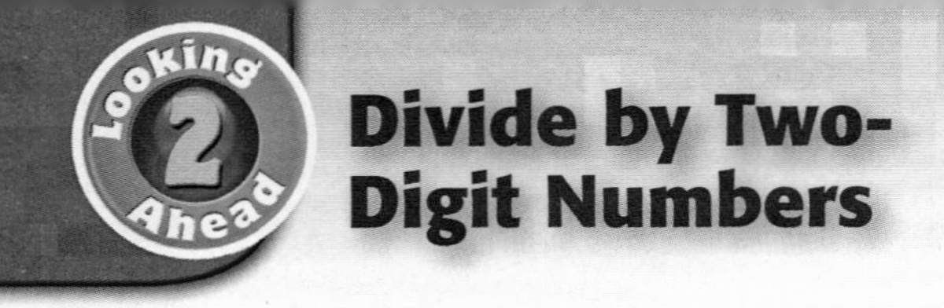

# Divide by Two-Digit Numbers

## 1 Introduce

**Activity Choice 1 • Hands-On** 

- Review estimating quotients with students.
- Write five three-digit by two-digit division problems on the board.
- Have students estimate each quotient. Ask volunteers to explain how they estimated.
- **What do you notice about the number of digits in your estimated quotients?** The quotients all have either one or two digits.
- **Will you ever have a three-digit quotient when you divide a three-digit number by a two-digit number?** no

## 2 Teach

### Scaffolding Questions

Guide groups to model 143 ÷ 11 with base-ten blocks as you model the division for the class.

- **How many equal groups will you divide 143 into?** 11
- **Can you divide 1 hundred by 11?** No; regroup 1 hundred as 10 tens for a total of 14 tens.
- **How can you divide 14 tens into 11 groups?** Place 1 ten in each group with 3 tens left.
- **What will you do next?** Regroup 3 tens as 30 ones and divide the 33 ones into 11 groups.
- **What is 143 ÷ 11?** 13

**GET READY to Learn**

Have students open their books and read the information in **Get Ready to Learn**. Review **dividend**, **divisor**, and **quotient**. As a class, work through **Examples 1 and 2**.

# Divide by Two-Digit Numbers

**MAIN IDEA**

I will divide up to a three-digit number by a two-digit number.

**GET READY to Learn**

A certain squid can measure up to 720 inches in length. What is the length of this squid in feet?

In Lesson 8-7, you learned how to divide multi-digit dividends by one-digit divisors. You can follow the same steps when dividing multi-digit dividends by two-digit divisors.

**Real-World EXAMPLE** Divide by a Two-Digit Divisor

**1 ANIMALS What is the length of a 720-inch squid in feet?**

There are 12 inches in one foot. Divide 720 by 12 to find the length of the squid in feet.

**Step 1** Divide the tens.

```
    6      Divide. 72 ÷ 12 = 6
12)720     Put 6 in the quotient over the tens place.
  -72      Multiply. 12 × 6 = 72
    0      Subtract. 72 − 72 = 0
           Compare. 0 < 12
```

**Step 2** Divide the ones.

```
   60      Bring down the ones.
12)720     Divide. 0 ÷ 12 = 0
  -72↓     Put 0 in the quotient above the ones place.
    00     Multiply. 12 × 0 = 0
   - 0     Subtract. 0 − 0 = 0
     0     Compare. 0 < 12
```

So, the length of the squid is 60 feet.

**Real-World EXAMPLE** Division with a Remainder

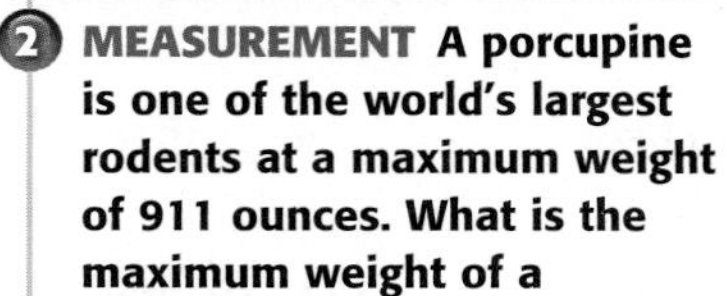

**2 MEASUREMENT A porcupine is one of the world's largest rodents at a maximum weight of 911 ounces. What is the maximum weight of a porcupine in pounds?**

There are 16 ounces in one pound. So, divide 911 by 16 to find the maximum weight in pounds.

**Step 1** Divide the tens.

| | |
|---|---|
| 5 | Divide. 91 ÷ 16 = 5 |
| 16)911 | Put 5 in the quotient over the tens place. |
| −80 | Multiply. 16 × 5 = 80 |
| 11 | Subtract. 91 − 80 = 11 |
| | Compare. 11 < 16 |

**Step 2** Divide the ones.

| | |
|---|---|
| 56 R15 | Bring down the ones. |
| 16)911 | Divide. 111 ÷ 16 = 6 |
| −80↓ | Put 6 in the quotient above the ones place. |
| 111 | Multiply. 16 × 6 = 96 |
| −96 | Subtract. 111 − 96 = 15 |
| 15 | Compare. 15 < 16 |
| | The remainder is 15. |

So, 911 ÷ 16 = 56 R15. Therefore, the maximum weight of a porcupine is a little more than 56 pounds.

**Remember**

When a real-world problem has a remainder, you have to interpret the remainder.

## CHECK What You Know

**Find each quotient.** See Examples 1 and 2 (pp. LA6–LA7)

**1.** 14)168
12

**2.** 17)391
23

**3.** 589 ÷ 21
28 R1

**4.** 717 ÷ 33
21 R24

**5.** A mountain located on the island of Kauai in Hawaii, receives 460 inches of rain each year. How many feet of rain does this mountain receive each year?
38 R4 feet

**6.** Talk About It Explain how you can decide where to place the first digit in the quotient. See margin.

Divide by Two-Digit Numbers **LA7**

### Additional Answer

**6.** Sample answer: Place the first digit in the quotient above the first place value in the dividend the divisor will divide into.

### Divide by a Two-Digit Divisor

**Example 1** Explain that, when dividing a three-digit number by a two-digit number, you always begin by trying to divide the tens. If necessary, have students attempt to divide hundreds first.

### ADDITIONAL EXAMPLES

**1** How many cartons are needed to hold 384 eggs if each carton holds 12 eggs? 32

**2** Find 764 ÷ 40. 19 R4

**3** Chris volunteered at the school 288 hours last year. If he volunteered the same number of hours each month, how many hours did he work each month? 24 hours

### CHECK What You Know

As a class, have students complete Exercises 1–6 in **Check What You Know** as you observe their work.

**Exercise 6** Assess student comprehension before assigning practice exercises.

## BL Alternate Teaching Strategy

**If** students have trouble using the division algorithm to divide by two-digit numbers…

**Then** use one of these reteach options:

**1** Model the method of dividing by using 10 groups and 1 group of the divisor, subtracted repeatedly from the dividend to find 165 ÷ 13. Record subtracting 130 from the dividend and label the group. Continue the process.

| | |
|---|---|
| 13)165 | |
| − 130 | ↓ 10 group |
| 35 | |
| − 13 | ↓ 1 group |
| 22 | |
| − 13 | ↓ 1 group |
| 9 | 12 R9 |

### COMMON ERROR!

Students may have difficulty placing digits correctly when dividing. Encourage students to turn lined paper horizontally and use the lines as a guide for where to place digits.

# 3 Practice

Differentiate practice using these leveled assignments for Exercises 7–21.

| Level | Assignment |
| --- | --- |
| BL Below/Approaching Level | 7–10, 15–18, 24–33 odd |
| OL On Level | 7–22 even, 23–33, 34–37 odd |
| AL Above/Beyond Level | 7–22, 23–33 even, 38–41 |

Have students discuss and complete the Higher Order Thinking problems. For Exercise 39, encourage students to use multiplication to help check.

**WRITING IN MATH** Have students complete Exercise 41 in their Math Journals. You may choose to use this exercise as an optional formative assessment.

## Practice and Problem Solving

**Find each quotient.** See Examples 1 and 2 (pp. LA6–LA7)

**7.** $13\overline{)234}$ 18

**8.** $14\overline{)434}$ 31

**9.** $15\overline{)510}$ 34

**10.** $16\overline{)688}$ 43

**11.** $18\overline{)324}$ 18

**12.** $17\overline{)476}$ 28

**13.** $19\overline{)589}$ 31

**14.** $22\overline{)572}$ 26

**15.** $706 \div 24$ 29 R10

**16.** $715 \div 26$ 27 R13

**17.** $764 \div 27$ 28 R8

**18.** $823 \div 29$ 28 R11

**19.** $851 \div 31$ 27 R14

**20.** $892 \div 35$ 25 R17

**21.** $913 \div 36$ 25 R13

**22.** $995 \div 38$ 26 R7

**23.** Parker's vacation was 336 hours long. How long was his vacation in days? 14 days

**24.** Mrs. Jones bought a pumpkin that weighed 112 ounces. How many pounds does the pumpkin weigh? 7 pounds

**Algebra** **Find $578 \div n$ for each value of $n$.**

**25.** $n = 17$ 34

**26.** $n = 19$ 30 R8

**27.** $n = 26$ 22 R6

**28.** $n = 39$ 14 R32

**Compare. Use >, <, or =.**

**29.** $18\overline{)319}$ ● $25\overline{)498}$ <

**30.** $31\overline{)634}$ ● $28\overline{)537}$ >

**31.** $742 \div 35$ ● $829 \div 38$ <

**32.** $981 \div 46$ ● $883 \div 42$ >

**The table shows the height of three of the tallest sports equipment monuments in the United States. Use the table to solve Exercises 33–35.**

**33.** What is the height of the bowling pin in feet? 24 feet

**34.** What is the height of the soccer ball in feet? 12 feet

**35.** What is the difference in height of the bowling pin and the arrows in feet? 6 feet

**Sports Equipment Monuments**

| Monument | Height (inches) |
| --- | --- |
| Bowling pin | 288 |
| Arrows | 216 |
| Soccer Ball | 144 |

**36.** Audrey's cat is 416 weeks old. There are 52 weeks in one year. How many years old is the cat? 8

**37.** The time a person has spent balancing on one foot is about 77 hours. How many days did the person balance on one foot? 3 R5 days

**Real-World PROBLEM SOLVING**

*Science* The table shows the weights of various birds.

| Bird Weights | |
|---|---|
| **Bird** | **Weight (ounces)** |
| Bald Eagle | 240 |
| Flamingo | 144 |
| Owl | 144 |
| Pelican | 272 |
| Stork | 320 |

**38.** Identify the bird that weighs 17 pounds. (hint: 16 ounces = 1 pound) pelican

**39.** Identify the two birds that have a weight difference of 5 pounds. bald eagle and stork

**40.** What is the difference in weight between a flamingo and a bald eagle in pounds? 6 lb

**41.** Identify the bird that weighs 8 pounds more than an owl. pelican

45. Sample answer: The same steps are involved in both types of division problems.

## H.O.T. Problems

**42. NUMBER SENSE** The quotient of a division problem is 23 R17. If the divisor is 36, what is the dividend? Explain. Sample answer: 845; $36 \times 23 + 17 = 845$

**43. CHALLENGE** Find $52{,}347 \div 18$. 2,908 R3

**44. FIND THE ERROR** Shiloh and Mario are finding $29\overline{)536}$. Who is correct? Explain. Sample answer: Shiloh; Mario subtracted wrong when subtracting 53 − 29.

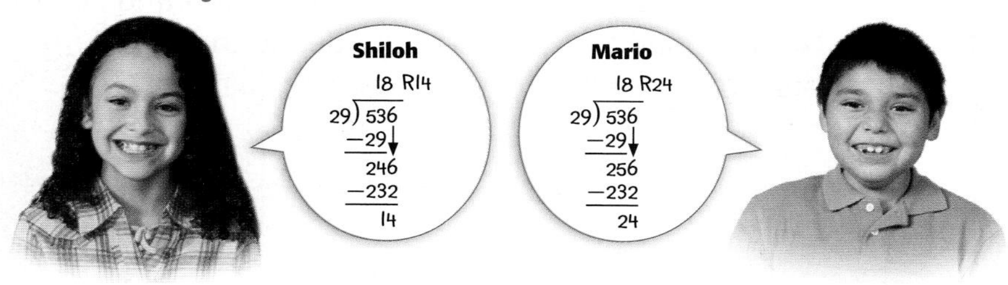


**45. WRITING IN MATH** Explain how dividing by a two-digit number is similar to dividing by a one-digit number.

Divide by Two-Digit Numbers LA9

# 4 Assess

## Formative Assessment

- **Estimate $24\overline{)497}$. Then divide.**
  Estimate: $20\overline{)500} = 25$
  Divide $24\overline{)497} = 20$ R17
- **How could you check your answer?** Sample answer: multiply $24 \times 20 = 480 + 17 = 497$

**Quick Check** **Are students continuing to struggle with dividing up to a three-digit number by a two-digit number?**

**If Yes** → Small Group Options (p. LA6B)

**If No** → Independent Work Options (p. LA6B)

**Ticket Out the Door** Write $287 \div 48$ on the board. Have students divide and show their work on a piece of paper that they give to you as they leave class.

# Decimals: Addition and Subtraction

Looking Ahead 3

## Lesson Planner

### Objective

Add and subtract decimals.

### Review Vocabulary

**sum, difference**

### Resources

**Materials:** notebook

**Manipulatives:** play coins

**Teacher Technology**

TeacherWorks • Interactive Classroom

### Focus on Math Background

Decimals must be added and subtracted in many real-world applications, especially in finance and science. Decimal points are lined up when decimals are added or subtracted vertically (which is not the case for multiplication). This ensures that digits with the same place value are combined or separated.

For addition and subtraction of so-called "ragged decimals" that have unequal numbers of decimal places, extra zeros are annexed as placeholders. This is particularly important for subtraction when regrouping is needed.

Thus, $\begin{array}{r} 63.4 \\ -\ 11.265 \\ \hline \end{array}$ becomes $\begin{array}{r} 63.400 \\ -\ 11.265 \\ \hline \end{array}$

Note that the zero placeholders do not change the value of the minuend. To subtract, the 4 tenths must be renamed as "3 tenths plus 9 hundredths plus 10 thousandths" so that the hundredths and thousandths place subtractions can be carried out. The result is $\begin{array}{r} 63.4\overset{9}{\cancel{0}}\overset{10}{\cancel{0}} \\ -\ 11.265 \\ \hline \end{array}$ or 52.135. Since students often make errors when subtracting across zeros in the minuend, estimation can be especially helpful here.

## Daily Routine

Use these suggestions before beginning the lesson on p. LA10.

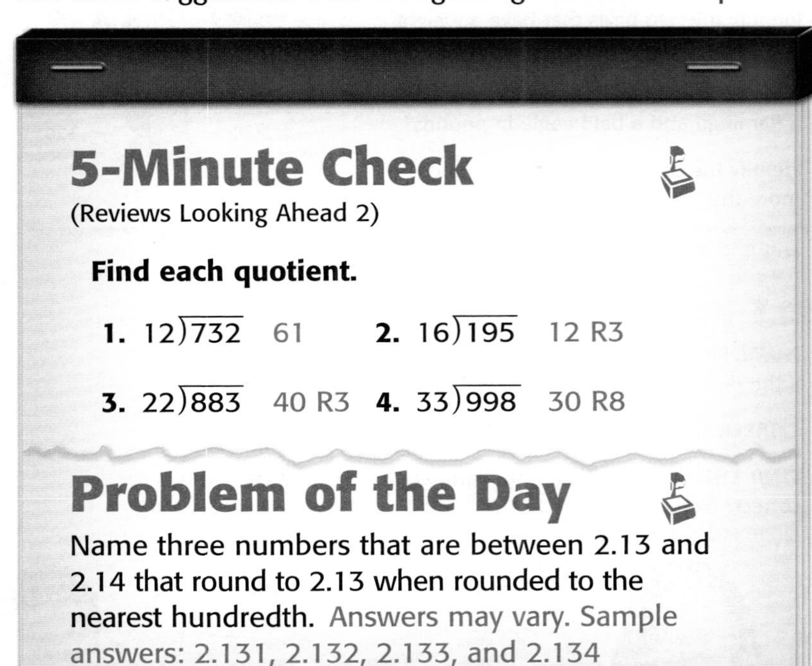

### 5-Minute Check

(Reviews Looking Ahead 2)

**Find each quotient.**

**1.** 12)732 61 **2.** 16)195 12 R3

**3.** 22)883 40 R3 **4.** 33)998 30 R8

### Problem of the Day

Name three numbers that are between 2.13 and 2.14 that round to 2.13 when rounded to the nearest hundredth. Answers may vary. Sample answers: 2.131, 2.132, 2.133, and 2.134

### Review Math Vocabulary

Write the review vocabulary words and their definitions on the board.

Before putting the definitions on the board, have students copy the words from the board, and write their own definitions for each word.

Once students have written their own definitions, put the definitions on the board. Have students compare their definitions to the actual meaning of each of these words. If needed, have them revise their own definitions to make them more accurate.

# Differentiated Instruction

## Small Group Options

KINESTHETIC, LINGUISTIC

### Option 1 Gifted and Talented AL

**Materials:** paper and pencil

Have students write two word problems with a sum of 61.43 and two problems with a difference of 61.43.

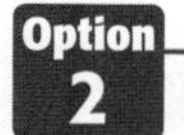

VISUAL, SPATIAL, SOCIAL

### Option 2 English Language Learners ELL

**Materials:** construction paper shapes listed below (several of each shape, could be different sizes), glue
**Core Vocabulary:** costs, use shapes, create
**Common Use Verb:** afford to make

**Do Math** This strategy activates background knowledge to help students integrate their understanding of adding and subtracting decimals.

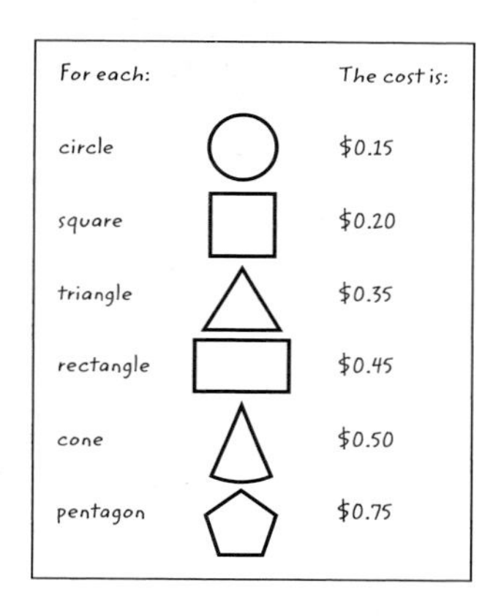

| For each: | | The cost is: |
|---|---|---|
| circle | | $0.15 |
| square | | $0.20 |
| triangle | | $0.35 |
| rectangle | | $0.45 |
| cone | | $0.50 |
| pentagon | | $0.75 |

- All students will make a picture out of shapes of a city, house, or car and start with $5.00. Students' pictures can use only the shapes they can afford (costs listed above).
- Multiple shapes may be used. Students are not allowed to spend more than $5.00.
- Have students tell how much they spent and how much they had left over from the $5.00.
- Allow students who made the same scenes to compare their pictures and costs.
- Discuss the differences and commonalities within group pictures. Have groups confirm the costs of materials.

## Independent Work Options

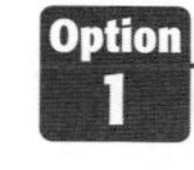

LINGUISTIC

### Option 1 Early Finishers OL AL

**Materials:** index cards, notebook

- Have students write real-world problems on the front of an index card that can be solved using the numbers in Examples 2 and 3.
- Have them show the solution processes for the problems they wrote on the back of the cards.
- Have each student exchange cards with another student. Have them solve the other problems. Tell students to compare their processes and discuss their results.

### Option 2 Student Technology

**Math Online** macmillanmh.com

Personal Tutor • Extra Examples

# Decimals: Addition and Subtraction

## 1 Introduce

**Activity Choice 1 • Hands-On**

- Pass out pennies, nickels, dimes, quarters, and half dollars to individuals or small groups. Ask students the value of each coin.
- **Using these coins, how can you make one cent?** one penny
- **How many ways can you make 5 cents? Name them.** two: one nickel, and five pennies
- **How can you make 10 cents?** Sample answer: 10 pennies, 5 pennies and a nickel, two nickels, one dime
- Ask students to make combinations for other amounts such as $0.36, $0.78, and $1.00.

## 2 Teach

**Scaffolding Questions**

Have each student draw a 10 × 10 grid on a sheet of centimeter grid paper. Then write the following on the board: 0.53 + 0.3

- **How many squares are in a 10 × 10 grid?** 100
- Tell students to shade the grid to show 0.53.
- **How did you know how many to shade?** Sample answer: I needed to show 53 hundredths, so I shaded 53 squares.
- **How can you show 0.3 on the grid?** Sample answer: annex a zero to change the number to hundredths. Therefore, 0.3 is equivalent to 0.30.
- Tell them to shade in 0.3 on the grid.
- **How much did you shade in and why?** Shade in 30 squares to show 30 hundredths.
- **How many squares in all are shaded?** 83
- **How would you write this as a decimal?** 0.83

Have students open their books and read the information in **Get Ready to Learn**. Review **sum** and **difference**. As a class, work through **Examples 1–6**.




# Decimals: Addition and Subtraction

**MAIN IDEA**

I will add and subtract decimals.

**GET READY to Learn**

The table shows the weights of two American eagle bullion coins. What is the total weight of these coins?

| Coin Weights | |
|---|---|
| Coin | Weight (grams) |
| Gold | 8.483 |
| Platinum | 7.780 |

**Source:** U.S. Mint

To add or subtract decimals, add or subtract digits in the same place-value position. Remember to align the decimal points.

**Real-World EXAMPLE** Add Decimals

1 **MEASUREMENT What is the total weight of the coins?**

Find the sum of 8.483 and 7.780.

**Estimate** $8.483 + 7.780 \longrightarrow 8 + 8 = 16$

$$\begin{array}{r} {}^{1\,1}\phantom{000} \\ 8.483 \\ +\,7.780 \\ \hline 16.263 \end{array}$$

Line up the decimal points.
Add as with whole numbers.
Regroup if needed.

So, the total weight of the coins is 16.263 grams.

**Check for Reasonableness** 16.263 ≈ 16 ✓

**EXAMPLE** Subtract Decimals

2 **Find 9.496 − 5.243.**

**Estimate** $9.496 - 5.243 \longrightarrow 9 - 5 = 4$

$$\begin{array}{r} 9.496 \\ -\,5.243 \\ \hline 4.253 \end{array}$$

Line up the decimal points.
Subtract as with whole numbers.
Regroup if needed.

So, 9.496 − 5.243 = 4.253.

**Check for Reasonableness** 4.253 ≈ 4 ✓

Sometimes it is necessary to annex zeros before you subtract.

**Remember**

Annexing zeros means writing zeros in a number without changing the number's value.

**EXAMPLE** Subtract Decimals

**3 Find 6.85 − 2.319.**

**Estimate** 6.85 − 2.319 ⟶ 7 − 2 = 5

```
   4 10
  6.850
− 2.319
  4.531
```

Annex zeros so both numbers have the same place value.
Subtract as with whole numbers.
Regroup if needed.

So, 6.85 − 2.319 = 4.531.

**Check for Reasonableness** 4.531 ≈ 5 ✓

**Real-World EXAMPLE** Subtract Decimals

**4 The table shows the masses of some of the planets in our solar system. What is the difference in mass of Earth and Venus?**

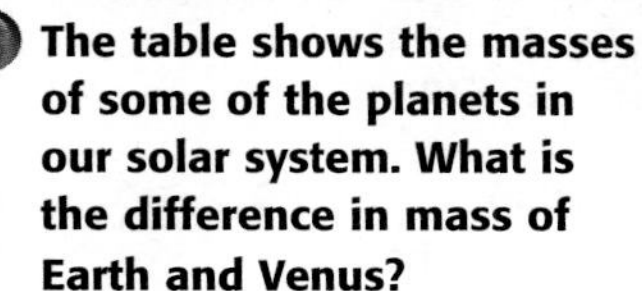

| Mass of Planets | |
|---|---|
| **Planet** | **Mass** |
| Earth | 1 |
| Mars | 0.107 |
| Saturn | 95.16 |
| Venus | 0.815 |

**Source:** *The World Almanac*

Find 1 − 0.815.

**Estimate** 1 − 0.815 ⟶ 1 − 1 = 0

```
   9 9
 0 10 10 10
  1.000
− 0.815
  0.185
```

Annex zeros so both numbers have the same place value.
Subtract as with whole numbers.
Regroup if needed.

So, the difference in mass of Earth and Venus is 0.185.

**Remember**

Compare the answer to the estimate to check your answer.

**EXAMPLE** Subtract Decimals

**5 Find 26 − 3.275.**

**Estimate** 26 − 3.275 ⟶ 26 − 3 = 23

```
     9 9
   5 10 10 10
  26.000
−  3.275
  22.725
```

Annex zeros so both numbers have the same place value.
Subtract as with whole numbers.
Regroup if needed.

So, 26 − 3.275 = 22.725.



### Add Decimals

**Example 3** Make sure students remember to line up the decimal points when they write one number under the other. Remind them that they should always estimate the answer before finding the exact answer.

## ADDITIONAL EXAMPLES

**Find each sum.**

1.
```
  2.354
+3.123
  5.477
```

2. 13.214 + 9.953 23.167

**Find each difference.**

3.
```
  3.752
−1.256
  2.496
```

4. 16.322 − 12.432 3.890

## CHECK What You Know

Have students complete Exercises 1–14 in **Check What You Know** as you observe their work.

**Exercise 14** Assess student comprehension before assigning practice exercises.

## BL Alternate Teaching Strategy

**If** students fail to align the numbers correctly when adding or subtracting a whole number and a decimal…

**Then** use this reteach option:

1 Tell them to remember this saying, "If the decimal isn't there, it's at the end of the number." Suggest that they make the saying into a song or chant. Practice it several times, "If the decimal isn't there … where is the decimal in the number 6? It's at the end of the number (meaning 6. or 6.0)."

Remind students that the 6 can be thought of as the whole number part of a decimal. Explain that all the digits after the 6 are less than one and that the decimal point separates the whole amount (6) from the part less than one (.0).

### Additional Answer

**14.** Sample answer: Write a decimal point and three zeros after the 7. Then subtract each place value, starting with the thousandths. Regroup if neeeded.

### COMMON ERROR!

**Exercises 33 and 34** Some students may have difficulty finding the difference between a whole number and a decimal. Remind them to put a decimal point after the whole number and annex zeros so that both numbers have the same place value.

## CHECK What You Know

**Find each sum.** See Example 1 (p. LA10)

1. 3.147 + 5.365 **8.512**
2. 6.098 + 2.415 **8.513**
3. 11.619 + 7.836 **19.455**
4. 14.817 + 8.329 **23.146**
5. 18.354 + 15.027 **33.381**
6. 21.865 + 17.428 **39.293**

**Find each difference.** See Examples 2–5 (pp. LA10–LA11)

7. 4.785 − 1.364 **3.421**
8. 7.098 − 3.174 **3.924**
9. 9.43 − 6.219 **3.211**
10. 12.32 − 8.257 **4.063**
11. 8 − 2.458 **5.542**
12. 15 − 9.823 **5.177**
13. A bee hummingbird weighs 0.056 ounces. A black-legged falconet weighs 1.25 ounces. What is the difference in the weight of the birds? **1.194 ounces**
14. Talk About It Explain how you would find the difference of 7 and 2.163. **See margin.**

## Practice and Problem Solving

**Find each sum.** See Example 1 (p. LA10)

15. 1.098 + 2.571 **3.669**
16. 3.837 + 4.526 **8.363**
17. 7.692 + 5.048 **12.74**
18. 9.486 + 8.973 **18.459**
19. 12.092 + 6.363 **18.455**
20. 16.816 + 3.755 **20.571**
21. 17.489 + 7.302 **24.791**
22. 19.971 + 9.646 **29.617**
23. 13.407 + 11.689 **25.096**
24. A millimeter is 0.039 of an inch. What is the length of two millimeters in inches? **0.078 inches**
25. A centimeter is 0.394 of an inch. What is the length of three centimeters in inches? **1.182 inches**

**Find each difference.** See Examples 2–5 (pp. LA10–LA11)

**26.** $\begin{array}{r} 3.798 \\ -\ 1.258 \\ \hline \end{array}$ **2.54**

**27.** $\begin{array}{r} 5.647 \\ -\ 2.379 \\ \hline \end{array}$ **3.268**

**28.** $\begin{array}{r} 6.723 \\ -\ 3.919 \\ \hline \end{array}$ **2.804**

**29.** $\begin{array}{r} 8.072 \\ -\ 4.546 \\ \hline \end{array}$ **3.526**

**30.** $\begin{array}{r} 7.36 \\ -\ 5.891 \\ \hline \end{array}$ **1.469**

**31.** $\begin{array}{r} 9.78 \\ -\ 7.308 \\ \hline \end{array}$ **2.472**

**32.** $13.56 - 6.164$ **7.396**

**33.** $18 - 8.398$ **9.602**

**34.** $31 - 4.663$ **26.337**

**The table shows boat water speed records. Use the table to solve Exercises 35–37.**

**35.** What is the difference in the two fastest speeds? **14.999 mph**

**36.** What is the difference in Roy Duby's and Jack Regas's speeds? **12.792 mph**

**37.** Which two boat drivers have a difference of speed equal to 13.493 miles per hour? **Russ Wicks and Bill Muncey**

**Water Speed Records**

| Boat Driver | Speed (miles per hour) |
|---|---|
| Dave Villwock | 220.493 |
| Russ Wicks | 205.494 |
| Roy Duby | 200.419 |
| Bill Muncey | 192.001 |
| Jack Regas | 187.627 |

**41. Sample answer: Cailin's hair is 10.875 inches long. Christy's hair is 2.275 inches shorter than Cailin's. How long is Christy's hair?**

## H.O.T. Problems

**38. NUMBER SENSE** Arrange the digits 1, 2, 3, 4, 5, 6, 7, and 8 into two decimals so that their difference is as close to 0 as possible. Use each digit only once. **$0.2 - 0.1876543 = 0.0123457$**

**39. CHALLENGE** Find $2{,}175.4982 + 5{,}368.0479$. **7,543.5461**

**40. NUMBER SENSE** Find a counterexample to the following statement.

*If two decimals each have their last nonzero digit in the hundredths place, their sum also has its last nonzero digit in the hundredths place.*
**Sample answer: $5.65 + 3.25 = 8.9$**

**41. WRITING IN ► MATH** Write a real-world problem involving subtraction of decimals in which the difference is between 8.5 and 9.



## 3 Practice

Differentiate practice using these leveled assignments for Exercises 15–44.

| Level | Assignment |
|---|---|
| BL Below/Approaching Level | 15–17, 21–23, 26, 27–29, 33–35, 39 |
| OL On Level | 15–18, 21–25, 26, 27–38, 40 |
| AL Above/Beyond Level | 15–40 odd, 41–44 |

Have students discuss and complete the Higher Order Thinking problems. For Exercise 42, have students use the Guess and Check strategy or logical reasoning to solve the problem.

**WRITING IN ► MATH** Have students complete Exercise 44 in their Math Journals. You may choose to use this exercise as an optional formative assessment.

## 4 Assess

### Formative Assessment

- **What is the sum of 56.78 and 13.9?** 70.68

**Quick Check** **Are students continuing to struggle with adding and subtracting decimals?**

**If Yes** → Small group options (p. LA10B)

**If No** → Independent Work Options (p. LA10B)

**Name the Math** Ask students to write and solve an addition and a subtraction problem involving decimals.

# Add and Subtract Fractions with Unlike Denominators

## Lesson Planner

### Objective

Add and subtract fractions with unlike denominators.

### Review Vocabulary

**equivalent fractions**

### Resources

**Materials:** grid paper

**Manipulatives:** fraction tiles

**Teacher Technology**
TeacherWorks • Interactive Classroom

## Daily Routine

Use these suggestions before beginning the lesson on p. LA14.

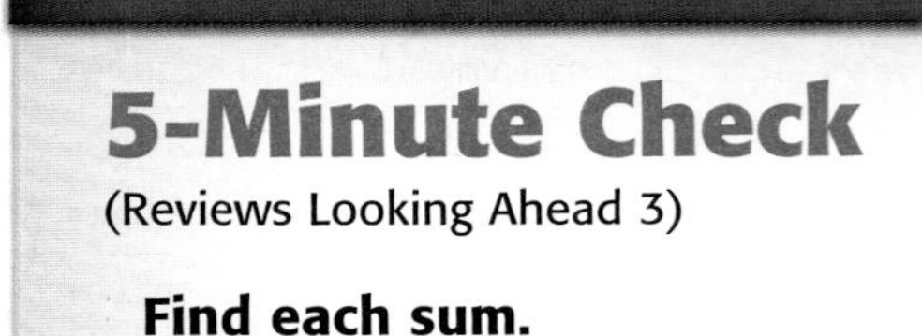

### 5-Minute Check

(Reviews Looking Ahead 3)

**Find each sum.**

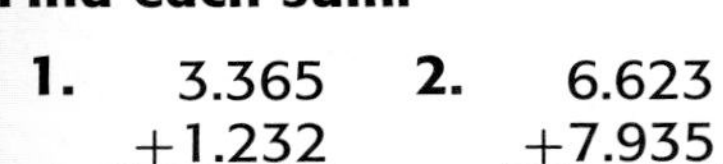

**1.** 3.365 + 1.232 = 4.597

**2.** 6.623 + 7.935 = 14.558

**Find each difference.**

**3.** 6.692 − 1.325 = 5.367

**4.** 19.993 − 12.875 = 7.118

### Problem of the Day

David ran the race in 6.65 seconds. Shaun ran it 19 thousandths of a second slower. What was Shaun's time? 6.669 sec.

### Focus on Math Background

Students will use models to learn that when they add fractions with *like* denominators, they are adding like units (the denominator that they have in common). So, when they add $\frac{1}{5}$ and $\frac{2}{5}$, they will understand that they are adding 1 fifth and 2 more fifths to get 3 fifths. With this conceptual understanding, it is unlikely that they will add the denominators and get 3 tenths. Students will then extend their knowledge of adding fractions to fractions with *unlike* denominators. It is here that students are tempted to add the numerators and the denominators, so it is very important that students develop understanding through models before moving to paper and pencil. When students have gained that understanding and have studied equivalent fractions (Lesson 13-4), they are ready to apply what they know. In general, if two fractions have unlike denominators, you can rename one or both of the fractions so that the denominators are the same. Then the sum can be found.

### Review Math Vocabulary

Write the review vocabulary word and its definition on the board.

Ask each student to write two equivalent fractions, one per index card. Have the class combine and mix up their cards, placing them face down on a large table or on the floor. Then have students take turns flipping over cards. If they turn over two equivalent fractions, they remove that pair. Play until all equivalent fractions have been matched.

# Differentiated Instruction

## Small Group Options

LOGICAL

### Below Level BL

**Materials:** fraction models, paper and pencil

- Have students use fraction models as needed.
- Hand this problem to students:

  *JiLyn's mom has 2 cups of sugar in the house. She wants to make 2 kinds of cookies. One recipe requires $\frac{1}{2}$ cup of sugar, and the other recipe requires $\frac{2}{3}$ cup. Does she have enough sugar or must she go buy some?* She has enough sugar to make both kinds of cookies.

SPATIAL, LINGUISTIC

### English Language Learners ELL

**Materials:** paper
**Core Vocabulary:** one-fourth, unlike denominators, label
**Common Use Verb:** replace
**Write Math** This strategy lets students experiment with finding like denominators.

- Students fold paper twice, creating $\frac{1}{4}$s. They rip and label. Students make two more $\frac{1}{2}$s with other sheet.
- Explain, "If you have **unlike denominators**, you need to change one so they match." Hold up two $\frac{1}{4}$s; encourage students to use their papers to find what it equals. $\frac{1}{2}$
- Say, "What is $3\frac{1}{2} + 1\frac{1}{4}$?" Students write the number sentence. "***Replace*** two $\frac{1}{4}$s for the $\frac{1}{2}$, then solve." Continue with less scaffolding each time.

## Independent Work Options

VISUAL, SPATIAL

### Early Finishers OL

**Manipulatives:** number cubes with 0–5 and 5–10

- Have one partner choose *numerators* and the number cube 0–5. The other partner chooses *denominators* and the number cube 5–10.
- Have partners take turns rolling their cubes and writing the numbers to create two fractions, each with a numerator from 1–5 and a denominator from 5–10. If a 0 is rolled for the numerator, have that partner roll again.
- Ask partners to use the paper and pencil method to add the two fractions. Repeat for several rounds of play.

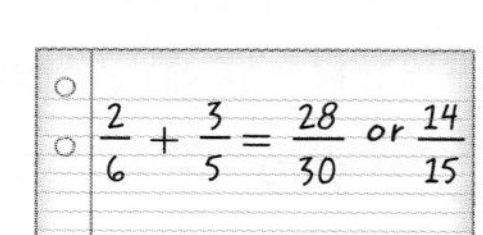

### Student Technology

**Math Online** macmillanmh.com

Personal Tutor • Extra Examples

# Add and Subtract Fractions with Unlike Denominators

## 1 Introduce

**Activity • Hands-On** 

- Ask students to get out their fraction models and have them work in pairs. Show them how to model simple addition and subtraction problems using these manipulatives.
- **What is $\frac{1}{4} + \frac{2}{4}$?** $\frac{3}{4}$
- **What is $\frac{1}{3} + \frac{2}{3}$?** $\frac{3}{3}$ or 1
- **What is $\frac{3}{5} - \frac{1}{5}$?** $\frac{2}{5}$
- Next, write $\frac{1}{3}$ and $\frac{3}{4}$ on the board. Have students use their fraction models to write two equivalent fractions for $\frac{1}{3}$ and $\frac{3}{4}$. $\frac{1}{3}$ : $\frac{2}{6}$ and $\frac{4}{12}$; $\frac{3}{4}$ : $\frac{6}{8}$ and $\frac{9}{12}$
- Have students examine their models and choose one equivalent fraction for $\frac{1}{3}$ and one for $\frac{3}{4}$ that together show two fractions with like denominators. $\frac{4}{12}$ and $\frac{9}{12}$
- Emphasize that $\frac{1}{3} = \frac{4}{12}$ and $\frac{3}{4} = \frac{9}{12}$.

## 2 Teach

### Scaffolding Questions

- **How did we change the two fractions to have like denominators?** We found equivalent fractions for each fraction that had the same denominator.
- **How could these equivalent fractions help us add $\frac{1}{3}$ and $\frac{3}{4}$?** Since the equivalent fractions have the same denominator, we can add them to find the sum.
- Place the fraction models for $\frac{9}{12}$ to the right of those for $\frac{4}{12}$. **How many twelfths are there in all?** 13
- **What is the sum of $\frac{4}{12}$ and $\frac{9}{12}$ as a mixed number?** $1\frac{1}{12}$.
- **What is the sum of $\frac{1}{3}$ and $\frac{3}{4}$?** $1\frac{1}{12}$



# Add and Subtract Fractions with Unlike Denominators

**GET READY to Learn**

A butterfly traveled $\frac{3}{4}$ mile on Monday and $\frac{5}{6}$ mile on Tuesday. How many miles did the butterfly travel in all?

The fractions $\frac{3}{4}$ and $\frac{5}{6}$ have unlike denominators. You can use paper and pencil to add fractions with unlike denominators.

**EXAMPLE** Add Fractions with Unlike Denominators

**1** **MEASUREMENT Add $\frac{3}{4}$ and $\frac{5}{6}$ to find how many miles the butterfly traveled in all.**

You need to find $\frac{3}{4} + \frac{5}{6}$.

**Step 1** Write the problem.

$$\begin{array}{r} \frac{3}{4} \\ + \frac{5}{6} \\ \hline \end{array}$$

**Step 2** Find equivalent fractions.

$$\begin{array}{rcr} \frac{3}{4} & \longrightarrow & \frac{9}{12} \\ + \frac{5}{6} & \longrightarrow & + \frac{10}{12} \\ \hline \end{array}$$

Write $\frac{3}{4}$ and $\frac{5}{6}$ as equivalent fractions.

**Step 3** Add the fractions with like denominators. Then write the sum as a mixed number.

$$\begin{array}{rcr} \frac{3}{4} & \longrightarrow & \frac{9}{12} \\ + \frac{5}{6} & \longrightarrow & + \frac{10}{12} \\ \hline & & \frac{19}{12} = 1\frac{7}{12} \end{array}$$

So, the butterfly traveled $1\frac{7}{12}$ miles in all.

Paper and pencil can also be used to subtract fractions with unlike denominators.

**EXAMPLE**

**2 MEASUREMENT This morning, $\frac{5}{6}$ of an inch of snow was on the ground. By noon, $\frac{2}{3}$ of an inch of snow melted. How much snow is left on the ground?**

You need to find $\frac{5}{6} - \frac{2}{3}$.

**Step 1** Write the problem.

$$\begin{array}{r} \frac{5}{6} \\ -\frac{2}{3} \\ \hline \end{array}$$

**Step 2** Find equivalent fractions.

$$\begin{array}{r} \frac{5}{6} \\ -\frac{2}{3} \\ \hline \end{array} \longrightarrow \begin{array}{r} \frac{5}{6} \\ -\frac{4}{6} \\ \hline \end{array}$$

Write $\frac{5}{6}$ and $\frac{2}{3}$ as equivalent fractions.

**Step 3** Subtract the fractions with like denominators.

$$\begin{array}{r} \frac{5}{6} \\ -\frac{2}{3} \\ \hline \end{array} \longrightarrow \begin{array}{r} \frac{5}{6} \\ -\frac{4}{6} \\ \hline \frac{1}{6} \end{array}$$

So, $\frac{1}{6}$ of an inch of snow is left on the ground.

**Check**

The model shows $\frac{5}{6} - \frac{2}{3}$.

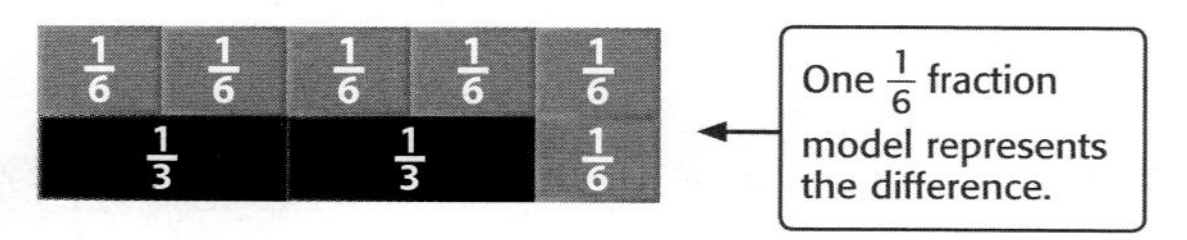


One $\frac{1}{6}$ fraction model represents the difference.

So, $\frac{5}{6} - \frac{2}{3} = \frac{1}{6}$. The answer is correct. ✓

**Remember**

After subtracting fractions, always look to see if the answer can be written in simplest form.



**GET READY to Learn**

Have students open their books and read the information in **Get Ready to Learn**. Introduce **equivalent fractions**. As a class, work through **Examples 1 and 2**.

## Real-World Example

**Example 2** Encourage students to make connections between the fraction tile model and the paper and pencil methods of subtraction. For Step 2 in the paper and pencil method, point out that the larger denominator, 6, is divisible by the smaller denominator, 3, so the greater denominator can be used as the like denominator.

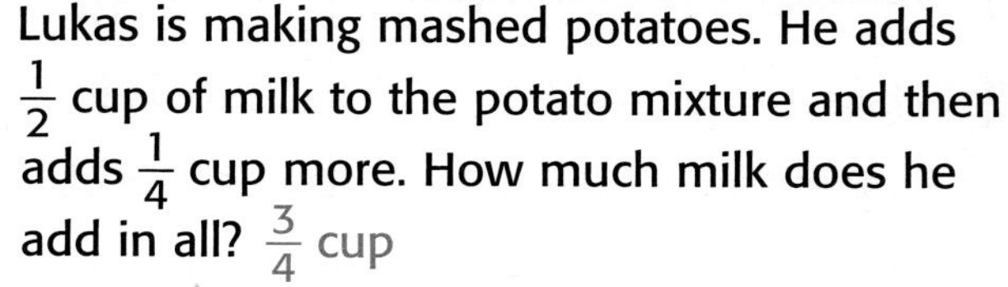

**ADDITIONAL EXAMPLES**

1. Lukas is making mashed potatoes. He adds $\frac{1}{2}$ cup of milk to the potato mixture and then adds $\frac{1}{4}$ cup more. How much milk does he add in all? $\frac{3}{4}$ cup
2. Subtract $\frac{7}{10} - \frac{1}{2}$. $\frac{1}{5}$

**COMMON ERROR!**

Students may subtract numerators before finding equivalent fractions. Suggest that students write the like denominator for the two fractions in the difference before they subtract.

## CHECK What You Know

Have students complete Exercises 1–8 in **Check What You Know** as you observe their work.

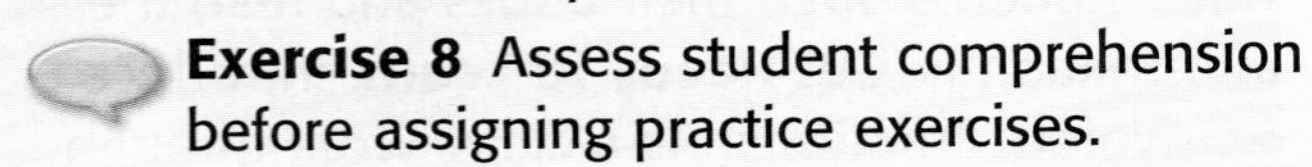

**Exercise 8** Assess student comprehension before assigning practice exercises.

## BL Alternate Teaching Strategy

**If** students have trouble adding fractions with unlike denominators…

**Then** use this reteach option:

Write $\frac{1}{2} + \frac{2}{5}$ on the board. Guide students to create an area model on grid paper that can be evenly divided into both halves and fifths: two rectangles each with 2 rows of 5 squares. Point out that there are 10 squares in each rectangle, so each square stands for $\frac{1}{10}$.

Have students shade 1 of the 2 rows in the first rectangle to show $\frac{1}{2}$. Note that 5 of the 10 squares, or $\frac{5}{10}$, are shaded. Then have the students shade 2 of the 5 columns in the second rectangle to model $\frac{2}{5}$. Have students count the squares and explain that 4 out of 10 or $\frac{4}{10}$ are shaded. Ask students to count the total number of squares to find the sum, $\frac{9}{10}$.

# 3 Practice

Differentiate practice using these leveled assignments for Exercises 6–26.

| Level | Assignment |
|---|---|
| BL Below/Approaching Level | 9–13, 25, 29–32 |
| OL On Level | 10–16, 17–18, 33–34 |
| AL Above/Beyond Level | 9–28 even, 20–26, 33–34 |

Have students discuss and complete the Higher Order Thinking problems. For Exercise 25, suggest that students list the three pairs that can be made with the three fractions and find all three sums.

**WRITING IN MATH** Have students complete Exercise 34 in their Math Journals. You may choose to use this exercise as an optional formative assessment.

## CHECK What You Know

**Add or subtract. Use fraction models if needed. Write in simplest form.**

See Examples 1 and 2 (pp. LA14–LA15)

1. $\frac{1}{3} + \frac{1}{4}$ $\frac{7}{12}$
2. $\frac{5}{8} + \frac{3}{4}$ $1\frac{3}{8}$
3. $\frac{3}{10} + \frac{3}{5}$ $\frac{9}{10}$
4. $\frac{3}{4} - \frac{1}{2}$ $\frac{1}{4}$
5. $\frac{4}{6} - \frac{1}{3}$ $\frac{1}{3}$
6. $\frac{3}{4} - \frac{1}{3}$ $\frac{5}{12}$
7. Russ poured $\frac{3}{4}$ gallon of liquid from a container that holds $\frac{7}{8}$ gallon. How much liquid is left in the container? $\frac{1}{8}$ gal

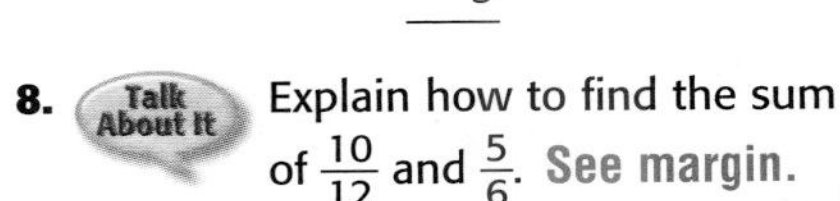


8. Explain how to find the sum of $\frac{10}{12}$ and $\frac{5}{6}$. See margin.

## Practice and Problem Solving

**Add or subtract. Use fraction models if needed. Write in simplest form.**

See Examples 1 and 2 (pp. LA14–LA15)

9. $\frac{1}{5} + \frac{3}{10}$ $\frac{1}{2}$
10. $\frac{2}{3} + \frac{1}{12}$ $\frac{3}{4}$
11. $\frac{2}{4} + \frac{7}{12}$ $1\frac{1}{12}$
12. $\frac{1}{3} + \frac{1}{6}$ $\frac{1}{2}$
13. $\frac{1}{5} + \frac{1}{6}$ $\frac{11}{30}$
14. $\frac{1}{3} + \frac{5}{7}$ $1\frac{1}{21}$
15. $\frac{3}{6} + \frac{1}{4}$ $\frac{3}{4}$
16. $\frac{7}{9} + \frac{2}{3}$ $1\frac{4}{9}$
17. $\frac{7}{9} - \frac{1}{3}$ $\frac{4}{9}$
18. $\frac{7}{8} - \frac{3}{4}$ $\frac{1}{8}$
19. $\frac{5}{6} - \frac{1}{3}$ $\frac{1}{2}$
20. $\frac{7}{8} - \frac{1}{2}$ $\frac{3}{8}$
21. $\frac{3}{5} - \frac{1}{2}$ $\frac{1}{10}$
22. $\frac{3}{4} - \frac{1}{6}$ $\frac{7}{12}$
23. $\frac{2}{3} - \frac{1}{4}$ $\frac{5}{12}$
24. $\frac{6}{8} - \frac{1}{6}$ $\frac{7}{12}$
25. Selena fed her two dogs. How much more food did the big dog get than the puppy? $\frac{2}{3}$ cup

| Dog Food Fed to Dogs | |
|---|---|
| **Dog** | **Amount of Food (cups)** |
| Big dog | $\frac{11}{12}$ |
| Puppy | $\frac{1}{4}$ |



### Additional Answer

8. Sample answer: Find a common denominator by using fraction models to see which piecess fit under $\frac{10}{12} + \frac{5}{6}$. 20 twelfths fit, so the sum is $\frac{20}{12}$, which equals $1\frac{2}{3}$.

**26.** Stella's favorite recipe is shown below. If she makes one serving, will she be able to use a glass that holds 1 cup of liquid? Explain. See margin.

Stella's Cranberry Drink

$\frac{2}{3}$ c cranberry juice

$\frac{3}{8}$ c water

Makes: one serving

**27. Measurement** The table below shows how much paint Mr. Price needs in his art classes. How many gallons will he use in all? $1\frac{1}{6}$ gallons

| Paint Supply List | |
|---|---|
| **Class** | **Paint (gal)** |
| Class 1 | $\frac{1}{5}$ |
| Class 2 | $\frac{2}{3}$ |
| Class 3 | $\frac{3}{10}$ |

**28.** Paula lives $\frac{1}{4}$ mile from school. Cris lives $\frac{4}{5}$ mile from school. How much farther from school does Cris live than Paula? $\frac{11}{20}$ mi

**29.** A stew has $\frac{1}{4}$ cup of onions and $\frac{1}{2}$ cup of celery. How much more celery is in the stew than onions? $\frac{1}{4}$ cup

## Real-World PROBLEM SOLVING

*Science* The table shows the sizes of various newborn animals.

**30.** What is the total weight of the heaviest and lightest animals listed? $\frac{15}{16}$ lb

**31.** Which two animals have a total weight of $\frac{7}{16}$ pound? flamingo and giant panda

**32.** What is the total weight of the alligator and the cheetah? $\frac{3}{4}$ lb

**33.** What is the total weight of all of the animals? 2 lb

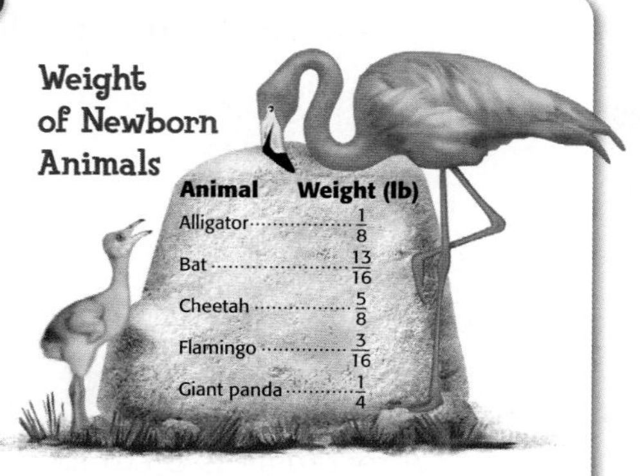

Weight of Newborn Animals

| Animal | Weight (lb) |
|---|---|
| Alligator | $\frac{1}{8}$ |
| Bat | $\frac{13}{16}$ |
| Cheetah | $\frac{5}{8}$ |
| Flamingo | $\frac{3}{16}$ |
| Giant panda | $\frac{1}{4}$ |

## H.O.T. Problems

**34. NUMBER SENSE** Is the sum of $\frac{4}{6}$ and $\frac{5}{8}$ greater or less than 1? How can you tell without adding? 34, 35. See margin.

**35. WRITING IN MATH** Could you use 8 as a denominator to add $\frac{1}{2}$ and $\frac{3}{4}$? Explain.



# 4 Assess

### Formative Assessment

- **How is adding fractions with unlike denominators similar to adding fractions with like denominators?** When the denominators are the same, I add the numerators then write the sum in simplest form.
- **How is it different?** Before I can add, I need to find equivalent fractions to get like denominators for the addends.

**Quick Check** **Are students continuing to struggle with adding fractions with unlike denominators?**

**If Yes** → Small Group Options (p. LA14B)

**If No** → Independent Work Options (p. LA14B)

**Into the Future** Have students predict what they might learn next about fractions. Ask them to write a problem they think they may be asked to solve.

### Additional Answers

**26.** No; $\frac{2}{3} + \frac{3}{8}$ is greater than 1.

**34.** Sample answer: Greater than 1; both addends are greater than $\frac{1}{2}$, so their sum will be greater than 1.

**35.** Sample answer: yes; Eight is a common multiple of 2 and 4.

### COMMON ERROR!

**Exercises 12 and 13** Students may have difficulty identifying like denominators for $\frac{1}{5}$ and $\frac{1}{6}$ and $\frac{1}{3}$ and $\frac{5}{7}$. Have students use a multiplication table to locate common multiples. Demonstrate how to find a common multiple for 5 and 6 by finding where the row for 5 and the column for 6 meet at 30. Have students do the same for 3 and 7 to find the like denominator 21.

# Looking Ahead 5 Volumes of Rectangular Prisms

## Lesson Planner

### Objective

Find the volumes of rectangular prisms.

### Review Vocabulary

**volume**

### Resources

**Manipulatives:** rulers, centimeter cubes, connecting cubes
**Teacher Technology**
TeacherWorks • Interactive Classroom • Concepts in Motion

## Daily Routine

Use these suggestions before beginning the lesson on p. LA18.

### 5-Minute Check

(Reviews Looking Ahead 4)

**Add. Use fraction models if needed.**

**1.** $\frac{2}{5} + \frac{4}{8}$ $\frac{36}{40}$ or $\frac{9}{10}$

**2.** $\frac{5}{10} + \frac{1}{5}$ $\frac{7}{10}$

### Problem of the Day

A rectangle is 8 cm long and 4 cm wide. It has the same perimeter as a square. How much less area does it have? Draw a picture and explain.
4 $cm^2$ less; see students' work.

### Focus on Math Background

Students have already identified rectangular prisms and estimated their volumes in a previous lesson. In this lesson, they will use a formula to find the volumes of rectangular prisms.

Volume is the number of cubic units that fit inside a three-dimensional figure. A cubic unit is a cube that is 1 unit in length, 1 unit in width, and 1 unit in height. At this level, only volumes of rectangular prisms are considered. To determine the volume of a three-dimensional figure, ask: How many cubes fill the base and how many layers of cubes are in the given figure?

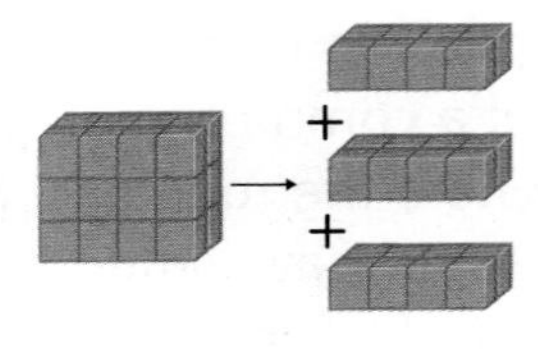

### Building Math Vocabulary

Write the lesson vocabulary word and its definition on the board.

Have students discuss how they would explain the term *volume* to a third-grade student.

# Differentiated Instruction

## Small Group Options

### Option 1 Below Level BL

SPATIAL

**Materials:** one-inch cubes for each student

- Review the properties of a rectangular prism.
- Have students build cubes that measure 2 red cubes wide, 2 blue cubes deep, and 2 green cubes high. **How many cubes do you need to build this prism?** 8
- Have students build cube that measure 2 green cubes wide, 2 blue cubes deep, and 2 red cubes high. **How many cubes did it take to build this cube?** 8
- **What do you notice about these answers and why?** The answer is the same because the Commutative Property of Multiplication states that the order of the factors does not change the product.

### Option 2 English Language Learners ELL

VISUAL/SPATIAL

**Materials:** blocks, index cards
**Core Vocabulary:** layers, diagram, following instruction
**Common Use Verb:** will build
**Do Math** This strategy uses model building to develop the language and concept of volume in three dimensions.

- Say: "Today we ***will build*** rectangular prisms **following instructions** on a **diagram.**"
- Draw a **diagram.**

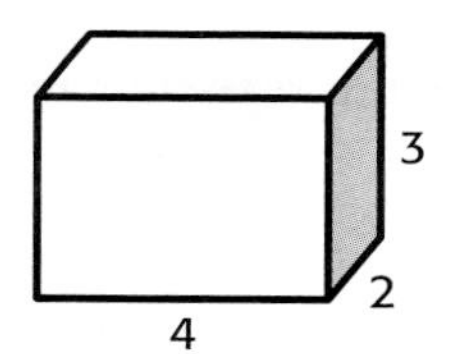


- Say: "According to this **diagram**, I have to put 2 rows of each of 4 blocks on the bottom, and then do 3 more **layers** of it."
- Model how to follow the **diagram.** Write **"layer"** next to the 3 to help reinforce the vocabulary.
- Students draw their own **diagrams** on an index card with up to 6 blocks on either side and exchange with someone in their group. They build one according to the **diagram.**
- Ask, "How many blocks did you use to make your prism?"

## Independent Work Options

### Option 1 Early Finishers OL AL

KINESTHETIC

**Materials:** rulers

- Challenge students to measure to the nearest inch the lengths, widths, and heights of several classroom objects that are rectangular prisms.
- Have students calculate the volume for each object they measured.
- You may extend the activity by having students build nets from their measurements.

### Option 2 Student Technology

**Math Online** macmillanmh.com

Personal Tutor • Extra Examples

# Volumes of Rectangular Prisms

## 1 Introduce

**Activity Choice 1 • *Hands-On***

- Review linear and square units of measure.
- Provide students with rulers and have them draw a line segment that is 1 inch long. **What kinds of things can you measure in inches?** Answers will vary.
- Sketch a rectangle on the board. **What can you measure about this rectangle using inches?** length, width, perimeter
- Next, have students use their rulers to draw a square that is 1 inch on each side. **What unit does the square show?** 1 square inch
- **What can you measure about the rectangle using square inches?** its area

## 2 Teach

### Scaffolding Questions

Give each student a centimeter cube and a ruler.

- **Is a centimeter cube a two- or three-dimensional figure? How do you know?** three-dimensional; it has length, width, and height.
- **What do you notice about the edges and faces of the cube?** The faces are congruent squares, and the edges are all the same length.
- Have students measure one edge. **What is the length?** 1 cm **width?** 1 cm **height?** 1 cm
- Tell students that the cube represents 1 cubic centimeter or 1 $cm^3$.
- **How can you use cubic units to measure three-dimensional figures?** Count the number of cubic units that fill a three-dimensional figure.

**GET READY to Learn**

Have students open their books and read the information in **Get Ready to Learn**. Introduce **volume**. As a class, work through **Examples 1 and 2**.



# Volumes of Rectangular Prisms

**GET READY to Learn**

Cathy's jewelry box is 6 inches long, 4 inches wide, and 3 inches high. What is the volume of Cathy's jewelry box?

As you learned in Lesson 12-8, volume is the amount of space a three-dimensional figure contains. Volume is measured in cubic units. A cubic unit has length, width, and height.

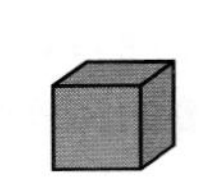

1 cubic unit

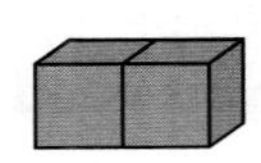

2 cubic units

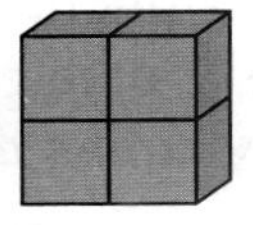

4 cubic units

Some common units of volume are *cubic inch*, *cubic foot*, *cubic yard*, *cubic centimeter*, and *cubic meter*.

You can find the volume of a rectangular prism by using models or a formula.

**Volume of a Rectangular Prism** — Key Concept

**Words** The volume $V$ of a rectangular prism is length $\ell$ times width $w$ times height $h$.

**Symbols** $V = \ell \times w \times h$

**Model**

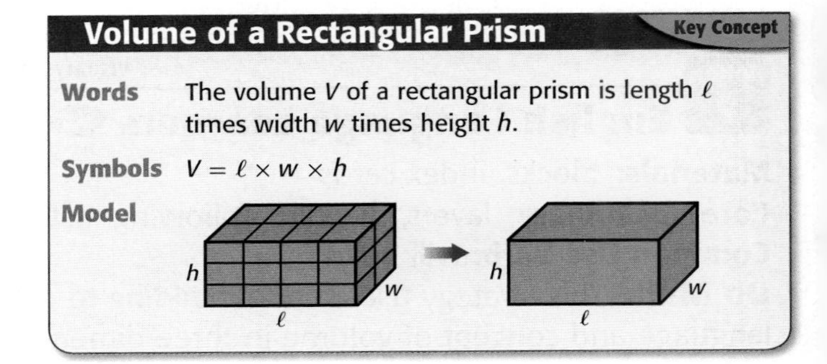

**Remember**

The volume of a solid equals the number of cubic units needed to fill the solid.

**Real-World EXAMPLE** Volume of a Prism

1 **JEWELRY BOX** **What is the volume of Cathy's jewelry box?**

### One Way: Use a Model

Count the number of 1-inch cubes that will fill the bottom of the rectangular prism. The prism is 6 cubes long and 4 cubes wide. So, there are 24 cubes on the bottom.

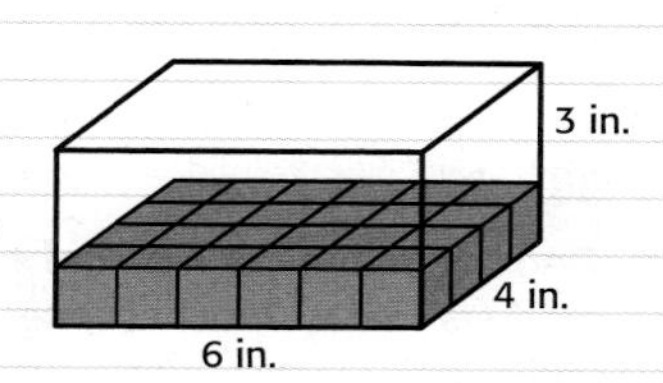


There are 3 layers of cubes. So, there are 3 × 24 or 72 cubes.

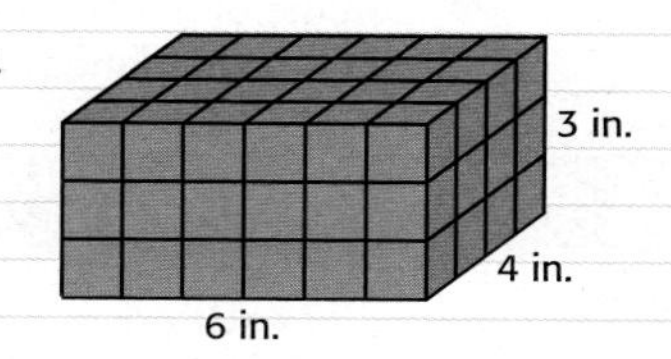


### Another Way: Select and Use a Formula

| | |
|---|---|
| $V = \ell \times w \times h$ | Formula for the volume of a rectangular prism |
| $V = 6 \times 4 \times 3$ | $\ell = 6, w = 4, h = 3$ |
| $V = 72$ | Multiply. |

The volume of the jewelry box is 72 cubic inches.

**EXAMPLE** Volume of a Prism

2 **Find the volume of the prism.**

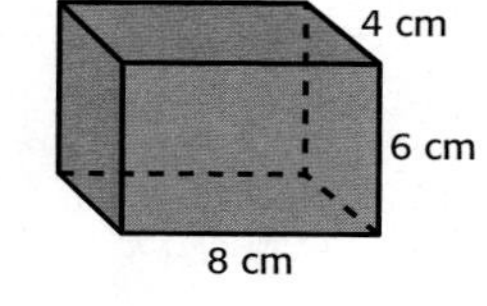


| | |
|---|---|
| $V = \ell \times w \times h$ | Formula for the volume |
| $V = 8 \times 4 \times 6$ | $\ell = 8, w = 4, h = 6$ |
| $V = 192$ | Multiply. |

The volume of the prism is 192 cubic centimeters.



### Volume of a Prism

**Example 2** Remind students of the procedure for multiplying three factors: multiply two factors first, then multiply that product by the third factor.

Remind students of the difference between *capacity* and *volume*. Volume refers to the space taken up by an object itself. Capacity refers to the amount of liquid or other substance a container can or does hold.

**ADDITIONAL EXAMPLES**

1. What is the volume of tank that is 6 inches long, 4 inches wide, and 4 inches tall? 96 cubic inches
2. Find the volume of the rectangular prism. 240 cubic meters

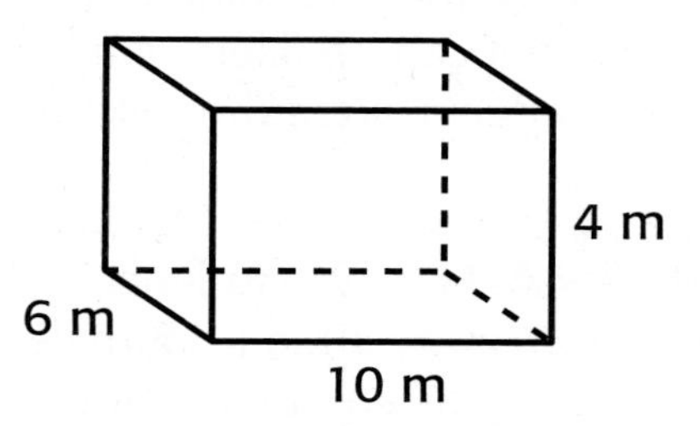


**CHECK What You Know**

As a class, have students complete Exercises 1–6 in **Check What You Know** as you observe their work.

**Exercise 7** Assess student comprehension before assigning practice exercises.

## BL Alternate Teaching Strategy

**If** students have trouble understanding the concept of volume…

**Then** use this reteach option:

1 Have each student make one rectangular prism using exactly 24 connecting cubes. Then ask students to show their prisms to the class and write the length, width, and height of the prism in units in a table you create on the board.

- Next, have students use the formula $V = \ell \times w \times h$ to find the volume of each prism in the table.
- Discuss how the different prisms all have the same volume of 24 cubic units. Have students explore how volume is related to length, width, and height.

# 3 Practice

Differentiate practice using these leveled assignments for Exercises 8–24.

| Level | Assignment |
|---|---|
| BL Below/Approaching Level | 7–10, 14–15, 18–19, 21–22 |
| OL On Level | 7–12, 14–22, 27 |
| AL Above/Beyond Level | 9–19 odd, 21–27 |

Have students discuss and complete the Higher Order Thinking problems. If students have difficulty describing a real-life situation for Exercise 27, encourage them to think about rectangular prisms that can be filled with something. Have students share their examples with the class.

**WRITING IN MATH** Have students complete Exercise 27 in their Math Journals. You may choose to use this as an optional formative assessment.

## CHECK What You Know

**Find the volume of each prism. Use models if needed.** See Examples 1 and 2 (p. LA19)

**1.**
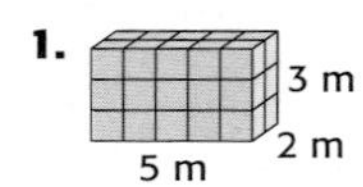


30 cubic meters

**2.**
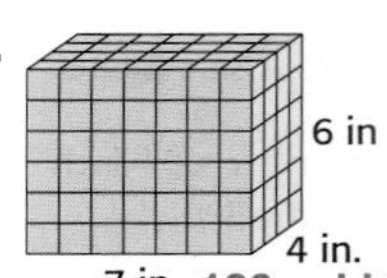


168 cubic inches

**3.**
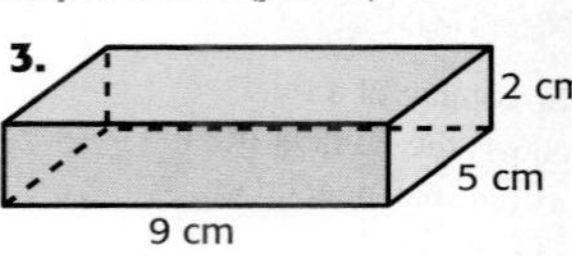


90 cubic centimeters

**4.** Find the volume of a box of animal crackers that is 7 inches long, 3 inches wide, and 9 inches high. 189 cubic inches

**5.** Find the volume of a toy box that is 5 feet long, 4 feet wide, and 3 feet high. 60 cubic feet

**6.** Talk About It Identify which units would be appropriate to measure the volume of a match box. Would it be reasonable to use the same units to measure the volume of a garage? Explain.

6. Sample answer: centimeters; no; the dimensions of a garage are too great to measure in centimeters

## Practice and Problem Solving

**Find the volume of each prism. Use models if needed.** See Examples 1 and 2 (p. LA19)

**7.**
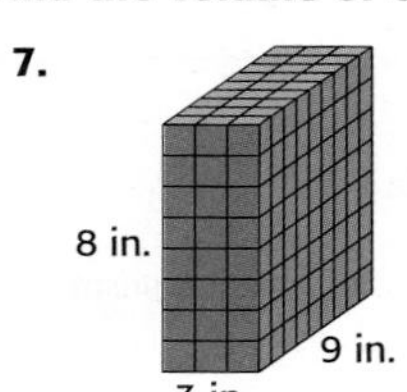

216 cubic inches

**8.**
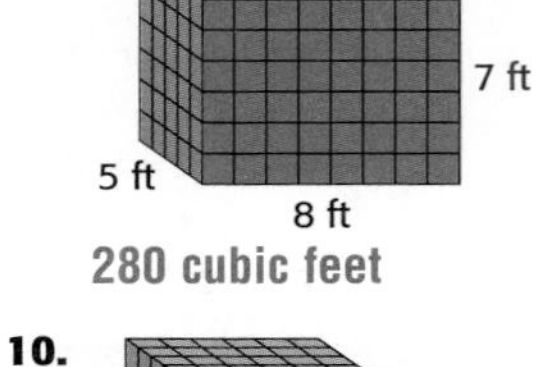


280 cubic feet

**9.**
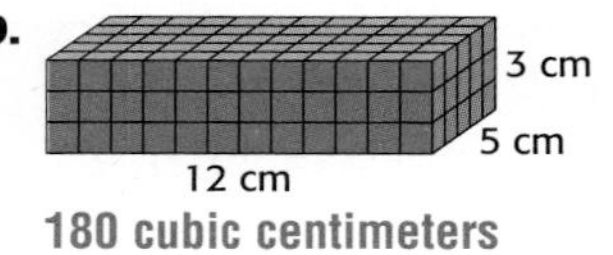

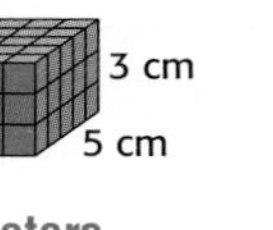

180 cubic centimeters

**10.**
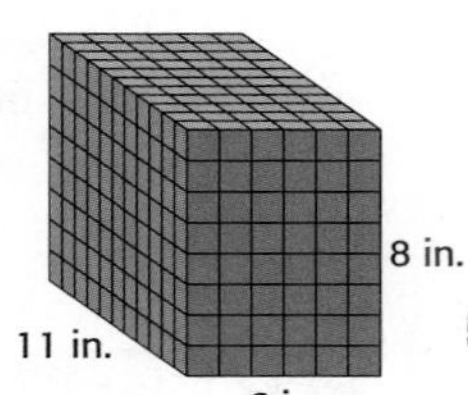


528 cubic inches

**11.**
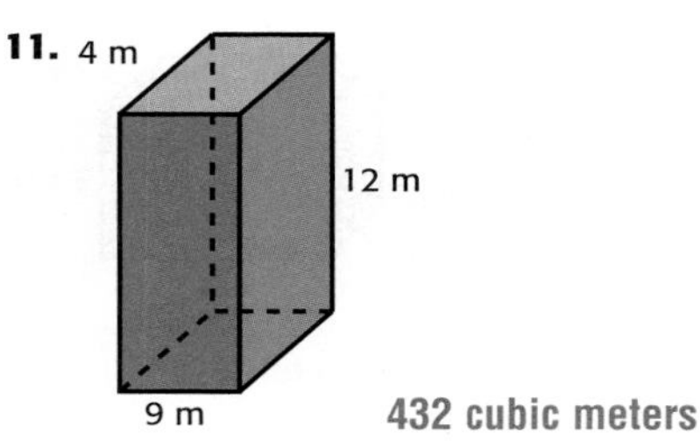


432 cubic meters

**12.**
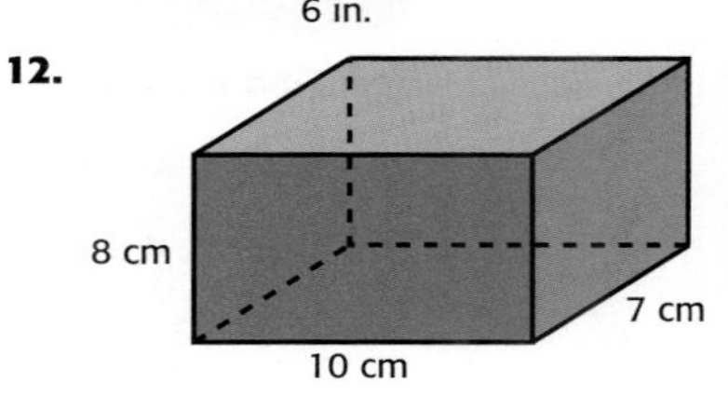


560 cubic centimeters



### COMMON ERROR!

Students may make multiplication errors when multiplying length × width × height. Remind students of the Commutative Property of Multiplication, which states that the order in which numbers are multiplied does not change the product. This means that the formula $V = \ell \times w \times h$ could also be written as $V = w \times \ell \times h$ or $V = h \times w \times \ell$, etc., and still produce the same volume. If students consistently make multiplication errors, suggest that they look carefully at the three factors (length, width, height) and arrange them in a new order that would make it easier to multiply.

**Find the volume of each prism.** See Examples 1, 2 (p. LA19)

**13.** Find the volume of the trunk of a car that is 5 feet long, 4 feet wide, and 2 feet high. **40 cubic feet**

**14.** A fish tank that has the shape of rectangular prism has a length of 4 feet, a width of 3 foot, and a height of 2 foot. What is its volume? **24 cubic feet**

**15.** A tissue box is 12 centimeters long, 8 centimeters wide, and 6 centimeters tall. What is its volume? **576 cubic centimeters**

**16.** Find the volume of a pool that is 20 feet long, 10 feet wide, and 5 feet high. **1,000 cubic feet**

**17.** Find the volume of a suitcase that is 12 centimeters long, 8 centimeters wide and 10 centimeters high. **960 cubic centimeters**

**18.** Copy and complete the table below.

| Length | Width | Height | Volume (cubic units) |
|---|---|---|---|
| 7 | 5 | 11 | ■ 385 |
| 12 | 3 | ■ 8 | 288 |
| ■ 6 | 10 | 9 | 540 |
| 11 | ■ 7 | 4 | 308 |

**For Exercises 19–22, the dimensions of various rectangular prisms are given. Find each volume. Then compare using >, <, or =.**

**19.** $\ell = 5,\ w = 9,\ h = 6$ ● $\ell = 10,\ w = 4,\ h = 8$ $<$

**20.** $\ell = 12,\ w = 10,\ h = 5$ ● $\ell = 6,\ w = 8,\ h = 11$ $>$

**21.** $\ell = 4,\ w = 12,\ h = 3$ ● $\ell = 6,\ w = 2,\ h = 12$ $=$

**22.** $\ell = 8,\ w = 10,\ h = 3$ ● $\ell = 4,\ w = 7,\ h = 9$ $<$

## H.O.T. Problems

**23. OPEN ENDED** Estimate the volume of a desk. Then measure the desk. Check your estimate by finding the actual volume. **See students' work.**

**24. NUMBER SENSE** How will the volume of the car trunk in Exercise 14 change if the length is doubled? Explain. **Sample answer: the volume will also double; the volume was 40 cubic feet and the new volume is 80 cubic feet**

**25. CHALLENGE** A store sells lunch boxes that measure 10 inches by 6 inches by 4 inches. How many lunch boxes will fit in a box that measures 20 inches by 12 inches by 8 inches? Explain. **Sample answer: 8; each dimension of the box is twice the size of each dimension of the lunch box, so, 4 lunch boxes will fit in the bottom of the box. 2 rows of lunch boxes will fit in the box.**

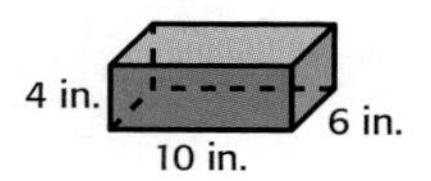


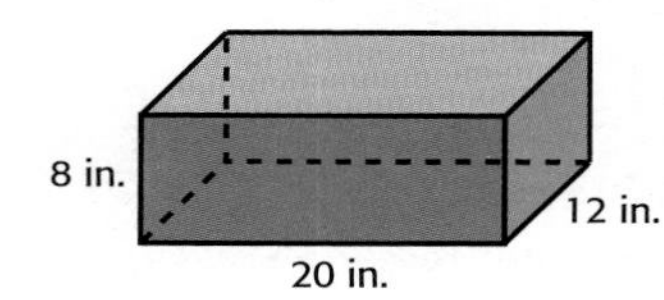


**26. WRITING IN MATH** Write about a real-life situation that can be solved by finding the volume of a prism. Then solve. **Sample answer: What is the volume of a dresser drawer that is 3 feet long, 2 feet wide, and 1 foot tall?**

# 4 Assess

## Formative Assessment

Tell students they have a box with a length of 6 cm, a width of 4 cm, and a height of 9 cm.

- **How could you use a model to find the volume of box?** Sample answer: Fill the bottom of the box with centimeter cubes and count or multiply to find the number of cubes in that layer: 24. Fill the box with 9 layers and multiply $9 \times 24$ to find the number of cubes, 216.
- **How could you use a formula to find the volume?** Use the formula $V = \ell \times w \times h$ and substitute, $V = 6\text{ cm} \times 4\text{ cm} \times 9\text{ cm}$. Multiply to get a volume of 216 $cm^3$.
- **Which method do you prefer to use? Why?** Answers will vary. Sample answer: I prefer to use the formula because it is the fastest method, and I can do it with pencil and paper.

**Quick Check**

**Are students continuing to struggle with finding the volumes of rectangular prisms?**

**If Yes** → Small Group Options (p. LA18B)

**If No** → Independent Work Options (p. LA18B)

# Looking Ahead 6 Surface Areas of Rectangular Prisms

## Lesson Planner

### Objective

Find the surface areas of rectangular prisms.

### Vocabulary

**surface area**

### Resources

**Materials:** grid paper, scissors, tape, ruler

## Daily Routine

Use these suggestions before beginning the lesson on p. LA22.

### 5-Minute Check

(Reviews Looking Ahead 5)

**Find the volume of each prism.**

1. length: 5 yd, width: 2 yd, height: 6 yd 60 cubic yards
2. length: 3 ft, width: 5 ft, height: 2 ft 30 cubic feet
3. length: 7 cm, width: 2 cm, height: 4 cm 56 cubic centimeters

### Problem of the Day

Find the volume of a rectangular prism with the length of 3 centimeters, width of 3 centimeters and height of 4 centimeters. 36 cubic centimeters

### Focus on Math Background

In Lesson 9-1, students learned that a net is a two-dimensional representation of a three-dimensional figure. In Lesson 11-6, students learned to measure the area of rectangles and squares. They have also learned to use the area formula. In this lesson students will learn about surface area. They will apply their prior knowledge to find the surface area of rectangular prisms.

### Building Math Vocabulary

Write the lesson vocabulary word and its definition on the board.

Have students write the new term in their notebooks or Math Journals. Provide pairs of students with various rectangular prisms. Have the partners work together to draw two-dimensional views of each of the faces. Explain how these views are related to the surface area of the prism.

# Differentiated Instruction

## Small Group Options

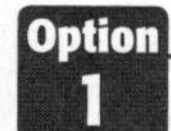

### Option 1 Gifted and Talented AL

**Materials:** grid paper, pencils

Explore what happens with the dimensions of a rectangular prism double.

- **Will the surface area double as well? Why or why not?** No, it will get 4 times as large because the area of each face quadruples.
- **What happens if only the height is doubled?** The surface area will be less than double.
- **What happens to the volume of the prism?** The new volume is 8 times greater than before.

### Option 2 English Language Learners ELL

**Materials:** different sized cardboard boxes, markers
**Core Vocabulary:** back/front, top/bottom, side A/B
**Common Use Verb:** locate

**Do Math** This strategy helps students vocalize the surface area of rectangular prisms.

- Model holding a box in front of you against your stomach. Put your hand on top of your head and say: "My top." Put your hand on the top of the box and say: "top of the box." Label it with a sticky note.
- Give each student a box. Have students repeat, labeling their box directly.
- Repeat for bottom, back, front, and sides A and B. Always reorientate and restate placement vocabulary after each label is placed.
- When students have labeled all the sides of their boxes, call out a placement and have all students place their hand appropriately.

## Independent Work Options

### Option 1 Early Finishers

**Materials:** boxes, rulers

- Students will measure the length, height and width of a box.
- Then they will find the volume of the box.
- They will find the area of each side of the box and then combine them to find the surface area of the box.

### Option 2 Student Technology

**Math Online** macmillanmh.com

Personal Tutor • Extra Practice

# Surface Areas of Rectangular Prisms

## 1 Introduce

**Activity Choice 1 • Hands-On**

Provide grid paper.

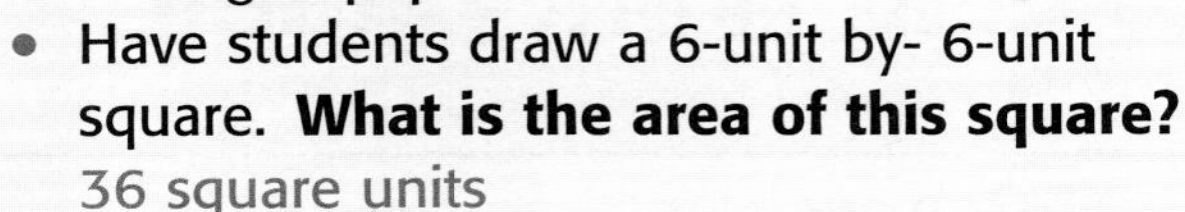

- Have students draw a 6-unit by- 6-unit square. **What is the area of this square?** 36 square units
- **How many faces does a cube have?** 6
- **Suppose each face has an area of 36 square units. What would be the area of all 6 faces?** 216 square units

## 2 Teach

### Scaffolding Questions

Have students measure the length, the width, and the height of their math books to the nearest half-inch.

- **Which dimensions would you use to find the area of the front and back covers?** length and width
- **Which dimensions would you use to find the area of the book's spine?** length and width

**GET READY to Learn**

**Hands-On Mini Lab** Distribute grid paper, scissors, and tape to students. Before they begin the activity, review the definition of a net. A net is a two-dimensional figure that can be used to make a three-dimensional figure. For Exercise 1, suggest that students make a table of each face and its area to make sure that they do not miss any of the faces.



# Surface Areas of Rectangular Prisms

In Lesson 9-1, you learned that a net is a two-dimensional figure that can be used to make a three-dimensional figure. You can also use a net to explore the sum of the areas of the faces of a prism.

**GET READY to Learn**

**Hands-On Mini Lab**

**Step 1** Draw and cut out the net below.

**Step 2** Fold along the dashed lines. Tape the edges.

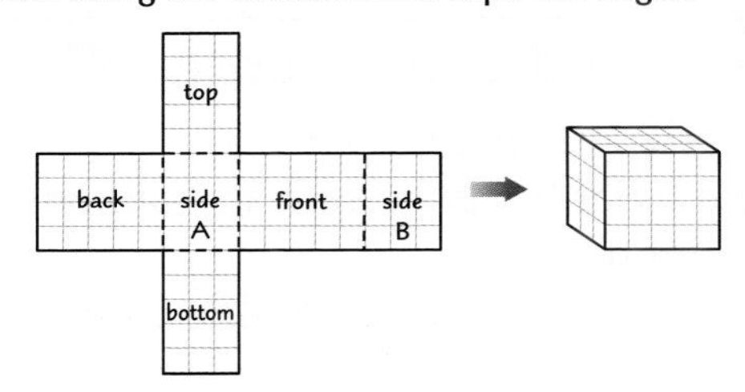


1. Copy the table shown.

| | Top | Bottom | Front | Back | Side A | Side B |
|---|---|---|---|---|---|---|
| Number of Squares | 15 | 15 | 20 | 20 | 12 | 12 |

2. Count the squares on each face of the prism.
3. Complete the table.
4. What is the sum of the areas of the faces of the prism? **94 square units**
5. What do you notice about the areas of opposite sides of the prism? **Sample answer: Opposite sides of the prism have the same area.**
6. How could you use the formula area = length × width to find the areas of the faces of the prism? **See margin.**



### Additional Answer

6. Sample answer: The formula area = length × width finds the area of a rectangle. Since each face of a rectangular prism is a rectangle, this formula can be used to find the area of each face.

The sum of the areas of all the faces of a prism is called the **surface area** of the prism.

## Surface Area of a Rectangular Prism

**Key Concept**

**Words** The surface area $S$ of a rectangular prism with length $\ell$, width $w$, and height $h$ is the sum of the areas of the faces.

**Model**

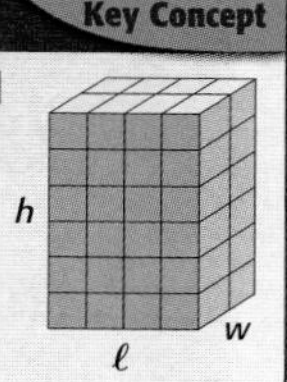


Counting is one way to find the surface area of a prism. You can also use the area formula for a rectangle, area = length × width to find a rectangular prism's surface area.

**EXAMPLE** Find Surface Area

**Find the surface area of the rectangular prism.**

Find the area of each prism face by using the formula area = length × width.

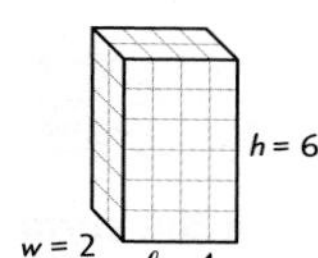


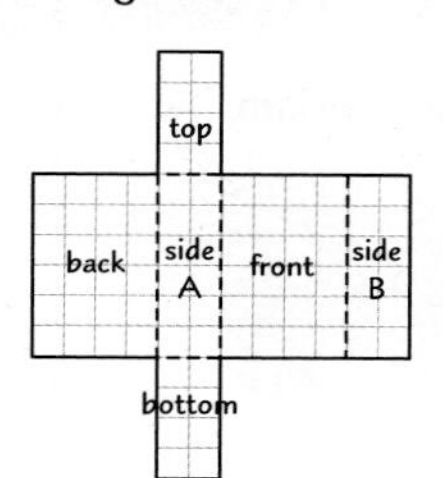


| top and bottom | front and back | side A and side B |
|---|---|---|
| $A = \ell \times w$ | $A = \ell \times w$ | $A = \ell \times w$ |
| $A = 4 \times 2$ | $A = 4 \times 6$ | $A = 2 \times 6$ |
| $A = 8$ | $A = 24$ | $A = 12$ |

Add the areas of all the faces to find the surface area of the prism.

| 8 | + | 8 | + | 12 | + | 12 | + | 24 | + | 24 | = | 88 |
|---|---|---|---|---|---|---|---|---|---|---|---|---|
| top | | bottom | | front | | back | | side A | | side B | | surface area |

So, the surface area of the prism is 88 square units.



## Real-World

**Example 1** Make sure students understand they must find the sum of the areas of all six faces. Have them draw a diagram and label the dimensions. Have them mark off the faces as they substitute the values into the formula to make sure they do not miss any of the faces.

## ADDITIONAL EXAMPLES

1. Find the surface area of the rectangular prism. 136 cm$^2$

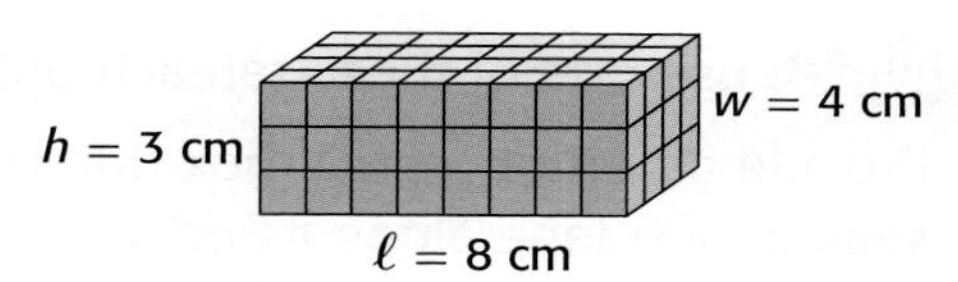


2. A box measures 13 inches long, 7 inches wide, and 4 inches deep. What is the surface area of the box? 342 in$^2$

## ✓ CHECK What You Know

As a class, have students complete Exercises 1–5 in **Check What You Know** as you observe their work.

**Exercise 5** Assess student comprehension before assigning practice exercises.

## BL Alternate Teaching Strategy

**If** students have trouble with surface area of rectangular prisms…

**Then** use one of these reteach options:

1 Provide an empty cereal box that has been sealed with tape along its edges. Have students cut it open and unfold it to form a net.

- **How many faces does the carton have?** 6
- **What kind of shape is each face?** rectangle
- **How can you find the total amount of surface area of cardboard?** Sample answer: Find the sum of the areas of the six rectangular faces.

# 3 Practice

Differentiate practice using these leveled assignments for Exercises 6–22.

| Level | Assignment |
|---|---|
| BL Below/Approaching Level | 6–12 even, 15, 17, 18, 21, 22 |
| OL On Level | 6–12, 14–18, 21, 22 |
| AL Above/Beyond Level | 7–19 odd, 20–22 |

Have students discuss and complete the Higher Order Thinking problems.

**WRITING IN ▸MATH** Have students complete Exercise xx in their Math Journals. You may choose to use this exercise as an optional formative assessment.

## ✓ CHECK What You Know

**Find the surface area of each rectangular prism.** See Example 1 (p LA23)

1. 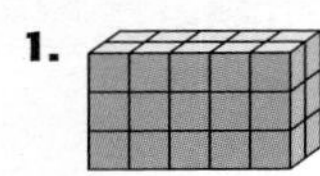
62 square units

2. 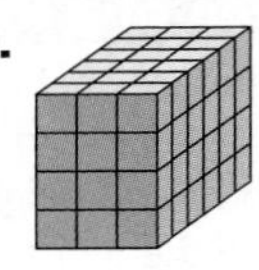
108 square units

3. 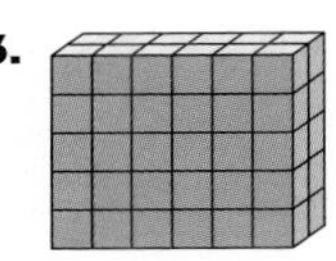
104 square units

4. Find the surface area of the gift box at the right. Use a model if needed. 136 square units

5. **Talk About It** Explain how a net can help you find the surface area of a rectangular prism.
Sample answer: Add all of the squares on the net.

## Practice and Problem Solving

**Find the surface area of each rectangular prism.** See Example 1 (p. LA23)

6. 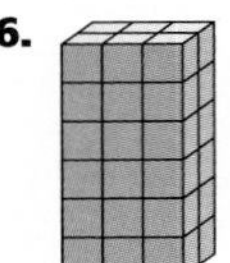
72 square units

7. 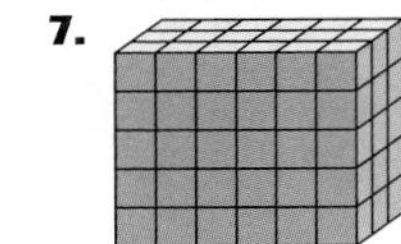
126 square units

8. 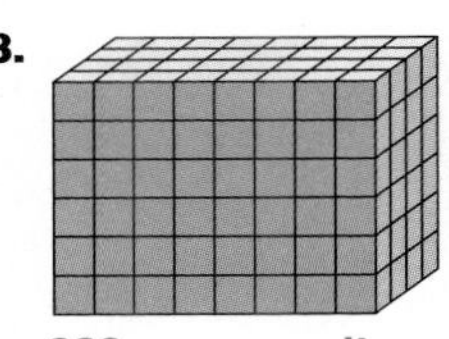
208 square units

9. 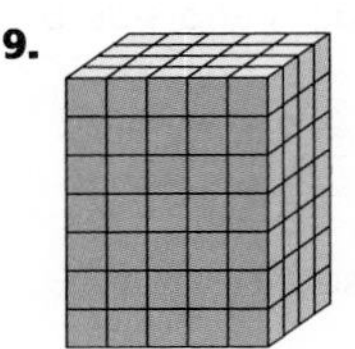
166 square units

10. 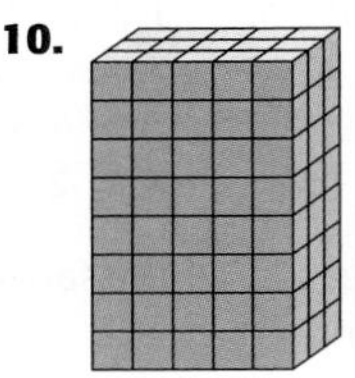
158 square units

11. 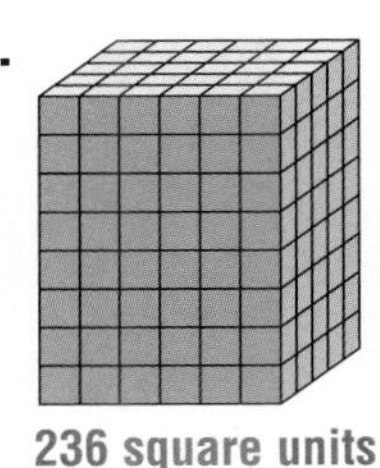
236 square units

12. Find the surface area of a music box that is 5 units long, 4 units wide, and 2 units tall. Use a model if needed.
76 square units

13. Find the surface area of a pencil box that is 8 units long, 5 units wide, and 2 units high. Use a model if needed.
132 square units

Find the surface area of each object. Use models if needed.

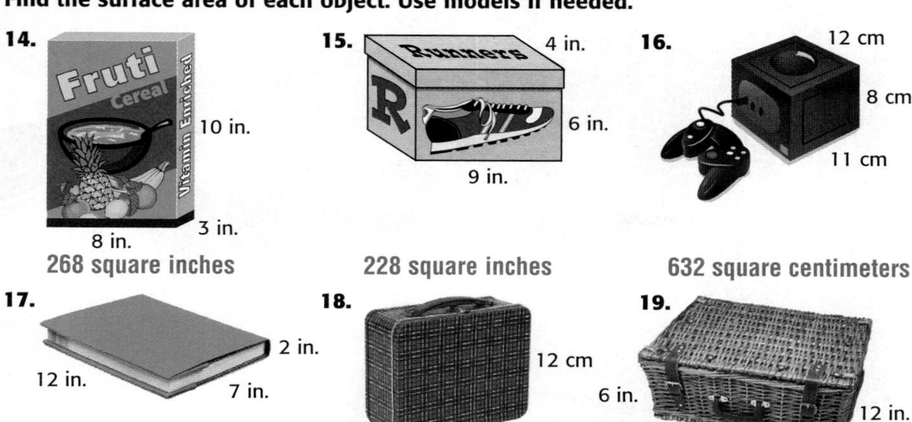


14. 268 square inches

15. 228 square inches

16. 632 square centimeters

17. 2 in. 12 in. 7 in.
244 square inches

18. 12 cm 8 cm 16 cm
832 square centimeters

19. 6 in. 12 in. 18 in.
792 square inches

**For Exercises 20–22, use the rectangular prisms at the right.**

**20.** What is the surface area of figure A? 82 square units

**21.** Which figure has a greater surface area? Explain. Sample answer: figure B, 104 square units $>$ 82 square units

**22.** If the lengths of the sides of figure B are doubled, will the surface area be four times greater? Explain. Sample answer: yes; the new surface area would be $4 \times 104$ or 416 square units

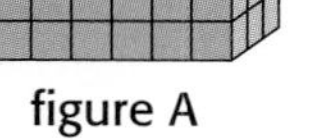
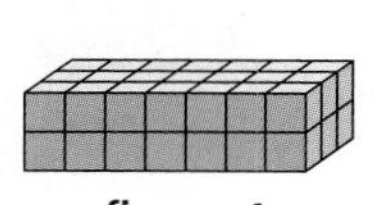
figure A

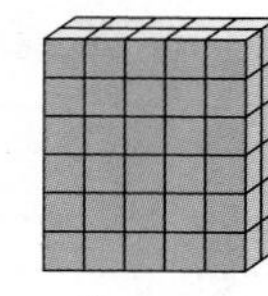
figure B

25. Sample answer: How much wrapping paper is needed to wrap a present that is 8 inches long, 6 inches wide, and 4 inches high?

## H.O.T. Problems

**23. OPEN ENDED** Draw a rectangular prism that has a surface area of 148 square units. See students' work.

**24. CHALLENGE** Find the surface area of the figure at the right. 60 square units

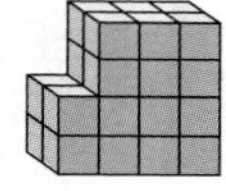

**25. WRITING IN ▶MATH** Write a problem about a real-world situation in which you would need to find the surface area of a rectangular prism.



# 4 Assess

## Formative Assessment

- **Describe the steps you would use to find the surface area of a rectangular prism.** Sample answer: Find the area of the front and back, top and bottom, and two sides. Add the areas of the faces together.
- **Explain what $2 \times \ell \times w$ means.** Sample answer: Since the top and bottom of the rectangular prism are congruent, find the area of one and multiply by 2 to get the area of both.

**Quick Check** **Are students continuing to struggle with surface area of rectangular prisms?**

**If Yes** → Small Group Options (p. LA22B)

**If No** → Independent Work Options (p. LA22B)

**Ticket Out the Door** Select a classroom object and give its measurements. Have students determine the size of the box in which it would fit and the least amount of paper they would need to wrap that box.

### COMMON ERROR!

**Exercises 12 and 13** Students may have trouble finding the area of all the faces of the rectangular prism without a diagram. Have them make a drawing of the prism and label the dimensions. Have them count to see that they have included all six faces.

# Problem-Solving Projects

The **Problem-Solving Projects** apply the math concepts and skills that the students have learned during the year. By completing the projects, students will use and connect Grade 4 mathematics to everyday situations and activities.

## End-of-Year Assessment

Use the **End-of-Year Test** to assess student comprehension of the skills and concepts presented in Grade 4.

**Chapter 15 Resource Masters**

End-of-Year Test (p. 66)

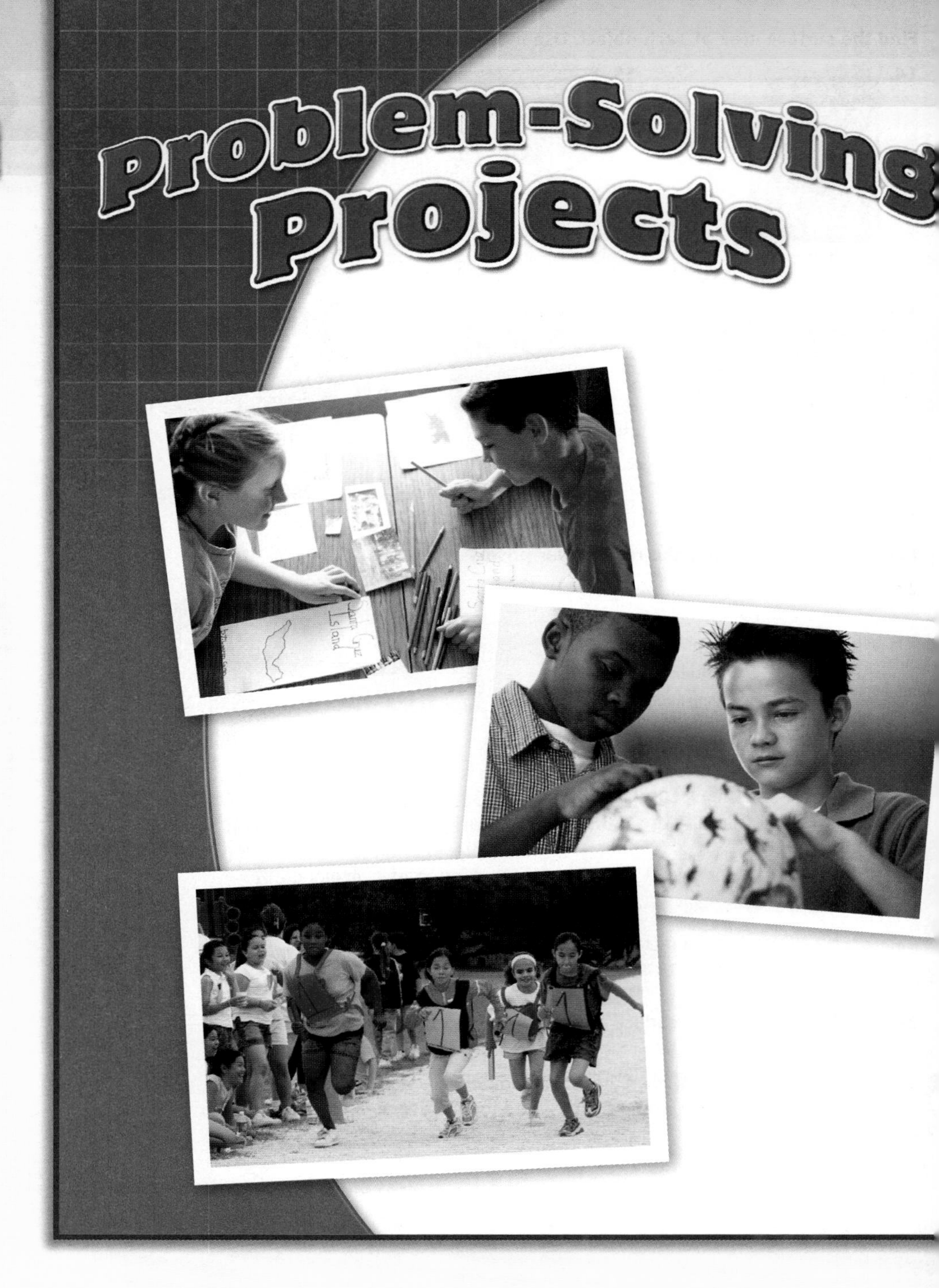

# Problem-Solving Projects

# Lesson Planner

## Objectives

Students create a math game based on the chapters they have covered in class.

## Resources

**Materials:** paper poster board, markers

### Day 1

- List the chapters in your math book. Then have students name concepts from the chapters.
- Encourage students to be specific with their concepts. For example, instead of naming *multiplication*, students could name *multiplication facts.*
- Divide students into small groups.
- Have groups choose a concept from among those listed. Tell groups that the concept they have chosen is going to be the basis for a math game that they are going to create.

### Day 2

- In their groups, students brainstorm specific ideas about their games, such as important vocabulary words, facts, and figures that will be needed to play the game.
- Groups should then determine how the game will be played. They should include several different strategies for the game.
- Students develop a scoring system for their game. They should determine how points are scored and if points can be lost as well as won.

Have you ever made up a board game? In this project, you can invent a new board game or combine two board games that already exist.

#### Getting Started

**Day 1 Choose the Subject**

- Decide what your game will be about by choosing one of the chapters that was covered in math class this year.
- Determine which concepts in the chapter you want to focus on, such as multiplication facts, two-dimensional figures, or fractions.

**Day 2 Brainstorm Ideas**

- Work as a group to determine what facts, figures, or important vocabulary will be a part of your game.
- Discuss different ways this game can be played.
- Design several alternative ways to play the game.

P2

- Discuss a point system.
- How many points can you earn and how can you earn them?
- Can you lose points? How?

**Day 3 Rules and Regulations**

- Choose one of the alternative games that were designed on Day 2.
- Write clear instructions for the game. Include any rules or regulations that may affect the scoring and outcome of the game. All players must have a fair chance of winning.
- Give some examples of how to play and score the game.

**Day 4 Create and Practice**

- Review the instructions for the game. List any items that you will need to make, such as pictures of shapes or flash cards.
- Make all items that are needed to play the game.
- Make a score card or board to keep track of the score.
- Practice your game to make sure that it works.

**Day 5 Presentation Day**

- Present the instructions along with the rules for the game to the class.
- Ask for volunteers to play your game.
- Play and enjoy.

## Wrap Up

- Could you use this game for other math concepts? Describe what changes would need to be made.
- Do all players of your game have a fair chance of winning? Explain.
- How would the game have been different if you chose a different alternative game?

P3

Projects

## Day 3

- Students choose which strategy they are going to use to play their game.
- Using the strategy, they write rules to the game that specify how the game is to be played and ensure fairness.
- Ask students to include several specific examples of how the game is to be played.

## Day 4

- Have groups review their game instructions and make any necessary changes.
- Provide students with any materials they will need to create game pieces, game boards or other items. Ask students to create a scorecard.
- Have students practice their games to make sure that everything works.

## Day 5

- In groups, students present their games to the rest of the class. They should explain the rules and use their examples to demonstrate how the game is played.
- As a class or in groups, have students play each other's games.
- Discuss which games were most successful and why.

## Wrap-Up

- Use the Wrap-Up questions to assess students' work.
- **Which new game was the most creative? the most fun? the most difficult?** Answers will vary.
- **Which games can the class play together?** Answers will vary.

# Lesson Planner

## Objectives

Students will:

- plan a dinner for a real-world special occasion for their family, and
- calculate the total cost of the meal as well as the cost per person.

## Review Vocabulary

**cost**

## Resources

**Materials:** grocery store advertisements, Internet access

### Day 1

- Have students select an occasion for which a large meal is prepared.
- Students choose the day and time for the celebration.
- Make a timeline to help organize the preparation for the celebration based on the amount of time before the event takes place. Students may use a calendar to help with the organization.

### Day 2

- Students plan a meal for the number of guests who will attend a celebration of a special occasion at their home. The meal should include at least one main dish and three side dishes. The meal should also include traditional or ethnic foods that are usually prepared for this celebration.
- Students find recipes at home for dishes that need to be prepared.
- Students adjust the amounts of the ingredients needed to double the recipes.

Plan a celebration for your family. It can be a known holiday, special event, or you can create your own holiday.

### Getting Started

**Day 1 Decide What to Celebrate**

- Decide on a special occasion for your family. Some examples are a family reunion, Independence Day, or "Juneteenth."
- Choose the day and time to have this celebration.
- Use a calendar to calculate the number of weeks, days, and hours that you have until the celebration.
- Create a timeline to help you organize how to prepare for the celebration.

P4

**Day 2 The Number Makes a Difference**

- Think carefully about the number of people you want to invite.
- Plan a meal that will feed everyone.
- Using cookbooks and family recipes, choose foods for the celebration.
- Double the recipes if needed.
- Calculate the amounts of each ingredient you will need.
- Calculate a total for all food items.

**Day 3 What's the Cost?**

- Use the list of ingredients as a shopping list.
- Determine the cost of each item by using the Internet or advertisements from a grocery store.
- Add the prices together to find the total cost of the ingredients.
- Choose any other food items you might want to serve. Determine their cost and add it to your previous total.

**Day 4 What Else Do I Need to Buy?**

- Make a list of any nonfood items that may be needed.
- Research the cost for these items.
- Make a table to show the amount spent on food and nonfood items.
- Determine the total cost for food and nonfood items.

**Day 5 Presentation Day**

- Present your celebration to the class. Use your timeline to describe your plan.
- Share what you will serve, the total cost for each item, and the amount spent for each individual.
- Explain your reasoning for the total cost.

## Wrap Up

- Why did you choose this celebration?
- Would you like your family to use your plan for this celebration?
- Did the price of the food help you decide what you would have at your celebration?

P5

Projects

## Day 3

- Students use the Internet or grocery store advertisements to determine the total cost of each individual item they need for recipes. Then they should find the total cost of the meal.
- Students use the list of items as a shopping list.
- Choose other food items.
- Add the cost of all items to get the total.

## Day 4

- Have students research the cost of any nonfood items they need for their celebrations.
- Students calculate the total cost of food and nonfood items for the celebration.
- Students calculate the total amount spent per person.
- Make a table to show the amount spent on food and nonfood items.

## Day 5

- Students present their celebrations to the class. They share what they served, the total cost for each item, and the amount spent per individual.
- Students also share the meaning of the celebration, the number of people they invited, and how they used math to plan the celebration.
- Students explain their reasoning for the total cost.

# Wrap-Up

- Use the Wrap-Up questions to assess students' work.
- **Why did you choose this celebration?** Answers will vary.
- **Would you like your family to use your plan for this celebration?** Answers will vary.
- **Did the price of food help you decide what you would serve at your celebration?** Answers will vary.

# Lesson Planner

## Objectives

Students will:

- research the area in which they live, finding its land area, population, elevation, and other details,
- create a survey to find out what would make it a better place and display their data, and
- create a map of the community, using their own scale.

## Review Vocabulary

**scale, bar graph, survey**

## Resources

**Materials:** Internet, paper, pencils, atlas or maps of the community

### Day 1

- Have students research their community.
- Students should find the land area used for their community.
- Find the area used for parks and recreation.
- Determine the area used for housing.

### Day 2

- Students create survey questions about possible improvements to their community. The questions should be multiple choice so that they can graph the data.
- Students poll their classmates to see what they think about making the community a better place to live.
- Students create a bar graph to display the results of their survey.

Have you ever wanted to design a community? When city planners construct a new development, they create a model of the development. Then that development becomes a community.

### Getting Started

**Day 1 Where Do You Live?**

- Research your community. What interesting information can you find?
- Find the total area of the land used for your community.
- Find the area used for parks and recreation.
- Determine the area used for housing.

P6

### Day 2 Make It Better

- Think about what makes your community a nice place to live.
- Survey the class for ideas on how to improve communities.
- Create a bar graph to display the data you have collected.

### Day 3 Various Viewpoints

- Discuss with other students whether their surveys showed similar data. If not, explain why.
- Research the cost of one idea from the survey.
- Identify three ways that you can raise money to improve your community.

### Day 4 Map It Out

- Examine the scale of a map of your community. The scale is a chosen distance that represents an actual distance. For example, you may wish to use a scale of 1 inch = 1 mile.
- Recreate the map of your community using a different scale than what is shown on the map.
- Look at your classmates' maps. What do you notice about the scales and the sizes of the maps?

### Day 5 Presentation Day

- Present your community research, survey, and map to the class.
- Is there anything you wanted to add to your community that no one else thought of?

### Wrap Up

- How would changing the scale of your map affect the map?
- How can you work toward improving your community?
- Who can help you achieve your community improvement goals?

P7

Projects

## Day 3

- Allow students who had similar survey questions to collaborate with each other to see if their data matches.
- Discuss with students how survey data can be used to mislead people.
- Students research the cost of one of the ideas from the survey.
- Ask students to decide on three ways to raise money to improve the community.

## Day 4

- Students use a map of their community. They look at the scale of the map and choose another scale to use for their own maps.
- Students recreate a map of their community using the scale they have chosen. Be sure to review the definition of scale on a map. Students may also include improvements to the community.
- Ask students to compare the way their maps look with those of students who chose a different scale.

## Day 5

- Have students present their survey results and maps to the class.
- Discuss information about the community that the students did not know before doing this project. Also discuss what students might like to add to the community that no one has thought of.

# Wrap-Up

- Use the Wrap-Up questions to assess students' work.
- **How would changing the scale of your map affect the map?** Answers will vary.
- **How can you work toward improving your community?** Answers will vary.
- **Who can help you achieve your community improvement goals?** Answers will vary.

# Lesson Planner

## Objectives

Students will plan a road trip in which they determine their destination, cost, and route for the trip.

## Review Vocabulary

**gallon, mile**

## Resources

**Materials:** U.S. map or atlas, ruler, calculator, daily calendar pages, 4 × 6 index cards, markers, Internet

### Day 1

- Have student groups plan a road trip, which must cross at least three states and is about 500 miles from home.
- Students can use U.S. maps and atlases to determine all possible combinations of their destinations. Review with students the idea of scale, and help them use their rulers to measure distances.
- Students find the distance to their destinations.
- Have students estimate all the costs for their trip.
- Then have students create a table with the estimates to organize their data as they collect it.

### Day 2

- Have students estimate how long the trip would take if they traveled 60 miles per hour.
- Have students calculate how many times they will have to stop for gas if their car gets 30 miles per gallon and holds 18 gallons of gas.
- Have students calculate how much they will spend for gas for the trip if gas costs $2.50 per gallon.
- Have students make a list of items to bring on the trip.
- Tell students to place the cost of the gas on the table created in Day 1.

Plan a road trip in which you will determine the destination, cost, and route for the trip.

### Getting Started

**Day 1 Plan the Trip**

- Plan a trip that includes at least three states and is about 500 miles from home.
- Use a map or atlas to determine all possible combinations of states you can visit.
- Choose the route for your trip. Add all the distances to determine the total miles to your final destination.
- Multiply by two to determine the round-trip mileage.
- Estimate all costs for the trip.
- Create a table to organize and display this data.

Projects

**Day 2 Research Items Needed for Your Trip**

- Estimate how long the trip will take if you travel 60 miles per hour.
- Determine how many stops for gas you will need to make if your car can travel 30 miles per gallon and holds 18 gallons of gas.
- Write an equation to determine how much you will spend on gas for the entire trip if gas costs $2.50 per gallon.
- Place the cost of the gas in the table from Day 1.

**Day 3 What To Do When You Get There**

- Research what you would like to do when you reach your final destination.
- Design a calendar for the week. Account for how each hour is spent.
- Draw a clock next to each event to show the time it will occur. Write the elapsed time for each event.
- Research prices on the places you will visit and the food you will eat. Add these figures to the table that was created on Day 1.

**Day 4 What Is the Cost?**

- Research prices for the hotel. Place this on the table from Day 1.
- Calculate the total cost of the trip using the table from Day 1.
- Prepare a poster to present to the class that shows the information about your trip.

**Day 5 Presentation Day**

- Present your trip to the class.
- Include a summary of where you would go, your calendar, the total cost, and the poster you created.

## Wrap Up

- How many possible destinations did your group identify?
- Why did you choose your destination?
- Did the costs of places help you decide where you wanted to go?
- Estimate how much faster you will arrive at your destination if you travel 65 miles per hour. Explain.

P9

## Day 3

- Students research activities they would like to do when they reach their final destination.
- Students design a week-long calendar in which they write down what they do for each hour of the day. You may wish to give them blank daily calendar pages to record their activities.
- Have students research prices for the places they will go and food they will eat.
- Students put these figures into the table created on Day 1.

## Day 4

- Have students research the cost of lodging for their stay. Place the amount in the table.
- Have students calculate the total cost for their trip, using the prices that they found during the previous days.
- Students prepare posters showing the information about the trip.

## Day 5

- Student groups present trips to the class.
- Each student presents his or her poster and has a speaking role in presenting the summary of the trip, the schedule of activities on the trip, the total cost of the trip, or recommendations for others.

# Wrap-Up

- Use the Wrap-Up questions to assess students' work.
- **How many possible destinations did your group identify? Why did you choose your destination?** Answers will vary.
- **Was the cost a factor in your choice?** Answers will vary.
- **Estimate how much faster you will arrive at your destination if you travel 65 miles per hour. Explain.** Answers will vary.

# Student Handbook

## Built-In Workbooks



## Reference

# How to Use the Student Handbook

The Student Handbook is the additional skill and reference material found at the end of books. The Student Handbook can help answer these questions.

### What If I Need More Practice?

You, or your teacher, may decide that working through some additional problems would be helpful. The **Extra Practice** section provides these problems for each lesson so you have ample opportunity to practice new skills.

### What If I Need to Prepare for a Standardized Test?

The **Preparing for Standardized Tests** section provides worked-out examples and practice problems for multiple-choice, short-response, and extended response questions.

### What if I Want to Learn Additional Concepts and Skills?

Use the Concepts and Skills Bank section to either refresh your memory about topics you have learned in other math classes or learn new math concepts and skills.

### What If I Forget a Vocabulary Word?

The **English-Spanish Glossary** provides a list of important, or difficult, words used throughout the textbook. It provides a definition in English and Spanish as well as the page number(s) where the word can be found.

### What If I Need to Find Something Quickly?

The **Index** alphabetically lists the subjects covered throughout the entire textbook and the pages on which each subject can be found.

### What If I Forget Measurement Conversions, Multiplication Facts, or Formulas?

Inside the back cover of your math book is a list of measurement conversions and formulas that are used in the book. You will also find a multiplication table inside the back cover.

# Extra Practice

## Lesson 1-1

Pages 17–19

**Write the value of the underlined digit.**

**1.** 1,637 600 **2.** 37,904 30,000 **3.** 56,572 70 **4.** 209,631 200,000

**Write each number in word form and expanded form.**

**5.** 2,493 **6.** 6,319 **7.** 7,085 **8.** 9,160

**9.** 28,482 **10.** 71,045 **11.** 523,608 **12.** 347,281

5–12. See Student Handbook Answer Appendix.

**Write each number in standard form and expanded form.**

**13.** fifty-six thousand, seven hundred twenty 56,720; 50,000 + 6,000 + 700 + 20

**14.** two hundred thirty-four thousand, eight hundred three 234,803; 200,000 + 30,000 + 4,000 + 800 + 3

## Lesson 1-2 1–11. See Extra Practice Answer Appendix.

Pages 22–25

**Write each number in word form and expanded form.**

**1.** 9,005 **2.** 19,860 **3.** 26,010 **4.** 360,508

**5.** 408,040 **6.** 26,053,107 **7.** 730,000,520 **8.** 800,530,700

**Write each number in standard form and expanded form.**

**9.** nine million, twenty-four thousand, ten

**10.** six hundred thirty-five million, eight hundred fifty-seven thousand, five

**11.** Write in word form and standard form.

300,000 + 20,000 + 1,000 + 50 + 8

## Lesson 1-3

Pages 26–27

**Solve. Use the four-step plan.**

**1.** Mrs. Beal's students earned a class party. An extra large pizza cost $28. If she bought 3 pizzas, how much did she spend? $84

**2.** Carisa can draw 3 pictures in the morning and 3 pictures in the afternoon. If she draws for 5 days, how many pictures can she make? 30 pictures

**3.** Tom watched 45 movies this year. Each movie was two hours long. How many hours did he spend watching movies this year? 90 hours

**4.** A basketball game has 4 quarters. If 5 players each score 2 points during each quarter, how many total points are scored? 40 points



## Lesson 1-4

Pages 28–30

**Compare. Use >, <, or =.**

**1.** 9,719 ● 9,791 <

**2.** 3,780 ● 3,080 >

**3.** 34,925 ● 34,952 <

**4.** 89,629 ● 89,635 <

**5.** 47,283 ● 42,283 >

**6.** 72,036 ● 72,300 <

**7.** 325,614 ● 235,614 >

**8.** 758,438 ● 758,438 =

**9.** 7,863,403 ● 7,863,304 >

**10.** 9,604,138 ● 9,064,946 >

**Copy and complete to make the number sentence true.**

**11.** 4,■58 < 4,859 8 or less

**12.** 34,199 = 3■,199 4

**13.** 214,166 > 2■4,166 0

**14.** 5,877,820 > 5,877,8■0 0 or 1

## Lesson 1-5

Pages 32–34

**Order the numbers from greatest to least.**

**1.** 1,443; 1,434; 1,444; 1,344 — 1,444; 1,443; 1,434; 1,344

**2.** 6,519; 6,600; 3,941; 4,872 — 6,600; 6,519; 4,872; 3,941

**3.** 19,400; 9,400; 19,004; 10,440 — 19,400; 19,004; 10,440; 9,400

**4.** 52,951; 49,384; 51,954; 52,865 — 52,951; 52,865; 51,954; 49,384

**5.** 85,610; 85,185; 85,611; 85,625 — 85,625; 85,611; 85,610; 85,185

**6.** 94,846; 49,846; 84,694; 46,948 — 94,846; 84,694; 49,846; 46,948

**7.** 275,391; 2,086,344; 258,983 — 2,086,344; 275,391; 258,983

**8.** 361,259; 361,084; 61,999; 846,465 — 846,465; 361,259; 361,084; 61,999

**9.** 568,208; 559,876; 59,986; 58,869 — 568,208; 559,876; 59,986, 58,869

**10.** 768,635; 792,456; 741,056; 78,318 — 792,456; 768,635; 741,056; 78,318

**11.** 3,849,257; 38,492,570; 38,492,057 — 38,492,570; 38,492,057; 3,849,257

**12.** 4,608,056; 4,608,942; 4,608,924 — 4,608,942; 4,608,924; 4,608,056

## Lesson 1-6

Pages 36–39

**Round each number to the given place-value position.**

**1.** 451; hundred 500

**2.** 949; hundred 900

**3.** 4,965; thousand 5,000

**4.** 20,368; thousand 20,000

**5.** 36,801; hundred 36,800

**6.** 42,204; ten thousand 40,000

**7.** 70,988; thousand 71,000

**8.** 83,756; ten 83,760

**9.** 437,947; ten thousand 440,000

**10.** 455,877; ten 455,880

**11.** 849, 604; thousand 850,000

**12.** 934,567; hundred thousand 900,000

## Lesson 1-7
Pages 40–41

**Use the four-step plan to solve.**

1. Lisa lives 7 miles from school. She bikes to school and back every day. How many miles does she bike in 1 school week? 70 miles
2. A chicken runs 5 miles an hour. An ostrich runs 40 miles an hour. How many hours would it take a chicken to run the same distance it took an ostrich to run in two hours? 16 hrs
3. Aaron bought a shirt that cost $27 and a hat that cost $3. How much change will he receive if he pays with two $20 bills? $10
4. A bag of 15 oranges costs $20. Oranges that are sold individually cost $2. Is it cheaper to buy 15 oranges in a bag or 15 oranges sold individually? Explain. bag; 15 individual oranges cost $30, which is more than $20.

## Lesson 2-1
Pages 55–57

**Copy and complete each number sentence. Identify the property or rule used.**

1. $20 - ■ = 0$ 20; Subtraction Rule
2. $14 + 37 = ■ + 14$ 37; Commutative Property (+)
3. $7 + (4 + 8) = (7 + 4) + ■$ 8; Associative Property (+)
4. $197 + 0 = ■$ 197; Identity Property
5. $233 - ■ = 233$ 0; Subtraction Rule
6. $72 + 9 = ■ + 72$ 9; Commutative Property (+)
7. $(14 + 3) + 8 = 14 + (3 + ■)$ 8; Associative Property (+)
8. $863 + 44 = ■ + 863$ 44; Commutative Property (+)
9. $21 + (■ + 9) = (21 + 17) + 9$ 17; Associative Property (+)
10. $541 - ■ = 0$ 541; Subtraction Rule

## Lesson 2-2
Pages 58–61

**Estimate. Round to the indicated place value.**

1. 43 + 29; tens $40 + 30 = 70$
2. 664 + 49; tens $660 + 50 = 710$
3. 1,329 + 755; hundreds $1{,}300 + 800 = 2{,}100$
4. 9,488 + 2,061; thousands $9{,}000 + 2{,}000 = 11{,}000$
5. \$34,163 + \$29,982; hundreds \$34,200 + \$30,000 = \$64,200
6. 59 − 34; tens $60 - 30 = 30$
7. 859 − 42; tens $860 - 40 = 820$
8. 2,495 − 468; hundreds $2{,}500 - 500 = 2{,}000$
9. \$6,295 − \$1,402; thousands \$6,000 − \$1,000 = \$5,000
10. 37,423 − 18,196; ten thousands $40{,}000 - 20{,}000 = 20{,}000$



## Lesson 2-3
Pages 62–63

**Tell whether an estimate or exact answer is needed. Then solve.**

1. Nina bought a CD that cost $11. She gave the cashier a $20 bill. About how much change should she get back? estimate; about $10
2. Carlos wants to buy a new football that costs $32. He earns $6 every week delivering newspapers. How many weeks will it take to save enough money for the ball? exact; 6 weeks
3. The 29 students in Jin's science class are riding in vans on a field trip. Each van can hold 8 students. How many vans will be needed? exact; 4 vans
4. Mika spends about $1\frac{1}{2}$ hours practicing the piano each day, Monday through Friday. About how many hours does she practice each month? estimate; about 40 h

## Lesson 2-4
Pages 64–67

**Find each sum. Check your work by estimating.**

1. 456 + 233 = 689
2. \$3,879 + \$348 = \$4,227
3. 5,678 + 2,431 = 8,109
4. \$38,406 + \$6,744 = \$45,150
5. 60,483 + 98,218 = 158,701
6. \$32,819 + \$67,375 = \$100,194
7. 357,816 + 93,402 = 451,218
8. \$572,938 + \$118,476 = \$691,414
9. \$983,107 + \$645,815 = \$1,628,922

## Lesson 2-5
Pages 72–74

**Subtract. Use addition or estimation to check.**

1. 721 − 563 = 158
2. \$807 − \$328 = \$479
3. 926 − 644 = 282
4. \$1,766 − \$819 = 947
5. 9,663 − 5,201 = 4,462
6. \$6,741 − \$3,983 = \$2,758
7. \$24,509 − \$7,625 = \$16,884
8. 55,788 − 34,223 = 21,565
9. 71,864 − 49,667 = 22,197

## Lesson 2-6

Pages 76–77

**Use any strategy to solve. Tell what strategy you used.**

1. Mr. Lee spent about $23 on paintbrushes, $50 dollars on paint, and $15 on colored chalk. How much did he spend on art supplies? $88
2. Tia is hanging lights around her window. The window is a square with sides that are 28 inches. How many inches of lights will Tia need? 112 in.
3. The cats in the animal shelter eat 18 pounds of food each day. How many pounds of food do the cats eat each week? 126 lbs
4. Casey has $6. He buys a sandwich for $2, a salad for $2, and milk for $1. How much money will he have left? $1

## Lesson 2-7

Pages 80–83

**Subtract. Use addition to check.**

1. $400 − $298 = $102
2. 800 − 567 = 233
3. 1,000 − 703 = 297
4. 3,600 − 1,695 = 1,905
5. 5,000 − 2,367 = 2,633
6. $9,000 − $4,890 = $4,110
7. 7,000 − 5,804 = 1,196
8. 6,400 − 3,166 = 3,234
9. 9,600 − 1,879 = 7,721
10. $2,200 − $883 $1,317
11. $4,700 − $2,864 $1,836
12. 8,600 − 7,621 979
13. 7,000 − 4,386 2,614

## Lesson 3-1 1, 2. See Extra Practice Answer Appendix.

Pages 95–97

**Organize each set of data in a tally chart and a frequency table.**

1. George recorded the types of pets that his classmates have. His recordings are shown at the right.

| Pets | | |
|---|---|---|
| cat | cat | dog |
| cat | dog | lizard |
| dog | fish | bird |
| bird | dog | fish |

2. Tina conducted a survey to find out the favorite sports of the children in the park. Her recordings are shown at the right.

| Favorite Sports | | |
|---|---|---|
| soccer | baseball | football |
| soccer | basketball | football |
| football | football | basketball |
| basketball | soccer | tennis |



## Lesson 3-2

Pages 98–101

**Find the mode and median of the set of data. Identify any outliers.** 1. 22; 24; no outliers 2. no mode; 39; outlier: 17

1.

| Students in Each Grade | | | | | |
|---|---|---|---|---|---|
| Grade | 1 | 2 | 3 | 4 | 5 |
| Number of Students | 26 | 22 | 27 | 24 | 22 |

2.

| Roller Coaster Riders at an Amusement Park | | | | | | | |
|---|---|---|---|---|---|---|---|
| Roller Coaster | 1 | 2 | 3 | 4 | 5 | 6 | 7 |
| Number of Riders | 46 | 38 | 41 | 17 | 45 | 39 | 36 |

## Lesson 3-3

Pages 102–103

**Solve. Use the make a table strategy.**

1. Akira mailed invitations to his birthday party. The postage to mail each invitation was 42¢. Akira paid 252¢ in all for postage. How many invitations did he send? 6 invitations
2. During the soccer season, for every 3 penalty kicks he took, Jamil scored on 2 of them. If he scored on 12 penalty kicks, how many penalty kicks did he take? 18 kicks
3. Nick earns $7 an hour walking dogs. He works the same number of hours each week. Nick earns $252 in 1 month. How many hours does he work each week if there are 4 weeks in a month? 9 h
4. Maria bought some six-packs of soda. She bought 48 cans of soda in all. How many six-packs of soda did she buy? 8 six-packs

## Lesson 3-4 1, 2. See Extra Practice Answer Appendix.

Pages 104–107

**Organize each set of data in a line plot.**

1. Number of seeds that sprouted

| Seeds That Sprouted | |
|---|---|
| Week | Seeds |
| Week 1 | 6 |
| Week 2 | 9 |
| Week 3 | 11 |
| Week 4 | 10 |
| Week 5 | 9 |
| Week 6 | 6 |
| Week 7 | 9 |

2. Miles hiked by campers

| Miles Hiked per Day | |
|---|---|
| Day | Miles Hiked |
| Monday | 5 |
| Tuesday | 7 |
| Wednesday | 6 |
| Thursday | 4 |
| Friday | 5 |
| Saturday | 4 |
| Sunday | 3 |

## Lesson 3-5
Pages 108–110

**For Exercises 1–4, use the graph shown.**

1. Which animal has the longest life span? killer whale
2. Which animal has a life span of 70 years? African elephant
3. Which animal has a life span that is 45 years longer than a gorilla's life span? blue whale
4. How many years would three generations of humans last? 225 years

## Lesson 3-6
Pages 112–114

**For Exercises 1–4, use the graph shown.**

1. Which fruit did the farm produce the most of? apples
2. Which fruit did the farm produce the least of? plums
3. How many more pounds of strawberries were produced than pounds of plums? 150 lb
4. Which two fruits added together equal the amount of the fruit that the farm produced the most of? strawberries and peaches

## Lesson 3-7
Pages 118–119

**Use any strategy to solve. Tell what strategy you used.**

1. Luis has an aquarium with 47 fish. There are 12 orange fish, 13 blue fish, 9 white fish, and 8 yellow fish. The rest of the fish are red. How many are red? 5 fish
2. There were 45 action, 60 comedy, 25 drama, and 50 mystery movies rented from a video store in one day. How many more comedies than dramas were rented? 35



## Lesson 3-8 1–4. See Extra Practice Answer Appendix.
Pages 124–127

1. Draw a grid to find the number of possible outcomes if two counters are tossed once. Each counter is red on one side and yellow on the other.
2. Draw a grid to find the number of possible outcomes if a coin is tossed and a 0–5 number cube is rolled.
3. Draw a tree diagram to find the number of possible outcomes if a coin is tossed and a spinner with four equal sections labeled 1, 2, 3, and 4, is spun.
4. Draw a tree diagram to find the number of possible outcomes if a spinner with three equal sections labeled 1, 2, and 3, is spun twice.

## Lesson 3-9
Pages 128–130

**Describe the probability of each outcome. Write *certain, likely, equally likely, unlikely,* or *impossible.***

1. What is the probability of rolling a number? certain
2. What is the probability of rolling a number that is less than 5? likely
3. What is the probability of rolling an even number? equally likely
4. What is the probability of rolling a number that is greater than 6? impossible

## Lesson 4-1
Pages 147–149

**Algebra Copy and complete each fact family.**

1. $3 \times 8 = $ ■ 24; $8 \times$ ■ $= 24$ 3; $24 \div$ ■ $= 3$ 8; $24 \div 3 =$ ■ 8
2. $9 \times$ ■ $= 72$ 8; $8 \times$ ■ $= 72$ 9; $72 \div 9 =$ ■ 8; $72 \div 8 =$ ■ 9

**Algebra Divide. Use a related multiplication fact.**

3. $27 \div 3 =$ ■ 9; $3 \times 9 = 27$
4. $54 \div 9 =$ ■ 6; $9 \times 6 = 54$
5. $36 \div 6 =$ ■ 6; $6 \times 6 = 36$
6. $88 \div 11 =$ ■ 8; $11 \times 8 = 88$
7. $32 \div 8 =$ ■ 4; $8 \times 4 = 32$
8. $50 \div 5 =$ ■ 10; $5 \times 10 = 50$

## Lesson 4-2

Pages 150–153

**Identify the property or rule shown by each number sentence.**

1. $7 \times 4 = 4 \times 7$ Comm. Prop. (×)
2. $0 \div 15 = 0$ Zeros in Division
3. $3 \times (4 \times 5) = (3 \times 4) \times 5$ Assoc. Prop. (×)
4. $24 \div 1 = 24$ Divide by 1
5. $36 \div 36 = 1$ Ones in Division
6. $(5 \times 8) \times 6 = 5 \times (8 \times 6)$ Assoc. Prop. (×)

**Algebra Copy and complete each number sentence. Identify the property or rule used.**

7. $6 \div ■ = 1$ 6; Ones in Division
8. $16 \times ■ = 0$ 0; Zero Prop. of Multiplication
9. $14 \div ■ = 1$ 14; Divide by the same number
10. $■ \times 8 = 8 \times 5$ 5; Commutative Property (×)

## Lesson 4-3

Pages 154–157

**Multiply or divide. Use arrays or area models if needed.**

1. $3 \times 8$ 24
2. $5 \times 5$ 25
3. $4 \times 7$ 28
4. $2 \times 9$ 18
5. $9 \times 4$ 36
6. $2 \times 7$ 14
7. $3 \times 6$ 18
8. $12 \times 3$ 36
9. $27 \div 3$ 9
10. $32 \div 4$ 8
11. $30 \div 5$ 6
12. $15 \div 3$ 5
13. $45 \div 5$ 9
14. $28 \div 4$ 7
15. $24 \div 4$ 6
16. $45 \div 3$ 15

## Lesson 4-4

Pages 158–159

**Tell which operation you would use to solve each problem. Then solve.**

1. Sanjay and 3 of his teammates together scored 52 points in a basketball game. They each scored the same number of points. How many points did each boy score? division; 13 points
2. Sherri jogged 9 miles last week, which is 3 times as many miles as her sister and half as much as her brother. How many miles did her sister and brother jog? division, multiplication; 3 miles, 18 miles
3. There are 6 rows of desks in a classroom. There are 7 desks in each row. How many desks are in the classroom? multiplication; 42 desks
4. Roger earns $3,600 a year delivering papers. How much does he earn in one month? division; $300



## Lesson 4-5

Pages 160–162

**Multiply or divide. Use arrays or area models if needed.**

1. $9 \times 6$ 54
2. $6 \times 8$ 48
3. $7 \times 7$ 49
4. $8 \times 10$ 80
5. $5 \times 8$ 40
6. $9 \times 5$ 45
7. $6 \times 10$ 60
8. $7 \times 9$ 63
9. $42 \div 6$ 7
10. $48 \div 6$ 8
11. $90 \div 10$ 9
12. $56 \div 7$ 8
13. $35 \div 5$ 7
14. $81 \div 9$ 9
15. $36 \div 6$ 6
16. $72 \div 8$ 9

## Lesson 4-6

Pages 166–169

**Multiply or divide. Use arrays or area models if needed.**

1. $3 \times 11$ 33
2. $4 \times 12$ 48
3. $11 \times 6$ 66
4. $8 \times 12$ 96
5. $7 \times 11$ 77
6. $4 \times 12$ 48
7. $11\overline{)88}$ 8
8. $11\overline{)110}$ 10
9. $12\overline{)48}$ 4
10. $120 \div 12$ 10
11. $99 \div 11$ 9
12. $96 \div 12$ 8

## Lesson 4-7

Pages 170–171

**Use any strategy to solve. Tell what strategy you used.**

1. Manuel earns $4 for every 3 dozen cookies he sells. How much will Manuel earn if he sells 9 dozen cookies? 12 dozen cookies? $12; $16
2. Laura has 24 jazz CDs and 7 country CDs. She has 2 times as many pop CDs as country CDs. How many CDs does she have in all? 45 CDs
3. Kim wants to buy a snowboard that costs $160. She has $88 in the bank. If she earns $6 an hour babysitting, how many hours will Kim have to work to earn enough money to buy the snowboard? 12 hrs
4. An art gallery has paintings on display in 7 rooms. There are 12 paintings in each room. How many paintings are on display in the art gallery? 84 paintings





Extra Practice

## Lesson 4-8

Pages 172–174

**Multiply.**

1. $6 \times 3 \times 4$ 72
2. $5 \times 7 \times 3$ 105
3. $8 \times 2 \times 5$ 80
4. $9 \times 3 \times 2$ 54
5. $6 \times 4 \times 5$ 120
6. $9 \times 1 \times 4$ 36
7. $8 \times 4 \times 3$ 96
8. $3 \times 3 \times 12$ 108
9. $10 \times 3 \times 5$ 150
10. $6 \times 11 \times 1$ 66
11. $9 \times 4 \times 2$ 72
12. $12 \times 2 \times 4$ 96

## Lesson 4-9

Pages 176–179

**Find all of the factors of each number.**

1. 36 1, 2, 3, 4, 6, 9, 12, 18, and 36
2. 18 1, 2, 3, 6, 9, and 18
3. 16 1, 2, 4, 8, and 16
4. 35 1, 5, 7, and 35
5. 11 1 and 11
6. 24 1, 2, 3, 4, 6, 8, 12, and 24
7. 48 1, 2, 3, 4, 6, 8, 12, 16, 24, and 48
8. 40 1, 2, 4, 5, 8, 10, 20, and 40
9. 23 1 and 23

**Identify the first six multiples for each number.**

10. 4 0, 4, 8, 12, 16, and 20
11. 7 0, 7, 14, 21, 28, and 35
12. 6 0, 6, 12, 18, 24, and 30
13. 12 0, 12, 24, 36, 48, and 60
14. 8 0, 8, 16, 24, 32, and 40
15. 9 0, 9, 18, 27, 36, and 45
16. 10 0, 10, 20, 30, 40, and 50
17. 11 0, 11, 22, 33, 44, and 55
18. 3 0, 3, 6, 9, and 12

## Lesson 5-1

Pages 193–195

**Find the value of each expression if $x = 6$ and $c = 7$.**

1. $c + 5$ 12
2. $x - 3$ 3
3. $c + 9$ 16
4. $7 + x$ 13
5. $c - 2$ 5
6. $14 - x$ 8
7. $(x - 2) + 9$ 13
8. $16 - (c + 5)$ 4
9. $5 + (6 + x)$ 17

**Write an expression for each situation.**

10. five less than $y$ $y - 5$
11. the sum of $b$ and seventeen $b + 17$
12. $d$ minus twenty-four $d - 24$
13. fifty-one subtracted from $f$ $f - 51$



## Lesson 5-2

Pages 198–201

**Solve each equation.**

1. $4 + b = 12$ 8
2. $7 + m = 18$ 11
3. $p - 8 = 6$ 14
4. $18 - 13 = y$ 5
5. $9 - x = 2$ 7
6. $q + 14 = 22$ 8
7. $8 + d = 18$ 10
8. $7 + 6 = f$ 13

**Write and solve an equation for each situation.**

9. Twelve less than a number is sixteen. What is the number? $y - 12 = 16$; 28
10. Eight subtracted from a number equals thirteen. What is the number? $n - 8 = 13$; 21
11. The sum of nine and a number is twenty-eight. Find the number. $9 + b = 28$; 19
12. A number plus eleven equals twenty-five. What is the number? $q + 11 = 25$; 14

## Lesson 5-3

Pages 202–203

**Identify any missing or extra information. Then solve if possible.** 2. extra: There are 3 tennis balls in each can; 5

1. Monkeys at the zoo eat 9 bananas and 4 apples each day. How many pieces of fruit do the monkeys eat in one week? missing: the number of monkeys at the zoo
2. Sandra has $21. She wants to buy cans of tennis balls for $4 each. There are 3 tennis balls in each can. How many cans can she buy?
3. Marco has soccer practice 3 days a week. He has 17 teammates. Practice lasts for 2 hours each day. How many hours does Marco practice soccer each week? extra: He has 17 teammates; 6
4. Kayla earns $5 per hour. She is saving to buy a new game that costs $36 dollars. How many weeks will Kayla have to work to earn enough money for the game? missing: how many hours Kayla works each week

## Lesson 5-4

Pages 204–206

**Identify, describe, and extend each pattern.**

1. 3, 7, 11, 15, 19, ■ + 4; 23
2. 27, 22, 17, 12, 7, ■ − 5; 2
3. 2, 5, 3, 6, 4, ■ + 3 then − 2; 7
4. 5, 1, 7, 3, 9, ■ − 4 then + 6; 5
5. Sara jogs on a track five days a week. What is the rule for the pattern shown in the table? × 8
6. Trevor practices the guitar every day. What is the rule for the pattern shown in the table? × 45

| Distance Jogged | | | | | |
|---|---|---|---|---|---|
| Day | 1 | 2 | 3 | 4 | 5 |
| Laps | 8 | 16 | 24 | 32 | 40 |

| Time Spent Practicing | | | | | |
|---|---|---|---|---|---|
| Day | 1 | 2 | 3 | 4 | 5 |
| Minutes | 45 | 90 | 135 | 180 | 225 |

## Lesson 5-5

Pages 208–211

**Write an equation that describes each pattern. Then use the equation to find the next three numbers.**

1.

| Rule: ■ | | | | | | |
|---|---|---|---|---|---|---|
| Input ($b$) | 4 | 6 | 10 | 14 | 20 | 24 |
| Output ($x$) | 13 | 15 | 19 | ■ | ■ | ■ |

$b + 9 = x$; 23, 29, 33

2.

| Rule: ■ | | | | | | |
|---|---|---|---|---|---|---|
| Input ($y$) | 11 | 15 | 19 | 23 | 27 | 31 |
| Output ($c$) | 4 | 8 | 12 | ■ | ■ | ■ |

$y - 7 = c$; 16, 20, 24

3.

| Rule: ■ | | | | | | |
|---|---|---|---|---|---|---|
| Input ($f$) | $24 | $32 | $40 | $48 | $56 | $64 |
| Output ($q$) | $16 | $24 | $32 | ■ | ■ | ■ |

$f - 8 = q$; $40, $48, $56

4.

| Rule: ■ | | | | | | |
|---|---|---|---|---|---|---|
| Input ($m$) | $16 | $19 | $22 | $25 | $28 | $31 |
| Output ($p$) | $27 | $30 | $33 | ■ | ■ | ■ |

$m + 11 = p$; $36, $39, $42

## Lesson 5-6

Pages 214–216

**Find the value of each expression if $v = 4$ and $x = 8$.**

1. $x \div 4$ 2
2. $6 \times v$ 24
3. $x \div v$ 2
4. $v \div v$ 1
5. $x \times 7 =$ 56
6. $5 \times v$ 20
7. $(v \times 4) \div x$ 2
8. $32 \div (x \div v)$ 16
9. $(x \div 2) \times 9$ 36

**Write an expression for each situation.**

10. a number divided by 5 $n \div 5$
11. The product of 3 and a number $3 \times n$
12. a number divided by 10 $n \div 10$
13. 9 times a number $9 \times n$

## Lesson 5-7

Pages 218–219

**Use any strategy to solve. Tell what strategy you used.**

1. Ty wants to buy posters that cost $7 each. He has $50. How many posters can he buy? 7 posters
2. Ian is eating pizza with 5 friends. They ordered 3 pizzas. If each pizza is cut into 6 slices, how many slices can each person have? 3 slices
3. A vine in the park grows 2 inches every week. The vine is 13 inches tall now. How many inches tall will the vine be in 2 weeks? 4 weeks? 8 weeks? 17 in.; 21 in.; 29 in.
4. Amy is putting photos in an album. Each page in the album can hold 4 photos. There are 32 pages in the album. How many photos can Amy put in the album? 128 photos





## Lesson 5-8

Pages 220–223

**Write an equation that describes each pattern. Then use the equation to find the next three numbers.**

1.

| Input ($a$) | Output ($q$) |
|---|---|
| 2 | 12 |
| 4 | 24 |
| 6 | 36 |
| 8 | ■ |
| 10 | ■ |
| 12 | ■ |

Multiply by 6; $a \times 6 = q$; 48, 60, 72

2.

| Input ($g$) | Output ($v$) |
|---|---|
| 21 | 3 |
| 28 | 4 |
| 35 | 5 |
| 42 | ■ |
| 49 | ■ |
| 56 | ■ |

Divide by 7; $g \div 7 = v$; 6, 7, 8

## Lesson 6-1

Pages 237–239

**Multiply. Use basic facts and patterns.**

1. $4 \times 5$ 20<br>$4 \times 50$ 200<br>$4 \times 500$ 2,000<br>$4 \times 5{,}000$ 20,000
2. $3 \times 7$ 21<br>$3 \times 70$ 210<br>$3 \times 700$ 2,100<br>$3 \times 7{,}000$ 21,000
3. $8 \times 6$ 48<br>$8 \times 60$ 480<br>$8 \times 600$ 4,800<br>$8 \times 6{,}000$ 48,000
4. $3 \times 9$ 27<br>$3 \times 90$ 270<br>$3 \times 900$ 2,700<br>$3 \times 9{,}000$ 27,000
5. $5 \times 6$ 30<br>$5 \times 60$ 300<br>$5 \times 600$ 3,000<br>$5 \times 6{,}000$ 30,000
6. $7 \times 4$ 28<br>$7 \times 40$ 280<br>$7 \times 400$ 2,800<br>$7 \times 4{,}000$ 28,000

**Multiply. Use mental math.**

7. $7 \times 80$ 560
8. $60 \times 6$ 360
9. $90 \times 3$ 270
10. $500 \times 7$ 3,500
11. $9 \times 400$ 3,600
12. $8{,}000 \times 5$ 40,000

## Lesson 6-2

Pages 240–241

**Decide whether each answer is reasonable. Explain your reasoning.**

1. Ebony practices the guitar 30 minutes every day. Is it reasonable to say that she practices the guitar 3,000 minutes each month?
2. The soccer fields in a park are each 130 yards long. Is it reasonable to say that 4 soccer fields are a total of 1,560 feet long? yes; $(4 \times 130) \times 3 = 1{,}560$
3. The chickens on a farm produce about 4,200 eggs per week. Is it reasonable to say that the chickens produce 600 eggs each day? yes; $600 \times 7 = 4{,}200$
4. An album can hold 24 stamps on each page. There are 200 pages. Is it reasonable to say that the album can hold 48,000 stamps? no; $24 \times 200 = 4{,}800$

1. no; Ebony practices for 210 minutes each week, so 3,000 is not a good estimate.

## Lesson 6-3

Pages 242–244

**Estimate each product. Then tell if the estimate is *greater than* or *less than* the actual product.**

1. 584 × 3 — 600 × 3 = 1,800; greater
2. 484 × 5 — 500 × 5 = 2,500; greater
3. 723 × 8 — 700 × 8 = 5,600, less
4. 3 × 692 — 3 × 700 = 2,100; greater
5. 6 × $472 — $6 × 500 = $3,000; greater
6. 9 × $460 — 9 × $500 = $4,500; greater
7. 7 × 1,986 — 7 × 2,000 = 14,000; greater
8. 8 × $5,420 — 8 × $5,000 = $40,000; less
9. 5 × 6,752 — 5 × 7,000 = 35,000; greater
10. 3 × $478 — 3 × $500 = $1,500; greater
11. 6 × $9,810 — 6 × $10,000 = $60,000; greater
12. 8 × 3,755 — 8 × 4,000 = 32,000; greater

## Lesson 6-4

Pages 246–248

**Multiply. Check for reasonableness.**

1. 18 × 6 108
2. 28 × 5 140
3. $17 × 9 $153
4. 2 × 99 198
5. 6 × 25 150
6. 7 × $43 $301
7. 5 × 73 365
8. 4 × $86 $344
9. 9 × 39 351
10. 3 × $92 $276
11. 8 × 78 624
12. 7 × $56 $392

## Lesson 6-5

Pages 250–251

**Use any strategy to solve. Tell what strategy you used.**

1. Jesse bikes 224 miles each month. He bikes the same number of miles each week. How many miles does Jesse bike each week? Assume that there are four weeks in each month. 56 miles
2. Movie tickets are $7 for adults and $4 for children. What is the total cost if three adults and five children go to the theater? $41
3. Rita is making muffins. There are 36 muffins in each batch. How many muffins will be in 3 batches? How many muffins will be in 7 batches? 108 muffins; 252 muffins
4. At the zoo, the big cats are in a row. The lions are last. The jaguars are to the left of the tigers. The cheetahs are to the left of the jaguars. In what order are the big cats? cheetahs, jaguars, tigers, lions



## Lesson 6-6

Pages 252–255

**Multiply. Check for reasonableness.**

1. 538 × 3 1,614
2. 392 × 6 2,352
3. $256 × 8 $2,048
4. 734 × 7 5,138
5. $493 × 6 $2,958
6. $724 × 4 $2,896
7. 6 × 5,630 33,780
8. 6 × $8,562 $51,372
9. 5 × 2,845 14,225
10. 4 × 3,488 13,952
11. 8 × 2,376 19,008
12. 9 × 5,670 51,030

## Lesson 6-7

Pages 258–261

**Multiply. Check for reasonableness.**

1. 408 × 4 1,632
2. 507 × 8 4,056
3. 906 × 7 6,342
4. 2 × 6,009 12,018
5. 7 × $3,408 $23,856
6. 5 × 9,206 46,030
7. 3 × $8,702 $26,106
8. 6 × 4,090 24,540
9. 9 × $6,205 $55,845
10. 4 × 7,084 28,336
11. 8 × 9,502 76,016
12. 5 × 5,047 25,235

## Lesson 7-1

Pages 273–275

**Multiply.**

1. 18 × 30 540
2. 24 × 50 1,200
3. 48 × 90 4,320
4. 47 × 60 2,820
5. 75 × 40 3,000
6. 56 × 90 5,040
7. 64 × 30 1,920
8. $49 × 60 $2,940
9. 85 × 70 5,950
10. $28 × 30 $840
11. 92 × 70 6,440
12. 63 × 90 5,670

## Lesson 7-2
Pages 276–279

**Estimate. Tell whether the estimate is *greater than* or *less than* the actual product.**

1. 38 × 26 — $40 \times 30 = 1{,}200$; greater
2. 63 × 44 — $60 \times 40 = 2{,}400$; less
3. 59 × 37 — $60 \times 40 = 2{,}400$; greater
4. \$98 × 57 — $\$100 \times 60 = \$6{,}000$; greater
5. 43 × 82 — $40 \times 80 = 3{,}200$; less
6. \$67 × 38 — $\$70 \times 40 = \$2{,}800$; greater
7. 322 × 64 — $300 \times 60 = 18{,}000$; less
8. 668 × 27 — $700 \times 30$; 21,000 greater
9. 982 × 34 — $1{,}000 \times 30 = 30{,}000$; less
10. 441 × 33 — $400 \times 30 = 12{,}000$; less
11. 877 × 59 — $900 \times 60 = 54{,}000$; greater
12. 799 × 87 — $800 \times 90 = 72{,}000$; greater

## Lesson 7-3
Pages 280–281

**Solve. Use the act it out strategy.**

1. There are 4 tennis players at the court. Each one played one set of tennis against every other player. How many sets of tennis were played? 6 sets
2. Keisha has 450¢ in her piggy bank. She has the same number of dimes and quarters. She has half as many nickels as dimes. What coins does she have?
   6 nickels, 12 dimes, 12 quarters
3. Linda is 12 years old. Her mother is 2 years less than 3 times her age. How old is Linda's mother?
   34 years old
4. Jaime has 17 coins in his pocket. The coins have a value of 120¢. What coins does he have?
   5 pennies, 7 nickels, 3 dimes, and 2 quarters

## Lesson 7-4
Pages 284–286

**Multiply.**

1. 17 × 25 = 425
2. 56 × 33 = 1,848
3. \$84 × 42 = \$3,528
4. 62 × 55 = 3,410
5. 74 × 93 = 6,882
6. \$65 × 48 = \$3,120
7. 36 × 56 = 2,016
8. 49 × 77 = 3,773
9. \$44 × 83 = \$3,652
10. 64 × 95 = 6,080
11. \$58 × 17 = \$986
12. 75 × 73 = 5,475



## Lesson 7-5
Pages 288–291

**Multiply.**

1. 104 × 18 = 1,872
2. 186 × 32 = 5,952
3. 207 × 49 = 10,143
4. 275 × 64 = 17,600
5. 377 × 53 = 19,981
6. 309 × 81 = 25,029
7. 452 × 37 = 16,724
8. 438 × 27 = 11,826
9. 588 × 39 = 22,932
10. 542 × 64 = 34,688
11. 663 × 46 = 30,498
12. 738 × 56 = 41,328

## Lesson 7-6
Pages 294–295

**Use any strategy to solve. Tell what strategy you used.**

1. Natalie is thinking of two numbers with a sum of 13 and a product of 36. What are the two numbers?
   9 and 4
2. The fish at the pet store eat 28 jars of food every week. How many jars of food will the fish eat in 4 weeks? in 6 weeks? in 8 weeks?
   112; 168; 224
3. Ramón saves \$15 every week to buy a skateboard. The skateboard costs \$105. How many weeks will it take him to save half as much as he needs to buy the skateboard?
   $3\frac{1}{2}$ weeks
4. Every fourth grader washed 4 cars at the car wash. The fourth graders washed 284 cars in all. How many fourth grade students are there?
   71

## Lesson 7-7
Pages 296–298

**Multiply.**

1. 1,877 × 24 = 45,048
2. 2,345 × 62 = 145,390
3. 3,906 × 59 = 230,454
4. 5,792 × 48 = 278,016
5. 6,504 × 96 = 624,384
6. 7,708 × 85 = 655,180
7. 8,544 × 38 = 324,672
8. 12,304 × 65 = 799,760
9. 17,455 × 92 = 1,605,860

## Lesson 8-1

Pages 313–315

**Divide. Check each answer.**

1. 36 ÷ 3
   12; 3 × 12 = 36
2. 60 ÷ 5
   12; 5 × 12 = 60
3. 54 ÷ 3
   18; 3 × 18 = 54
4. 70 ÷ 5
   14; 5 × 14 = 70
5. 98 ÷ 7
   14; 7 × 14 = 98
6. 91 ÷ 7
   13; 7 × 13 = 91
7. 79 ÷ 3
   26 R1; 3 × 26 + 1 = 79
8. 66 ÷ 4
   16 R2; 4 × 16 + 2 = 66
9. 95 ÷ 7
   13 R4; 7 × 13 + 4 = 95

## Lesson 8-2

Pages 316–319

**Copy and complete each set of patterns.**

1. 48 ÷ 6 = ■ 8
   480 ÷ 6 = ■ 80
   4,800 ÷ 6 = ■ 800
2. 63 ÷ 9 = ■ 7
   630 ÷ 9 = ■ 70
   6,300 ÷ 9 = ■ 700
3. $40 ÷ 8 = ■ $5
   $400 ÷ 8 = ■ $50
   $4,000 ÷ 8 = ■ $500
4. 72 ÷ 9 = ■ 8
   720 ÷ 9 = ■ 80
   7,200 ÷ 6 = ■ 800
5. $27 ÷ 3 = ■ $9
   $270 ÷ 3 = ■ $90
   $2,700 ÷ 3 = ■ $900
6. 35 ÷ 7 = ■ 5
   350 ÷ 7 = ■ 50
   3,500 ÷ 7 = ■ 500

**Divide. Use patterns.**

7. 420 ÷ 6 70
8. 300 ÷ 5 60
9. $280 ÷ 7 $40
10. $210 ÷ 3 $70
11. 5,600 ÷ 7 800
12. 7,200 ÷ 8 900
13. 8,100 ÷ 9 900
14. 1,600 ÷ 4 400
15. 3,000 ÷ 6 500
16. $2,700 ÷ 3 $900
17. 4,500 ÷ 9 500
18. 5,400 ÷ 9 600

## Lesson 8-3

Pages 320–321

**Solve. Use the guess and check strategy.**

1. Ren bought 5 CDs for $55. One of the CDs cost $5 more than the others. How much did each CD cost? 4 of the CDs each cost $10 and 1 of them cost $15.
2. Carmen has 49 more mystery novels than adventure novels. She has 223 novels in all. How many mystery novels and adventure novels does Carmen have? 2. 136 mystery novels and 87 adventure novels
3. The chickens on a farm eat 3 times as much grain as the turkeys do per week. The chickens and turkeys eat a total of 52 pounds of grain every week. How much grain do the chickens and turkeys each eat every week? turkeys: 13 pounds, chickens: 39 pounds
4. A toy store has at least 10 wagons and at least 10 tricycles on sale. There are a total of 89 wheels. How many tricycles and how many wagons are on sale? 11 tricycles and 14 wagons



## Lesson 8-4

Pages 322–324

**Estimate. Check your estimate.**

1. 24 ÷ 4
   20 ÷ 4 = 5
2. 510 ÷ 7
   490 ÷ 7 = 70
3. 433 ÷ 5
   430 ÷ 5 = 86
4. 476 ÷ 8
   480 ÷ 8 = 60
5. $537 ÷ 6
   $540 ÷ 6 = $90
6. 298 ÷ 4
   280 ÷ 4 = 70
7. 337 ÷ 8
   320 ÷ 8 = 40
8. $259 ÷ 5
   $250 ÷ 5 = $50
9. 1,244 ÷ 6
   1,200 ÷ 6 = 200
10. 2,240 ÷ 3
    2,400 ÷ 3 = 800
11. $6,580 ÷ 9
    $6,300 ÷ 9 = $700
12. 8,256 ÷ 9
    8,100 ÷ 9 = 900

## Lesson 8-5

Pages 326–329

**Divide. Use estimation to check.**

1. 7)47
   6 R5; 49 ÷ 7 = 7
2. 8)39
   4 R7; 40 ÷ 8 = 5
3. 9)71
   7 R8; 72 ÷ 9 = 8
4. 6)33
   5 R3; 30 ÷ 6 = 5
5. 5)44
   8 R4; 40 ÷ 5 = 8
6. 8)62
   7 R6; 64 ÷ 8 = 8
7. 9)25
   2 R7; 27 ÷ 9 = 3
8. 6)45
   7 R3; 42 ÷ 6 = 7
9. 554 ÷ 8
   69 R2;
   560 ÷ 8 = 70
10. 462 ÷ 9
    51 R3;
    450 ÷ 9 = 50
11. 368 ÷ 6
    61 R2;
    360 ÷ 6 = 60
12. 659 ÷ 8
    82 R3;
    640 ÷ 8 = 80

## Lesson 8-6

Pages 330–331

**Use any strategy to solve. Tell what strategy you used.**

1. At the drugstore, pencils are on sale for 10 for $1. Pens are on sale for 4 for $2. How much do 20 pencils and 12 pens cost? $8
2. A plant produces about 45 new flowers every 2 weeks. After 8 weeks, how many flowers will the plant have produced? 180 flowers
3. There are 9 seals at a zoo. Altogether, the seals eat about 750 fish each day. About how many fish does each seal eat every day? 80 fish
4. Mei hiked for 20 minutes every morning from her campsite to the lake. She hiked back to the campsite every afternoon. Mei hiked for a total of 8 hours to and from the lake. How many days was Mei at camp? 12 days

## Lesson 8-7

Pages 332–334

**Divide. Use estimation to check.**

1. $3\overline{)693}$ 231
2. $2\overline{)764}$ 382
3. $7\overline{)875}$ 125
4. $4\overline{)936}$ 234
5. $3\overline{)1,677}$ 559
6. $6\overline{)2,558}$ 426 R2
7. $5\overline{)3,697}$ 739 R2
8. $9\overline{)2,938}$ 326 R4
9. 1,539 ÷ 2 769 R1
10. 7,564 ÷ 8 945 R4
11. 4,255 ÷ 7 607 R6
12. 2,687 ÷ 4 671 R3

## Lesson 8-8

Pages 336–338

**Divide. Use estimation to check.**

1. $3\overline{)315}$ 105
2. $4\overline{)837}$ 209 R1
3. $4\overline{)\$432}$ $108
4. $9\overline{)976}$ 108 R4
5. $3\overline{)625}$ 208 R1
6. $4\overline{)438}$ 109 R2
7. $2\overline{)414}$ 207
8. $7\overline{)756}$ 108
9. $3\overline{)\$317}$ $105 R2
10. $5\overline{)1,039}$ 207 R4
11. $3\overline{)\$2,721}$ $907
12. $9\overline{)9,459}$ 1,051
13. 1,615 ÷ 2 807 R1
14. 4,363 ÷ 4 1,090 R3
15. $611 ÷ 3 $203 R2
16. 1,236 ÷ 4 309

## Lesson 8-9

Pages 342–345

**Divide. Use estimation to check.**

1. $2\overline{)3,664}$ 1,832
2. $3\overline{)4,671}$ 1,557
3. $5\overline{)5,847}$ 1,169 R2
4. $6\overline{)7,248}$ 1,208
5. $4\overline{)6,184}$ 1,546
6. $8\overline{)9,872}$ 1,234
7. $7\overline{)9,256}$ 1,322 R2
8. $6\overline{)57,888}$ 9,648
9. $8\overline{)18,816}$ 2,352
10. $9\overline{)33,786}$ 3,754
11. $7\overline{)25,984}$ 3,712
12. $6\overline{)23,678}$ 3,946 R2
13. 9,634 ÷ 8 1,204 R2
14. 59,510 ÷ 5 11,902
15. 67,651 ÷ 9 7,516 R7
16. 95,785 ÷ 5 19,157



## Lesson 9-1

Pages 359–361

**Tell the number of faces, edges, and vertices. Then identify each figure.**

1. 0 faces, 0 edges, 0 vertices; sphere
2. 2 faces, 0 edges, 0 vertices; cylinder
3. 5 faces, 9 edges, 6 vertices; triangular prism
4. 6 faces, 12 edges, 8 vertices; cube
5. 5 faces, 8 edges, 5 vertices; square pyramid
6. 1 face, 0 edges, 1 vertex; cone

## Lesson 9-2

Pages 362–365

**Identify each polygon.**

1. hexagon
2. quadrilateral
3. octagon

**Tell whether each shape is a polygon.**

4. yes
5. no
6. no

## Lesson 9-3

Pages 366–367

**Solve. Use the look for a pattern strategy.**

1. A flowering plant produces 15 seeds on the first day of spring. On the second day, it produces 23 seeds. On the third day, it produces 31 seeds. Describe the pattern. How many seeds will the plant produce on the sixth day?
   Add 8; 55
2. Copy and complete the table. What is the pattern?

| Input | Output |
|---|---|
| 3 | 21 |
| 5 | 35 |
| 7 | ■ 49 |
| ■ 8 | 56 |

Multiply by 7.

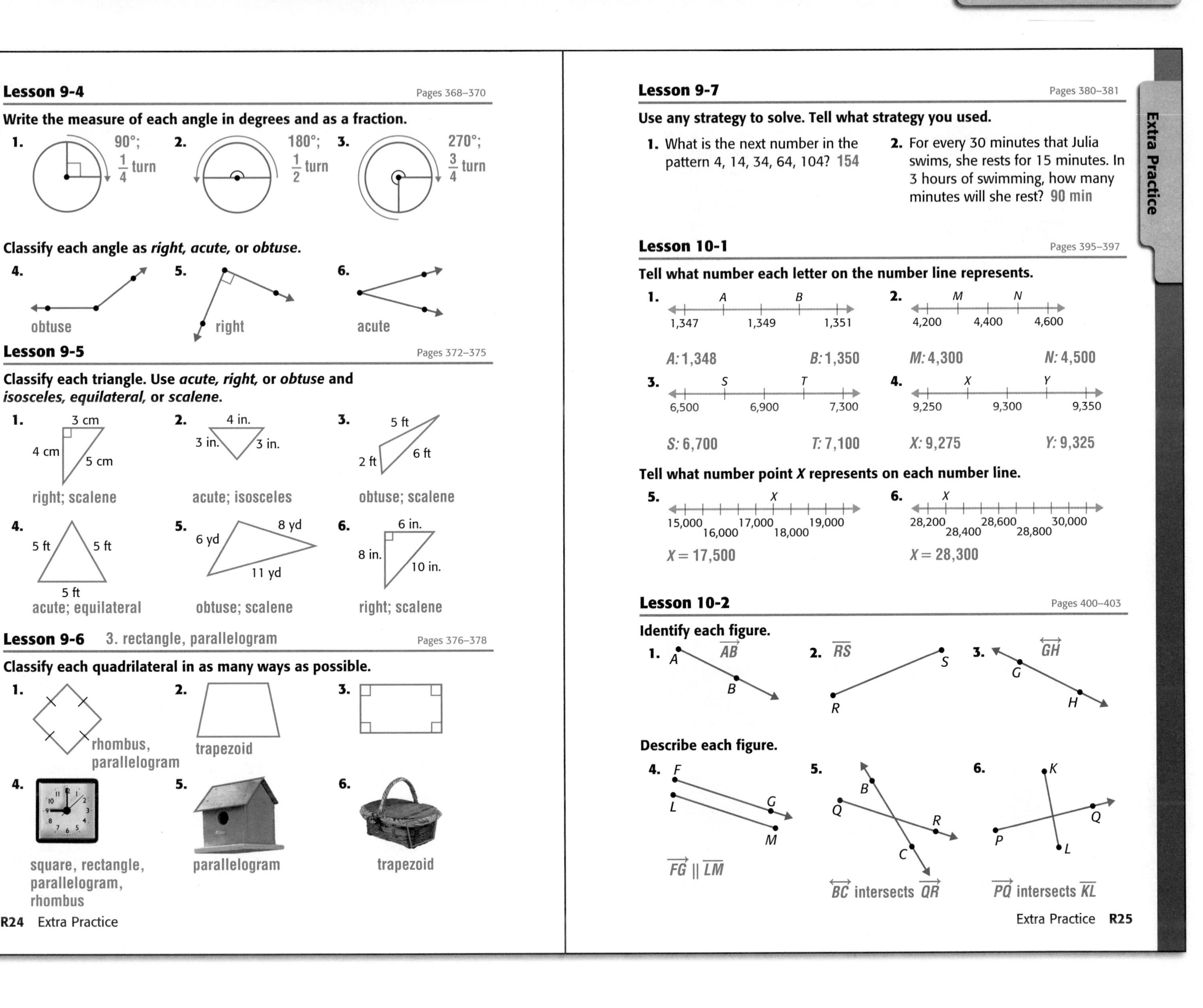



## Lesson 9-4
Pages 368–370

**Write the measure of each angle in degrees and as a fraction.**

1. 90°; $\frac{1}{4}$ turn
2. 180°; $\frac{1}{2}$ turn
3. 270°; $\frac{3}{4}$ turn

**Classify each angle as *right, acute,* or *obtuse.***

4. obtuse
5. right
6. acute

## Lesson 9-5
Pages 372–375

**Classify each triangle. Use *acute, right,* or *obtuse* and *isosceles, equilateral,* or *scalene.***

1. 3 cm, 4 cm, 5 cm — right; scalene
2. 4 in., 3 in., 3 in. — acute; isosceles
3. 5 ft, 2 ft, 6 ft — obtuse; scalene
4. 5 ft, 5 ft, 5 ft — acute; equilateral
5. 6 yd, 8 yd, 11 yd — obtuse; scalene
6. 6 in., 8 in., 10 in. — right; scalene

## Lesson 9-6 3. rectangle, parallelogram
Pages 376–378

**Classify each quadrilateral in as many ways as possible.**

1. rhombus, parallelogram
2. trapezoid
3.
4. square, rectangle, parallelogram, rhombus
5. parallelogram
6. trapezoid



## Lesson 9-7
Pages 380–381

**Use any strategy to solve. Tell what strategy you used.**

1. What is the next number in the pattern 4, 14, 34, 64, 104? 154
2. For every 30 minutes that Julia swims, she rests for 15 minutes. In 3 hours of swimming, how many minutes will she rest? 90 min

## Lesson 10-1
Pages 395–397

**Tell what number each letter on the number line represents.**

1. 1,347 1,349 1,351 — *A*: 1,348 *B*: 1,350
2. 4,200 4,400 4,600 — *M*: 4,300 *N*: 4,500
3. 6,500 6,900 7,300 — *S*: 6,700 *T*: 7,100
4. 9,250 9,300 9,350 — *X*: 9,275 *Y*: 9,325

**Tell what number point *X* represents on each number line.**

5. 15,000 16,000 17,000 18,000 19,000 — $X = 17,500$
6. 28,200 28,400 28,600 28,800 30,000 — $X = 28,300$

## Lesson 10-2
Pages 400–403

**Identify each figure.**

1. $\overrightarrow{AB}$
2. $\overline{RS}$
3. $\overleftrightarrow{GH}$

**Describe each figure.**

4. $\overrightarrow{FG} \parallel \overline{LM}$
5. $\overleftrightarrow{BC}$ intersects $\overrightarrow{QR}$
6. $\overrightarrow{PQ}$ intersects $\overline{KL}$

## Lesson 10-3

Pages 404–405

**Solve. Use the make an organized list strategy.**

1. Jim has 1 blue jacket, 1 green jacket, and 1 brown jacket. He has 1 tan hat and 1 black hat. How many different combinations of a jacket and hat can he wear? 6
2. Lee, Diego, Tara, and Irena will ride the Ferris wheel. Two people can sit in each car. What pairs are possible for the four friends to ride the Ferris wheel?

2. Lee/Diego and Tara/Irena; Lee/Tara and Diego/Irena; Lee/Irena and Diego/Tara

## Lesson 10-4

Pages 406–408

**Identify the letter that is located at each ordered pair.**

1. (2, −4) *K*
2. (−3, 4) *J*
3. (7, 6) *C*
4. (−4, −2) *M*
5. (−2, 1) *P*
6. (4, 0) *H*
7. (−7, −6) *Q*
8. (7, −6) *X*
9. (0, 0) *A*

## Lesson 10-5

Pages 412–415

**Identify each transformation. Write *rotation*, *reflection*, or *translation*.**

1. translation
2. rotation
3. reflection
4. translation



## Lesson 10-6

Pages 416–417

**Use any strategy to solve. Tell what strategy you used.**

1. Sam is replacing the wheels on 6 bicycles. He is also replacing the wheels on 4 tricycles and 3 wagons. How many wheels is Sam replacing in all? 36 wheels
2. Suna wants to make 5 bracelets and 3 necklaces. She plans to use 3 shells for every bracelet and 4 shells for every necklace. How many shells does she need? 27 shells
3. Evan has twice as many pairs of mittens as boots. He has 6 times as many pairs of socks as boots. He has 18 pairs of socks. How many pairs of boots and mittens does he have? 3 pairs of boots and 6 pairs of mittens
4. Mike makes $4 an hour babysitting. Omar makes $6 an hour gardening. How many hours will Mike have to work to make the same amount that Omar makes in 8 hours? 12 hrs

## Lesson 10-7

Pages 418–420

**Tell whether the figures appear to be congruent. Write *yes* or *no*. If they are, describe the movements that show the congruence.**

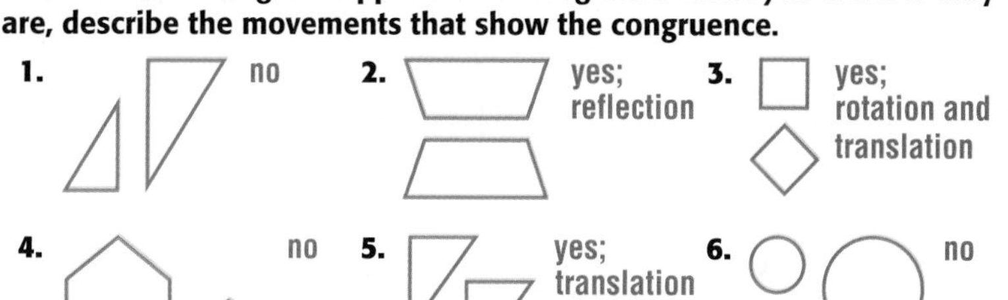

1. no
2. yes; reflection
3. yes; rotation and translation
4. no
5. yes; translation
6. no

## Lesson 10-8

Pages 422–424

**Tell whether each figure has line symmetry. Write *yes* or *no*. Then tell how many lines of symmetry the figure has.**

1. yes; 1
2. no
3. yes; 4

**Tell whether each figure has rotational symmetry. Write *yes* or *no*.**

4. yes
5. no
6. yes

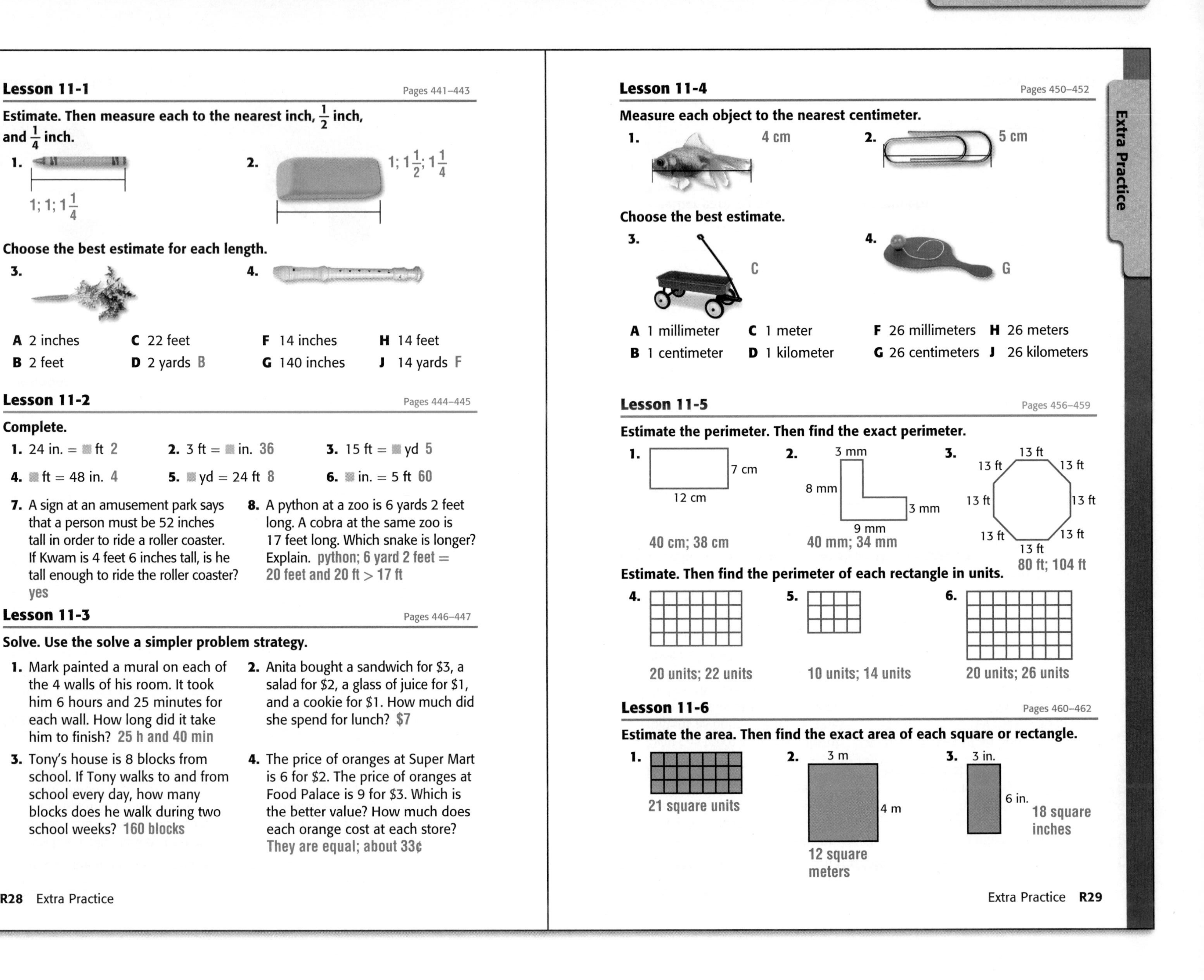



## Lesson 11-1

Pages 441–443

**Estimate. Then measure each to the nearest inch, $\frac{1}{2}$ inch, and $\frac{1}{4}$ inch.**

**1.** $1; 1; 1\frac{1}{4}$

**2.** $1; 1\frac{1}{2}; 1\frac{1}{4}$

**Choose the best estimate for each length.**

**3.**

**A** 2 inches
**B** 2 feet
**C** 22 feet
**D** 2 yards B

**4.**

**F** 14 inches
**G** 140 inches
**H** 14 feet
**J** 14 yards F

## Lesson 11-2

Pages 444–445

**Complete.**

**1.** 24 in. = ■ ft 2
**2.** 3 ft = ■ in. 36
**3.** 15 ft = ■ yd 5
**4.** ■ ft = 48 in. 4
**5.** ■ yd = 24 ft 8
**6.** ■ in. = 5 ft 60

**7.** A sign at an amusement park says that a person must be 52 inches tall in order to ride a roller coaster. If Kwam is 4 feet 6 inches tall, is he tall enough to ride the roller coaster? yes

**8.** A python at a zoo is 6 yards 2 feet long. A cobra at the same zoo is 17 feet long. Which snake is longer? Explain. python; 6 yard 2 feet = 20 feet and 20 ft > 17 ft

## Lesson 11-3

Pages 446–447

**Solve. Use the solve a simpler problem strategy.**

**1.** Mark painted a mural on each of the 4 walls of his room. It took him 6 hours and 25 minutes for each wall. How long did it take him to finish? 25 h and 40 min

**2.** Anita bought a sandwich for $3, a salad for $2, a glass of juice for $1, and a cookie for $1. How much did she spend for lunch? $7

**3.** Tony's house is 8 blocks from school. If Tony walks to and from school every day, how many blocks does he walk during two school weeks? 160 blocks

**4.** The price of oranges at Super Mart is 6 for $2. The price of oranges at Food Palace is 9 for $3. Which is the better value? How much does each orange cost at each store? They are equal; about 33¢



## Lesson 11-4

Pages 450–452

**Measure each object to the nearest centimeter.**

**1.** 4 cm

**2.** 5 cm

**Choose the best estimate.**

**3.** C

**A** 1 millimeter
**B** 1 centimeter
**C** 1 meter
**D** 1 kilometer

**4.** G

**F** 26 millimeters
**G** 26 centimeters
**H** 26 meters
**J** 26 kilometers

## Lesson 11-5

Pages 456–459

**Estimate the perimeter. Then find the exact perimeter.**

**1.**

40 cm; 38 cm

**2.**

40 mm; 34 mm

**3.**

80 ft; 104 ft

**Estimate. Then find the perimeter of each rectangle in units.**

**4.** 20 units; 22 units

**5.** 10 units; 14 units

**6.** 20 units; 26 units

## Lesson 11-6

Pages 460–462

**Estimate the area. Then find the exact area of each square or rectangle.**

**1.** 21 square units

**2.**

12 square meters

**3.**

18 square inches

## Lesson 11-7
Pages 466–467

**Use any strategy to solve. Tell what strategy you used.**

1. The perimeter of a rectangular yard is 20 meters. What are the possible lengths of the sides? Sample answer: length: 8 units, width: 2 units
2. Stella bought 5 pencils for 25¢. How much would she pay for 15 pencils? 75¢
3. Each bunch of flowers has 12 tulips and 23 daisies. There are 6 bunches of flowers. How many flowers are there in all? 210 flowers
4. There are 324 apples. There are 68 fewer apples than oranges and 127 more apples than limes. How many limes and oranges are there? limes: 197; oranges: 256

## Lesson 11-8
Pages 468–471

**Write the approximate temperature in degrees Fahrenheit and Celsius.**

1. 54°F; 12°C
2. 78°F; 26°C
3. The thermometer reads 2° Celsius. Would Gabrielle go swimming or build a snowman? build a snowman
4. An average person's body temperature is about 99° Fahrenheit. About how many degrees Celsius is this temperature? 37°C

## Lesson 12-1
Pages 486–489

**Choose the most reasonable estimate for each capacity.**

1. A 15 fluid ounces
B 15 pints
C 15 quarts
D 15 gallons A

2. F 2 fluid ounces
G 20 fluid ounces
H 2 quarts
J 2 gallons H

3. A 6 fluid ounces
B 6 cups
C 6 pints
D 6 quarts B

4. F 6 fluid ounces
G 60 fluid ounces
H 6 cups
J 6 pints F

5. A 1 fluid ounce
B 1 cup
C 1 quart
D 1 gallon D

6. F 1 fluid ounce
G 1 cup
H 1 pint
J 1 quart G



## Lesson 12-2
Pages 490–491

**Complete.**

1. 6 c = ■ pt 3
2. 32 fl oz = ■ c 4
3. 8 qt = ■ pt 16
4. 2 gal = ■ qt 8
5. ■ fl oz = 5 c 40
6. 10 pt = ■ c 20

**Compare. Use >, <, or =.**

7. 3 qt ● 1 gal <
8. 3 c ● 4 fl oz >
9. 3 qt ● 5 pt >

## Lesson 12-3
Pages 492–495

**Choose the more reasonable estimate for each capacity.**

1. 11 mL 11 L 11 L
2. 710 mL 710 L 710 mL
3. 1 mL 1 L 1 L
4. 235 mL 235 L 235 mL

## Lesson 12-4
Pages 498–500

**Choose the most reasonable estimate for the weight of each object.**

1. A
A 8 ounces
B 80 pounds
C 8 pounds
D 8 tons

2. J
F 70 ounces
G 7 pounds
H 700 pounds
J 7 tons

3. B
A 8 ounces
B 8 pounds
C 80 pounds
D 8 tons

4. F
F 1 ounce
G 10 ounces
H 1 pound
J 10 pounds

## Lesson 12-5

Pages 502–503

**Solve. Use logical reasoning.**

1. Mr. Myers is thinking of a number between 20 and 30. The number is not even, not prime, and not divisible by 3. What is the number? 25
2. There are three buildings on a block. The bank is to the left of the school. The museum is not first. What is the order of the buildings? bank, school, museum
3. A group of 3 adults and 7 students rode a ferry. The cost for the entire group was $36. If the cost of a student to ride was $3, what was the cost for an adult? $5
4. The Bears won 18 games. The Lions won one game for every three games the Bears won. The Sharks won 8 more games than the Lions. How many games did the Lions win? 6 games

## Lesson 12-6

Pages 504–507

**Complete.**

1. 2 lb = ■ oz 32
2. 4,000 lb = ■ T 2
3. 64 oz = ■ lb 4
4. 2 T = ■ lb 4,000
5. 1 lb and 2 oz = ■ oz 18
6. 3 T and 400 lb = ■ 6,400

7. **Algebra** Copy and complete the table below.

| Pounds | ■ 3 | 5 | ■ 6 | 8 | ■ 10 |
|---|---|---|---|---|---|
| Ounces | 48 | ■ 80 | 96 | ■ 128 | 160 |

## Lesson 12-7

Pages 508–510

**Choose the more reasonable estimate for the mass of each object.**

1. 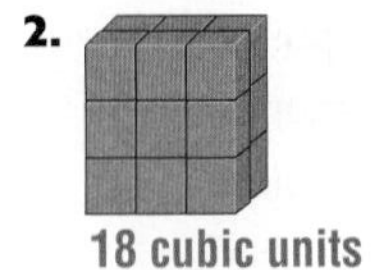

4 g 4 kg 4 kg

2. 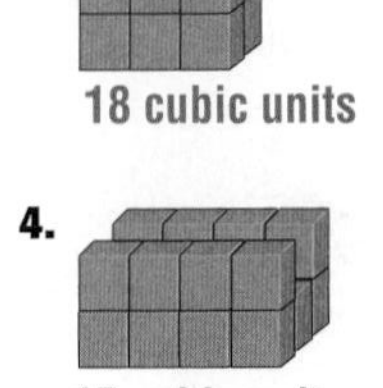

350 g 350 kg 350 g

3. 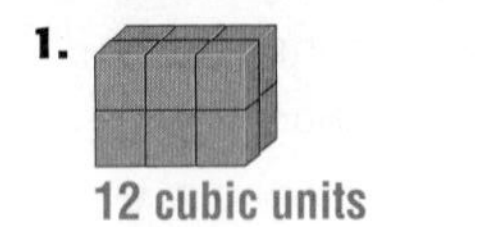

250 g 250 kg 250 kg

3. 300 g 300 kg 300 g



## Lesson 12-8

Pages 512–515

**Find the volume of each figure.**

1. 12 cubic units
2. 18 cubic units

**Estimate the volume of each figure.**

3. 12 cubic units
4. 15 cubic units

## Lesson 12-9

Pages 518–519

**Use any strategy to solve. Tell what strategy you used.**

1. Leila bought a hat for $5, mittens for $7, and a scarf for $11. The cashier gave her $7 in change. How much did Leila give the cashier? $30
2. Radio station ABC plays songs that are 3 minutes long. How many songs can the station play in 50 minutes? 16 songs
3. Emilio's sister is twice his age. In 6 years, his sister will be 3 times his age right now. How old are Emilio and his sister? Emilio is 6; his sister is 12.
4. A model home has 8 windows on the first floor and 7 windows on the second floor. There are 180 windows all together. How many model homes are there? 12 models

## Lesson 12-10

Pages 520–523

**The following are times of tennis matches. Find the length of each match.**

1. Start Time End Time

2 hours 15 minutes

2. Start Time End Time

2 hours 30 minutes

**Find each elapsed time.**

3. The clock shows when Lydia started ice skating. It is 12:45 when she stops.

1 hour 15 minutes

4. The clock shows when Helki's hockey practice started. It is 6:30 when it stops.

1 hour 45 minutes

## Lesson 13-1
Pages 537–539

**Write the fraction that names part of the whole.**

1. $\frac{3}{10}$
2. $\frac{4}{7}$
3. $\frac{12}{24}$
4. $\frac{5}{8}$
5. $\frac{3}{4}$
6. $\frac{3}{10}$

**Draw a picture and shade part of it to show the fraction.**

7. $\frac{3}{7}$ 8. $\frac{6}{7}$ 9. $\frac{2}{10}$ 10. $\frac{4}{5}$ 11. $\frac{7}{8}$

7–11. See Extra Practice Answer Appendix.

## Lesson 13-2
Pages 540–543

**Write the fraction for the part of the set that is blue. Then write the fraction for the part that is *not* blue.**

1. $\frac{5}{8}, \frac{3}{8}$
2. $\frac{4}{10}, \frac{6}{10}$
3. $\frac{2}{5}, \frac{3}{5}$
4. $\frac{4}{7}, \frac{3}{7}$
5. $\frac{9}{12}, \frac{3}{12}$
6. $\frac{6}{9}, \frac{3}{9}$

## Lesson 13-3
Pages 544–545

**Solve. Use the draw a picture strategy.**

1. Four dogs are standing in a row. The Great Dane is ahead of the poodle. The terrier is not next to the poodle. The collie is to the right of the terrier and is not first. What is the order of the dogs? terrier, collie, Great Dane, poodle
2. There are 30 children at the park. $\frac{1}{2}$ are playing soccer. $\frac{1}{3}$ are playing football. The rest are on the swings. How many children are on the swings? 5 children
3. There are 16 CDs on a shelf. $\frac{1}{4}$ of the CDs are jazz. 5 are classical music, and 3 are blues. The rest are pop music. How many CDs are pop music? 4 CDs
4. There are 4 books on display. The cookbook is next to the history book but not next to the art book or the novel. The art book is third. What is the order of the books? cookbook, history book, art book, novel



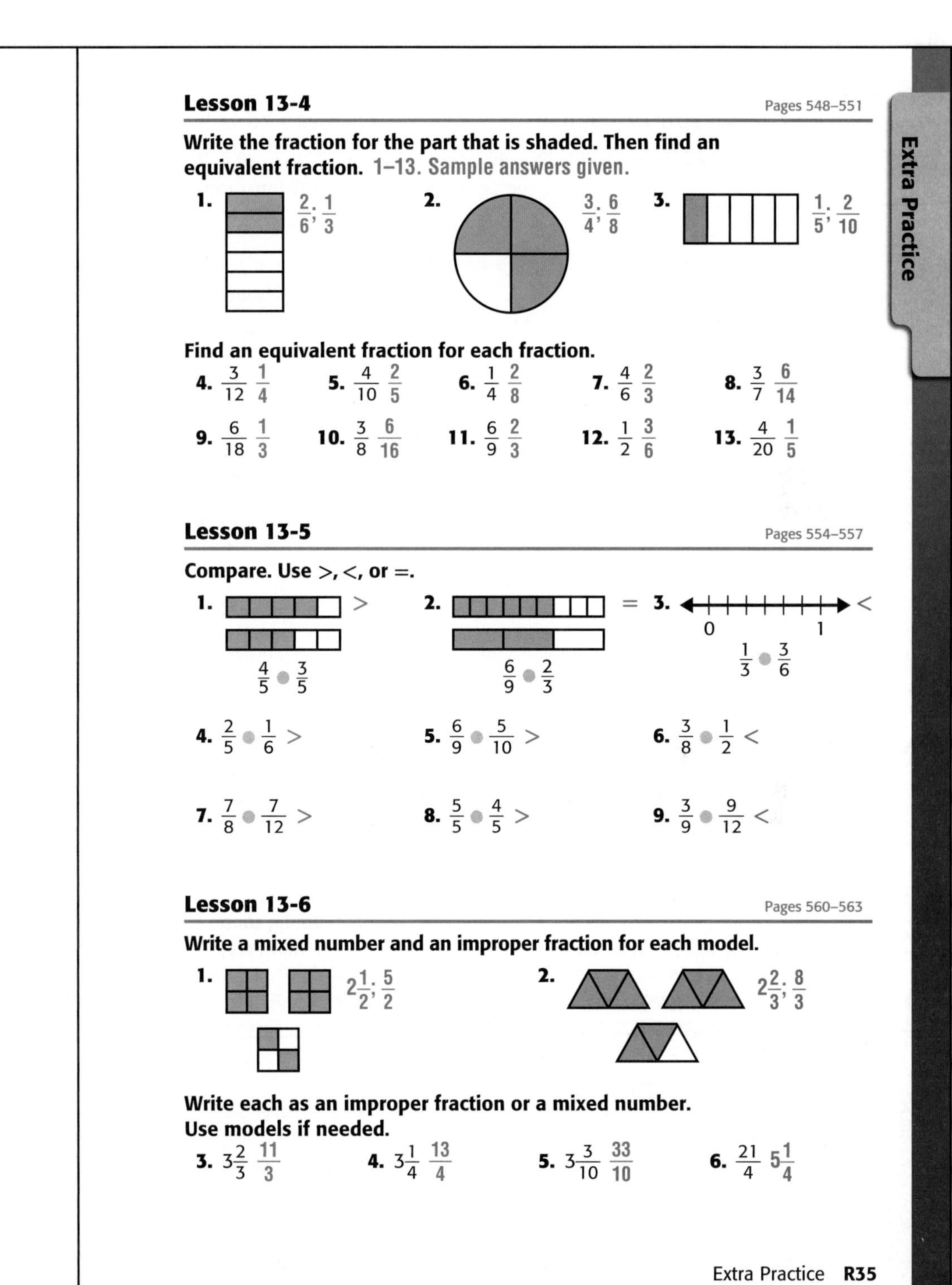

## Lesson 13-4
Pages 548–551

**Write the fraction for the part that is shaded. Then find an equivalent fraction.** 1–13. Sample answers given.

1. $\frac{2}{6}, \frac{1}{3}$
2. $\frac{3}{4}, \frac{6}{8}$
3. $\frac{1}{5}, \frac{2}{10}$

**Find an equivalent fraction for each fraction.**

4. $\frac{3}{12}$ $\frac{1}{4}$ 5. $\frac{4}{10}$ $\frac{2}{5}$ 6. $\frac{1}{4}$ $\frac{2}{8}$ 7. $\frac{4}{6}$ $\frac{2}{3}$ 8. $\frac{3}{7}$ $\frac{6}{14}$

9. $\frac{6}{18}$ $\frac{1}{3}$ 10. $\frac{3}{8}$ $\frac{6}{16}$ 11. $\frac{6}{9}$ $\frac{2}{3}$ 12. $\frac{1}{2}$ $\frac{3}{6}$ 13. $\frac{4}{20}$ $\frac{1}{5}$

## Lesson 13-5
Pages 554–557

**Compare. Use >, <, or =.**

1. $\frac{4}{5}$ ● $\frac{3}{5}$ >
2. $\frac{6}{9}$ ● $\frac{2}{3}$ =
3. $\frac{1}{3}$ ● $\frac{3}{6}$ <

4. $\frac{2}{5}$ ● $\frac{1}{6}$ > 5. $\frac{6}{9}$ ● $\frac{5}{10}$ > 6. $\frac{3}{8}$ ● $\frac{1}{2}$ <

7. $\frac{7}{8}$ ● $\frac{7}{12}$ > 8. $\frac{5}{5}$ ● $\frac{4}{5}$ > 9. $\frac{3}{9}$ ● $\frac{9}{12}$ <

## Lesson 13-6
Pages 560–563

**Write a mixed number and an improper fraction for each model.**

1. $2\frac{1}{2}, \frac{5}{2}$
2. $2\frac{2}{3}, \frac{8}{3}$

**Write each as an improper fraction or a mixed number. Use models if needed.**

3. $3\frac{2}{3}$ $\frac{11}{3}$ 4. $3\frac{1}{4}$ $\frac{13}{4}$ 5. $3\frac{3}{10}$ $\frac{33}{10}$ 6. $\frac{21}{4}$ $5\frac{1}{4}$

## Lesson 13-7
Pages 564–565

**Use any strategy to solve. Tell what strategy you used.**

1. Juan has 9 coins that equal 85¢. None of them are pennies. What are the coins? 4 nickels, 4 dimes, and 1 quarter
2. Ramona started reading at 4:20. She stopped reading at 5:15. For how many minutes did she read? 55 min
3. Ten students are in the library. Three students leave the library as 5 students go in. How many students are in the library now? 12 students
4. There are 20 fish in an aquarium. $\frac{1}{5}$ of the fish are blue. $\frac{1}{4}$ of the fish are red. The rest are yellow. How many yellow fish are there? 11 yellow fish

## Lesson 14-1
Pages 579–581

**Write a fraction and a decimal for each shaded part.**

1. $\frac{7}{10}$; 0.7
2. $\frac{2}{10}$; 0.2
3. $\frac{5}{10}$; 0.5
4. $\frac{88}{100}$; 0.88
5. $\frac{7}{100}$; 0.07
6. 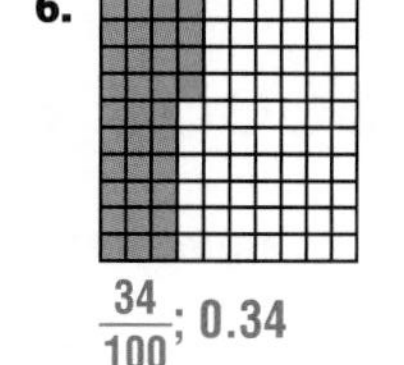 $\frac{34}{100}$; 0.34

## Lesson 14-2
Pages 582–585

**Write each as a mixed number and decimal.**

1. $1\frac{3}{10}$; 1.3
2. 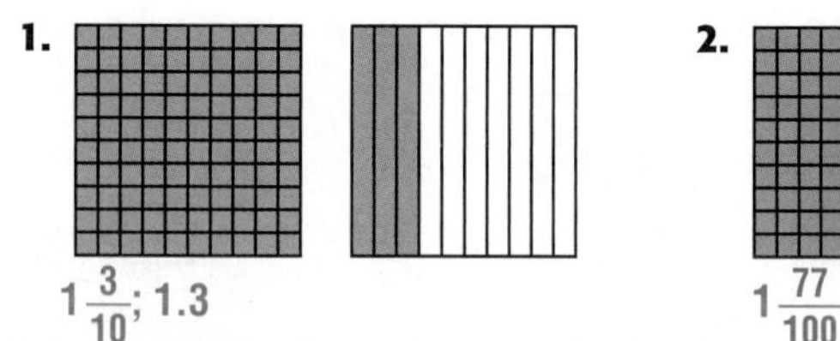 $1\frac{77}{100}$; 1.77

**Write each mixed number as a decimal.**

3. $4\frac{6}{10}$ 4.6
4. $36\frac{33}{100}$ 36.33
5. $83\frac{45}{100}$ 83.45
6. $99\frac{8}{10}$ 99.8
7. $15\frac{74}{100}$ 15.74
8. $75\frac{3}{10}$ 75.3
9. $62\frac{87}{100}$ 62.87
10. $24\frac{5}{10}$ 24.5



## Lesson 14-3
Pages 586–587

**Solve. Use the make a model strategy.**

1. Marcus has 20 coins. One fourth are dimes. One fifth are nickels. The rest are quarters. How much are Marcus's coins worth? $3.45
2. There are 3 plants in a garden. The first plant is 3 times taller than the second and 2 times taller than the third. The plants are a total of 22 feet tall. How tall is each plant?
3. Simon is hanging wallpaper on 3 walls of his room. Each wall is 10 feet wide and 8 feet tall. Each roll of wallpaper covers 40 square feet. How many rolls of wallpaper does Simon need? 6 rolls
4. Emily walked halfway home from school. She walked back 3 blocks to find a book. Then she walked home. She walked 20 blocks in all. How many blocks is it from Emily's house to school? 14 blocks

2. The first plant is 12 feet tall, the second is 4 feet tall, and the third is 6 feet tall.

## Lesson 14-4
Pages 588–589

**Tell which letter represents each mixed number on the number line. Write as a decimal.**

1. $1\frac{1}{5}$ A; 1.2
2. $1\frac{4}{5}$ C; 1.8

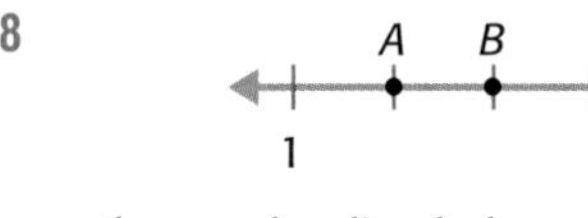


3. Name the point $N$ represents on the number line below.

N

7  $7\frac{1}{2}$  8  $8\frac{1}{2}$  9

$7\frac{3}{4}$

4. Latisha is measuring her height. the top of her head reaches the fifth mark out of 7 marks between 1 feet and 5 feet. How many feet tall is Latisha? $3\frac{1}{2}$ feet
5. A zookeeper measured the length of a newborn kangaroo. The kangaroo ends at the fourth mark out of nine marks between 0 and 1 inch. How many inches long is the kangaroo? 0.4 inches

## Lesson 14-5
Pages 590–592

**Compare. Use >, <, or =.**

1. 6.7 ● 0.67 >
2. 3.96 ● 3.09 >
3. 55.5 ● 55.50 =
4. 0.67 ● 0.76 <
5. 13.80 ● 13.8 =
6. 4.91 ● 4.9 >

**Order from greatest to least.** 8. 53.33, 53.13, 53.03

7. 2.08, 2.98, 2.88 2.98, 2.88, 2.08
8. 53.03, 53.33, 53.13
9. 65.02, 6.86, 6.5 65.02, 6.86, 6.5
10. 0.78, 0.87, 0.08 0.87, 0.78, 0.08

## Lesson 14-6

Pages 594–595

**Use any strategy to solve. Tell what strategy you used.**

1. A basement is rectangular in shape. One wall is 16 feet long. If the area is 304 square feet, what is the length of the other walls? 16 ft; 19 ft; 19 ft
2. What is the next number in the pattern? What is the rule?
   8, 5, 12, 9, 16, 13, 20, 17
   24; −3, +7
3. Bina began her chores at 3:30 P.M. She stopped at 4:20 to walk her dog. She started her chores again at 5:15 and stopped at 5:45. How long did Bina do her chores? 1 hr and 20 min
4. A pepperoni pizza is cut into 10 slices. A veggie pizza the same size is cut into 6 slices. Which is greater: 4 slices of pepperoni pizza or 3 slices of veggie pizza? 3 slices of veggie pizza

## Lesson 14-7

Pages 596–599

**Write a fraction and decimal to describe the shaded part of each model.**

1. $\frac{3}{4}$; 0.75
2. $\frac{3}{5}$; 0.60
3. $\frac{1}{5}$; 0.20
4. $\frac{1}{4}$; 0.25
5. $\frac{3}{10}$; 0.30
6. $\frac{1}{2}$; 0.50

## Lesson 14-8

Pages 602–604

**Use a number line or model to compare. Use >, <, or =.**

1. $\frac{25}{5}$ ● 4 >
2. 12.34 ● 12.3 >
3. $6\frac{1}{2}$ ● 6.89 <
4. $8\frac{1}{10}$ ● 8.75 <
5. 72.07 ● 72.70 <
6. 52 ● 5.02 >

**Use a number line to order from greatest to least.**

7. $67\frac{2}{100}$, 67.0, 67.70
8. 50.80, $\frac{4}{10}$, $\frac{4}{5}$ 50.80, $\frac{4}{5}$, $\frac{4}{10}$
9. $\frac{25}{100}$, $\frac{2}{3}$, 33.3 33.3, $\frac{2}{3}$, $\frac{25}{100}$
10. $\frac{70}{100}$, 0.75, $\frac{4}{10}$ 0.75, $\frac{70}{100}$, $\frac{4}{10}$

7. 67.70, $67\frac{2}{100}$, 67.0



## Lesson 15-1

Pages 617–620

**Round to the nearest whole number.**

1. 19.8 20
2. 46.21 46
3. 73.81 74
4. 32.41 32
5. 55.79 56
6. 38.11 38
7. 82.7 83
8. 25.5 26

**Round to the nearest tenth.**

9. 16.72 16.7
10. 93.39 93.4
11. 47.11 47.1
12. 33.76 33.8
13. 29.28 29.3
14. 73.64 73.6
15. 51.82 51.8
16. 85.83 85.8
17. A CD costs the amount shown. What is this amount rounded to the nearest whole number? $12
18. The European mole is 12.7 centimeters long. What is this amount rounded to the nearest whole number? 13

## Lesson 15-2

Pages 622–625

**Estimate. Round to the nearest whole number.**

1. 4.7 + 2.1; 5 + 2 = 7
2. 5.3 + 4.2; 5 + 4 = 9
3. $14.96 + $23.17; $15 + $23 = $38
4. 17.67 + 23.78; 18 + 24 = 42
5. 9.8 − 3.7; 10 − 4 = 6
6. 13.3 − 7.2; 13 − 7 = 6
7. 26.2 − 14.8; 26 − 15 = 11
8. $25.85 + $16.27; $26 + $16 = $42
9. 34.95 − 18.50; 35 − 19 = 16
10. 27.8 − 14.7; 28 − 15 = 13
11. $38.91 − $26.78; $39 − $27 = $12
12. 59.5 − 23.12; 60 − 23 = 37
13. $83.32 − $54.86; $83 − $55 = $28

## Lesson 15-3

Pages 626–627

**Solve. Use the work backward strategy.**

1. Pedro has $3.75 left from lunch. He bought the items shown in the table below. How much money did he have before lunch? $8.75

| Pedro's Lunch | |
|---|---|
| Item | Cost |
| taco | $1.60 |
| salad | $2.45 |
| milk | $0.95 |

2. Allison completed the chores shown in the table below. If she finished her chores at 8:30, what time did she start? 7:00

| Allison's Chores | |
|---|---|
| Chore | Time to Complete (minutes) |
| Rake leaves | 30 |
| Pull Weeds | 15 |
| Mow Grass | 45 |

3. What is the least number of coins worth 25¢ or less that could be used to make $3.49? What are the coins? 19 coins; 13 quarters, 2 dimes, 4 pennies

4. A number is divided by 4. Next, 7 is subtracted from the quotient. Then, the difference is multiplied by 3. The result is 15. What is the number? 48

## Lesson 15-4

Pages 630–632

**Add. Use estimation to check for reasonableness.**

1. 0.5 + 0.7 1.2
2. 0.8 + 0.7 1.5
3. 2.3 + 0.15 2.45
4. 6.4 + 9.34 15.74
5. 7.65 + 9.38 17.03
6. $7.25 + $6.49 $13.74
7. 14.79 + 5.55 20.34
8. 11.46 + 4.93 16.39
9. 22.48 + 18.67 41.15
10. 17.99 + 12.99 30.98
11. 42.52 + 21.84 64.36
12. 6.4 + 3.6 + 2.8 12.8
13. 5.2 + 8.3 + 7.4 20.9
14. 6.6 + 4.7 + 9.9 21.2



## Lesson 15-5

Pages 634–635

**Use any strategy to solve. Tell what strategy you used.**

1. There are two numbers whose product is 48 and difference is 8. What are the numbers? 12 and 4

2. A number is multiplied by 3. The product is subtracted from 50. The result is 11. What is the number? 13

3. A flower shop is selling roses at the price shown at the right. How much would 12 roses cost? $9.60



4. Dion surveyed 500 students to find out their favorite color. Blue was the favorite color of 7 out of 10 students. How many students' favorite color is blue? 350

## Lesson 15-6

Pages 638–641

**Subtract. Use estimation or addition to check.**

1. 4.8 − 2.3 = 2.5
2. 6.9 − 3.3 = 3.6
3. 8.3 − 2.7 = 5.6
4. 5.2 − 2.8 = 2.4
5. 3.78 − 1.44 = 2.34
6. 7.56 − 4.43 = 3.13
7. $9.45 − $2.06 = $7.39
8. 8.55 − 4.38 = 4.17
9. 12.61 − 8.75 = 3.86
10. $19.23 − $12.86 = $6.37
11. $26.74 − $16.95 = $9.79
12. 48.03 − 27.12 = 20.91
13. 54.50 − 46.72 7.78
14. 38.04 − 23.60 14.44
15. 41.93 − 15.98 25.95
16. $62.35 − $28.90 $33.45
17. 76.40 − 39.24 37.16
18. 93.19 − 65.38 27.81

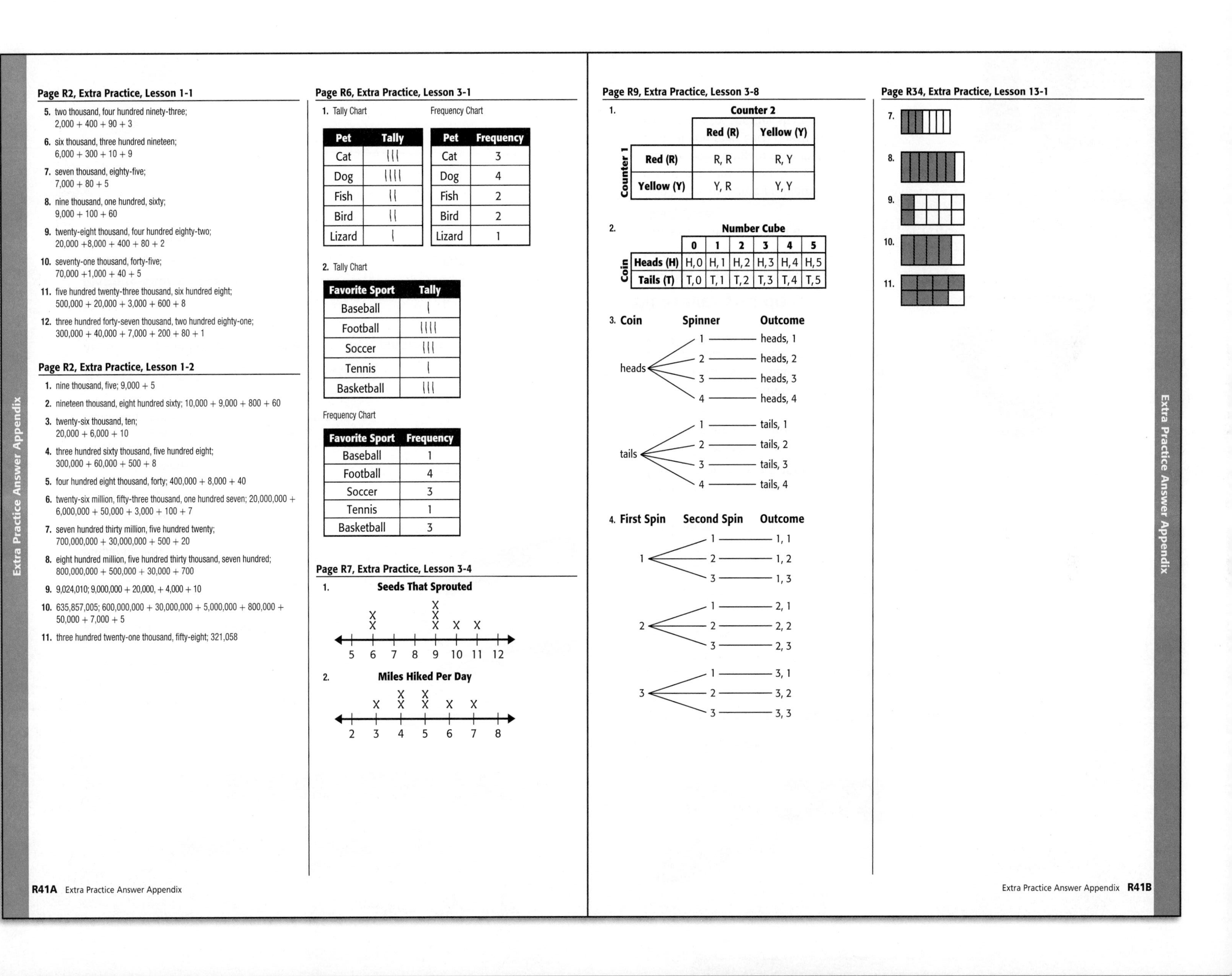



## Page R2, Extra Practice, Lesson 1-1

5. two thousand, four hundred ninety-three; 2,000 + 400 + 90 + 3
6. six thousand, three hundred nineteen; 6,000 + 300 + 10 + 9
7. seven thousand, eighty-five; 7,000 + 80 + 5
8. nine thousand, one hundred, sixty; 9,000 + 100 + 60
9. twenty-eight thousand, four hundred eighty-two; 20,000 +8,000 + 400 + 80 + 2
10. seventy-one thousand, forty-five; 70,000 +1,000 + 40 + 5
11. five hundred twenty-three thousand, six hundred eight; 500,000 + 20,000 + 3,000 + 600 + 8
12. three hundred forty-seven thousand, two hundred eighty-one; 300,000 + 40,000 + 7,000 + 200 + 80 + 1

## Page R2, Extra Practice, Lesson 1-2

1. nine thousand, five; 9,000 + 5
2. nineteen thousand, eight hundred sixty; 10,000 + 9,000 + 800 + 60
3. twenty-six thousand, ten; 20,000 + 6,000 + 10
4. three hundred sixty thousand, five hundred eight; 300,000 + 60,000 + 500 + 8
5. four hundred eight thousand, forty; 400,000 + 8,000 + 40
6. twenty-six million, fifty-three thousand, one hundred seven; 20,000,000 + 6,000,000 + 50,000 + 3,000 + 100 + 7
7. seven hundred thirty million, five hundred twenty; 700,000,000 + 30,000,000 + 500 + 20
8. eight hundred million, five hundred thirty thousand, seven hundred; 800,000,000 + 500,000 + 30,000 + 700
9. 9,024,010; 9,000,000 + 20,000, + 4,000 + 10
10. 635,857,005; 600,000,000 + 30,000,000 + 5,000,000 + 800,000 + 50,000 + 7,000 + 5
11. three hundred twenty-one thousand, fifty-eight; 321,058

## Page R6, Extra Practice, Lesson 3-1

1. Tally Chart

| Pet | Tally |
|---|---|
| Cat | ||| |
| Dog | |||| |
| Fish | || |
| Bird | || |
| Lizard | | |

Frequency Chart

| Pet | Frequency |
|---|---|
| Cat | 3 |
| Dog | 4 |
| Fish | 2 |
| Bird | 2 |
| Lizard | 1 |

2. Tally Chart

| Favorite Sport | Tally |
|---|---|
| Baseball | | |
| Football | |||| |
| Soccer | ||| |
| Tennis | | |
| Basketball | ||| |

Frequency Chart

| Favorite Sport | Frequency |
|---|---|
| Baseball | 1 |
| Football | 4 |
| Soccer | 3 |
| Tennis | 1 |
| Basketball | 3 |

## Page R7, Extra Practice, Lesson 3-4

1. Seeds That Sprouted



2. Miles Hiked Per Day



## Page R9, Extra Practice, Lesson 3-8

1.

| Counter 1 \ Counter 2 | Red (R) | Yellow (Y) |
|---|---|---|
| Red (R) | R, R | R, Y |
| Yellow (Y) | Y, R | Y, Y |

2. Number Cube

| Coin | 0 | 1 | 2 | 3 | 4 | 5 |
|---|---|---|---|---|---|---|
| Heads (H) | H, 0 | H, 1 | H, 2 | H, 3 | H, 4 | H, 5 |
| Tails (T) | T, 0 | T, 1 | T, 2 | T, 3 | T, 4 | T, 5 |

3.



4.



## Page R34, Extra Practice, Lesson 13-1

7.

8.

9.

10.

11.

# Preparing for Standardized Tests

Throughout the school year, you may be required to take several tests, and you may have many questions about them. Here are some answers to help you get ready.

## How Should I Study?

The good news is that you've been studying all along—a little bit every day. Here are some of the ways your textbook has been preparing you.

- **Every Day** The lessons had multiple-choice practice questions.
- **Every Week** The Mid-Chapter Check and Chapter Test also had several multiple-choice practice questions.
- **Every Month** The Test Practice pages at the end of each chapter had even more questions, including short-response and extended-response questions.

## Are There Other Ways to Review?

Absolutely! The following pages contain even more practice for standardized tests.





# Tips for SUCCESS

## Before the Test

- Go to bed early the night before the test. You will think more clearly after a good night's rest.
- Become familiar with common measurement units and when they should be used.
- Think positively.

## During the Test

- Read each problem carefully. Underline key words and think about different ways to solve the problem.
- Watch for key words like *not*. Also look for order words like *least, greatest, first,* and *last*.
- Answer questions you are sure about first. If you do not know the answer to a question, skip it and go back to that question later.
- Check your answer to make sure that it is reasonable.
- Make sure that the number of the question on the answer sheet matches the number of the question on which you are working in your test booklet.

## Whatever you do...

- Don't try to do it all in your head. If no figure is provided, draw one.
- Don't rush. Try to work at a steady pace.
- Don't give up. Some problems may seem hard to you, but you may be able to figure out what to do if you read each question carefully or try another strategy.

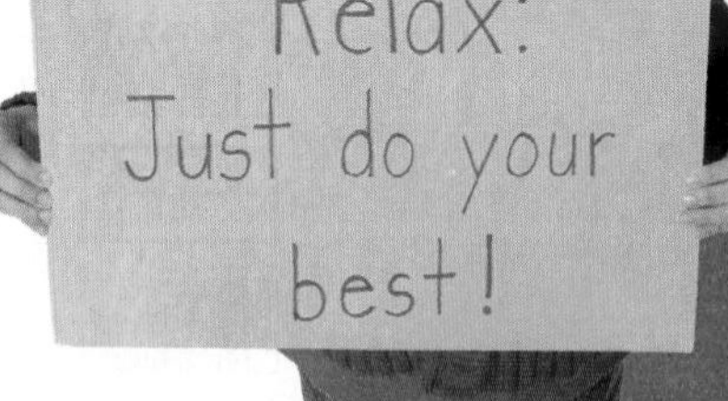

# Multiple-Choice Questions

Incomplete shading (A) (B) (C) (D)
Too light shading (A) (B) (C) (D)
Correct shading (A) (B) (C) (D)

Multiple-choice questions are the most common type of questions on standardized tests. You are asked to choose the best answer from four possible answers.

To record a multiple-choice answer, you may be asked to shade in a bubble that is a circle or an oval. Always make sure that your shading is dark enough and completely covers the bubble.

**STRATEGY**
**Patterns** Can you find a pattern to solve the problem?

**Example**

**1 The graph shows how many sit-ups a student did each day.**

**If this pattern continues, how many total sit-ups will be done on Friday and Saturday?**

**A** 88 **B** 48 **C** 40 **D** 8

**Read the Problem Carefully** You know how many sit-ups were done each day from Monday to Thursday. Find how many total sit-ups will be done on Friday and Saturday.

**Solve the Problem** Look for a pattern. The student did 8 sit-ups on Monday, 16 on Tuesday, 24 on Wednesday, and 32 on Thursday. Each day, the student did 8 more sit-ups.

Extend the pattern to find how many sit-ups were done on Friday and Saturday. Then add the numbers to find the total.

$32 + 8 = 40$ sit-ups on Friday
$40 + 8 = 48$ sit-ups on Saturday

$40 + 48 = 88$ total sit-ups

So, 88 sit-ups were done on Friday and Saturday.

The correct choice is A.



**STRATEGY**
**Elimination** Can you eliminate any of the choices?

**Example**

**2 The shaded part of the figure represents the fraction $\frac{4}{6}$. Which fraction represents the part that is not shaded?**

**F** $\frac{1}{2}$ **G** $\frac{1}{3}$ **H** $\frac{1}{4}$ **J** $\frac{4}{5}$

**Read the Problem Carefully** You are asked to find which fraction represents the part of the figure that is not shaded.

**Solve the Problem** The part that is not shaded is less than half of the figure. Since the answer is less than $\frac{1}{2}$, the choices $\frac{1}{2}$ and $\frac{4}{5}$ can be eliminated. The figure can be divided into 3 equal parts. One of the three, or $\frac{1}{3}$, of the figure is not shaded.

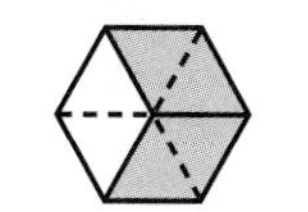

So, the correct choice is G.

**STRATEGY**
**Work Backward** Can you work backward from the total to find the number of days?

**Example**

**3 A family traveled 900 miles. They traveled half of the distance on the first day. How many total days did they travel if they traveled 150 miles each day for the rest of the trip?**

**A** 3 **B** 4 **C** 5 **D** 6

**Read the Problem Carefully** You are asked to find the total number of travel days. You know how many miles were traveled each day and the total number of miles traveled.

**Solve the Problem** First find the number of miles traveled the first day. Then add 150 miles each day until you reach 900 miles. Count the number of travel days.

Day 1 $900 \div 2 = 450$ miles
Day 2 $450 + 150 = 600$ miles
Day 3 $600 + 150 = 750$ miles
Day 4 $750 + 150 = 900$ miles

The family traveled for 4 days.

So, the family traveled for 4 days.

The correct choice is B.

# Multiple-Choice Practice

**DIRECTIONS**
**Read each question. Choose the best answer.**

**1.** Josh counted 29 desks in each of 3 classrooms in the 4th grade hall. If there are 8 classrooms in the 4th grade hall, about how many desks are there in all? B

**A** 250
**B** 240
**C** 200
**D** 180

**2.** Which number sentence best represents the model below? G

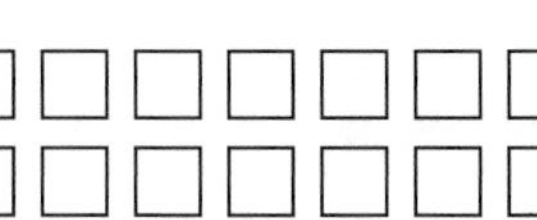
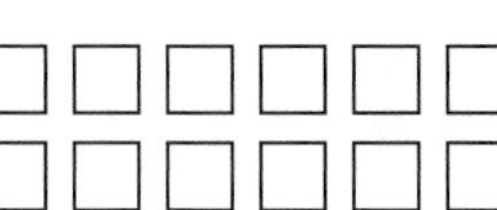

**F** $7 + 7 = 14$
**G** $3 \times 7 = 21$
**H** $3 + 7 = 10$
**J** $3 + 3 + 3 = 9$

**3.** What rule best describes the pattern of ordered pairs? C

(1, 10) (2, 20) (3, 30)
(4, 40) (5, 50) (6, 60)

**A** Add 10.
**B** Add 9.
**C** Multiply by 10.
**D** Divide by 10.

**4.** When you multiply a number by 100, you move the decimal point of the number 2 places to the right.

$$630 \times 100 = 63{,}000$$

What is $409 \times 100$? G

**F** 49,000
**G** 40,900
**H** 4,900
**J** 4,090

**5.** Which of the following objects has a capacity of about 1 gallon? A

**A**

**C**

**B**

**D**
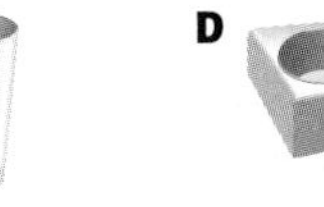

**6.** Which of the following is the best estimate for the weight of a car? J

**F** 1,900 tons
**G** 1,900 ounces
**H** 1,900 grams
**J** 1,900 kilograms



**7.** Look at the three-dimensional figures below. Which figure has exactly two faces? D

**A** **C**
**B** **D**

**8.** Which quadrilateral has 2 pairs of parallel opposite sides and 4 right angles? H

**F** parallelogram
**G** pentagon
**H** square
**J** trapezoid

**9.** A piggy bank contains 1 quarter, 3 dimes, 2 nickels, and 2 pennies. If Lindsay picks a coin without looking, what is the probability she will pick a dime? B

**A** 3 out of 5
**B** 3 out of 8
**C** 5 out of 8
**D** 5 out of 3

**10.** Refer to the bar graph below. It shows the number of absent students each day last week at Reggie's school. J

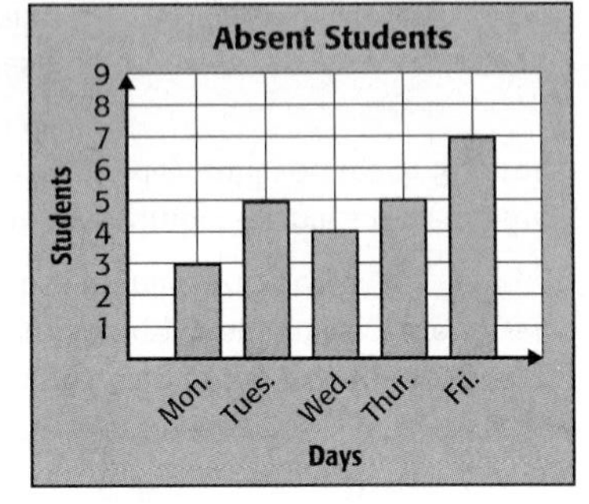


How many students were absent on Thursday and Friday combined last week?

**F** 5 students
**G** 7 students
**H** 11 students
**J** 12 students

**11.** Each player in a game spins the spinner below on his or her turn. What is the probability that Carla will spin an odd number on her next turn? A

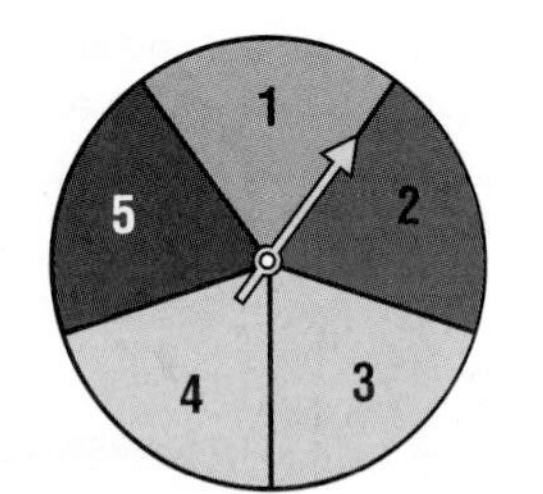


**A** 3 out of 5
**B** 3 out of 2
**C** 2 out of 5
**D** 2 out of 3

# Short-Response Questions

Short-response questions ask you to find the answer to the problem as well as any method, explanation, and/or justification you used to arrive at the solution. You are asked to solve the problem, showing your work.

The following is a sample rubric, or scoring guide, for scoring short-response questions.

| Credit | Scores | Criteria |
|---|---|---|
| Full | 2 | Full Credit: The answer is correct and a full explanation is provided that shows each step in arriving at the final answer. |
| Partial | 1 | Partial Credit: There are two different ways to receive partial credit. • The answer is correct, but the explanation provided is incomplete or incorrect. • The answer is incorrect, but the explanation and method of solving the problem is correct. |
| None | 0 | No credit: Either an answer is not provided or the answer does not make sense. |

**Example**

**STRATEGY**
**Find the Operation** Which operation can be used to perform repeated addition?

**2** **Pencils are on sale at a store. Four pencils cost $1. How many pencils can be bought with $6?**

## Full Credit Solution

First, I will decide which operation to use. Since each dollar can buy four pencils, I can use repeated addition or multiplication. I will use multiplication to find $6 × 4 pencils.

6 dollars
× 4 pencils
24 pencils

The steps, calculations, and reasoning are clearly stated.

So, $6 can be used to buy 24 pencils.

The correct answer is given.



## Partial Credit Solution

In this sample solution, the answer is correct. However, there is no explanation for any of the calculations.

$6,4 pencils

24 pencils

There is no explanation of how the problem was solved.

## Partial Credit Solution

In this sample solution, the answer is incorrect. However, the calculations and reasoning are correct.

Each dollar can be used to buy 4 pencils, so I can use repeated addition or multiplication. I will use multiplication to find 6 × 4.

6 dollars
× 4 pencils
12 pencils

The student did not multiply correctly.

12 pencils can be bought with $6.00.

## No Credit Solution

In this sample solution, the answer is incorrect, and there is no explanation for any calculations.

6 + 4 = 10

There are $10.

The student does not understand the problem and adds 6 and 4.

## Short-Response Practice

**DIRECTIONS**
**Solve each problem.**

**1.** Mrs. Henderson brought 42 boxes of raisins to her daughter's class. She gave 33 of the boxes away to the students. How many boxes of raisins were left? **9 boxes**

**2.** What fraction is represented by the shaded part of the figure below? $\frac{2}{7}$

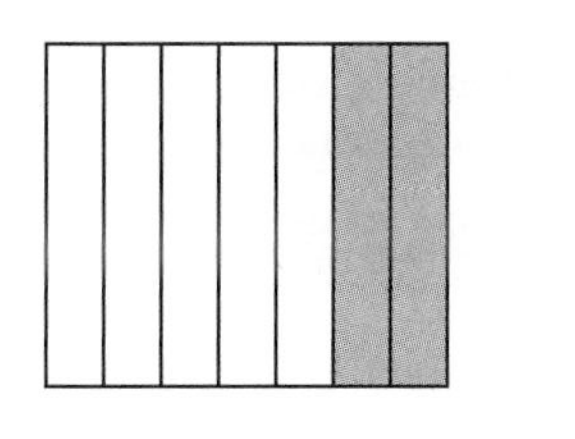

**3.** There are 14 buses at Millwood Elementary School. Each bus holds up to 56 students. How many students in all can be transported by the buses? **784 buses**

**4.** Juan walks at the park every morning for exercise. The table shows the total number of miles he has walked after different numbers of days.

| Morning Walks | |
|---|---|
| **Number of Days** | **Number of Miles** |
| 1 | 6 |
| 2 | 12 |
| 3 | 18 |
| 4 | 24 |

If Juan walks the same distance each day, how many miles will he have walked in a week? **42 miles**

**5.** Binta has 11 pages of stickers in a binder with 12 stickers on each page. She calculates that she has $11 \times 12 = 132$ stickers in all. Which number sentence can she use to check her calculation? **$132 \div 11 = 12$**

**6.** Molly's patio has the dimensions shown below.

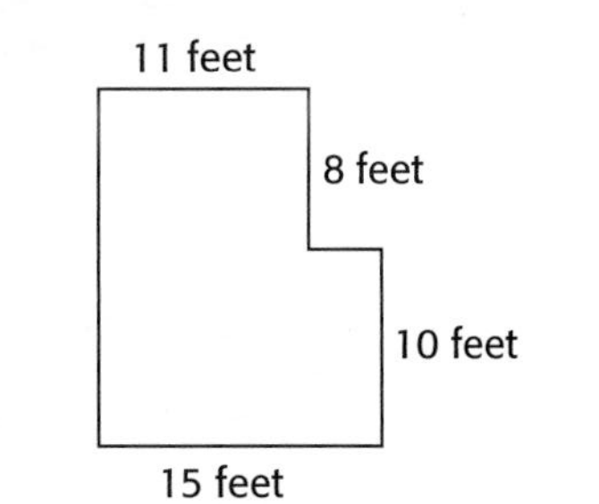


What is the area of the patio? **238 square feet**

**7.** Before leaving for school, Taye checks the outside temperature. What temperature is shown on the thermometer? **62°F**

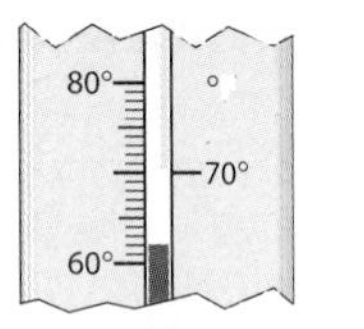


**8.** How many lines of symmetry does a square have? **4 lines of symmetry**

**9.** What type of angles are formed by two perpendicular lines? **right angles**

**10.** Draw a pair of figures that show reflection. **See students' work.**

**11.** To play a board game, each player rolls a number cube and chooses a card at random from a deck. There are red and green cards in the deck.

How many possible outcomes are there on each turn? **12 outcomes**

**12.** Refer to the rules for the game in Exercise 11. What is the probability that Eduardo will roll a 3 and select a red card on his next turn? **1 out of 12**

**13.** Look at the bar graph below. It shows the number of points scored by 4 players in a basketball game.

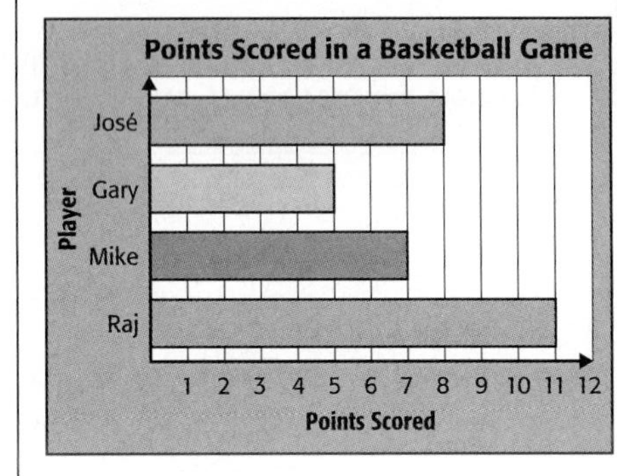


Which players scored a total of 12 points? **Gary and Mike**

**14.** Refer to the bar graph in Exercise 13. How many points were scored in all? **31 points**

**15.** Suppose Matt tosses a beanbag onto the game board below. What is the probability that the beanbag will land on a shaded space? **12 out of 32**

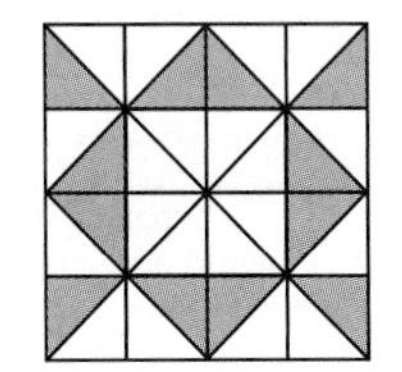

**16.** Kyle has 70 baseball cards. Write a number sentence that shows how many cards Kyle would have if he gave away half of his cards. **$70 \div 2 = 35$**

# Extended-Response Questions

Most extended-response questions have multiple parts. You must answer all parts to receive full credit.

In extended-response questions, you must show all of your work in solving the problem. A rubric is used to determine if you receive full, partial, or no credit. The following is a sample rubric for scoring extended-response questions.

| Credit | Score | Criteria |
|---|---|---|
| Full | 4 | Full Credit: The answer is correct and a full explanation is given that shows each step in finding the answer. |
| Partial | 3, 2, 1 | Partial Credit: Most of the solution is correct, but it may have some mistakes in the explanation or solution. The more correct the solution, the greater the score. |
| None | 0 | No credit: Either an answer is not provided or the answer does not make sense. |

Make sure that when the problem says to *show your work,* you show every part of your solution. This includes figures, graphs, and any explanations for your calculations.

**Example**

**1 Find how much longer it took each student to read *Sounder* than *Charlotte's Web*. Make a bar graph to show the results.**

| Student | *Charlotte's Web* (hours to read) | *Sounder* (hours to read) |
|---|---|---|
| Lisa | 9 | 27 |
| Jason | 15 | 45 |
| Torres | 6 | 18 |
| Monique | 12 | 36 |

## Full Credit Solution

In this sample answer, the student explains what calculations need to be done and finds the correct solution.

First, I will list each student's name and write the expression that will show the difference. Then I will subtract.

Lisa: $27 - 9 = 18$ Jason: $45 - 15 = 30$ Torres: $18 - 6 = 12$ Monique: $36 - 12 = 24$

The steps, calculation and reasoning are clearly stated.

The difference in hours spent reading the two books for each student is: Lisa: 18, Jason: 30, Torres: 12, and Monique: 24 hours.

The correct answer is given.

Now I will use the data from the first part to make the bar graph.

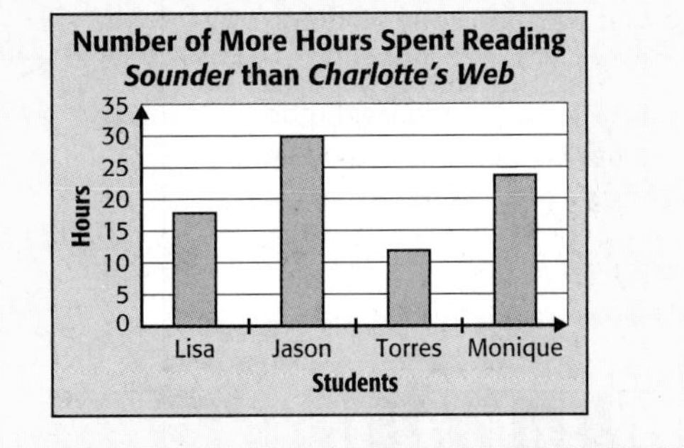


## Partial Credit Solution

This sample answer receives partial credit because the student explains how they got each answer, but did not create a bar graph.

First, I will list each student's name and write the expression that will show the difference. Then I will subtract.

| Lisa | Jason | Torres | Monique |
|---|---|---|---|
| 27 | 45 | 18 | 36 |
| − 9 | − 15 | − 6 | − 12 |
| 18 | 30 | 12 | 24 |

The number of more hours spent on *Sounder* than *Charlotte's Web* for each student is: Lisa: 18, Jason: 30, Torres: 12, and Monique: 24 hours.

## No Credit Solution

A solution for this problem that will receive no credit may include incorrect answers and an inaccurate or incomplete bar graph.

# Extended-Response Practice

**DIRECTIONS** 1–16. See students' explanations.
**Solve each problem. Show all your work.**

**1.** What is the smallest possible number you can make with the digits below? How did you decide how to arrange the digits? 24,568

5, 2, 8, 6, 4

**2.** Mark says the model below shows the fraction $2\frac{3}{4}$. Gina says that the model shows $\frac{11}{4}$. Who is correct? Explain.

They are both correct.

**3.** A pizza is cut into 8 equal slices. How many slices would you have to eat to have eaten $\frac{1}{4}$ of the pizza yourself? Draw a picture and write an equivalent fraction to show how to find the answer. 2 slices

**4.** Look at the number sentences below.

532 × 10 = 5,320
75 × 10 = 750
1,248 × 10 = 12,480
49 × 10 = 490

How can these number sentences help you find the product of 35 and 10?

**5.** The table shows input and output numbers.

| Input | Output |
|---|---|
| 2 | 5 |
| 4 | 7 |
| 6 | 9 |
| 8 | 11 |
| 10 | 13 |

Describe what happened to each input number to result in the output number. add 3

**6.** Describe two ways to find the perimeter of a soccer field with the dimensions shown below.

75 meters

110 meters

75 + 75 + 110 + 110; 2 × (75 + 110)

**7.** Suki returned home at the time shown on the clock, which is 2 hours 15 minutes after school ended. Explain how to find the time that school ended.



**8.** Artie estimates that the pitcher of lemonade has a capacity of 2 quarts. How can he find whether or not he is correct using a measuring cup that holds 1 cup?

**9.** Explain why the two figures below are congruent.

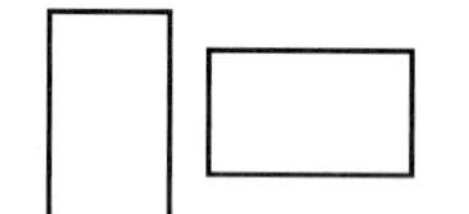

**10.** Use the figures below to write a definition for *isosceles triangles* and *right triangles.*

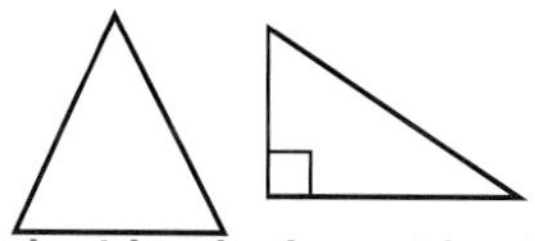

Isosceles triangles have at least two equal sides. Right triangles have one right angle.

**11.** Suppose Kathi tosses a coin and records the result. Then she tosses a second coin and records the result. Let H represent a coin landing on heads, and let T represent a coin landing on tails. List all of the possible outcomes. HH, HT, TH, TT

**12.** Four coins are placed in a bag. They add up to 41¢. What is the probability that a coin pulled from the bag has a value greater than 10¢? Show how you found the answer. 1 out of 4

**13.** Two bags of grapes cost \$5. Four bags of grapes cost \$10. Suppose this pattern continues. Make a bar graph to show the cost of 6, 8, and 10 bags of grapes.

**14.** The double bar graph shows the number of points scored by two different players during the first 4 games of a basketball season.

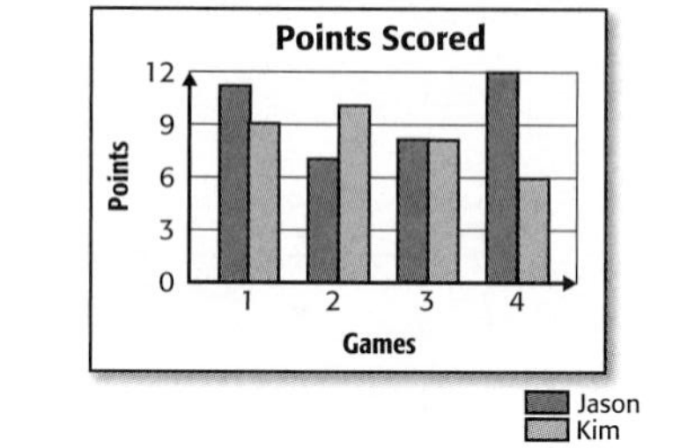


How can you find the overall difference in points scored by both players?

**15.** Compare and contrast a tally chart and a frequency table. How are they similar? How are they different?

**16.** There is ham, turkey, mayonnaise, mustard, and two types of bread in a refrigerator. How can a tree diagram be used to find the possible sandwich combinations?

# Concepts and Skills Bank

 Order of Operations

# Lesson Planner

## Objective

I will use order of operations to solve expressions containing two or more operations.

## Vocabulary

**order of operations**

## Activate Prior Knowledge

Write a few expressions on the board.

- Ask students to copy expressions, such as 629 + 176, 3 + 8 + 12, and 58 – 40 – 3, from the board. Ask for volunteers to share their solutions.
- Now, write expressions containing more than one operation on the board, such as 16 + 9 × 5, 45 – 5 + 30, and 20 – 8 × 2. Again, ask students to copy and solve. Call on volunteers to share their answers, expecting two different answers to each problem.

### Using student page R56.

- Explain to students that when solving an expression with more than one operation, order of operations must be used instead of solving from left to right.
- Tell students that in order to perform order of operations, they can use the saying "**P**lease **E**xcuse **M**y **D**ear **A**unt **S**ally." The first letter of each word in this phrase represents a step in the order of operations. Exponents will be taught in a later grade, and can be skipped for now.

| **P**lease | Parentheses |
|---|---|
| **E**xcuse | Exponents |
| **M**y | Multiplication |
| **D**ear | Division |
| **A**unt | Addition |
| **S**ally | Subtraction |





## Order of Operations

To find the value of an expression with more than one operation, you need to follow the rules for the **order of operations**.

**Order of Operations** — Key Concept

1. Do the operations in the parentheses first.
2. Multiply and divide in order from left to right.
3. Add and subtract in order from left to right.

**EXAMPLE** Use the Order of Operations

**1** **Find 3 + (2 × 4) – 6.**

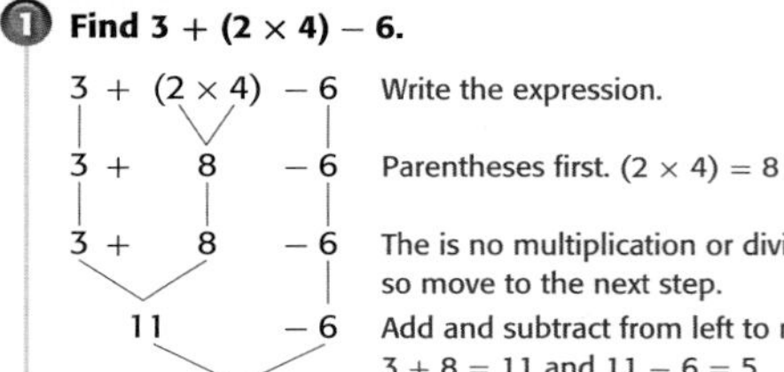


Write the expression.

Parentheses first. (2 × 4) = 8

The is no multiplication or division, so move to the next step.

Add and subtract from left to right. 3 + 8 = 11 and 11 – 6 = 5

So, 3 + (2 × 4) – 6 = 5.

### Exercises

**Find the value of each expression.**

1. (7 + 1) × 3 – 5 **19**
2. (8 – 5) ÷ 3 + 2 **3**
3. 13 + 4 – (7 × 2) **3**
4. 5 (2 + 3) **25**
5. (5 + 4) × 7 – 3 **60**
6. 8 × (14 – 8) + 7 **55**
7. 6 × (8 – 5) + 9 **27**
8. (8 + 6) ÷ (12 – 5) **2**

**Write and find the value of an expression for the situation.**

9. **Measurement** Todd walked 2 miles a day for 4 days and 3 miles on the fifth day. How many miles did he walk? **(2 × 4) + 3; 11**



- Solve the three expressions again using order of operations.
- Introduce expressions involving parentheses, such as (3 × 7) + 10 and 4(12 – 7). Show students how to find the value of each of these expressions. Then give them a few to solve on their own.

### Using the Exercises

**Exercises 1–8** Advise students to write each line of the solution on a different line of notebook paper to help them keep their solution organized. Students may need support when finding the value of the expression in Exercise 8 since it contains two sets of parentheses.

**Exercise 9** Some students may need guidance with using parentheses when writing the expression for this exercise.

## Assess and Close

**Made to Order** Ask each student to write five multi-operation expressions. Tell students they must use parentheses and each of the operations at least once in their five expressions. Then, have students exchange expressions with someone in the classroom and solve.

## Divisibility Rules for 2, 5, and 10

A whole number is **divisible** by another number if the remainder is 0 when the first number is divided by the second. The divisibility rules for 2, 5, and 10 are stated below.

| Divisibility Rules for 2, 5, and 10 (Key Concepts) | |
|---|---|
| **Words** | **Examples** |
| A whole number is divisible by: | |
| • 2 if the ones digit is divisible by 2. | 2, 4, 6, 8, 10, 12, ... |
| • 5 if the ones digit is 0 or 5. | 5, 10, 15, 20, 25, ... |
| • 10 if the ones digit is 0. | 10, 20, 30, 40, 50, ... |

A whole number is **even** if it is divisible by 2. A whole number is **odd** if it is not divisible by 2.

**EXAMPLE** Use Divisibility Rules

1. **Tell whether the number 340 is divisible by 2, 5, or 10. Then classify the number as even or odd.**

Use the divisibility rules to determine if 340 is divisible by 2, 5, or 10.

2: Yes, the ones digit, 0, is divisible by 2.

5: Yes, the ones digit is 0.

10: Yes, the ones digit is 0.

Since 340 is divisible by 2, it is an even number.

So, 340 is divisible by 2, 5, and 10, and it is an even number.

### Exercises

**Tell whether each number is divisible by 2, 5, or 10. They classify each number as even or odd.**

1. 40 2, 5, 10; even
2. 65 5; odd
3. 78 2; even
4. 91 none; odd
5. 115 5; odd
6. 136 2; even
7. 150 2, 5, 10; even
8. 194 2; even
9. 216 2; even
10. 280 2, 5, 10; even
11. 311 none; odd
12. 345 5; odd
13. Find a number that is divisible by both 2 and 5. 50
14. Find a number that is divisible by 2, 5, and 10. 90





# Concepts and Skills Bank

## 2 Divisibility Rules for 2, 5, and 10

# Lesson Planner

## Objective

I will draw conclusions about the divisibility of a number by looking at its ones place.

## Vocabulary

**divisible, even, odd**

**Materials:** hundreds charts (1 per group); crayons, markers, or colored pencils; One Hundred Hungry Ants by Elinor J. Pinczes

## Activate Prior Knowledge

Lead a discussion about how to identify the ones place of a number.

- Write various numbers on the board, such as 4,321, 950, and 2,453. Ask students to identify the ones place of each number. 1, 0 and 3
- Tell students that they will be using the ones place of numbers to tell whether the numbers are divisible by 2, 5, and 10.

### Using student page R57.

- Discuss with students the divisibility rules displayed in the table on page R57.
- Pass out hundreds charts to small groups of students. On each hundreds chart, have students mark each number that is divisible by 2 with a blue dot. Second, ask students to mark each number that is divisible by 5 with a green dot. Lastly, ask students to mark each number that is divisible by 10 with a red dot.
- Have students search for patterns on the chart. Possible patterns include: all marked numbers are either even or have 5 in their ones place, every other column is marked in blue (divisible by 2), etc. Have students share and discuss the patterns they find.
- Revisit the numbers written on the board (36, 950, and 2,453). Work with students to determine their divisibility by 2, 5, and 10 to conclude whether they are even or odd.

### Using the Exercises

**Exercises 1–12** Have students copy the number from each exercise and underline the digit in its ones place before determining its divisibility.

**Exercises 13–14** Challenge students who finish early to find numbers in the tens, hundreds, and thousands that fit the descriptions given.

## Assess and Close

**Ant Arrays** Read aloud One Hundred Hungry Ants. In the book, 100 marching ants are arranged into various arrays, including a 2-by-50 array and a 5-by-10 array. Therefore, 100 is divisible by 2, 5, and 10. Have students determine another number that is divisible by 2, 5, and 10. Then, have students write their own story using that number of hungry, marching ants who divide into arrays. Students should write about the arrays involving 2, 5, and 10 in their stories and they should tell whether their chosen number is even or odd.

## 3 Even and Odd Numbers and Products

# Lesson Planner

## Objective

I will draw conclusions about the products of expressions involving the multiplication of even and/or odd numbers.

## Vocabulary

**even, odd**

**Materials:** index cards or sticky notes (1 per student)

## Activate Prior Knowledge

Lead a discussion about how to identify even and odd numbers.

- Recall that even numbers have 0, 2, 4, 6, or 8 in the ones place while odd numbers have 1, 3, 5, 7, or 9 in the ones place.
- Write several numbers, such as 439, 3,567, and 93,020, on the board. Then have students determine whether they are even or odd.

### Using student page R58.

- Write a two- or three-digit number on each index card or sticky note. Make about half of the numbers even and the other half odd. Then, write a letter on each card so that two cards have As on them, two have Bs, two have Cs, etc. Some of the matching cards should contain two even numbers, one even and one odd number, and two odd numbers.
- Pass out the cards to students. Tell them to find their partner by looking for a card with the same letter on it.
- After students find their partners, refer them to page R58 to determine whether the product of their two numbers will be even or odd.





### Even and Odd Numbers and Products

A whole number is **even** if it is divisible by 2. A whole number is **odd** if it is not divisible by 2.

| Even Numbers | Odd Numbers |
|---|---|
| 0, 2, 4, 6, 8, 10, 12, 14, 16, 18, 20, ... | 1, 3, 5, 7, 9, 11, 13, 15, 17, 19, ... |

The factors in a multiplication problem can help you determine if the product will be even or odd.

**Odd and Even Products** — Key Concepts

| Words | Examples |
|---|---|
| even number × even number = even number | $2 \times 4 = 8$ or $6 \times 8 = 48$ |
| even number × odd number = even number | $2 \times 3 = 6$ or $4 \times 5 = 20$ |
| odd number × odd number = odd number | $3 \times 5 = 15$ or $7 \times 9 = 63$ |

**EXAMPLE** Tell Whether a Product Will Be Even or Odd

**1 Tell whether the product of 14 and 23 will be even or odd.**

Classify each factor as even or odd. Then use the information in the Key Concept box to determine if the product will be even or odd.

14 × 23

14 → even number; 23 → odd number

The product of an even and odd number will be even. So, the product of 14 and 23 will be even.

#### Exercises

**Tell whether each product will be even or odd.**

**1.** $13 \times 21$ odd
**2.** $34 \times 56$ even
**3.** $41 \times 118$ even
**4.** $73 \times 129$ odd
**5.** $134 \times 155$ even
**6.** $143 \times 167$ odd
**7.** $184 \times 192$ even
**8.** $212 \times 257$ even



- Have students share their number cards and whether they believe the product will be even or odd with the class.

### Using the Exercises

**Exercises 1–8** Encourage students to identify whether each product will be even or odd before using the "Odd and Even Products" table of page R58 to confirm their thinking.

## Assess and Close

**Product Predictions** On a piece of notebook paper, ask students to determine whether the products of three expressions, such as $11 \times 19$, $38 \times 192$, and $521 \times 410$, will be even or odd without access to the table on page R58. Have students explain their thinking in words.

## Relate Fractions, Decimals, and Percents

Fractions, decimals, and percents are related. A **percent** compares a number to 100.

100%

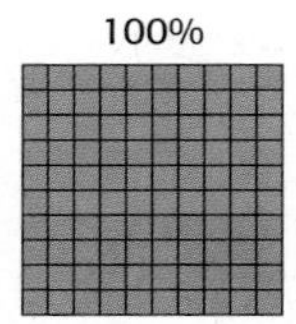

100 out of 100

$\frac{100}{100} = 1 = 1.0$

67%

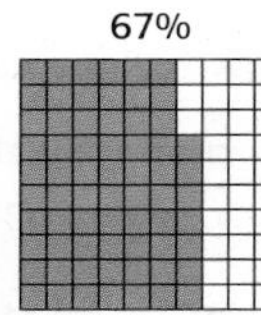

67 out of 100

$\frac{67}{100} = 0.67$

25%

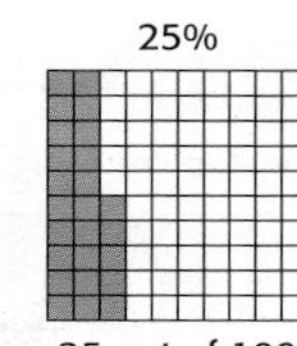

25 out of 100

$\frac{25}{100} = \frac{1}{4} = 0.25$

**EXAMPLE** Write a Fraction, Decimal, and Percent

**1 Write the amount shown by the model as a fraction, decimal, and percent.**

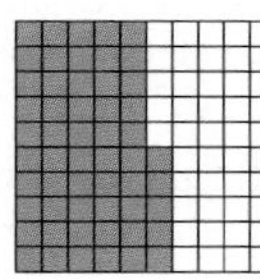

55 out of 100 squares in the model are shaded.

So, the amount shown by the model as a fraction, decimal, and percent is $\frac{55}{100}$, 0.55, and 55%.

### Exercises

**Write the amount shown by each model as a fraction, decimal, and percent.**

**1.**

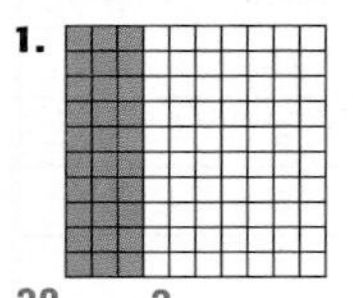

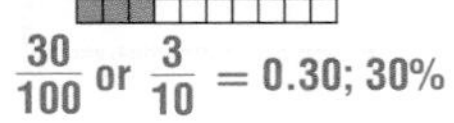

$\frac{30}{100}$ or $\frac{3}{10} = 0.30$; 30%

**2.**

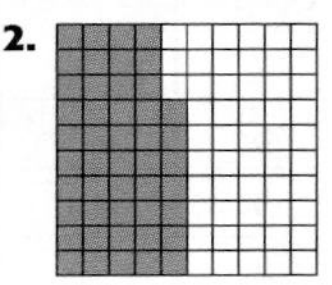

$\frac{47}{100} = 0.47$; 47%

**3.**

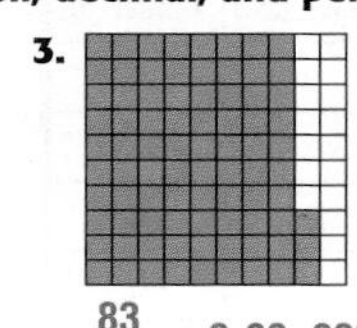

$\frac{83}{100} = 0.83$; 83%

**4.** Carisa plays soccer. She makes 0.75 of the goals she shoots. What is the percentage of shots she makes? 75%

**5.** Miguel read 35 of the 50 pages in his book. What percent of the book has Miguel read? 70%



Concepts and Skills

# Concepts and Skills Bank

## 4 Relate Fractions, Decimals, and Percents

# Lesson Planner

## Objective

I will explore equivalent fractions, decimals, and percents.

## Vocabulary

**percent**

**Materials:** transparency of hundredths grid

**Manipulatives:** base-ten blocks (ones and tens), dice (2 per student)

# Activate Prior Knowledge

Initiate discussion about fractions of a hundred.

- Display a transparency of a hundredths grid. Place 3 tens rods and 5 ones units in the hundredths grid to model the fraction $\frac{35}{100}$. Model a few more fractions this way.

### Using student page R59.

- Show students how to write a percent. If the denominator of a fraction is 100, then the percent is written as the numerator followed by a percent sign. For example, $\frac{25}{100} = 25\%$.
- When a fraction already has a denominator of 100, it is easy to write the decimal equivalent. Say the fraction aloud to know how to write the decimal. For example, $\frac{35}{100}$ is read as "thirty-five hundredths," so the decimal equivalent is 0.35, or "thirty-five hundredths."

| Read | Say | Write |
|---|---|---|
| $\frac{35}{100}$ | "thirty-five hundredths" | 0.35 |

- The same rule applies when starting with a decimal and writing the fraction equivalent.

| Read | Say | Write |
|---|---|---|
| 0.35 | "thirty-five hundredths" | $\frac{35}{100}$ |

- If time allows, challenge students by giving them a fraction that is less than $\frac{10}{100}$. For example, $\frac{4}{100} = 0.04$, not 0.4.

## Using the Exercises

**Exercises 1–3** Advise students to carefully count the shaded squares before writing the fraction, decimal, and percent.

**Exercise 5** Students may need help with Exercise 5. The 35 pages will need to be doubled to determine the percent since the book is only 50 pages total.

# Assess and Close

**I Can Relate** Have students roll two dice three times to create three 2-digit numbers. Students are to write each 2-digit number as a numerator over 100 to create three fractions. Then have students write an equivalent decimal and precent for each fraction.

## 5 Skip Counting Forward and Backward

# Lesson Planner

## Objective

I will skip count to find missing numbers in function tables.

**Materials:** blank paper (1 piece per group); crayons, markers, or colored pencils

## Activate Prior Knowledge

Review how to find unknown values in function tables.

- Display a table on the chalkboard with a simple function, such as $y = 2x$. Write the first output value. Invite student volunteers to fill in the rest of the output values.
- Demonstrate how to skip count to find the output values by drawing arrows and showing the addition or subtraction process along the right side of the function table.

### Using student page R60.

- As a class, work through examples 1 and 2. Have students brainstorm strategies for determining unknown values. For example, determine whether the output values are increasing or decreasing to decide whether to skip count forward or backward.
- Create a function table using an item in the classroom or a fact from a recent social studies or science unit of study. For example, a function table could be written about the fact that butterflies have six legs. The input values would represent the number of butterflies and the output values would represent the total number of legs the butterflies have.





### Skip Counting Forward and Backward

You can skip count forward and backward to find missing numbers in a function table.

**EXAMPLES** Skip Counting on Function Tables

**Use skip counting to find the missing number.**

1

| $y = 20x$ | |
|---|---|
| Input (x) | Output (y) |
| 1 | 20 |
| 2 | 40 |
| 3 | 60 |
| 4 | ■ |

+20, +20, +20

This function table shows $y = 20x$. You can skip count forward by 20 to find the missing number.

$60 + 20 = 80$

So, the missing number is 80.

2

| $y = 1{,}000x$ | |
|---|---|
| Input (x) | Output (y) |
| 8 | 8,000 |
| 7 | 7,000 |
| 6 | 6,000 |
| 5 | ■ |

−1,000, −1,000, −1,000

The function table shows $y = 1{,}000x$. You can skip count backward by 1,000 to find the missing number.

$6{,}000 - 1{,}000 = 5{,}000$

So, the missing number is 5,000.

### Exercises

**Use skip counting to find the missing number.**

1.

| $y = 100x$ | |
|---|---|
| Input (x) | Output (y) |
| 5 | 500 |
| 6 | 600 |
| 7 | 700 |
| 8 | ■ |

800

2.

| $y = 50x$ | |
|---|---|
| Input (x) | Output (y) |
| 7 | 350 |
| 6 | 300 |
| 5 | 250 |
| 4 | ■ |

200

3.

| $y = 25x$ | |
|---|---|
| Input (x) | Output (y) |
| 10 | 250 |
| 9 | 225 |
| 8 | 200 |
| 7 | ■ |

175

4.

| $y = 10{,}000x$ | | | | |
|---|---|---|---|---|
| Input (x) | 2 | 3 | 4 | 5 |
| Output (y) | 20,000 | 30,000 | 40,000 | ■ |

50,000



### Using the Exercises

**Exercises 1–4** Help students in finding the missing values by drawing arrows and recording their skip counting as shown in the examples. Encourage students to work backward to check their work by skip counting in the opposite direction.

## Assess and Close

**Mascot Mania** Divide students into small groups, or teams, and assign them the task of creating team mascots. Each group is to draw and color a mascot on a blank piece of paper. Mascots should have a multiple number of an item, such as a monster with 10 eyes, a ladybug with 6 spots, or a dragon with 2,000 scales. Groups will then create a function table that relates to their mascot. For example, a group using the dragon as a mascot could skip count by 2,000 in the output column to determine how many scales 1, 2, 3, and 4 dragons would have.

## Negative Numbers

The numbers +1 and +3 are **positive numbers**. They can be written with or without a + sign. The numbers −1 and −3 are **negative numbers**. A negative number has a − sign.

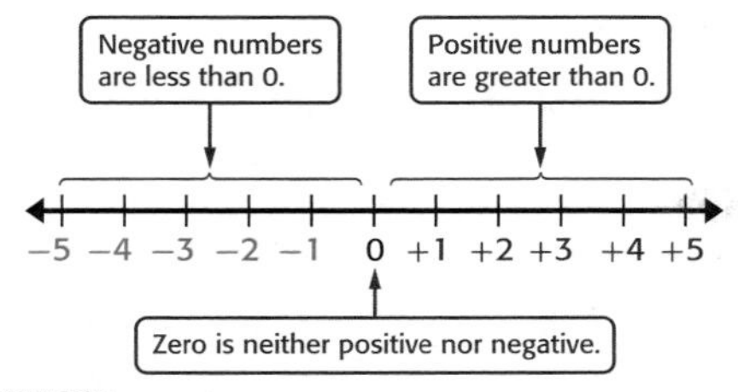


**EXAMPLES** Write Positive and Negative Numbers

**Write the number that represents each situation.**

**1 WEATHER 4 degrees below zero**

The temperature is below zero. The number is −4.

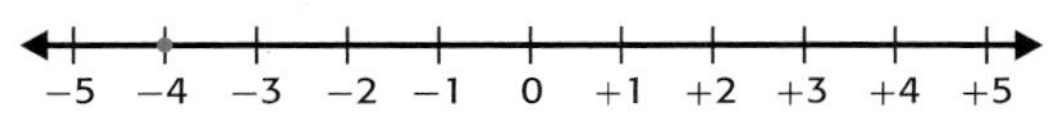


**2 FOOTBALL a gain of 3 yards**

The word *gain* means an increase. The number is +3 or 3.

−5 −4 −3 −2 −1 0 +1 +2 +3 +4 +5

### Exercises

**Write the number that represents each situation.**

1. move back 3 spaces −3
2. move 12 steps forward +12
3. score 10 points +10
4. owe $7 −7
5. 8 degrees below 0 −8
6. distance increases by 5 miles +5
7. earn $15 +15
8. cut 10 seconds off a running time −10

**Write the number of each letter on the number line.**

**9.** 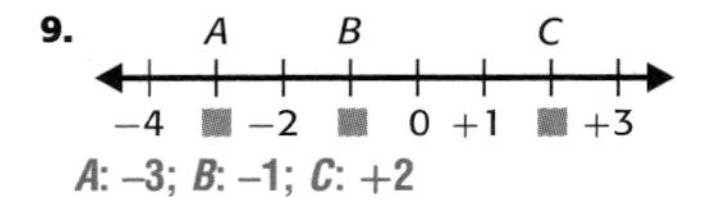

A: −3; B: −1; C: +2

**10.** 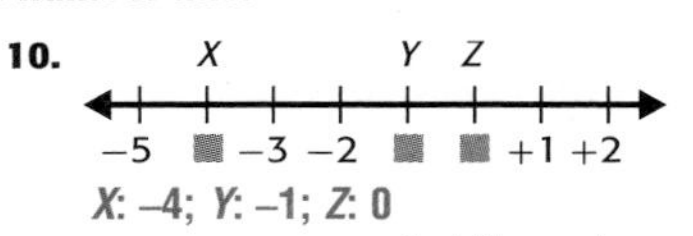

X: −4; Y: −1; Z: 0



Concepts and Skills

# Concepts and Skills Bank

## 6 Negative Numbers

# Lesson Planner

## Objective

I will explore positive and negative numbers using a number line.

## Vocabulary

**positive numbers, negative numbers**

**Materials:** sticky notes (1 per student)

## Activate Prior Knowledge

Lead a discussion about positive and negative numbers.

- Tell students that up to this point, all the numbers they have worked with have been positive numbers. Positive numbers are located to the right of the number 0 on a number line. As you move to the right on a number line the values of the numbers increase.
- Emphasize that 0 is neither a positive nor a negative number.
- Tell students that negative numbers are located to the left of the number 0 on a number line. They are always preceded by a negative sign. As you move to the left on a number line the values of the numbers decrease.

### Using student page R61.

- Write the numbers -10 through +10 on sticky notes, one per note. Pass out the notes to the class.
- Ask students to line up in the correct order to simulate a number line.
- Toss a soft object to a student holding a number that is between -10 and +5. Ask that student to toss it to another student for a gain of 5 (or +5). Then, ask the student who just caught the ball to toss it to another student for a loss of 3 (or -3).
- Continue with the game by using vocabulary seen in the exercises, such as "move back/forward," "increase/decrease," "gain," etc.
- If time allows, play again. This time, have the student who catches the ball decide on and announce the loss or gain.

## Using the Exercises

**Exercises 1–8** Ask students to think about whether something is being added or taken away when trying to determine if each number should be positive or negative.

**Exercises 9–10** Remind students that all numbers to the right of 0 are positive, whereas those to the left of 0 are negative.

## Assess and Close

**Number Line Know-How** Ask students questions like the ones shown below.

Which word, "less" or "greater" would fit correctly in each phrase?

+11 is_____ than -21   -9 is_____ than -4

# Concepts and Skills Bank

## Graphing Functions

# Lesson Planner

## Objective

Given a function, I will create a table. Then I will graph the ordered pairs from the table.

**Materials:** transparency containing a grid, graph paper (2 pieces per student)

**Manipulatives:** rulers (1 per student)

## Activate Prior Knowledge

Students found unknown values in function tables in a previous lesson. Tell students they will not be able to skip count to determine unknown values in this lesson.

- Solve several simple algebraic expressions on the board such as $y = 4x$ where $x$ equals 2 and $3 + 5x = y$ where $x$ equals 5. $y = 8; 28 = y$

### Using student page R62.

- When graphing ordered pairs, always start with the $x$-coordinate. Since students are used to working in this order, it may be helpful for them to write functions this way too. For example, the function $y = 2x + 1$ can be written as $2x + 1 = y$. It may also benefit students to add a function column to their tables, as seen below.
- Create a function table for $y = 2x + 1$.
- Display a grid using a transparency or large poster paper and invite volunteers to graph the ordered pairs for the function $y = 2x + 1$. Show students how to connect the points using a ruler.

| Input ($x$) | Function $2x + 1 = y$ | Output ($y$) | ($x$, $y$) |
|---|---|---|---|
| 0 | (2 x 0) + 1 | 1 | (0,1) |
| 1 | (2 x 1) + 1 | 3 | (1,3) |
| 2 | (2 x 2) + 1 | 5 | (2,5) |
| 3 | (2 x 3) + 1 | 7 | (3,7) |
| 4 | (2 x 4) + 1 | 9 | (4,9) |

Concepts and Skills

## Graphing Functions

Functions can be placed in a table and then graphed. First, make a table for the function. Then graph the function using the ordered pairs found.

**EXAMPLE** Graph a Function

**Graph ten points on the graph of the function $y = 2x + 1$.**

Complete a table to find the ordered pairs. Then graph the ordered pairs. Connect the points with a straight line.

| Input ($x$) | Output ($y$) | ($x$, $y$) |
|---|---|---|
| 0 | 1 | (0, 1) |
| 1 | 3 | (1, 3) |
| 2 | 5 | (2, 5) |
| 3 | 7 | (3, 7) |
| 4 | 9 | (4, 9) |
| 5 | 11 | (5, 11) |
| 6 | 13 | (6, 13) |
| 7 | 15 | (7, 15) |
| 8 | 17 | (8, 17) |
| 9 | 19 | (9, 19) |

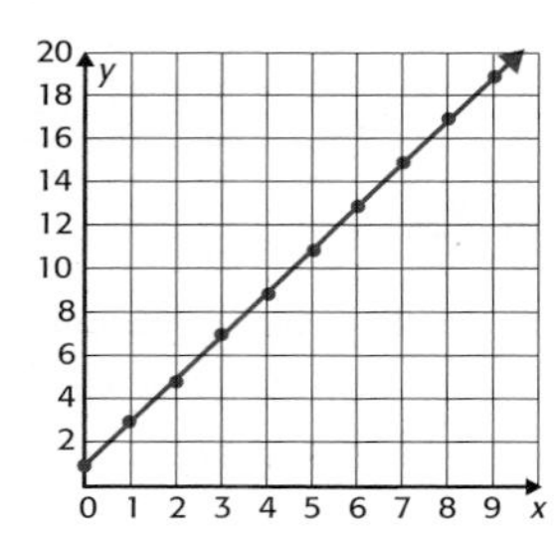


### Exercises

**Graph ten points on the graph of the function.**

1. $y = 1x$
2. $y = 6x$
3. $y = x + 6$
4. $y = 2x - 1$
5. $y = 4x + 2$
6. $y = 5x - 3$
7. Laine gives $3 of her weekly allowance to a charity. The rule can be written as $y = 3x$. The function table shows the amount of money Laine has given to a charity after 1, 2, 3, and 4 weeks. Create a graph to show the amount of money given to charity after 10 weeks.

| Input ($x$) Weeks | Output ($y$) Amount to Charity | ($x$, $y$) |
|---|---|---|
| 1 | $3 | (1, 3) |
| 2 | $6 | (2, 6) |
| 3 | $9 | (3, 9) |
| 4 | $12 | (4, 12) |

1–7. See students' work.

R62 Concepts and Skills Bank

### Using the Exercises

**Exercises 1–6** Have students use rulers to connect the ordered pairs.

**Exercise 7** Tell students that they will have to extend the table to 10 in the input column before graphing the ordered pairs.

## Assess and Close

**Figuring Functions** Have students complete the function table below and then graph the ordered pairs.

| Input ($x$) | Function $2x + 1 = y$ | Output ($y$) | ($x$, $y$) |
|---|---|---|---|
| | | | (1,2) |
| 2 | | | |
| 3 | | | (3,8) |
| | | 11 | |

## Units of Time

**Time** is a unit of measure. It measures the interval between two or more events. Like other units of measure, units of time can also be converted.

- To convert from larger units to smaller units, multiply.
- To convert from smaller units to larger units, divide.

| Units of Time |
| --- |
| 60 seconds (s) = 1 minute (min) |
| 60 minutes = 1 hour (h) |
| 24 hours = 1 day |
| 7 days = 1 week |
| 12 months = 1 year |
| 52 weeks = 1 year |
| 365 days = 1 year |

Concepts and Skills

**EXAMPLES** Convert Units of Time

**MEASUREMENT Complete each conversion.**

**1** **5 hours = ■ minutes**

$$\begin{array}{r} 60 \\ \times 5 \\ \hline 300 \end{array}$$

Since 1 hour = 60 minutes, multiply by 60.

So, 5 hours = 300 minutes.

**2** **42 days = ■ weeks**

$$7\overline{)42}^{\;6}$$

Since 7 days = 1 week, divide by 7.

So, 42 days = 6 weeks

### Exercises

**MEASUREMENT Complete each conversion.**

**1.** 52 weeks = ■ days 365

**2.** 7 days = ■ hours 168

**3.** 24 hours = ■ seconds 86,400

**4.** 3 years = ■ days 1,095

**5.** 120 months = ■ years 10

**6.** 15 minutes = ■ seconds 900

**7.** 49 days = ■ weeks 7

**8.** 4 weeks = ■ days 28

**9.** 1,470 days = ■ weeks 210

**10.** 216 months = ■ years 18

**11.** A calendar typically shows one year. Some calendars can show many years. If a calendar shows 5 years, how many months does it show? 60 months

**12.** James was looking at his calendar and noticed it was a 2-year calendar. How many weeks is that? how many days? 104; 730

Concepts and Skills Bank **R63**

## Using the Exercises

**Exercises 1–10** Remind students to write the related conversion information on their papers and to solve the problem under it. Also, help students recall that they should multiply when converting from larger units to smaller units and divide when converting from smaller units to larger units.

**Exercises 11–12** Ask students to think carefully about whether they are converting from larger units to smaller units or vice versa.

# Assess and Close

**Two-Step Problems** Pose two-step word problems involving time conversions. For example: "Lia walked the family dog for 1 hour. The next day, her mom walked the dog for 2 hours. On the third day, Lia's sister walked the dog for $1\frac{1}{2}$ hours. How many minutes was the dog walked during those three days? 270 minutes

# Concepts and Skills Bank

## 8 Units of Time

# Lesson Planner

## Objective

I will convert units of time.

## Vocabulary

**time**

# Activate Prior Knowledge

Discuss units of time as a class.

- Ask students to share facts about time. Record their thoughts in an idea web with the word "time" as the center.
- If students do not offer units of time during the brainstorming session, prompt them by asking how time can be measured.

### Using student page R63.

- When making a conversion involving units of time, follow the steps shown below.
- First, read the problem carefully: "James has to practice the piano for 7 hours each week. How many minutes is that?"
- Second, find the conversion information that will help solve the problem. Then write it on a piece of paper. Since the problem deals with hours and minutes, write the conversion information involving hours and minutes.
- Third, under the conversion information, write an equation using information from the problem. Make sure the hours and minutes are lined up. Think, "How do I figure out how many minutes are in 7 hours? I multiplied 1 hour by 7 to get 7 hours. So I will multiply 60 minutes by 7. The answer is 420 minutes because 60 × 7 = 420."

1 hour = 60 minutes

↓x7 ↓x7

7 hours = ____ minutes

# Concepts and Skills Bank

## Parts of a Circle

# Lesson Planner

## Objective

I will identify the parts of a circle

## Vocabulary

**circle, center, radius, diameter**

**Materials:** sticky notes (1 per student), blank paper (2 pieces per student)

**Manipulatives:** compasses (1 per student), rulers (1 per student)

Concepts and Skills

### Parts of a Circle

A **circle** is a two-dimensional figure in which all points are the same distance from a point called the **center**. The parts of a circle are shown below.

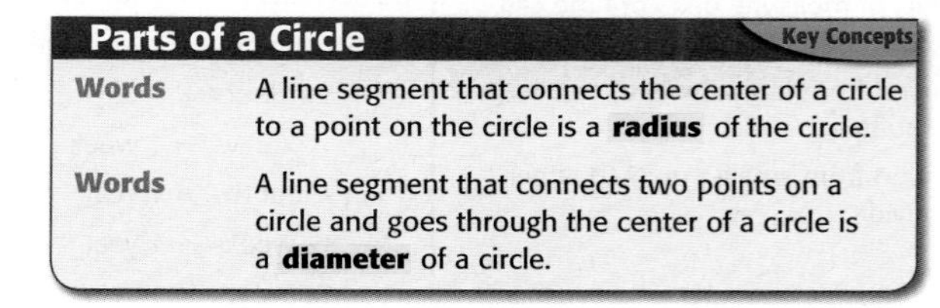

**Parts of a Circle** — Key Concepts

| | |
|---|---|
| **Words** | A line segment that connects the center of a circle to a point on the circle is a **radius** of the circle. |
| **Words** | A line segment that connects two points on a circle and goes through the center of a circle is a **diameter** of a circle. |

**EXAMPLES** Parts of a Circle

**Identify the part of the circle.**

1.

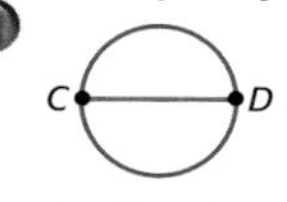



The line segment connects two points on the circle and goes through the center. This is a diameter.

2.

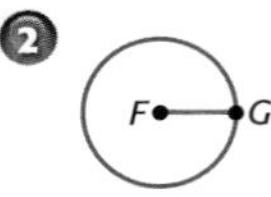



The line segment connects the center of the circle to one point on the circle. This is a radius.

### Exercises

**Identify the part of the circle.**

**1.** C center

**2.**

radius

**3.** G H F diameter

**Identify the part of the circle.**

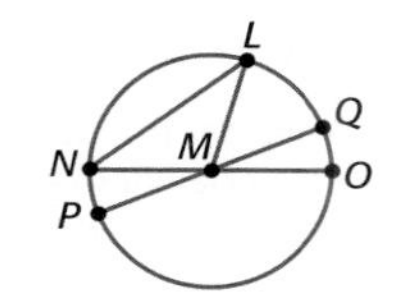



**4.** $\overline{LM}$ radius

**5.** $\overline{ON}$ diameter

**6.** $\overline{NM}$ radius

**7.** $\overline{ML}$ radius

**8.** $M$ center

**9.** $\overline{PQ}$ diameter



# Activate Prior Knowledge

Discuss items with circular shapes.

- Have each student draw a circular object and write its name on a sticky note.
- Have students share their ideas as they post their notes on the board.

## Using student page R64.

- Demonstrate for students how to use a compass to draw a circle.
- Then, have students use compasses to draw different-sized circles on a blank piece of paper.
- After allowing a few minutes of experimentation with the compasses, have students construct a circle with a center point.
- Instruct students to use a ruler to draw a line segment through the center of the circle with endpoints located on the circle. Tell students that this line segment is called the diameter of the circle. Label this distance as the diameter.
- Next, tell students to draw a line segment from the circle's center to any point on the circle. Label this distance as the radius.
- Show students how to label the endpoints of the radius and diameter with letters of the alphabet.
- If time allows, measure the length of the radius in centimeters or inches. Measure the length of the diameter and then compare the lengths of the two segments. Lead students to draw the conclusion that the length of the diameter is twice the length of the radius.

## Using the Exercises

**Exercises 1–9** Encourage students to identify each circle part on their own before looking at the information located at the top and middle of page R64 to confirm their thinking.

# Assess and Close

**Constructing Circles** Have students draw a circle according to directions. For example, draw a circle and its center, draw a radius and label it GH, and draw a diameter and label it JK. Have students write the definitions of the parts of a circle under their drawings.

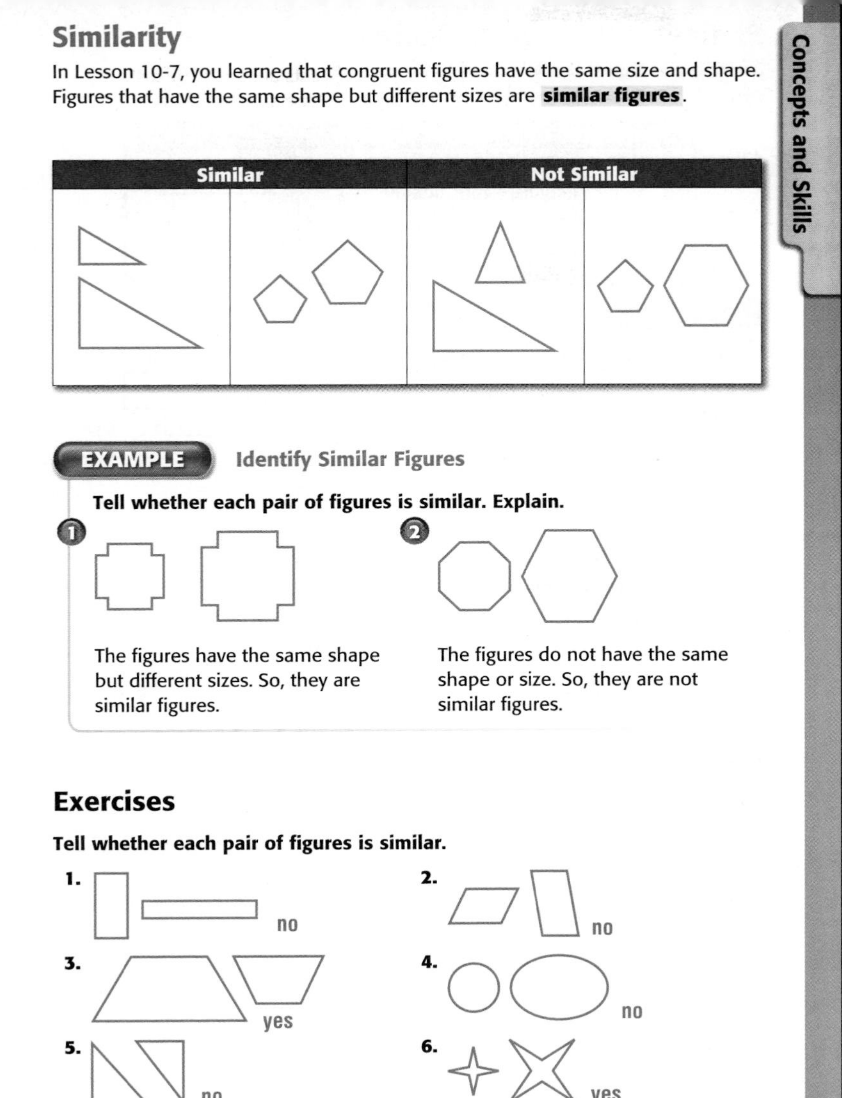

### Similarity

In Lesson 10-7, you learned that congruent figures have the same size and shape. Figures that have the same shape but different sizes are **similar figures**.

| Similar | | Not Similar | |
|---|---|---|---|
| | | | |

**EXAMPLE** Identify Similar Figures

**Tell whether each pair of figures is similar. Explain.**

1. The figures have the same shape but different sizes. So, they are similar figures.

2. The figures do not have the same shape or size. So, they are not similar figures.

**Exercises**

**Tell whether each pair of figures is similar.**

1. no
2. no
3. yes
4. no
5. no
6. yes

Concepts and Skills Bank R65

Concepts and Skills

# Concepts and Skills Bank

## 10 Similarity

# Lesson Planner

## Objective

I will identify similar figures.

## Vocabulary

**similar figures**

**Materials:** large piece of blank paper (1 per group), crayons, markers, or colored pencils, page of figures on colored paper (1 per student), blank paper (1 piece per student), scissors, glue

**Manipulatives:** pattern blocks

## Activate Prior Knowledge

Discuss the concept of similarity as a class.

- Write the word "similar" on the chalkboard and ask students what it means.
- Draw two equilateral triangles of varying sizes and one scalene triangle on the chalkboard. Ask students whether they think these figures are similar. Have students discuss their thoughts with a partner and then invite them to share with the class.
- Tell students that the first and second triangles (the equilaterals) are similar because they have the same shape but different sizes. The third triangle is not similar to the first two because it does not have the same shape.
- If students have not determined what similarity means, explain its defintion in mathematical terms.

### Using student page R65.

- Pass out piles of pattern blocks to small groups of students. Challenge students to create similar figures using the blocks. For example, create similar squares by using one square pattern block for one of the figures and four square pattern blocks for the other.
- Have groups who finish early trace their similar figures onto pieces of blank paper and color them.

### Using the Exercises

**Exercises 1–6** Remind students that figures have to have the same shape to be considered similar.

## Assess and Close

**Similarity Search** Create a page of figures, some similar and some not, and make copies on colored paper. Pass out this page and a blank piece of paper to each student. Have them fold the blank paper in half three times and then unfold it to reveal eight boxes. Then, ask students to cut out the similar figures and glue each pair in a different box on the blank piece of paper. Vary the difficulty of the task by either telling students how many pairs of similar figures to find (the easier option) or leaving it to students to determine this fact.

## 11 Perimeter of Irregular Figures

# Lesson Planner

## Objective

I will find the perimeter of an irregular figure by adding the lengths of its sides.

## Vocabulary

**irregular figure**

**Materials:** irregular figures drawn on half pieces of paper (1 figure per paper) with the lengths of their sides labeled (1 per student)

## Activate Prior Knowledge

Discuss the meaning of the word "perimeter" as a class.

- Write the word "perimeter" on the board. Ask students to share what they know about its meaning.
- The distance around the outside of an object or shape is its perimeter. You can remember that it is the distance *around* the shape because perimeter has the word "rim" in it, which means edge or border.

### Using student page R66.

- Draw an irregular figure on the board and label the lengths of its sides.
- Have students find its perimeter by recording the lengths of each side in a horizontal addition problem on a piece of paper. Tell students to estimate the figure's perimeter first by rounding each side to the nearest ten. After they have finished estimating, have students find the figure's actual perimeter.

Concepts and Skills

### Perimeter of Irregular Figures

An **irregular figure** is made up of two or more figures. You can find the perimeter, or distance around an irregular figure.

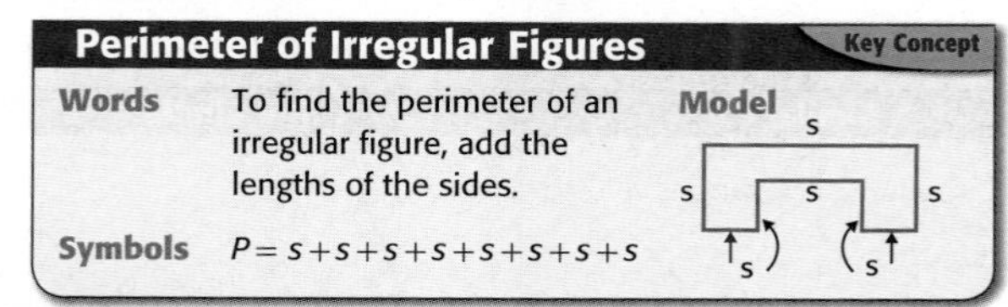


**EXAMPLE** Estimate and Find Perimeter

**1 Estimate then find the perimeter of the figure.**

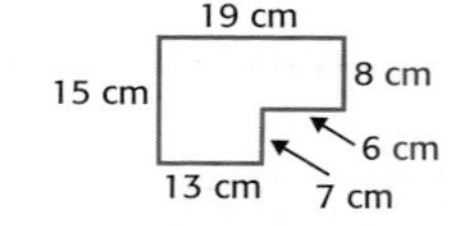


To estimate the perimeter you first need to round each side measure to the nearest ten.

$P = 19 + 8 + 6 + 7 + 13 + 15$

$P = 20 + 10 + 10 + 10 + 10 + 20$

$P = 80$

So the figure is about 80 centimeters.

Next, add the exact measures.

$P = 19 + 8 + 6 + 7 + 13 + 15 = 68$

So, the perimeter of this figure is 68 centimeters.

**Check for Reasonableness**

The answer, 68, is close to the estimate, 80. ✓

### Exercises

**Estimate then find the perimeter of each irregular figure.**

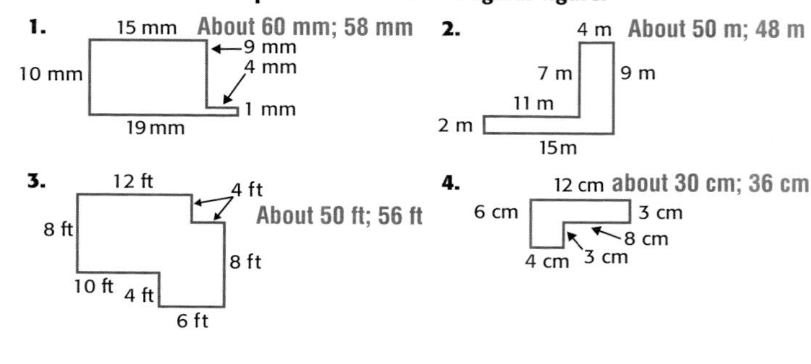




- Show students how to make sure each side's length was counted only once by marking off each side of the figure with an *x* after it has been added to the number sentence.
- Next, pass out irregular figures to students (see materials section at top). Give students time to determine the perimeter of the figure. Then, have students switch figures with a classmate and find that figure's perimeter.

### Using the Exercises

**Exercises 1–4** Remind students to double-check that all sides have been counted only once. They should also estimate before finding the actual perimeter of each figure.

## Assess and Close

**Perimeter Practice** Pose problems that provide students with the perimeter and polygon type and ask them to brainstorm possible side lengths. For example: "A square has a perimeter of 36 centimeters. What are lengths of the four sides?" 9 cm, 9 cm, 9 cm, and 9 cm Another example is: "The perimeter of a rectangle is 28 feet. The length of one of the sides is 8 feet. What are the lengths of the other three sides?" 8 ft, 6 ft, and 6 ft

# Concepts and Skills Bank

## 12 Area of Irregular Figures

# Lesson Planner

## Objective

I will calculate the areas of irregular figures by breaking them into smaller parts.

**Materials:** page containing four large irregular figures

### Area of Irregular Figures

To find the area of an irregular figure, break the figure into smaller parts.

**EXAMPLE** Area of Irregular Figures

**1 Find the area of the irregular figure.**

**Step 1** Break the figure into smaller parts. Look for rectangles and squares.

12 in., 5 in., 6 in., 6 in.

Rectangle 12 in., 5 in. Square 6 in., 6 in.

**Step 2** Find the area of each part.

| Rectangle | Square |
|---|---|
| $A$ = length × width | $A$ = side × side |
| $A = \ell \times w$ | $A = s \times s$ |
| $A$ = 12 in. × 5 in. | $A$ = 6 in. × 6 in. |
| $A$ = 60 square inches | $A$ = 36 square inches |

**Step 3** Add the areas.

The area of the figure is 60 + 36 or 96 square inches.

### Exercises

**Find the area of each figure.**

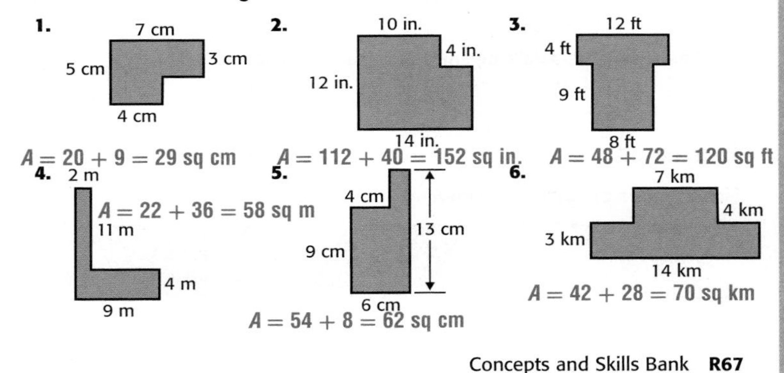




## Activate Prior Knowledge

Explore the formulas for finding the areas of rectangles and squares.

- Draw a rectangle on the board and label two of its adjacent sides with their lengths. Then, ask students to work at their desks to calculate its area. Call on student volunteers to show how they found its area. If students did not write the formula for area in their solutions, remind students that the formula for a rectangle's area is $A$ = length x width.
- Repeat the steps above with a square.

### Using student page R67.

- Tell students that breaking an irregular figure into smaller parts is an effective strategy for finding its area. It is also helpful to label the lengths of all the sides of the smaller figures it has been broken into (see example to the left).
- Next, tell students to write the area formula in each of the smaller parts.
- Finally, determine each smaller part's area. Then add all of the areas together to determine the area of the entire irregular figure.

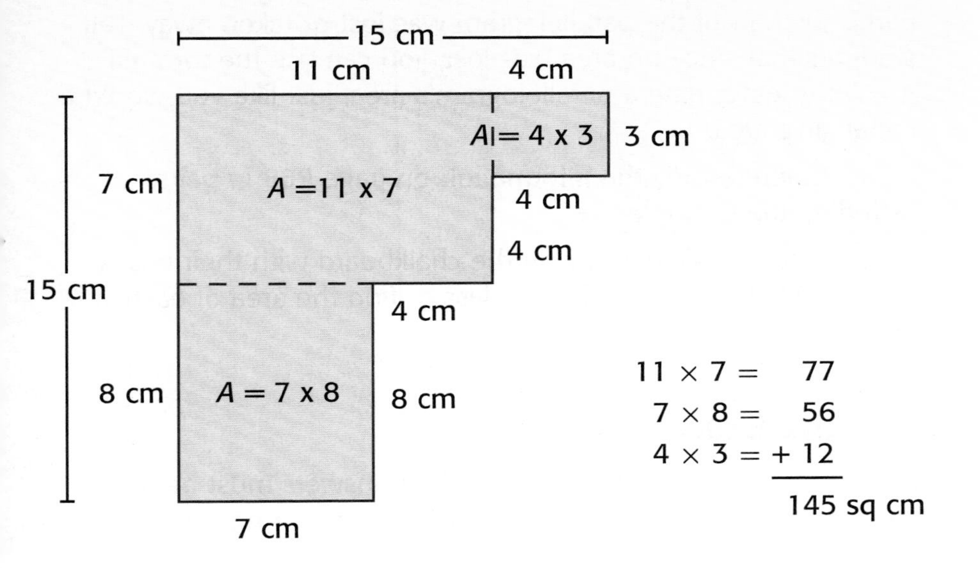


### Using the Exercises

**Exercises 1–6** Students may wish to trace each figure onto another piece of paper so they can draw lines to divide it into smaller parts and write the area formula in each of these parts. Remind students to write their answers in square units.

## Assess and Close

**Area Awareness** Provide students with a page containing four large irregular figures. Then have students measure and label each figure's sides to the nearest inch before breaking it into smaller parts and calculating its total area.

# 13 Areas of Parallelograms

# Lesson Planner

## Objective

I will find areas of parallelograms by using the formula *area = base x height.*

**Materials:** page of parallelograms (1 per student), scissors, page containing parallelogram areas (1 per student)

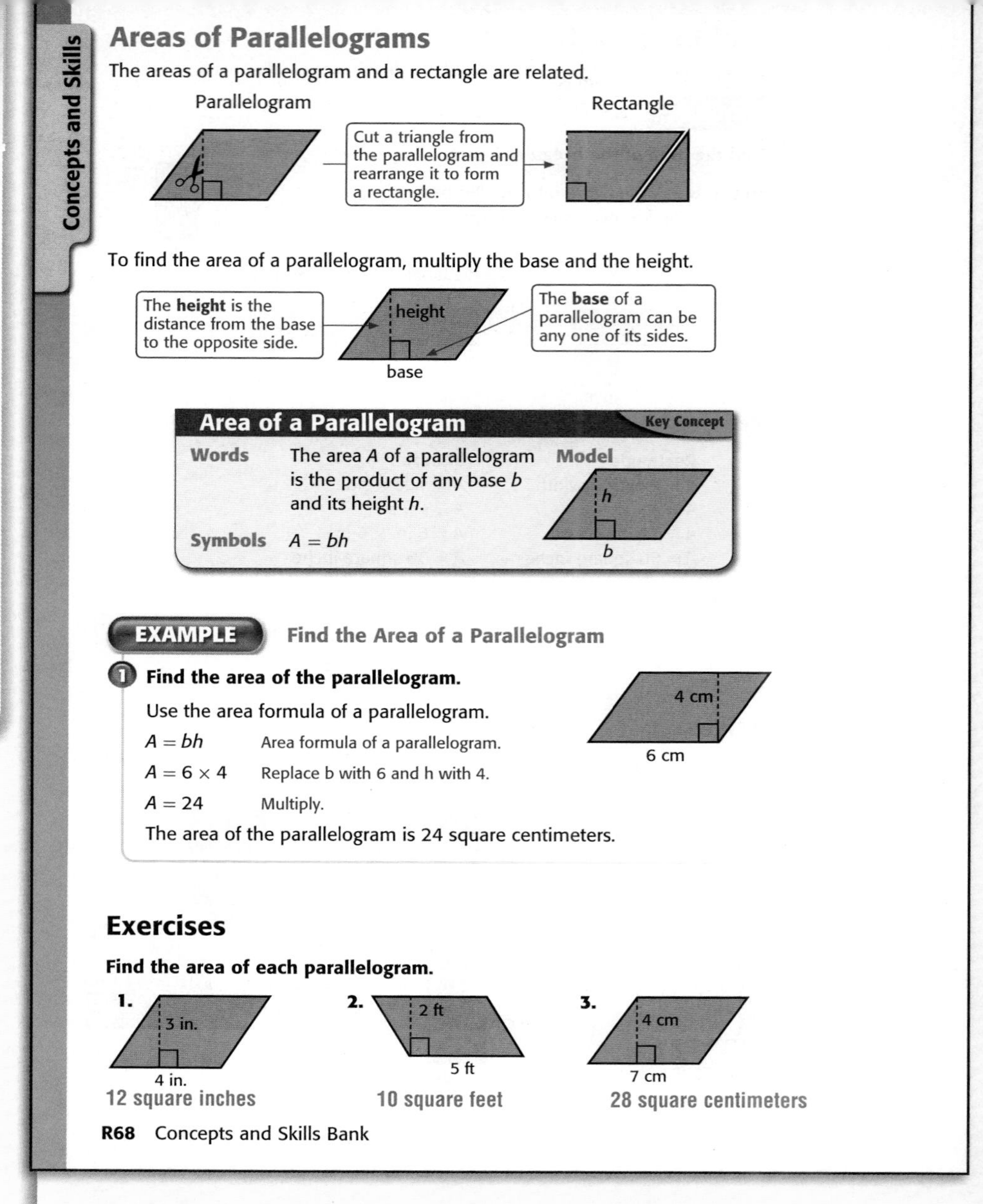

Concepts and Skills

### Areas of Parallelograms

The areas of a parallelogram and a rectangle are related.



To find the area of a parallelogram, multiply the base and the height.



**Area of a Parallelogram** — Key Concept

**Words** The area $A$ of a parallelogram is the product of any base $b$ and its height $h$.

**Symbols** $A = bh$

**Model**



**EXAMPLE** Find the Area of a Parallelogram

**1 Find the area of the parallelogram.**



Use the area formula of a parallelogram.

| | |
|---|---|
| $A = bh$ | Area formula of a parallelogram. |
| $A = 6 \times 4$ | Replace b with 6 and h with 4. |
| $A = 24$ | Multiply. |

The area of the parallelogram is 24 square centimeters.

**Exercises**

**Find the area of each parallelogram.**

**1.** 3 in., 4 in. — 12 square inches

**2.** 2 ft, 5 ft — 10 square feet

**3.** 4 cm, 7 cm — 28 square centimeters

**R68** Concepts and Skills Bank

## Activate Prior Knowledge

Discuss parallelograms as a class.

- Draw a parallelogram on the board. Ask students to identify the figure. If students offer the term "quadrilateral," tell them that they are correct, but that squares, rhombuses, rectangles, etc. are also quadrilaterals. Inform students that you want the specific name of this quadrilateral.
- Discuss why parallelograms are named so. Ask students to name properties of parallelograms. four sides; two pairs of opposite, parallel sides; two pairs of opposite, equal sides and angles, etc.

### Using student page R68.

- Pass out a page containing the outlines of five parallelograms to each student. Give students the task of cutting out the parallelograms, and then making one cut to turn them into different shapes (by manipulating the two new shapes created). Give students about five minutes to work, but tell them to save one of the parallelograms on their page.
- Invite volunteers to share their new shapes with the class. If any student shares a rectangle with the class, ask him/her to explain how it was created. If not, then show the class how to do so.
- Have all students cut out their last parallelogram and make one cut along its height to turn it into a rectangle.
- Ask students if, by making the cut and rearranging the two small parts, any part of the parallelogram was lost or taken away. Tell students that since no area was lost, you can use the formula $A = bh$ to determine a parallelogram's area, just like you would a rectangle's area.
- Have students study the information on page R68 in pairs, including the example.
- Draw a few parallelograms on the chalkboard with their bases and heights labeled. Work as a class to find the area of each figure.

### Using the Exercises

**Exercises 1–3** Remind students that their answers must be in square units. Also, point out that all of the units are not the same.

## Assess and Close

**Parallelogram Practice** Hand out a page containing the areas of six parallelograms. Ask students to write down all the possible lengths of each parallelogram's base and height. At the bottom of the page, ask students to explain how to determine a parallelogram's area.

## Areas of Triangles

Notice that a parallelogram is made of two congruent triangles. So, the formula for the area of a triangle can be found by dividing the formula for the area of a parallelogram by two.

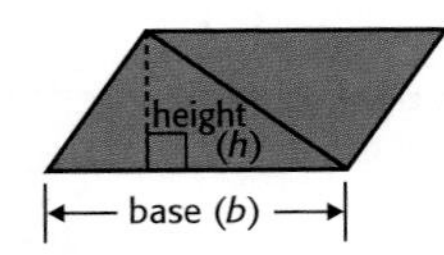


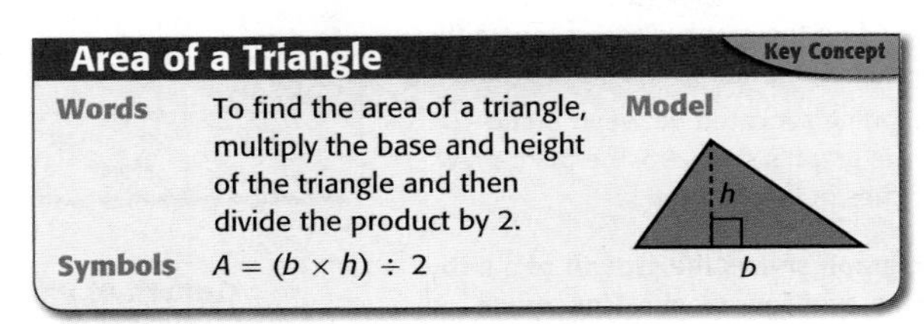

**Area of a Triangle** — Key Concept

**Words** To find the area of a triangle, multiply the base and height of the triangle and then divide the product by 2.

**Model**

**Symbols** $A = (b \times h) \div 2$

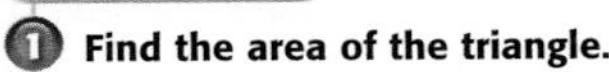

**EXAMPLE** Find the Area of a Triangle

**1 Find the area of the triangle.**

Use the area formula of a triangle.

| | |
|---|---|
| $A = (b \times h) \div 2$ | Area formula of a triangle. |
| $A = (8 \times 4) \div 2$ | Replace $b$ with 8 and $h$ with 4. |
| $A = 32 \div 2$ | Multiply. |
| $A = 16$ | Divide. $32 \div 2 = 16$ |

The area of the triangle is 16 square centimeters.

### Exercises

**Find the area of each triangle.**

**1.**

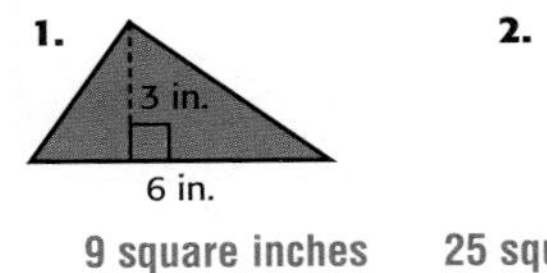


9 square inches

**2.**

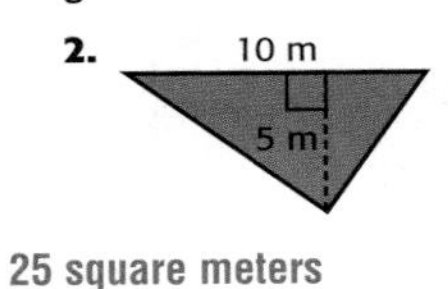


25 square meters

**3.**

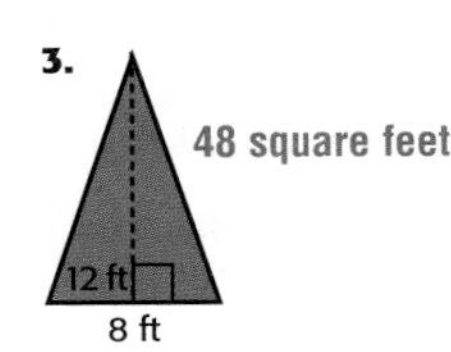


48 square feet



Concepts and Skills

## Using the Exercises

**Exercises 1–3** Remind students to write their answers in square units. Also, help students notice that not all of the answers will be in inches, as in Exercise 1.

# Assess and Close

**Trying Triangles** Provide students with a page of ten triangles where each triangle has the length of every side listed (see below). Ask students to find the area of each triangle and to record the appropriate unit (i.e., sq ft, sq km, etc.) in the answer.

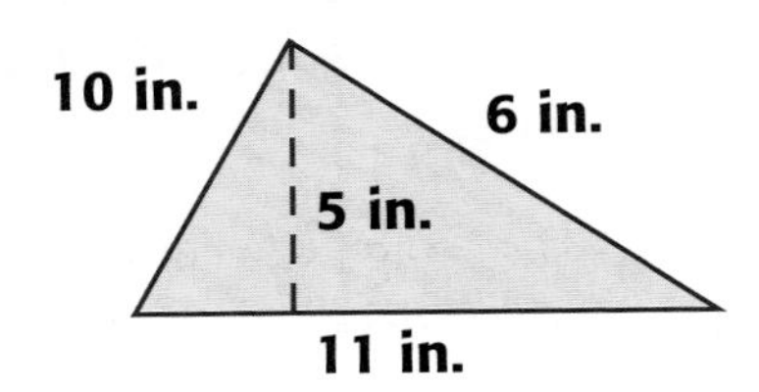


# Concepts and Skills Bank

## 14 Areas of Triangles

# Lesson Planner

## Objective

I will use the formula *Area = (base × height) ÷ 2* to find the areas of triangles.

**Materials:** page containing pairs of congruent triangles (1 per group), scissors, cut-out of paper parallelogram, page of ten triangles (1 per student)

# Activate Prior Knowledge

Explore making new shapes by manipulating congruent triangles.

- Pass out a page containing pairs of congruent triangles to small groups of students. Ask groups to cut out each pair and rearrange it to create a new shape. Give students five to ten minutes to experiment.
- Have students share their findings with the class. Students' findings should include triangles forming parallelograms.

## Using student page R69.

- Display a paper parallelogram with the measure of its base and height labeled. Ask students to find its area. Invite volunteers to the board to share their solutions.
- Now, cut the parallelogram in half to create two equal triangles. Pose the question, "What is the area of each triangle?" Tell students that each triangle's area is exactly half of the parallelogram's area, since the parallelogram was cut in half.
- Write the formula for finding the area of a triangle on the board and have students discuss with a partner why they think it ends with "÷2". Invite volunteers to share their answers with the class.

## 15 Line Graphs

# Lesson Planner

## Objective

I will create and interpret line graphs.

## Vocabulary

**line graph**

**Materials:** Materials: bar graph and line graph examples (1 of each), transparency containing a grid, index cards (1 per student), line graph with corresponding questions (1 per student)



### Line Graphs

A **line graph** shows how data changes over time. You can use a line graph to make predictions about future events.

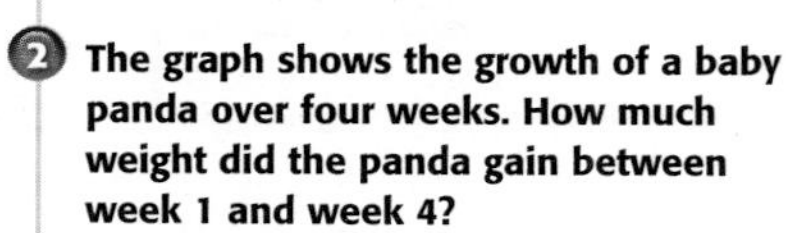

**EXAMPLES** Interpret a Line Graph

**1** **Refer to the graph at the right. How tall did the flower grow in three months?**

The third month is May.

Move up to find where the point is located on the graph. Then compare the height of the point to the scale on the left.

The point is located between 8 and 10 on the graph's scale. So, the plant grew 9 inches in three months.

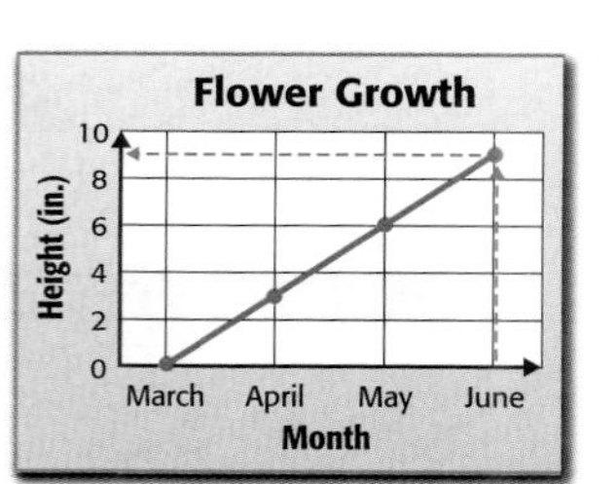


**2** **The graph shows the growth of a baby panda over four weeks. How much weight did the panda gain between week 1 and week 4?**

Subtract the panda's weight at week 1 from its weight at week 4.

Week 1: 11 pounds
Week 4: 14 pounds

$14 - 11 = 3$

So, the baby panda gained 3 pounds between week 1 and week 4.

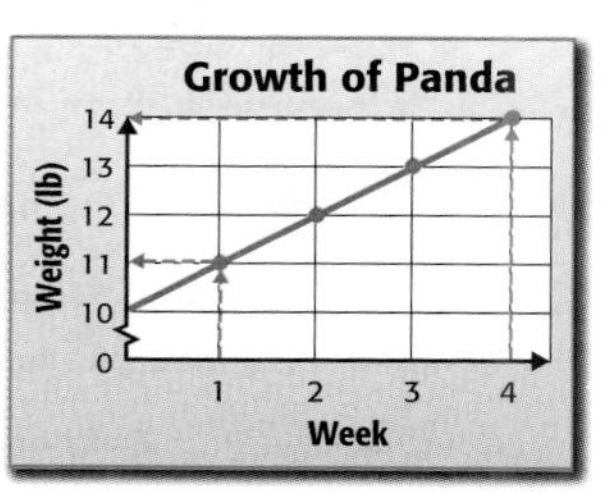


### Exercises

**For Exercises 1–3, use the line graph.**

1. At what time is the least amount of snow on the ground? **6 P.M.**
2. How much snow is on the ground at 8:00 P.M.? **3 in.**
3. How much snow fell over the 5-hour period shown on the graph? **6 in.**

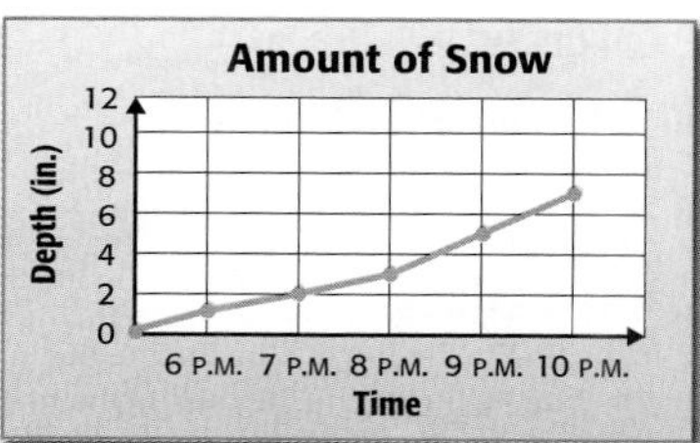

## Activate Prior Knowledge

Compare bar graphs and line graphs as a class.

- Draw a Venn diagram on the board. Entitle one region "bar graph" and the other "line graph."
- Ask students if they know the difference between a bar graph and a line graph. Record similarities and differences in the Venn diagram.
- Show students an example of each type of graph to inspire more ideas to record in the diagram.

### Using student page R70.

- Tell students that a line graph uses points and lines to show how data changes over time.
- Ask students whether a line graph would be used in the following scenarios: to show how many students like pears (no), to show how the population of a city has grown over ten years (yes, because it would show change over time), to show how much it snowed each month during the winter (yes, because it would show change over time).
- Have small groups of students study the line graph examples on page R70. Then ask them to create a list of the various parts that are needed to make a line graph.

  title (tells the main idea of the line graph)
  horizontal axis (shows the change over time)
  vertical axis (displays what is changing over time, the scale always starts at 0)
  labels for both axes (to show what type of data is represented in graph)
  points connected by line segments (will show a change over time)

- Now, create a line graph as a class on a grid using a transparency. Possible themes include rainfall over a period of time or amount of money made at a lemonade stand over a week's time. Be sure to include all of the aspects previously listed.
- Pose two questions about the graph for students to answer. Then, pass out index cards to small groups (one per student). Ask students to write their own questions about the line graph. Present the questions to the class.

### Using the Exercises

**Exercises 1–3** Tell students to study the graph before answering the questions. Advise them to look at the title, the labels for each axis, the shape of the data (is it going up or down over time?), etc.

**For Exercises 4–8, use the line graph.**

**4.** What was Roberto's height when he was 9 years old? 53 inches

**5.** How many inches did Roberto grow between the ages of 10 and 12? 5 inches

**6.** How many inches did Roberto grow from age 8 to age 12? 9 inches

**7.** At this rate, predict how tall Roberto will be when he is 14 years old. See students' work.

**8.** Can the data shown in the line graph be displayed in a bar graph? Explain. Sample answer: yes; make the height of each bar the same as each point on the line graph.

**For Exercises 9–13, use the line graph.**

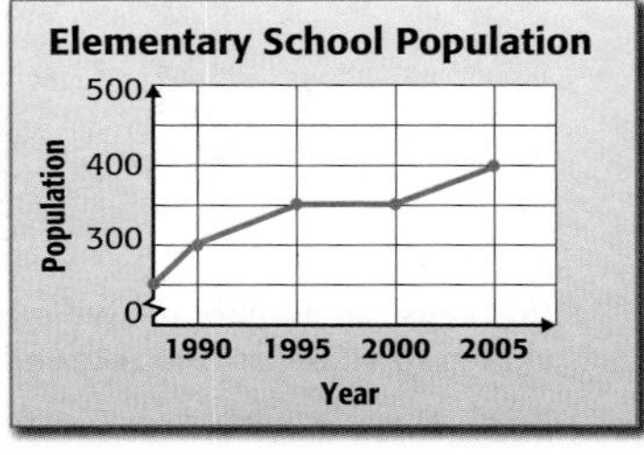


**9.** Is the school population increasing, decreasing, or varying over time? increasing

**10.** What was the population in 1995? 350

**11.** How much did the population grow between 1995 and 2005? 50

**12.** During which time period did the population stay the same? 1995 and 2000

**13.** Predict the population in 2020. Explain your reasoning. Sample answer: 600; the population grew by 200 students in the previous 15 years, so if the pattern continues the population in 2020 will be $400 + 200 = 600$

**Represent each set of data in a line graph.**

**14.**

| Plant Growth | |
|---|---|
| **Week** | **Height (in.)** |
| 1 | 1 |
| 2 | 2 |
| 3 | 3 |
| 4 | 5 |
| 5 | 8 |

**15.**

| One Day's Temperatures | |
|---|---|
| **Time** | **Temperature (°F)** |
| 12 P.M. | 62° |
| 1 P.M. | 65° |
| 2 P.M. | 72° |
| 3 P.M. | 66° |
| 4 P.M. | 64° |

14–16. See students' work.

**16.** Collect and organize data about a week's daily high temperatures in your city. Display the data on a line graph.

**17.** Analyze the graph you made in Exercise 16. Would a bar graph be a more effective way to display the data? Explain. Sample answer: no; A bar graph does not show change over time as effectively as a line graph.



Concepts and Skills

## Using the Exercises

**Exercises 4–13** Again, have students study each graph before answering the related questions. Also, point out the broken scale and explain that it is used because the data does not start until 51 in the first graph and 100 in the second.

**Exercises 14–15** Advise students to begin the scales of their graphs at 0, even though the data begins at 1 in Exercise 14 and 62° in Exercise 15. They should remember all the parts that are necessary to include in a graph.

**Exercises 16–17** Direct students to an appropriate source for gathering the weather data needed to complete Exercise 16, such as a local website or newspaper.

## Assess and Close

**Interpreting Importance** Give students an example of a line graph. Then ask them to explain in words why each aspect (such as the title, axes labels, etc.) is important.

# Concepts and Skills Bank

## 16 More Ways to Display Data

# Lesson Planner

## Objective

I will interpret data displayed in circle graphs, Venn diagrams, and stem-and-leaf plots.

**Materials:** compasses

## Activate Prior Knowledge

Introduce the data used in the examples and ask students to think about how best to display it.

- Write the test scores from page R72 on the board. Ask students which ways they think the data could be organized and displayed well. Make a list of students' ideas on the board.

### Using student page R72.

- Work through example 1.
- Take a close look at the circle graph on page R72. Are there any components that students might add to make the graph easier to understand? Sample answers: a title could be added; each region could include a number telling how many scores fall in that range, such as 4 in the A region because 4 students received As
- Have students work in small groups to brainstorm additional questions that can be answered by looking at the circle graph. Have them share their questions with the class.
- Ask students to share what type of information they have seen in Venn diagrams in the past. This method for displaying data is very common and can be used in all subject areas.
- Work through example 2.
- Challenge students to find a different way to list the data in a Venn diagram so that the circles are more balanced. Sample answer: by setting 80 or 85 as the cutoff point



## More Ways to Display Data

There are many ways to display sets of data. Three of them are shown.

**EXAMPLES** Different Displays of Data

**Three teachers are reviewing the same test scores. The test scores are: 95, 68, 87, 100, 23, 56, 85, 93, 85, 70, 98, 45, and 85. Each teacher displayed the data in a different way.**

1. Teacher 1 displayed the data in a circle graph where it was organized by letter grade. A circle graph shows data as parts of a circle.

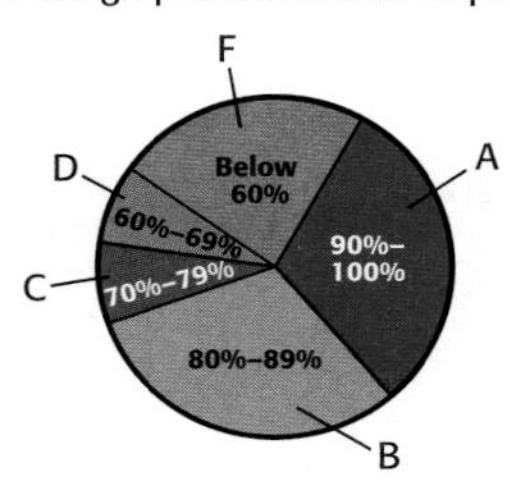


**How does the number of students who received an A compare to the number of students who received a B?**

The number of students who received an A or B on the test is the same because the sections marked as A and B on the circle graph are the same size.

2. Teacher 2 displayed the data using a Venn diagram showing which students scored 70s or above and 70s or below. A Venn diagram is made of circles and shows the relationships between sets of data.

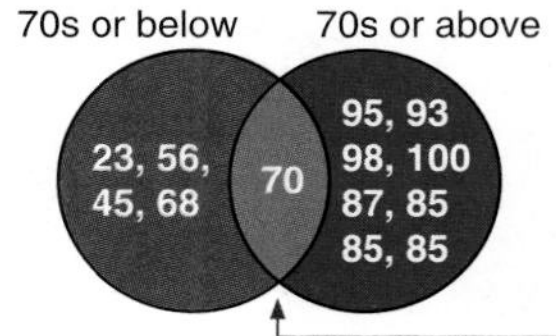


**What score did most students receive: 70s or above or 70s or below?**

There are 9 scores in 70s or above. There are 5 scores in the 70s or below. So, most students' test scores were 70s or above.

**3** Teacher 3 displayed the data using a Stem-and-Leaf plot. A stem-and-leaf plot is a display of data with digits to the left of ones digits as stems and ones digits as leaves.

**What are the mode and the median of these test scores?**

| Stems | Leaves |
|---|---|
| 2 | 3 |
| 4 | 5 |
| 5 | 6 |
| 6 | 8 |
| 7 | 0 |
| 8 | 5 5 5 7 |
| 9 | 3 5 8 |
| 10 | 0 |

The median is the middle number in a set of data. In this set of data the middle number is 85.

The mode is the number that is repeated most. In this set of data it is 85.

So, both the median and mode are 85.

Concepts and Skills

## Exercises

**For Exercises 1–4, use the circle graph.**

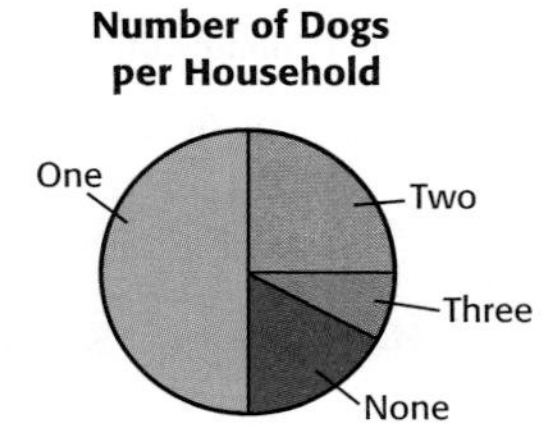


1. What fraction of students owns 2 dogs? $\frac{1}{4}$
2. What fraction of students owns one dog? $\frac{1}{2}$
3. How many dogs do most students own? **One**
4. What is the greatest number of dogs a student owns? **Three dogs**

**For Exercises 5–7, use the Venn diagram.**

Favorite Sports

Indoor Outdoor

12 7 15

5. What may have been the survey question for this Venn diagram? **Sample answer: Which type of sport is your favorite, indoor or outdoor?**
6. What is the favorite type of sport, indoor or outdoor? **Outdoor**
7. What does the number 7 mean? **7 students like indoor and outdoor sports the same amount.**

**For Exercises 8–10, use the stem-and-leaf plot.**

| Stems | Leaves |
|---|---|
| 1 | 0 5 6 |
| 2 | 2 4 5 6 |
| 6 | 6 8 |
| 7 | 5 8 9 |
| 8 | 2 3 3 5 |
| 9 | 5 |

8. What is the greatest number in this set of numbers? **95**
9. What is the median for this set of number? **68**
10. What is the mode for this set of numbers? **83**



## Using student page R73.

- Introduce students to a third way the test scores can be displayed, a stem-and-leaf plot. Some students may not have seen this method of displaying data before, so give them time in small groups to study it. Visit each small group to ensure students understand how a stem-and-leaf plot displays data.
- Ask students to explain why a stem-and-leaf plot might be a better choice than the other two methods when finding the mode and median of a data set.

## Using the Exercises

**Exercises 1–4** Point out how this circle graph differs from the one shown on page R72. This circle graph has a title and tells how many pieces of data belong in each region of the circle.

**Exercises 5–7** Before answering this set of questions, ask students to think of types of indoor and outdoor sports. If time allows, create a class list using students' suggestions.

**Exercises 8–10** Students may find it helpful to list the pieces of data in numerical order to determine the median and mode.

# Assess and Close

**Data Decisions** Ask students to take another look at the examples of a circle graph, Venn diagram, and stem-and-leaf plot on pages R72 and R73. Have students explain in writing which method helps them to best understand the data and why.

Then, have students take a data set (such as the ages of the first ten presidents when they took office – 57, 61, 57, 57, 58, 57, 61, 54, 68, 51) and display it using one of the three methods. Provide students with compasses if they decide to create a circle graph or Venn diagram.

## 17 Minimum, Maximum, and Range

# Lesson Planner

## Objective

I will analyze a data set to determine its minimum, maximum, and range.

## Vocabulary

**range**, **maximum**, **minimum**

**Materials:** small paper bag (1 per student), reading book (1 per student)

**Manipulatives:** differently colored links, blocks, or another type of colorful manipulative (between 10 and 30 per student)

## Activate Prior Knowledge

Explore the meanings of the terms "minimum" and "maximum."

- On the board create two different word webs using "minimum" and "maximum." Ask students to use thesauruses to find synonyms for the words. Record their findings in the webs.

### Using student page R74.

- Pass out a small bag of colorful manipulatives to each student.
- Have students open their bags and record the total of all items. Next, have students' record the total of each color.
- Record students' totals in a list on the board. Rearrange the numbers so they are in numerical order. Show students how to find the data set's minimum, maximum, and range.
- Record the values of each of the colors on the board. Have students work in small groups and assign each group a color that appears in the bag. Assign groups the task of determining their data set's minimum, maximum, and range.





## Minimum, Maximum, and Range

The **range** of a set of data describes how much the data varies. It is the difference between the greatest (**maximum**) and least (**minimum**) values of the set.

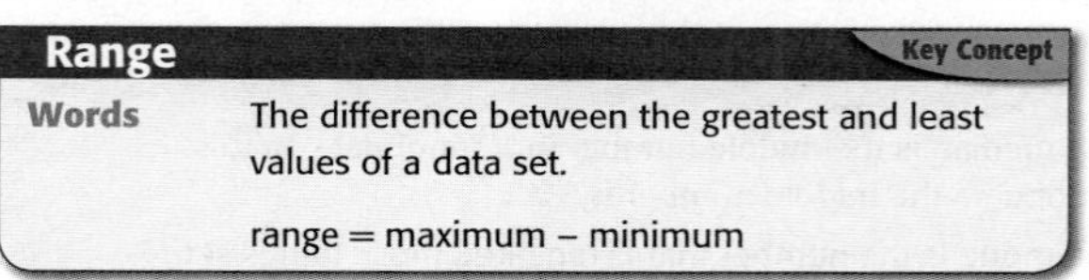

| Range | Key Concept |
|---|---|
| Words | The difference between the greatest and least values of a data set. |
| | range = maximum − minimum |

**EXAMPLE** Find Range

**1** **Find the range of the data set {39, 86, 21, 57, 14, 62}.**

Identify the maximum and minimum of the data set. Then find the range of the data set.

**Step 1** Identify the maximum and minimum.

{39, 86, 21, 57, 14, 62}

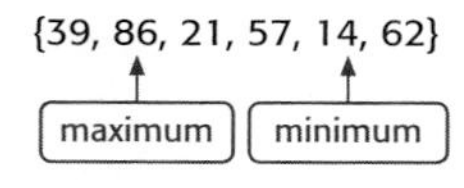


**Step 2** Subtract the minimum from the maximum to find the range.

86 − 14 = 72

So, the range of the data set is 72.

### Exercises

**Identify the maximum, minimum, and range of each data set.**

1. Birthdays in May: {4, 22, 18, 2, 29, 15} **29; 2; and 27**
2. Ages: {18, 59, 83, 42, 27, 70} **83; 18; and 65**
3. Students per grade: {44, 61, 38, 59, 65, 42} **65; 38; and 27**
4. Bowling scores: {145, 98, 110, 128, 152, 105} **152; 98; and 54**
5. Cailin's test scores were 89, 92, 85, 76, 82, and 98. Find the maximum, minimum, and range of the data set. **98; 76; and 22**
6. The daily high temperatures during one week were 45, 53, 58, 62, 64, 55, and 57. Find the maximum, minimum, and range of the data set. **64; 45; and 19**



## Using the Exercises

**Exercises 1–6** Remind students to order numbers from least to greatest to aid in finding the minimum, maximum, and range.

## Assess and Close

**Page Turner** Have each student locate their favorite book or the book they are currently reading. Instruct the class to randomly flip to ten different pages in their books. Record the page number of each page on a piece of notebook paper. Then, identify the minimum and maximum, and calculate the range. Have students repeat the experiment with the same book, or have them swap books with a partner. If time allows, have students give a quick book talk about the book they swapped to their partner.

## Mean

You have already learned how to find the median, mode, range, maximum, and minimum of a data set. You will now learn how to find the **mean** or average of a set of data.

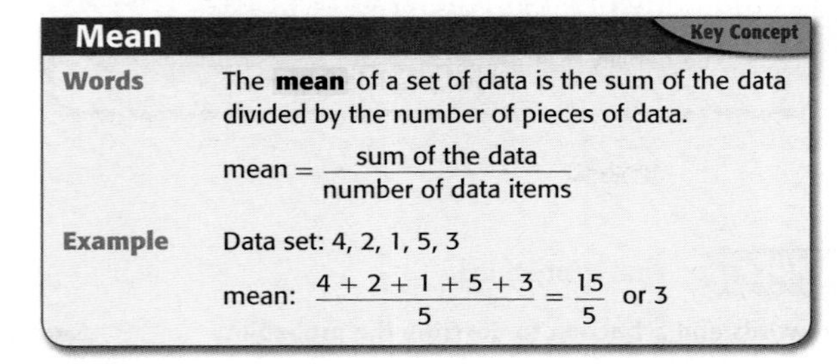

**Mean** — Key Concept

| | |
|---|---|
| **Words** | The **mean** of a set of data is the sum of the data divided by the number of pieces of data. mean = $\frac{\text{sum of the data}}{\text{number of data items}}$ |
| **Example** | Data set: 4, 2, 1, 5, 3 mean: $\frac{4+2+1+5+3}{5} = \frac{15}{5}$ or 3 |

**EXAMPLE** Find the Mean

**1** **SPORTS** **Henry is playing miniature golf. His scores on the first 6 holes are: 5, 2, 6, 3, 7, and 1. What is Henry's mean score?**

Use the definition to find Henry's mean score.

$$\text{mean} = \frac{\text{sum of the data}}{\text{number of data items}}$$
$$= \frac{5+2+6+3+7+1}{6}$$
$$= \frac{24}{6}$$
$$= 4$$

So, Henry's mean score is 4.

### Exercises

**Find the mean for each set of data.**

1. Weekly allowances: \$3, \$5, \$4, \$0, \$2, \$4 \$3
2. Number of siblings: 2, 1, 3, 0, 1, 3, 4 2
3. Number of songs on a CD: 9, 10, 14, 12, 15, 13, 11 12
4. Test scores: 87, 90, 84, 93, 86 88



Concepts and Skills

# Concepts and Skills Bank

## 18 Mean

# Lesson Planner

## Objective

I will determine the mean of a set of data.

## Vocabulary

**mean**

## Activate Prior Knowledge

Build knowledge of the word "mean."

- Tell students that today they will learn the definition of the word "mean." Ask students to share their thoughts about its meaning.
- If students do not know the mathematical definition of mean, explain that it has the same meaning as the word "average." A student's grades in a particular subject are usually averaged to determine his/her final grade.

### Using student page R75.

- Have students suggest different types of numerical data, such as ages, test scores, allowance earned, etc. Inform students that a group of numbers is always needed when finding the mean or average.
- Model the formula for finding the mean of a data set. For example: "Here are the life spans of different animals: camel– 50 years, prairie dog– 10 years, bottlenose dolphin– 20 years, hippopotamus– 45 years, and African grey parrot– 50 years. What is the average life span of these animals?" 35 years
- Ask students to study the example about miniature golf on page R75. Change the score of 7 to a score of 1 and ask students to work with a partner to refigure the mean. 3 If time allows, challenge students to use the original scores on page R75, except they are to change the score of 2 to a different score to arrive at a mean of 5. change the score of 2 to 8

### Using the Exercises

**Exercises 1–4** Inform students that 0 counts as a data point and should be included in the calculations used to determine mean. Advise students to double check their answers to each exercise to ensure they are correct.

## Assess and Close

**On Average . . .** Pose the following problem to students: "Mr. Walsh gave a test, and his students received the following scores: 84, 70, 95, 91, 68, 97, 80, 84, and 96. He gave a homework pass to each student who scored higher than the class's mean score. How many students received a homework pass?" 4 students After students solve the problem on a piece of notebook paper, ask them to explain, in words, the steps they took to solve the problem.

# Concepts and Skills Bank

## 19 Probability and Fractions

# Lesson Planner

## Objective

I will use a fraction to describe the favorable outcome of an event.

## Vocabulary

**favorable outcome**

**Materials:** sticky notes (1 per student), index cards (1 per every 2 students), blank paper (1 piece per student), compasses

## Activate Prior Knowledge

Expand students' knowledge of probability by relating it to fractions.

- Pass out a sticky note to each student. Tell the class to look around the room to find something that can be expressed in a fraction, like 10 out of 19 students, or $\frac{10}{19}$, are girls.
- Invite volunteers to come to the board, one at a time, to post their fractions. Either have students tell what their fractions represent, or give the class three guesses before they are told the fraction's meaning.

### Using student page R76.

- Begin by discussing the probability of a coin landing heads-down after a toss. $\frac{1}{2}$ or 1 out of 2 possible outcomes Next, discuss the probability of rolling either a 1 or 4 when using a 0-5 number cube. $\frac{2}{6}$ or 2 chances out of 6 possible outcomes
- Ask students to work with a partner to study the example on page R76. Have each pair of students develop a probability question about the spinner on an index card. Collect the cards and ask the class as many questions as time allows.

Concepts and Skills

## Probability and Fractions

You have already used words to describe probability. You can also use a fraction to describe the probability of a desirable result, called a **favorable outcome**.

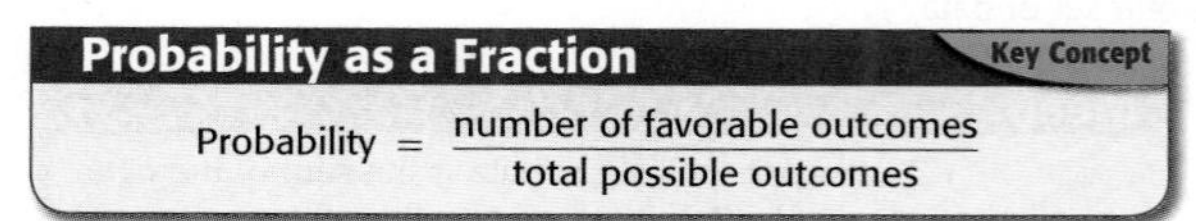

**Probability as a Fraction** — Key Concept

$$\text{Probability} = \frac{\text{number of favorable outcomes}}{\text{total possible outcomes}}$$

**EXAMPLE** Find Probability

**1** **Use words and a fraction to describe the probability of spinning a star.**

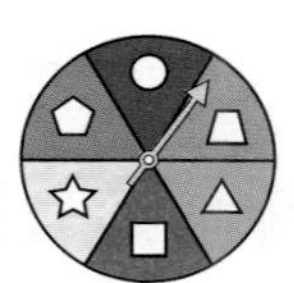

One out of six of the shapes is a star.

$$\text{Probability} = \frac{\text{number of favorable outcomes}}{\text{total possible outcomes}}$$

$$= \frac{\text{number of stars}}{\text{total number of shapes}}$$

$$= \frac{1}{6}$$

So, the probability of spinning a star is 1 out of 6, or $\frac{1}{6}$.

### Exercises

**The spinner is spun. Use words and a fraction to describe the probability of each outcome.**

**1.** yellow 1 out of 5; $\frac{1}{5}$

**2.** green or blue 2 out of 5; $\frac{2}{5}$

**3.** white 0 out of 5; $\frac{0}{5}$

**4.** *not* green 4 out of 5; $\frac{4}{5}$

**5.** red 1 out of 5; $\frac{1}{5}$

**6.** a color *not* in the United States' flag 3 out of 5; $\frac{3}{5}$

**7.** Kylie has 6 pencils, 3 pens, 8 markers, and 2 highlighters in her back pack. If she chooses 1 item without looking, what is the probability that she will choose a pen? 3 out of 19; $\frac{3}{19}$



## Using the Exercises

**Exercises 1–7** Explain to students that using words to describe probability means writing "4 out of 7" for the fraction $\frac{4}{7}$. Also, let students know that when determining the probability of one event or another, as in Exercise 2, the probabilities must be added together. For example, the probability of spinning yellow or green or red is 3 out of 7, or $\frac{3}{7}$.

## Assess and Close

**Super Spinners** Tell students they have to design spinners for board games. They will have to listen carefully to the directions to create two different spinners on their pieces of paper. Have students fold a piece of blank paper in half and then unfold it to reveal two regions. Provide students with compasses to aid them in drawing the spinners. Each spinner will have 8 sections. In the first box, draw a spinner containing numbers upon which the probability of spinning an even number is $\frac{6}{8}$. In the second box, design a spinner containing letters of the alphabet upon which the probability of spinning a vowel is $\frac{2}{8}$.

# Photo Credits

Unless otherwise credited, all currency courtesy of the US Mint.
**v** Thomas Barwick/Getty Images; **vi** Doug Martin; **vii** (br)courtesy Dinah Zike; (others)Doug Martin; **x–xi** Isidor Stankov/iStockphoto; **xii–xiii** Creatas/SuperStock; **xiv–xv** Kevin Schafer/zefa/CORBIS; **xvi–xvii** Daniel A. Bedell/Animals Animals; **xviii–xix** Brand X/SuperStock; **xx–xxi** CORBIS; **xxii–xxiii** Keren Su/Getty Images; **xxiv–xxv** David Muench/CORBIS; **xxvii** The McGraw-Hill Companies; **xxviii** Tim Fuller; **xxix** Ed-Imaging; **1** Thinkstock/CORBIS; **2** Carl Heilman II/Wild Visions, Inc.; **3** Philip Scalia/Alamy Images; **4** David A. Northcott/CORBIS; **5** (t)Stephen J. Krasemann/Photo Researchers, Inc.; (b)Jeremy Woodhouse/Getty Images; **6** Eduardo Garcia/Getty Images; **7** Siede Preis/Getty Images; **8** David R. Frazier/PhotoEdit; **9** Panoramic Images/Getty Images; **10** Janel Cherry; **11** (l to r, t to b)Colin Young-Wolff; Spencer Grant; Dennis MacDonald; David Frazier/CORBIS; Walter Bibikow/CORBIS; **12** Getty Images; **13** Tom Grill/CORBIS; **14–15** Isidor Stankov/iStockphoto; **19** Elizabeth DeLaney/Index Stock Imagery; **20** Ed-Imaging; **23** Claver Carroll/Jupiterimages; **24** (t)Brand X/SuperStock; (b)Pixtal/SuperStock; **26** Paul Seheult/Eye Ubiquitous/CORBIS; **28** Robert E Daemmrich/Getty Images; **32** (l)Ingram Publishing/Alamy Images; (r)G.K. Vikki Hart/Getty Images; **35** Ed-Imaging; **36** (t)Lon C. Diehl/PhotoEdit; (b)Matthias Kulka/CORBIS; **39** (l)Ed-Imaging; (r)Ryan McVay/Getty Images; **40** Ed-Imaging; **42** (inset) J.Berndes/A.B./Zefa/CORBIS; **42–43** (bkgd)Stuart Westmorland/Getty Images; (inset)J.Berndes/A.B./Zefa/CORBIS; **52–53** The McGraw-Hill Companies; **54** (l)CORBIS; (r)C Squared Studios/Getty Images; **57** Ed-Imaging; **58** (t)Image Source/Jupiterimages; (b)Index Stock Imagery; **60** Ralf-Finn Hestoft/CORBIS; **62** Gary Rhijnsburger/Masterfile; **65** (t)Brand X Pictures/Alamy Images; (b)2006 Photos To Go/Index Open; **66** (l)CORBIS; (2)Ryan McVay/Getty Images; **70** Ed-Imaging; **73** CORBIS; **74** Raymond Forbes/AgeFotostock; **75–76** Ed-Imaging; **77** (t)Photodisc/Getty Images; (b)Getty Images; **78–79** (bkgd)Jeff Rotman/Getty Images; **79** (cr)Paul Springett/Alamy Images; **81** C Squared Studios/Getty Images; **82** (cr)CORBIS; (others)Ed-Imaging; **83** CORBIS; **92–93** Kwame Zikomo/SuperStock; **96** G.K. Vikki Hart/Getty Images; **98** Creatas/SuperStock; **101** Ed-Imaging; **102** Oliver Benn/Royal Philharmonic Orchestra; **103** (l)C Squared Studios/Getty Images; (br)PhotoLink/Getty Images; **104** Darren Bennett/Animals Animals; **115 through 118** Ed-imaging; **119** (br)Ryan McVay/Getty Images; (others)The McGraw-Hill Companies; **120** Stock Disc/Getty Images; **120–121** Tony Craddock/Getty Images; **124** David Young-Wolff/PhotoEdit; **126** Getty Images; **134** CORBIS; **139** (r)Jupiterimages; (others)Stockdisc/PunchStock; **142–143** Denis Scot/CORBIS; **147** The McGraw-Hill Companies; **149** Daniel Dempster Photography/Alamy Images; **151** C Squared Studios/Getty Images; **152** BananaStock/Alamy Images; **154** Lon C. Diehl/PhotoEdit; **160** Getty Images; **162** (cr)Stockdisc/PunchStock; (r)Brian Hagiwara/PictureArts/CORBIS; **164** (l to r)Bettmann/CORBIS; John Van Hasselt/CORBIS Sygma; Webster & Stevens Collection/Museum of History and Industry, Seattle/CORBIS; **164–165** (bkgd)Tracy Hebden/Alamy Images; **165** (l)SuperStock; (r)Rachel Epstein/PhotoEdit; **166** Tetra Images/Alamy Images; **167** D. Hurst/Alamy Images; **168** Kevin Schafer/zefa/CORBIS; **170** David Young-Wolff/PhotoEdit; **172** Ed-Imaging; **174–175** Ed-Imaging; **176** Dennis Macdonald/PhotoEdit; **177** Mark Richards/PhotoEdit; **178** StockTrek/Getty Images; **179** Ed-Imaging; **181** (leaf)Getty Images; (others)The McGraw-Hill Companies; **190–191** Digital Vision/PunchStock; **193** Don Smetzer/PhotoEdit; **198** Stockdisc/Jupiter Images/Getty Images; **200** (l)Ed-Imaging; (r)William Howard/Getty Images; **202** Ed-Imaging; **211** G.K. Vikki Hart/Getty Images; **212–213** (bkgd)Roine Magnusson/Getty Images; **213** Joe McDonald/CORBIS; **214** Jim Cummins/CORBIS; **215** Getty Images; **216** Shaun Cunningham/Alamy; **217 218** Ed-Imaging; **220** Michael nan/PhotoEdit; **226** Getty Images; **229** (l)C Squared Studios/Getty es; (r)The McGraw-Hill Companies; **234–235** Denis Scott/CORBIS; urgen Freund/JACANA/HOA-QUI/ImageState; **238** George Hall/ IS; **239** CORBIS; **240** (tr)C Squared Studios/Getty Images; (tl)G.K. Hart/Getty Images; **242** Ren Long/AP Images; **245 through 250** Ed-ing; **252** Richard Hutchings/PhotoEdit; **254** Age Fotostock/SuperStock; :d-Imaging; **256** Daniel A. Bedell/Animals Animals;
**257** (bkgd)David Tipling/Lonely Planet Images; **258** Robin Lynne/ Images; **259** AgeFotostock/SuperStock; **261** (l)Jack Hollingsworth/ Images; (r)Ed-Imaging; **270–271** David Young-Wolff/PhotoEdit; :ooperphoto/CORBIS; **275** Robert Lubeck/Animals Animals; **276** G.K. ki Hart/Getty Images; **278** Colin Keates/Getty Images; **280** CORBIS; ;etty Images; **285** (l)Ryan McVay/Getty Images; (r)Michael Houghton/StudiOhio; **286** C Squared Studios/Getty Images; **288** Getty Images; **290** (l, r)Ed-Imaging; (t)Getty Images; **292–293** JUPITERIMAGES/Thinkstock/Alamy Images; **294** BananaStock/Jupiterimages; **296** Mark Newman/Photo Researchers, Inc.; **297** Christian Petersen/Getty Images; **299** Ed-Imaging; **308–309** Dennis MacDonald; **311** Ed-Imaging; **313** Craig Lovell/CORBIS; **315** (l to r, t to b)GK & Vikki Hart/Getty Images; Patti Murray/Animals Animals; Brand X/Jupiter Images; Ed-Imaging; **321** Ryan McVay/Getty Images; **323** Stockbyte/Getty Images; **324** David Muench/CORBIS; **326** CORBIS; **327** Tony Freeman/PhotoEdit; **328** ThinkStock/Wonderfile; **329 330** Ed-Imaging; **334** Brand X/SuperStock; **336** CORBIS; **339** Ed-Imaging; **340** Mauritius/SuperStock; **342** SuperStock, Inc./SuperStock; **343** Sergio Pitamitz/Robert Harding World Imagery/CORBIS; **348** (l)G.K. Vikki Hart/Getty Images; (r)Getty Images; **352** C Squared Studios/Getty Images; **356–357** Masterfile; **358** Getty Images; **359** (t)GK Hart/Vikki Hart/Getty Images; (b)Thomas Northcut/Getty Images; **360** The McGraw-Hill Companies; **361** (l)C Squared Studios/Getty Images; (tl)Brand X Pictures/Getty Images; (tr)Stockdisc/PunchStock; **362** (t)Getty Images; (c)CORBIS; (b)Comstock Images/Alamy Images; (tr)S. Wanke/PhotoLink/Getty Images; **363** (l)Davies and Starr; (r)Getty Images; **364** (l)C Squared Studios/Getty Images; (r)Ed-Imaging; (t)Ryan McVay/Getty Images; (b)Bridgeman-Giraudon/Art Resource, NY; **365** Ed-Imaging; **370** The McGraw-Hill Companies; **371** Photos.com/Jupiterimages; **372** David Young-Wolff/PhotoEdit; **373** Lawrence Manning/CORBIS; **376** Werner H. Mueller/CORBIS; **377** (l to r, t to b)Alan King/Alamy Images; Stockbyte/Getty Images; Image Source/Alamy Images; Creatas/SuperStock; Purestock/Jupiterimages; Peter Miller/eStock Photo; **378** (l to r, t to b)Jorg Greuel/Getty Images; Burke/Triolo/Brand X Pictures/Jupiterimages; Thomas Northcut/Getty Images; DK Limited/CORBIS; Purestock/Alamy Images; **379 380** Ed-Imaging; **382–383** (bkgd)Visions of America, LLC/Alamy Images; (inset)Mary Ann Sullivan/Bluffton University; (inset)Visions of America, LCC/Alamy Images; **385** Jupiterimages; **392–393** Lawrence Manning/CORBIS; **396** Stockbyte/SuperStock; **399** (l)The McGraw-Hill Companies; (c)David Young-Wolff; (r)Tony Arruza/CORBIS; **400** CORBIS; **402** (tc)Brand X/ImageState; (c)C Squared Studios/Getty Images; (cr)Getty Images; **404** Rob Gage/Getty Images; **407** Getty Images; **409** Photos.com/Jupiterimages; **416 417** Getty Images; **419** Photos.com/Jupiterimages; **420** (cl)Ralph A. Clevenger/CORBIS; (cr, bl)Ryan McVay/Getty Images; (br)Ed-Imaging; **422** Darrell Gulin/CORBIS; **423** Comstock/Alamy Images; **424** Gallo Images/Getty Images; **425** Ed-Imaging; **426–427** (bkgd)The McGraw-Hill Companies; **427** (l to r)SuperStock; The McGraw-Hill Companies; CREATAS; John Pitcher; **430** Getty Images; **436–437** Gary Gerovac/Masterfile; **438** (l)Design Pics Inc./Alamy Images; (r)Creatas Images/Jupiterimages; **439** PhotoLink/Getty Images; **440** 2006 Photos to Go/Index Open; **441** (l to r, t to b)Chris Newbert/Minden Pictures; C Squared Studios/Getty Images; The McGraw-Hill Companies; Jupiterimages; **442** (l to r, t to b)GK Hart/Vikki Hart/Getty Images; Siede Preis/Getty Images; C Squared Studios/Getty Images; The McGraw-Hill Companies; C Squared Studios/Getty Images; **443** (l to r, t to b)Stockdisc/PunchStock; G.K. Vikki Hart/Getty Images; Ken Cavanaugh/The McGraw-Hill Companies; Siede Preis/Getty Images; Image Ideas Inc./Index Stock; **444** STACY GOLD/National Geographic Society Images; **446** C Squared Studios/Getty Images; **447** Getty Images; **449** Jupiterimages; **450** (l to r, t to b)D. Hurst/Alamy Images; Jupiterimages; Michael Grimm; D. Hurst/Alamy Images; **451** (l to r, t to b)Jeffrey Coolidge/CORBIS; Hans Christoph Kappel/npl/Minden Pictures; W.A.N.T. PHOTOGRAPHY/Animals Animals; Comstock Images; The McGraw-Hill Companies; **452** (l to r, t to b)The McGraw-Hill Companies; David Young-Wolff/Photo Edit; Getty Images; Lon C. Diehl/Photo Edit; CORBIS; **453** (tl, b)Getty Images; (tr)Photosindia.com/SuperStock; (c)Jupiterimages; **454** (inset)James Hackett/eStock Photo; **454–455** (bkgd)CORBIS; **455** CORBIS; **458** Michael Freeman/CORBIS; **459** (l)Getty Images; (r)The McGraw-Hill Companies; **463–466** Ed-Imaging; **467** (t)Getty Images; (b)AgeFotostock/SuperStock; **471** Ed-Imaging; **473** (tl)Getty Images; (tr)Stockbyte/PictureQuest; (b)C Squared Studios/Getty Images; **475** (tl)Getty Images; (tr)Creatas/PunchStock; (b)CORBIS; **479** (t)C Squared Studios/Getty Images; (cl)USDA Natural Resources Convservation Service; (b)Joe Polillo/The McGraw-Hill Companies; **484** Getty Images; **483–484** (bkgd)Keren Su; (inset)Getty Images; **485** Ed-Imaging; **486** (polish)Lawrence Manning/CORBIS; (others)Ed-Imaging; (fish)GK Hart/Vikki Hart/The Image Bank/Getty Images; **487** (l to r, t to b)Burke/Triolo Productions/Jupiterimages; Didier Robcis/CORBIS; 2006 Photos to Go; Photos.com/Jupiterimages; CORBIS; David Young-Wolff/



# Photo Credits

PhotoEdit; Colin Young-Wolff/PhotoEdit; **488** (l to r, t to b)Jeff Greenberg/PhotoEdit; Jupiterimages; Burke/Triolo/Jupiterimages; The McGraw-Hill Companies; Burke/Triolo Productions/Brand X/CORBIS; Spencer Grant/PhotoEdit; Getty Images; **489** The McGraw-Hill Companies; **490** Ed-Imaging; **492** (t)Amon/PhotoCuisine/CORBIS; (bl)Michael Newman/PhotoEdit; (br)Ed-Imaging; **493** (t)Comstock/Jupiterimages; (c)Getty Images; (bl)Dynamic Graphics Value/SuperStock; (bc)Lawrence Manning CORBIS; (br)Elizabeth Whiting & Associates/CORBIS; **494** (l to r, t to b)Joson/zefa/CORBIS; David Young-Wolff/PhotoEdit; Lawrence Manning CORBIS; The McGraw-Hill Companies; Andy Crawford; DK Limited/CORBIS; **495** (l)Getty Images; (r)Andrea Rugg/Beateworks/CORBIS; **496** (t)Lew Robertson/Jupiterimages; (c, b)Ed-Imaging; **498** (br)Rachel Epstein/Photo Edit; (c, cl)Getty Images; (cr)Paul Gapper/worldphotos.org/Alamy Images; Caren Alpert/Jupiterimages; Rachel Epstein/Photo Edit; **499** (l to r, t to b)Getty Images; C Squared Studios/Getty Images; Thinkstock/Alamy Images; PunchStock; CORBIS/Jupiterimages; **500** (l to r, t to b)Getty Images; CORBIS; Getty Images; David Stares/Alamy Images; G.K. Vikki Hart/Getty Images; Jeffrey Coolidge/CORBIS; AgeFotostock/SuperStock;
**501** (l to r, t to b)Michael Matisse/Getty Images; Photodisc/Getty Images; Envision/CORBIS; Russell Illig/Getty Images; G.K. & Vikki Hart/Getty Images; **502** Photodisc/Getty Images; **503** G.K. & Vikki Hart/Getty Images; **504** Envision/CORBIS; **506** Design Pics/FotoSearch; **507** (l to r, t to b) C Squared Studios/Getty Images; G.K. & Vikki Hart/Getty Images; 2006 Photos to Go; **508** Ed-Imaging; **509** (l to r, t to b)Big Cheese Photo/Jupiterimages; Ron Chapple/Jupiterimages; Photodisc/Getty Images; CORBIS; **510** (l to r, t to b)Monotype, LLC; Dave Mager/Index Stock Imagery; C Squared Studios/Getty Images; ThinkStock LLC; Image Farm Inc./Alamy Images; Charlie Roy/Jupiterimages; C Squared Studios/Getty Images; **511** Ed-Imaging; **512** The McGraw-Hill Companies;
**515** (l)Stockdisc/PunchStock; (r)Photos.com/Jupiterimages; **516** (l)Mark Cassino/SuperStock; (c)Iconotec/Alamy Images; **516–517** (bkgd)Renee Morris/Alamy Images; (r)Jupiter Images; **518** Ed-Imaging; **519 520** 2006 Photos To Go; **523** (l to r, t to b)Ed-Imaging; G.K. Vikki Hart/Getty Images; G.K. Vikki Hart/Getty Images; G.K. & Vikki Hart/Getty Images;
**525** (l)Masterfile; (tr)Hirdes/f1online/Alamy Images; (cr)Mick Broughton/Alamy Images; (br)Jupiterimages; **526** (l to r, t to b)Colin Young-Wolff/Photo Edit; Judith Collins/Alamy Images; Jan Tadeusz/Alamy Images; Purestock/Getty Images; Jeffrey Coolidge/Getty Images; Joe Schmelzer/Beateworks/CORBIS; **527** Rick Gayle Studio/CORBIS; **528** (l to r, t to b)Ed-Imaging; G.K. Vikki Hart/Getty Images; Getty Images; Ann Cutting/Jupiterimages; Siede Preis/Getty Images; **529** (l)Siede Preis/Getty Images; (r)Getty Images; **531** (l to r, t to b)The McGraw-Hill Companies; Brand X Pictures/Alamy Images; Jose Fuste Raga/CORBIS Brand X Pictures/Punchstock; Mitch Diamond/Index Stock Imagery; DARREN BENNETT/Animals Animals; **534–535** (inset)C Squared Studios/Getty Images; (bkgd)Siede Preis/Getty Images; **539** (cr)Photodisc/Getty Images; (r)C Squared Studios/Getty Images; **540** The McGraw-Hill Companies; **541** (l)Don Farrall/Getty Images; (c)Stockdisc/PunchStock; **542** Richard Wear/Design Pics/CORBIS; **543** (l)Ed-Imaging; (r)Getty Images; **544** Stockdisc/PunchStock; **545** (c)Ton Kinsbergen/Beateworks/CORBIS; (r)C Squared Studios/Getty Images; (others)Koopman/CORBIS; **551** (t)Getty Images; (b)Ed-imaging; **552** Ed-Imaging; **557** Getty Images; **558** (inset)Ed Taylor/Getty Images; **558–559** (bkgd)The McGraw-Hill Companies, Inc.; (inset)Ed Taylor/Getty Images; **563** (l)Punchstock; (r)Getty Images; **564** Ed-Imaging; **568** The McGraw-Hill Companies; **570** Photodisc/Getty Images; **574–575** CORBIS; **579** MedioImages/SuperStock; **582** David Muench/CORBIS; **583** Martin Harvey/CORBIS; **584** Scenics of America/PhotoLink/Getty Images; **585** (l)Ed-Imaging; (r)Getty Images; **586 594** Ed-imaging; **595** Michael Houghton/StudiOhio; **596** Greg Probst/CORBIS; **600–601** (bkgd)Digital Vision/Getty Images; (inset)Getty Images; **602** Stockdisc Classic/Alamy Images; **604** (l)Ed-Imaging; (r)Brad Wilson/Getty Images; **605** Ed-Imaging; **614–615** Steve Satushek; **617** Time & Life Pictures/Getty Images; **618** Sam Greenwood/NewSport/CORBIS; **621** Ed-Imaging; **623** Michael Houghton/StudiOhio; **624** Mauritius/SuperStock; **626** CORBIS; **627** G.K. Vikki Hart/Getty Images; **628** Ed-Imaging; **630** BigStockPhoto.com; **631** Deborah Meeks/SuperStock; **634** Getty Images; **635** The McGraw-Hill Companies; **636** Ed-Imaging; **638** Bettmann/CORBIS; **639** John Cancalosi/Peter Arnold, inc.; **641** (l)Image Source/Getty Images; (r)CORBIS; **642–643** (bkgd)Donald Miralle/Getty Images; **643** (l)Empics/SportsChrome; (r)Rob Tringali/SportsChrome; **LA0** Mark Steinmetz/Amanita Pictures; **LA1** Tim Fuller; **LA2** Walter Geiersperger/CORBIS; **LA3** PictureNet/CORBIS; **LA4** Comstock Images/Alamy Images; (r)C Squared Studios/Getty Images; **LA5** (t)The McGraw-Hill Companies; (bl)Ed-Imaging; (br)CORBIS; **LA6** Jeffrey L. Rotman/CORBIS; **LA7** PureStock/AGE fotostock; **LA8** Ryan McVay/Getty Images; **LA9** (t)The McGraw-Hill Companies; (b)Ed-imaging; **LA10** Tom Grill/CORBIS; **LA11** (t)StockTrek/Getty Images; (b)The McGraw-Hill Companies; **LA13** Getty Images; **LA14** Stockbyte; **LA15** (l)Comstock/Alamy Images; (b)D. Hurst/Alamy Images; **LA16** C Squared Studios/Getty Images; **LA18** Chev Wilkinson; **LA25** (l)The McGraw-Hill Companies; (r)2006 Photos To Go/Index Open; (c)Photolibrary; **P0** (t)Getty Images; (c)Punchstock; (b)Bob Daemmrich/PhotoEdit; **P1** (t)Tim Fuller; (b)2006 Photos To Go; **P2** (t)BananaStock/Alamy Images; (b)2006 Photos To Go/Index Open; **P4** (t)Food Image Source/O'Gara/Bissell/StockFood; (b)2006 Photos To Go/Index Open; **P5** Photos.com/Jupiterimages; **P6** Sindre Ellingsen/Alamy Images; **P7** Brand X Pictures/Alamy Images; **P8** (t)Laurie Rubin/Getty Images; (b)Getty Images; **P9** Photos.com/Jupiterimages; **R0** Ed-Imaging; **R9** McGraw-Hill Companies Inc; **R24** (l)gds/zefa/CORBIS; (c)Nancy R. Cohen/Getty Images; (r)Burke/Triolo Productions/Getty Images; **R28** (tl)The McGraw-Hill Companies; (tr)Getty Images; (bl)D. Hurst/Alamy; (br)C Squared Studios/Getty Images; **R29** (tr)C Squared Studios/Getty Images; (bl)C Squared Studios/Getty Images; (br)Photos.com/Jupiterimages; **R30** (l to r, t to b)The McGraw-Hill Companies; Ingram Publishing/Superstock; The McGraw-Hill Companies; CORBIS; Jupiterimages; **R31** (l to r, t to b) Jupiterimages; Photos.com/Jupiterimages; Photos.com/Jupiterimages; Photos.com/Jupiterimages; Stockdisc/PunchStock; Jeremy Woodhouse/Getty Images; Photos.com/Jupiterimages; Image Source/Jupitierimages; **R32** (l to r, t to b)Getty Images; G.K. & Vikki Hart/Getty Images; Jupiterimages; **R39 R41** Getty Images; **R43** Ed-Imaging; **R64** (l)The McGraw-Hill Companies; (r)Masterfile

McGraw-Hill would like to acknowledge the artists and agencies who contributed to illustrating this program: **Cover** Mick McGinty represented by Mendola Artists; Argosy Publishing; Gary Ciccarelli, Keith Batcheller, Jean-pascal Donnot represented by AA Reps. Inc; Dick Gage, Mark Collins, Richard Carbajal represented by Deborah Wolfe Ltd.

**Teacher Edition Photo Credits**

Unless otherwise credited, all currency courtesy of the US Mint.

**T3** LWA-JDC/CORBIS; **T8** Bloom Works Inc./Alamy Images; **T12** CORBIS; **T13** Bananastock/Punchstock; **T14** Blend Images/Alamy Images; **14H** Ed-Imaging; **17 through 36** Eclipse Studios; **52G 52H** Ed-Imaging; **55 through 58** Eclipse Studios; **58B** Ed-Imaging; **62 through 80** Eclipse Studios; **92I** Ed-Imaging; **98 through 128** Eclipse Studios; **142H** Ilene MacDonald/Alamy Images; **147 through 176** Eclipse Studios; **190H** Ed-Imaging; **193 through 220** Eclipse Studios; **234G** Ed-Imaging; **237 through 246** Eclipse Studios; **270G** Ed-Imaging; **270H** (t)Mike Parry/Minden Pictures, (b)Ed-Imaging; **273 through 288** Eclipse Studios; **308G** Ed-Imaging; **316 336** Eclipse Studios; **336B** Ed-Imaging; **342** Eclipse Studios; **342B** Ed-Imaging; **356G** Ed-Imaging; **356H** Daniel Templeton/Alamy Images; **359 362** Eclipse Studios; **363** Ingram Publishing/SuperStock; **366 372** Eclipse Studios; **377** Getty Images; **392H** (t)Ed-Imaging, (b)Steve Kaufman/CORBIS; **395 through 422** Eclipse Studios; **436I** (t)Ed-Imaging, (b)Don S. Montgomery/CORBIS; **436J** Ed-Imaging; **440A** Nick Koudis/Getty Images; **441 444** Eclipse Studios; **444A** The McGraw-Hill Companies; **446A** Eclipse Studios; **450B** Ed-Imaging; **456** Eclipse Studios; **456A** The McGraw-Hill Companies; **460** Eclipse Studios; **482I** 2006 Photos to Go/Index Open; **482J** (t)Peter Arnold/Alamy Images, (c)Getty Images, (b)Tetra Images/Alamy Images; **498A** (l)Christian Darkin/Alamy Images, (r)Jupiterimages; **498B** G.K. Vikki Hart/Getty Images; **502A** (l)Eclipse Studios, (r)G.K. & Vikki Hart/Getty Images; **504** Eclipse Studios; **510** G.K. Vikki Hart/Getty Images; **512** Eclipse Studios; **512A** (t)The McGraw-Hill Companies, (b)CORBIS; **534H** Ed-Imaging; **544 554** Eclipse Studios; **574G** Michael Houghton/StudiOhio; **574H** Ed-Imaging; **579 582** Eclipse Studios; **586B** Ed-Imaging; **588 through 602** Eclipse Studios; **614G 614H** Ed-Imaging; **617 622** Eclipse Studios; **622B** Michael Houghton/StudiOhio; **626** Eclipse Studios.

McGraw-Hill would like to acknowledge the artists and agencies who contributed to illustrating this program: **Cover** Mick McGinty represented by Mendola Artists.





Photo Credits



Photo Credits

# Glossary/Glosario

**Math Online** A mathematics multilingual glossary is available at www.macmillanmh.com.
The glossary includes the following languages.

| | | | |
|---|---|---|---|
| Arabic | Cantonese | Korean | Tagalog |
| Bengali | English | Russian | Urdu |
| Brazilian Portuguese | Haitian Creole | Spanish | Vietnamese |
| | Hmong | | |

**Cómo usar el glosario en español:**
1. Busca el término en inglés que desees encontrar.
2. El término en español, junto con la definición, se encuentran en la columna de la derecha.

## English

**A**

**acute angle** (p. 369) An *angle* with a measure greater than 0° and less than 90°.

**acute triangle** (p. 372) A *triangle* with all three *angles* less than 90°.

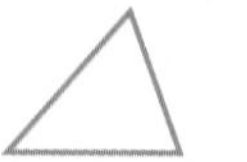

**addend** (p. 64) Any numbers being added together.

**add (adding, addition)** (p. 52) An operation on two or more *addends* that results in a *sum*.

$$9 + 3 = 12$$

**algebra** (p. 193) A branch of mathematics that uses symbols, usually letters, to explore relationships between quantities.

**angle** (p. 368) A figure that is formed by two *rays* with the same *endpoint*.

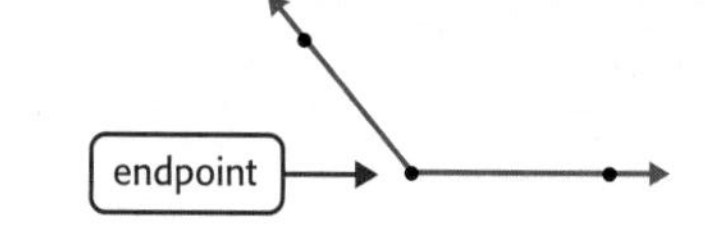


## Español

**ángulo agudo** Un *ángulo* que mide más de 0° y menos de 90°.

**triángulo acutángulo** Un *triángulo* cuyos tres *ángulos* miden menos de 90°.

**sumando** Cualquier número que se suma a otro.

**suma (sumar, adición)** Operación en dos o más *sumandos* que resulta en una *suma*.

$$9 + 3 = 12$$

**álgebra** Rama de las matemáticas que usa símbolos, generalmente letras, para explorar relaciones entre cantidades.

**ángulo** Figura formada por dos *rayos* con el mismo *extremo*.

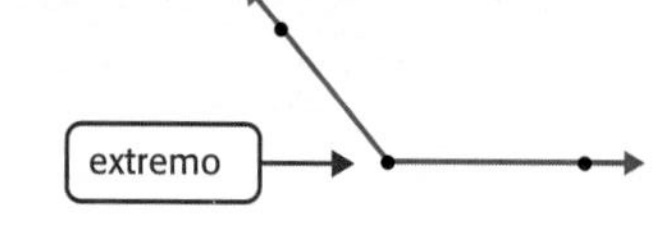

**area** (p. 460) The number of *square units* needed to cover the inside of a region or plane figure without any overlap.

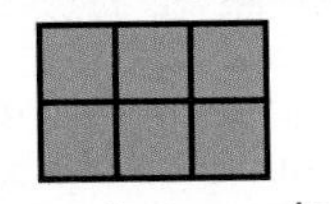

area = 6 square units

**Associative Property of Addition** (p. 55) The property states that the grouping of the *addends* does not change the *sum*.

$(4 + 5) + 2 = 4 + (5 + 2)$

**Associative Property of Multiplication** (p. 150) The property that states that the grouping of the *factors* does not change the *product*.

$3 \times (6 \times 2) = (3 \times 6) \times 2$

**área** El número de *unidades cuadradas* necesarias para cubrir el interior de una región o figura plana sin traslapes.

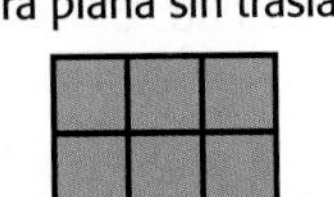

área = 6 unidades cuadradas

**propiedad asociativa de la suma** Propiedad que establece que la agrupación de los *sumandos* no altera la *suma*.

$(4 + 5) + 2 = 4 + (5 + 2)$

**propiedad asociativa de la multiplicación** Propiedad que establece que la agrupación de los *factores* no altera el *producto*.

$3 \times (6 \times 2) = (3 \times 6) \times 2$

## B

**bar graph** (p. 108) A graph that compares *data* by using bars of different lengths or heights to show the values.

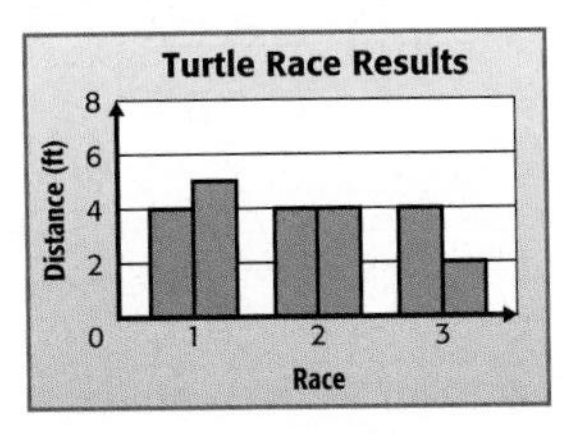


**bilateral symmetry** (p. 422) The property of a figure that allows it to be folded so the two halves match exactly.

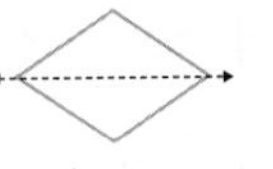

**gráfica de barras** Gráfica que compara los *datos* usando barras de distintas longitudes o alturas para mostrar los valores.

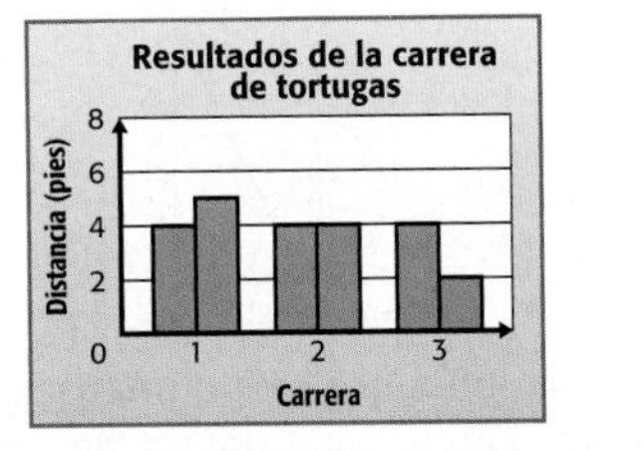


**simetría bilateral** Propiedad de una figura que le permite ser doblada de manera que las mitades se correspondan exactamente.

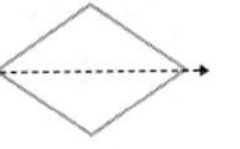







## C

**capacity** (p. 485) The amount of liquid a container can hold.

**circle** (p. R64) A closed figure in which all points are the same distance from a fixed point, called the center.

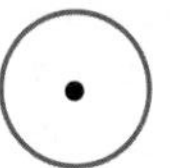

**Commutative Property of Addition** (p. 55) The property that states that the order in which two numbers are added does not change the *sum*.

$12 + 15 = 15 + 12$

**Commutative Property of Multiplication** (p. 150) The property that states that the order in which two numbers are multiplied does not change the *product*.

$7 \times 2 = 2 \times 7$

**compatible numbers** (p. 322) Numbers in a problem or related numbers that are easy to work with mentally.

720 and 90 are compatible numbers for division because $72 \div 9 = 8$.

**cone** (p. 359) A 3-dimensional figure with a curved surface, a circular base, and one *vertex*.

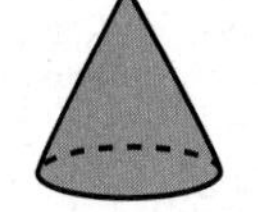

**congruent figures** (p. 418) Two figures having the same size and the same shape.

**capacidad** Cantidad que puede contener un envase, medida en unidades de volumen.

**círculo** Figura cerrada en la cual todos los puntos equidistan de un punto fijo llamado centro.

**propiedad conmutativa de la suma** Propiedad que establece que el orden en el cual se suman dos o más números no altera la *suma*.

$12 + 15 = 15 + 12$

**propiedad conmutativa de la multiplicación** Propiedad que establece que el orden en el cual se multiplican dos o más números no altera el *producto*.

$7 \times 2 = 2 \times 7$

**números compatibles** Números en un problema o números relacionados con los cuales es fácil trabajar mentalmente.

720 y 90 son números compatibles en la división porque $72 \div 9 = 8$.

**cono** Figura tridimensional con una superficie curva, una base circular y un *vértice*.

**figuras congruentes** Dos figuras con la misma forma y el mismo tamaño.

**coordinate** (p. 406) One of two numbers in an *ordered pair*.

In (1, 5), the 1 is the number on the *x*-axis. The 5 is on the *y*-axis.

**coordenada** Uno de los dos números de un *par ordenado*.

(1, 5) El 1 es el número en el eje *x* y el 5 está en el eje *y*.

**coordinate plane** (p. 406) A graph that displays a set of points and gives the position of a point on a line.

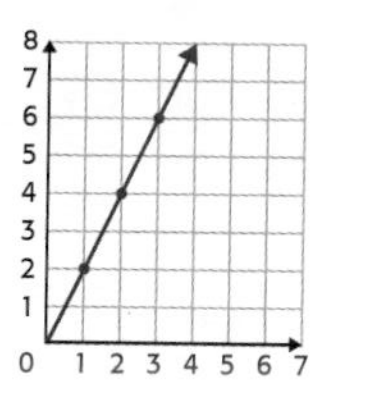


**gráfica de coordenadas o cuadriculado** Gráfica que representa un conjunto de puntos y da, en términos numéricos, la posición de un punto sobre una recta.

**cube** (p. 359) A 3-dimensional figure with six *congruent* square *faces*.

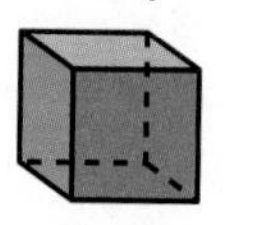

**cubo** Figura tridimensional con seis *caras* cuadradas *congruentes*.

**cylinder** (p. 359) A 3-dimensional *figure* having two *parallel congruent* circular *bases* and a curved surface connecting the two *bases*.

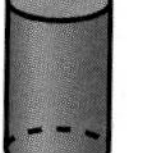

**cilindro** Figura tridimensional que tiene dos bases circulares *paralelas* y *congruentes* y una superficie curva que las une.

## D

**data** (p. 95) Numbers or symbols, sometimes collected from a *survey* or experiment, to show information. Datum is singular; data is plural.

**datos** Números o símbolos que muestran información, algunas veces reunidos de una *encuesta* o un experimento.

**decimal** (p. 579) A number that uses *place value,* numbers, and a *decimal point* to show part of a whole.

**decimal** Número con uno o más dígitos a la derecha del punto *decimal*, tales como 8.37 ó 0.05.







**decimal equivalents** (p. 596) Decimals that represent the same number.

0.3 and 0.30

**decimales equivalentes** Decimales que representan el mismo número.

0.3 y 0.30

**decimal point** (p. 579) A period separating the ones and the *tenths* in a decimal number.

0.8 OR $3.77

**punto decimal** Punto que separa las unidades de las *décimas* en un número decimal.

0.8 ó $3.77

**degrees (°)** (p. 468) The units of measurement used to describe temperature.

**grado (°)** Unidad de temperatura.

**denominator** (p. 537) The bottom number in a *fraction*.

In $\frac{5}{6}$, 6 is the denominator.

**denominador** El número inferior en una *fracción*.

$\frac{5}{6}$ 6 es el denominador.

**digit** (p. 17) A symbol used to write numbers. The ten digits are 0, 1, 2, 3, 4, 5, 6, 7, 8, and 9.

**dígito** Símbolo que se usa para escribir números. Los diez dígitos son 0, 1, 2, 3, 4, 5, 6, 7, 8 y 9.

**Distributive Property of Multiplication** (p. 166) To multiply a *sum* by a number, multiply each *addend* by the number and add the *products*.

$4 \times (1 + 3) = (4 \times 1) + (4 \times 3)$

**propiedad distributiva de la multiplicación** Para multiplicar una *suma* por un número, puedes multiplica cada *sumando* por el número y suma los *productos*.

$4 \times (1 + 3) = (4 \times 1) + (4 \times 3)$

**division (divide)** (p. 142) An operation on two numbers in which the first number is split into the same number of equal groups as the second number.

**división (dividir)** Operación en dos números en que el primer número se separa en tantos grupos iguales como indica el segundo número.

**dividend** (p. 311) A number that is being divided.

$3\overline{)19}$ 19 is the dividend

**dividendo** El número que se divide.

$3\overline{)19}$ 19 es el dividendo

**divisor** (p. 311) The number by which the *dividend* is being divided.

$3\overline{)19}$ 3 is the divisor

**divisor** El número entre el cual se divide el *dividendo*.

$3\overline{)19}$ 3 es el divisor

**double bar graph** (p. 113) A *bar graph* that compares two related groups of *data*.

## E

**edge** (p. 359) The *line segment* where two *faces* of a *solid figure* meet.

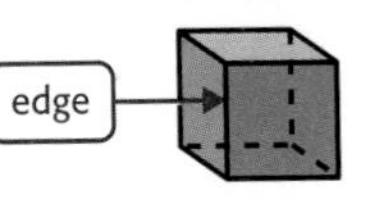


**elapsed time** (p. 520) The amount of time that has passed from beginning to end.

**endpoint** (p. 400) The point at either end of a *line segment* or the point at the beginning of a ray.

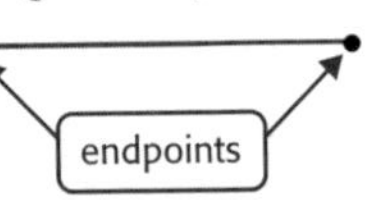


**equally likely** (p. 128) Having the same chance of occurring.

In a coin toss, you are equally likely to flip a head or a tail.

**equation** (p. 198) A sentence that contains an equals sign (=), showing that two *expressions* are equal.



**gráfica de barras dobles** *Gráfica de barras* que compara dos grupos de *datos* relacionados.

**arista** El *segmento de recta* donde concurren dos *caras* de una *figura sólida*.

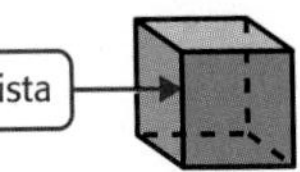


**tiempo transcurrido** Cantidad de tiempo que ha pasado entre el principio y el fin.

**extremo** El punto en cualquiera de los dos lados en que termina un *segmento de recta* o el punto al principio de un rayo.

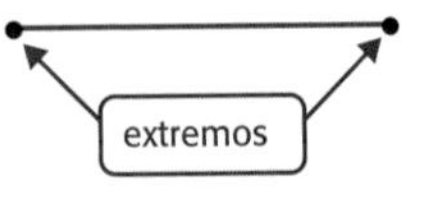


**equiprobable** Que tiene la misma posibilidad de ocurrir.

Al lanzar una moneda, es equiprobable que caiga cara o cruz.

**ecuación** Oración matemátia que contiene el signo de igualdad, =, el que indica que las dos *expresiones* son iguales.





**equilateral triangle** (p. 373) A *triangle* with three *congruent* sides.

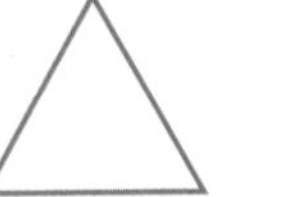

**equivalent fractions** (p. 548) *Fractions* that represent the same number.

$\frac{3}{4} = \frac{6}{8}$

**estimate** (p. 58) A number close to an exact value. An estimate indicates *about* how much.

47 + 22 is about 50 + 20 or 70.

**expanded form/expanded notation** (p. 18) The representation of a number as a sum that shows the value of each digit.

536 is written as 500 + 30 + 6.

**expression** (p. 193) A combination of numbers, variables, and at least one operation.

## F

**face** (p. 359) The flat part of a 3-dimensional figure.

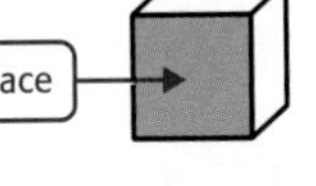


**fact family** (p. 147) A group of related facts using the same numbers.

| | |
|---|---|
| $5 + 3 = 8$ | $5 \times 3 = 15$ |
| $3 + 5 = 8$ | $3 \times 5 = 15$ |
| $8 - 3 = 5$ | $15 \div 3 = 5$ |
| $8 - 5 = 3$ | $15 \div 5 = 3$ |

**factor** (p. 176) A number that divides a whole number evenly. Also a number that is multiplied by another number.



**triángulo equilátero** *Triángulo* con tres lados *congruentes*.

**fracciones equivalentes** *Fracciones* que representan el mismo número.

$\frac{3}{4} = \frac{6}{8}$

**estimación** Número cercano a un valor exacto. Una estimación indica *aproximadamente* cuánto.

47 + 22 es aproximadamente 50 + 20; ó 70.

**forma desarrollada/notación desarrollada** Representación de un número como una suma que muestra el valor de cada dígito.

536 se escribe como 500 + 30 + 6.

**expresión** Combinación de números, variables y por lo menos una operación.

**cara** Parte llana de una figura tridimensional.

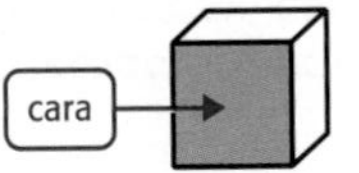


**familia de operaciones** Grupo de operaciones relacionadas que usan los mismos números.

| | |
|---|---|
| $5 + 3 = 8$ | $5 \times 3 = 15$ |
| $3 + 5 = 8$ | $3 \times 5 = 15$ |
| $8 - 3 = 5$ | $15 \div 3 = 5$ |
| $8 - 5 = 3$ | $15 \div 5 = 3$ |

**factor** Número que divide exactamente a otro número entero. También es un número multiplicado por otro número.

**fraction** (p. 537) A number that represents part of a whole or part of a set.

$\frac{1}{2}, \frac{1}{3}, \frac{1}{4}, \frac{3}{4}$

**frequency table** (p. 95) A table for organizing a set of *data* that shows the number of times each result has occurred.

**function** (p. 208) A relationship in which one number depends on another number.

**function table** (p. 208) A table of ordered pairs that is based on a rule.

## H

**hexagon** (p. 362) A *polygon* with six sides and six *angles*.

**hundredth** (p. 580) A place value position. One of one hundred equal parts.

In the number 0.05, 5 is in the hundredths place.

## I

**Identity Property of Addition** (p. 55) For any number, zero plus that number is the number.

$3 + 0 = 3$ or $0 + 3 = 3$

**Identity Property of Multiplication** (p. 150) If you multiply a number by 1, the product is the same as the given number.

$8 \times 1 = 8 = 1 \times 8$



**fracción** Número que representa parte de un todo o parte de un conjunto.

$\frac{1}{2}, \frac{1}{3}, \frac{1}{4}, \frac{3}{4}$

**tabla de frecuencias** Tabla para organizar un conjunto de *datos* que muestra el número de veces que ha ocurrido cada resultado.

**función** Relación en que una cantidad depende de otra cantidad.

**tabla de funciones** Tabla de pares ordenados que se basa en una regla.

**hexágono** *Polígono* con seis lados y seis *ángulos*.

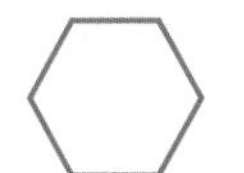

**centésima** Un valor de posición. Una parte de cien partes iguales.

En el número 4.57, 7 está en el lugar de las centésimas.

**propiedad de identidad de la adición** Para todo numero, cero más el numero es el número.

$3 + 0 = 3$ ó $0 + 3 = 3$

**propiedad de identidad de la multiplicación** Si multiplicas un número por 1, el producto es igual al número dado.

$8 \times 1 = 8 = 1 \times 8$





**impossible** (p. 128) An event that cannot happen. It has a probability of zero.

It is impossible to choose yellow.

**improper fraction** (p. 560) A fraction with a *numerator* that is greater than or equal to the *denominator*.

$\frac{17}{3}$ or $\frac{5}{5}$

**intersecting lines** (p. 401) *Lines* that meet or cross at a point.

**irregular figure** (p. R66) A shape that is made up of two or more shapes.

**is greater than** > (p. 28) An inequality relationship showing that the number on the left of the symbol is greater than the number on the right.

$5 > 3$ 5 is greater than 3

**is less than** < (p. 28) The number on the left side of the symbol is smaller than the number on the right side.

$4 < 7$ 4 is less than 7

**isosceles triangle** (p. 373) A *triangle* with at least 2 sides of the same length.



**imposible** Un evento que no puede suceder, cuya probabilidad es cero.

**fracción impropia** Fracción con un *numerador* mayor que o igual al *denominador*.

$\frac{17}{3}$ ó $\frac{5}{5}$

**rectas secantes** *Rectas* que se intersecan o cruzan entre sí.

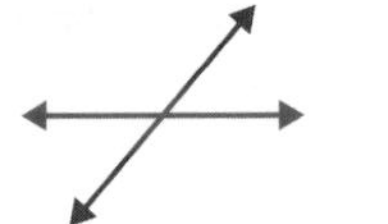

**figura compleja** Figura compuesta por dos o más formas.

**es mayor que** > Relación de desigualdad que muestra que el número a la izquierda del símbolo es mayor que el número a la derecha.

$5 > 3$ 5 es mayor que 3

**es menor que** < El número a la izquierda del símbolo es más pequeño que el número a la derecha.

$4 < 7$ 4 es menor que 7

**triángulo isósceles** Un *triángulo* que tiene por lo menos 2 lados del mismo largo.

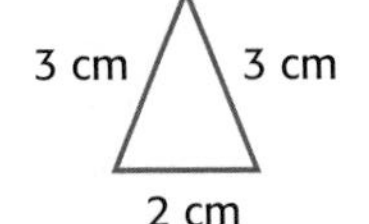

## L

**length** (p. 441) The measurement of a line between two points.

**likely** (p. 128) An event that will probably happen.
It is likely you will choose a red tile.

**line** (p. 400) A straight set of points that extend in opposite directions without ending.

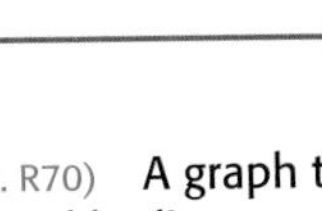

**line graph** (p. R70) A graph that uses points connected by *line segments* to represent data.

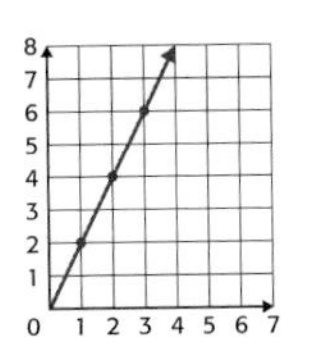

**line of symmetry** (p. 422) A *line* on which a figure can be folded so that its two halves match exactly.

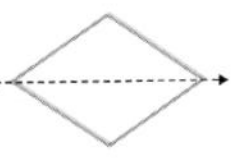

**line plot** (p. 104) A graph that uses columns of Xs above a *number line* to show frequency of data.

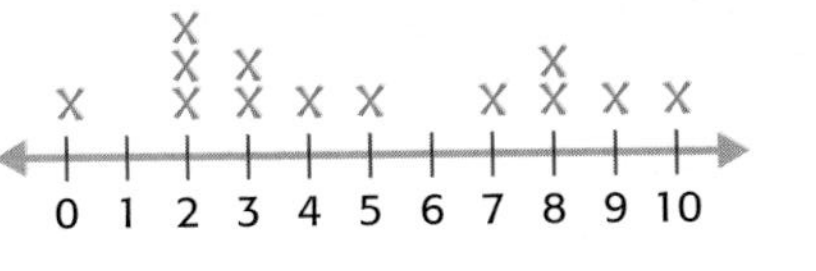



**longitud** Medida de la distancia entre dos puntos.

**posible** Un evento que probablemente sucederá
Es posible que elijas una baldosa rojo.

**recta** Conjunto de puntos dispuestos rectamente que se extienden en direcciones opuestas y sin fin.

**gráfica lineal** Gráfica que usa puntos unidos por *segmentos de recta* para representar datos.

**eje de simetría** *Recta* sobre la cual se puede doblar una figura de manera que sus mitades se correspondan exactamente.

**esquema lineal** Gráfica que usa columnas de X sobre una *recta numérica* para representar frecuencias de datos.





**line segment** (p. 400) A part of a *line* between two *endpoints*. The length of the line segment can be measured.

**line symmetry** (p. 422) A figure has *line symmetry* if it can be folded so that the two parts of the figure match, or are *congruent*.

## M

**median** (p. 98) The middle number in a group of numbers arranged in numerical order.
The median of 3, 5, 6, 7, and 8 is 6.

**minuend** (p. 71) The first number in a subtraction sentence from which a second number is to be subtracted.

8 − 3 = 5
(8: minuend; 3: subtrahend; 5: difference)

**mixed number** (p. 560) A number that has a *whole number* part and a *fraction* part.

$6\frac{3}{4}$

**mode** (p. 98) The number(s) that occurs most often in a set of numbers.

7, 4, 7, 10, 7, and 2
The mode is 7.

**multiple** (p. 177) A multiple of a number is the *product* of that number and any whole number.
15 is a multiple of 5 because $3 \times 5 = 15$.

**multiply (multiplication)** (p. 142) An operation on two numbers to find their *product*. It can be thought of as repeated *addition*.



**segmento de recta** Parte de una *recta* entre dos *extremos*. La longitud de un segmento de recta se puede medir.

A B

**simetría lineal** Una figura tiene *simetria lineal* si puede doblarse de modo que las dos partes de la figura correspondan o sean *congruentes*.

**mediana** El número central de un grupo de números ordenados numéricamente.
La mediana de 3, 5, 6, 7 y 8 es 6.

**minuendo** El primer número en un enunciado de sustracción del cual se restará un segundo número

8 − 3 = 5
(8: minuendo; 3: sustraendo; 5: diferencia)

**número mixto** Número compuesto por un *número entero* y una parte *fraccionaria*.

$6\frac{3}{4}$

**moda** Número o números que ocurre(n) con mayor frecuencia en un conjunto de números.

7, 4, 7, 10, 7 y 2
La moda es 7.

**múltiplo** Un múltiplo de un número es el *producto* de ese número y cualquier otro número entero.
15 es múltiplo de 5 porque $3 \times 5 = 15$.

**multiplicar (multiplicación)** Operación en dos números para calcular su *producto*. También se puede interpretar como una *adición* repetida.

## N

**net** (p. 360) A flat pattern that can be folded to make a 3-dimensional figure.

**red** Patrón llano que se puede doblar para formar una figura tridimensional.

**number line** (p. 395) A line with numbers on it in order at regular intervals.

0 1 2 3 4 5 6 7 8 9 10

**recta numérica** Recta con números ordenadosa intervalos regulares.

0 1 2 3 4 5 6 7 8 9 10

**numerator** (p. 537) The number above the bar in a *fraction*; the part of the fraction that tells how many of the equal parts are being used.

**numerador** El número que está encima de la barra de *fracción*; la parte de la fracción que te indica cuántas partes iguales están siendo usadas.

## O

**obtuse angle** (p. 369) An *angle* that measures greater than 90° but less than 180°.

**ángulo obtuso** *Ángulo* que mide más de 90° pero menos de 180°.

**obtuse triangle** (p. 372) A *triangle* with one *obtuse angle*.

**triángulo obtusángulo** *Triángulo* con un *ángulo obtuso*.

**octagon** (p. 362) A *polygon* with 8 sides.

**octágono** *Polígono* de 8 lados.

**operation** (p. 52) A mathematical process such as addition, subtraction, multiplication, or division.

**operación** Proceso matemático como la suma (+), la resta (−), la multiplicación (×) o la división (÷).





**order of operations** (p. R56) Rules that tell what order to follow use in evaluating an expression:
(1) Do the operations in parentheses first.
(2) Multiply and divide in order from left to right.
(3) Add and subtract in order from left to right.

**orden de las operaciones** Reglas que te indican qué orden seguir cuando evalúas una expresión:
(1) Evalúa primero las operaciones dentro de los paréntesis ( ).
(2) Multiplica o divide en orden de izquierda a derecha.
(3) Suma o resta en orden de izquierda a derecha.

**ordered pair** (p. 406) A pair of numbers that are the *coordinates* of a point in a coordinate plane.

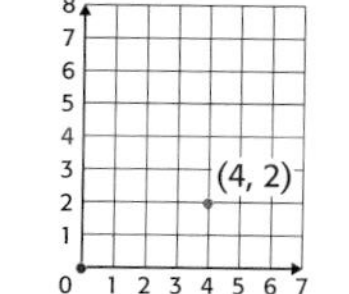


**par ordenado** Par de números que son las *coordenadas* de un punto en un plano de coordenadas.

(4, 2)

**origin** (p. 406) The point (0, 0) on a *coordinate plane* where the vertical axis meets the horizontal axis.

**origen** El punto (0, 0) en una *gráfica de* coordenadas donde el eje vertical interseca el eje horizontal, (0, 0).

**outcome** (p. 124) A possible result of an experiment.

**resultado** Resultado posible de un experimento.

**outlier** (p. 99) A number in a set of data that is much larger or much smaller than most of the other numbers in the set.

**valor atípico** Número en un conjunto de datos que es mucho mayor o mucho menor que la mayoría de los otros números del conjunto.

## P

**parallel lines** (p. 401) Lines that are the same distance apart. Parallel lines do not meet.

A B
C D

**rectas paralelas** Rectas separadas por la misma distancia. Las rectas paralelas no se intersecan.

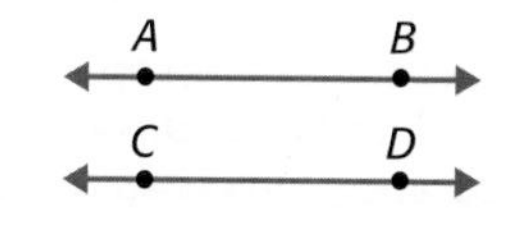

**parallelogram** (p. 376) A quadrilateral with four sides in which each pair of opposite sides are parallel and equal in length.

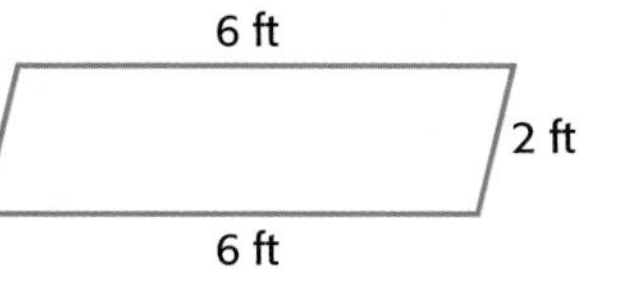


**pentagon** (p. 362) A *polygon* with five sides.

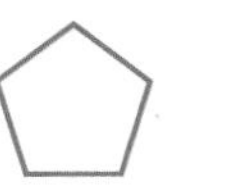

**percent** (p. R59) A ratio that compares a number to 100.

**perimeter** (p. 456) The distance around a shape or region.

**period** (p. 17) The name given to each group of three digits on a place-value chart.

**perpendicular lines** (p. 401) *Lines* that meet or cross each other to form *right angles*.

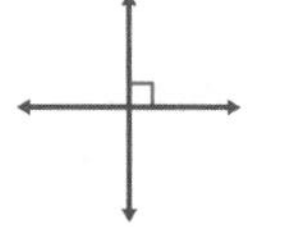

**place value** (p. 14) The value given to a *digit* by its position in a number.

**polygon** (p. 362) A closed *plane figure* formed using *line segments* that meet only at their *endpoints*.

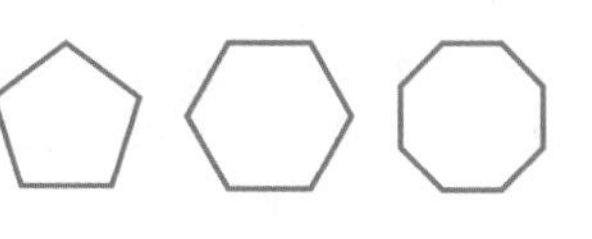



**paralelogramo** Cuadrilátero de cuatro lados en el cual cada par de lados opuestos son paralelos y de la misma longitud.

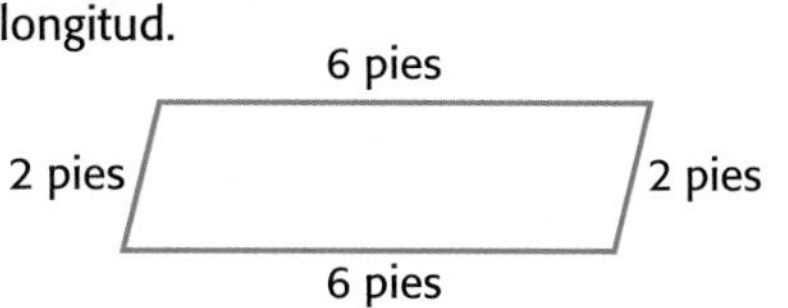


**pentágono** *Polígono* de cinco lados.

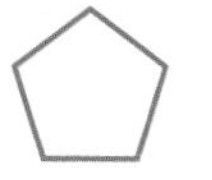

**porcentaje** Razón que compara un número con 100.

**perímetro** Distancia alrededor de una figura o región.

**período** Nombre dado a cada grupo de tres dígitos en una tabla de valores de posición.

**rectas perpendiculares** *Rectas* que se intersecan o cruzan formando *ángulos rectos*.

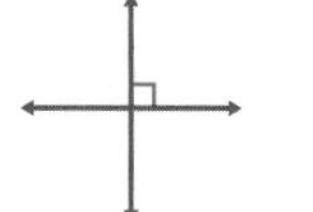

**valor de posición** El valor dado a un *dígito* según su posición en un número.

**polígono** *Figura plana* cerrada formada por *segmentos de recta* que sólo se unen en sus *extremos*.

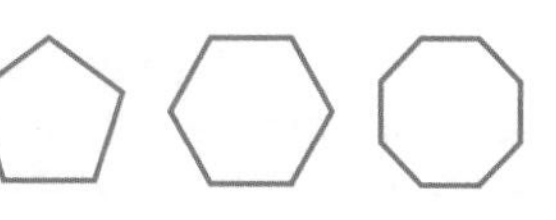





**probability** (p. 128) A number between 0 and 1 that measures the likelihood of an event happening.

**product** (p. 145) The answer or result of a multiplication problem. It also refers to expressing a number as the product of its factors.

**pyramid** (p. 359) A 3-dimensional figure with a polygon as a base and triangular shaped faces that share a common vertex.

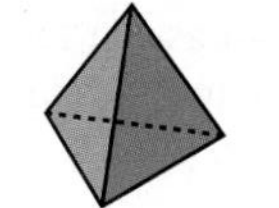

## Q

**quadrilateral** (p. 362) A shape that has 4 sides and 4 *angles*.

square, rectangle, and parallelogram

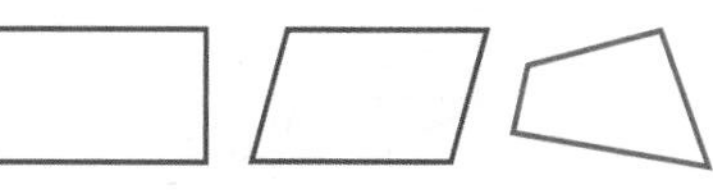
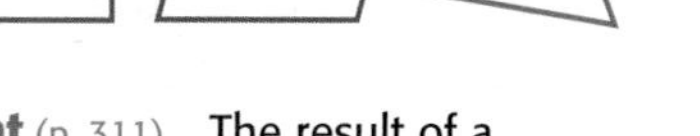

**quotient** (p. 311) The result of a *division* problem.

## R

**range** (p. R74) The *difference* between the greatest and the least numbers in a set of data.

**ray** (p. 400) A part of a *line* that has one *endpoint* and extends in one direction without ending.

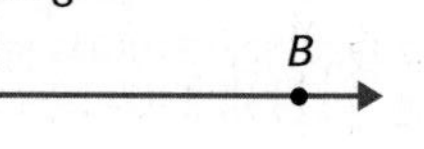




**probabilidad** Número entre 0 y 1 que mide la posibilidad de que ocurra un evento.

**producto** Repuesta o resultado de un problema de multiplicación. También se refiere a la expresión de un número como el producto de sus factores.

**pirámide** Figura sólida con un polígono como base y caras triangulares que comparten un vértice común.

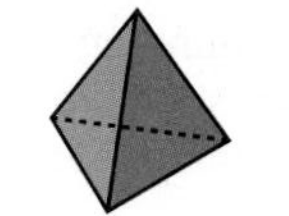

**cuadrilátero** Figura que tiene 4 lados y 4 *ángulos*.

cuadrado, rectángulo y paralelogramo

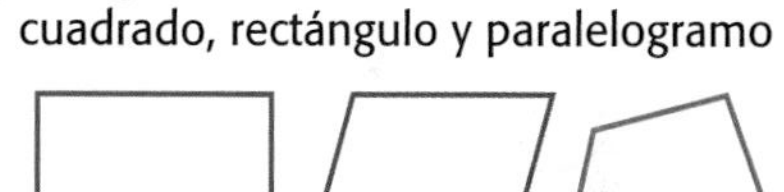

**cociente** Respuesta o resultado de un problema de *división*.

**rango** La *diferencia* entre el mayor y el menor de los números en un conjunto de datos.

**rayo** Parte de una *recta* que tiene un *extremo* y que se extiende en una dirección sin fin.

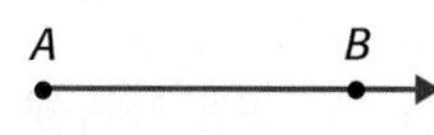

**rectangle** (p. 376) A *quadrilateral* with four *right angles*; opposite sides are equal and *parallel*.

**rectangular prism** (p. 359) A 3-dimensional figure with six faces that are rectangles.

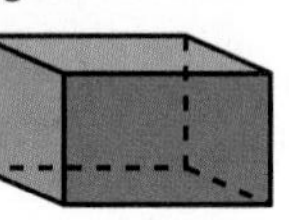

**reflection** (p. 412) A type of transformation that flips a figure.

**remainder** (p. 312) The number that is left after one whole number is divided by another.

**rhombus** (p. 376) A *parallelogram* with four *congruent* sides.

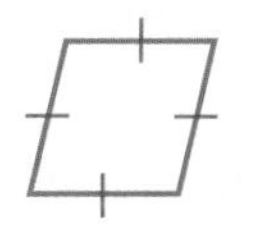

**right angle** (p. 369) An *angle* with a measure of 90°.

**right triangle** (p. 372) A *triangle* with one *right angle*.

**rotation** (p. 412) A type of transformation in which a figure is turned about a central point.



**rectángulo** *Cuadrilátero* con cuatro *ángulo rectos*; los lados opuestos son iguales y *paralelos*.

**prisma rectangular** Figura tridimensional de seis caras rectangulares.

**reflexion** Tipo de transformación en que seleda vuelta a una figura.

**residuo** Número que queda después de dividir un número entero entre otro número entero.

**rombo** *Paralelogramo* con cuatro lados *congruentes*.

**ángulo recto** *Ángulo* que mide 90°.

**triángulo rectángulo** *Triángulo* con un *ángulo recto*.

**rotación** Tipo de transformación en que se hace girar una figura alrededor de un punto central.





**rotational symmetry** (p. 423) A figure has rotational symmetry if, after a rotation of the figure about a point, the figure lies in its original position.

**round** (p. 37) To change the value of a number to one that is easier to work with. To find the nearest value of a number based on a given *place value*.

## S

**scalene triangle** (p. 373) A *triangle* with no *congruent* sides.

2 in. 4 in. 3 in.

**similar figures** (p. R65) Figures that have the same shape but different sizes.

**sphere** (p. 359) A solid or 3-dimensional figure that is set of all points that are the same distance from a given point, called the center.

**square** (p. 376) A rectangle with four *congruent sides*.

**square unit** (p. 460) A unit for measuring area.



**simetría de rotación** Una figura posee simetría de rotación si después de rotarla sobre un punto la figura yace en su posición original.

**redondear** Cambiar el valor de un número a uno con el cual es más fácil trabajar. Calcular el valor más cercano a un número basado en un *valor de posición* dado.

**triángulo escaleno** *Triángulo* sin lados *congruentes*.

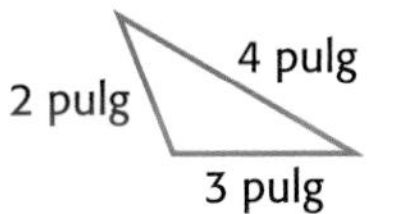


**figuras semejantes** Figuras que tienen la misma forma, pero diferente tamaño.

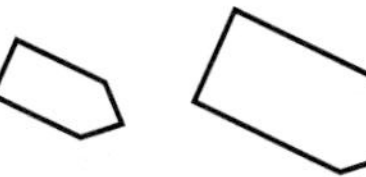

**esfera** *Figura tridimensional* formada por el conjunto de todos los puntos equidistantes de un punto dado llamado *centro*.

**cuadrado** Rectángulo de cuatro *lados congruentes*.

**unidad cuadrada** Unidad para medir el área.

**standard form/standard notation** (p. 18) The usual way of writing a number that shows only its *digits*, no words.

537     89     1642

**subtract (subtraction)** (p. 52) An operation on two numbers that tells the *difference*, when some or all are taken away. Subtraction is also used to compare two numbers.

$14 - 8 = 6$

**subtrahend** (p. 71) A number that is subtracted from another number.

$14 - 5 = 9$
↑
subtrahend

**sum** (p. 58) The answer to an addition problem.

**surface area** (p. LA22) The area of the surface of a three-dimensional figure.

**survey** (p. 95) A method of collecting data.

## T

**tally chart** (p. 95) A way to keep track of *data* using tally marks to record the number of responses or occurrences.

| What is Your Favorite Color? | |
|---|---|
| **Color** | **Tally** |
| Blue | 𝍸 ||| |
| Green | |||| |

**tally mark(s)** (p. 95) A mark made to keep track and display *data* recorded from a survey.





**forma estándar/notación estandard** Manera habitual de escribir un número que sólo muestra sus dígitos, sin palabras.

537     89     1642

**restar (resta)** Operación en dos números que indica la *diferencia*, cuando algunos o todos son eliminados. La sustracción también se usa para comparar dos números.

$14 - 8 = 6$

**sustraendo** Un número que se sustrae de otro número.

$14 - 5 = 9$
↑
sustraendo

**suma** Respuesta o resultado de un problema de suma.

**área de superficie** Área de la superficie de una *figura tridimensional.*

**encuesta** Método para reunir datos.

**tabla de conteo** Manera de llevar la cuenta de los datos usando marcas de conteo para anotar el número de respuestas o sucesos.

| ¿Cuál es tu color favorito? | |
|---|---|
| **Color** | **Conteo** |
| Azul | 𝍸 ||| |
| Verde | |||| |

**marcas(s) de conteo** Marca que se hace para llevar un registro y representar datos reunidos de una encuesta.



**tenth** (p. 580) One of ten equal parts or $\frac{1}{10}$.

**three-dimensional figure** (p. 359) A solid figure has three dimensions: length, width, and height.

**transformation** (p. 412) A movement of a figure.

**translation** (p. 412) A type of transformation in which a figure is slid horizontally, vertically, or both.

**trapezoid** (p. 376) A *quadrilateral* with exactly one pair of *parallel* sides.

**tree diagram** (p. 125) A diagram of all the possible *outcomes* of an event or series of events or experiments.

**triangle** (p. 362) A *polygon* with three sides and three angles.

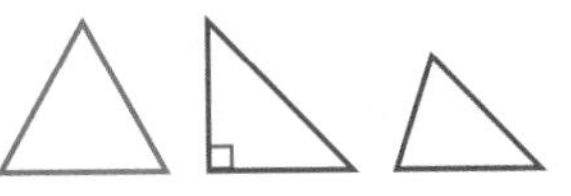

**triangular prism** (p. 359) A prism whose bases are triangular with *parallelograms* for sides.

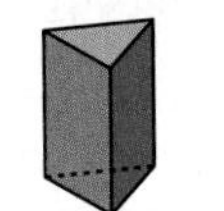



**décima** Una de diez partes iguales ó $\frac{1}{10}$.

**figura sólida** Una figura sólida tiene tres dimensiones: largo, ancho y alto.

**transformación** Movimiento de una figura.

**traslación** Tipo de transformación en que una figura se desliza en sentido vertical, en sentido horizontal o en ambos sentidos.

**trapecio** *Cuadrilátero* con exactamente un par de lados *paralelos*.

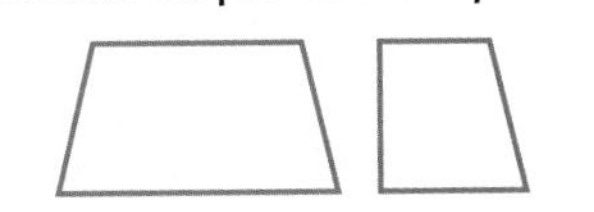

**diagrama de árbol** Diagrama de todos los *resultados* posibles de un evento o series de eventos o experimentos.

**triángulo** *Polígono* con tres lados y tres ángulos.

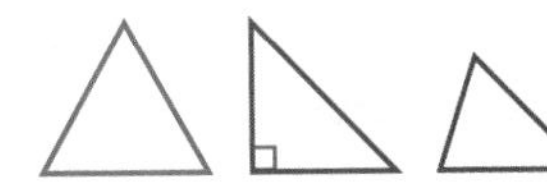

**prisma triangular** Prisma cuyas bases son triangulares con *paralelogramos* como lados.

**triangular pyramid** (p. 359) A pyramid whose base is a *triangle*.

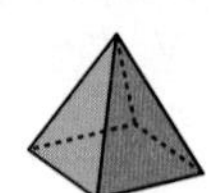

**pirámide triangular** Pirámide cuya base es un *triángulo*.

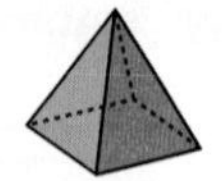

**two-dimensional figure** (p. 362) A figure that lies entirely within one plane.

**figura plana** Figura que yace completamente en un plano.

## U

**unlikely** (p. 128) An event that is improbable or it will probably *not* happen.

It is unlikely you will choose a yellow tile.

**improbable** Evento que es improbable o que es probable que *no* suceda.

Es improbable que elijas una baldosa amarilla.

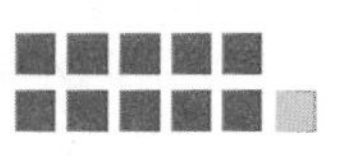

## V

**variable** (p. 193) A letter or symbol used to represent an unknown quantity.

**variable** Letra o símbolo que se usa para representar una cantidad desconocida.

**Venn diagram** (p. R72) A diagram that uses circles to display elements of different sets. Overlapping circles show common elements.

Factors of 42 | Factors of 56: 3, 6, 21, 42 | 1, 2, 7, 14 | 8, 4, 28, 56

**diagrama de Venn** Diagrama que usa círculos para mostrar elementos de diferentes conjuntos. Círculos sobrepuestos indican elementos comunes.

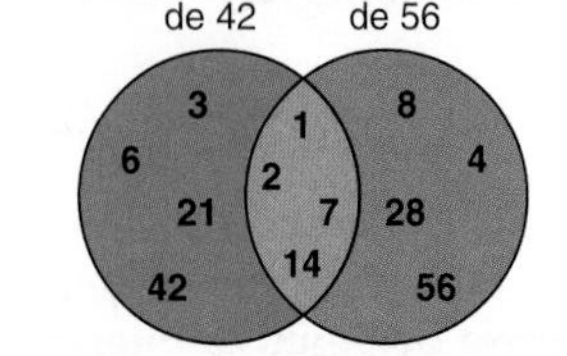








**vertex** (p. 359) The point where two rays meet in an *angle*.

**vértice** Punto donde concurren dos o más rayos.

**volume** (p. 512) The number of cubic units needed to fill a three-dimensional figure.

**volumen** Número de unidades cúbicas necesarias para llenar una figura tridimensional o sólida.

## W

**weight** (p. 498) A measurement that tells how heavy an object is.

**peso** Medida que indica la pesadez un cuerpo.

## X

***x*-axis** (p. 406) The horizontal axis (↔) in a coordinate graph.

**eje *x*** El eje horizontal (↔) en una gráfica de coordenadas.

***x*-coordinate** (p. 406) The first number in an *ordered pair* that indicates how far to the left or the right of the *y*-axis a point is. In (2, 3), 2 is the *x*-coordinate.

**coordenada *x*** El primer número en un *par ordenado* que indica la distancia a la izquierda o a laderecha del eje *y* a la cual se encuentra un punto. En (2, 3), 3 es la coordenada *x*.

## Y

***y*-axis** (p. 406) The vertical axis (↕) in a coordinate graph.

**eje *y*** El eje vertical (↕) en una gráfica de coordenadas.

***y*-coordinate** (p. 406) The second number in an *ordered pair* that indicates how far above or below the *x*-axis a point is. In (2, 3), 3 is the *y*-coordinate.

**coordenada *y*** El segundo número en un *par ordenado* que indica la distancia hacia arriba o hacia abajo del eje *x* a la cual se encuentra un punto. En (2, 3), 3 es la coordenada *y*.

## Z

**Zero Property of Multiplication** (p. 150) The property that states any number multiplied by zero is zero.

$0 \times 5 = 0$ $5 \times 0 = 0$

**propiedad del producto nulo de la multiplicación** Propiedad que establece que cualquier número multiplicado por cero es igual a cero.

$0 \times 5 = 0$ $5 \times 0 = 0$

# Index

Index

Index

Index

## M



Index

## N



Index

## Q



## R